87TH CONGRESS, 1ST SESSION, HOUSE DOCUMENT NO. 29

THE YEARBOOK OF
AGRICULTURE · 1961

THE UNITED STATES DEPARTMENT OF AGRICULTURE

Washington, D.C.

SEEDS

The Yearbook of Agriculture

1961

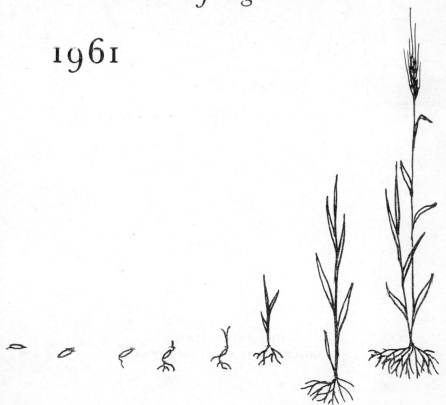

THE UNITED STATES
GOVERNMENT PRINTING OFFICE

FOR SALE BY THE SUPERINTENDENT OF DOCUMENTS, WASHINGTON 25, D.C., PRICE $2

FOREWORD

ORVILLE L. FREEMAN

Secretary of Agriculture

GOOD SEEDS ARE both a symbol and a foundation of the good life our people have gained. A basic factor in our realization of mankind's most sought goal, agricultural abundance, good seeds can be a means of our bringing about an Age of Plenty and an Age of Peace and Freedom. We can use our good seeds to help end hunger and fear for the less fortunate half of the human family. So used, our seeds can be more meaningful to a hungry world than can the rocket that first carries man to the moon.

This Yearbook of Agriculture seeks to provide a new and improved basis for understanding the complex order of Nature's forces so that man can better shape them in a positive and creative fashion.

Seeds are ever a positive and creative force. Seeds are the germ of life, a beginning and an end, the fruit of yesterday's harvest and the promise of tomorrow's. Without an ample store of seeds there can be no national treasure, or no future for a Nation.

Finding and developing better seeds is the oldest continuous service our Federal Government has rendered to our farmers—indeed, to all our people. We have collected valuable and curious seeds from all corners of the world. From the founding ninety-nine years ago of this branch of Government, our Department of Agriculture has worked continuously to aid the selection, advance the harvest, and further the development of improved seeds required to produce crops that could better resist drought, heat and cold, the threat of disease, the attacks of insects.

What success we have realized! The seeds we use today enable our farmers to produce a variety of healthy and hardy food and fiber crops that were virtually unknown a few years ago. Our plant breeders and geneticists have accomplished miracles in the development of more useful plants. In our seeds we have a wealth we all enjoy in abundant foods.

v

This work has concerned all Americans. Now it must concern all members of the human family who fear hunger.

Now, often to the same foreign lands from which we gathered the parent plants, we return more useful seeds. We can do more.

In our seeds we have a wealth we can transmit—without the need of translation—to people of other lands who draw their living from land and forest. The message of seeds that flourish and produce an abundant harvest is one that all the human family can understand. Exported with vigorous purpose and direction, our seeds can be a vital factor in reaching the goals we seek through Food for Peace. Although we cannot feed the entire world, we can supply the technology and the abilities the world can use to feed itself.

This Yearbook of Agriculture, compiling our vast knowledge of seeds for greater application in the United States, also serves well the peoples of the world. By designation of the Food and Agriculture Organization of the United Nations, 1961 is World Seed Year in an international campaign against hunger.

This Yearbook of Agriculture can be regarded as a contribution of the United States and the Department of Agriculture to World Seed Year, and to the continuing search by the peoples of the world for freedom from hunger.

As a contribution to World Seed Year, the Crop Production and Improvement Branch of FAO in Rome undertook to prepare an agricultural study, *Agricultural and Horticultural Seeds—Their Production, Control and Distribution,* in English, French, and Spanish versions.

PREFACE

ALFRED STEFFERUD

Editor of the Yearbook

JOHN CHAPMAN is in this book. He was the near-legendary Johnny Appleseed, who for almost fifty of his seventy-odd years planted apple trees through the pioneer wilderness. The seeds he got from cider presses in Pennsylvania he carried in canoes down the Ohio River and on his back to clearings in Ohio and Indiana. He walked hundreds of miles to tend his orchards and share his dream and the good health he believed was in apples and herbs. He was an original, a doer; he gave no speeches, wrote no books, attended no committee meetings. To the settlers he was a kindly, helpful visitor, who now and then asked a few pennies or old clothes for his efforts. To the Indians he was a welcome medicine man, to whom service was a privilege. To us he is a lesson in greatness, for he who plants a seed plants life.

Wendelin Grimm also is in this book. In 1857, when he was nearly forty years old, he emigrated from his home in Baden, Germany, to Carver County in Minnesota. He brought with him as a prized possession a few pounds of alfalfa seeds, which he planted on some of the 137 acres he bought near Chaska. In the cold Minnesota winter, the first year and later years, some plants winterkilled. Sometimes nearly all died. Each year Grimm saved and planted seeds of the plants that survived. His cattle thrived on the alfalfa, which in time became acclimatized and winterkilled no longer. He let neighbors have some of the seeds. It did not occur to him that his work had scientific importance—he was just being a good farmer—but the value of his "everlasting clover" came to be recognized. Modest, hardworking Wendelin Grimm surely expected no monument, but he has two: A bronze tablet, unveiled in 1924, on a boulder on his old farm and the crop that is grown and prized as Grimm alfalfa. An editorial George W. Kelley wrote about him in the Northwest Farmstead said in part: "The world knows not its greatest benefactors. . . . Sometimes, though, it is given

vii

to a few to recognize and pay tribute to a patient man or woman who in obscurity and perhaps in poverty has worked out great benefits to humanity. . . ."

Gregor Johann Mendel, too, is here. He was the gentle, unknown, incurably curious Austrian monk who kept on planting peas in a monastery garden, checking the traits of each generation, and wondering about the reasons for the differences. His report on his records was the beginning of much of our knowledge of heredity and genetics. The horizon of knowledge he pointed to is a limitless one.

Here also are men and women who stand alongside Johnny Appleseed, Wendelin Grimm, and Gregor Johann Mendel in dedication, accomplishment, and vision.

They are the scores of scientists whose work is explained and made into tools for the hands of all. Their efforts helped to make available seeds of superior varieties that have made it possible for Americans to enjoy a bountiful and continuing food supply and to share their good fortune with other people.

They are also the research scientists, plant breeders, seedsmen, economists, production specialists, seedgrowers, and administrators who, drawing on the knowledge of centuries and the notable developments of recent years, have written these chapters. They have written for technicians, because in a day of specialization there is much to be shared and explored; for farmers and gardeners and foresters and others who work in the fields of applied biology; for students and pupils, who some day will discover new things because, despite our big strides forward, there is still much room for improvement; and for the rest of us, who are incurably curious about life and living things. Their subject is as broad as life itself, for seed or seeds (words that we use interchangeably in this book without any special distinction) are life.

The planning of this book began in 1959 and was in charge of the members of the 1961 Yearbook Committee:

Agricultural Research Service: Martin G. Weiss, CHAIRMAN; Carlton S. Garrison, SECRETARY; Donald T. Black; Victor R. Boswell; G. J. Haeussler; C. L. Lefebvre; John W. McKay.

Agricultural Conservation Program Service: Thomas L. Ayers.

Federal Extension Service: John R. Paulling.

Forest Service: H. A. Fowells.

Agricultural Marketing Service: Walter A. Davidson, Thomas J. Kuzelka, Stanley F. Rollin.

Foreign Agriculture Service: W. H. Youngman.

Commodity Stabilization Service: Wilson E. Westbrook.

American Seed Trade Association: John F. Schiffman.

CONTENTS

THE PRODUCTION OF SEEDS

THE PROCESSING OF SEEDS

THE CERTIFICATION OF SEEDS

THE TESTING OF SEEDS

THE MARKETING OF SEEDS

ON A SEED

This was the goal of the leaf and the root.
For this did the blossom burn its hour.
This little grain is the ultimate fruit.
This is the awesome vessel of power.

For this is the source of the root and the bud . . . .
World unto world unto world remolded.
This is the seed, compact of God,
Wherein all mystery is enfolded.

GEORGIE STARBUCK GALBRAITH.

THE NEW YORK TIMES
MAY 6, 1960

THE

IMPORTANCE

OF SEEDS

What Seeds Are and Do:

An Introduction

VICTOR R. BOSWELL

SEEDS are many things.

Above all else, they are a way of survival of their species. They are a way by which embryonic life can be almost suspended and then revived to new development, even years after the parents are dead and gone.

Seeds protect and sustain life. They are highly organized fortresses, well stocked with special supplies of food against long siege.

Seeds are vehicles for the spread of new life from place to place by the elements and by animals and people.

Seeds are food for man and animals and other living things.

Seeds are raw material for the fash-ioning of myriad products by people.

Seeds are wealth. They are beauty. They are a symbol—a symbol of begin-nings. They are carriers of aid, of friendship, of good will.

Seeds are a source of wonder. They are objects of earnest inquiry in man's ceaseless search for understanding of living things.

Seeds of unwanted kinds are as ene-mies; they are a source of trouble.

Seeds are many things, but every-thing about seeds—their numbers and forms and structures—has a bearing on their main purpose, to insure con-tinuing life. Seeds are containers of embryonic plants, the embryos of a new generation.

SEEDS are borne by two great and different classes of plants.

One group, less highly developed than the other, produce "naked" seeds that develop from "naked" ovules.

In plants of the more highly de-veloped and much larger class, the

I

ovule and the seed develop within an ovary, the seed vessel. The ovary is the part of the flower that contains the ovule with its egg, or female sex cell. The ovary later becomes a fruit with the developed ovule or ovules—seeds—inside. This group of plants we call angiosperms, a word that means vessels for seeds.

Plants of the other group, the gymnosperms, the "naked seed" plants, have no ovaries, no flowers, and no fruits, although they do have seeds. Gymnosperms include the cone-bearing trees, the conifers. Their seeds are borne in pairs at the bases of the scales of the cones.

DEEP WITHIN the ovary of the mother flower (or between the scales of a seed cone) lies the ovule, which contains an embryo sac and its tiny egg. The egg must be fertilized by a sperm cell from a pollen tube before it can start to develop into an embryo and so perpetuate the parent's life.

Along with the embryo there develops a special store of food, the embryo's own special "formula" or diet for its use after it is separated from its mother plant.

Every seed contains carbohydrates, proteins, fats, and minerals to nourish the embryonic plant within. The nature and proportions of each of them differ among the many kinds of seeds. Some seeds, like corn, are predominantly starchy. Seeds of flax and sunflower are oily or fat. Others, such as peas and beans, are notable for their high content of protein.

Some seeds (such as the seeds of orchids, which are like specks of dust) contain only tiny bits of stored food because they are so small. Large seeds may contain a billion times more food than the smallest ones.

Some kinds of seed have most of their reserve supplies packed inside their seed leaves. Others have it packed in tissues developed from the embryo sac, called endosperm, or from the cells of the ovule that surrounded the embryo sac.

THE SEED usually is well protected through its development. This protection differs greatly among different kinds in degree and in the way it is provided.

The ovary and the tissues that are attached to it become the fruit of the plant. The seeds (formed by ovules in the ovary) of plants having large or fleshy fruits are deeply protected therefore so that we never see them before maturity unless we open the fruit to find them.

Although the seeds of gymnosperms are said to be naked, they nearly always have some protection during development. The seeds of the pine tree and other conifers, for example, are hidden at the bases of the scales of the cone. The cone scales of some pines separate to release the seeds as soon as they are mature. Others remain closed for years.

The fruit tissues that enclose some seeds are scanty and are attached to the coat of the seed. A kernel of corn, for example, is more than a seed—it is a one-seeded fruit. The kernel is nearly all seed, but a thin layer of ovary tissue surrounds the seed and has grown together with the seedcoat in such a way that we can hardly see the tissue.

Many structures that we call seeds are actually fruits. Most of them, such as the fruits of the cereals and other grasses, lettuce, and spinach, contain only one seed. Members of the carrot family produce two-parted fruits, each with one seed. Some fruits, such as those of beets, have one or several seeds.

Botanists identify the various types of fruits and give them specific names, but our purpose here is served if we deal with the small, dry, one- or few-seeded fruits, which we are accustomed to plant like seeds, as though they were seeds.

Seeds of some species develop in the mother plant with amazing speed. Some others are surprisingly slow. A chickweed plant that is pulled from the garden and thrown aside at the time its flowers first open may form some seeds before it withers and dies.

Most familiar plants form their seeds during a period of several days to a few weeks following pollination. Pine trees, however, take 2 to 3 years to mature their seeds. The fruit of the sea palm is said to need 7 to 10 years to mature.

ANOTHER ASPECT of the survival of plants is that the seed-bearing species can be perpetuated in two ways.

One, which we have been discussing, is sexual—that is, by means of seeds, which develop from fertilized egg cells.

The other is asexual, or vegetative, as we usually say, by means of such parts as buds, pieces of root, and pieces of stem with attached buds, bulbs, and tubers.

The seeds of some plants—like potatoes, cultivated tree fruits, grapes, berries, and many ornamental garden plants—do not come true to variety. Their seeds therefore are worthless for perpetuating the varieties we plant in gardens and orchards.

For them, we must use vegetative propagation. We can grow apple trees, grapevines, potatoes, or strawberry plants from seeds, but the plants and their fruits (or tubers) will be unlike those of the varieties that produced the seeds.

That is because most seeds, as we have seen, develop after the union of male and female reproductive cells. The seeds perpetuate the hereditary characteristics contributed by both the male and female cells. Seeds of plants like potatoes, apples, pears, and tulips fail to come true to variety because their sex cells carry random assortments of mixed-up sets of characters. Among the offspring of the numberless chance unions that occur in such plants, hardly any two are alike. The plants from seeds of most species come reasonably true to variety if precautions are taken to keep the pollen of undesired types from reaching the flowers of desired types.

We must note a rare exception. A few kinds of plants, such as some species of grasses and of *Citrus*, produce asexual seeds, whose embryos develop entirely from cells of the ovule outside the egg apparatus. No fertilization of an egg cell is involved. There is no mixture of characters from pollen cells with those of the mother cells. The embryo is formed entirely from mother-plant cells and therefore is identical with the mother plant in its hereditary makeup. Such asexual seeds, therefore, come true to variety and afford the unusual opportunity of accomplishing "vegetative" propagation by means of seeds. Except for such rare instances, however, seed propagation means sexual propagation, and asexual or vegetative propagation means propagation by some means other than seeds.

Plants that do come true to variety from seed of sexual origin can also be propagated asexually from stem cuttings or other appropriate parts of the plant under favorable conditions.

Why, then, do we consider the seeds of such plants of great importance? Why are seeds essential if we can perpetuate the plants without seeds?

The answer is that conditions rarely are favorable or practicable for their vegetative propagation.

A prohibitive amount of work would be required for the vegetative propagation of the billions upon billions of such plants that we need to grow every year. An even greater obstacle is that there is no feasible way to keep these "vegetative" plants alive through periods of great cold, drought, or flood. If such plants are killed before they produce seed, that is the end of their line.

The kinds and varieties of plants that fail to produce viable seeds—that is, seeds that can grow or develop—must be perpetuated by asexual means. There is no other way. Such diverse plants as certain grasses, bananas, and garlic produce no seeds, but each has an asexual feature (a vegetative structure) by which it can be multiplied.

Sometimes, for a particular reason, growers resort to vegetative propagation of a kind of plant that is normally grown only from seeds.

Small farmers in the hills of Vietnam grow cabbage year after year without the use of seeds. The climate there is not cool enough at any time to induce flowering and seed production in cabbage, and the farmers cannot import seeds for each planting. The farmers therefore make cuttings from the stumps of the cabbage plants after the heads are harvested. They plant the pieces of stump, each of which has one or more side buds. Roots soon develop. The buds grow and produce new cabbage plants that will develop heads. The process is repeated for each crop.

This method of growing cabbage would be impossible where the seasons become too cold, too hot, too wet, or too dry for the continued survival of the vegetative stage of the plant.

THE ENORMOUS NUMBERS of seeds that single plants of some species produce make it feasible to increase seed supplies at almost fantastically rapid rates. Single plants of other species produce few seeds, and the rates of increase are ploddingly slow.

One tobacco plant may produce as many as 1 million seeds. The average is about 200 thousand seeds. The garden pea plant produces a few dozen seeds at best.

The possible rate of spread of some plants over an area by seeds therefore is astronomical. With other plants, the rate is modest or slow.

Even the relatively slow rates of seed increase among annual and biennial plants are fast and easy, compared to most vegetative propagation.

Species and varieties of hardy perennial plants that spread by runners (creeping stems above the soil surface), stolons (creeping stems below the soil surface), bulbs (arrangements of fleshy leaf bases on a drastically shortened stem), and tubers (greatly thickened underground stems), are especially adapted to survival for long periods without depending on seeds, although they may also produce seeds. Seeds of these kinds of plants often do not come true to variety.

Plants are able to spread naturally only very slowly if seeds are absent. They can only creep. Their vegetative structures do not fly on the wind, float on the water, or ride on animals to distant sites as easily as seeds do. Vegetative reproductive parts may be torn from parent plants by animals or by storms and later may take root after being carried some distance. Vegetative spread nevertheless is slow and cumbersome in nature, compared to spreading by seeds.

SEEDS are the protectors as well as the propagators of their kinds. Thousands of kinds of plants have evolved in such ways that they cannot survive, even in the regions where they are best adapted, if they produce no seeds.

Seeds of most plants are the very means of survival of the species. They carry the parent germ plasm, variously protected against heat, cold, drought, and water from one growing season that is suitable for growth of the species to the next.

Most kinds of seeds will live considerably longer than the time from one growing season to the next if their surroundings are not too extreme for their respective characteristics. Some seeds normally keep alive under natural conditions above ground only a year or two. Others can keep alive for a score of years or more. A few, such as the seeds of silver maple, remain viable only a few days if they are not kept moist and cool.

Some kinds can survive deep burial in the soil, dry or moist, for 10 to 20 years or longer. In one famous experiment, started in 1902, J. W. T. Duvel, of the Department of Agriculture, placed some seeds in soil in flowerpots, so he could find them later. He then buried the pots and all. At intervals he dug up the pots, recovered the seeds, and then planted them under favorable conditions for germination. More than 50 of 107 species tested were viable after 20 years. Many weed seeds remain viable for a very long time if they are buried deeply.

Seeds of common evening-primrose and mullein have been known to remain viable after 70 years in soil.

Most crop seeds keep best for one or a few years when they are stored in a dry place. Exposure to warm, moist air shortens their life. Repeated wetting or submergence in water soon kills most of them. Seeds of plants that grow in water, on the other hand, are not soon harmed by water.

Onion seeds kept in a warm, humid place will lose their life in a few months. When they are well dried and sealed in glass, they remain viable more than a dozen years at room temperature. If seeds are relatively dry, most kinds will tolerate for years extreme cold that would quickly kill their parent plants.

Most seeds also tolerate prolonged hot weather if they are dry. Seeds of muskmelon have produced good plants in the field after storage in a hot, dry office for 30 years. Seeds of Indian-mallow, a common weed, have germinated after 70 years of dry storage. Seeds of *Mimosa*, *Cassia*, and some other genera have germinated after being kept in a herbarium more than 200 years.

The seeds of *Lagenaria*, a gourd, are not harmed by the immersion of the fruits in sea water for a year, long enough for the fruits to float across an ocean. Water may enter the fruits and wet the seeds. Lotus seeds estimated to be 800 to 1,200 years old have germinated.

The stories, however, about the finding of viable seeds 2 thousand to 3 thousand years old in Egyptian tombs are not true. Viable barley seeds found in the wrappings of a mummy were traced to the new straw in which the mummy was packed for shipment to a museum. Viable seeds of corn, squash, and beans found in caves and ancient ruins of cliff dwellings had not lain there for hundreds of years—pack rats or other creatures had carried them in not long before the archeologists found them.

The long "storage" life of the embryo within the seed not only helps insure survival of the species, it makes possible the distribution or spread of the species over long distances, either in the wild or by the agency of man.

VIABLE SEEDS probably are never completely inactive. Vital processes go on as a seed awaits conditions favorable for germination and plant growth. If we knew how to arrest or suspend all these processes completely, it would be possible theoretically to retain viability indefinitely. We do not know how to do that.

Activity within the seed may be so low that we cannot measure it by any known method. In time, however, if the seed does not encounter conditions that will permit it to grow, unidentified substances become exhausted or they deteriorate, and germinating power is lost. The seed dies. Warmth and moisture hasten the exhausting life processes and shorten the life of the seed. Dryness and cold slow down activities, conserve vital substances, and protect the delicately balanced systems within the seed.

SEEDS POSSESS remarkably complex and effective protective mechanisms that help insure survival.

Consider a tender plant that grows in a region of sharply different seasons and matures its seeds and drops them to the ground while the weather is still favorable for growth. If those seeds grow promptly, the new plant surely will be killed when winter comes.

In such situations, seeds that grow promptly are wasted because they fail to perpetuate the parents.

Many seeds therefore have a rhythm of ability to grow that coincides with the rhythm of the seasons. They have a delayed-action mechanism, a natural timeclock, which insures that the seeds will remain dormant until another growing season rolls around—a season long enough to permit another generation of seeds to mature.

Many kinds of seeds remain dormant—fail to grow upon planting—for a while after separation from the mother plant. The length of the dormancy and the nature of the delaying mechanism differ greatly among species and varieties.

Dormancy that is due to water-resistant ("hard") seedcoats may last for years, until enough water has soaked into the seed for it to germinate. Tiny nicks or scratches in the seedcoat will permit water to enter, thus breaking the dormancy. Natural abrasion of the seeds—by the freezing and thawing of soil or by their movement among rock particles by water—permits water to enter the seed. Hard seeds of crop plants are abraded artificially to induce germination. Dormancies due to some other mechanisms may be overcome less easily.

Some dormant seeds, before they will grow, must go through a long period of cool temperature while they are moist. They must go through conditions that simulate a cold, moist soil during autumn or winter. The rhythm of the seasons must be simulated in the environment of the seeds if they are to grow.

Some seeds lie dormant, although they are in moist soil, until they are exposed to light. Certain weed seeds never germinate deep below the soil surface, but grow quickly after they are brought to the surface when the soil is worked.

Still other seeds fail to grow soon after separation from the mother plant because they are immature. Structural developments or chemical processes, or both, must be completed before they can grow. The naked seed of the ginkgo tree drops to the ground in the autumn long before its embryo is fully grown. The embryo must continue its development for many months, nourished by the foods stored around it, before it is mature enough to break out of the seedcoat and grow.

Some seeds in a nondormant state after harvest can be pushed into a dormant state. Upon exposure to unfavorably warm and moist conditions, some varieties of lettuce seed become dormant, although they are capable of germinating under favorable conditions. It is as though their growth processes recoiled, or went into reverse, in the face of a situation that would be unfavorable for the plants developed from those seeds.

Witchweed, a semiparasitic seed-bearing plant, has an unusual survival device. Witchweed is a parasite on many species of crop plants and weeds. Its almost microscopic seeds may lie dormant in the soil for many years if no suitable stimulator plant grows close to them. When the root of a stimulator plant grows close to them, some substance from the root causes the seeds to germinate. The young witchweed plants promptly become parasitic on the roots of any host that caused the seeds to germinate. If a nonhost should cause the seeds to germinate in the absence of a host, the witchweed seedlings die.

MANY species of plants are widespread because their seeds are great travelers. Besides the special features that insure perpetuation of their respective species, plants have other features for spreading the species as far and wide as they are able to grow.

Most of the familiar structures that aid in the natural transport of seeds involve fruits rather than the seeds alone. (As I said, a large proportion of the plant parts we call seeds are actually tiny, dry fruits containing one or a few seeds.)

The windblown dandelion and thistle "seeds" are one-seeded fruits, called achenes. To each is attached a feathery pappus that serves as a sail and a parachute.

The "sticktights" of Spanish-needle are barbed achenes that catch in the coats of animals and people to be carried afar.

A "tickseed" of the beggarweed plant is a one-seeded fragment of its leguminous pod (fruit). It is covered with minute hooks that make it "sticky."

The flying "seed" of the maple tree

is a samara, a one-seeded, one-winged fruit.

The water-resistant seeds in buoyant fruits, large or small, one-seeded or many-seeded, may be carried great distances by water. Coconuts, gourds, and the tiny berries of asparagus are examples.

A few kinds of plants distribute their seeds widely as the entire aboveground part of the mature plant tumbles about over the land, blown by the wind. The Russian-thistle is noteworthy among these tumbleweeds. They sometimes roll for many miles, even over fences and other obstructions, scattering seeds as they go.

Some seeds travel on their own. They need not depend on features of their enclosing fruits or of their mother plants as aids to transportation. The coats of some seeds resemble certain surface features of fruits.

The coat of the pine seed is expanded into a wing, which carries it a short distance.

The seed of the milkweed has a tuft of long, silky hairs attached to its coat. The wind carries this seed far.

When a seed of flax becomes wet, as by rain, its surface becomes gelatinous. It adheres to whatever touches it and is carried away.

The coats of many seeds are resistant to moisture and to the digestive fluids of animals. If such seeds happen to escape grinding by stones in the crops of birds or by the teeth of animals that eat them, the seeds will pass unharmed through the alimentary tract. Some of them reach congenial soil many miles from where the animal got them.

The seeds of the mesquite tree have been distributed by cattle over millions of acres of formerly good grazing lands in the Southwest.

Seedlings of cherry, dogwood, and holly commonly appear where seeds have been dropped by birds far from any parent tree.

UNWANTED PLANTS make seeds, too. It seems that undesirable or unwanted plants generally are more pro-
lific seed producers than most of the crop plants that we strive to grow. One investigator estimated that one large tumbling pigweed produces more than 10 million seeds. Many kinds produce 100 thousand to 200 thousand seeds per plant.

Weeds are the pests they are partly because they produce so many seeds. More than that, though: The seed and the plants that grow from them have a remarkable capacity for survival. Reproductiveness and survival value have evolved to a high level by natural selection. Seeds of many weeds are such potent survivors and successful travelers that their species have become nuisances over much of the world.

Farmers and gardeners must contend with weeds that arise from seeds. They appear to come suddenly from nowhere—or everywhere. They arrive unnoticed by air, by water, by animals, and by man's devices.

Earlier arrivals have accumulated in the soil and lie there waiting for the husbandman to stir them up to the surface, where they seemingly explode into growth. One investigator recovered 10 thousand to 30 thousand viable weed seeds in patches of soil about a yard square and 10 inches deep. Various kinds of seeds kept dormant a long time by their respective mechanisms persistently produce successive waves of noisome seedlings each time the soil is cultivated.

Weeds thus continue to appear although the grower has not allowed a parent plant to produce seed on the site for years. Survival value! Many weed seeds will survive in the soil 20 years and some for longer than 70 years.

Many weed seeds have nearly the same size, shape, and density as the crop seeds with which they may become mixed. The complete removal of such weed seeds from crop seeds is difficult and expensive. Weed seeds that contaminate seeds for food or industrial use lower the grade and value of the latter. Weed seeds will continue to pose problems for gardeners, farmers, and processors.

SEEDS are an aid in efforts to improve plants.

It is said sometimes—incorrectly—that plant improvement can occur only through seeds. Many improved varieties of plants have originated as mutations in vegetative (asexual) cells and have been perpetuated vegetatively (asexually). No seeds are involved in such instances, although the plants may be seed producers.

Most purposeful plant "improvements," however, have come about through sexual reproduction and the consequent formation of seeds. Useful variations in hereditary characteristics occur much oftener incidental to sexual propagation than in asexually propagated plants. Plant improvement would be extremely slow and uncertain, indeed, if we could only sit and wait for useful mutations to occur.

Man learned long ago that like begets like among annual and biennial plants. He learned that he could gradually upgrade the plants he grew year after year by saving and planting the seeds produced by the most desirable plants.

We speak of "seed selection" when we really should say "parent selection." Man nevertheless has made productive use of the capacity of seeds to contain, preserve, and perpetuate the properties of selected parent plants. For thousands of years he has been gradually improving plants by the parental characters he has helped to perpetuate.

As research has revealed more and more about how plant characters are inherited, seeds have become an increasingly valuable element in the purposeful modification of plants. Seeds are not only a means of perpetuating and multiplying plants but an essential feature of the most rapid and practicable way of progressively improving them.

As additional desirable plant characters (or more desirable degrees of existing traits) are found in a potential parent plant, they can be combined with other desirable characters in a second potential parent by mating the two. Through the seed that results from this planned union, the desired combination of characters is captured and retained. A step upward is taken.

Large progenies generally can be developed rather quickly and inexpensively through the agency of seeds. Large numbers greatly increase the probability of finding truly superior plants for further increase and selection or for further mating with other desirable parent plants.

The compactness and longevity of most seeds enable the plant breeder to store collections of germ plasm in small space at small cost and safely and also to distribute germ plasm readily to distant points. Seeds thus help man in his efforts to produce better plants so that he may live better.

SOMEWHAT DIFFERENT but related aspects of survival have to do with the utility and beauty of seeds—the reasons why we grow them, breed them, and husband their spark of life.

Seeds are the world's principal human food. The American Indians, for example, gathered the seeds of about 250 species in more than 30 families of plants for food. Among these were seeds of more than 50 kinds of pine, nut trees, and oak; more than 40 kinds of grasses, of which corn is most important; 30-odd members of the thistle family (like sagebrush and sunflower), and 20 of the goosefoot family (like saltbush and lambsquarters).

Seeds of the wild species used by the Indians are no less wholesome and nutritious today than in the distant past. Most of those species, however, are less productive or are more trouble to grow or harvest than our present crop plants. Or, the seeds are more trouble to prepare or less attractive to our tastes than the ones we now depend on.

All dry edible seeds are highly concentrated foods.

For human food, the seeds of certain grasses, the cereals, are by far the most important group. The seeds of wheat provide more human food than any other plant or animal product, and the seeds of rice are second in importance the world over.

The seeds of rye, barley, corn, sorghums, millets, and oats are also important for human food in different regions of the world. Rye and corn are most important in the Americas and Europe. Rice, wheat, and sorghums are dominant in the Far East.

About one-fourth of the supply of human energy in the United States comes from seeds of the cereals; in Europe, about one-half; and in the Far East, about three-fourths. These seeds are relatively easy to grow, harvest, and store. One or another of them can be grown wherever there is any agriculture at all.

SEEDS are the raw materials for making a great diversity of important products for use in industry and the arts and for making pharmaceuticals, cosmetics, and alcoholic beverages.

Among these various purposes, the oilseeds have the widest range of uses.

Millions of tons of both oily and starchy seeds are used every year in this country for products other than food and feed.

MOST SEEDS are objects of beauty of form, proportion, surface, and color.

Many seeds are so small that their beautiful features escape us. Many others, although large enough to see easily, are such common, everyday objects that we do not really see them. They are, however, worth our careful observation.

The first and most obvious beauty in most true seeds is in the perfection of their simple forms. Their outlines or silhouettes exhibit endless variations in the curve of beauty. In their entirety, too, we find wide ranges of proportion and different graceful and simple masses that are pleasing to look upon.

The sphere is a thing of beauty in itself, although quite unadorned. Artists have tried to produce nonspherical "abstract" forms that possess such grace and proportion as to call forth a satisfying emotional or intellectual response in the beholder. Some of the nicest of such forms lie all about us, unnoticed, in seeds. The commonest are such basic forms as the sphere, the teardrop, and the ovoid and other variations of the spheroid.

Some of these curving shapes are flattened, elongated, or tapered in pleasing ways. Sometimes they are truncated or sculptured into somewhat rough and irregular form. They may bear prominent appendages, such as wings, hooks, bristles, or silky hairs. Most seeds show a smooth flow of line and surface that is perfection itself.

The details of the surface relief of many seeds are even more beautiful in design and precision than the mass of the seed as a whole. Often you can find minute surface characters of surprising kinds. Surfaces that appear plain and smooth to the unaided eye may be revealed under a good hand lens to have beautiful textures.

Surfaces may be grained or pebbled. They may have ridges like those of Doric columns. They may bear geometric patterns in tiny relief, forming hexagons, as in a comb of honey, or minute dimples may cover the surface. Some irregular surface patterns of surprising beauty sometimes appear under the lens. Surfaces may be a dull matte, or highly glossy, or anywhere in between.

Last but not least in the beauty of seeds are their surface colors. They may be snow white or jet black. The color may be a single solid one, or two or more may be scattered about at random. Colors may form definite patterns that are distinctive and characteristic of the species and variety. The colors may be almost any hue of the rainbow—reds, pinks, yellows, greens, purples—and shades of ivory, tan, brown, steely blue, and purplish black.

Look for all you can see with the un-aided eye. Then look at smaller seeds and the surfaces of large seeds with a good hand lens. You will be delighted with what you find.

There is still another beauty, a potential beauty in seeds, that can be seen only as the seed fulfills its ultimate purpose—the production of a new plant possessing its own beauty. This is perhaps the greatest of all: Beauty of general form; grace of stem; the shape, sheen, and color of the leaf; and finally the loveliness of the flower or the lusciousness of a fruit. The cycle is complete, and so we are back to the beauty of a seed.

SEEDS are a symbol. They color our language and habits of thought.

From prehistoric times man has understood the role of seeds. Ancient languages, ancient cultures, and our own contain many words and concepts based on this understanding. The Bible contains several such examples, including the parable of the sower, the use of the word "seed" to mean offspring or progeny, and references to good and bad seed.

Our language contains both common and technical terms involving "seed," although the meanings are quite unrelated to the subject of plants.

The meanings recognize, however, some metaphoric connection in one way or another. "Seed" is a noun, an adjective, and a verb.

Watermen speak of seed oysters, seed pearls, and seed fish. The optician speaks of seeds in glass. The chemist seeds a solution with a crystal to induce crystallization. We speak of the seed of an idea or a plan.

WE KNOW a great deal about how seeds are formed and what they do, but we know only a little about why that is so. Many purely practical questions still cannot be answered. We wonder about many features of seeds and their behavior.

Scientists study seeds for two kinds of reasons. It is desirable to learn everything possible about seeds in order that man can produce and use them more efficiently and effectively. Seeds or parts of seeds are especially convenient forms of living material for the study of the fundamentals of life processes in plants.

RESEARCHERS are conducting more inquiries into seeds today than ever before, and still our wonder grows.

Why does a very dry seed become so well protected and so insensitive that it can tolerate sharp, deep-freeze temperatures for years, with no harm and no loss of vigor?

A light-sensitive seed, while dry, may be so well protected and so insensitive that it is quite unaffected by daylong exposure to sunlight, yet, after it becomes moist, it may respond to a light exposure from a flash lamp as short as one one-thousandth of a second. Exactly what chain of events is set in motion by that flash, and how?

Why do some seeds require alternating temperatures in order to grow, while others do not?

Why do some seeds live for decades and scores of years, while others, apparently as well protected, die in 2 or 3 years?

Why do some small plants produce seeds that are much larger than the seeds of some much larger plants?

Why does one kind of seed develop completely in a few days while another takes years?

How is it that seeds are so wondrously different among species, and yet all are quite evidently evolved to accomplish exactly the same thing?

Seeds are a source of wonder.

Seeds are many things.

VICTOR R. BOSWELL *is a horticulturist with special interest and experience in vegetable plants. He is Chief of the Vegetables and Ornamentals Research Branch in the Crops Research Division of the Agricultural Research Service. He received his undergraduate training at the University of Missouri and his graduate training at the University of Maryland.*

How Seeds
Are Formed

JOHN W. MCKAY

A FLOWER exists to produce seed.

For that, two organs are essential.

The stamen produces pollen grains that later form the male cells, or sperms. The stamen has a stalk, or filament, at the tip of which is the pollen sac, or anther.

The pistil, usually in the center of the flower, is the female organ. Normally it has three fairly distinct parts: The ovary, which contains one or more immature seeds, called ovules; above the ovary, a slender style, or tube; at the tip of the style, the stigma, on which the pollen is deposited.

The stamen and pistil are called essential organs because they are necessary if there is to be seed.

Two other organs—sepals and petals—are not directly involved in sexual reproduction. Some flowers do not have them. We call them accessory organs. A flower that has all four organs is a complete flower.

The sepals are the lowermost of the four organs. Usually they look like leaves. Their main function is to protect the bud until it has developed into a flower. The sepals collectively are called the calyx.

Above and inside the calyx are the petals, known collectively as the corolla. In many flowers they are brightly colored. The petals of many flowers have glands—nectaries—in which a sweet liquid, called nectar, is secreted.

The colors, the nectar, and the odors of essential oils produced by the petals of many flowers attract insects, hummingbirds, people, and other creatures, which, with wind and gravity, may transfer the pollen from the anther to the stigma to fertilize the ovules.

Sometimes the reproductive organs are formed in separate flowers on the same plant. Such plants are said to be monoecious. The watermelon, cucumber, and other members of the gourd family are examples.

Individual plants of some species have one-sexed flowers—that is, flowers on a plant may have only stamens, and the flowers of another plant of the species may have only pistils. To such plants the term dioecious is applied. The holly is an example.

A SEED is a ripened ovule containing an embryo.

A fruit, in terms of origin, is a ripened ovary containing the seeds.

Both ovule and ovary are in the pistil of the flower. To identify seeds and fruits correctly, one has to follow the development of these parts to maturity.

The botanical definition of a fruit is much broader than the popular meaning of the word. For example, the mature bean pod is the fruit of the bean plant, and bean seeds are ripened ovules. The bean pod originates in the bean flower as a minute ovary, which contains ovules so small as to be scarcely visible without a magnifying glass.

Fruit and seeds are present in miniature form in the flower as ovary and ovules, hence the importance of the flower in the development of the seed.

Each female flower in the corn plant has an ovary containing a single ovule, and the mature grain, or fruit, is single seeded, and the ovary wall and the seedcoat are united to form a single covering. Many ovaries are arranged together on a common receptacle, which later becomes the cob of the ear of corn. The long, slender silk is the style through which the pollen tube grows to reach the ovule. A grain of corn is a familiar example of a single-seeded fruit that is commonly called a seed.

All the important cereals are members of the grass family, and have one-seeded fruits.

The large sunflower and other members of the aster family, such as lettuce, dandelion, and aster, produce one-seeded fruits.

By contrast, the ovary of the watermelon flower contains many ovules, which mature to produce the many-seeded watermelon (fruit).

The plants that produce seed are in two natural divisions.

Gymnosperms, the "naked-seeded" plants, bear cones and produce seeds on the surface of cone scales. Among them are such trees as pine, fir, cypress, cedar, and redwood. In the gymnosperms, ovules are produced in female cones, and the pollen is produced in male cones. Pollen is carried to the ovule-bearing female cones by the wind, and each ovule matures into a "naked" seed. This group has no structure comparable with the fruit of the angiosperms, the other division, which are the true flowering plants.

THE SEED-PRODUCING plants—spermatophytes—originated from lower forms of the plant kingdom through a long series of evolutionary changes in both the reproductive and vegetative structures.

The four great divisions of the plant kingdom, beginning with the simplest and ending with the most complex, are algae and fungi; liverworts and mosses; ferns and fern allies; and the seed plants, the spermatophytes.

Algae and fungi lack differentiation of the plant body into true roots, stems, and leaves, although some of the forms may have structures that resemble those organs. Sexual reproduction makes its appearance in this group, but the sex organs and spore-producing structures are usually one celled and primitive. Most of the algae live in water, and the simple, reproductive structures seem to depend on water for functioning and distribution.

Liverworts and mosses are essentially land plants. The zygote—the fertilized egg—is retained in the female sex organs for some time, during which it divides to form a mass of cells,

A Typical Flower

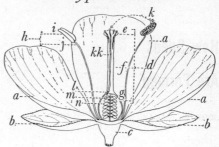

a–a–a, petals (corolla); b–b, sepals (calyx); c, receptacle; d, pistil (composed of: e, stigma; f, style; g, ovary); h, stamen (composed of: i, anther; j, filament); k, pollen, kk, pollen tube; l, sperm nuclei; m, egg cell; n, ovule.

the young sporophyte—or asexual phase of the plant's life cycle. During this period, the sporophyte gets its food, water, and other essentials of life from the gametophyte—the part of the plant which produces gametes, or sex cells—and thus is parasitic on it.

The many-celled and differentiated sporophyte is structurally adapted to withstand drying out and is linked with the beginning of the existence of plants on land. In water plants, such as algae, the zygote is protected against drying, since it is bathed in water at all times.

Mosses have sporophytes that are about equal in size to the gametophyte but depend on the latter for nourishment.

The ferns and fern allies are the first great group of plants that develop an independent sporophyte with true roots, stems, and leaves.

This is one of the most important steps in the evolution of the plant kingdom. The development of a vessel system, which allows water and food to be conducted rapidly through stems, roots, and leaves, was mainly responsible for this advance.

The sporophyte is the dominant plant body in this group, and the gametophyte is usually quite small, though still independent and self-sustaining. Spores are disseminated as asexual bodies when conditions are favorable and develop into small, separate gametophytes.

In seed plants, the last big step in plant evolution, the sporophyte is completely dominant over the gametophyte. Spores are retained in special organs of the sporophyte (essential parts of the flower), and male and female gametophytes are formed within these organs.

The fertilized egg in all lower plants develops immediately into the mature sporophyte, but in seed plants it grows for a time and then goes into a dormant condition to form the seed.

Some of the lower algae multiply only by mitotic cell division—a process of exact splitting of the chromosomes, resulting in two identical cells where one existed before.

Beginning with the higher algae and extending through the rest of the plant kingdom, a process known as alternation of generations is the framework of evolutionary change.

That means that a sexual generation (gametophyte) alternates with an asexual phase (sporophyte). In algae and fungi, the gametophyte generation is the dominant plant body, and the sporophyte, usually quite small, is parasitic on the gametophyte.

Evolutionary differentiation from this point on involved a gradual reduction in size of the gametophyte and consequent increase of the sporophyte.

In the seed plants, reduction of the gametophyte generation has reached the point at which the male gametophyte (pollen tube) and the female gametophyte (embryo sac) are much reduced and are parasitic on the sporophyte—an exact reversal of the relation of the two phases in algae.

Special cells of the ovule and anther differentiate into embryo-sac-mother-cells and pollen-mother-cells, all having the diploid or sporophytic number of chromosomes.

The mother cells divide by a process called meiosis, which results in the daughter cells receiving half the number of chromosomes characteristic of the species. Male and female gametophytes derived from the daughter cells—pollen grains and embryo sacs—thus have nuclei with the reduced gametophytic number of chromosomes. Fusion of sperm and egg at fertilization restores the double, or diploid, chromosome number in the new embryo or sporophyte.

The goal of plant evolution seems to have been the vegetative development and specialization of the sporophyte, with consequent reduction in the gametophyte.

Sexual reproduction in seed plants, resulting in the formation of a young resting sporophyte, the embryo of the seed, is highly efficient. The success of the seed plants in dominating the vegetation of the earth undoubtedly can be ascribed to development of the seed, which makes possible the dispersal of plant species over wide areas and their survival through periods of unfavorable environmental conditions.

THE FORMATION of seed in the higher plants depends on processes of sexual reproduction in the flower. One should know the nature of these processes and where they occur.

Six steps in the development of reproductive plant structures leading to formation of seed are:

The formation of stamens and pistils in flower buds;

the opening of the flower, which signals the sexual maturity of these organs;

pollination, which consists in transfer of the pollen from the stamen to the pistil; germination of the pollen; and formation of the pollen tube;

fertilization of the egg and polar nuclei by the sperm nuclei from the pollen tube;

growth of the fertilized egg and its differentiation into an embryo plus a surrounding coat—the seed; and

maturing of the seed, usually with an accumulation of stored food.

Pollen grains are carried from the stamens to the stigma of the pistil by

Watermelon from Flower to Fruit

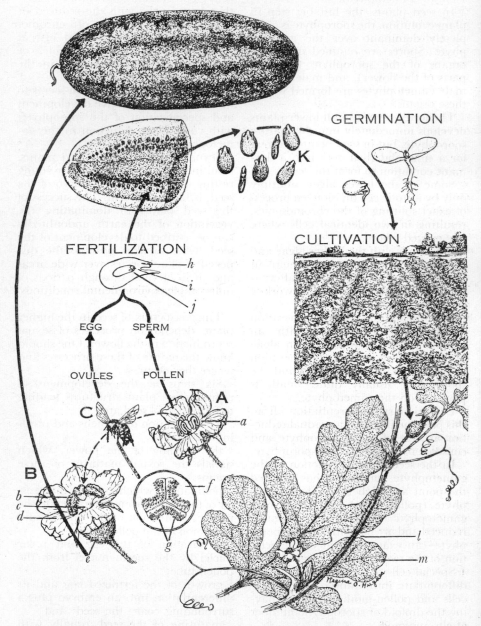

A, *male flower;* B, *female flower;* C, *pollinating insect (honey bee);* a, *stamens;* b, *stigma;* c, *style;* d, *petals (corolla);* e, *ovary (develops into mature watermelon fruit);* f, *cross section of ovary;* g, *ovules;* h, *ovule at time of fertilization;* i, *egg;* j, *sperm nucleus;* K, *mature seeds (Honey Cream variety);* l, *portion of mature plant (vine) bearing male and female flowers and tendrils;* m, *mature leaf.*

insects, wind, or gravity. This crucial step may be seriously impeded if conditions are not right.

An example: Honey bees pollinate clover flowers in fields grown for seed production. If the clover flowers during a long rainy period, the bees cannot fly, and the seed crop may fall far short of the normal because of inadequate pollination.

Insects are attracted to flowers by odor, color, or nectar. Some of the clovers produce great amounts of nectar. Much of the commercial honey available in markets is made by bees working in clover fields. This is an example of partnership in Nature, in which the bees, by pollinating the clover blossoms, play a necessary part in seed production and in return receive nectar for their services.

The pollen grain germinates on the surface of the stigma and produces a long, slender tube, which grows through tissue of the style to the ovule. Two male nuclei, or sperms, move down each pollen tube to the ovule. One unites with the egg in the embryo sac of the ovule; the other with the two polar nuclei. This is called double fertilization.

The fertilized egg develops into a rudimentary plant, the embryo of the seed, the starting point of the next plant generation. The fertilized polar nuclei develop into a tissue called the endosperm, which surrounds and nourishes the growing embryo.

The endosperm in most seeds is absorbed completely by the embryo by the time the seed matures. Among the plants whose seeds contain no endosperm are bean, watermelon, garden pea, and pumpkin. The edible part of the coconut is endosperm. In corn, wheat, and other cereals, the endosperm makes up a large part of the nutriment in the seed.

AFTER FERTILIZATION, the embryo, which starts as a single cell, grows rapidly, and the ovule expands to accommodate the enlarging structures within. The embryo is a mass of un-differentiated cells in its early stages.

As enlargement continues, three well-defined structures are formed: The epicotyl, or young shoot; the hypocotyl, or young root; and the one or two cotyledons, or seed leaves.

Usually the cotyledons of the embryo become thickened to permit storage of food materials, such as starch, sugar, oil, or protein. The accumulation of stored food in the embryo or other parts of the seed usually signals maturity. The period of "filling" of the embryo, or endosperm, is one of stress on the mother plant, because large amounts of organic food materials must be manufactured by the leaves and transported to the developing seeds.

Finally, enlargement of the embryo ceases, the parts become dry, and the seed becomes a dormant living organism prepared to withstand adverse conditions.

THE MATURE SEED we have discussed so far from the standpoint of origin as a ripened ovule. Structurally, though, the seed is a resting embryo plant, which is surrounded by a seedcoat and may have an endosperm.

The embryo has one or more cotyledons, which in many instances will serve as foliage leaves when the seed has germinated.

Between the cotyledons are located two growing points—the hypocotyl, which will produce the root, and the epicotyl, which will give rise to the shoot.

One of the wonders of the seed is that the entire aboveground part of the plant develops from the tiny epicotyl, and the elaborate root system originates in the small hypocotyl.

Because the early growth and enlargement of epicotyl and hypocotyl after germination of the seed will depend on the food supplies stored in the cotyledons and other parts of the seed, the seed is important as a storage organ.

The seedcoat, or testa, is developed from one or two outer layers or integu-

Soaked (A) and Germinating (B) Seeds of Dent Corn (Left) and Great Northern Bean (Right)

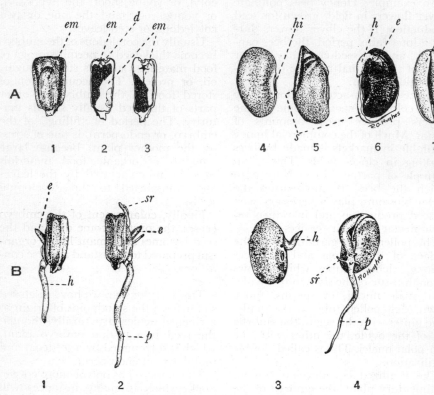

A₁, *flat side of grain;* A₂, *longitudinal section of grain, narrow side showing starchy endosperm stained dark with iodine—embryo not stained;* A₃, *longitudinal section of grain, narrow side, showing embryo stained dark with Sudan IV, a dye that is specific for fats and oils. The starchy endosperm is unstained;* A₄, *side view of soaked bean;* A₅, *unstained cotyledon of bean with attached portion of seedcoat;* A₆, *cotyledon of bean stained with iodine to show high starch content—epicotyl and hypocotyl low in starch;* A₇, *longitudinal section of soaked bean showing two fleshy cotyledons.* B₁ *and* B₂, *germinating grains;* B₃ *and* B₄, *germinating beans; c, cotyledon; d, dent in grain; e, epicotyl; en, endosperm; em, embryo; h, hypocotyl; hi, hilum; p, primary root; s, seedcoat; sr, secondary root.*

ments of the ovule. These layers form a covering, whose function is to protect the embryo against drying out, mechanical injury, and attacks by insects, fungi, and bacteria. Usually the outer coat is hard and durable, and the inner one is thin and membranous. Often the two seem to be fused into one layer.

The seedcoat and fruit wall may develop appendages or special structures that adapt the seed to certain ways of dissemination. In cotton, for example,

long fibers produced by epidermal cells of the cotton seed cling to passing objects, and the seeds thus are carried from place to place.

THE SEED usually matures at the same time the fruit ripens.

Fruits are classified as simple, aggregate, or multiple.

The simple fruits are further classified as dry and fleshy.

In certain fruits, the wall, or pericarp, which sometimes is called the seed vessel, is composed of three layers—exocarp, mesocarp, and endocarp.

The peach is a one-seeded fleshy fruit whose pericarp has three layers—the outer skin (exocarp); the fleshy edible part (mesocarp); and the hard, bony pit (endocarp), which surrounds the seed.

One has to have some knowledge of fruit classification if he wants to identify seeds correctly as to origin and structure. The fact that a blackberry is not a berry but an aggregate fruit and watermelon is a hard-rinded berry indicates that common terms do not always indicate the true structure of a fruit.

We should remember that the fruit is a device for seed distribution and that its structure is related to the way in which seeds of each species are dispersed.

FROM THE STANDPOINT of function, a seed is a device for the reproduction, preservation, increase, and dissemination of the plant species.

The many different ways in which seeds are dispersed illustrate the complexity of Nature's plan in providing for the perpetuation of plant species. Dryness is a factor of great importance in this connection. At low moisture content, the living embryo respires very slowly, and some seeds remain viable for many years, even if they are subjected to harsh conditions.

The food stored in seeds is also important. The reserves supply energy to the embryo as it resumes growth during germination. The young seedling plant is thus given a start in its new location, often a long distance from the mother plant that produced the seed.

Furthermore, the stored food has a part in Nature's plan of seed distribution, for it is attractive to animals. Squirrels bury many more acorns and nuts in the soil than they ever consume as food. Some of these seeds sprout and grow into young oak and hickory trees

to replace overmature individuals in the forest.

Many examples may be cited of the interdependence of plants and animals based upon stored food in the seed. Notable is man's use of seeds for food.

This point leads to a related one. Despite the marvelous mechanisms that produce and disperse seed, many of the improved varieties of crop plants would perish under natural conditions. People, who need the seeds for food, have bred and selected crop plants adapted to their needs. Such improvement and specialization have been possible only because the seed is a product of sexual reproduction in the flower. The sexual reproduction means that the plant, represented by the embryo of the seed, may show traits inherited from either or both parents and consequently be different from either.

That is the key to the improvement of useful, beautiful plants.

THUS, seeds serve us in at least three ways. A large part of agriculture has to do with producing seeds that are used for food and as materials for many other uses. Many seeds are grown for planting, so farmers can have the best seed for the next crop. Seeds are the basis of all procedures to improve plants through breeding.

Plant explorers search all parts of the world for unusual plants that might furnish valuable characters for the plant breeder. Resistance to disease has been bred into many crop plants by use of a wild seed that in itself was worthless. Desert plants frequently provide drought-resistance characters valuable in breeding dryland crops.

Man's dependence on the crops he has developed through work with seeds behooves us to learn more about their origin, structure, and function.

JOHN W. MCKAY *is a horticulturist at the Plant Industry Station, Beltsville, Md. He is a graduate of the University of Texas and University of California at Berkeley.*

The Greatest Service

to Any Country

MARGUERITE GILSTRAP

OUR MAIN crops came from all parts of the world. None of them originated in the United States. Indians, colonists, traders, immigrants, Government people, and plant hunters in turn have brought them.

Those who first imported seeds and plants sought crops that were known to be the best in the regions where they grew.

The goal has changed since then to a search for germ plasm, the substance of life by which hereditary traits are transmitted, because our widening knowledge of genetics has shown that the wild relatives of crop plants are also a rich source of improvement.

Crop breeders today use huge collections of seeds of cultivated plants and related wild species to select germ plasm for improved varieties of crops grown here and to find new crops.

The task of assembling and maintaining plant genes from the whole world has become a far-ranging, continuing, and highly productive activity of the Department of Agriculture, an activity shared by every State where plant breeders seek new frontiers.

Our crops were domesticated in many parts of the world. Corn, potatoes, and tomatoes grew in the Andes of Bolivia and Peru. Wheat, rye, and lentils along the Euphrates Basin of the Near East. Soybeans in China. Rice in southeastern India. Citrus fruit in Burma. Peas in Middle Asia, the Near East, and Ethiopia. Cherries, apples, and certain plums in the Caucasian Mountains of the Near East. Oats in northern Europe.

Their introduction to what is now the United States began with the Indians of ancient America. We do not know precisely when the crops native to Central and South America were moved northward and dispersed.

The oldest remains of cultivated corn are those found in the refuse in Bat Cave in New Mexico. They are more than 5 thousand years old. They came from plants that have disappeared from the earth, from species more akin to popcorn and pod corn than the field corns of today. The wild plants looked more like grasses. They had many short stalks, bore the ear high on the stalk, and had brittle branches, which broke easily and allowed the seeds to fall to the ground.

The great turning point in Indian culture—when seeds formerly collected for food were first saved for planting— probably occurred more than 7 thousand years ago.

Colonists from Europe found North American Indians growing corn, often with beans and squash, from the eastern seaboard to the foot of the Rocky Mountains and up the Missouri River to Montana. Some plantings covered hundreds of acres.

Columbus began the introduction of Old World crops in 1493. He carried barley, wheat, sugarcane, and grapes on his second voyage west.

The colonists who followed the Spanish armies into Florida, Mexico, and Peru took with them seeds of those and other crops they knew. They, like the immigrants through the years, settled in places that reminded them of the homes they left. Many crops brought from Spain therefore did well in the new environment.

They needed more seeds—and more. The Spanish Government consequently ordered all ships sailing for the Indies to carry plants and seeds in the cargo. Among the 147 species and varieties of introductions to New Spain cataloged from early histories are alfalfa, flax, oats, apricots, lemons, olives, oranges, peaches, pears, walnuts, cabbage, lettuce, peas, spinach, turnips, anise, fennel, mustard, saffron, thyme, bamboo, carnations, daffodils, iris, and poppies.

The Indians distributed some of them. The wild peaches found by the first settlers in Pennsylvania, for instance, very likely came from Spanish plantings a century earlier in St. Augustine, Fla.

The Spaniards likewise adopted crops of the Indians—corn, white potatoes, tobacco, cotton, avocado, kidney and lima beans, cacao, the chili pepper, gourd, guava, cassava, maté, pineapple, pricklypear, pumpkin, quinoa, squash, sweetpotato, and tomato.

The first introduction from Spanish America, Orinoco tobacco, was brought by Jamestown planters from Trinidad in 1611. It became the source of colonial Virginia's most profitable crop.

Most of the food and feed crops now grown in the United States were established in colonial America by the end of the 17th century.

The ideas that were to govern the introduction of plants during the next two centuries were current then, as well—the belief that agriculture everywhere could be improved by the adoption of new methods; that the colonies could grow all the cash crops then in demand in Europe, among them rice, indigo, cotton, sugar, spices, tea, grapes for wine, and mulberry trees for silkworms; that new crops could be adapted if planting materials were brought from many different sources and grown experimentally; and that plants of all kinds should be collected for study and classification.

The colonists failed again and again in their efforts to establish the crops so urgently wanted on the European market. Few of the plants introduced repeatedly from the subtropics survived the winters of even the southernmost Colonies.

But finally, in the 1690's, South Carolina planters found—in seeds from Madagascar—the hardy productive rice that could be grown on their lowlands. And in 1745, Eliza Lucas, then only 18, introduced the indigo seeds that gained a foothold for this highly prized crop. They came from Antigua, West Indies, where her father was governor and she had formerly lived.

To tobacco, rice, and indigo, planters of the Southern Coastal Plains added a fourth profitable crop shortly after the American Revolution.

This was sea-island cotton, the seeds of which were introduced from the Bahamas. Its advantage over upland cotton, which had been introduced by the Indians, was that the lint separated easily from the seeds. The cotton gin, patented by Eli Whitney in 1793, however, overcame this difficulty for upland cotton and soon paved the way for the expansion of the crop.

Plant introduction during the 18th century reflected the keen interest in experimentation then beginning to rise in the Western World.

An example is the colonists who left England for Georgia in 1735. Even before they left, they set aside 10 acres for an experimental garden. They hired a competent botanist to explore for "usefull Plants . . . found wanting in America." Neither the botanist first engaged nor the one who was hired to succeed him introduced any seeds or plants—they did not even reach Georgia. But the men in charge of the Trustees' Garden in Savannah proved to their own satisfaction that the climate was too severe for the subtropical plants under study. They turned the plot into a nursery for grapevines and mulberry trees. Fifteen years after the garden was laid out, they decided to abandon the enterprise, but it had served a purpose.

Many of the fruits and ornamentals imported during the 18th century were first grown in the gardens of able plantsmen such as George Robbins of Easton, Md., Henry Laurens and Charles Drayton of Charleston, S.C., and John Bartram of Philadelphia.

Bartram, a farmer who taught himself botany, was considered by the great Swedish botanist Carolus Linnaeus to be "the greatest natural botanist in the world." His botanical garden near Philadelphia, the best known in colonial America, specialized in the plants of this continent. It was also the point of introduction for many different kinds of seeds sent to him by Benjamin Franklin and other Americans traveling abroad and by the directors of the botanical gardens in Europe.

Franklin and Thomas Jefferson were among the leading citizens of colonial America whose interest in plant introduction was no less practical than it was scientific.

On missions abroad they carried on a brisk exchange of seeds with growers at home. Franklin introduced two Scottish crops to America—rhubarb and kale.

Jefferson risked the death penalty in northern Italy to obtain seeds of an upland rice for South Carolina. The provincial government, seeking to protect its monopoly, prohibited the export of seed. Jefferson smuggled them out in his coat.

Franklin and Jefferson, like other influential men of their times, had studied the work of Linnaeus and other botanical authorities. They were well acquainted with the directors of botanical gardens of Europe and exchanged seeds and other plant material with them. Before members of agricultural and scientific societies then being organized on both sides of the Atlantic, they discussed their observations of plantlife.

With the founding of the Republic, the societies became powerful forces in plant introduction. Their members were wealthy men who could afford to try new methods and make mistakes. They believed the success of agriculture depended on the diversification of crops and the cultivation of new and unusual ones.

A fluent spokesman for these ideas was Elkanah Watson, one of the founders of the New York Society for the Promotion of Useful Arts and the Berkshire Agricultural Society in Massachusetts.

Watson in 1817 sent a circular letter requesting seeds from the consuls in Europe. An enthusiastic response came from Valencia, Spain. There, at Watson's suggestion, the consul turned to an eminent Spanish botanist for help in selecting varieties of grain that should do well in this country. The seeds of 14 kinds of wheat, one of oats, and one of barley were sealed in a cask and sent to Watson.

Farmers in a Shaker community near Albany, N.Y., were among those who grew the wheat and reported with favor on one variety. The results so impressed James Madison, then president of the Virginia Agricultural Society, that he mentioned them in an address to the society. The address was published in the American Farmer, a new and influential journal.

Government officials perceived the importance of Watson's work.

William H. Crawford, Secretary of the Treasury, in 1819 issued a circular to consuls and naval officers asking them to send useful plants and seeds to collectors at American ports. The Congress appropriated no funds for the work, but the Agricultural Society of South Carolina allotted 200 dollars a year, beginning in 1823, to pay naval officers for the costs of correspondence.

President Monroe meanwhile had selected a skilled botanist to go as ship's surgeon with an American Commission to South America. Dr. William Baldwin collected seeds and plant specimens near Rio de Janeiro, Montevideo, and Buenos Aires and met the leading botanists of the countries he visited.

A member of the Commission, Theodorick Bland, introduced a wheat that gained wide attention. The variety, which came from Chile, was distributed by the American Farmer and grown for a time in Maryland and Pennsylvania.

CROP SEEDS were indispensable to 9 out of 10 households in the early days of the Nation. Most of the seed was homegrown. Seeds for new land were obtained by purchase or trade from other farmers.

The first seedhouse—David Landreth & Son of Philadelphia—was opened in the 1780's. The seed industry grew slowly. Forty-five seed firms, most of them in the East, flourished in 1850.

Growers in New York and Pennsylvania were supplying timothy and clover seeds for export in the early 1800's. Later the center of production moved into the Ohio Valley, and Toledo for a time was the largest market of grass seed in the world.

Seeds for many of the vegetables grown in this country before the Civil War were brought by the wives of immigrants, who then saved seed from each year's harvest.

The early colonists brought fruit trees with them, but most of the trees were grown from seed during the days of the westward migration.

John Chapman earned the name of "Johnny Appleseed" by washing seeds out of the pomace at cider mills and planting orchards as he strode through the wilderness. He was not alone. The first orchards in almost every State began in that way.

Farmers liked to get free seeds from whatever source. At the time Elkanah Watson distributed seeds from Spain, farmers in the Middle Atlantic States desperately were seeking varieties with resistance to hessian fly, a pest first observed in the 1760's. The susceptibility of varieties most used in Pennsylvania and New York helped the fly spread wherever wheat was grown.

Watson's introduction had habits of growth that made it appear resistant for a time, but it was not the answer.

The late-seeding wheat that helped eastern growers gain some control over the pest was sent to a New York farmer by a friend on Navy duty in the Mediterranean. Andrew J. Beaumont, a Pennsylvania farmer who obtained some of the seeds, advertised the wheat in the Pennsylvanian late in the 1830's and received orders from all parts of the country.

Dr. Henry Perrine, consul at Campeche, Mexico, strongly advocated the introduction of new crops and avidly collected fiber-producing agaves and other subtropical plants. After 10 years in Mexico, he persuaded the Congress to grant him and his associates a township of more than 30 thousand acres on Indian Key, near what is now Miami.

He imported more than 200 varieties of tropical plants and made sisal plantings on every section of the grant before he was killed in an Indian massacre on Christmas morning of 1838.

The Perrine grant was the last one the Congress made in attempts to introduce new crops. Two previous ones in Ohio and Alabama had failed.

Henry L. Ellsworth, Commissioner of Patents, had wide support in 1838 when he asked the Congress to appropriate money for collecting and distributing seeds. Agricultural societies, which were dedicated to the introduction of superior varieties and completely new crops, helped Ellsworth distribute the seeds and plants sent by consuls and naval officers. Congressmen distributed some of the seeds.

Ellsworth wrote: "Inventors are sanguine in the belief (and probably not without reason) that the time is not far distant when ploughing machines will be driven by steam, and steampower applied to many other operations of the husbandryman. . . . A subject intimately connected with this is the aid which husbandry might derive from the establishment of a regular system for the selection and distribution of seeds of the choicest varieties for agricultural purposes."

The Congress responded in 1839 by appropriating 1 thousand dollars of fees collected by the Patent Office to support his work in agriculture. Part of the money was allotted to the collection of information on agriculture in the 1840 census. The remainder was for collecting and distributing seed.

Thus began the distribution of free seeds, an activity that continued until 1923 and supplied Americans, through their Congressmen, with billions of packages of seeds. Most of them were seeds of vegetables and flowers, but also included were seeds of sorghums, sugarbeets, soybeans, and many others.

The demand for seeds rose sharply in the 1840's as pioneer families moved across the continent into new territories and as more and more immigrants arrived.

By the end of the decade, the Patent Office was distributing more than 80 thousand packages of seeds each year. Some of them were gifts of European governments.

Complaints of poor germination led to questions as to the reliability of the sources of supply. Some questioned the wisdom of those who had selected sugar and tea as the most urgently desired new crops.

Sugar was the costliest food item. Louisiana canes, the only domestic supply, were dying out. The Patent Office in 1856 sent Townend Glover, an English entomologist, to the northern coast of South America to assemble a cargo of cuttings. The *Release*, a Navy vessel, was assigned to bring the cargo to New Orleans. The canes, selected and packed by the best means then known, were infested with borers when the ship reached port. Even so, the cargo was unloaded, and growers were urged to take whatever planting material they could use. The high risks of introducing crop pests were not fully recognized for more than 50 years.

Chinese Amber sorgo, which had just been introduced into Europe, was among seeds of many kinds purchased by D. J. Browne in 1854 on the first official trip abroad to buy seeds for free distribution. He also arranged with reliable firms in Paris, Hamburg, Liverpool, and London to supply the Government with seeds.

Even his political enemies agreed that the new sorgo should be widely known and grown. Orange Judd, editor of the influential American Agriculturist, wrote about it, and gave away 36 thousand pounds of free seeds.

A 5-acre plot was set aside in Washington for the increase of the sorgo seeds. It was the first Federal plant propagating garden. It was the forerunner of experimental plots that now cover thousands of acres for cooperative use by the Department and State agricultural experiment stations.

So great was the interest in sirup-producing crops that South Carolina hired an English planter to introduce superior selections from Africa. Along with Chinese Amber, the 16 sorgos Leonard Wray brought to the United States in 1857 were planted on thousands of acres. The sorgos never lived up to expectations as a sugar-producing crop, however, and were discarded for that purpose when sugarbeets became established.

Hardy alfalfas arrived in the United States in the decade before the Civil War. The valued forage had been introduced time and again and grown during colonial days under the name of "lucerne." The variety that took hold in the eastern half of the country carries the name of Wendelin Grimm, a German immigrant who carried the seeds to Minnesota.

The Forty-niners introduced a Chilean alfalfa. They got seeds of it when they were on their way to California by way of Cape Horn. The Patent Office got seeds of it for free distribution from a dealer in San Francisco.

The Rev. Chauncy Goodrich, of Utica, N.Y., reported in the Cultivator in 1850 that he hoped to "renovate" the potato by using true seed of importations from South America. He wanted a variety with resistance to the blight that led to the Irish famine. He did not achieve that goal, but he laid the foundation for potato breeding in this country by selecting highly desirable germ plasm. His selection of Garnet Chili, a seedling of the imported Rough Purple Chili, was widely grown and used in parent stock of 170 varieties, including Green Mountain, Burbank, Early Ohio, and Early Rose.

MORE AND MORE of the supplies of the free seed distribution program came from domestic sources. For example, American seedsmen in 1912 supplied nearly all of the vegetable seeds in the 63 million packets distributed by the Department. Most of the flower seeds, however, came from Germany, France, and North Africa.

The outbreak of the First World War stopped the flow of seeds from Europe to the United States. It created new markets for the American seed industry. At home, victory gardens met wartime demands for food. In Europe, seeds from the United States replaced supplies disrupted by the war. After the Armistice, the demand for American seeds on the home market continued. Seedsmen expanded plantings, chiefly in the West, to serve the rapidly growing canning industry.

The end of the distribution of free seeds in 1923 raised an important question. How should the Department release superior new varieties of crop breeding research? The answer was found in cooperative agreements with the State agricultural experiment stations and the seed industry. An elaborate machinery has been set up to provide the seed industry with small amounts of seeds of new varieties. From these, the industry builds up commercial supplies.

THREE MEASURES enacted by the Congress in 1862 stimulated Federal plant introduction in strikingly different ways.

The Homestead Act, which gave land to those who would settle it, attracted thousands of people to the West immediately after the Civil War. Soon they were asking the Government for seeds of crops suited to the drylands, the river valleys, and the western plains.

The act of 1862, which established the U.S. Department of Agriculture, directed the new agency to "collect new and valuable seeds and plants; to test, by cultivation, the value of such of them as may require tests; to propagate such as may be worthy of propagations; and to distribute them among agriculturists."

The Federal Land-Grant Act of 1862 supplied the States with funds for colleges where young people could be trained in arts and sciences relating to agriculture. It was possible to build up in the colleges scientific staffs for collecting, testing, propagating, and distributing crop seeds. Fifteen years later, the Hatch Act gave further impetus to agricultural research by adding Federal support for State agricultural experiment stations.

Three important crops introduced in the 1860's were durum wheats, sugarbeets, and the navel orange.

The wheat we got from the Russian Ukraine made available on the Northern Plains varieties that were suited to a cold, dry climate and supplied the emerging milling industry with flours for macaroni and other pastas.

Seeds of sugarbeet from France and Germany took hold in Illinois and gave the Midwest the long-sought productive sugar crop.

In the navel orange from Brazil, California had a crop that soon had a value of millions of dollars. Many previous attempts to introduce this superior orange failed. William Saunders, a botanist and superintendent of the Department's propagating gardens, turned his exceptional skills to the task, gave directions for packing the buds for shipment from Bahia, made the grafts, and produced the vigorous young trees that were shipped to California.

James Wilson, who became Secretary of Agriculture in 1897, was the first man in the office who was thoroughly familiar with crop needs in the Western States and the possibilities of crop improvement through research. A farmer himself, he had gained recognition as an agricultural leader through his work in the Iowa Legislature, his widely published writings, and his service as director of the Iowa Agricultural Experiment Station.

Shortly after Secretary Wilson entered the Cabinet, he sent Prof. Niels E. Hansen of South Dakota State College to Russia to collect cold-resistant fruits and cereals for the Great Plains.

Hansen, a Dane who grew up in Iowa, first visited Russia during vacation while he was a graduate assistant in horticulture at Iowa State College. When he went again as a plant explorer in 1897, he traveled 2 thousand miles by wagon and sleigh from the southern part of Turkestan to western China. The five carloads of seeds and plants he shipped to the United States on that first trip included seeds of several hundred different grains and forages. Among them was seed of a hay crop he found on the steppes of Siberia that survived the severest drought and subzero weather. It was the seed of crested wheatgrass.

As Hansen's vast collections began to arrive in Washington, David Fairchild and Walter T. Swingle, young scientists of the Department, suggested a way to finance further explorations. They would set aside a portion of the funds for distribution of free seed to introduce carefully selected crops.

Secretary Wilson liked the idea, presented it to the Congress, and gained approval. The appropriation act of 1898 specified that 20 thousand dollars of the appropriation of 150 thousand dollars for free seed be used for the introduction of seeds. Secretary Wilson established a Section of Seed and Plant Introduction. Fairchild headed it.

The first assignments of the newly formed section went to Mark Carleton and Seaman A. Knapp, men well qualified to be agricultural explorers.

Carleton, a cereals specialist, grew up on a Kansas farm and knew firsthand the hardships of wheatgrowers who lost their crops to bad weather and disease. He proved in research at the Kansas Agricultural Experiment Station that rusts are specific for each kind of grain. Then he joined the Department of Agriculture and demonstrated, through research on more than a thousand varieties of wheat, that only a few of them could stand up to the worst conditions under which wheat was grown here.

His search for hardy, rust-resistant wheats in Russia took him across the Urals to western Asia. His great contributions were the introduction of Kabunka and Khrakov wheats, which could "stand the worst years."

Dr. Knapp went to the Orient to look for rice varieties for the Coastal Plains of Louisiana and Texas. Then 65, he was an influential spokesman for scientific agriculture. He was the driving force in building a rice industry in Louisiana in the 1890's. Seeking markets for farmers associated with him in a great land-development program in the western part of the State, he established the first rice mill west of the Mississippi, helped organize the Rice Association of America, and founded and edited the Rice Journal and Gulf Coast Farmer.

Dr. Knapp's interest and experience in agriculture were far broader than the rice crop. He was a strong advocate of diversified farming. A former professor and then president of Iowa State College, he had drafted the proposal for Federal aid to agricultural research on which the Hatch Act was based. After his agricultural explorations, he carried on farm demonstration work in the South that led to the passage of the Smith-Lever Act in 1914 and the establishment of the Federal Extension Service.

From his first trip to Japan in 1898, Dr. Knapp introduced Kiushu rice, which yielded a fourth more than the varieties formerly grown in Louisiana. Two years later he obtained seeds of other varieties of rice and other crops on a trip by train and mule that covered much of Japan, China, Siam, Burma, Ceylon, the Philippines, and Hawaii.

Plants sent home by Hansen, Carleton, and Knapp had become well established by 1920. Hansen's important finds—crested wheatgrass and bromegrass—supplied farmers of the Northern Plains with forage for livestock. Carleton's hard red winter wheats had begun to transform the Great Plains into a breadbasket of the world. The short-grained rice varieties Knapp brought from Japan assured the mid-South and California a vigorous new industry

Fairchild, Swingle, and other agricultural explorers combed the world for crop plants of all kinds that might be grown in the United States and for ornamentals to add beauty wherever they could be grown.

The prized Chinese elm of farmsteads and towns across the Plains and the zoysia grasses that carpet many lawns were introduced by Frank N. Meyer, a young Dutchman, who between 1905 and 1918 walked thousands of miles in Asia as a plant explorer for the Department.

IT WAS NOT enough to find plants, identify them, and ship them home.

Plant introduction gardens were set up in Chico, Calif., Glenn Dale, Md., and Coral Gables, Fla., to receive the new material, grow it under constant inspection, and make the first tests for adaptation.

O. F. Cook organized an ingenious, highly necessary system of keeping records of the vast flow of material from our agricultural explorers, private firms and public agencies of other countries, and American officials on duty abroad.

Ever since 1898 each plant immigrant has been listed by number and identified by name. More than 265 thousand items were listed in the inventory of plant introductions by 1961.

At first the explorers sought plant immigrants that could make themselves immediately at home in the United States and could be grown commercially. Among those widely planted as fast as the growers could get seeds of them were alfalfas from Peru, Arabia, and Turkestan and Siberia; wheats from Australia and Russia; date palms and the insects to pollinate them from Turkey; and grapes from Italy and Greece.

Scientists learned to identify the genes responsible for certain plant traits, draw up specifications for genes desired in a new variety, locate those genes in breeding stocks, and recombine them in improved varieties.

They learned very soon that this genetic approach would require large reservoirs of plant germ plasm.

W. G. Wight, a Department explorer who collected 250 sorts of cultivated and wild potatoes at various places in the Andes in 1913, initiated a practice that was to become routine for every crop—the search for plant genes in centers of high variability, often near the place of origin of the crop. A striking example of the benefits of seed and plant exploration is the soybean crop.

The soybean was one of the slowest crops to become established in North America. In 1907, more than a century after the first recorded introduction, fewer than 50 thousand acres were in soybeans in the United States.

Scientists learned that a crucial difficulty was the unusual sensitivity of the soybean to the day-night cycle. Daylength controls its flowering and maturing. A soybean planted very far north of its zone of adaptation matures so late it is damaged by frost. Planted south of its adapted zone, the soybean yields poorly.

The selections that took hold in the United States were chosen from more than a thousand introductions between 1900 and 1912 under test in the Department of Agriculture. Twenty of these immigrants were included in the free seed distribution after 1914.

Soybeans were grown on more than 2 million acres in 1927, when the Department sent W. J. Morse and P. H. Dorsett to Asia to make an exhaustive search for additional soybean breeding material. During the next 2 years they assembled seeds of more than 3 thousand selections to give the United States a bank of soybean germ plasm unmatched in the world.

Soybean breeders in Federal-State cooperative work make continuing appraisal of the germ plasm collection. It supplied the genes for 22 improved varieties released for field crops between 1936 and 1960. These include specific varieties for each zone where soybeans are grown commercially, a total area in the United States of more than 26 million acres. The improved varieties produce 10 to 20 percent more beans, have a higher content of oil, stand more erect in the field, and can be harvested by machine more easily than the plants they replaced.

The bank of germ plasm has become a weapon against crop pests. When soybean cyst nematodes were observed for the first time in the United States in 1954, none of the commercial varieties carried resistance to the disease. When the 4 thousand selections in the germ plasm bank were evaluated, three sources of resistance were found.

The reservoir of germ plasm so carefully built and carefully watched over by soybean breeders has its counterpart in world collections of breeding material of all the main—and some lesser—crops of the United States.

As the store of germ plasm has grown and the demands for it have multiplied, our national policy for handling it has been revised. The Congress broadened the base in 1946 in certain provisions of the Agricultural Research and Marketing Act. These provide funds for the support of introduction centers in the regions where the plant is most widely grown or most likely to be adapted. The act also gives Federal support to research on introduced material at State agricultural experiment stations.

The Department has responsibility for the exploration for seeds and plants and their introduction, inspection, and quarantine. Much of the material goes directly to the primary introduction center where it is to prove its value to agriculture.

Peanuts, sesame, castorbeans, and subtropical grasses go to the regional center at Experiment, Ga.

Corn, alfalfa, soybeans, and other crops suited to the Midwest are sent to the center at Ames, Iowa.

Beans, peas, safflower, and similar western crops go to the center at Pullman, Wash.

In the Northeast, forage introduc-

tions go to Geneva, N.Y.; and fruit and other crops of regional interest are sent to the Plant Introduction Garden at Glenn Dale, Md.

All potato introductions are sent to the interregional potato introduction station at Sturgeon Bay, Wis.

The regional introduction stations propagate the seeds, make a preliminary check for growth and disease characters, retain some of the seeds on file, and distribute the remainder to experiment stations for evaluation.

MANY VALUED sources of plant germ plasm have been lost.

Many of them were discarded because they did not serve the immediate interest of a crop breeder. They were susceptible to insects or disease or unsuited to machine production. They gave poor yields in the field.

Many seeds of once prized commercial varieties also have disappeared as those varieties became obsolete.

It is estimated that 75 percent of the alfalfa breeding material and more than 90 percent of the different kinds of clovers introduced over a period of 40 years have been lost. The full measure of the loss cannot be taken. Most of the seeds had been studied for only one or two characters. Their potential can only be guessed, but the estimates rise as crop breeders improve their skills in screening germ plasm and recombining the genes in improved varieties.

To safeguard the treasures in plant germ plasm already assembled and those to be added through the years, our Government has built a national repository—the National Seed Storage Laboratory—in Fort Collins, Colo. The first seeds were accepted for storage in 1958, just 60 years after the Department of Agriculture began an organized search for new crops.

The stocks come from crop breeders in the Federal-State agricultural network, the universities, commercial seed companies, private individuals, and interested groups. For instance, the American Seed Trade Association has taken the responsibility for assembling seeds of vegetables that once were sold commercially but are now obsolete. Along with the sample, each donor provides a record to show why the seeds are considered of value.

All seeds become the property of the Federal Government. To be accepted, they must pass a test for viability. They are then placed in containers and stored in rooms where humidity and temperature can be held at the best levels to maintain viability. In nine of the storage rooms, the temperatures are held at 20° to 40° F.; in the tenth, between 0° and 30°.

Research in the National Seed Storage Laboratory is devoted to physiological problems in viability of seeds as it relates to longevity. The laboratory rejuvenates the stocks of seeds in storage and publishes periodical inventories of the collection. It also supplies, without charge, material not readily obtained from other stores of plant germ plasm to any bona fide research worker in the United States.

It is not designed to service requests from other countries. These are handled by the New Crops Research Branch of the Agricultural Research Service, and the material may be supplied from various centers.

The laboratory is a symbol of the growing public awareness of the great value of the plant germ plasm brought together from all parts of the world. The genes can serve, like money in the bank, for meeting new and continuing threats of crop pests and as capital for new ventures to open wider markets.

As Jefferson pointed out when the Nation was young, "The greatest service which can be rendered to any country is to add a useful plant to its culture."

MARGUERITE GILSTRAP, *an information specialist with the Agricultural Research Service, began writing about scientific work in the Department of Agriculture when she joined the staff of the Bureau of Plant Industry, Soils, and Agricultural Engineering in 1946.*

Age-Old Uses of Seeds and Some New Ones

FREDERIC R. SENTI AND W. DAYTON MACLAY

THE FOOD stored in seeds for their early growth also is food for people and animals.

Wheat is the world's bread grain. Rice is used almost entirely as food and is the main crop of southern Asia. Sorghum and millet are staples in parts of China and Africa. Corn is popular in South Africa and Latin America. Barley, rye, and oats also contribute to the world's food supply.

Nine-tenths of all seeds cultivated are cereal grains—the breadstuffs of the world. By far the greater part of the food of all the people in the world consists of seeds.

Civilization developed in Egypt and Mesopotamia because of their favorable climate for cereal grains. The civilizations in ancient America were the product of those Indian races who knew best how to grow corn. Ceres was the Roman goddess of growing vegetation and her name we associate with grain—cereals.

Legume seeds are the second great group of seeds we use for food. All kinds of beans, peas, and lentils supply protein. Dry, they contain 25 to 40 percent protein, and some are rich in carbohydrates.

Some legumes, such as soybeans and peanuts, are high in oil and protein, as are certain other seeds, particularly rape, sesame, and sunflower. Soybeans are 20 percent oil. Peanuts are 50 percent. Seed oils furnished about 55 percent of the world's edible oils and fats in 1959. (Nearly half the edible oils came from soybeans and peanuts.) Animal fats provided about 42 percent, and the marine oils provided 3 percent.

The soybean seed is the most important leguminous food in the world. In the United States, where half of the world crop is grown, soybeans are processed for their edible oil. The residue from soybean processing goes mainly into animal feeds.

Soybeans are extensively processed into a remarkable number of food products in the Orient. American chemists, seeking to increase exports of soybeans, have adapted modern techniques and fermentation methods to improve their use in such traditional Japanese foods as tofu and miso and in tempeh of Indonesia. Soybean flour, grits, flakes, "milk," and curd can be bought in the United States.

Peanuts are the world's second most important legume. They are used mainly for their oil. We produce peanut oil, but to a much greater extent we eat the entire seed. Blanched peanuts, as prepared for making peanut butter or for eating as nuts, are roasted seeds whose seedcoats have been rubbed off.

Cereal grains, supplemented with soybeans or dry edible peas or beans, comprise about two-thirds or three-fourths of the diet in parts of Asia and Africa.

In western Europe and North America, where the level of economic development is higher, grains and other seed products furnish less than one-third of the food consumed. Rather, meat and potatoes, sugar, and dairy products are the main sources of carbohydrate, protein, oils, and fats. People depend less on seeds for foods in Australia, New Zealand, and Argentina, where extensive grazing lands support sheep or cattle, and the consumption of meat is high.

Feeds for livestock took about one-sixth of the world's cereal crop in 1957–1958. Most of the grain is fed to swine and dairy cows and lesser amounts to beef cattle and poultry. About 90 percent of the corn used in the United States is fed to animals.

The rest is used for human food and industrial products. More than half of the sorghum and barley seeds we produce and most of the byproducts of the milling of cereals and the crushing of oilseeds are fed to livestock.

More than 200 million tons of seeds and seed products are fed to livestock annually in the United States.

The efficiency with which animals convert grains and forages to meat has risen steadily in the United States since the 1930's and has paralleled the increased feeding of the cake and meal that are a byproduct when seeds are processed for oil.

THE DEMAND for food is so great in the world that little arable land can be given over to growing the nonfood crops. Seeds grown for industrial uses hold a relatively minor position.

Chief among the seed crops grown primarily for industrial uses are the oil-bearing seeds—flax, castor, tung (nuts from the China wood-oil tree), perilla (from an Oriental mint), and oiticica (from a Brazilian tree).

Oils, or liquid fats, from the seeds of flax and tung have long been the principal constituents of paints and varnishes for protecting and beautifying the surfaces of wood and metal. These oils develop hard, smooth films when they dry and form resinlike substances.

The artist who paints in oil uses drying oils to carry the pigments and to protect his finished work for the ages. One of the finest of artists' oils comes from poppy seeds.

Seeds of soybean, cotton, corn, sesame, and rape yield semidrying oils. Some are used in paints along with drying oils. Palm oil protects the surfaces of steel sheets before they are plated with tin.

Castor oil, made from castorbeans, has gone out of style as a medicine. This nondrying oil, however, is now more in demand than ever before as a fine lubricant, as a constituent of fluids for hydraulically operated equipment, and as a source of chemicals to make plastics.

Almond oil, another nondrying oil, was once used extensively in perfumery to extract flower fragrances. It is still used in drugs and cosmetics, but it is rather scarce and sometimes is adulterated with oils from peach and plum seeds.

Liquid fats from all these oilseeds enter into the manufacture of soaps for industry and the household and of glycerin for such industrial uses as making explosives.

Sizable amounts of soybean, coconut, and palm kernel oil—seed oils that are produced primarily for food purposes—also are used to make soaps, detergents, and paint resins.

Solid fats from the seeds of the mahua tree, the shea tree, and the coconut palm are used to make candles in tropical countries.

Seeds are a main source of starch for industrial and food use in many parts of the world. Corn and wheat supply most of the starch in the United States, Canada, and Australia. In other countries where cereal grains are not among the principal crops of a region, starchy tubers or roots are processed for starch. Starch is used in the paper, textile, and food-processing industries and in a multitude of other manufacturing operations.

Gums were extracted from quince, psyllium (fleawort), flax, and locust (carob) seeds in ancient times. Today the yearly import into the United States of locust bean gum is more than 15 million pounds; of psyllium seed, more than 2.6 million. The discovery during the Second World War that guar gum was similar to imported locust gum increased its cultivation in western Asia and initiated it in the United States.

Water-soluble gums are used in foods and drugs and in the manufacture of pulp and paper as thickeners, stabilizers, or dispersing agents. Guar gum thickens salad dressings and stabilizes ice cream. Quince seed gum is the main ingredient in wave-setting lotions. Once regarded as an agricultural nuisance, psyllium was sold in the 1930's as a mechanical laxative under 117 different brands. Locust gum is added to pulp slurries to break up the lumps of fibers in making paper.

THE SEEDS of hard, fibrous, stony fruits, called nuts, provide highly concentrated foods, oils, and other materials of value. Most nuts consist of the richly packaged storage kernel and its thick, adherent, brown covering—the seedcoat.

The kernels of brazil nuts, cashews, coconuts, filberts, hazelnuts, hickory nuts, pecans, walnuts, and pine nuts are predominantly oily. Almonds and pistachio nuts are not so high in oil but are rich in protein. Chestnuts are starchy. All nut kernels are rich in protein.

The world production of familiar seed nuts—almonds, brazil nuts, filberts, and the English walnuts—totals about 300 thousand tons annually.

Coconuts, the fruit of the coconut palm, have the largest of all known seeds and are grown in South Pacific islands as a crop for domestic and export markets. The oil palm of West Africa yields edible oil from both the flesh and the seed or kernel of its fruit. World production of copra, the oil-bearing flesh of the coconut, was a little more than 3 million tons in 1959. Exports from producing countries in terms of equivalent oil were a little more than 1 million tons, about half of which was palm kernels or oil from them and about half was palm oil.

Other nuts consumed in lesser quantity include the spicy nutmeg; the soap nut, which owes its sudsing power to natural saponins; the marking nut, used for ink and varnish; the aromatic sassafras nut of South America; and the sweet-smelling cumara nut, which is suited for perfumes.

A forest crop that has not been extensively cultivated is ivory nuts from the tagua palm. The so-called vegetable ivory is the hard endosperm of the egg-sized seed. It is used for making buttons and other small, hard objects of turnery. Seeds of the sago palm are used in Bermuda to make heads and faces of dolls sold to tourists.

THE COLOR AND SHAPE of seeds have long made them attractive for ornaments and decorations.

Since Biblical times, rosaries have been made from jobs-tears—the seeds of an Asiatic grass. Bead tree seeds are the necklaces of South Pacific islanders and the eyes of Buddha dolls in Cuba. Victorian ladies had a fad of stringing unusual seeds to wear as jewelry.

Handmade Christmas wreaths and trees often contain a variety of seeds collected during the year.

Tradition has assigned medicinal values to seeds because of their alkaloids, aromatic oils, and highly flavored components. Although science has given us more effective materials, preparations from anise, castorbean, colchicum, nux vomica, mustard, fennel, and stramonium are familiar to many for the relief of human ailments. Flaxseed poultices and mustard plasters still are used by some persons.

Peanut and sesame oils often are used as carriers or diluents for medicines administered by injection.

Still another group of seeds (sometimes tiny, dry, seed-bearing fruits) provide distinctive flavors and odors to foods, although the nutrients they supply are quite negligible. The common spices, flavorings, and condiments make up this group.

Each year millions of pounds of anise, caraway, mustard, celery, and coriander and the oils extracted from them are imported.

Single-seeded dry fruits used for flavoring include several of the carrot family, such as cumin, dill, fennel, and angelica. Less common seeds used in cooking and beverages include fenugreek (artificial maple flavor) and cardamom. White pepper is the ground seed of the common black pepper fruit.

Sesame seed, which comes from the tall pods of a plant grown in Egypt, Brazil, and Central America, has a toasted-nut flavor and can be used in almost any dish calling for almonds.

It is a main flavoring for halvah, the candy of the Middle East. Sesame sticks, a snack dip, originated in the Southwest.

Beverages are made from seeds the world over.

Coffee is made from the roasted and ground seeds of the coffee tree. World production of coffee broke all previous records in 1959 and 1960 at more than 5 million tons. Per capita consumption remains around 16 pounds in the United States.

Cocoa, chocolate, and cocoa butter come from the ground seeds of the cacao tree. World production of about 1 million tons is divided primarily between Africa (63 percent) and South America (27 percent).

Several soft drinks contain extracts from kola nuts, the seed of the kola tree cultivated in the West Indies and South America.

Cereal grains have been used for centuries to prepare fermented beverages. The Japanese sake is wine fermented from rice grain. Arrack is distilled from fermented rice in India.

Beer, generally fermented from barley, is an old alcoholic beverage. Beer was brewed by the Babylonians and Egyptians more than 6 thousand years ago. Brewers today use corn, rice, and malted barley.

Distillers use corn, malt, wheat, grain sorghum, and rye in making beverage alcohol.

SEED CROPS hold a prominent place in the agricultural economy of the United States.

The farm value of seeds produced in this country for all purposes, including the cereals, is nearly 10 billion dollars a year. Cereal grains, oilseeds, and dry beans and peas account for about 57 percent of the farm value of all crops raised.

The economic importance of seed crops actually is even greater, because additional returns are obtained from most of the corn, oats, barley, and sorghum—as well as the cake and meal from the processing of flaxseed, cottonseed, and soybeans—through conversion to poultry, meat, and dairy products.

Seeds furnish about 40 percent of the total nutrients consumed by all livestock. Hay and pasture are the other chief sources of livestock feed.

Seeds are the essential raw materials for milling grain, baking, crushing oilseed, refining edible oil, brewing, distilling, and mixing feed.

More than 11 thousand business establishments in the United States were based on cereals and oilseeds in 1954. The value of products from these industries was 15.8 billion dollars, of which about one-third was created by manufacturing processes. Not included was the value of seed oil in paints and varnishes or the value of the coffee and chocolate industries that are based on imported seed or seed products.

Cereal grains furnish about one-fourth of the total food calories in the American diet and about one-third of the total nutrients consumed by all livestock and poultry. More than 40 percent of all grain fed to livestock is fed to hogs and about 25 percent to poultry. Industrial uses of cereal grain products depend mainly on starch.

Cereal seeds are predominantly starchy, but are fairly rich in protein. They are low in fat or oil. As prepared for human food, the seedcoats usually are milled off, together with most of the germ. The part eaten thus consists almost entirely of endosperm. A great array of bakery and other factory-made products is based on the endosperm of cereal seeds.

Most wheat is milled to flour from which bread, cake, pastry, crackers, and macaroni are made. About 475 million bushels of wheat are used for food purposes annually.

Wheat is generally conceded to be the most satisfactory bread material, but the various words that indicate "bread" mean different things. In the Orient it would mean rice cakes; in Germany or Russia, rye bread; in Norway, barley loaves; in Scotland, oaten cakes; in Georgia or Texas, corn pones. In England, Canada, and most parts of the United States, it means wheat bread made with yeast. In northern India, thin griddle cakes or chapatties are eaten as unleavened bread.

Before man baked bread, he made bulgur by parboiling wheat and spreading it out in the sun to dry. He rubbed it to remove some of the bran and then cracked it to a coarse or fine meal. Every household in the Near East prepared a year's store of bulgur in the fall after the wheat harvest.

As the Armenians dispersed during the 14th century, they took bulgur with them. Today it is used in one form or another in many parts of the world. Bulgur that is cooked in broth or soup stock and suitably flavored is called pilaf.

Modern American flour mills prepare and ship bulgur to foreign markets. Cereal chemists began working to develop a compressed wheat wafer of expanded bulgur to serve as a base for food stockpiles in shelters.

Wheat differs from all other seed grains in the special properties of its endosperm proteins. When flour is made into dough with water, the wheat proteins hydrate and form gluten, a coherent, elastic mass. Gluten gives to the dough its gas-retaining properties that make light, leavened bread and rolls possible. Other cereal proteins (except rye) do not possess this property.

The uses of wheat flour reflect the characteristics of the wheat from which it is milled. Wheats are classified into five major groups: Hard red spring and hard red winter, which make the best bread; soft red winter, which possesses properties needed for cake, pastry, cracker, and pretzel flours; durum, which is grown almost exclusively for macaroni, spaghetti, and other alimentary pastes; and white wheat, which is used for bread or pastry, depending on its content of protein and whether it is classed as hard or soft.

A relatively small amount of wheat grain is fed to animals in this country—about one-twelfth of the amount used for food. Mill feeds, byproducts of flour milling, serve as supplements to grains in animal rations by raising the content of protein and other nutrients. About 30 percent of the wheat ends up as byproduct mill feeds.

The chief nonfood use of wheat flour is for wallpaper paste and as an extender for plywood glues. Some flour is separated into gluten (protein) and starch. Wheat gluten goes into specialty breads, breakfast cereals, and some other food products.

At one time the main source for monosodium glutamate (used to enhance the flavors of food) was wheat gluten, but lower cost sources have taken this market. Wheat starch is used in foods and textile sizing.

Corn is primarily a feed grain— about 84 percent of the 3.8 billion bushels used in the United States for all purposes in 1958 went for animal feeding. It makes up nearly 65 percent of the hog feed and 40 percent of the poultry feed. Corn as food amounts to about 130 million bushels annually, and is second to wheat as a food grain in this country.

In the four and one-half centuries that the white man has cultivated corn, the only important improvements accomplished are the selection of present-day dent varieties and the development of hybrids. The Indian had already developed the six nations of corn—popcorn, sweet corn, flour corn, flint corn, dent corn, and pod corn. The Peruvian Indians bartered maize for other foods.

The tools and methods of preparing corn for food probably were discovered over and over again in many places. However corn was ground, the resulting meal or dough was the energy food of the Americas. Cornmeal makes tortillas in Mexico, johnny-cake in the South, scrapple in Pennsylvania, and corn chips in many places.

Two industries—dry milling and wet milling—process corn for food as well as industrial uses with simultaneous production of byproduct feed.

In the dry milling of corn, the whole kernel may simply be ground to a coarse meal with or without bolting to remove the coarser particles of the hull. This type of cornmeal produced from white dent corn is preferred in the South. Most northern mills employ a more elaborate process that separates the bran and part of the germ from the endosperm, which is recovered in the form of hominy, meal, and flour.

A considerable amount of corn grits, meal, and flour goes into breakfast foods and pancake mixes and confections. Brewers use a large amount of grits. Some livestock feed is supplied by the hominy feed from dry milling and also by the germ cake that remains after oil is extracted.

Some corn flour is used as a component of oil-well drilling muds and other applications in which starch can be used but high purity is not required.

In wet milling of corn, the kernel is more completely separated into hull, endosperm, and germ. The endosperm is further separated into its starch and gluten protein components, and the germ is processed for oil. The 300 million pounds of corn oil produced in 1959 from both dry and wet milling in the United States went mainly into salad and cooking oils and margarine. Most of the byproduct germ cake, hull, and gluten go into livestock feeds. Some gluten is a source of industrial protein.

Zein, the alcohol-soluble protein from corn gluten, serves as an adhesive in printing inks, as a coating for wrapping paper for packaging frozen foods, as a glaze for candy and cookies, and as a coating for pills.

A new and water-soluble zein gives tough, grease-resistant films and is useful in rubless floor polishes, water-based inks, and leather finishes.

Cornstarch, the principal product of wet milling, has numerous uses: In canned foods as a thickening agent, in puddings, pie fillings, and pastries, and in confections. The starch also is a diluent or carrier for vitamins and food adjuncts.

Most wet-milled starch for human consumption, however, is converted into corn sirup or corn sugar. Between 800 million and 900 million pounds of corn sugar and about 2 billion pounds of corn sirup are used yearly as sweetening agents in foods, candies, confections, and soft drinks and for table use as sirup.

Nearly 1.5 billion pounds of cornstarch, one of the most widely used organic chemicals in this country, are used each year in industry. The largest outlet is in paper and paper products, in which cornstarch is an internal bonding agent, surface size, and coating adhesive. It also is a prime adhesive for corrugating and laminating boxboard and hardboard. The textile industry consumes large quantities of starch as a sizing to protect yarns in looming of fabrics. Laundry starch is applied as a textile finish.

Low-quality starches are components of oil-well drilling muds that lubricate the bit and carry cuttings to the surface. Starch also is used in explosives, in gypsum board, and in core binders. Flour, particularly from corn and sorghum, can replace starch in many applications.

Starch of cereal grains is the starting raw material from which several organic chemicals are made.

Corn sugar, obtained from starch, is converted chemically to sorbitol and saccharic acid and by fermentation to lactic, gluconic, and 2-ketogluconic acids, which are used as humectants, food acidulants, metal-sequestering agents in hard water, and as intermediates in the synthesis of other chemicals.

A new starch-derived polymer, called dialdehyde starch, was put into production on a semicommercial scale in 1959. It is made by oxidation of starch with periodic acid which is electrolytically regenerated.

Industrial alcohol can be produced by fermenting starch as such or in the grain, although petroleum provides the chief source. About 15 million bushels of corn, grain sorghum, and wheat are converted to industrial alcohol annually.

Waxy corn, so called because of the waxy appearance of the cut surface of the kernel, is wet milled to obtain a starch whose properties resemble imported tapioca starch. Each year 20 thousand to 30 thousand acres of waxy corn are grown for starch for special food and industrial needs. Waxy starch gels are softer and clearer than ordinary cornstarch gels and more stable at low temperature. Waxy starch, therefore, is preferred in such food products as puddings and thickeners for pie fillings and sauces.

Another familiar type of corn is popcorn. The farm value of the 485 million pounds produced in 1958 was more than 11 million dollars. Whether freshly popped or in confections, popcorn is mainly a food, but some is used as a packaging material for fragile items. Garlands of "parched maize like a very white flower" were worn by Aztec temple maidens. We used to make strings of fluffy white popcorn for our Christmas trees.

Sweet corn represents another food use of seed, although the crop is harvested before maturity. The commercial crop of sweet corn of 1958 was more than 2 million tons and had a farm value of 80 million dollars.

Oats are primarily a feed grain, although about 37 million bushels (about 3 percent of the total volume) went into food products in 1958. Oats for food go mostly into prepared cereals, rolled oats, and oatmeal.

Furfural, obtained by the chemical industry from oat hulls, is important both as a chemical raw material and as a solvent.

About two-thirds of the 340 million bushels of barley used in the United States in 1958 was fed to livestock. Small amounts were hulled and milled into pearled or pot barley for soups. Most of the remainder was used as malt, made from germinated seed. Barley malt is an ingredient of malted milkshakes, special infant and diet foods, and prepared cereals. Barley malt in fermenting alcohol and alcoholic beverages accounted for one-fourth of the total barley used in 1958.

Byproduct residues remaining after fermentation of cereal grains and malt provide a high-protein supplement for animal feeding. These residues, sold as brewer's dried grains and distiller's solubles, average about 450 thousand tons a year.

Rice ranks third in the United States as a staple food grain. The per capita consumption is 6 pounds. Rice is eaten as the polished whole grain and also as an ingredient in many familiar foods. Rice flour has uses similar to those for corn flour and cornstarch. Broken rice kernels screened from milled or polished rice are known as brewer's grits and utilized by the brewing industry.

Rice is sometimes used in the Tropics as a drying agent for photographic film to keep it from becoming moldy.

Rye and buckwheat furnish flour that is blended with wheat flour to make rye bread and flour for pancakes, muffins, and light baked goods. About 4.6 million bushels of rye and 1 million bushels of buckwheat were milled in 1958.

Buckwheat groats—kernels with the hulls removed—may be sold toasted or raw for breakfast food, porridge, and thickening for soups, gravies, and dressing.

Buckwheat flour and groats must be used fresh, as they soon become rancid because of their high content of fat.

This poor keeping quality makes buckwheat products difficult to handle in the summer.

If buckwheat is eaten in too large quantities, it sometimes causes a rash to appear on the skin of man and on white-colored animals, especially animals exposed to direct sunlight.

Sorghum grain is attracting increasing attention as an animal feed. It also is finding industrial outlets similar to those for corn in dry and wet milling. Of more than 117 million tons of cereal grains fed to animals in 1958, sorghum grain comprised 6 percent, compared with 70 percent for corn, 17

percent for oats, 5 percent for barley, and 2 percent for wheat and rye.

SEED OILS supply about 60 percent of the food fats produced in this country. Of this total in 1958, about two-thirds was from soybeans, one-fourth from cottonseed, and about one-tenth from other seeds, including corn and peanuts. The amount of these oils used for shortening, margarine, and salad or cooking oils in 1958 was about 5.7 billion pounds. (About 1.5 billion pounds each of butter and lard were consumed.)

Nonfood uses of vegetable oils generally are classed in three groups: Soap, drying oils, and other industrial products.

The only seed oil used to any extent for soap is coconut oil, but for other uses many oils are interchangeable. About one-fourth of the 630 million pounds of coconut oil, imported as such or as copra in 1958, was made into soap. Soapmaking, which also uses inedible tallow and greases, has declined as an outlet for all oils and fats because of the increasing use of synthetic detergents. The effect on coconut oil has been offset somewhat by an increase in its other industrial uses, including synthetic detergents.

Drying oils are made from about 1 billion pounds of seed oils each year. Linseed oil, about 50 percent of this total, is used mainly in the manufacture of exterior house paints, other paints and varnishes, and also floor coverings.

Soybean oil supplies 20 percent of the drying oil, primarily in modified oils and alkyd resins for trim paints.

Dehydrated castor oil, tung oil, and safflower oil account for about 15 percent of all drying oils and find application in such specialty coatings as varnishes, alkyd resins for metal coatings, and other industrial finishes.

These needs for industrial drying oils are the main reasons for growing three crops—flaxseed, castorbeans, and tung nuts—in the United States.

The flaxseed crops, ranging from

about 25 million to 40 million bushels, produce about 500 million to 800 million pounds of linseed oil each year. Some of this oil is available for export, since domestic needs are about 500 million pounds.

Most of our castor oil is imported to meet the yearly need for about 135 million pounds. However, the domestic crop of castorbeans is expanding because of the development of improved varieties and harvesting machinery. About 20 million pounds of oil came from domestic beans in 1959.

Imported tung oil amounts to about 25 million pounds annually to supplement our domestic crop and to supply the total need for about 50 million pounds of oil.

The third major outlet for seed oils—other industrial uses—provides a market for about 600 million pounds each year.

About 35 percent in 1958 was coconut oil used in making synthetic detergents, resins, and other chemicals.

About 30 percent was soybean oil for use in plastics and resins (either as epoxidized oils or as dimer acids for polyamide resins), textile lubricants, and other specialty applications. A considerable proportion of the 60 million pounds of animal fats and vegetable oils used a year as plasticizers—those agents that make plastics soft and flexible—is soybean oil.

Castor oil, about 10 percent of the total, is an ingredient of lubricants, plasticizers, and waxes. It also is a source of sebacic acid used to make synthetic fibers, lubricants for jet engines, and plastics.

Cottonseed, linseed, and palm oil supplied the remaining 25 percent of the domestic market.

Oilseed proteins, obtained as the cake or meal after removal of oil, are used mainly in feeds. Soybean, cottonseed, linseed, and peanut oil meals total between 10 million and 12 million tons. Soybean meal makes up more than 60 percent of all the oilseed meals fed.

Industrial uses for oilseed proteins are limited mainly to soybean proteins. About 95 million pounds of soybean meal, which contains 40 to 50 percent protein, were used to make plywood glue in 1959. Some 50 million pounds of isolated soybean protein are used each year for adhesives, mainly as binder for clay coatings on high-quality paper, and for emulsifiers. Soybean protein is a constituent of firefighting foams.

SEVERAL OTHER seed crops are grown in the United States, primarily for food. They are leguminous seeds and tree nuts. They provide a considerable variety of staple foods and special food values.

About 750 thousand tons of dry edible beans are grown annually, including white navy, red kidney, mottled pinto, and lima beans and edible soybeans and mung beans.

Mung bean seeds and sometimes the seeds of other beans are germinated in large masses in special vessels and allowed to form sprouts up to about 3 inches long in the dark. The sprouts make a succulent, nutritious food that is high in vitamin content.

Green beans generally are eaten without removing the seed pod. Immature or green seeds of peas are also eaten as vegetables. Split peas, popular in this country for making soup, consist of the mature cotyledons only. The annual consumption of dry peas is about 150 thousand tons.

The yield of tree nuts in the United States in 1960 was about 190 thousand tons, in-the-shell basis, of almonds, filberts, walnuts, and pecans. About the same amount of tree nuts was imported. The per capita consumption of shelled nuts was about 1.5 pounds in 1960.

AMERICAN AGRICULTURE currently produces a surplus of cereal grains. New seed crops are sought as alternative sources of income for the American farmer.

Safflower has potentialities as a new crop. Centuries ago the Middle East knew about safflower. Its yellow and orange florets were sources of dyes. Safflower has been a profitable crop in the Central Valley of California since 1956, and its production in the Great Plains States has increased substantially. Edible safflower oil is an outstanding source of unsaturated fats. Increasing amounts of safflower oil are used in exterior house paints and interior finishes because it retains color well.

The canarygrasses are a new crop of interest to farmers in the Northwest. The seed of *Phalaris canariensis* has long been used as canary bird feed. Imports run about 20 thousand tons.

Idaho grows rapeseed and North Dakota produces millet for birdseed mixtures. A carload of birdseed, it is said, would be required daily for an estimated 7 million parakeets and "budgies" in New York City alone. Sunflower seed is a health food, an hors d'oeuvre, and a source of edible oil. It also is a popular feed for parrots and wild birds at outdoor feeders.

Man through the ages has sampled and screened plants for useful products. Botanists know about 250 thousand species of higher plants. Some 15 thousand are native to North America, but only 100 produce economic crops in the United States—that is, each has an annual value exceeding a million dollars. Seed crops made up 70 percent of the total acreage in 1958 and 57 percent of the total crop value.

The Agricultural Research Service in 1956 began a coordinated and greatly expanded research program with State agricultural experiment stations to find crops, particularly seed crops, that will be profitable for the farmer to grow and will permit him to diversify his agricultural program and will satisfy present or anticipated industrial needs—crops that may supply strategic or critical raw materials and replace nonrenewable resources.

In this search, seeds yielding new raw materials for industrial markets hold most promise. Although very young, the new crops program has developed a number of leads, particularly in the field of oilseeds, that appear encouraging.

More and more we realize that seeds of the plant kingdom contain many unexplored and potentially useful chemical raw materials.

Modern scientific tools and knowledge permit us to probe deeper into the composition of plants. Changing industrial needs and an expanding economy mean markets for new and different raw materials.

The future is bright for greater uses of the world's seed crops and for the development of new ones with compositions and growth characteristics that will make them profitable for the farmer to grow and for industry to process.

FREDERIC R. SENTI, *Director of the Northern Utilization Research and Development Division, Agricultural Research Service, Peoria, Ill., since 1959, has spent more than 20 years conducting research on agricultural products. Dr. Senti, whose graduate degrees are from Kansas State and The Johns Hopkins Universities, received a Superior Service Award in 1956 for his contributions on properties of seed grains and oilseeds and their industrial uses. Many analytical techniques and scientific principles now being applied in a search for new, industrially useful materials through chemical and microbiological transformation of cereal grains, oilseeds, and unusual plant seeds, or their constituents, were developed under his guidance.*

W. DAYTON MACLAY, *Assistant Administrator of Utilization Research, Agricultural Research Service, Washington, D.C., obtained his doctor's degree in 1932 in organic chemistry at the University of Nebraska. Before serving as Director of the Northern Utilization Research and Development Division from 1954–1959, he worked at the Western Division, the Pacific coast counterpart of the Peoria laboratory, as head of sections responsible for research programs on sugarbeets, alfalfa, wheat, and rice for an 11-State area. His research work has led to publication of 75 scientific papers and numerous patents.*

THE

LIFE PROCESSES

OF SEEDS

꽃꽃꽃꽃꽃꽃꽃꽃꽃꽃꽃꽃꽃꽃꽃꽃꽃꽃꽃꽃꽃꽃꽃꽃꽃꽃꽃꽃꽃꽃꽃꽃꽃꽃꽃꽃꽃

Light, Flowering, and
the Production of Seed

HARRY A. BORTHWICK

ONE MINUTE of artificial light each night holds back the flowering of certain plants, promotes the flowering of some, and has no measurable effect on others.

Our understanding of how we can use light to control flowering—a matter that has practical applications and a direct bearing on the organs in which seeds are produced—has grown in the past few years.

For countless generations people have known that external conditions influence the flowering of plants.

They knew, for example, that the flowering dates of fruit trees vary somewhat from year to year. They attributed this variation largely to seasonal differences in temperature.

They also knew, however, that despite these relatively small differences in time of flowering, their fruit trees always bloomed in early spring, their cereals in early summer, and many of their ornamentals, such as chrysanthemums and cosmos, in late summer or early autumn. These plants thus were able to recognize the onset of the various seasons and to synchronize their development with the change of season.

The mechanism by which certain plants are able to time the events of their lives in such a way that they always bloom at a particular time of year remained undetected until 1919.

In that year Dr. W. W. Garner and Dr. H. A. Allard, plant physiologists in the Department of Agriculture, discovered that Maryland Mammoth tobacco and Biloxi and other varieties of soybean, which normally bloom in autumn, could be made to flower in

37

June or July by subjecting them to artificially shortened days and lengthened nights.

This discovery was one of the most significant advances in botanical science in this century. It marked the recognition of a hitherto unsuspected feature of the environment, the daily duration of light and darkness, as a most important factor regulating plant growth and development.

Dr. Garner and Dr. Allard called the phenomenon photoperiodism, an appropriate name because it recognized the importance of both a light-requiring (*photo-*) reaction and a time-measuring one (*period*) in the response.

Their discovery was confirmed promptly by countless investigators. The phenomenon was found to occur among many flowering plants.

Many kinds, the short-day ones, flower only when the daily light periods are short and the dark periods are long. Examples include numerous fall-flowering plants, such as cosmos, chrysanthemum, and cocklebur.

Others, the long-day ones, flower only when days are long and the dark periods are short. Sugarbeet, garden beet, spinach, wheat, oats, and barley are examples.

In still others, the day-neutral or indeterminate ones, flowering apparently is not influenced by daylength over a wide range of daylengths. Among such plants are tomato and many kinds of garden beans.

THE PROCESS by which plants form flowers is complex and takes time. One can measure the time in some plants by transferring them at a given moment from daylength conditions that prevent flowering to daylength conditions that lead to flowering.

The date of transfer thus gives us a known starting point, which is important because we cannot see the first steps of flowering. Under natural conditions, therefore, one never knows when the flowering process really starts.

We should keep in mind that before we can see any microscopic evidence of flower formation, some most important biochemical changes must occur to cause this shift from vegetative development to floral development.

It is to the initial causal reactions of this change that we give special attention. When we learn more about these first reactions, we should be in a better position to study the remaining steps in flowering.

The entire flowering process is completed in some species in several days. In others it may require many weeks or even months. We can recognize the earliest visible stages of flower formation in a soybean or cocklebur 3 or 4 days after the plants receive short-day treatment if we examine the growing points with a microscope. In another week or more we might be able to see them without a microscope.

The start of flower formation in the chrysanthemum can be seen microscopically a week or 10 days after the beginning of short-day treatment. The flowers are not ready for harvest, however, until 8 to 10 weeks later, or more, depending on the variety.

In some plants, such as apple, the flower primordia are formed during the summer. They develop throughout the rest of the growing season, remain in the bud over winter, and open during the following spring. The entire process takes 8 or 9 months.

We know that the entire process of flower formation and in some instances the formation of fruit and seed are influenced profoundly by daylength.

In some plants, however, the initiation of flowering is so clearly under control of the daylength reaction that we can advantageously restrict the observations to that step in the flowering process. For example, a cocklebur that receives only one short day in its entire life may flower.

The chain of reactions leading to flowering, once they are started by a short-day treatment, can proceed to completion in long days. This does not mean that these reactions might not go faster if more short days were given.

It permits us, for experimental convenience, however, to deal with this initial effect of light without becoming involved with the complexities of the many reactions that make up the flowering process itself.

THE MECHANISM by which light acts to control flowering received attention immediately after Garner's and Allard's discovery of photoperiodism.

Scientists soon learned that the day-length stimulus is received by the leaves and that its controlling action on flowering is transmitted in some way through the leafstalks to the growing points of the stem where the flowers are formed. They found they could bring about flowering in some short-day plants by subjecting a single leaf to short days even though all other leaves receive long days. That fact indicates that a flower-promoting stimulus is produced in the short-day leaf—not a flower-inhibiting one in the long-day ones.

Many workers have searched without success for a flower-inducing hormone in leaves of photoperiodically induced plants.

Because plants flowered on some photoperiods and not on others, it was evident that plants were able to measure time. Whether they measured duration of darkness or light, however, was not apparent until experiments were performed in which each long dark period of daily short-day cycles was broken into two short dark periods by insertion of a few minutes of light near the middle. The effect, which was equivalent to that of a treatment with long days and short nights, inhibited the flowering of short-day plants and promoted that of long-day ones.

The opposite kind of experiment, in which a short period of darkness was placed in the middle of a long light period, resulted in no detectable difference in plant response.

These experiments showed that the time measured was the dark period.

The effectiveness of the brief period of light during a long dark period depends markedly on whether the light period is placed in the middle of the dark period or elsewhere.

It has maximum effect if it is placed near the middle. It may have no observable influence on flowering if it comes near the beginning or end of the dark period.

Flowering of many short-day plants, such as soybean, chrysanthemum, and Japanese morning-glory, can be completely inhibited—checked and held up—by less than a minute of light of 25 to 50 foot-candles in the middle of dark periods at least 12 hours long. Long-day plants, such as barley and other small grains, are induced to flower by similar light treatments in the middle of 12-hour dark periods.

The discovery of this remarkable responsiveness of plants to irradiances of such brief duration and low energy suggested that a further way to investigate the nature of the light reaction would be to interrupt the dark periods with light of narrow wavelength limits and of known energies.

Such experiments done quantitatively show, for example, whether the photoperiod reaction depends on light absorption by chlorophyll or by some other pigmented substance that has light-absorbing characteristics different from those of chlorophyll. The method thus permits one to learn whether responses of plants to light that seem quite different superficially are controlled by the same photoreactions or by different ones.

The procedure involves measuring the minimum light energy required at each wavelength position to cause a particular response, such as promotion of flowering of long-day plants or inhibition of flowering of short-day ones.

Such experiments require special equipment to obtain light that is sufficiently pure and has enough energy to cause the plant to react. This is sometimes done by the use of light filters that permit passage of only the wavelengths desired, or it may be done by passing a strong beam of light through a spectrograph, an instrument containing a system of mirrors and prisms arranged to produce a spectrum. Such an instrument, when illuminated with very high-intensity light from a carbon-arc or other high-intensity source, produces a spectrum of sufficient size that small plants or whole leaves of larger ones can be irradiated with enough light of the desired wavelength range to cause the plant to exhibit some developmental response that we can measure.

THE EFFECTIVENESS of the different colors of light was measured with such an instrument for several long- and short-day plants. The results were remarkably similar.

Red light of about 6,500 A (A= angstrom, a unit of wavelength of light equivalent to about one hundred-millionth of a centimeter) was found to be far more effective than any other color for inhibiting flowering of short-day plants and promoting flowering of long-day ones. Blue light of less than 4,400 A was slightly effective in some plants but far less than red. Other colors were less effective than blue.

These results proved that the photochemical reaction regulating flowering was the same in short- and long-day plants despite the fact that it inhibited flowering of the former and promoted flowering of the latter.

SCIENTISTS investigated also the action of light on some other responses of plants to learn whether the light reaction of photoperiodism might also cause these effects.

One such response was seed germination, the light relations of which are considered in a later chapter. Because some of the studies of seed gave new insight into the flowering reaction, we should consider a few findings here.

It was learned that the action of light in the control of germination is remarkably like its action in control of flowering. Red light promoted germination in seeds. Other colors had little or no promotive effect. This result alone was strong evidence that the light reaction in photoperiodic control of flowering is the same as that for promotion of germination of seed.

Another important observation, however, which had special significance for studies of flowering, also came from the studies of seed germination.

Short-wavelength infrared, the so-called far red (7,000–7,400 A), was found to inhibit the germination of certain seeds that normally would germinate in the dark. This waveband also reinhibited the germination of seeds that had first been irradiated with red. These reinhibited seeds, moreover, could be immediately repromoted to germinate by another brief red treatment.

The germination results, in brief, showed that the promotive action of red on seed germination was reversed by far red and that the far-red inhibition in turn was reversed by red. Moreover, the results suggested that since opposing actions of red and far red were exhibited in germination they might also be present in photoperiodism.

The presence of red, far-red reversibility in flowering was tested in experiments with cocklebur, soybean, and other short-day plants.

The object of the experiments was to reinduce flowering in the plants by means of a radiation treatment immediately after they had received enough red light in the middle of the night to inhibit flowering.

The experiments were successful. Plants given far red after an inhibitory treatment with red that made control lots of the plants vegetative, flowered nearly as well as plants that received no light treatment during the night.

The discovery that flowering and seed germination were both reversibly controlled by red and far-red light was extremely strong evidence that the same basic photochemical reaction was involved in both responses.

Similar studies of the photoreactions regulating stem growth and leaf expansion (which are vegetative responses), production of anthocyanin, and several other light responses showed that these also were photoreversible by red and far red.

Photoperiodic control of flowering thus proved to be just one manifestation of a photoreaction that plants use to regulate many features of their growth and development.

Details of the reaction can be studied in the response that best serves a particular experimental purpose because the same light reaction is involved in all of these different phenomena. Thus some of our present knowledge of how light controls flowering has come from studies of how it controls seed germination and stem elongation.

DETAILS of the flowering reaction for which there had been no apparent experimental approach could now be investigated by making use of this characteristic.

For example, one could learn how quickly the flower-inhibiting action of red light actually takes place by starting it with a red treatment and then finding how long a far-red treatment could be delayed without loss of reversibility.

Such experiments required two light sources, one of red light and one of far red. A satisfactory red source consists of a fluorescent lamp equipped with a red cellophane filter to remove the light of wavelength shorter than 6,000 A. The fluorescent lamp is used instead of an incandescent-filament one because it emits very little far red. The resulting filtered light is, therefore, reasonably pure red.

A suitable far-red source is an incandescent-filament lamp filtered with blue and red cellophane. The cellophane filters remove almost all of the visible light but are transparent to far red, which is abundant in the radiation from such lamps.

One notes that a 1-minute treatment with red light in the middle of the night prevents flowering of a cocklebur plant, but that a far-red treatment after the red one is completed stops the flower-inhibiting reaction before it has actually gone far enough to interfere seriously with flowering.

If one delays giving the far-red treatment after the red treatment, however, he finds that after 30 minutes to an hour the far red no longer reinduces flowering. This shows that the flower-inhibiting reaction started by the red light does not go to completion immediately, but continues to operate for at least an hour after the light is turned off: Some product made by the red light persists therefore after the light is turned off and functions in some way to interfere with the reactions leading to flowering.

Flowering is much more completely reversible by red and far red in some plants than in others.

Flowerbuds reinduced in cocklebur by far red after an inhibitory treatment with red, for example, are often almost as large as those of untreated control plants.

In soybean the reinduced buds are less numerous and usually smaller than in the controls. In chrysanthemum the buds of reinduced plants frequently are only one-half to two-thirds the size of those of controls.

In *Pharbitis nil*, the Japanese morning-glory, reinduction of flowering by far red in the middle of the dark period fails completely. Seedlings of this plant only a few days old initiate flowerbuds readily when subjected to only 2 or 3 long nights. If irradiated with red in the middle of each dark period, however, flowering is prevented and is not reinduced by far red. However, weak reinduction of flowering by far red in older seedlings of *Pharbitis* that have developed true leaves has been observed.

The reasons for this variation in response to far red from one species to another or within the same species are not yet fully understood.

Repeated reversals of flowering response have been made in cocklebur, chrysanthemum, and a few other plants. In these experiments, a group of plants is subjected alternately in the middle of each night to a brief treatment with red light followed by a brief far-red one, and so on for as many as four alternating treatments with each kind of light. At each step in the treatment one lot is withdrawn to darkness until finally the last remaining lot received its final far-red treatment. In these experiments, half of the lots flower and half remain vegetative. The flowering ones in all instances are the ones that receive far red last.

SCIENTISTS deduce the nature of the light reaction from results of these various experiments on flowering and of others on germination of seed, elongation of stems, and other phenomena that are controlled by the red, far-red reaction.

The response to red or far-red light occurs because the plant preferentially absorbs the energy of those wavelengths and transfers this absorbed energy to some chemical reaction. The response of a plant to red therefore requires the presence in the plant of a red-absorbing compound. Thus, without actually seeing it, one knows that a special pigment is present, because the plant responds to red light. He also knows the color of the pigment, because red-absorbing compounds are necessarily blue or green.

The amount of these pigmented compounds is very low, however, as can be shown in albino seedlings. The elongation of the stems of albino barley seedlings is regulated by the red, far-red reaction and is as effectively controlled in them as in the normal green ones. Concentrations of the pigment in the albino plants thus are adequate to control lengthening response but so low that the eye detects no color.

THE PIGMENT exists in two interconvertible forms, as shown by experiments on photoreversible control of flowering, germination of seed, and other plant responses.

When the plant is irradiated with red light, for example, the pigment molecules absorb some of the light and thereby are changed in structure. The changed pigment molecules have the property of absorbing far red very effectively. They are changed back to the original red-absorbing form when they are irradiated with far red. The pigment thus can be converted repeatedly from one form to the other.

One pigment form or the other apparently is a necessary link in the chain of chemical reactions leading to flowering, germination, and so on.

Evidence from experiments strongly suggests—but does not prove—that the active form is the far-red-absorbing one.

The active form, irrespective of which one it is, however, functions as an enzyme in a reaction that is still unidentified. Red light thus either activates or inactivates this enzyme.

If the radiation treatment activates the enzyme, the latter continues in the active form even though the light is turned off. Thus, in the prevention of flowering of such short-day plants as cocklebur or soybean, interrupting the dark period briefly with light completely inhibits flowering if the plants are allowed to remain in the dark for 30 minutes or more before they are reirradiated with far red.

DIRECT DETECTION of the pigment in plant material by chemical methods was not possible because of lack of knowledge of its biochemical reactions. The extremely low concentration of the pigment in the plant, moreover, made its detection by ordinary laboratory spectrophotometers improbable.

Physiological experiments, which gave detailed knowledge of the pigment, however, indicated that a spectrophotometer of special design should detect its presence. Such an instrument, constructed at the Plant Industry Station for a purpose unrelated to this problem, was used successfully.

The pigment was found in several kinds of dark-grown seedlings. It was detected, in fact, in a single intact corn seedling, in which it proved to be most abundant in the uppermost part of the elongating first internode and in the coleoptile. The reversibility of the pigment was still present after the seedling was fragmented and ground under proper conditions, and it remained in the liquid portion upon filtration. This meant that the scientists could now study the biochemistry of the reversible photoperiodic pigment.

WHERE DOES this kind of work with light on flowering lead us?

What is its promise in agriculture?

The long-range objective is more complete understanding of the growth and development of plants. This knowledge will help crop specialists develop more efficient methods of production.

We see that light plays a fundamental role in the regulation of flowering and the production of seed. It is important in germination. Light regulates the habit of growth of seedlings and the adult plants.

Moreover, we find that a single light reaction is concerned with each of these expressions of growth and development—probably with others that are still to be studied.

This reaction of plants to light thus gets right to the heart of the regulation of many aspects of plant growth.

IMPROVEMENTS in procedures of plant production came immediately from the discovery of photoperiodism.

One of the first uses made of the information was by cereal agronomists as early as 1922. They used supplemental light over small-grain crops to promote the flowering and fruiting of a winter-grown crop in the greenhouse.

They soon found that they could produce two successive greenhouse crops and still have time to grow a third crop in the field during the normal growing season. This procedure enabled them to complete programs of plant breeding in much shorter time than formerly.

In these first applications, the artificial light was turned on before sundown and continued for several hours to obtain a long-day response. The assumed necessity of following this procedure was based on the feeling that the light, not the dark, was the controlling time period of the daily cycle.

The discovery in 1937 that the reverse was true and that a brief period of light in the middle of the night was about as effective as continuous light from sundown until midnight resulted in modification of lighting procedures.

Agronomists and others found that a few minutes or an hour of light in the middle of winter nights promoted flowering of small grains, for example, as well as did the former method of prolonged lighting.

Florists also were quick to use light to extend the productive period of chrysanthemums. They, too, originally gave the supplemental light in conjunction with the daily period of natural light. Dark-period interruptions proved to be as effective as prolonged lighting, however, and avoided objectionable stem elongation that prolonged lighting often brings about.

Breeders of sugarbeets began almost at once to use supplemental light to induce flowering. They found that incandescent-filament lamps effectively induced flowering. The fluorescent lamps were almost without effect. This difference in response apparently was connected with differences in the wavelength composition of the two kinds of light—incandescent-filament light contains much more far red in proportion to red than does fluorescent light.

We now know that this response of beets is in some way a result of the red, far-red reaction.

The results with sugarbeets emphasize the importance of knowledge of the detailed effects of different wavelengths.

The most extensive commercial application of control of daylength in the United States is made by growers of chrysanthemums. They supply cut flowers in a range of varieties and colors throughout the year.

During periods when natural nights are long enough to induce flowering, the growers use supplemental light to delay blossoming until the plant attains proper size and to time the harvest for dates of their choice. They bring the plants into bloom by discontinuing the light treatments several weeks before the desired harvest date, thus allowing the natural long nights to induce flower formation. The procedure is practiced widely in greenhouses and out of doors in places where winter temperatures are warm enough for chrysanthemums.

Several hundred acres of chrysanthemums were grown under lights out of doors in the United States in 1961.

During periods of the year when daily night length is too short to promote the flowering of chrysanthemums, the growers cover the plants with black cloth for a few hours morning or evening, or both, to create adequately long daily dark periods. This procedure is practiced in the greenhouse and sometimes out of doors.

The practices of the chrysanthemum growers are applied commercially but less extensively by growers of orchids, asters, tuberous-rooted begonias, *Kalanchoe blossfeldiana*, feverfew, and *Stevia*.

Poinsettia, a short-day plant, usually is grown in the greenhouse in periods of natural long nights. It would seem that no special attention need be paid to its daylength requirements. In practice, however, poinsettias are lighted during the second half of September and the first third of October. Lighting is then discontinued, and often the plants are given artificially lengthened dark periods for a week or two so that the flower-inducing reactions will begin promptly. After that, the natural dark periods are long enough to promote flowering.

Poinsettias are so sensitive to light that special care must be used to avoid low intensities, such as from the watchman's flashlight, a nearby street lamp, or passing automobiles, which would delay or inhibit flowering.

The use of artificial light on field crops presents difficulties.

Although it is used commercially to control flowering of chrysanthemums and a few other ornamentals, artificial light is not used in the commercial production of field crops. It is not probable that extensive field use will be made of it in the foreseeable future. The reason is that the cost of providing an extensive lighting installation makes it impractical.

Sugarcane, as grown in Hawaii and Puerto Rico, illustrates the problems. The yield of sugar is less when cane forms flowers because flowering stops the growth of leaves and stems. The further growth of the plant thus is restricted. Sugarcane begins to form flower primordia about the first of September—only at that time of year does the natural daylength become favorable.

Cane, moreover, is unusual in that it is unable to flower when the daylength is longer or shorter than these September days. Therefore it is unnecessary to use light for more than a period of 2 or 3 weeks in September to prevent flowering throughout the entire year. Light applied properly during this period is 100 percent effective in preventing the formation of flowers, and the amount of light needed each night is trivial. Nevertheless, the costs of an adequate lighting installation preclude use of this procedure.

One might therefore reasonably question the wisdom of devoting so much time and money to the study of flower control by light if the knowledge has so little promise of extensive field application.

KNOWLEDGE of the light reactions of plants does have practical applications in other than the direct use of light.

An important one is that it helps us find or breed varieties of crops that are adapted to the natural daylength conditions of an area. If we can do that, we do not have to try to change the daylength conditions of large regions to meet crop requirements.

Soybeans are grown extensively in

the United States, but no one variety is widely grown. Instead, certain varieties are restricted to comparatively narrow latitudes 75 to 100 miles wide. In areas either to the north or south, other varieties are sown because they are better adapted to the slightly different daylength conditions and they are therefore more apt to mature at the proper time and have greater yields.

It seems almost incredible that daylength differences such as occur between points only 100 or so miles apart north and south could cause measurable differences in plant response. An experiment with soybeans at the Agricultural Research Center at Beltsville, Md., however, demonstrated that this was indeed true.

The durations of natural light, including twilight, were calculated for each day of the growing season at Beltsville, and points in southern Virginia and central North Carolina.

Soybeans grown at Beltsville on these three artificially maintained daylength schedules matured at different times. Those of the southernmost schedule were significantly earlier than the middle one. The middle one was earlier than the northern one. The greatest difference in daylength between neighboring lots occurred on the longest day of the season and was only about 15 minutes. Since all of the lots were subjected equally to all other fluctuating environmental variables except daylength, the differences in maturing must be attributed to the effects of daylength.

Daylength influences the further growth and development of flowers after they are initiated, although I did not stress this point in the earlier part of this discussion.

One long night causes floral initiation in cocklebur, but repeated treatments with long night are necessary for more rapid development of the flowers.

Flowers of soybean plants often drop, unless the plants are given long nights until after the pods are set.

Initiation of flowers by red kidney bean occurs regardless of daylength, but at some temperatures daylength markedly influences the yield of beans.

In the blue-mist spirea, the visible flowerbuds form on any daylength but never open on long days. On short days, however, the young buds grow rapidly and the flowers open in about 3 weeks.

The effects of daylength may thus be expressed at any or all stages in the development of flowers.

THE FUTURE of our knowledge and understanding of the action of light in the control of flowering and many other features of plant growth and development is bright.

At the beginning of 1961, when I prepared this chapter, the photoreactive pigment had been extracted from dark-grown corn seedlings and held for several months without loss of photoreversibility. Its presence had also been detected in a dozen or more other kinds of plants, and initial steps in its purification had been made. Its complete purification and identification are expected, and with identification one hopes may come knowledge of the reaction catalyzed by its active form.

This work leads to understanding of a basic reaction controlling growth and development of plants, but the immediate objectives are not the solution of individual problems of plant production.

When the fundamental principles of light action on plants are understood, specialists will apply them intelligently to many production problems peculiar to their individual crops.

HARRY A. BORTHWICK *is Director of the Plant Physiology Pioneering Research Laboratory, Plant Industry Station, Beltsville, Md. This laboratory was chartered in 1957. Its purpose is to investigate the various effects of light on the growth and development of plants and to find and understand the basic photoreactions that control these plant responses.*

Temperatures and Fruits and Seeds

JOHN H. WEINBERGER

DURING the warm months nearly all deciduous trees and many other plants in the United States form leaves, manufacture their food, and grow actively. During the colder months leaves are lost, visible growth ceases, and the plants rest. Temperature, like light, thus may influence the dormancy of buds and consequently flowering and the production of fruits and seeds.

This pattern of behavior is necessary for survival, because all actively growing tissues in plants are harmed or killed by temperatures only a little below the freezing point. Plants could not survive in most parts of this country if somewhere in their system they did not have a mechanism to keep them safely dormant through periods of freezing temperatures.

The mechanism involved is called rest, and the stage at which buds are unable to grow (even though external conditions are favorable for growth) is the rest period.

The rest is of particular advantage in the fall and early winter, when temperatures may be warm enough for growth but freezing temperatures are apt to occur. The buds need the rest to hold them dormant while they are becoming hardened by exposure to increasingly colder temperatures and are acquiring resistance to cold. The hardening process will not take place while the tree is growing.

The rest begins fairly early, soon after terminal growth ceases. As leaves are formed on the actively growing twig, buds develop in the axil of the leaf where the petiole is attached to the shoot. The bud is well formed by the time the leaf is fully developed.

The rest seems to develop in buds from the base upward, and individual buds at the base of the shoot may be in the rest while the shoot is still growing terminally. The fact that lateral buds on a shoot do not grow during the summer does not indicate they are in the rest. Hormones from the growing tip may check development of the buds. Cutting off the tip of the shoot would remove the inhibitory influence, and the bud may be forced into growth.

The rest influence in the bud develops gradually as the shoot becomes more mature and the bud older. The inhibitory influence from the shoot apex, which keeps them dormant, becomes less essential. The rest is easily broken early in bud development by leaf injury, wet weather, pruning, or other stimuli.

The practice of June budding in commercial nurseries is based on the principle that newly formed buds may readily be forced into growth. The resting influence becomes stronger as the summer progresses, and buds are less readily forced into growth.

Nurseries successfully practice dormant budding in late summer without stimulating growth of the transferred bud during that season. Although buds are essentially dormant during the summer and winter, they are still undergoing changes and development without making externally visible growth, if temperatures are above the minimum for growth.

Certain of the buds, because of internal influences, are transformed into flowerbuds, usually during late summer. During fall and winter, while their rest is being broken, these flowerbuds continue to develop flower initials very slowly.

All buds are well into their rest at time of leaf-fall, although there is no causal relationship between leaf-fall and rest. The shortened length of daylight of the fall season causes the leaves of many species of trees to drop.

Additional illumination postpones leaf-fall, but even under continuous illumination on trees under street lights foliage is not retained indefinitely. In other species, length of day, or photoperiod, has no effect on the trees entering dormancy. The cooler weather of fall, or simply the physiological aging of the leaf, is responsible for leaf-fall in some species.

Evergreen trees undergo periods of active growth followed by periods of dormancy, or quiescence. This is more of a cyclic growth habit, and the dormant buds of evergreens are not necessarily in a resting condition.

MUCH OF THE WORK on the mode of breaking of the rest period of buds has been done with deciduous fruit trees, particularly the peach, *Prunus persica*. Other species of deciduous trees would differ somewhat in the intensity of the rest or duration of rest, but their pattern of behavior would be similar.

The peach is grown commercially in areas where the rest is sometimes not completely broken, and serious economic losses occur. The rest period of peaches is broken in the natural sequence of events during winter. The buds then are able to resume normal growth with the arrival of warm temperatures of spring.

Periods of low temperatures are responsible for breaking the rest. Chilling weather may occur even before the leaves are shed, and emergence from the rest then begins.

As the periods of chilling accumulate, the emergence is gradual, and it becomes increasingly easier to force the buds into growth by external stimuli. Extreme cold is not necessary. Temperatures of 45° F. are adequate, and even a temperature of 50° is effective but less efficient.

Probably the optimal temperature for breaking the rest of peach buds is around 40°—fully as effective as freezing temperatures. In climates with long winters like those of the Northern States, the rest is broken long before the winter is over—often by early December. The time at which it is broken is determined easily by bringing shoots from the orchard into a warm room, placing the cut ends in water, and observing the development of the buds.

When peach trees have had their chilling requirements partly satisfied, many buds are in position to develop very slowly at temperatures favorable for growth.

If no further chilling occurs, straggly development and a condition called prolonged dormancy results. Blossoming may extend over 2 months. The flowers are generally weak and underdeveloped, and the style and stigma may fail to grow, although the ovary develops. Pollen development is weak. Many anthers fail to dehisce. Fruit set is poor. Some early-opening blossoms may have developed fruits the size of walnuts while the foliage is still sparse. Variable percentages of flowerbuds will drop off without opening.

Leafbuds generally require more chilling than flowerbuds do. If their chilling requirements are not satisfied, leafbuds may remain dormant or may make a small flush of growth and then become dormant.

In certain districts of southern California where winters are warm and summers are cool, growth sometimes starts before the rest is completely broken, fails to elongate normally, and then reverts to a resting condition. The tree is never completely out of the rest, and the rest inhibition dwarfs the tree.

The older buds in the center of the trees are the first to break dormancy when chilling is inadequate. They have undergone two or more chilling periods and need less chilling the second time than 1-year-old buds. The next buds to develop are terminal shoot buds. Buds on shoot spurs and lateral buds are last.

Flowerbuds on certain varieties may drop off completely after extremely warm winters in the Southeast. No leafbuds develop. The tree is left completely dormant until very late spring. Then high temperatures of late April and May exert their influence in breaking the rest of the leafbuds and forcing them into sudden growth. Normal development follows during the summer.

The problem of warm winters in the commercial production of peaches was described by S. H. Rumph, the originator of the Elberta peach, as early as 1890. Thirty years later research workers proved that lack of chilling is responsible.

In the Proceedings of the Georgia Horticultural Society for 1890, Mr. Rumph reported:

"The fruit growers in this section will long remember 1890 as the most peculiar and disastrous season ever witnessed. The extremely dry winter or some other unknown cause prevented peaches from blooming in February and March at their usual time. Our first cold wave during the winter came January 16, and then the thermometer registered only 30 degrees above zero. . . . Belle, Elberta . . . commenced blooming about April 5 . . . but the blooms were almost void of petals and the trees . . . did not leaf until late in April and May. It was a strange sight to see orchards of Alexanders without a leaf, as late as May 20th, the time that this variety usually ripens. . . ."

The mean temperature for November to February of that winter was 7.2° above average.

THE TIME element, or the length of time during which chilling occurs, is important.

An accumulation by early February of 750 hours during which temperatures were 45° or lower at Fort Valley, Ga., is sufficient to break the rest period of buds of Southland peach. That is the minimum requirement when the chilling is spread over 3 months. The rest could be broken earlier, by January 22 on occasion, but in this shorter period an accumulation of 1 thousand hours of chilling is necessary. Continuous chilling breaks the rest in the shortest length of time, but actually requires a greater number of hours of chilling than if the chilling

alternated with warmer temperatures and was spread over a period of 3 months.

Most other important varieties of peaches have chilling requirements equal to that of Southland or greater. Mayflower has one of the longest requirements, about 1,200 hours. On the other extreme are varieties like St. Helena and Red Ceylon, which are nearly evergreen and require very little chilling.

The chilling requirements of peach varieties expressed in hours of chilling apply only to the southeastern United States where the observations were made.

Weather patterns are different in the Southwest and California, and other measures or adjustments must be applied.

In the Central Valley of California, the principal peach-growing area of the West, winter weather is characterized by fogs or low clouds, which keep temperatures constant at around 50° or slightly lower for days at a time. Each hour of chilling under such conditions appears to be nearly 50 percent more effective than under normal conditions in the Southeast. After winters with little fog, the responses of peach buds in the two areas seem to be alike.

Temperatures in December and January are much more important in breaking the rest of peach buds in the Southeast than temperatures in November or February. The mean temperatures for December and January are just as reliable an indicator of the progress of rest breaking as hours of chilling, and the two measures may be used interchangeably.

Thus varieties that require an accumulation of 750 chilling hours have their rest broken if the December-January average temperature is 51° or below.

Satisfactory crops are produced if the temperature averages a little higher, but the trees show some symptoms of a prolonged dormancy trouble.

Varieties like Elberta that need 850 hours for flowerbuds blossom normally after 49.6° in December and January, but with a 950-hour leafbud requirement, Elberta trees leaf out normally only after a 48.3° in December–January.

Dixired trees, which need 1,050 hours for leafbuds, foliate normally only if December–January temperatures average 47° or lower. These temperature relations apply only in the Southeast.

High temperatures during the rest-breaking period counteract the effects of chilling instead of advancing development. Buds on trees in the shade of some object require less chilling than exposed trees.

Warm, sunny days increase the chilling requirements of buds. A few days of extremely high temperature during the first part of the rest may produce abnormalities in flowerbuds of peaches that subsequent chilling fails to overcome. Typical abnormal blooming occurs, even though the winter has been cold.

Leafbuds differ from flowerbuds in that subsequent chilling may be effective in overcoming the influences of high temperatures. The resting condition is a reversible process in leafbuds and to a limited extent in flowerbuds.

BUD DROP, a serious problem for some species of fruit, particularly apricot, is associated with warm winters. The temperature relation is not the direct cause, however.

Anthers in buds of stone fruits start to deteriorate and turn brown in late winter and early spring about the time visible swelling of buds occurs. The condition spreads to other flower parts, and as many as 95 percent of apricot buds may fall off. A 50-percent bud drop in peaches is not uncommon.

Among pome fruits having mixed buds, like the apple and the pear, all or only some of the flowers may fall off. A spur is left that has only a cluster of leaves or leaves and a reduced number of flowers.

The condition has been correlated with high temperatures in early fall, although bud drop is also greater in winters having fewer chilling hours. Generally it is more serious in peach varieties that have a long chilling requirement, but exceptions occur, particularly in varieties having a moderate chilling requirement.

Peach varieties of Peento origin that require little chilling may be affected severely by bud drop. High maximum temperatures during the winter are not responsible for the condition.

THE REST influence seems to be centered largely in the buds. It was once thought the cambium had no rest and only the bud was affected. The idea was disproved when active apple scions grafted on unchilled trees did not grow so well as those grafted on trees where the rest period had been broken by chilling. Both series of stocks had been disbudded to eliminate any bud influence on growth.

Thus far no adequate substitute has been found to replace chilling temperatures in breaking the rest of buds on orchard trees.

Heat, freezing, ether, alcohol, hydrochloric acid, oil, sodium nitrate, chloroform, ethylene dichloride, ethylene chlorhydrin, and other organic compounds have some influence if the rest has been partly broken. Mechanical injury or wounding is effective.

Spraying orchards with an emulsified oil, either lubricating, linseed or seal oil, has hastened blossoming and foliation of apple and pear trees.

Fortifying the oil with dinitrocresol increases effectiveness. Too often in this country injury results from this treatment without adequate bud response. The basis of the stimulation seems to be largely an influence of injury. The closer a treatment comes to killing a bud, the greater appears to be its stimulating properties.

As yet there is no safe, cheap, and dependable means of preventing prolonged dormancy on orchard trees where the winters are warm.

THE CAUSE of the rest has been a subject for investigation for many years. Diffusible auxins, sometimes thought responsible, generally are higher in rest-broken buds and deficient in buds during the rest. It is unlikely therefore that they are agents. C. H. Hendershott and D. R. Walker, of the North Carolina State College, identified a growth inhibitor in dormant peach flowerbuds as naringenin (5,7,4' trihydroxyflavanone). It was eight times more plentiful in buds collected December 1, 1958, than in those collected February 2, 1959.

THE SOUTHERN limits of successful production of many fruits and nuts in the United States is determined by the chilling requirements of their buds. When prolonged dormancy and subsequent crop losses occur too often, production becomes unprofitable, and susceptible kinds or varieties of fruit disappear from an area.

Acceptable varieties of fruits having relatively short chilling requirements are being developed, and the frontiers of the commercial production of these fruits are being extended southward. The problem in this country is of consequence only in the southern border States, including North Carolina, South Carolina, and Georgia.

Varieties of peaches vary widely in their chilling requirements. The southernmost area of production of the leading varieties is in south-central Georgia, but less acceptable varieties are adapted to the winter climate of Miami, Fla.

The Babcock variety, which has a short chilling requirement, is planted extensively in southern California. Maygold is grown commercially as far south as northwestern Florida. Jewel and the new Tejon, Red Ceylon, and Rochon varieties require less chilling than Babcock or Maygold. Many good varieties are in the class that need 750 hours of chilling or are adapted to December–January winters that average 51°. Among them (in order of ripening) are Springtime, Earligold,

Hiland, Robin, Redcap, Keystone, Sunhigh, Southland, July Elberta, Merrill 49'er, and Redskin.

Breeders in time will develop varieties suitable for commercial production in all southern regions.

Nectarines—sports of peaches—are like peaches in their adaptability to a warm climate, but no extremely short-chilling varieties are known. Silver Lode and Panamint have a moderately short chilling requirement.

Apples generally require more chilling than peaches, but the range among varieties is wide. Some varieties, as Hume and Beverly Hills, are adapted to the warm winters of southern California. Important apple districts in the United States generally have cold winters, and winter chilling is a minor aspect.

Pears are similar to apples in chilling requirements of varieties. Leading producing areas are in cooler climates. Baldwin, Garber, Kieffer, LeConte, Orient, and Pineapple are varieties having short chilling requirements.

THE ORIENTAL plums (*Prunus salicina*) require relatively little chilling, compared with other fruits. Varieties like Mariposa and Burmosa are adapted to winters of southern California. The European plum varieties (*Prunus domestica*) blossom much later as a group than the Oriental plums. Tragedy and Sugar require less chilling than others.

American plums, *Prunus americana*, have long chilling requirements. *Prunus angustifolia* are native throughout the Southeast. Bruce and Six Weeks, commercial varieties that are hybrids of *Prunus salicina* and *Prunus angustifolia*, are adapted to warm areas of the Southeast.

Apricot buds require relatively little chilling and begin development even before almonds. Apricot trees shed their flowerbuds following warm winters, however, and the crop suffers. Thus, although the species is adapted by chilling requirements to warm winters, bud drop prevents successful commercial production in the warm sections.

Because buds of the sweet cherry and sour cherry (*Prunus avium* and *P. cerasus*) have moderately high chilling requirements, they generally are unsuited to warm sections.

Grape buds require little chilling to break their rest. The eastern grape, *Vitis labrusca*, is native to areas having long, cold winters, but it has an extremely short chilling requirement.

The European grape, *Vitis vinifera*, requires no chilling after the vine becomes dormant to make normal growth. A period of 10 to 12 weeks, however, elapses before growth starts. Time appears to be the controlling factor in breaking the dormancy of *vinifera* buds.

Almonds have short chilling requirements. Their rest is broken early in the winter. This trait, plus the fact the buds will grow at rather low temperatures, makes the frost hazard a serious problem for growers of almonds.

Trees of Persian walnut, *Juglans regia*, and filberts are sometimes affected by lack of winter chilling in warmer climates. Placentia variety of walnut is the best known among those having shorter chilling requirements. The Barcelona variety of filbert generally suffers least from lack of chilling.

Pecans, which are native to southeastern United States, require little winter chilling. Some forms of pecan growing wild in Indiana need more chilling than those that grow in Mississippi.

FLOWERING and the production of fruits and seeds in many deciduous trees therefore depend on a certain rhythmic response to temperature during the dormant season. Doubtless many other plants not so well studied are similarly affected by temperature in the formation of seed.

JOHN H. WEINBERGER *is a horticulturist in the Fruit and Nut Crops Research Branch, Crops Research Division, Department of Agriculture, Fresno, Calif.*

Growth Regulators, Stimulants, and Seeds

PAUL C. MARTH AND JOHN W. MITCHELL

SOME KINDS of woody plants have been made to grow six times faster than normal by treating them with one of the chemicals we call plant-regulating compounds or plant regulators.

Minute amounts of the compounds can alter the growth and behavior of plants in many ways. They can increase or restrict or otherwise influence the production of flowers and seeds. Many of the effects are as striking as those produced on animals by animal hormones.

A number of the compounds have been used beneficially and safely for years. Others have been discovered recently, and methods of correctly using them are being developed.

It takes 10 to 18 years to produce flowers and fruits on some slow-growing plants, such as fruit, nut, and forest trees. That long period makes a problem for growers and plant breeders who work with them to produce new, good, disease-resistant varieties. Seeds of some wild desert plants, on the other hand, germinate, grow, and produce flowers in a few days after a light rain.

We have various theories as to why plants flower when they do. The discovery of a natural, universally occurring, flowering hormone, or "florigen," would offer a simple explanation.

A great difficulty in conducting research in this field has been the lack of methods of detecting and identifying natural hormones that we now know occur in tiny, changing amounts in different parts of plants.

Modern refined methods, such as chromatography (a technique that permits a scientist to remove, purify, and identify infinitesimal quantities of organic compounds that occur in plant tissues and which may be the causal agents for regulating growth); the use of radioisotopes (which are of aid in tracing the movement and chemical behavior of small quantities of organic compounds); and the adaptation of newly developed physical equipment (such as the ultra centrifuge, the electron microscope, and improvement in the spectrophotometer), have facilitated this research and are opening new approaches to the problem.

By the use of the older methods, which were relatively crude, scientists learned that naturally occurring plant regulators reached a low concentration in the young vegetative tips of plants just before they changed to the flowering state.

Scientists all over the world have long been searching for a simple, effective chemical method of altering growth so that the plant flowers.

The research has been especially successful with pineapple. Growers of pineapples now load their sprayers with a dilute solution of plant-regulating chemical and thoroughly wet the foliage. The plants show visible flowerbuds within a few weeks. The flowering of pineapples, which usually requires a year or more, has been shortened as much as 11 months by the spray treatment. It is not desirable to apply the plant regulator too early after planting, because small plants, chemically induced to flower too soon, ultimately produce small, undesirable fruits. Naphthaleneacetic acid (NAA) once was considered effective, but scientists have found that low concentrations of 2,4-D, which also is used widely as a herbicide, is less costly and more effective in causing pineapples to flower.

Many hundreds of acres of pineapple in Hawaii and Puerto Rico were sprayed commercially in 1959 to regulate flowering. The sprays are applied carefully so that the fruit is of a size to fit processing machines. If the sprays are applied too early, the fruit does not develop to full size. If they are applied too late, flowering is delayed and the fruit matures late and is too big.

In other words, one growth regulator can bring about opposite flowering effects, depending on the concentration and the time it is applied.

Plant regulators that differ chemically also produce opposite effects sometimes. N-meta-tolylphthalamic acid (a plant regulator that affects flowering), for instance, has induced numerous terminal flowers to develop in the greenhouse on varieties of tomato that ordinarily blossom laterally on the plant and never at the top. This chemical, applied under certain conditions, causes unusual fasciated, or doubled, flowers. The development of individual flower parts apparently can be drastically changed by the chemical.

THE GIBBERELLINS, potent growth regulators produced as a metabolic byproduct by the fungus *Gibberella fujikuroi*, a serious disease of growing rice, have stimulated research and widespread interest. They bring about a wide variety of responses on many different kinds of plants.

Rapid production of seedstalks and flowers within a few weeks after treatment occurred in numerous species of biennial plants, such as beets, carrots, radishes, celery, and cabbage, which require 2 years to flower. It is believed generally that under natural conditions of development of a seedstalk, bolting, or stem elongation, in these plants is due to the production of a natural plant hormone produced by the developing flowers.

Gibberellins, applied externally, apparently can substitute effectively for this hormone.

To demonstrate this phenomenon, F. Lona, of Parma, in Italy, placed the developing seedstalks of bolting radish plants in alcohol. He applied this extract to young radish plants and induced them to bolt in a manner and at a rate like those of comparable plants sprayed with gibberellin.

Gibberellins or substances like gibberellins occur rather widely in many species.

An early demonstration of their existence and potency was given in experiments by John W. Mitchell. In searching for plant hormones of high potency from natural sources, he found that the translucent juice in young developing bean seeds about 7 to 9 days after fertilization is an extremely rich source of what is now called gibberellinlike hormones. This research was done in 1950, long before the purified gibberellins were available in this country. An extract of one tiny bean seed (slightly larger than the head of a pin), applied to four young bean plants, caused them all to develop new stem growth at a rate 25 times greater than the controls. This rate of growth would be comparable to that resulting from a heavy application of gibberellin.

Another scientist of the Department of Agriculture, Frank H. Stodola, of the Northern Utilization Research and Development Division, Peoria, Ill., prepared the first pure gibberellin in the United States.

Biennial plants are not the only ones that produce earlier flowers when treated with gibberellic acid. Neil Stuart and others, in experiments conducted at the Agricultural Research Center at Beltsville, Md., were able to induce early flowering in more or less woody plants, such as hydrangeas and Pfitzer juniper.

Some plants require a period of cold treatment to stimulate production of flowers. Hydrangea plants, for instance, are generally stored 3 months at $40°$ F. before they are forced in the greenhouse to produce flowers for Easter or Mother's Day. Spraying the plants with dilute solutions of gibberellic acid brought about the flowering of hydrangea bushes without any cold treatment. The best flowers, however, were produced by plants that received a short cold treatment, 2 or 3 weeks, before they were sprayed with the substance.

Pecan trees produce flowers and fruits when they are about 18 years old. Breeding for new varieties of pecans is consequently a slow process. Research by L. W. Martin and S. C. Wiggans, of Oklahoma State University, indicates that this long waiting period may be shortened considerably by stimulating the rapid overall growth of the trees with gibberellic acid.

At Beltsville we increased the size of black walnut trees growing in a greenhouse from an average of 1.5 feet (untreated) to 8.5 feet (treated) by placing a narrow band of lanolin paste containing 1 percent of gibberellic acid around the stems one-half inch from the terminal bud. We applied the paste three times during the summer and spaced the treatments so that the terminal buds never ceased growing until the short days of fall.

Some trees, including the black walnut, produce a flush of spring growth, often less than a foot long. Then the buds become dormant. Before producing additional new growth, the buds generally must be subjected to cold or overwintering temperature. Treatment with gibberellin substitutes for the cold requirement, overcomes summer dormancy, and causes the plants to produce the equivalent of several years' growth in one season.

We do not know yet whether this stimulation in vegetative growth will mean earlier flowering and fruiting.

Plant breeders who work with various annual crops would like to obtain two or more generations in one season, thereby speeding up their program.

On the basis of research in California on barley, that is possible experimentally. Two crops of barley were obtained in one season by accelerating overall plant growth and maturity by applications of gibberellic acid.

CONSIDERABLE RESEARCH has gone into tests to find a chemical means of retarding flowering of crop plants.

A few weeks' delay in the flowering of fruit trees, for instance, may avoid damage from frost. Some investigators have effected a delay of a few days by the use of spray applications of such chemicals as naphthaleneacetic acid and maleic hydrazide to apples, peaches, pears, and cherries.

The margin of safety with regard to injury to trees from the chemical is too narrow and the delay in flowering is too small to justify a recommendation of these chemicals for this purpose. The fact that they have been successful in some experiments, however, gives us hope that new and better chemicals or methods of application will be developed for this purpose.

Many vegetables grown for market or home use sometimes flower prematurely, and the edible crop is therefore not usable because of woody seedstalks.

The flowering of celery and cabbage grown for table use in Michigan is delayed by spraying the plants with a growth regulator at the time flowerbuds are forming during cold temperatures, which favor flower initiation. S. H. Wittwer, of Michigan State University, found that alpha-orthochlorophenoxyacetic acid spray at a concentration of 100 p.p.m. (parts per million) was effective on cabbage and celery.

In California the premature bolting of sugarbeets grown for processing has been retarded experimentally by the application of 2,4-dichlorophenoxyacetic acid (2,4-D) at 50 p.p.m. The time of application is critical.

After floral initiation is well underway, the bolting of lettuce has been greatly accelerated by applications of 2,4-D or parachlorophenoxyacetic acid at spray concentrations of 10 to 25 p.p.m. This response is of importance to seedsmen who grow certain varieties for seed production. For instance, varieties of lettuce, such as the Imperial and Great Lakes types, frequently are relatively slow and irregular in bolting, thereby causing a seed harvest problem for the grower. A treatment applied just as the plants began to form heads stopped formation of heads and induced the rapid elongation of seedstalks.

Ornamental trees sometimes produce fruit that is objectionable when it matures and falls to the lawn or street. Chemical sprays remove the blossoms and prevent fruit set without injury to the trees. A spray of naphthaleneacetic acid, 20 p.p.m., applied to the flowers of horsechestnut prevented production of burs, which litter the lawn and damage mowers. The same treatment applied to mulberry eliminated the purple staining of clothes and streets from the ripe fruits otherwise produced in abundance.

Horace V. Wester, of the Department of the Interior, and Paul C. Marth, of the Department of Agriculture, prevented growth of the vile-smelling fruits of ginkgo trees in Washington by spraying them with 250 p.p.m. of 3-chloro-isopropyl N-phenylcarbamate (Chloro IPC) at blossomtime.

THE GROWTH-REGULATING chemicals sometimes are used to stimulate the development of parts of the fruit other than seeds. In other instances the production of viable seeds has been increased by their use.

Scientists have worked with a number of economically important varieties of fruit—such as the Marsh grapefruit, Washington navel orange, and Thompson seedless grape—in order to develop good fruits that are free of seeds. Fruits so produced are called parthenocarpic.

Some plants apparently produce enough natural hormones so that they do not require the stimulus of developing seeds to prevent the falling off, or abscission, of flowers and young fruits.

Synthetic plant regulators have been discovered that, applied externally, simulate the effects of natural hormones so that now we can produce seedless or partly seedless fruits of tomatoes, blackberries, eggplants, peppers, cucumbers, green beans, and others by a simple spraying procedure.

The production of greenhouse-grown tomato fruits has been increased by the use of a suitable plant regulator treatment. Many of the fruits produced in this way are seedless. The greatest benefit is that tomato crops can be grown during periods of cloudy weather and low-light intensity, as during the short days of winter and early spring, when the fruit-setting stimulus of pollination reaches a low ebb, flower drop is excessive, and yields are low.

Sprays containing beta-naphthoxyacetic acid, alpha-ortho-chlorophenoxyacetic acid, parachlorophenoxyacetic acid, and others have been used effectively by commercial growers of greenhouse tomatoes. If the flower clusters are sprayed just before pollen is shed, most of the fruits will be entirely or almost seedless.

The yield of field-grown tomatoes, particularly in the first pickings, has been increased by the use of these regulators, notably when crops bloom under conditions of low-night temperatures that are unfavorable for fruit set. Therefore, perhaps, the greatest and most consistent increases in yield of field-grown tomatoes have been reported in England, where the crop may be almost entirely lost because of excessive flower drop during cool growing seasons.

R. J. Weaver, of the California Agricultural Experiment Station at Davis, has reported that the Black Corinth grape normally produces fruit that contains only thin, papery seedcoats. The variety is generally considered seedless. Experimentally, the application of parachlorophenoxyacetic acid sprays of 10-p.p.m. concentration at full bloom induced numerous hard seeds (seedcoats) to develop. When the same spray treatment was delayed until 3 days after full bloom, the fruits produced were seedless and larger than those produced on untreated vines or on those that were mechanically girdled to increase the size of berries.

Dr. Weaver also discovered that gibberellic acid is superior to other growth regulators he tested as an aid in increasing the size of the grapes, particularly the Thompson seedless variety.

The size of apricot fruits has been increased as much as 40 percent through the application of 2,4,5-trichlorophenoxyacetic acid at 75 p.p.m. to the trees when the pits were beginning to harden. These experiments were conducted by J. C. Crane and his coworkers at Davis.

In attempting to explain the cause for this increase in the size of the fruit because of the treatment, they studied the rate of growth of all parts of the fruits both on the sprayed and unsprayed trees.

They concluded that the growth of the seed about midseason competed with the fleshy parts of the fruits for naturally occurring hormones and thereby greatly retarded growth of the flesh for a rather long period until the seed stopped enlarging. Applications of the 2,4,5-T spray just before the period of rapid seed development eliminated this competition, so that the flesh did not slow down in rate of growth and at harvest was much larger than that of the untreated fruits. The final size of the seeds was about the same in both instances.

PLANT-REGULATING chemicals have been used as an aid in obtaining viable seed in the breeding of new plants that are of good quality and resistant to diseases.

In the breeding of new resistant types of cantaloups, for instance, C. P. Burell and T. W. Whitaker, of the Horticultural Field Station of the Department of Agriculture in La Jolla, Calif., found that the young fruit fell off without maturing seeds, even though an abundance of viable pollen was used in their hand crosses. Often the hybridizations were between varieties where there should be no question of compatibility between the pollen of one plant and ovules of another.

They learned that the application of an infinitesimal amount of indoleacetic acid, applied to the female flowers soon after pollination, reduced fruit abscission and so increased production of seed by more than 40 percent.

Plant breeders sometimes wish to obtain hybrid seeds by crossing species that differ considerably in growth characteristics. The growth rate of the pollen of one plant may be so slow that the ovules of the female plant wither and die before the pollen germinates.

In working with difficult crosses between certain species of lima beans, Robert E. Wester and Paul C. Marth, working at Beltsville, found that the application of a mixture of indolebutyric acid and parachlorophenoxyacetic acid increased markedly the yield of fertile hybrid seed.

Sometimes the pollen of a plant lacks the facility of fertilizing its own ovules as well as those ovules of a closely related species—a serious handicap to the plant breeder that occurs fairly commonly.

Self-incompatibilities in a number of varieties of Easter lilies has been overcome by Dr. S. L. Emsweller and Dr. Neil Stuart by the proper use of indoleacetic, indolebutyric, naphthaleneacetic, naphthaleneacetamide, parachlorophenoxyacetic, and 2,4,5-trichlorophenoxyacetic acids. Their work opened up new possibilities in breeding lilies and made it possible to produce new plant types unobtainable by usual breeding methods.

The growth regulators, applied at a concentration of 0.1 to 1.0 percent, were mixed with lanolin to form a paste. A dab of the mixture is applied to a small wound made at the base of the ovary by merely breaking a flower petal where it is joined to the pistil.

AN EXCITING NEW development in plant research is the possibility of using chemicals as an aid in securing hybrid vigor.

Corn is an example of the increases in yields due to hybrid vigor. The unwanted or pollen-bearing male parts of the corn plants are large and easy to remove by hand or machine. Many of our crop plants bear pollen in such a way that they are difficult to remove, even by hand.

Scientists discovered that maleic hydrazide suppressed the growth of corn tassels. Perhaps, because of phytotoxic effects on other parts of the plant, this effect could not be used practically.

Later, however, F. M. Eaton reported that the pollen mother cells in flowers of the cotton plant could be destroyed chemically without injuring the female parts of the flower. The chemical he found effective for this purpose, sodium-gamma, beta-dichloroisobutyrate, is called a gameticide—that is, a substance that kills gametes.

Water solutions of 0.2 to 0.4 percent concentration of this gameticide induced male sterility in cotton, and the plants set seed from pollen transferred from plants of another unsprayed variety growing nearby.

Favorable experimental results with the gameticide have been reported by R. A. Hensz and H. C. Mohr, of Texas Agricultural and Mechanical College, in experiments with watermelon. The Rohm & Haas Co. of Philadelphia, suppliers of the gameticide, have indicated that the results with apples, peaches, grapes, and strawberries were less promising.

Some plant-growth regulators are translocated into the developing seeds. Amo-1618 (2-isopropyl-4-dimethylamino-5-methylphenyl 1-piperidinecarboxylate methyl chloride) suppresses the growth of some kinds of plants and causes them to grow as dwarfs.

Pole-type snap beans, such as Kentucky Wonder and Blue Lake, have been induced to grow as a bush type when the young plants were treated with Amo-1618. When the seeds produced by the chemically suppressed plants were sown, the resulting first generation plants were semidwarf. Seeds produced in the second generation, however, reverted to the usual pole-type growth habit.

Amo-1618 may be unusual in its ability to get into seeds.

The chemical 2,4-dichlorobenzyltributyl phosphate (Phosfon) also causes beans and certain other plants to grow as dwarfs, so that they resemble plants treated with Amo-1618. Applied to the roots or stems, it apparently is not translocated into seeds.

In experiments for comparative purposes, we collected seeds from Kentucky Wonder plants that we had treated with massive doses of Amo-1618 and from others that received Phosfon treatment. The seed from Amo-1618-treated plants grew as a bush type. Seed from the Phosfon treatment produced plants that were of the pole type, like the control plants.

The shattering of seed at harvesttime often causes a loss of 25 percent or more of the productivity of rice, beans, alfalfa, clovers, and like crops. Seed-bearing organs, pods, and capsules develop well-defined, thin-walled layers of cells, or abscission zones, as they mature. When the cells separate, the seeds are released, sometimes with surprising force, so that they may be physically thrown for some distance. Even a brief delay in separation of the cells would reduce losses from shatter and thus increase yields.

Since plant regulators generally bring about their effects by altering some physiological mechanisms within plants, it seems likely that those involved in seed shatter may be quite different from those concerned with the abscission of leaves, flowers, and fruit.

Chemicals, not of the growth regulator type, have been used effectively to kill and desiccate crop plants and thereby reduce seed shatter. This practice, called spray curing, generally is accomplished with compounds used as herbicides or defoliants.

New regulating chemicals are being synthesized in laboratories, and other new regulators are being obtained directly from plants. Through further research with these compounds, additional ways will be found so that we can continue to use them safely and even more effectively in the production of seeds of high quality.

PAUL C. MARTH *and* JOHN W. MITCHELL *are plant physiologists in the Growth Regulator and Antibiotic Investigations Unit, Agricultural Research Service, Beltsville, Md. Dr. Mitchell is Investigations Leader.*

Flowering Habit and Production of Seeds

VICTOR R. BOSWELL

AMATEUR GARDENERS sometimes ask, "What should I do to get seeds of the plants that I grow in my garden?"

We could give almost as many answers to that question as there are kinds of plants in the inquirer's garden. If one's interest in the question goes beyond the garden to the field, orchard, and forest, we would have to give additional answers.

Before we can answer the question about any plant we must know a good many intimate things about it. The procedure for obtaining "good" seeds of a particular plant is determined by several of its major and most obvious characteristics.

First, we need to know whether the plant is an annual, a biennial, or a perennial one and how long it takes to grow from seed to seed.

We also need to know the nature of its sex expression. Does it produce flowers containing functional organs of both sexes? Are the flowers normally self-fertilized, or are they cross-fertilized? Are the sexes borne in different flowers, and where are the different flowers—on the same plants or on different plants? How are the flowers pollinated?

Our point of view in this chapter is that of the purposeful producer of seed rather than that of the incidental "saver" of a few seeds.

Plants that can grow from seed to seed in one season—the annuals—are easier to grow than those that require two seasons (biennials) or more (the perennials).

Some plants that are perennial in

the Tropics, such as cotton, castor-bean, tomato, and lima bean, complete a reproductive cycle (from planted seed to production of mature seed) within one season in a temperate climate. Bad weather then kills them; these perennials thus behave like annuals in the United States.

Conversely, such annuals as spinach, lettuce, wheat, and cornflower (*Centaurea cyanus*) are hardy enough to go through mild winters in a vegetative state, following planting in autumn. Cold or short days, or both, prevent flowering until spring. These annuals thus may be treated as biennials.

Annuals generally flower in a few weeks to 2 or 3 months after growth starts in the spring. Mature seeds develop in another 2 to 6 weeks. The times differ among species and varieties and depend on the temperature. The time of flowering of many species also depends largely on the length of day.

Some annuals, such as garden peas, tend to mature so fast during hot weather that they flower, produce seed, and die before they develop a plant large enough to yield a large crop of seeds.

Some other annuals tolerate hot weather but are sensitive to daylength. They will flower and form seeds when an effective daylength occurs even though the plants are still young and small. The Biloxi soybean and the cocklebur (*Xanthium*) are examples.

Spinach and some other annuals are sensitive to both heat and daylength. They "shoot to seed" during warm, long days much too soon to have formed a plant of highly productive size.

All the species that are sensitive to heat or daylength must be planted early in the spring if the plants are to grow large enough to yield well.

Hardy species, including the so-called winter legumes, the winter grains, and certain vegetables, such as spinach, are most productive of seeds in regions of mild to moderate winters when they are planted in the

autumn so as to produce seeds the following spring or summer.

Many cultivated annuals present no special problems of adjustment to daylength or to the normal range of growing-season temperatures, once their requirements are known. Among them are various beans grown for food, other legumes grown for forage, annual oilseed and fiber crops, and the grain crops.

The fruit-bearing vegetables, such as tomatoes, peppers, the vine crops—melons, cucumbers, squash—and okra, also are in this group. Reasonably early planting of all of them encourages the development of larger plants, more flowers, and better yields of seed than late plantings do, other things being the same.

BIENNIAL PLANTS present more difficulties for the seed producer than annuals or perennials do.

Biennials produce only a vegetative phase of the mother plant in the first season. They flower, produce seed, and die in the second season.

Some plants, such as the true clovers (*Trifolium*), are actually perennials but generally they become relatively unproductive after they produce their first seed crop, in their second year.

They are therefore usually plowed under after their second year.

Producing seed of sugarbeets and biennial vegetables is troublesome and costly. It is sometimes feasible to leave the mother roots or plants (such as cabbage and celery) in place where they grow the first season and to harvest commercial seed from them the next season without disturbing them over winter. If the winters are too severe, however, it is necessary to remove the mother plants (or their bulbs or storage roots) of many species from the field in the autumn for artificial protection and to plant them back the following spring.

If mother roots or bulbs are to be selected for good type, they must be harvested and selected in the autumn and stored over winter. It is wise to reselect them for good storage behavior when they are removed from storage in the spring and before they are planted in the seed field.

In the second season, the flowers of biennial vegetables develop on a strong stalk that arises from the apex of the stem within a bulb, atop a root, or within a rosette of leaves. Stalks also may arise from strong lateral buds, especially if the apex has been injured. The flower stalk generally begins to develop deep within the mother structure during early winter to midwinter. The flower parts, too, start development in many species during midwinter to late winter, completely out of sight.

Whether a flower stalk will form, when it will emerge, and how prolific it will be all depend on the interplay of several factors.

For a good yield of seed, the mother plant must have developed to the required size and physiological state in its first season. It must go through a requisite period of low temperature, not too cold but just cool enough. One to two months at 40° to 50° F. is effective for most biennial crops.

The weather must be moderate when the mother structure resumes visible growth. The daily mean temperatures should not be much over 70°. Freezing of the tissues at any time does not help induce floral development but may hinder it. Long days in the second season favor flowering in beets and some other species.

Species and even varieties within species differ in their requirements and in their responses to these several factors. Flowering and seed production are generally satisfactory when mother plants have been grown to market stage (or nearly so) and then allowed to go through a winter cold enough to keep them from growing but not cold enough to damage them visibly.

Production difficulties of various kinds are most likely to be encountered in sections where the winter gets so cold that artificial storage is necessary or is so mild that flower stalks fail to form. Planting the mother crop too late the first season may mean failure of floral induction. Planting too early or too late may mean winter injury.

Storing mother bulbs or roots near the freezing point from autumn harvest to spring planting will largely or entirely prevent floral initiation during storage and it may prevent flowering and seed production in the second season.

Hot weather immediately after the emergence of flower stalks can interrupt floral development and cause a resumption of vegetative growth in such plants as beet and cabbage. It may cause sparse or abnormal development of flowers. If the days are long enough, however, the adverse effects of high temperature are less serious on long-day seeders, like the beet, than if high temperature occurs during shorter days.

To avoid the high costs of harvesting, storing, and planting mother bulbs, roots, and plants, seedsmen sometimes produce seed of a biennial plant by the seed-to-seed method. They leave the mother plants in place to go to seed the second season. Because they thus have no opportunity to rogue out off-type bulbs or roots, they must maintain strict control of type and uniformity through the stock seed to assure satisfactory quality of the commercial seed.

Cabbage is produced seed-to-seed by sowing stock seed in late summer and letting the plants go through the winter in the rosette stage and shoot to seed in the spring without ever forming heads.

Cabbage seed also can be grown from the stumps of selected plants from which typical heads have been harvested, without moving the stumps. The practice is feasible only in regions of mild winters and with stumps of a crop harvested in autumn or winter.

Most of these biennials flower from early to late spring and produce mature seed from midsummer to late summer, depending on the species and the climate where each is grown.

THE REQUIREMENTS for flowering and
the times of flowering of perennials are
no less diverse than those of annuals
and biennials.

Many perennial grasses and most of
our forest and fruit trees flower early
in the spring. Some perennial grasses,
such as sugarcane, and trees and
shrubs, such as filbert (*Corylus ameri-cana*) and *Osmanthus*, flower in late
autumn to early spring. Perennials of
some kind or another can be found in
bloom all through the growing season.

The seeds in many perennial grasses
and herbaceous ornamentals mature 2
to 3 weeks after bloom. They must be
harvested promptly before they fall
from the plant and are lost.

Some perennials, such as hollyhock,
produce flowers and seeds successively
over many weeks, and the seeds must
be harvested repeatedly lest they be
lost. Others, such as asparagus, hold
their fruits firmly until autumn har-vest, although they flower and form
fruits over many weeks.

Most of the cultivated, herbaceous,
seed-bearing perennials begin flower-ing and producing seed a year or two
after they are grown from seed. One,
the ornamental "century plant" (*Agave
americana*), takes 10, 20, even 50 years
or more to flower.

Seeds of some fruit trees are required
for growing rootstocks, and seeds of
forest trees for planting in nurseries of
ornamental, windbreak, and timber
trees.

Some trees develop mature seeds in
no more than 2 months after flowering.
Certain cherries, poplars, maples, and
elms are examples. Others, such as
plums, peaches, chestnuts, and mag-nolias, take 3 to 4 months. Apples (late
varieties), ash, beech, most nut trees,
dogwood, and most oaks mature their
seeds in autumn about 5 months after
flowering. Pine seeds mature 2 to 3
years after bloom. The so-called
double coconut or coco du mer (*Lodoi-cea maldivica*) matures 7 to 10 years
after bloom.

The age at which fruit, ornamental,
and forest trees begin to bloom and
produce seeds is generally a major
obstacle to seed propagation of im-proved or selected types. When grown
to fruiting on their own roots, these
kinds of trees produce negligible or
small amounts of seeds for a few years
before they can be said to have become
truly productive. Seed production by
many of these can be speeded up by
grafting scions from very young seed-lings in the top of large, established
trees so as to force the young seedling
to earlier maturity.

The citrus and stone fruits become
productive of seeds after 5 or 6 years;
apples, after 8 to 10 years. Good yields
of seed of most forest trees begin still
later. Various species of pines become
productive in 10 to 40 years; cedars
and junipers in about 10 years; elms
and Douglas-fir, about 15 years; oaks,
ash, and redwood, about 20 years.
The bigtree (*Sequoia gigantea*) takes
about 125 years.

Foresters have sought for many years
to develop special methods of hasten-ing flowering and seed production of
selected forest species. They have made
progress with some of them, including
important conifers, through establish-ment of seed orchards of grafted trees.
Other species, such as the elms, still
defy all efforts to hurry them.

WE HAVE BEEN concerned so far with
some of the requirements as to time,
temperature, and daylength for flower-ing for the production of seeds.

Next we shall see how sex expression
and flower structure in species and
varieties determine spatial arrange-ments and certain other practices in
seed production.

Suppose a seedsman plans to grow a
stock of a species that bears complete
flowers that are so constructed that
they are seldom or never naturally
cross-pollinated. He can grow that
stock relatively close to other stocks or
varieties of the same species with very
little danger of any genetic mixture.
Such plants include garden and field
peas, common bean and soybean, cow-pea, and some other legumes; wheat,

oats, barley, and other self-pollinated or apomictic grasses (those that reproduce without sexual union); and tomatoes, flax, and tobacco.

In producing ordinary commercial seed of these, plots of different varieties need to be separated by no more than the width of a driveway. Such distance will prevent an objectionable degree of chance cross-pollination. For producing foundation, or stock, seed, however, a separation of 150 feet or more is necessary.

Most of our other major field and vegetable crops have flowers that either require cross-pollination or may be readily cross-pollinated to a large extent, although both sexes are functional in the individual flower.

Flowers require cross-pollination for any of these reasons: They may form no functional pollen; the pollen may be discharged at the wrong time; or the plant (or a clone) may be sterile to its own pollen.

Alfalfa flowers are bisexual but only partly self-fertile. They produce some seed in the absence of insects, but their seed production is much better when bees are present to effect cross-pollination. The lima bean, on the other hand, produces flowers that are fully self-fertile and do not benefit from the intervention of insects. Still, a high degree of cross-pollination occurs in lima bean where bumble bees are numerous. Thus the mere presence of both sexes in a legume flower proves nothing about its requirements for cross-pollination.

The seedgrower must separate varieties of all such kinds of plants that are cross-pollinated with the help of insects by distances up to one-fourth mile if he is to avoid an unwanted genetic mixture.

The pollen of some cross-pollinated species is fine and dustlike and is carried long distances by the wind. Beets, spinach, and rye are noteworthy for the great distances that their pollen can be blown and effect cross-fertilization. Fields of different varieties of one type of beet (as garden beet or sugar-

beet) should be at least one-half mile apart—preferably 2 miles. Spinach varieties should be separated at least one-fourth mile. A mile is better.

In practice, sugarbeets and garden beets are never purposely grown for seed within the same district because of the danger of crossing over distances of miles. Swiss chard, stock beets, garden beets, and sugarbeets are of the same species (*Beta vulgaris*) and all intercross. They should be separated by many miles when they are grown for seed.

Veritable clouds of pollen blow from a rye field that is in bloom. Although most flowers in a field of one variety of rye will be fertilized by pollen of nearby plants of the same variety, there is some danger of intervarietal crossing over distances of a mile or more.

The pollen of corn (maize) also is windblown but is relatively heavy. Generally there is little danger of undesirable crossing between plants in fields more than one-fourth mile apart. Cross-pollination, however, may sometimes occur over distances of more than a mile.

The pollen of many forest trees is as fine as dust. The male inflorescences, called catkins, hang in the breeze in a manner that is ideally adapted for dislodgment and dispersal of the discharged pollen. During the height of bloom in forests of oak or pine and other conifers, the light may become tinted by great quantities of pollen. Cross-fertilization occurs over long distances. It is not surprising that the seeds of such trees are highly variable genetically.

The flowers of some plants, such as alfalfa and beans, produce pollen that is too sticky to be dispersed by the wind. The pollen-bearing anthers are also well enclosed by the flower parts. The pollen is dislodged by insects. Varieties of such plants need not be separated so distantly as most wind-pollinated kinds, but they still need to be a moderate distance apart.

The flowers of a large group of vegetable and ornamental plants must be cross-fertilized by insects.

Some examples: Flowers of the onion and carrot families contain both sexes, but the anthers of any one flower discharge their pollen before the stigma of that flower is receptive. The flowers on one plant of members of the cabbage family generally are largely sterile to the pollen of that plant. The members of the gourd family (cucumbers, melons, squash) all produce the two sexes in separate flowers on the same plant. The pollen of all of these—and many others—is too sticky and heavy to be dislodged and carried by the wind.

Bees are the chief pollen carriers for the kinds of plants I just mentioned. Bees may work over fairly long distances and carry pollen from one variety to another within a species.

Varieties of these species therefore should be separated by about one-fourth mile for the production of ordinary commercial seed. For producing foundation or stock seed of a very high degree of purity—that is, freedom from intervarietal crossing—varieties should be separated by a mile or more.

The seedsman must be sure that an ample number of pollinating insects, chiefly bees, will be present if he is to get a good crop of seed of these insect-pollinated species. If enough insects do not occur naturally, he must raise bees or rent them for the purpose. In commercial seed-growing districts (and districts where cucumbers and melons are extensively grown for market), apiaries are operated to provide custom pollinating service.

During the flowering season of insect-pollinated crops, growers must be careful in the way they use insecticides for the control of harmful insects lest they kill essential pollinating insects, including honey bees.

A FEW CROP PLANTS and trees of economic importance are dioecious—they bear one-sexed flowers on separate plants. Among vegetable crops, asparagus is almost entirely so. Strictly

dioecious strains of spinach have been developed for the production of hybrid seed.

Some plants in most spinach varieties normally are monoecious—they bear some flowers of both sexes, although they bear predominantly one or the other.

Plants of a species bearing the sexes separately usually occur in approximately equal numbers. Thus, unless the seedsman can identify the male plants early in their life and remove some of them, a great surplus of them may take space that he would prefer to have occupied by seed-bearing individuals. In general, 10 to 20 percent of males in a planting will furnish effective pollination.

Excess males in a seed spinach field can be chopped out as they become recognizable to allow a higher proportion of females and more space for them.

The sex of asparagus plants can be identified the first year, and a suitable ratio of the two sexes can be transplanted for a perennial seed plot, if desired.

Many fruit and other trees are dioecious. Some have complete flowers but are self-sterile. In either case, the female parent will require the presence of a pollinator tree within a reasonable distance of bee flight or for wind pollination. If no pollinator is nearby and bees are plentiful, small branches of flowers that bear compatible pollen may be cut from distant trees and placed in buckets of water in the trees to be pollinated.

American holly (*Ilex opaca*) is a common example of a dioecious species. Male trees bloom but never produce fruits and seeds. Their flowers contain pollen-bearing anthers that are visible to the naked eye, but no pistils. Female trees produce flowers having pistils but only rudimentary or shriveled-up anthers without pollen.

THE COMMERCIAL PRODUCTION of hybrid seed depends on suitable flowering habits of the plants to be hybridized.

Hybrid seed of corn is relatively simple to produce because the male and female inflorescences are large and well separated on the plant. To control pollination in a seed field, one needs only to pull the tassels from the rows of female parent plants as they appear and leave the rows of pollinator plants undisturbed. The pollinator must, of course, be one that discharges its pollen at the time the seed plants are in silk.

Hybrid seed of tomato is expensive because it must be produced by hand pollination, flower by flower, usually after emasculation of the flower of the seed parent, also by hand. The pollen is not dispersed by wind and very little by any insect. The flowers are naturally self-pollinated almost entirely.

Hybrid onion seeds became commercially feasible about 1940 with the development of seed-parent inbred lines possessing what is commonly called cytoplasmic male sterility. Such a line produces no pollen but is perpetuated by recurrent fertilization by an appropriate self-fertile line that possesses cytoplasmic male fertility. This second line must be bred and maintained solely for perpetuating the male-sterile line. The 100-percent male-sterile progeny of these two is then planted to produce mother bulbs.

They, in the next year, produce flowers that are field pollinated by a third inbred to produce commercial hybrid seed. Every fifth or sixth row in the seed field usually is a pollinator line. Bees do the pollinating.

The principle of male sterility has been applied commercially to the producing of hybrid seed of other crops such as corn, sorghum, and sugarbeets.

Hybrid seed of spinach is produced commercially by the use of newly developed inbred parent lines, which consist of purely staminate (male) and purely pistillate (female) plants. The male plants are chopped out of the seed-parent rows as they become recognizable. Thus the complete cross-pollination by nearby rows of an inbred pollinator is insured.

Japanese seedsmen produce hybrid seed of cabbage and related plants. They use selected parent lines that are rather highly (but not completely) self-sterile and highly cross-fertile. When plants of two such lines are set alternately in the seed field, about 98 percent of the harvested seed is hybrid. The seedlings that arise from seeds resulting from self-pollination in such a seed lot are smaller than the hybrid seedlings (from cross-pollinated flowers). These nonhybrids are largely left behind in the plant bed at transplanting time so that the transplanted cabbage field consists of practically 100 percent hybrids.

The Japanese also first developed seedless watermelon seed and produced it commercially. This involves a relatively difficult and expensive procedure that may never become popular in the United States, but it illustrates a remarkable application of an unusual flower behavior.

Seedless watermelons are seedless because they develop from flowers that are both self-sterile and cross-sterile. Although these flowers cannot produce seeds, they do respond to the stimulus of pollination sufficiently to form fruits that are normal except for seedlessness. Then where do the seeds come from, for growing the seedless melons? They are produced by hybridizing two parent lines, the seed line of which is a special kind.

The seed-parent line is a tetraploid, produced by doubling the normal number of chromosomes of a watermelon variety through the use of colchicine. Flowers of selected tetraploid plants are then crossed with a selected pollen parent that has the normal (diploid) number of chromosomes. This crossing is done either by hand pollination of artificially protected flowers or by insect pollination of flowers on isolated plants from which all male flowers are removed before they open. The resulting hybrid seed is abnormal. It is triploid—it has 1.5 times the normal number of chromosomes. It can produce a plant capable of fruiting when pollinated by suitable diploid pollen, but it is too abnormal to reproduce itself by seeds.

I HAVE mentioned only examples of why and how the seed producer must take into account the flowering behavior of the plants from which he wants to obtain seed. There are almost endless variations in detail of behavior among species and varieties that seedsmen handle. Furthermore, flowering behavior is but one part of the complex subject of seed production, although it is a large and vitally controlling part.

The more we can learn about the details of the flowering habit, including sex expression, and the factors that affect flowering, the more effective the work of producing seed can be.

IN CONCLUSION, then, the incidental or casual saving of seeds can lead to disappointing results with the crops grown from them. The flowering habit of the species underlies a large share of the disappointments. Indeed, flowering habit is a major factor in determining whether any seeds will form to be saved. Unless the gardener and farmer know something of the flowering habit of plants, they often are in no position to get good seeds from them. Sometimes, even when they know a plant's flowering habits, the requirements for getting good seeds may be beyond their control in their particular situation—especially with varieties having flowers that are readily cross-pollinated and that are not well isolated from other plantings of the same species. We look with little or no favor on the casual saving of seed because of its hazards.

VICTOR R. BOSWELL *joined the Department of Agriculture in 1928. His own research has dealt primarily with the growth, development, behavior, responses, and inherent qualities of a wide range of vegetable crops and seeds thereof. He has written research, review, and popular articles for many publications.*

The Thread of Life Through Seeds

MARTIN G. WEISS AND JOHN E. SASS

THE ORIGIN of each new seed-bearing plant traces back to the time of flowering. The end product of flowering is the seed. The thread of life that persists through the process of seed formation long has captivated the interest of man. If we wish to trace the processes that result in the transmission of life, we must start by examining the basic structural units, the cells of the parent plant.

The contents of cells are complex. Young cells of plants are filled with protoplasm, the physical basis of life. Its main components are the plastids, the nucleus, and the cytoplasm, a clear semifluid matrix, which contains the plastids, the nucleus, and many smaller bodies.

Plastids in green plants contain the chlorophylls, which give the plants their green color and enable them to carry on photosynthesis. Some plastids contain other pigments. Others carry no coloring matter but may contain starch or fat.

The nucleus is regarded as the specific center of many cell activities. The nucleus contains the chromosomes, which carry most of the hereditary materials of the plant.

The development of a number of scientific instruments made it possible for us to study in detail the contents of cells.

The electron microscope enables us to see particles that are only one five-hundredth to one one-thousandth as large as the smallest particles that can be resolved with the standard light microscope.

The phase contrast microscope permits examination of unstained living cells by converting slight differences in the indices of refraction of the cell parts to visible differences.

The ultraviolet microscope is immensely useful because of the selective absorption of ultraviolet light by nucleic acids.

The spectrometer permits detailed studies of the chemical composition through differential absorption by cell components of the different wavelengths of light.

With high-speed centrifuges one can separate the many different types of cellular particles.

Such detailed studies disclose that many bodies, much smaller than the plastids, exist in the protoplasm of the cells.

One group of such bodies are granular or rod shaped, are known as mitochondria, and are believed to give rise to plastids and to be involved in the metabolism of the cell.

Certain of the plastids and smaller bodies are transmitted from one generation of plants to the next through the sex cells and transmit a few characters from the mother plant to the offspring. We do not yet know the specific bodies that are involved.

The plant cell, as it matures, develops one or more cavities, the vacuoles within the cytoplasm. Vacuoles are filled with a water solution of sugars, salts, acids, and other substances. In large cells the cytoplasm eventually becomes a saclike layer surrounding a large vacuole.

One class of plant pigments, called the anthocyanins, at times occurs in solution in the vacuole. The red color of autumn leaves, for instance, is associated with pigments in the vacuole.

The chromosomes contain the factors, or genes, that govern development of most plant structures and traits. Chromosomes are the major means by which germ plasm, the vital stuff in the germ cells, is passed on from one generation to the next.

In a mature cell that is not dividing, the chromosomes are long, thin, fibrous threadlike bodies. Because they are so long and intertwined, we have not yet been able to examine a single whole chromosome.

Actually, we may say a chromosome is a bundle of fibrils, or threads. The number of the threads, or fibrils, seems to differ in different organisms. The chromosomes of corn may have just a few. Those of certain lilies may comprise eight fibrils.

Other organisms, in which chromosomes were tagged with radioactive substances or studied with the electron microscope, may have chromosomes of 32 to 64 units and possibly even 128 fibrils.

Studies of the chemistry of chromosomes indicate that they are comprised of complex organic molecules, including protein and ribose and deoxyribonucleic acids.

Irregularities in thickness and density occur along the length of a chromosome. The thickened parts, which resemble knots in a string, are called chromomeres. Some geneticists believe that chromomeres are accumulations of nucleic acids. Others believe they are expressions of different patterns of coiling along the chromosome thread.

No one has yet seen an individual gene. We can only speculate upon its nature and composition. Geneticists believe that genes, like chromosomes, consist of complex organic molecules, probably composed mainly of deoxyribonucleic acid, and that genes may differ from each other according to their molecular construction.

We know from genetic studies, however, that genes occur in linear order in the chromosome. This order is maintained through countless generations unless the chromosome is broken.

In corn, for instance, a gene locus, which influences the color of the endosperm, is located on a specific chromosome, known as the No. 6 chromosome, near a locus that controls the color of the plant. Scientists measure the distance between genes in terms of crossover units. These two genes are approximately 28 units apart. This distance remains constant generation after generation.

We know also that genes are stable, although occasionally they change, or mutate, to another form, as evidenced by the change in the character they influence.

We know that certain agencies, such as irradiation by X-rays, gamma rays, or ultraviolet rays, can increase the rate of mutation.

We know that certain genes mutate more frequently than others. Under normal conditions, however, most genes would not be expected to mutate oftener than once in hundreds of thousands or even millions of cell generations.

Genes reproduce themselves. Chromosomes duplicate themselves longitudinally. On the basis of genetic evidence, the genes must also be reproduced in kind.

Several times we have said a character, or trait, is caused or influenced by a gene. How, one asks, can a gene located on a chromosome in corn govern whether the color of the kernel will be red or yellow?

Here is another gap in our knowledge.

It is presumed that a gene of certain construction is responsible for the production of a specific enzyme within the protoplasm. The enzymes influence the activities of the cells and thereby determine the final expression of the character in question. We have only fragmentary evidence as to the way in which this is done.

INNUMERABLE cell divisions take place during the growth of a plant.

The dividing of vegetative cells is mitosis. The process is an orderly one—the individuality and stability of the number of chromosomes and the number of genes are maintained through the many cell cycles.

Let us examine this process.

During the early phases of nuclear division we can recognize the long, threadlike chromosomes, which contract and thicken to a degree that enables us to identify individual chromosomes. The contraction is actually a coiling of the chromosome, and the final form is somewhat like a coiled spring. When they are fully contracted, the coils may be closed so tightly that the chromosome appears to be a cylinder.

During mitosis, at some phase that has not been determined with absolute certainty, each chromosome becomes longitudinally visibly doubled and then consists of two chromatids, which are closely twisted around each other.

The physical doubling, or reduplication, of each chromosome provides that succeeding cells carry the exact genetic complement as the mother cell. As cell division proceeds, each of the chromatids develops into an individual chromosome in each of the two new cells that are formed.

Each of the chromatids consists of two further subdivisions, known as chromonemata. The two chromonemata comprising a chromatid are thought to be wound about each other very tightly, like twisted strands of a rope.

The chromonemata are the forerunners of chromatids of the next cell division and in time become the individual chromosomes in the four succeeding granddaughter cells.

When one projects this manner of regeneration of new chromosomes, it is not surprising to learn that the chromonemata in turn consist of further subdivisions and already carry the prototype of chromosomes for a number of cell generations in the future.

After the chromosomes contract, they migrate toward the center of the cell. A spindle-shaped figure of fibers forms in the cell. The membrane that encloses the nucleus had previously disappeared. The chromosomes become arranged in a central plane, which is perpendicular to the axis of the spindle.

The two chromatids that comprise each chromosome separate from each other and thus give rise to daughter chromosomes. The daughter chromosomes separate and move toward opposite ends of the cell.

The movement of the two chromatids is initiated at a constricted portion of the chromosome, known as the centromere, or spindle fiber attachment. The latter name is given this region because through the microscope it appears that a spindle fiber from one of the poles becomes attached at the restricted region of one chromatid, whereas a spindle fiber from the other pole similarly is attached to the sister chromatid.

The forces that cause the daughter chromosomes to migrate from each other and toward the poles are not fully understood. The daughter chromatids may be drawn toward the poles by the spindle fiber, or the daughter chromosomes may repel one another in the spindle fiber attachment region. In fact, it is not known if the spindle fibers are really fibers at all. They may be mere protoplasm arrangements, which demark lines of force that have developed in the nucleus.

Suffice it to say that the daughter chromosomes first separate in the centromere region and, as these regions move apart, the chromosomes uncoil until they are completely separated. Thereupon they migrate to the opposite poles of the cell.

Since this process takes place in each of the 20 chromosomes of corn, it follows that 20 daughter chromosomes migrate to each of the poles. A cell wall is formed between the separated groups of chromosomes, new nuclear membranes are formed, and the result is two daughter cells, each of which carries the same chromosome complement as the mother cell.

THE PROCESS of cell division may take only a few minutes or as much as many hours.

The significance of cell division as related to heredity may be summed up, first, as the exact duplication of each chromosome and the genes which it carries and, second, the mechanism that provides each of the daughter cells with the same chromosome complement as the parent cell.

Each vegetative cell of the plant therefore has the same complement of chromosomes and heredity potentials as the initial cell from which the plant arose.

SINCE THE complement of chromosomes and the genetic complement of all vegetative cells of the plant are alike, one may question why all cells of the plant are not identical in appearance when mature.

For instance, some cells develop into epidermis, the surface cells of plants. Other cells develop into the cells of the xylem and the phloem, through which materials are transported in the plant. Others become growth regions, such as cambium, which occurs under the bark of trees. Still others give rise to the egg or pollen grain, which are involved in sexual reproduction.

Differentiation of cells into the various tissues largely depends on the inheritance of tissue pattern, a subject that is not understood at present. The differentiation of cells, moreover, may be influenced by the neighboring cells or by the position in the plant in which the cells are located.

Regardless of the stimulus, we know that cells differentiate and fit a pattern of special uses and that such differentiation is controlled at least partly by the genes of the chromosomes carried in the cells.

ONE TYPE of cell differentiation that is particularly pertinent in a study of seeds is the production of sex cells in the flowers.

During the growth of a plant, certain groups of rapidly dividing cells, the floral primordia, form the flower structures. Flowers are produced on the tip of a stem, either of the main stem, as in the case of the corn tassel, or on the tip of a side branch, like an ear of corn.

The female flower cluster of the corn plant is differentiated from a group of meristematic cells in the axil of a leaf. This flower cluster eventually develops into an ear of corn. Flowers bearing the male portion of germ plasm are located at the top of the corn plant, and the inflorescence, or flower cluster, is known as the tassel.

Anthers, the organs that later shed pollen grains, are formed during the development of the male flowers in the tassel.

The cells of young anthers when seen under the microscope seem very much alike. As an anther enlarges, however, certain cells in each of the four lobes of the anther enlarge and become different from cells of the surrounding tissues. Each of the enlarged cells develops into a pollen mother cell, which divides twice to form four daughter cells—the microspores, which later develop into pollen grains.

When the anther is mature, it splits open. Then the pollen grains are released.

In the female flower cluster, which becomes the ear of corn, the process of cell division is somewhat different. The form of the ear and very young kernels can be recognized at a very early stage. The forerunner of the corn kernel is the ovary, which will become the kernel proper, and the stigma and style, which in combination constitute the silk.

The ovary contains an ovule, which fills the entire space in the ovary. One cell near the tip enlarges greatly as the ovule enlarges. This cell is the megaspore mother cell. It undergoes two divisions, providing four megaspores. Not all four of these megaspores are functional. Three of them disintegrate. One, usually the cell nearest the base of the ovule, continues to develop.

The cell divisions that produce the microspores and megaspores warrant special attention. The nuclei in these spores contain only half as many chromosomes as the spore mother cells. This reduction in number of chromosomes is brought about by two distinctive cell divisions, a process known as meiosis or reduction division.

When we discussed mitosis, or vegetative cell division, in corn, we stated that each nucleus contains 20 chromosomes, and after a mitotic division each daughter nucleus contains 20 chromosomes.

A study of the chromosomes in the contracted stage in a vegetative cell of corn shows that they constitute 10 pairs of chromosomes. The two chromosomes of each pair are structurally identical and genetically similar. They are said to be the homologous chromosomes.

The early stages of meiosis in the spore mother cell resemble vegetative cell division in that the chromosomes contract and thicken until they may be observed as distinct individual bodies.

At that point, however, a special phenomenon occurs. The homologous members of a pair of chromosomes become attracted to each other and become closely associated throughout their length. Coiling of the chromosome pairs results in a further shortening and thickening. The pairs become oriented in a plane at right angles to the axis between the poles at opposite ends of the cell. The members of each pair of chromosomes begin to separate at the centromere region, and the members migrate to opposite ends of the cell after uncoiling.

This process, which occurs in each of the 10 pairs of chromosomes, results in a complement of 10 single chromosomes at opposite sides of the mother cell. This represents half the number of chromosomes in a vegetative cell—hence the term "reduction division" applies to this part of meiosis.

Usually without pause, the chromosomes at each end of the cell undergo a second division. Each of the chromosomes, in which two chromatids are now evident, becomes oriented in a plane at right angles to their previous plane of orientation. Spindle fiber poles develop on opposite sides of the cell, with their axis perpendicular to the new plane of orientation.

The two chromatids comprising each chromosome thereupon separate from each other and migrate to the opposite poles. This cell division, which may be said to be equational, should be recognized as structurally identical to that occurring in vegetative cells, except that only half the number of chromosomes are involved. The two divisions of meiosis in the spore mother cell produce four spores, each containing one member of the homologous pairs of chromosomes that were present in vegetative cells.

The meiotic mechanism, followed by fertilization, assures constancy in the number of chromosomes in successive generations.

Following meiosis in the female flower, the nucleus of the surviving megaspore undergoes three successive mitotic divisions. An embryo sac with eight nuclei is produced. The nuclei form a pattern that is characteristic of the particular species.

Three nuclei are often located near the tip of the embryo sac. One nucleus becomes the egg cell. The other two, the synergids, are commonly nonfunctional.

Two nuclei, the polar nuclei, migrate to the center of the embryo sac.

The remaining three nuclei, the antipodals, are located at the base end of the embryo sac. In the corn plant, the antipodals undergo limited mitosis, but they have no known function and soon "disappear."

The nuclei that are concerned with fertilization are the egg nuclei and the polar nuclei.

At this stage of development of the embryo, the silk of the young corn kernel begins to elongate rapidly and soon protrudes from the tip of the husk.

When grains of corn pollen, which mostly are carried by wind, land on the branched silk, they germinate immediately and produce pollen tubes. The tubes penetrate the cells of the silk and grow down the silk through sheath cells that surround the vascular tissues. Before shedding, the microspore nucleus of the pollen grain of corn undergoes mitotic division and produces a tube nucleus and a generative nucleus. The latter divides and produces the two sperms, the male nuclei that take part in the fertilization process. The tube nucleus seems to have a function directly concerned with the growth of the pollen tube down the silk and into the ovule. It remains near the tip of the growing pollen tube.

The pollen tube can grow rapidly down the silk of the ear. The distance from the tip of the silk to the ovule may be as much as 12 inches. The pollen tube may reach it in about 24 hours.

After reaching the base of the silk, the pollen tube grows through additional sheath cells until it reaches the ovule cavity. It twists and turns through this cavity until it reaches the opening, or micropyle, left by incomplete closing of the integuments that cover the ovule.

The pollen tube thereupon enters the embryo sac, the tip enlarges greatly, and the tube membrane disintegrates. Then the two sperm nuclei are released.

One male gamete fuses with the nucleus of the egg, thereby producing a zygote. This is fertilization, and the zygote is the first cell of the embryo.

This one cell, in which all potentialities of structural and functional development are present, may be said to be a living plant—a corn plant.

The other male gamete fuses with the two polar nuclei, producing a triple-fusion nucleus that carries three homologous chromosomes of each of the ten distinct chromosomes in corn.

Further divisions of this nucleus produce the endosperm, which is a food storage structure in the seed of corn.

The fusion of one male gamete with the egg and the other male gamete with the polar nuclei is referred to as double fertilization. It occurs in most flowering plants.

Every cell of the embryo contains the same genetic constitution. Minor differences in structure and striking differences in cell activity and orientation soon become evident, however.

The symmetrical profile of the em-

Development of Sex Cells and Growth of Pollen Tube in Corn

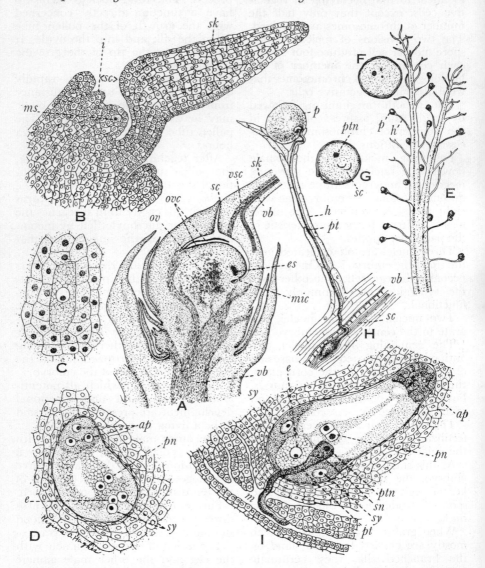

A, *longitudinal section of young corn kernel: ov, ovule; ovc, ovule coats; sc, stylar canal; vsc, sheathlike cells through which the pollen tube travels; sk, silk; vb, vascular bundle; es, embryo sac; mic, micropyle.* B, *longitudinal section of corn kernel as silk starts to elongate before nucleus of megaspore mother cell has divided: ms, megaspore mother cell; i, integument; sc, stylar canal; sk, silk.* C, *megaspore mother cell before division of nucleus.* D, *longitudinal section of embryo sac (mature female gametophyte): e, egg; ap, antipodals; pn, polar nuclei; sy, synergids.* E, *end of a silk: vb, vascular bundle; p, pollen grain; h, hair.* F, *cross section of pollen grain following mitotic division of nucleus.* G, *section of mature pollen grain; ptn, pollen tube nucleus; sc, sperm cell.* H, *single hair of a silk illustrating manner in which pollen tube penetrates sheath cells of the vascular bundle: p, pollen grain; h, hair; pt, pollen tube; sc, sheath cells.* I, *longitudinal section of embryo sac at time of fertilization: sy, synergid; e, egg; ap, antipodals; pn, polar nuclei; ptn, pollen tube nucleus; sn, sperm nucleus; pt, pollen tube; m, micropyle.*

bryo persists only until lateral organs are initiated in orderly sequence and position.

Indications of unsymmetrical growth can be detected 4 to 5 days after pollination in a zone of cells on the upper and outward region of the embryo. These cells are less vacuolate, more deeply stainable, and undergo more rapid cell division than cells in other regions of the embryo.

This activity foreshadows the subsequent rapid elongation of the embryo and the initiation of lateral organs. The basal portion of the embryo, the suspensor, elongates considerably in some varieties of corn. The suspensor eventually becomes undercut and fractured by the scutellum.

The first lateral organ, the coleoptile, arises on the outward (anterior) surface of the embryo. The coleoptile eventually becomes the hollow cone that emerges from the soil during germination and contains the plumule, or aerial portion, of the plant.

The apex of the future stem, on which the tassel develops in due time, can be identified in 10 or 12 days. The first foliage leaf is evident in 12 days. The radicle, or first root of the embryo, usually is well defined at 10 or 12 days, deep in the tissues of the embryo.

At about this age, cell division is accelerated over an extensive area on the inward (posterior) surface of the embryo. This process produces the large, flat, shield-shaped scutellum, which has been interpreted to be the cotyledon of the grass embryo. Two meristematic ridges that arise on the anterior side of the scutellum eventually grow around and encase the plumule-radicle axis of the embryo.

The foregoing observations show that the first member of each organ category, stem, leaf, and root, is initiated soon after fertilization, and the development of the embryonic corn plant is well underway.

Additional foliage leaves are initiated at intervals of 4 or 5 days. In 30 to 35 days, the full complement of five embryonic foliage leaves is present in many lines and types of corn. This is the number in the mature kernel. No more foliage leaves are formed until the onset of germination. The primordia of the three "seminal," or secondary, roots that occur in the corn embryo, in addition to the radicle, are initiated 30 to 35 days after pollination. This completes the formation of organs of the embryo of corn.

THE BASIS on which characters, or traits, of plants or animals are inherited becomes clarified through an understanding of the chromosome mechanism during reproduction.

The formation of a zygote by the fusion of an egg and sperm nucleus is the mechanism by which germ plasm from two individuals combines to form the heritable complex of the offspring.

The divisions which precede the formation of the sex cells provide a basis for segregation of parental traits among the offspring in a precise and predictable manner. In fact, geneticists observed the precise manner of segregation long before they observed the cellular mechanism of heredity under the microscope.

SEED COLOR of corn gives an example of the mechanism of heredity. One should remember that the seed of corn has three types of tissue: The outer covering, or pericarp, which is the ovary wall of the mother plant; the embryo, which contains equal germ plasm from the sperm and egg; and the endosperm, in which the germ plasm consists of two-thirds from the female and one-third from the male parent.

A single gene locus in chromosome No. 1 determines whether the pericarp of the kernel will be pigmented.

Most commercial corn carries in each of the homologous No. 1 chromosomes a gene that provides colorless pericarp on the kernel so that the colors of the underlying structures, usually yellow or white, give the characteristic color to the ears.

In some types of corn, however, the

Fertilization and Embryogeny in the Development of a Seed

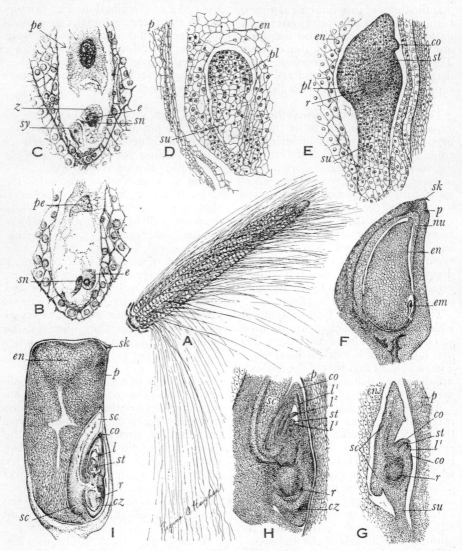

A, *a young ear of corn.* B, *formation of lily zygote—the union of male and female gametes: pe, primary endosperm (triple fusion) nucleus; sn, sperm nucleus; e, egg.* C, *the single-celled zygote and endosperm of lily: pe, primary endosperm nucleus; sn, sperm nucleus; e, egg; z, zygote; sy, synergid.* D, *the corn embryo 5 days after pollination: en, endosperm; pl, posterior lobe; su, suspensor; p, pericarp.* E, *the corn embryo 10 days after pollination: co, coleoptile; st, future stem tip; en, endosperm; pl, posterior lobe; r, root apex; su, suspensor.* F, *position and relative size of the corn embryo 10 days after pollination: em, embryo; en, endosperm; nu, nucellus remnant; p, pericarp; sk, silk remnant.* G, *the corn embryo 12 days after pollination: co, coleoptile; l¹, first leaf; st, stem tip; sc, scutellum; en, endosperm; r, root tip; p, pericarp; su, suspensor.* H, *the corn embryo 15 days after pollination: sc, scutellum; co, coleoptile; l¹, first foliage leaf; l², second foliage leaf; l³, third foliage leaf; st, stem tip; r, radicle; cz, coleorhiza.* I, *the corn kernel at 30–35 days after pollination: en, endosperm; sk, silk scar; p, pericarp; sc, scutellum; co, coleoptile; l, five folded leaves; st, stem tip; r, radicle; sc, scutellum; cz, coleorhiza.*

gene located at this locus has been altered to the degree that it causes the pericarp to have red coloration.

Let us assume that the ovule occurred on a plant having the normal yellow corn (which carries a colorless pericarp) and that the pollen grain that landed on the silk of this kernel of corn was from a plant carrying the gene for red pigmentation of the pericarp. A plant grown from a resulting kernel carries on one of its chromosome No. 1 homologs a gene that gives colorless pericarp. On the other homolog it carries a gene that gives red pericarp. The kernels of this plant will be red. The reason is that when the no-color and color-producing genes are in the same plant, the color gene has a dominant effect and suppresses the other factor.

During meiosis of the new plant, following the pairing of the two No. 1 chromosomes and their subsequent migration to opposite poles, two of the resulting megaspores carry color genes, and two carry no-color genes.

When the three megaspores disintegrate, there is an equal chance that the surviving megaspore will carry the color- or no-color-producing gene. When we consider all the kernels on an ear of corn, we can expect that half of the egg cells will carry a gene for red pigmentation and the other half will carry the no-color gene.

As we pointed out, meiosis also precedes the formation of pollen in the tassel of the plant. Half of the pollen therefore bears a no-color gene. The other half carries the gene for red grains.

Let us assume that we self-pollinate this plant: We collect pollen of the tassel and apply it to the silk in a way to keep away the pollen from nearby plants. There is an even chance that the egg cells will be fertilized with a sperm nucleus that carries a color gene. There also is an even chance that they will be fertilized by a sperm with the no-color gene. Because half of the egg cells carry the no-color gene and half of the pollen grains also carry this gene,

one-quarter of the new zygotes on an ear of corn will carry the no-color gene in each of the two No. 1 homologous chromosomes.

It follows that one-quarter of the corn kernels will give rise to plants bearing yellow or white ears of corn.

Similar reasoning establishes that one-quarter of the new zygotes will carry the color gene in both of the homologous chromosomes, and the resulting plants will have red kernels.

Finally, one-half of the new zygotes will be heterozygous—that is, they will be carrying the colorless factor on one chromosome and the color factor on the other. Because of dominance of the color gene over the colorless gene, this class of zygotes will give rise to plants with kernels that have colored pericarps.

If the pigments of underlying kernel parts were yellow in both parents, we would therefore expect three-quarters of the progeny of the self-pollinated ear of corn to give rise to red ears of corn and one-quarter of the progeny to bear yellow ears. Here we have the familiar 3:1 ratio that occurs with the segregation of gene pairs when one of the genes is completely dominant over the other. Such ratios, called Mendelian ratios, were discovered by Gregor J. Mendel in Austria about 100 years ago.

When a plant is heterozygous for two pairs of genes located on two different chromosome pairs, both of which may affect the same character or two different characters, their assortment during meiosis is completely independent and at random. When the plant is self-pollinated, the proportion of segregates of the various types in the resulting offspring can be predicted by simple mathematical calculations.

Many characters are determined by a large number of genes. The precise influence of any one gene cannot be measured. Studies on the inheritance of such characters are restricted to quantitative measurements that reflect the aggregate effect of a number of genes. Inheritance of characters controlled by many genes is known as quantitative inheritance.

Some genetic factors carried by the generative nuclei of pollen grains have an immediate effect on characteristics of the developing endosperm. It will be recalled the endosperm develops from a triple-fusion nucleus, two components of which are provided by the ovule parent and one component by the pollen parent. When the pollen parent carries a dominant endosperm character and the ovule parent carries the recessive counterparts, the effect of the pollen parent is observable in the developing seed. This immediate effect upon the endosperm is known as xenia.

If the ovule parent of the corn, for instance, carries the genetic factor resulting in white endosperm and the pollen parent carries the corresponding gene for yellow endosperm, the developing endosperm will have a light yellow appearance. If the pericarp is colorless so that the endosperm color can be seen, the end result will be that a yellow ear of corn will be borne on a genetically white plant.

Other factors that produce xenia have been found in corn. Several brown and blue colors exhibit xenia when crossed onto white corn. Similarly, the genetic factors that condition starchy field corn will exhibit xenia when crossed onto plants of sweet corn.

EARLIER we mentioned the linear arrangement of genes on the chromosomes. The genes conditioning two characters may be located on the same chromosomes. If the two genes are located close to each other on the chromosome, the two characters they control in most instances will be inherited together. This phenomenon is called linkage.

At times, however, the characters are not inherited together, particularly when the locations of the genes on the chromosome are distant. A disruption of linkage results when an exchange occurs between the chromosomes in the region separating the genes. It is called crossing over.

When the homologous members of a

The Mechanism of Heredity

Red coloration in the pericarp of corn is dominant to colorless pericarp. Hence the F_1 hybrid plant, which carries a gene from each parent, has red kernels. One-fourth of the F_2 plants carry two genes for red pericarp and one-half carry one gene for each color. Both types have red kernels, giving a ratio of three plants with red kernels and one plant with colorless pericarp.

pair of chromosomes begin to separate during reduction division, we mentioned that separation occurs first in the centromere region and subsequently the chromosomes uncoil. During the uncoiling process, numerous breaks may occur in the strands of chromonemata of the chromosomes, and the broken ends of chromonemata of homologous chromosomes may rejoin.

When such breaks occur in the chromosome region between two genes, a crossover occurs.

If the two genes lie at a considerable distance from each other, the frequency of gametes with crossovers may be as great as those containing the parental linkage, and from genetic evidence it will be difficult to determine if the genes actually are located on the same chromosome. The crossover mechanism provides a means of assortment of genes, even though they occur on the same chromosome.

IN CONCLUSION: Genes, which constitute the germ plasm and determine the hereditary traits of plants, are highly stable. Thought to be composed of complex organic molecules, they have the capacity to divide and reproduce themselves in kind.

The chromosome numbers of plants also are highly stable. Throughout the evolutionary process in plants, mechanisms that assure constancy of chromosome number through innumerable cell divisions of a growing plant and during the processes of sexual reproduction have developed.

During the processes of sexual reproduction, means are present, however, for assortment, segregation, and recombination of genetic factors. Tremendous genetic variability thereby is provided within a species. Occasional mutations of genes also contribute to the variability.

Genetic variability is especially significant in the evolution of plants. Plants that carry the proper combinations of factors are provided with the maximum opportunity to survive. Genetic variability also provides the basis for the potential improvement that man can make within a species to adapt it for his specific uses.

MARTIN G. WEISS *is Associate Director, Crops Research Division, Agricultural Research Service. He received his doctor's degree from Iowa State University in genetics and plant breeding, and taught courses in plant breeding at Iowa State University for 4 years. He has conducted research in the breeding of soybeans and forage crops since 1936.*

JOHN E. SASS *is a professor in the Department of Botany and Plant Pathology, Iowa State University. He received his doctor's degree from the University of Michigan in 1929. Since 1928 he has taught plant anatomy and related subjects at Iowa State University and has collaborated on the morphological phases of projects of the experiment station.*

Unusual Events in Seed Development

M. M. RHOADES

BEFORE CONSIDERING unusual nuclear phenomena in seed formation, let us review briefly the standard sequence of events leading to the formation of the embryo and endosperm.

Normal sexual reproduction in the angiosperms involves the fusion of egg and sperm nuclei to form the zygote. Both have one-half the number of chromosomes found in the sporophytic tissues. Their fusion results in a restoration of the diploid number of chromosomes.

The zygote, or fertilized egg, divides. As a consequence of the numerous mitotic divisions that ensue, the young sporophyte is formed. The embryo of the mature seed contains the future vegetative organs of the sporophyte.

Developmental patterns vary widely in different groups of plants, but the mature embryo invariably consists of a hypocotyl-root axis, with the root meristem at one end and the shoot meristem at the other.

One of the two sperm cells discharged into the embryo sac by the pollen tube unites with the two polar nuclei to form the primary endosperm cell. Secondary fertilization is characteristically and uniquely found in the angiosperms.

The rapidly dividing endosperm plays an important role—in most instances a decisive one—in providing nutrition for the young embryo. Nutrients from the enveloping sporophytic tissue are channeled to the embryo by the endosperm.

If the endosperm fails to develop normally, the embryo suffers; it may abort or remain in a rudimentary stage. In such plants as the common cereals, the endosperm continues to grow and forms a major portion of the mature seed. In other plants, the endosperm undergoes degeneration as the developing embryo utilizes its substance and only vestiges of the endosperm are present in the mature seed.

The endosperm in intercrosses is of a hybrid nature and may exhibit certain characteristics of the pollen parent. In corn, for example, when a strain with white endosperm is pollinated by one with yellow endosperm, the F_1 seeds will have the yellow color of the male parent. This direct effect of the pollen parent on the endosperm of the seed is called xenia.

Failure of normal seed development leading to seed collapse is due to a number of causes. In corn, a large number of simply inherited recessive genes are known which, when homozygous, result in defective or shriveled seeds.

Aneuploidy and genic unbalance also produce aborted seeds. The so-called seedless bananas and watermelons are triploids, which, because of an irregular assortment of the 3N number of chromosomes during meiosis, have unbalanced chromosomal complements in both megaspores and microspores. The aneuploid megaspores may fail to produce functional female gametophytes, but if they do give rise to an embryo sac and fertilization occurs, the ensuing proembryo and endosperm are arrested in early development and shriveled seed result.

Seedlessness in grapes results from an inhibited growth of the seed under the influence of a specific maternal genotype or from a lack of functional female gametophytes. In this latter situation, no fertilization is possible, but a parthenocarpic fruit develops.

The seedless fruits of most pineapple varieties are caused by pollen incompatibility—the inability of pollen tubes to grow down the style and discharge the sperm cells into the embryo sac. One commercial strain, however, the Cabenza of Florida and the West Indies, is a triploid, and seedlessness here, as in both triploid bananas and watermelons, results from the malfunctioning of unbalanced gametophytes or young sporophytes.

Since aborted seeds are found in the fruits of triploid watermelon, banana, and pineapple, the term "seedlessness" is hardly appropriate, but from a gastronomical point of view this is a matter of no consequence.

Normally one of the two sperm cells discharged into the embryo sac fuses with the egg nucleus to form the zygote, and the second sperm from the same pollen tube unites with the two polar nuclei to give rise to the primary endosperm cell.

Not uncommonly, however, in certain plants more than one pollen tube enters the embryo sac. When this occurs, a sperm cell from one pollen tube may fertilize the egg and a sperm cell from another pollen tube may fuse with the polar nuclei.

This phenomenon is known as heterofertilization. It results in embryo and endosperm of different genetic constitutions if the male parent is heterozygous and dissimilar sperm fertilize egg and polars.

Other phenomena that may occur when more than one pollen tube is present are the fusion of two sperm cells with the egg to give a triploid zygote and the fertilization of the synergid by a third sperm.

When fertilization of both egg and synergid takes place, the embryo sac will contain two zygotes, which will be diploid-diploid twins or triploid-diploid, depending on the number of sperm involved in fertilization of the egg.

Not all diploid-diploid twins come from fertilization of more than one cell of the same embryo sac. Some arise in ovules with two embryo sacs where both eggs are fertilized. Others stem from a cleavage of the proembryo.

In certain apomictic plants, such as *Citrus*, a number of sporophytes in a single seed are produced by sporophytic budding of the cells of the nucellus or integuments. Haploid-diploid twins in nonapomictic plants originate when the fertilized egg forms a diploid embryo and a synergid or antipodal is stimulated to divide and give rise to a haploid sporophyte.

Infrequently a haploid sperm cell which has entered the embryo sac will, under some unknown stimulus, divide to form a haploid embryo. This is the phenomenon of androgenesis. It occurs much less frequently than does the parthenogenetic development of the egg cell into a haploid sporophyte. As expected, an androgenetic haploid sporophyte has the characteristics of the pollen parent.

Fertilization of antipodals by accessory sperm has also been reported, but presumably this is a rarer event than fertilization of synergids, which are more like the egg cell in size and position.

Another kind of anomalous nuclear behavior due to polyspermy, which, however, is not well substantiated, is the separate fertilization of the polar nuclei by two different sperm cells. If one or both developed into the endosperm, it would be diploid rather than triploid. Reports exist in the literature that in plants with sexual reproduction the unfertilized polars may exceptionally give rise to the endosperm.

There is no question but that the haploid egg can occasionally develop into a haploid sporophyte, although the associated endosperm arising from fertilization of the polars is essential for continued growth of these haploid embryos.

It is possible that unfertilized polar nuclei may also be able to undergo division. This is certainly true in plants with autonomous apomixis where both embryo and endosperm arise from unfertilized, but unreduced, egg and polar nuclei, respectively.

The seeds produced in crosses between polyploid and diploid races are defective because of an upset in the 2:3 ratio of chromosome sets usually found in the embryo and endosperm.

In the cross of a tetraploid (4N) by a diploid (2N) pollen parent, a triploid (3N) zygote and a pentaploid (5N) endosperm result. Endosperm development is greatly restricted, and the young embryo consequently does not undergo full development, since it is dependent upon the meristematic endosperm for the transfer of nutrients from the mother plant.

In the reciprocal cross of 2N × 4N, the embryo is again 3N in constitution, while the endosperm is 4N. Poorly developed seed are formed. There is a departure in both kinds of crosses from the usual 2:3 ratio found in the embryo and endosperm of diploids, and this is reflected in a drastic impairment of seed development.

It is generally true, however, that there is a less drastic effect in the 4N × 2N cross than in the reciprocal.

The suggestion has been made that the genomic constitution of the maternal parent is a factor affecting seed development and that the production of normal seeds depends upon a specific ratio of chromosome sets in maternal tissue, embryo, and endosperm.

AN EXCEEDINGLY important technique for the plant breeder who wishes to obtain hybrids from crosses that produce aborted or nongerminable seed is that of embryo culturing.

Embryos removed from mature but nongerminable seed and placed on an artificial medium have given rise to viable seedlings. More spectacular is the finding that, when young embryos abort during development, seedlings have been obtained by excision of the young embryos and growth on a sterile nutrient medium.

Through the use of embryo culturing, it has been possible to obtain desired hybrids after repeated failures with conventional methods.

The F_1 hybrids between different species of the same genus or between species of different genera often are highly sterile and do not produce viable seed. The sterility may be caused by an irregular assortment of the chromosomes at meiosis, leading to aneuploid spores which abort, or to disharmonious (lethal) constellations of genes in the haploid spores if pairing of the chromosomes in meiosis is fairly regular.

These sterile hybrids in many instances have been converted into fertile amphidiploids by a doubling of the chromosome number. This occurs either by formation of unreduced gametes or in a somatic cell. Doubling of the chromosome number may readily be induced experimentally by chemical compounds, such as colchicine. The sterility of the hybrids has been overcome by a duplication of the chromosomes.

Some of our most valuable crop plants have arisen from sporadic crosses of different species followed by doubling of the chromosomes.

For example, the cultivated tobacco (*Nicotiana tabacum*) has been shown experimentally to be a tetraploid derived from a cross of two diploid species of *Nicotiana*.

The cultivated cotton (*Gossypium hirsutum*) races have arisen in a like manner from a hybrid of two related diploid species, and it has been demonstrated that the hexaploid (6N) common bread wheats (*Triticum aestivum*) have two sets of chromosomes from a diploid species of wheat and two sets each from two different species of the related genus *Aegilops*.

The induction of polyploidy in sterile hybrids can thus be seen to have played an exceedingly important role in the evolution of plant species and the development of crop plants.

In contrast to the high fertility of allotetraploids is the reduced fertility of autotetraploids, which arise following doubling of the chromosome number in a fertile diploid species.

Although most autotetraploids have larger seeds than do comparable diploids, there is a significant amount of seed abortion, and the potential yield is not realized. A large number of autotetraploids have been induced by colchicine treatment, but they have

not yet been of much commercial importance in plants where the grain is the marketable crop.

The sterility of autotetraploids has been ascribed to their somewhat irregular chromosomal assortment at meiosis, and the consequent aneuploidy is assumed to cause seed abortion. It has also been suggested that the sterility is due to genically determined pollen incompatibility.

Selection is possible for increased fertility of autotetraploids, however, and one tetraploid variety of rye with a satisfactory grain yield is grown commercially in Sweden. Work in progress in the United States indicates that similar success may be had for tetraploid corn.

Seeds normally arise from sexual reproduction, but in a number of plants found in families ranging from the grasses to the Compositae an asexual method has been substituted. Plants in which embryos arise without fertilization of the egg are called apomicts. The term "apomixis" is applied to this method of reproduction.

In plants with adventitious embryony, the young sporophyte arises directly from diploid somatic cells of the nucellus or integuments of the ovule. The progeny are uniformly alike, and all have the same genetic constitution. There is no segregation despite heterozygosity of the female parent. The female gametophyte, if formed, rarely functions to give an embryo of sexual origin.

There are three major variations of the course of events in adventitious embryony. In *Citrus*, for example, which has female gametophytes, fertilization of both egg and polars is necessary, and hybrids of sexual derivation are produced. These, however, cannot compete successfully with the adventitious embryos arising from the nucellus. Almost invariably it is the latter which are found in the ripened seed. In the second class, fertilization only of the polars is necessary for continued development of the adventitious embryos. Then there are those forms, such as *Opuntia*, in which neither egg nor polars are fertilized, but the adventitious embryos grow normally.

In pseudogamous and parthenogenetic apomicts, embryo sacs are formed, so there is an alternation of generations. The female gametophytes, however, are diploid and result from the failure of meiosis (diplospory), from development of an archesporial cell directly into a diploid female gametophyte (generative apospory), or from the division of a somatic cell (somatic apospory).

In pseudogamous apomicts, irrespective of the mode of origin of the diploid embryo sac, the egg cell divides without fertilization to form the embryo, but no endosperm is produced unless the polars are fertilized. Since an endosperm is essential for seed development in these forms, seed abortion occurs if there is no secondary fertilization.

In autonomous apomicts, where the diploid embryo sac can arise in the various ways cited above, both egg and polars are able to divide and form embryo and endosperm, respectively, without the stimulus of fertilization or even of pollination. Here fertilization has been entirely dispensed with and seed formation is wholly asexual.

It should be emphasized that in apomictic plants there is a substitution of meiosis and of the need of fertilization. Both substitutions must occur regularly, and the first must be followed by the second in plants that have apomixis as a recurrent method of reproduction.

It is of some interest that certain apomictic plants have progenies of sexual as well as of apomictic origin. These are called facultative apomicts. The proportion of sexual or apomictic embryos is known to be influenced by the constitution of the pollen parent. Obligate apomicts are plants that have offspring solely of apomictic origin. No sexual embryos are produced in them.

The precise genetic control of the mechanisms that make apomixis possible are not well understood, but most apomicts are both polyploid and are of hybrid ancestry. Neither polyploidy nor hybridity, however, alone will result in apomixis.

It is believed that genic combinations responsible for the substitution of meiosis and of fertilization are brought together by hybridization and that polyploidy brings about a more effective gene dosage for their expression. Since apomixis is genetically controlled, there will be a strong positive selection in sterile hybrids for any mechanism which affords an escape from sterility.

Despite the widespread occurrence of apomictic plants, they may well be doomed to eventual extinction since their asexual mode of reproduction precludes genic recombination. Barring somatic mutation, all of the offspring of an apomictic plant are as alike as identical twins. There is no opportunity to form new gene combinations that might enable adaptation to changing environments.

Many cases have been reported where an egg cell and occasionally a synergid, following a normal meiosis, underwent division to form a haploid embryo. In these embryo sacs, the polar nuclei were fertilized, so a 3N endosperm is formed. Since the haploid sporophyte is usually highly sterile the cycle is not repeated and nonrecurrent apomixis is of no significance as a method of reproduction.

Self-incompatibility, a widespread phenomenon, occurs in thousands of species distributed among at least 66 families of the angiosperms. A number of different genetic mechanisms for self-incompatibility, six in all, are known. They lead to the failure of fertilization. If seeds are necessary for normal fruit development in such nonapomictic plants as plums and cherries, it is essential that sources of compatible pollen be available.

M. M. RHOADES *is professor of botany and chairman of the Department of Botany of Indiana University.*

Plants Must Disperse
Their Seeds

PAUL G. RUSSELL AND ALBINA F. MUSIL

NOT ALL SEEDS survive the struggle for existence. Any marked change in environment, moisture, temperature, amount of sunlight, or soil composition may create conditions under which seeds of certain plants cannot germinate. Plants therefore must disperse their seeds in such a manner and in such quantity that some, at least, will survive so that the species may continue.

Devices for survival among plants are many.

The dormant embryonic plant within the seed of most kinds of plants is protected by a seedcoat until conditions are favorable for new growth to start. The seedcoat may be tough, as in the bean. It may be thin and delicate, as in the peanut, in which it is protected by the shell of the fruit.

The struggle for existence is reflected also in the amazing variety of shapes, structures, and sizes of seeds and fruits among the 300 families of flowering plants.

A variable proportion of seeds of many kinds of plants resists prompt germination and so assures survival if conditions are unfavorable for some of the seeds that germinate first. One example is the uneven ripening and shedding of the fruits of some grasses, such as giant foxtail (*Setaria faberi*). Another is the delayed shedding of the seeds (achenes) produced from the ray flowers of certain composites, such as some species of thistles.

Many legumes, such as the clovers, produce a variable proportion of seeds with impermeable seedcoats, which may resist germination for long periods.

Some species produce pods in which one segment remains indehiscent—closed—and the seed within it remains dormant for a long time, as in cocklebur (*Xanthium*), for example.

THE DISPERSAL of seeds is determined largely by the size, shape, and character of the seedcoat or the persisting structures of the fruit as, for example, the awns of grasses; the "fuzz" of cotton; spines and bristles of various forms; "wings" on the seeds of certain trees; plumes of dandelion and thistle; the forceful opening of the seed pod, as in witch-hazel (*Hamamelis virginica*); and a sticky surface when wet.

Such seeds are dispersed readily by such natural means as wind, water, animals, and birds.

When structures, such as awns and pubescence, have been removed in the process of harvesting and cleaning of crop seeds, such seeds may become widely distributed in any of several ways—with crop seeds, feeds (hay and grain), common carriers (trucks, automobiles, wagons, airplanes), farm implements, ships, birds, and insects.

The natural means of dispersal have been lost long since by most of our cultivated seed crops, like the cereals, beans, and peanuts. Many persons are not aware of that fact. Only the constant, watchful efforts of man enable these seed crops to withstand the effects of unfavorable weather and the onslaughts of insect pests and diseases and continue their roles as valuable sources of food.

Another fact is that the quality and quantity of production would begin to deteriorate very soon were it not for the continuous research of the plant breeders and geneticists. Through the selection and hybridization of plants, they are constantly developing new strains and varieties of all the main seed crops. The improved species are increasingly superior to the original wild types to which all would revert if left to the uncertain natural means of spreading.

WIND DISPERSAL is the commonest means of dispersal. Strong winds during storms may carry rather heavy

The witchweed has very tiny seeds, only ⅕ mm. long, and one plant produces 50 thousand to 500 thousand seeds. It is a dangerous parasitic weed (Striga asiatica), and attacks corn, sorghum, sugarcane, and other grasses.

seeds and seedlike fruits, regardless of structure, for miles. Even a light breeze may transport small, light seeds for some distance.

Dispersal by wind often is facilitated by the small size of certain seeds.

Possibly the smallest known are those of the witchweed (*Striga asiatica*), an Asiatic parasitic plant that has been found in two Southern States. The tiny seeds, only 0.0078 inch long, are produced in enormous quantities—50 thousand to 500 thousand on one plant. Because of their minute size, they are easily dispersed by water, wind, and farm implements. The witchweed has long been known in Old World Tropics and subtropics. It is a dangerous parasite that attacks corn, sorghum, sugarcane, and other grasses.

The orchid family (Orchidaceae) also has extremely small seeds. Some genera have seeds so fine they resemble dust. Freed from the capsule, they are

carried by the wind to great distances. Sometimes they float in the air for long periods. Seeds of some orchids are equipped with thin, tiny wings, which add to their buoyancy.

Tumbleweeds when they are dry and ripe may be torn loose by the wind and blown over the ground. Seeds drop along the way. Tumbleweeds are known on deserts, prairies, and steppes throughout the world.

An example is an amaranth (*Amaranthus graecizans*), a weed that is commonly found here and there in drier areas throughout the United States, especially in the western plains. The tumbleweed is so characteristic of our West that the name figures prominently in songs. Another example is the noxious Russian-thistle (*Salsola pestifer*), which is not a true thistle but is closely related to the pigweeds. The wind blows the plants in every direction, especially in winter when the ground is frozen, and the small, conical seeds are scattered in all directions.

Plants of the mustard family, such as the shepherds-purse (*Capsella bursa-pastoris*), an annual weed, have pods in which the seeds remain. The seeds are attached to a partition between the two halves of the pod. The partition and the seeds are blown away by the wind and are distributed widely. One large plant may bear 500 seed pods, each with about 24 seeds.

In the fieldcress (*Lepidium campestre*), wild peppergrass (*L. virginicum*), and other species of *Lepidium*, the small, round, flat, papery half pods, each with one flattened seed, are blown about by the wind for considerable distances.

Many plants have winged seeds or winged, seedlike fruits by which their distribution is facilitated through wind dispersal. They are more likely to occur on trees, tall shrubs, and high, woody vines than on low, herbaceous plants.

The winged keys of the maples are familiar to everyone. So are the winged nutlets of the ashes (*Fraxinus*). Many trees of the pine family have winged seeds that are samaroid—that is, they resemble the small, dry, winged, seedlike fruits of the maple and elms. Most of the pines (*Pinus*) have seeds of this type, as do the spruces (*Picea*), the firs (*Abies*), the cypresses (*Cupressus*), the tamaracks (*Larix*), and the true cedars (*Cedrus*). The elms (*Ulmus*) and the crapemyrtle (*Lagerstroemia indica*) also have small, samaroid seeds.

The handsome tree-of-heaven (*Ailanthus altissima*), popular as a street tree because of its adaptability to city conditions, has large clusters of samaras. The seed is in the center of the long, narrow wing. The sweetgum (*Liquidambar styraciflua*) has samaroid seeds about one-fourth inch long that are blown about freely by the wind in autumn.

The seeds in the samaroid group that have only one terminal wing rotate briskly in the wind as they travel, and the area of their distribution thus is greatly extended.

True yams (*Dioscorea*), of which there are more than 600 tropical and subtropical species, are climbers with winged seeds. The wings are attached to the seeds in various ways, but in most species the thin, papery seeds are winged on both sides.

The small, light, flat seeds of many of the rhododendrons are winged, usually all around, and fly readily in the wind. The leathery, ovoid capsules of the handsome paulownia (*Paulownia tomentosa*) enclose great numbers of small, delicate seeds, each of which has several wings.

We get quinine from South American trees (*Cinchona*). Their small, oblong, samaroid seeds are one-fourth to one-half inch long and have irregular, terminal wings. They are so light that they are easily carried for considerable distances by even gentle breezes.

The horseradish-tree (*Moringa oleifera*), grown throughout India, has curious, wind-dispersed, three-angled, winged seeds, which yield a valuable oil. The seeds are discharged from a large ribbed pod 9 to 18 inches long.

Many herbaceous plants also have seeds and seedlike fruits that are dispersed by wind with the aid of various

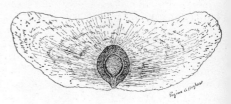

The airplane seed, borne by an East Indian cucurbit vine (Macrozanonia macrocarpa), *is about 6 inches wide, and derives its common name from the fact that it describes a spiral about 20 feet wide as it falls to the ground from the urn-shaped capsule.*

types of wing. One is an East Indian cucurbit vine (*Macrozanonia macrocarpa*), which has a flat seed an inch across. A wing about 3 inches long and 2 inches wide is on each end. It has been called the airplane seed, because it describes a spiral about 20 feet wide when it falls to the ground from its urn-shaped capsule on the high-climbing vine.

The true lilies (*Lilium*), popular as ornamentals throughout the Temperate Zones, have thin, flat seeds, distinctly winged all around. From the many-seeded capsules, often borne at the summit of the stalk, the seeds are blown away a few at a time, especially after the stalk becomes withered.

On the plains of South Africa, a similar method of dispersal may be observed in certain of the native gladiolus (*Gladiolus*).

Some of the rockcresses (*Arabis*) have long, narrow pods that release to the breeze small, elliptic seeds that have marginal wings. These low, herbaceous alpines, of the mustard family, have terminal clusters of attractive pink, white, or purple flowers.

The ovoid capsules of an attractive native white-flowered perennial, the turtlehead (*Chelone glabra*) enclose numerous small, flat, squarish seeds, which are surrounded by a broad, membranous wing, well suited for wind dispersal when it is released from the upper part of the plant.

The large carrot family has two principal means of seed dispersal. Each fruit consists of a pair of round or oblong carpels, which are attached to a slender axis, or columella. Each contains one seed, is usually indehiscent, and often is furnished on the outer side with several ribs that are sometimes elevated into wings. These fruits usually are borne on a tall stalk, which in some species is several feet high. When the whole plant becomes dry and brittle, the light, corky fruits are easily dislodged by the wind and carried away. The wings enhance the buoyancy.

Fruits of the wild carrot have developed bristles, with or without hooks, that enable the fruits to adhere to the fur of passing animals. Thus they get distributed.

Among the most serious pests of western ranges, the halogeton (*Halogeton glomeratus*) is especially dangerous, because it is poisonous to livestock. Its small, seedlike, winged fruits are dispersed easily by wind.

The Russian-thistle (*Salsola pestifer*), another noxious weed, also has small winged seeds.

A number of plants have seeds that are not actually winged but are flat and membranous, borne in capsules, and easily carried by wind. One example is the tulip (*Tulipa*). Its light, flattened seeds occasionally have narrow marginal wings. Another is the yucca (*Yucca*), native mostly to the more arid regions of our country. Its large, flat, black, windborne seeds are produced in great abundance.

The wind disperses the "seeds" of many grasses, although generally there is no special structural adaptation for this purpose except the lightness of the chaffy lemmas and paleas that enclose the grain and act as a wing. Many also have silky hairs on the callus. One is the common reed (*Phragmites communis*), whose long hairs enable the floret to fly away.

Plumed seeds and seedlike fruits generally fly much farther than winged ones. Some travel hundreds of miles. They usually are very light. They can rise and fall with the wind and even rise again from the ground. Most of them are weeds.

The common dandelion (*Taraxacum officinale*) has plumed achenes, which float gracefully in the breeze. Closely related genera in the chicory family that have similar structures are the sowthistles (*Sonchus*), wild lettuces (*Lactuca*), salsify (*Tragopogon*), and several others.

Among the grasses, the spike pappusgrass (*Enneapogon desvauxii*) has plumose awns, which enable the wind to carry off the mature florets.

In the aster family are a great many genera with seeds (achenes) that have bristles or hairs light enough to permit the wind to broadcast them. Some are pernicious weeds. The Canada thistle (*Cirsium arvense*) is one of the worst weeds in various parts of the North Temperate Zone because the plumed seeds are easily carried aloft. The knapweeds (*Centaurea*), ironweeds (*Vernonia*), and the erigerons (*Erigeron*) are other troublesome weeds that are similar to the common thistle in their adaptations for dispersal by wind.

Most of the milkweed family (Asclepiadaceae), many genera of the dogbane family (Apocynaceae), and some genera of the evening-primrose family, such as the fireweed (*Epilobium angustifolium*), have comose seeds—that is, with a tuft of hairs attached to one end.

An example from the dogbane family is the *Strophanthus* from tropical Africa and tropical Asia. The apex of the seed is prolonged into a long, slender beak that is densely feathered along the upper half with thin, white hairs. From the seeds of certain species of *Strophanthus*, sarmentogenin is derived; it contributed to the synthesis of cortisone, a drug used in the treatment of arthritis.

In the common milkweed (*Asclepias syriaca*), the large coma, or tuft of hairs, helps the wind carry the seed away.

Almost any type of seed can be

transported by some kind of water movement—rainwash, floods, and the action of streams. Very small seeds, those that are light in proportion to their size, and those with flat shapes that make for greater buoyancy, are moved greater distances than other kinds.

Many of the light, corky seedlike fruits of the carrot family float easily, some for several months, as do also seeds of some of the gourd family, which also owe their buoyancy to their light, corky structure. Seeds of both these groups are mostly transported by streams.

The thick-walled, buoyant achenes of the silverweed (*Potentilla anserina*) have been known to float in streams for 15 months. The weed therefore is widespread along riverbanks and in swampy meadows in the Northern Hemisphere.

The jimsonweed (*Datura stramonium*) has flat, corky seeds that float easily. In South Africa, and doubtless else-where, they are carried downstream by floodwaters and deposited on the river-banks, where they germinate.

The seedlike achenes of the buck-wheat family (Polygonaceae) are often dispersed by water, as shown by their common occurrence along riverbanks. In the docks (*Rumex*) that have winged seeds, the wings apparently serve for dispersal by both wind and water.

Certain sedges (*Carex*), of which there are about a thousand species, have seeds (achenes) that contain air pockets and float on water, sometimes for several months before the seed may find conditions favorable for germination.

Some seeds and seedlike fruits are carried by ocean currents. Such seeds are of the kind that can float for a long period without absorbing sea water and establish themselves finally in tidal mud or on beaches. They must have a hard, waterproof seedcoat and the ability to respond to external influences. Of the immense number of seeds floated down into the sea by streams all over the world, only a few fulfill

these and other conditions. They represent relatively few species, compared with those dispersed by wind and animals.

Several genera of the bean family appear among those successfully established by this means in widespread areas in the Tropics. They include *Mucuna, Guilandina, Entada, Erythrina,* and *Vigna*. In most of them, buoyancy is maintained by a relatively large cavity between the cotyledons. Seeds cast up on the Florida beaches and along the gulf coast picked up rather frequently by tourists nearly always belong to these genera. Some of them apparently have come from as far as eastern South America.

ANIMALS and birds disperse seeds, too. We often see them in late summer and early autumn with numerous seedlike fruits adhering to their hides or feathers—as happens also to the clothing of those of us who walk in the fields and woods. A large number of plants, including many weeds, owe their distribution to this type of seed dispersal. Hairs, bristles, or hooks on the surface of their fruits and muci-laginous seedcoats in some instances help them attach themselves to fur, feather, and fabric.

The bur-ragweed (*Franseria tomentosa*), a pernicious weed in the Western States, has burlike achenes that are armed with several rows of hooked spines, which adhere readily to passing animals. The barbed bristles of the beggarticks (*Bidens*) are well adapted to adhere to animal fur, bird's plumage, and clothing. The genus is known almost throughout the world.

The tick-trefoils (*Desmodium*) are equally adhesive. Their small, flat, indehiscent pods are covered with hooked hairs.

The wild carrot (*Daucus carota*) and some other species of *Daucus* have seeds (mericarps) with hooked bristles. The same is true of the species of the weedy snakeroots (*Sanicula*).

The seedlike nutlets of one stickseed (*Lappula echinata*) are armed with a double row of hooked prickles, which become embedded in sheep's wool in the Western States and are thus likely to lower the grade of the wool.

Another troublesome weed, the houndstongue (*Cynoglossum officinale*), closely related to the stickseed, also has nutlets with short, barbed prickles.

THE GLUEY SEEDCOATS of some species make it relatively simple for the seeds to become widely dispersed.

Seeds of the butterfly-pea (*Clitoria mariana*), a leguminous plant with showy, pale-blue flowers, are so viscid that they adhere to any passing animal. Several other species of *Clitoria* from tropical America and Asia also have sticky seeds.

Seeds of another rather large group of plants are viscid only after being wetted. The plantains (*Plantago*), with species, mostly weeds, all over the world, belong in this group, as do also many of the rushes (*Juncus*), some of the flaxes (*Linum*), and several of the members of the mustard family, including the garden cress (*Lepidium sativum*), the common falseflax (*Camelina sativa*), and the shepherds-purse (*Capsella bursa-pastoris*), all more or less weedy. Several genera of the phlox family have seeds that when wetted emit mucilage speedily in the form of fine threads. The seeds in this group do not become viscid until wetted, so that they may be blown about, when dry, until they reach a spot that is damp enough for them to exude mucilage and also to germinate.

Another way in which viscid seeds are spread is to become attached to dry leaves that the wind may carry off.

FORCEFUL dehiscence sometimes disperses seed.

One example is the squirting-cucumber (*Ecballium elaterium*), an annual vine whose fruit is an oblong berry about 2 inches long. When thoroughly ripe, the fruit detaches itself from its peduncle. Increasing tension within the fruit breaks the tissue, weakened at the point of detachment, and the seeds are violently ejected, together with the mucilaginous liquid with which they were surrounded. The explosion may throw the seeds as far as 20 feet. Sometimes these adhere to some passing animal that had set off the explosion by touching the ripe fruit.

The small mistletoe (*Arceuthobium pusillum*) of New England is parasitic on the black spruce. When its berries are ripe in September, the seeds are violently expelled. The mucilaginous matter on the seeds causes them to stick to other parts of the spruce or to nearby trees, upon which they germinate.

Another annual vine (*Cyclanthera explodens*) has small, spiny, gourdlike fruits about 1.5 inches long. They burst open into three lobes when they are ripe, and the seeds are thrown out.

In some species of *Oxalis*, as *O. stricta*, often a weed in gardens and elsewhere, the small, cylindrical capsule suddenly explodes when touched and scatters its seeds.

The pale touch-me-not (*Impatiens pallida*) and other species of *Impatiens* have narrow capsules that open suddenly to broadcast their seeds.

The violet-flowered Chinese wistaria (*Wisteria chinensis*) is a stout climber with woody pods. The hard, rounded seeds, when the pod opens, can fly 10 feet across a room. The native witchhazel (*Hamamelis virginica*) bears explosive capsular fruits.

Seed pods of many leguminous species open explosively when ripe. The large, thick pods of the West Indian swordbean (*Canavalia gladiata*) snap open, and the seeds are thrown 10 to 20 feet.

The sandboxtree (*Hura crepitans*) is known in the American Tropics for the force that accompanies the bursting of its round, 3-inch capsules, a force said to be enough to break open a small wooden box in which a capsule was kept.

TURTLES and tortoises often eat fleshy fruits. The box turtle of the

Eastern States feeds on wild strawberries and other succulent fruits, and the seeds pass uninjured through its digestive system.

Lizards, particularly the larger ones that are found in the Tropics, feed freely on all sorts of fruits, especially those of certain cactuses. They also disperse the seeds effectively.

Many freshwater fish feed on vegetation, including fruits of water plants like waterlilies, and may swim for long distances before expelling the seeds. The ability of some fishes to pass overland, usually through wet grass, from one body of water to another, is by no means uncommon, especially in some parts of the Tropics. Seeds are dispersed in their travels.

One curious method of seed dispersal was mentioned by Charles Darwin in his *Origin of Species*. Herons and other birds, he reported, have eaten fish in whose stomachs were viable seeds of the yellow waterlily. In this way the herons often carried the seeds many miles from their source.

Land crabs, which feed on fallen fruits, have increased in this way the distribution of the Malayan leguminous tree known as *Inocarpus edulis*. The large garden snail in England has been responsible for the dispersal of strawberries by eating the fruits.

The digestive tract of earthworms has been found, on dissection, to contain a very wide variety of small seeds.

SEEDS and seedlike fruits often are unusual and bizarre.

Probably the largest seed known among the flowering plants is the two-lobed seed of the so-called double coconut (*Lodoicea maldivica*), a tall, handsome palm native in the Seychelle Islands. One of them may weigh about 40 pounds and be more than a foot long and nearly 8 inches thick.

Among the smallest known seeds are those of *Striga*, which we discussed earlier, and certain orchid seeds.

Cuzco corn, from Peru, has large, flat kernels nearly an inch wide. Another grass, one of the Indian bamboos (*Melocanna baccifera*), has hard, woody seeds 4 inches long and nearly 2 inches in diameter.

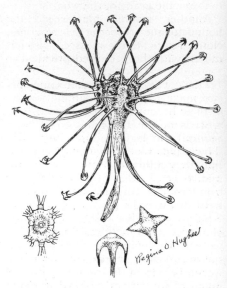

A half-shrubby plant, Uncarina peltata, *bears a capsule. The long, slender processes are terminated with four-winged barbs that cling to the hide or fur of passing animals.*

A native oak (*Quercus corrugata*) in southern Mexico bears enormous acorns with brown, wooly cups nearly 2.5 inches across. The scales are modified into concentric rings. A relative of our well-known catalpa that grows in India (*Oroxylon indicum*) is a tree with flat pods 3 feet long, filled with delicate, silky-papery, winged seeds about 3 inches wide.

The bizarre capsule of the unicorn plant of the Gulf States (*Martynia louisiana*) resembles a large hummingbird with two long, slender, upright tail feathers. These appendages have small recurved points, which readily attach the capsule to the fur of passing animals or to a person's clothing.

A similar method of dispersal is employed by the Malagasy plant *Uncarina peltata*, whose dry fruits, 3 inches in diameter, have numerous long, slender bristles, each terminated by four small, recurved hooks. One of these fruits attached to fur or clothing is very hard to dislodge.

One of the Chinese waterchestnuts (*Trapa bicornis*) has blackish fruits 3 inches across that closely resemble a bull's head, with two stout, curved, sharp-pointed horns. These fruits float for some distance before sinking to the bottom of the shallow river or pond, where they may germinate.

The dipterocarps (*Dipterocarpus*), tall trees from tropical Asia, are a source of the commercial gurjun balsam. Their fruits are small and globular and have a persistent calyx. Two of the sepals become greatly elongated up to 7 inches long, and the other three remain short. The elongated, winglike sepals enable the fruits to be wind propelled for long distances.

THE RECEIPT of a shipment of cabbage seed from Russia in February 1898 marked the beginning of a continuing program of plant introduction by the Department of Agriculture, which collects plant materials, mostly as seeds, from all parts of the world for experimental purposes.

The introductions are received from the Department's agricultural explorers, foreign institutions, and other sources. They usually represent special strains or varieties of existing crop plants, or they may be wild relatives of cereals, forage plants, fruit, vegetables, fiber plants, oil-yielding plants, and plants for special projects.

Seeds of weeds may come into the United States with imported crop seeds and on ships and airplanes. Most of the noxious weeds in this country were introduced from foreign sources in this manner. Familiar examples are field bindweed (*Convolvulus arvensis*) and Canada thistle (*Cirsium arvense*).

Some kinds of plants that are not important weeds in their native land sometimes become extremely objectionable under certain conditions in parts of this country—as, for example, giant foxtail (*Setaria faberi*) and St.-Johns-wort (*Hypericum perforatum*).

It is highly important therefore that all imported seeds, whether crop or weed, be correctly identified and evaluated before planting.

THE IDENTIFICATION of seeds and seedlike fruits usually is based on external morphological features, such as shape, size, color, and surface configuration or texture. Sometimes the internal anatomy of the seed—the size and position of the embryo or the nature of the endosperm, for example—furnishes useful clues to its identity.

For seed identification of special groups, particular attention is paid to the features that are characteristic of the group. For example, in determining species of the genus *Cucurbita*, which includes pumpkins, squashes, and cushaws, special attention is paid to the shape of the hilum (seed scar), the character and color of the seed margin, and the color of the seed face.

The identification of seeds of the genus *Phaseolus*, the cultivated beans, takes into account the position, shape, and size of the hilum, the nature of the caruncle and micropyle, the nature and color of the seedcoat, and the nature of the parahilum, which is a small area next to the hilum and is characterized by two small tubercules.

Seeds of two species of *Hibiscus*, the kenaf (*H. cannabinus*) and the roselle (*H. sabdariffa*), both of economic importance, are almost alike, except that glossy, pale-brown spots occur on the surface of *H. cannabinus*.

Seeds of the mimosa family (Mimosaceae), with one or two exceptions, are easily separated from the seeds of other legumes by a horseshoe-shaped design on the seed faces. A continuous elliptic or oval design on the seed faces would place the seed in the family Caesalpiniaceae.

A SEED HERBARIUM is essential for reference in identifying seeds, since published descriptions of plants rarely include the necessary morphological details of the seed and mature seeds are usually not present on specimens in plant herbariums. Newly introduced plant materials frequently must be identified promptly in order to be handled effectively.

The Department of Agriculture maintains a large general seed herbarium at the Plant Industry Station at Beltsville, Md., consisting not only of seeds, ranging in size up to 2 inches or more in diameter, but also seedlike fruits and certain types of dry fruits. The herbarium is used chiefly for identifying or checking the identification of newly introduced plant materials.

Another large seed herbarium, at the Agricultural Research Center, Beltsville, that consists mostly of actual and potential weeds and seeds of crop plants, is used mainly for identifications in carrying out the provisions of the Federal Seed Act.

Together, these seed herbariums total about 100 thousand samples, which come from all parts of the world. More than 250 plant families are represented, with 17 thousand species.

These herbariums may be used by anyone who cares to consult them.

Some persons have learned that the study of seeds is an absorbing and profitable hobby. It involves little expense and a small amount of time and energy. It is a field in which there are satisfying and practical returns. For the farmer or nurseryman, a collection of seeds of authentically identified plants is of value in checking new or little-known seed materials. The introduction of new and possibly dangerous weeds could very well be forestalled if authentic samples of them were on hand for comparison. Small glass vials and gummed labels from a pharmacy are ideal for filing small samples of seeds.

PAUL G. RUSSELL *is a collaborator in the New Crops Research Branch, Agricultural Research Service. Before retiring in 1959, he was a botanist in the same branch.*
ALBINA F. MUSIL *was a seed technologist in the Seed Branch, Grain Division, before she retired in 1960.*

Life Processes of the Living Seed

R. G. STANLEY AND W. L. BUTLER

THE EMBRYO in a seed draws on its endosperm for the nutrients it needs to germinate and grow. A delicate balance of internal conditions regulates its life processes.

The living seed is able to incorporate small molecules and simple substances—such as glucose, phosphorus, and sulfur—into complex chemical units of a cell. These organized parts are the cell wall and the protoplasm, which contains the cell nucleus. Enzymes act as the go-between in these conversions and building processes.

The energy for this work comes from the breakdown, or catabolism, of some of the cell's chemical components, usually by combining them with oxygen in the process called respiration.

Most of the seed components from which the enzymes of the protoplasm and cell walls form new cells can be classed as proteins, fats, carbohydrates, organic acids, and amino acids.

Thus the seed lives as long as its outside environment (against which its seedcoat helps protect it) and internal environment maintain active enzymes and a good balance of chemical substances. Only under these conditions can the embryo, the result of the fusion of the sperm and egg nuclei, produce new cells and a healthy plant.

Moisture, temperature, and gases, particularly carbon dioxide and oxygen, can affect markedly the enzymes and chemical components of the living seed. Fungi, insects, bacteria, chemicals, or light can diminish or destroy the seed's power to germinate. Many of the same factors, in the right concentration or combination, can enhance the life processes of the seed.

THE WATER CONTENT of the developing seed is similar to that of any actively growing tissue—about 70 to 80 percent. As the seed reaches maturity and the stage at which it is shed from the plant, however, its moisture drops rapidly.

How much water remains at maturity depends on the species of the plant and the environment in which the seed matures. When seeds are artificially extracted from the fruit, their moisture content is affected by the method of extraction and the storage conditions.

Seeds of the maple, wildrice, and orange illustrate the critical role of the water level in seeds at their time of harvest and during storage.

The silver maple (*Acer saccharinum*) sheds its seeds in June at a moisture content of about 58 percent. The seed dies if the water content falls below 30 percent. Seeds of sugar maple (*Acer saccharum*), however, mature in September, contain less than 30 percent water, and can be air dried to about 5 percent without lowering germination.

Some seeds, such as wildrice (*Zigania aquatica*), must actually be stored in water at 32° F. for maximum germination. They lose their ability to germinate if they are exposed to air for a few days.

Lela V. Barton, working at the Boyce Thompson Institute of Plant Research, Yonkers, N.Y., showed that citrus seeds stored at room temperature are injured if their high content of water drops. Orange seeds are injured by drying to 25 percent moisture. Grapefruit seeds became inactive when dried below 51 percent.

How the external environment in which a seed develops affects its moisture content is illustrated by a study of seed of ponderosa pine. N. T. Mirov, of the U.S. Forest Service, found that seed from trees growing at 2 thousand to 3 thousand feet contained 18 percent more moisture than those at 6 thousand to 7 thousand feet, although

he dried all the seeds under the same conditions.

This lower water-holding capacity of seeds from higher elevations supports Nicolai A. Maximov's theory that plant tissues that must survive severe cold usually contain less water than those of warmer climates. The mechanism by which the living seed is protected under such varying conditions of development can be related to their chemical composition.

Research at the Boyce Thompson Institute compared seeds high in fat content (pine and peanuts) with those low in fat and high in carbohydrate (tomato and onion). The amount of water held by seeds stored at the same temperature and relative humidity fell as the amount of fat and oil increased. Thus the ability of tissues of a low water content to withstand cold was related to their chemical composition, especially the amount of fat in them.

High temperatures may kill the seed, too. The seeds with a high content of water are less tolerant of high temperatures. Ponderosa pine and Douglasfir seeds remained viable after heating at 150° F. for 3 hours when they contained only 7 percent of water. With a water content of 60 percent, the seeds were rapidly killed by temperatures above 110°.

If seeds are stored with a high moisture content, internally produced heat may raise the temperature in the storage container and shorten the lifespan of the seed. This damage, as that from externally applied heat, results from changes in cell metabolism. The breakdown and conversion of chemical components and seed protein by enzymes is made easier by an abundance of water and is accelerated at high temperature.

Although enzymes are present in dry seed, they are activated only on movement of water into the seed. As the temperature increases, the rate of metabolism—enzyme activity—also increases.

One measurable product of this

metabolism is the amount of carbon dioxide given off and oxygen taken up. A rapidly metabolizing seed has a higher gas exchange rate than a quiescent seed. If the energy made available by respiration is not used in growth, it is liberated as heat, and the temperature of the stored seed goes up. Water content, one of the most important factors in seed viability, therefore cannot be considered alone.

Variations in water content influence the seed's metabolic activities, including respiration, its temperature, and its ability to germinate.

Increasing the amount of water in a seed above 10 to 15 percent strongly activates the cell enzymes. In stored sunflower and flax seeds, respiration rates increased with increasing water content up to 50 percent. The temperature inside the seeds increased after the increase in respiration. On heating at temperatures greater than 120°, the living cell protein coagulates irreversibly, just as an egg hardens on heating.

If the water content is too high, large amounts of the chemicals required for growth will be used up. The seeds will then be unable to germinate when they are placed under proper conditions.

Removal of too much water from the seed also causes death. The optimal water content of stored seed at 32° to 40° has been determined for most agriculturally important species.

The moisture content of the storage container is usually regulated by the use of chemical desiccants, such as calcium chloride or solutions of sulfuric acid, which maintain a constant relative humidity in the closed compartment or storage jar.

To maintain maximum viability, most seeds are stored at a fixed moisture content and at a fixed temperature, usually between 32° and 41°. In this temperature range, water in the seeds does not freeze, but enzyme activities are retarded.

Although the optimum storage water content and water-holding capacity may differ in seeds of different species, the universal nature of enzymes controlling metabolism in all living cells establishes the narrow temperature limits.

When enzyme activities are drastically reduced at low temperatures, the chemical substrates are preserved in a form essential to maintaining the maximum germinative capacity of the stored seed.

It is possible to store seeds at temperatures below 32° if the water content is low enough. Temperatures as low as minus 320°, the temperature of liquid nitrogen, do not injure wheat embryos with less than 10 percent of water, but kill embryos containing 50 percent of water.

So far, the technique of storing seeds at very low temperatures is merely an experimental laboratory procedure, which is neither necessary nor economically feasible.

Regardless of storage temperature or moisture content of the seed, as long as the protoplasm remains alive the enzymes continue some chemical activities, and respiratory changes occur.

Only the most sensitive instruments can detect these changes.

Changes in organic compounds also occur with the uptake of oxygen and release of carbon dioxide in living, but nongrowing, seeds. If these seeds are germinated, the rate of respiration increases, and the chemical changes, uptake of oxygen, and release of carbon dioxide are easy to detect.

By following respiratory changes over extended periods in the quiescent seed and comparing them to changes in the early phases of germination, we can compute more precisely the amount of gas exchange in stored seed.

THE GAS ATMOSPHERE surrounding mature seeds can determine if the seeds remain alive. If a container of seeds is evacuated and the oxygen pressure is reduced, the seeds keep better than in air. Lack of oxygen retards respiration. Some seeds are short lived in air even at low temperatures. Often they can be kept alive for many years in an atmosphere of nitrogen or hydrogen at temperatures near 40°.

Seeds planted too deeply in soil, where little oxygen is present, will not live. As the depth of planting increases, the available oxygen and seed survival decrease. Wet or poorly drained soils also lack oxygen and inhibit the living processes of the seed. Most seeds immersed in water will die unless air is bubbled through the water.

A shortage of oxygen usually kills the seed when the temperature or respiration is high. This happens because enzymes need oxygen to produce energy for growth of the embryo. The energy is released when the enzymes combine oxygen with various cell compounds.

Sometimes, however, high levels of oxygen are not required by the living cell to obtain energy from its chemical compounds. Some seeds have an abundance of the anaerobic enzymes, which function without oxygen. These enzymes produce enough energy for certain life processes.

Rice seeds (*Oryza*), for example, do not require much oxygen to function. The cells of the embryo and seedling have a system of anaerobic enzymes and a special kind of respiration that requires little oxygen. Seeds of rice, and of a few other plants, therefore can remain viable and germinate under water that contains too little oxygen for the survival of most seeds.

Carbon dioxide, the end product of respiration, also has marked effects on seed viability. If it accumulates inside the seed or in the soil environment surrounding the seed, injury may result.

The role of carbon dioxide is difficult to study, because gas concentrations inside and outside the seed may differ widely and the effects vary with the temperature. Research has shown, however, that the activity of most oxidative, energy-releasing enzymes is reduced by high levels of carbon dioxide.

Fifteen years ago this inhibiting effect was thought to be the result of the dissolving of carbon dioxide in the embryo cell sap and higher acidity.

We now recognize that living cells have many natural systems for buffering and counteracting such changes. Accumulation of an enzyme product, such as carbon dioxide, in the living cell slows down the enzyme that produces the product. When seeds are stored for a long time, factors that increase the carbon dioxide around them frequently must be controlled to assure maximum viability.

Fungi and bacteria can produce large amounts of carbon dioxide. These micro-organisms commonly occur on and in seeds. They, too, require water to grow, and drying the seed to a low moisture inhibits their activity.

Bacteria and fungi also contain enzymes, which metabolize and convert chemical compounds. They usually affect the chemicals on the seedcoat or in the seed.

Through respiration, micro-organisms produce energy, which may raise the temperature and cause the death of the seeds. Grains of stored wheat, for example, often appear to respire at a high rate. Actually, most of the carbon dioxide and heat is produced by micro-organisms growing inside the grain and not by the wheat embryos.

Micro-organisms may have many other effects.

Some fungi or bacteria produce chemicals that harm the embryo.

Some may produce compounds or excrete enzymes that soften the seedcoat, so that air and water diffuse into the seed and hasten its metabolism and loss of viability.

Others may metabolize and exhaust the seed's storage compounds. Old seeds and seeds that are stored under unsuitable conditions of moisture and temperature are particularly susceptible to attack by micro-organisms, usually to the detriment of the seed. The seedcoat therefore often is treated with a chemical disinfectant before it is stored.

Certain other chemical compounds inside and outside the seed may affect viability and germinative capacity.

By analyzing seeds before and after

storage under different conditions, we have detected several compounds that help keep quiescent seeds alive.

Enzymes, such as catalase, peroxidase, and cytochrome oxidase, have been found to be good indexes of seed viability. The activity of respiratory enzymes of this type, which add oxygen to a compound or remove hydrogen from it, is easily determined. A dye is placed on an embryo. If these oxidative-reductive enzymes are active they will add hydrogen to the dye and convert it to another color. Triphenyl tetrazolium chloride is one dye commonly used in this assay. The use of this and other biochemical tests of viability are discussed later.

UNSATURATED FATTY ACIDS in oily seeds are a good index of viability.

When a large percentage of the unsaturated fatty acids are oxidized or saturated with hydrogen, the seeds become rancid, and viability decreases.

The ability of seeds of Jeffrey pine to germinate after storage was found to be related to the content of linolenic acid. As this acid is saturated with hydrogen and changed to linoleic or oleic acid, the ability of the stored seed to germinate goes down.

The accumulation of citric and malic acids in lentil bean seeds during storage is recognized as beneficial for germination.

In cabbage seeds stored at 41°, enzymes convert the soluble sugars to acids. These changes also improved seed viability. If too much carbohydrate and protein are broken down, however, viability is reduced.

Old seeds, which show marked decreases in nonsoluble carbohydrate or protein, germinate poorly. The breakdown or coagulation of protein in old seeds may advance so far as to modify the protein present in the nucleus. When that occurs, the seeds usually die. If such seeds do germinate, they frequently produce mutant plants.

Corn grown from 5-year-old seeds showed many of the same mutations caused by X-rays and gamma rays.

Thus proper maintenance of the life processes of quiescent seed assures not only maximum viability but also the transmittance of desired characteristics from the parent plant to the offspring.

NEWLY DEVELOPED analytical techniques and instruments are beginning to clarify the role of such compounds as hormones, inhibitors, and light-sensitive pigments in seeds.

The endosperm of some seeds contains hormonelike substances, which the embryo absorbs during development and germination. Because of the suspected role of hormones in maintaining the viability and stimulating growth, many investigators have added hormonelike chemicals to seeds.

Most of the reports on treatment of seeds with synthetic growth substances were published between 1937 and 1946. Of 250 studies surveyed by Willem Kruyt in 1954, only one-third reported positive results. Poor experimental design was the cause of some conflicting reports.

Many problems must be considered when we attempt to demonstrate that hormones are essential to seed viability and growth.

The seedcoat may act as a physical barrier to the absorption of externally added hormones. The chemical added may be in a form that the seed cannot metabolize. Or the seed may contain sufficient natural hormone so that added growth substance will not be effective.

Although some form of plant hormone probably is involved in germination, its role has not been demonstrated conclusively.

Inhibitors, including many compounds that occur naturally in living seeds, keep the seeds dormant until conditions are favorable for germination. One such compound in tomato fruits prevents premature germination of their seeds.

Some seeds contain compounds that enforce dormancy until there is enough water in the soil to leach the inhibitors out of the seed. The concentration of such inhibitors diffusing out of seeds or roots may be great enough to prevent germination if seeds are sown too close together or too close to other plants.

But these same inhibitors, reduced to sufficiently low concentration, may stimulate germination. Many of these inhibitors are lactones; parasorbic acid and coumarin are two examples. They apparently prevent germination by inactivating certain enzymes necessary for elongation of the radicle.

LIGHT-SENSITIVE compounds are studied in the laboratory with a spectrophotometer.

Spectroscopic studies have the advantage that they nondestructively follow chemical changes occurring in intact seeds. Cytochrome oxidase and cytochrome c, two light-absorbing enzymes associated with respiration, can be measured in seeds by this technique. These enzymes are oxidized as the seed imbibes water. The higher oxidation state is related to the increase in respiration that occurs during the uptake of water. Spectrometry has also shown that the essential yellow carotene pigments are formed in the cotyledons of certain legumes before the radicle emerges.

The growth of many seeds and plants is affected by light in the red part of the spectrum. The pigment that mediates these effects was extracted from seeds and in seedlings in 1959 by a group of Department scientists—Sterling B. Hendricks, H. W. Siegelman, K. H. Norris, and W. L. Butler.

It is a soluble protein present in cells in very low concentrations. This pigment acts as an enzyme in some reaction so basic to plant development that it controls germination of certain seeds and several other phenomena of the growth and development in plants.

The pigment exists in two forms. One absorbs red light with an absorption maximum at wavelength of 660 mμ (millimicron). The other absorbs far-red light at a maximum of 730 mμ.

When the pigment absorbs light in one form, it is converted to the other chemical form.

$$P660 \underset{730\ m\mu}{\overset{660\ m\mu}{\rightleftarrows}} P730$$

Many seeds are stimulated to germinate by light.

Red light at a wavelength of 660 mμ is most effective in promoting germination of lettuce seed. Far-red light, 730 mμ, inhibits the stimulating effects of red light. The pigment controls the germination of such light-sensitive seeds by its response to light. Red light puts the pigment in the far-red absorbing form (P730). This change permits germination to proceed. If the red light is followed by far-red light, the pigment is returned to its red-absorbing form (P660), and germination is inhibited. Work with young seedlings and seeds has shown that in the dark the pigment exists in the P660 form. For this reason, germination of those seeds does not occur without light.

The control of germination by the photoresponsive pigment is an example of a cellular mechanism that keeps the seed dormant until conditions for survival are favorable.

A light-requiring seed buried deeply in the soil will not germinate until it is uncovered enough to allow light to reach it. It need not be completely bare, however, because only very low light energy is required.

Knowledge of the role of this pigment in maintenance of the living seed explains many seemingly unrelated observations.

For example, seeds of birch will not germinate on the forest floor beneath a tree canopy, but they will germinate in an opening that receives direct sunlight. We now recognize a likely reason. Probably the red wavelengths are absorbed out of light filtered through green foliage while far-red, inhibiting light is transmitted.

WE HAVE SEEN that keeping seeds alive requires the consideration of many important physical and chemical factors.

Details of the changes of simple organic constituents and respiratory processes of quiescent seeds have long been known. Information about complex organic compounds and seed hormones is just unfolding.

Other information and an understanding of facts already known must be sought.

We know enough about the manipulation of storage environments to minimize undesirable changes in most seeds for one or several years. Yet many so-called short-lived seeds do not retain their viability even under the best known procedures.

Perhaps the new research techniques and hypotheses will provide better ways to lengthen the lifespan and increase the germinative ability of the living seed.

R. G. STANLEY *is a biochemist at the Institute of Forest Genetics of the Pacific Southwest Forest and Range Experiment Station of the Forest Service, Berkeley, Calif. Dr. Stanley is a graduate of Michigan State University and the University of California.*

W. L. BUTLER *is a biophysicist associated with the Market Quality Research Division of the Agricultural Marketing Service at the Plant Industry Station, Beltsville, Md. He is a graduate of Reed College and the University of Chicago.*

For further reading:
　Barton, Lela V.: *Effect of Moisture Fluctuations on the Viability of Seeds in Storage.* Contribution Boyce Thompson Institute, volume 13, pages 35–46, 1943.
　Barton, Lela V.: *Effect of Subfreezing Temperatures on Viability of Conifer Seeds in Storage.* Contribution Boyce Thompson Institute, volume 18, pages 21–24; illus. 1954.
　Barton, Lela V.: *Relation of Certain Air Temperatures and Humidities to Viabilities of Seeds.* Contribution Boyce Thompson Institute, volume 12, pages 85–102, 1941.
　Barton, Lela V.: *Seed Packets and Onion Seed Viability.* Contribution Boyce Thompson Institute, volume 15, pages 341–352, 1949.
　Crocker, Wm.: *Life Span of Seeds.* Botanical Review, volume 4, number 5, pages 235–274, 1938.

How Long Can a Seed Remain Alive?

CLARENCE R. QUICK

PEOPLE USED to think that 150 years was about the maximum lifespan of the most durably viable seeds.

Some years ago, however, a Japanese botanist found some viable lotus (waterlily) seeds in a layer of peat under a layer of windblown soil in a dry lakebed in Manchuria. A geologist classified the peat and loess layers of the lakebed as Pleistocene deposits, but this geologic period—the Ice Age—in general came to an end 10 thousand to 15 thousand years ago.

The ancient Manchurian seeds are the size of small hazelnuts. They have thick, horny seedcoats. They closely resemble the seeds of *Nelumbo nucifera*, the East Indian lotus.

Several germination tests were made on the seeds. Almost all of them grew, even after having lain around in museums for a decade or two.

Was the estimation of age of the peat somehow in error, or are these viable seeds actually hundreds of years old?

Preliminary tests on several whole seeds by the residual carbon 14 isotope method of dating organic carbon residues indicated that the seeds were between 830 and 1,250 years old. More tests on larger numbers of seeds are needed to determine the probable maximum age. The seeds are reasonably common in the peat, but the old lakebed is in China, and there seems to be no immediate way to get more of the seeds.

SEEDS sometimes are divided into three classes according to their lifespan under the best possible conditions.

Seeds may be microbiotic (a lifespan of less than 3 years), mesobiotic (3 to 15 years), or macrobiotic (more than 15 years).

Such a classification is convenient but arbitrary. It assumes that we know the optimum conditions for preservation of viability in many kinds of seeds, but that is not entirely correct, even for the many economically important kinds of seeds.

Many—perhaps most—kinds of seeds of Temperate Zone wild plants are best preserved if they are carefully and thoroughly dried, placed in airtight containers, and stored under moderate refrigeration.

Many others, particularly seeds of numerous plants of the wet Tropics, would be killed by this treatment. Some seeds are dead if they become thoroughly dry. Immature seeds and seeds from diseased or otherwise unvigorous plants commonly have less longevity than more normal seeds.

Obviously, adequate methods for storage and adequate methods for germination must be known specifically before maximum longevity of seed can be approximated.

Most of our knowledge of longevity of seed comes from germination tests with three general types of stored seed samples: Seeds recovered from planned length-of-storage tests, "finds" of old seed samples, and old herbarium collections. The third method has led to valuable results, but it is not generally recommended, especially by herbarium curators! Collection data and storage conditions, furthermore, are not likely to be known so explicitly for seeds from herbarium samples and from finds of old samples.

Carefully planned length-of-storage tests have been made on many species of seeds and under many conditions of storage. Storage conditions and tests are highly important, especially for crop seeds. In this chapter I discuss only the tests that resulted in germination of seeds of ages well beyond common lengths of commercial storage of crop seeds.

Paul Becquerel, a French botanist, in 1907 and again in 1934 gave reports on germination tests on about 500 species of old seeds from a storage room in a museum. Of 13 species of viable seeds more than 50 years old, 11 species were legumes. Two species of Cassia (Leguminosae), one with seeds viable after 158 years and one after 115 years, were outstanding.

A. J. Ewart, an Australian, in 1908 reported tests on some 1,400 species and varieties of old seeds. Of the 49 samples of viable seeds more than 50 years old, 37 were legumes. Seeds of one species each of Hovea and of Goodia were viable after 105 years. Both plants are legumes.

J. H. Turner, Kew Gardens, England, in 1933 reported viable seeds in samples of seven species of legumes that were 80 or more years of age. The genera were Anthyllis, Cytisus, Lotus, Medicago, Melilotus, and Trifolium.

The Gardeners' Chronicle, London, in 1942 reported viable seeds of Albizzia julibrissin (a legume) after 149 years of storage and of Nelumbium speciosum (a waterlily) after about 250 years.

Many other germination tests on old seeds have been reported.

Frits W. Went, of the California Institute of Technology, and Philip A. Munz, of Rancho Santa Ana Botanic Garden, Calif., in 1948 started an elaborate longtime longevity test on seeds of more than 100 native California plants. Samples were dried in vacuum desiccators, packed in small glass tubes (20 tubes per seed sample), evacuated in the tubes to 0.1 millimeter of mercury or less, sealed, and placed in an insulated but unrefrigerated storage room. It is proposed that the last set of these samples be tested for germination in A.D. 2307.

We used to read reports that plants grew from "mummy" grains and pease found in ancient Egyptian tombs. It was also suggested somewhat later that viable seeds of Silene (a pink) and of Glaucium (a poppy) may have remained dormant for some 2 thousand years in the soil under heaps of ancient mining and smelting debris in the Laurian area of Greece.

Seed physiologists now consider all such claims erroneous. In all tests of authentic seed from Egyptian tombs, the seeds were dead. They disintegrated promptly.

FARMERS know that weed seeds can remain viable but dormant for many years in clean-cultivated land. Seeds of many garden plants react similarly to burial.

Seedlings of certain plants grow abundantly around old cow pads in pastures, an indication that some seeds can pass through the digestive system of grazing animals and remain viable, possibly to contaminate clean pastures. Sheep, horses, deer, bear, and rabbits are known to pass viable seeds. Some birds scatter many kinds of viable seeds. Other plant-eating and fruit-eating animals are presumed to do the same. Topsoil of fields and wildlands comes to contain considerable populations of viable seeds.

For example, 800 seedlings of field bindweed per acre emerged in 1941 in a 14-acre field, from which the original stand of bindweed had been eradicated in 1921. No bindweed plants had been permitted to fruit during the intervening period.

The plant ecologist, the farmer, and the seed physiologist are interested in these "soil-stored seeds" because of their importance to the long persistence of plant species that are thus scattered in time as well as in space.

The forest floor under stands of mature timber often contains surprising numbers of viable seeds. One study in Maine indicated a total viable seed population of 650 thousand per acre.

A research worker in California found 2,820 thousand viable seeds per acre. Seeds of trees in ecologically climax vegetation are seldom found in abundance in these studies.

Seeds and other plant residues in adobe buildings in the Southwest and sodhouses in the Midwest have been studied to estimate seed longevity and to date the introduction of weeds.

Drastic disturbances to the soil mantle, such as war bombings, often have caused seedlings of plant species to emerge in unexpected places.

The knowledge that some seeds remain viable in soil for decades stimulated several extensive buried-seed experiments. Investigators mixed seeds of known species, age, and condition with sand or soil and packed them in replicated bottles. They buried the bottles, mouth downwards, at one or several depths below the soil surface. They removed one or a set of bottles at planned intervals for testing. The remaining bottles were kept undisturbed.

These buried-seed tests simulate, but do not necessarily duplicate, environmental conditions of seeds naturally stored in the soil. One big advantage of the planned tests is that the age of the seed is known precisely.

Prof. W. J. Beal, of the State University of Michigan, started one of the earliest of these tests. He buried 20 pint bottles of weed seeds mixed with sand in the autumn of 1879. Each bottle contained 50 seeds each of 20 kinds of weedy plants. He buried the 20 bottles, with mouths tilted downward, 18 inches below the soil surface.

After 40 years in the soil, but not after 50 years, seeds of the following five plants were still viable: *Amaranthus retroflexus* (pigweed), *Ambrosia elatior* (ragweed), *Lepidium virginicum* (peppergrass), *Plantago major* (plantain), and *Portulaca oleracea* (purslane).

After 40 and 50 years, but not after 60 years, two additional species grew: *Brassica nigra* (mustard) and *Polygonum hydropiper* (knotweed).

After 40, 50, and 60 years, but not after 70 years, *Silene noctiflora* (catchfly) grew.

And after 70 years, three species were still germinable: *Oenothera biennis* (evening-primrose), *Rumex crispus* (a dock), *Verbascum blattaria* (mullein).

J. W. T. Duvel, of the Department of Agriculture, in 1902 buried multiple sets of seeds of 107 species of wild and cultivated plants near Rosslyn, Va. He packed the seeds in sterile soil in flowerpots covered with porous clay lids and buried the pots in the open at three depths—8, 22, and 42 inches. Sets of seeds were removed periodically and tested for germination.

Of the 107 species buried in 1902, 71 grew after 1 year, 61 after 3 years, 68 after 6 years, 68 after 10 years, 51 after 16 years, 51 after 20 years, 44 after 30 years, and 36 after 39 years. The tests were discontinued with the 39-year-old set of pots dug up in 1941.

W. L. Goss, of the California Department of Agriculture, in 1932 buried samples of seeds of 12 troublesome weeds. Seeds of bindweed (*Convolvulus arvensis*), a nightshade (*Solanum elaeagnifolium*), and Klamathweed (*Hypericum perforatum*) were the only ones viable after 10 years.

FROM THE MANY experiments and observations on seed longevity, we can now draw some generalizations in terms of seed morphology and chemistry and in terms of plant ecology and taxonomy.

Seeds vary widely in size. The coco de mer, a coconut of Praslin Island, Seychelles group, Indian Ocean, is credited with a maximum fruit weight of 40 to 50 pounds. The air-dry seeds of a small American plant in the figwort family (*Ilysanthes dubia*) are said to run about 137 million per pound. In the Temperate Zone, large, heavy seeds tend to be few and long lived, and small, easily distributed seeds tend to be numerous but short lived.

The number of seeds produced per plant also varies enormously. Relatively few seeds are produced by a coconut palm, but it has been estimated that one plant of *Amaranthus graecizans*, an annual tumbleweed, may produce as many as 6 million seeds.

Seedcoats are important in the longevity of seed. Seedcoats of most long-lived seeds have on or near the outside a palisade, or a Malpighian, layer made up of heavy-walled, tightly packed, radially placed, columnar cells. The cells are hard and horny. Usually they are lignified or cutinized. There are no intercellular spaces.

The palisade layer is mechanically protective and highly impervious to water and to respiratory gases. Morphologically, it is the most important structure in seed longevity; most seeds with exceptional longevity have a well developed palisade layer. This layer is not so all-important to buried seeds or to soil-stored seeds, because the soil habitat apparently provides some of the same or similar protective conditions necessary to longevity.

Little need be said here about seed extraction, cleaning, and storage, except to point out that the least damaged seeds—mechanically and biologically—and the best stored seeds will have the greatest longevity.

Many seeds with marked longevity look much alike. Typically they are larger and heavier than the average. Coats are thick and hard and often have a smooth, polished surface. The seeds commonly will not plump if soaked in cold water.

Some examples of well-known native macrobiotic seeds are: *Gymnocladus dioicus* (Kentucky coffeetree), about 240 seeds to the pound; *Gleditsia triacanthos* (honeylocust), about 2,840 seeds to the pound; *Robinia pseudoacacia* (black locust), about 25 thousand seeds; *Ceanothus cuneatus* (buckbrush), about 55 thousand seeds; and *Lotus americanus* (deervetch), about 110 thousand seeds to the pound.

Seeds of cultivated plants long used in their entirety as food commonly have thinner and weaker coats than closely related wild plants. The food seeds generally are shorter lived.

The chemical composition of many crop seeds, but few others, is well known. Seeds are sometimes classified broadly according to the kind of food reserves they store, as starchy seeds (such as those of the Gramineae, the grass family); proteinaceous seeds (for example, those of the Leguminosae, the legumes); and oily seeds (from most tree nuts and many other plants).

The classification is arbitrary, because the food reserves of seeds commonly are mixtures of various carbohydrates, proteins, and fats. I know of no comprehensive English summary of the chemical characteristics of seeds.

The longevity of the oily seeds of sugar pine (*Pinus lambertiana*) is related closely to the kind and amount of unsaturated fatty acids in the seeds. Another suggestion is that rancidity of seed fats in pine and other seeds varies inversely with seed viability.

The degeneration of proteins in food grains roughly parallels reduction of seed viability.

Some biochemical aspects of seed viability are known, but the precise reasons for loss of viability—death of the seed—are not yet clear.

The amazing thing about seeds is not that they degenerate with time but that some deteriorate so slowly.

One theory for the degeneration of long-lived seeds suggests that the various proteins slowly coagulate and denature with time and eventually cannot function in germination.

A related theory—perhaps the most plausible one in the present state of our knowledge—is that loss of viability is due to gradual degeneration, in the nuclei of cells, of the chromatin—the material basis of heredity—and of the delicate mechanism for mitosis, the process by which cells divide and increase in number.

Experiments that support this second theory show that aging, heating, and X-ray treatment of dry seeds all cause similar degeneration—increased mitotic aberrations and chromosome changes and increased plant mutations and abnormalities.

Degrees of aging and of treatment cause more or less proportional increases in extent of abnormalities and mutations until all viability is lost. An extension of this theory is that the mutations resulting from aged seeds is one means by which Nature produces varying races and strains of plants and advances evolution.

Seed longevity in a broad sense is an ecologic characteristic of a plant as well as a morphologic and a biochemical one. Over the great reaches of geologic time, the biology of most plant species and their seeds has come to fit approximately the habitat in which they are characteristically found.

Some plants are primary pioneers. They grow most commonly on ecologically tough sites where soil is scarce or poor.

Other plants are secondary pioneers. They are found commonly in abundance on well-developed soil profiles from which much or all of the previous plant cover has been removed by fire, logging, or clearing. And of course there are other comparable ecologic types of plants.

What about the life history of those secondary pioneers that are killed outright by fire but produce heavy seeds not scattered by wind?

How are these plants able to revegetate a burned area promptly and abundantly, as they so often do? Simply because they have mechanically durable, heat-resistant, and long-lived seeds.

In studies of soil-stored seed under ecologically mature forests, it is common to find more seeds of the pioneer vegetation, largely displaced by ecologic development, than of the climax tree species. There is an obvious and essential ecologic value to pioneer plants from long-lived seeds—that is, from seeds well distributed in time.

A few plants produce two kinds of seeds according to season and physiologic status of the plant. An example is *Halogeton glomeratus*, a serious weed of wildland desert ranges. One kind of seed will germinate immediately upon maturity. The second kind is dormant and will not germinate until some time after maturity. This again is distribution of seeds in time, with seed longevity as one requirement for success of the process.

Plants (particularly woody plants) characteristic of arid climates are believed in general to have longer lived seeds than plants of tropical or of humid-temperate habitats.

Plant taxonomy in relation to seed longevity is another interesting field of inquiry. The taxonomic plant families—for example, the Cruciferae, the Rosaceae, and the Leguminosae—commonly are rather uniform in flower structure, type and arrangement of leaves, and other traits.

Are these plant families also uniform in seed biology, or is seed longevity more a matter of ecology ("fit" to the environment) than of taxonomic relationships?

Species of the Leguminosae, considered here in a broad taxonomic sense to include the Mimosaceae, have turned up very frequently in lists of long-lived seeds, and it seems that this family has a marked tendency to longevity of seeds.

Other plant families that apparently have greater than average proportions of species with exceptionally long-lived seeds include the palms, cannas, waterlilies (lotuses), spurges, soapberries, buckthorns, mallows, and morning-glories. Within a single species, varieties and strains with somewhat differing genetic constitution may vary in germination and longevity.

IN CONCLUSION, let us say that we have a great many records—some amazing records—of long-lived seeds. Up to the present time, however, most data on seed longevity, particularly of wild plants, have been considered piecemeal, species by species.

Much more research and analysis must be done before broad generalizations can accurately relate seed longevity to an integrated consideration of seed and plant biochemistry, physiology, morphology, taxonomy, and ecology.

CLARENCE R. QUICK *is a forest pathologist in the Pacific Southwest Forest Experiment Station of the U.S. Forest Service, Berkeley, Calif. Previously he was a forest ecologist in the former Bureau of Entomology and Plant Quarantine.*

Until Time and Place Are Suitable

EBEN H. TOOLE AND VIVIAN KEARNS TOOLE

ONE MUST KEEP in mind the place of the seed in the life of the plant if he is to understand the processes of germination.

A seed is essentially a young plant whose life activities are at a minimum. The drying out of the young seed as it ripens on the plant brings about this reduction of activities. The dry seed thus is in a condition to be held, stored, and preserved until time and place are suitable for the start of a new plant.

Many seeds, especially crop seeds, begin to germinate as soon as they are planted under moist conditions and they absorb water. Thus new corn plants appear promptly when corn grains are kept over winter and planted in moist, warm soil.

The germination of other seeds, including seeds of many flowers and weeds, does not begin until special conditions, besides moisture, are provided. Such seeds have a block or blocks to the germination processes. They do not germinate until the blocks are removed.

If a crabgrass seed (*Digitaria*) should germinate when it fell to the ground at maturity in late summer, cold weather would soon kill the young seedlings. Special germination requirements of the freshly ripened crabgrass seed prevent it from germinating until the next season.

Seeds with special germination requirements are called dormant (blocked). The special conditions associated with seed dormancy are considered in the chapter that follows.

Development of a Bean

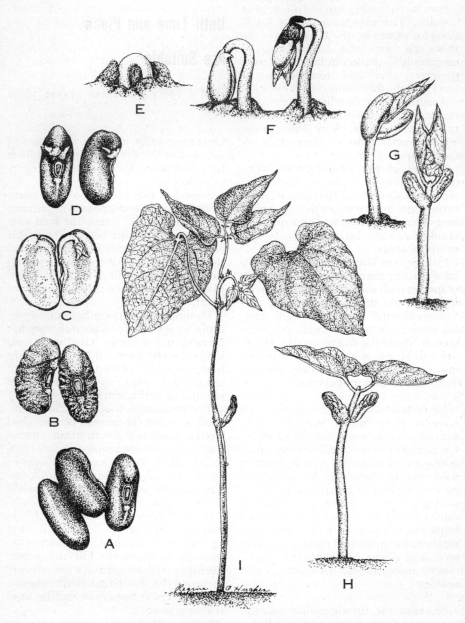

A, *dry seeds of beans;* B, *the seeds have imbibed water, the seedcoats are wrinkled;* C, *the seed opened to show the embryo;* D, *the radicle appears;* E, *the seedling is pushing up through the soil;* F, *the seedlings are up, part of the seedcoat still adheres to the one on the right;* G, *the seedlings are straightening up, the primary leaves are unfolding, and the seedling on the right shows how the two leaves are fitted together;* H, *the primary leaves are open and the stem has elongated;* I, *the trifoliate leaves have appeared.*

The first start toward germination is the absorption of water, which allows the protoplasm of the cells to carry on active life.

The imbibition of water by seeds involves two processes.

One is much like the taking up of water by any dry material, such as a sponge.

The other involves the osmotic nature of the living cells. The osmotically active cells of the living seed have great attraction for water. Seeds absorb enough water to start to germinate in soil that is so dry that it will not support subsequent growth of the seedlings.

Each kind of seed must absorb a fairly definite proportion of water before germination will start. The amount depends on the structure and the composition of the seed. When seeds have taken up enough water for germination to start, they contain about 40 percent of water (as in corn) to about 70 percent (as in beans).

The first visible evidence of germination is the breaking of the root tip through the seed covering.

The bean is typical of most seeds in regard to the start of germination. The root tip emerges as a result of the elongation of the hypocotyl (the stem tissue between the root tip and the cotyledons). At about this time, the cells of the root tip and hypocotyl begin to divide. The continuing elongation of the newly formed cells establishes the root in the soil and pushes the hypocotyl and cotyledons into the air.

Soon after the seedling is well above the surface, elongation of cells and then cell divisions start in the plumule, the young growing point of the stem. The elongation of newly formed cells pushes the stem tip and young leaves above the cotyledons.

The very first changes leading to germination, however, are not these visible growth activities, which require the energy and building materials that they obtain from chemical activity within the cells.

A marked increase of respiration occurs before we can see any growth. This early increase of respiration releases energy from food materials already present in usable form in the cells that start growth.

The mobilization of food reserves precedes visible signs of germination by many hours. In the tiny, oil-rich seed of foxglove (*Digitalis purpurea*), new starch grains appear in the root cap at least 12 hours before elongation of the cells of the radicle. Sugar and protein building materials increase in the root tip and in the plumule tip at an early stage.

As growth proceeds, the increasing demand for materials for energy and for new tissues is met by the digestion of reserve foods. After the small amounts of nearby reserves are used, the abundant stored foods of the cotyledons (as in bean) or of the endosperm (as in corn) are drawn upon.

The nature of the food reserves varies with the kind of seed.

The cells of the cotyledons of the bean are filled with starch and protein. Those of the soybean usually contain no starch but are filled with oil and protein.

The "germ" of wheat and corn (the embryo, including the scutellum or single cotyledon) contains much oil and is rich in protein, but the endosperm, which is much larger, is largely starch.

Much of the stored food of the date seed and the carrot seed is in thickened walls made of hemicellulose. These reserves of starch, oil, hemicellulose, and protein are large in amount.

Many other reserves must be present in smaller amounts for active germination and normal development of the seedling. Nucleic acids are present in the cotyledons of bean and in the endosperm of wheat and are transported to the growing axis during early germination. Organic phosphorus compounds, present during germination, are extremely important for the transfer of energy for growth. Inorganic phosphorus must be present for the formation of more organic phosphates.

A wide range of enzymes must be available to digest these reserves, make energy available from them through respiration, and build new tissues. The respiratory enzymes responsible for the initial release of energy must be present in the resting seed, but perhaps some of the others are produced as germination gets underway.

THE GERMINATION requirements of the seeds of many crop plants are much the same as the conditions for continued growth of the established plant.

Corn and bean plants grow best at moderately warm temperatures, and the seeds germinate best and most rapidly at similarly warm temperatures. Wheat and pea plants develop best at cool temperatures, and the seeds germinate best at similar temperatures. For these seeds, germination is simply the resumption of growth of the young plant. It is controlled by the same factors as later plant growth.

For varying periods after harvest, the seeds of many crop plants have special requirements for the initiation of germination. These seeds later will germinate readily at a wide range of conditions. The seeds of other plants (especially seeds of weeds) may require special conditions for germination throughout the life of the seed.

It is important to know the germination requirements of different seeds as a guide to the time and conditions for planting the seed, as a guide to any necessary special treatment, and, in the case of weeds, as an aid in the control of undesired plants.

We discuss germination requirements in relation to temperature, moisture, aeration, light, and the interaction of these factors.

MUCH ATTENTION used to be given to "cardinal" temperatures—the minimum, optimum, and maximum temperatures for germination. Early studies were limited to seeds that do not have special requirements as to temperature.

For many kinds of seeds, the rate of germination—the rate of growth of the seedling—increases with a rise of temperature until near the upper temperature limit for growth, when the rate of germination slows down.

In the early records, the temperature for the maximum rate of germination often was taken as the optimum temperature. Many individual seeds, however, may not germinate at all at the temperature of most rapid germination of other seeds.

One should consider therefore a compromise between highest percentage of germination and fastest rate of germination.

Most seeds germinate slowly at low temperatures. The reported minimum temperatures for germination therefore often depend on the patience of the observer. Several observations of seeds germinating on cakes of ice have been recorded.

Scientists now give emphasis to understanding the ways in which temperatures affect the germinating seeds rather than to establishing rigid limits of the overall effect of temperature.

The seeds of many plants will not start germination at high temperatures even though the seedlings will grow normally at high temperatures. In them, some step leading to the start of germination is blocked at higher temperatures but can proceed at lower temperatures. The temperature that keeps them from germinating varies with the kind of seed and the conditions under which the seeds mature.

Generally, the critical temperature is lowest just after harvest and gradually gets higher until the special temperature requirement disappears after a variable period of storage. Storing the seeds under very dry conditions and at very low temperatures delays such a change. Wheat often will not germinate at temperatures above 59° F. for 1 or 2 months after harvest. This condition varies with variety and with the weather at the time of maturity.

Most samples of lettuce seed will not germinate in soil that stays at high temperatures (76° to 86°). The critical temperature becomes higher as the seed ages in storage, but very few samples of lettuce seed will germinate at 86° even though seedlings will develop at that temperature.

Seeds of lettuce and many other plants that are held in darkness for several days at a temperature too high for germination become especially dormant and then will not grow when transferred to a lower temperature that previously would have favored germination.

The seeds of some plants have an opposite response to temperature. Seeds of alyceclover (*Alysicarpus vaginalis*), a semitropical plant, will germinate only at a temperature of 85° or higher when planted soon after harvest, but a year later they will germinate readily at lower temperatures.

The germination of seeds of coffee and the best growth of the young seedlings are restricted to a narrow temperature range (near 80° to 85°). The coffee tree thrives best at somewhat lower temperatures. The nurseries for young coffee plants therefore are usually at a lower elevation than the plantings of bearing trees.

The seeds of many grasses and flowers and of some vegetables germinate poorly at any temperature that is constantly maintained at a uniform level, but they germinate well if the temperature is alternated between a lower and a higher temperature.

Bluegrass seed will germinate well if the temperature is kept at about 60° for 16 hours and at about 75° for 8 hours each day or even at a daily alternation between 68° and 86°. These seeds usually germinate in nature in spring when the night and day temperatures vary sharply.

A satisfactory explanation of the physiological changes involved in this requirement for daily changes of temperature has not yet been given.

SEEDS need to absorb a fairly definite amount of water before germination will start. Different kinds of seeds vary in their response to surrounding moisture during germination. This probably is associated with the influence of the surrounding moisture on the aeration of the seeds.

Rice will germinate under water and with a low supply of oxygen.

The seeds of cattail (*Typha latifolia*) and probably those of other water plants, instead of being sensitive to a lack of oxygen, germinate only when the supply of oxygen is reduced.

Many other seeds, including clovers, will germinate under water. Others, such as cabbage, do not germinate if even a film of water surrounds the seed.

Spinach is especially sensitive to excess moisture; the spongy covering that surrounds the seed can become filled with water and so reduce aeration and prevent germination.

LIGHT does not influence the germination of many kinds of seeds, but the germination of others is controlled by the presence or absence of light.

When fully moist seeds of certain varieties of lettuce are held in total darkness at 68°, few of the seeds will germinate. If the seeds are exposed briefly to light, all the seeds are stimulated to germinate. The flash from a photographic flashlamp, in fact, is enough to cause them to germinate.

The promotion of seed germination is brought about by red light of a comparatively narrow range of wavelengths.

If moist lettuce seeds are promoted by exposure to red light and are then exposed to far-red light (just at the limit of visibility), the promoting effect of the red light is reversed, and the seeds will not germinate. This promotion and inhibition can be repeated many times, and whether germination occurs or not depends on the band of light that is given last.

THIS REVERSIBLE photoreaction that controls seed germination has been demonstrated in at least 20 kinds of seeds. Undoubtedly it occurs in many more.

It is interesting that the same mechanism that controls the germination of some kinds of seeds is also responsible for the photoperiodic control of flowering, for the control of the elongation of seedlings, for the coloring of seedlings and of certain fruits, and for the control of other phases of the development of plants.

BOTH RED AND FAR-RED light are present in daylight and in most artificial light, but the red light has the strongest effect on many light-sensitive seeds like lettuce. The germination of such seeds is stimulated by unfiltered light, but seeds of henbit (*Lamium amplexicaule*) are so sensitive to far-red light that their germination is prevented by long exposure to daylight or incandescent light.

Germination of the seeds of many plants, like those of lettuce, is promoted by a single brief exposure to red light, but the seeds of many grasses require repeated light exposures over a period of several days to stimulate the germination of all the seeds.

Not all of the seeds of some kinds of plants, such as loblolly pine (*Pinus taeda*) and white pine (*Pinus strobus*), are ready to respond to the light stimulus at the same time. After the seeds are held at a low temperature in darkness for 2 weeks, all are ready to respond to a single exposure to red light.

LIGHT and temperature and other factors that influence germination are interdependent.

Seeds of some samples of tobacco will germinate very little at temperatures held constant at any temperature from 59° to 86° unless the moist seeds have been exposed briefly to light. At daily alternations of temperature between 59° and 77° or between 68° and 86°, however, germination is complete either in light or in darkness.

The seeds of peppergrass (*Lepidium virginicum*) germinate only after the moist seeds have been exposed to light, but even after full promotion by red light only a part of the seeds germinate at constant temperatures, such as 59° or 68°.

If seeds of peppergrass that have been allowed to absorb moisture in darkness at about 70° for 24 hours are exposed to light and then returned to 70° in darkness, only about one-third of the seeds germinate. If, however, at the time the seeds are exposed to light, the temperature is raised to 95° for 2 hours, all of the seeds will respond to the light stimulus and germinate at 70°.

The short period at the high temperature removes some block that prevented the seeds from responding to the light stimulus. This short-time, high-temperature treatment is effective with a number of kinds of seeds in increasing the response to treatment with light.

When lettuce seeds of varieties that ordinarily germinate completely in darkness are held fully moist at a high temperature (86° to 95°) for 1 to 2 days in darkness, they will not germinate if placed at a low temperature (59° to 65°) that originally would have been very favorable for germination.

These dormant seeds, however, will germinate if they are exposed briefly to red light and are placed at the low temperature. The prolonged treatment at the high temperature changed the seeds from light insensitive to light requiring.

These examples of the interaction of the different germination requirements indicate that one should not consider any of these requirements separately. They all must be considered together to understand how to obtain the best germination of seeds.

THE VARIOUS requirements of different kinds of seeds have been learned from laboratory experiments, but this knowledge helps us to understand the behavior of seeds in the garden and in nature.

It is customary to give little or no soil covering when sowing many kinds of small seeds. Often it is stated that the seeds are planted near the surface because the seedlings are not strong enough to come up through much soil. The real explanation for most seeds is that they need to be exposed to light in order to germinate.

Weeds often appear in meadows where they had not grown for many years. They always appear where soil is brought to the surface by wheel tracks or other disturbance of the surface.

A SIMPLE experiment illustrates what takes place.

Seeds of peppergrass are planted on the surface of moist soil in three flower-pots. The seeds in two of the pots are quickly covered with about one-fourth inch of moist soil. The seeds in the other pot are left uncovered. Drying out is prevented by covering all the pots with a pane of glass. Abundant peppergrass seedlings appear in a few days from the seeds that were not covered. No seedlings appear in the other pots. If one then draws a pencil through the soil covering the seeds in one pot, seedlings appear in the disturbed area after a few days.

THE SEEDLING after germination must establish itself in the soil. The young plant is not fully independent. It is dependent on the reserve foods of the seed for further development of root, stem, and leaves until it can become established and can manufacture enough food for all its needs.

This means that the enzyme system of the germinating seed must continue to digest the starch and oil and protein of the cotyledons or endosperm. These digested materials must be moved to the growing regions. Here other parts of the enzyme system must release and make energy available.

The temperature, moisture, and other requirements for the establishment of the seedlings in general are the same as for the future development of that particular kind of plant. The structure of the seedling must be complete, however, to allow for the development of a normal, useful plant.

If some part of the seed has been injured by handling or by poor conditions of storage, the seedlings may be incapable of developing into a useful plant—it is an abnormal seedling.

Equal vigor is not manifested in all seedlings, even the ones that will produce normal plants. When seeds are stored under unfavorable conditions, the first evidence of deterioration is slower germination and slower growth of the seedling. Seeds that have been harvested before fully mature may germinate, but the seedlings often lack normal vigor.

A person with experience in the germination of seeds can detect many of the seed lots that will grow into seedlings that lack normal vigor. A dependable method of determining the relative vigor of seed lots has not been developed.

OUR present knowledge of the details of the changes that take place in the developing seed and during germination is not sufficient for us to know what determines seedling vigor.

There is much interest at present in learning how to insure that seeds that are produced will be of good vigor and how to detect, in the seedling stage, which seedlings will produce the most vigorous plants.

EBEN H. TOOLE *is a collaborator with the Crops Research Division and part-time consultant with the Asgrow Seed Co. of New Haven, Conn. Dr. Toole formerly was principal physiologist in charge of Vegetable Seed Investigations of the Vegetables and Ornamentals Research Branch, Agricultural Research Service. He was engaged in research on seed physiology from 1920 to 1959 in the Department of Agriculture.*

VIVIAN KEARNS TOOLE, *a plant physiologist, does research on seed physiology in the Vegetables and Ornamentals Research Branch, Crops Research Division, Agricultural Research Service. She has conducted research on seeds in the Department of Agriculture since 1930.*

Afterripening, Rest Period, and Dormancy

BRUCE M. POLLOCK AND
VIVIAN KEARNS TOOLE

SEED MATURITY and seed germination follow in direct sequence in the life of a plant, but normally they are separated in time and space.

The interval may be a few hours or many years. It may be a few inches or thousands of miles.

The function of the seed is to carry its embryo plant through the hazards of time and space to a time and place where the new plant can grow, flower, and in its turn produce seeds.

It is of advantage to the seed to remain in an inactive condition until it reaches a favorable time and place for germination: A young plant is vulnerable to lack of water and extremes of heat and cold—hazards that the embryo plant within the seed is adapted to withstand. In the nongrowing condition, the water content of the tissue is relatively low, the protoplasm of the cells is protected from damage, and the metabolic rate is low. Thus the seed can survive on its nutrient reserves for a long period.

DELAYED GERMINATION is not accidental. It is the result of physiological mechanisms that keep the seed in a nongerminating state.

The term "dormancy" is used to describe two inactive conditions. One results from an unfavorable environment. The other is due to internally imposed blocks. For example, germination may be delayed by inadequate water supply or unfavorable temperature. In some seeds, however, germination is prevented by blocking mech-anisms within the seed. They must be removed before the germination can occur.

The terms "rest" and "rest period" also have been used to describe seeds and buds that are inactive because of these internal blocks.

One should be aware of this confusion in terminology when he reads about seeds and germination, but he need not think the dual terminology is an exercise in scientific semantics. Our scientific terminology has to be precise. Often in writings it is difficult to tell whether the investigator was working with seeds that were "dormant" because they were dry or cold, or with seeds that were "dormant" because of blocks. It is simple to write on paper a definition of "dormancy" or "rest," but it is more difficult to apply the definitions to a seed or a seed lot.

An example illustrates the problem. The seed of silver maple (*Acer saccharinum*) can germinate as soon as it falls from the parent tree. You are familiar with the appearance of seedlings in early summer under the trees. This seed is "inactive dormant" at the time of maturity, but it is not "resting" or "blocked dormant," because it germinates as soon as it reaches the water supply in the soil.

At the other extreme, the seed of the apple tree (*Pyrus malus*) is "resting" or "blocked dormant" at maturity. It will not grow even under good conditions for germination until it has undergone changes, known as afterripening, to remove the germination blocks.

If one defines these two extremes as "dormant" and "resting" and then attempts to apply these definitions to other seeds, difficulties arise. Take the lettuce seed (*Lactuca sativa*). It germinates promptly in total darkness if it is planted in moist soil at 57° F. It does not contain a germination block. If the same seed is planted at 84°, however, it remains inactive. If, following 84° for a few days, the temperature drops to 57°, the seed still cannot germinate. Exposure of the imbibed seed to the high temperature induced the formation of a block that did not exist previously. This block may be removed by an exposure to red light.

Can one then easily apply a rigid definition of dormancy or rest to describe a lettuce or similar seed?

Obviously not, without qualifying the definition by listing carefully the conditions under which germination was attempted. The variety of the lettuce and the previous history of the seed also are important—not all varieties behave in the way we described, nor do all lots of one variety.

GERMINATION BLOCKS are relative, not absolute.

Close examination of some seeds, such as the sour cherry (*Prunus cerasus*), has disclosed that growth is not completely stopped, even in a blocked seed at a low temperature. Cells of the root and shoot can divide, and the whole embryonic axis grows slightly at a time when the seed cannot germinate even under good conditions.

This observation and the fact that something obviously does occur during afterripening to permit subsequent germination show that the blocks are only relative.

A blocked seed is like an automobile with its motor running at idling speed but with the gears disengaged—there is no motion.

Germination blocks are variable. Gardeners and farmers know that all the viable seeds they plant do not germinate. The proportion of those that do germinate varies with conditions of germination. A major reason for the variability is that all seeds are not genetically identical.

Conditions required for germination are the expression of the seed's heredity as influenced by environment during seed formation, maturity, and germination.

We do not know, even for a single kind of seed, exactly what are the critical environmental factors, when they act, or how they may be controlled experimentally or in commercial practice.

The result of the interaction of genetic and environmental factors is extreme variability in the rate at which germination of different kinds of seeds and different seeds of one kind begins.

The germination of seeds has a continuous range from prompt growth over a wide range of environmental conditions to sluggish growth over a narrow range of environmental conditions. Most farmers, scientific workers, seedsmen, and gardeners recognize this variability. It is the variability of Nature.

A species survives because of blocks that delay germination. They tend to spread germination over a period of years. One unfavorable growing season does not obliterate a species.

Consider weeds. All farmers and gardeners see how weeds emerge in soil clean cultivated for many years. Some may have been introduced recently by animal carriers or the wind, but most were already present in the soil from previous years. These seeds had germination blocks that previously prevented germination.

Blocked seeds are more obvious and more extreme in wild plants than in most of our cultivated forms. One inherited difference between seeds is the ability to develop germination blocks.

Through the years, man has tended to select seeds that give relatively prompt germination. The result is that some of our cultivated plants cannot survive without man to protect the seeds by proper storage until a favorable season for germination. In a sense, man has substituted himself for the germination blocks that probably were present in the ancestors of our common cultivated plants.

The term "block" is a convenient name for a mechanism that restricts germination. Blocks act through a number of different physiological mechanisms. Some blocks are simple and well understood. Others are complex and almost completely unknown.

The end result is the same in all instances: The seed is held in a nongrowing condition.

Germination is the Road a Seed Must Travel Before Becoming a Seedling

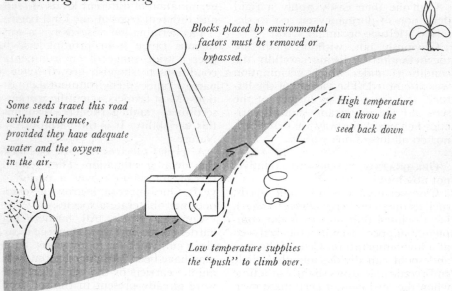

Blocks placed by environmental factors must be removed or bypassed.

Some seeds travel this road without hindrance, provided they have adequate water and the oxygen in the air.

High temperature can throw the seed back down

Low temperature supplies the "push" to climb over.

THE MOST complete block to germination is in seeds that have seedcoats impermeable to water. These hard seeds are common in the waterlily, mallow (cotton, okra), and legume (beans, clovers) families.

During ripening and drying of red and white clover seeds (*Trifolium pratense* and *T. repens*), the seedcoat becomes impermeable to water when the moisture content of the seed has reached a low level. The impermeable seedcoat has a fissure along the groove of the hilum, which functions as a hygroscopic valve. When the seeds are surrounded by dry air, the fissure opens and permits water vapor to escape. The fissure closes in moist air. Thus the seeds can dry further through outward diffusion of water vapor, while reentry of water is prevented. Such seeds remain impermeable to water until the seedcoat is somehow broken. If water cannot enter, the first steps toward germination are prevented.

Some germination blocks are local-

ized. Many blocks affect the whole embryo. Seeds of the apple are blocked and germinate only after undergoing a period of afterripening while moist at a temperature around 40°. Imbibed seeds that have been chilled for 2 to 3 months germinate promptly and produce normal seedlings.

The embryo in seed of the tree peony (*Paeonia suffruticosa*) has a root that will grow under normal germinating conditions. The shoot, however, is blocked and requires exposure to low temperature to permit growth. The chilling is not effective until after the root has grown. Seeds of the tree peony ripen in late summer, and the winter temperature is too low to permit germination. The root therefore cannot grow until spring. The required chilling is received during the next winter, and the shoot emerges above ground the second spring, 18 months after the seed matures.

The seed of *Trillium grandiflorum*, a wild flower found in the woods in early spring, requires chilling to remove the block to root growth and then a period of moderate temperature to permit root growth. This must be followed by a second period of chilling to remove a shoot block, and a second moderate temperature period for shoot growth.

CONDITIONS for removing blocks have been studied for many years, but we need to know much more about how blocks are removed naturally and how they may be removed artificially to produce plants out of their normal environment and season or to measure viability of seed in the laboratory.

One way to remove blocks is by a natural combination of time and exposure to the elements. A hard seedcoat may be softened in the soil by alternate freezing and thawing or wetting and drying. Micro-organisms may use the seedcoat as a source of nutrients and thus rot it off. At the same time, low soil temperature may meet a requirement for chilling.

Mere drying for a period induces changes that permit germination in some seeds. This is afterripening in the dry condition and is used often in the preparation of crop seeds.

A hard seedcoat may be artificially removed or its effect minimized by scarification. Seeds are scarified mechanically by blowing them against abrasive points or rubbing them over an abrasive surface. Chemical scarification with acid or hot water is used frequently in the case of such seed as black locust (*Robinia pseudoacacia*) and the dropseed grasses (*Sporobolus*).

The leaching action of water removes the blocks in some seeds. Desert plants are noteworthy in this respect. A seed in a desert needs enough water to germinate and much more to become established. It must be able to distinguish between a small amount of water and a large amount. The seed does this by means of inhibitors that are removed only by a large amount of water—an amount that will moisten the soil enough for the plants to become established.

Light initiates changes that permit germination of some seeds. The farmer when he plows his field and the gardener who spades a garden assists the germination of weed seeds by turning new seeds to the surface, where the light requirement is satisfied. A new crop of weeds is assured after each cultivation.

The conditions against which blocks protect the seed often are the same ones that serve to remove the blocks. This is closely related to the alternation of seasons a seed encounters.

Consider an annual plant of the Temperate Zone, such as ragweed (*Ambrosia artemisiifolia*), whose seeds mature in the late summer. It is not winter hardy. If the seeds germinate immediately upon maturity, the new plant will be killed by freezing during winter. Germination is blocked, however, and the block must be removed by some mechanism. This mechanism is controlled by exposure to low temperature during winter. Thus the seed is prevented from growing until the low temperature renders growth possible. The same low temperature that removes the block permits growth the following summer as the seed is warmed. The same condition occurs in the buds of trees.

Germination blocks are reversible. Afterripened seeds are ready to germinate. If they are in a place where they receive a deficiency of oxygen, an excess of water, or a temperature that is too high for germination, however, they will revert quickly to the blocked condition.

Afterripening also is reversible—undoubtedly a major factor in the longevity of weed seeds and a factor that often is overlooked in germinating seeds for garden purposes.

For example, seeds that have been afterripened carefully in a refrigerator may be planted at a high temperature, 76° or higher, and revert to the blocked condition instead of germinating. The seeds of pine, rose, apple, cocklebur, and many others are known to revert to the blocked condition—"secondary dormancy."

Blocks may be physical or chemical. Physical blocks are caused by the structures surrounding the embryo.

Chemical blocks are of two types— inhibiting chemicals in tissues surrounding the seed and an inhibition within the embryo itself.

Many seeds have more than one block. In the subterranean clover (*Trifolium subterraneum*), a hard coat is present in addition to a chemical block within the embryo.

PHYSICAL BLOCKS are associated with the structure of the seedcoats and other tissues surrounding the embryo. These tissues usually are considered to function primarily to protect the embryo from mechanical damage and from attack by micro-organisms. They may also act as germination blocks. The seedcoat of some seeds is so hard that it mechanically prevents expansion of the embryo. In others, the seedcoat is so impervious to water that the seed remains dry internally even though it is immersed in water.

The seedcoat and surrounding membranes also may act as blocks by preventing the entry of oxygen into the embryo or possibly the discharge of carbon dioxide. Most seeds require an abundant supply of oxygen during germination. Membranes restrict the oxygen supply in some seeds, and the resulting change in seed metabolism imposes a block.

Chemical blocks may be present in tissues surrounding the embryo. We commonly find that seeds do not germinate until freed from the outermost covering, the ovary or fruit wall. Seeds do not normally germinate within the fruit. Occasionally germination occurs on the parent plant. These viviparous seedlings may be economic problems, as in the case of some varieties of soft wheat. It may be that soft wheats lack an inhibitor that is present in seeds of hard wheat.

Germination-inhibiting chemicals in fruits may account somewhat for the failure of seeds to germinate in the fruit. Inhibitors are also known in the seedcoats and the other membranes around the embryo.

More than 120 sources of germination inhibitors were listed in an article in 1949. Many more are described each year. The chemical nature of many of these compounds is known. Most inhibitors are nonspecific. They block germination in many kinds of seeds besides those of the plant in which the inhibitor is found.

A word of caution concerning inhibitors: Inhibitors may be isolated from most or all seeds and other plant parts. The mere isolation of a chemical does not prove that it acts to inhibit germination in the seed. Many actively growing plant parts are excellent sources of the inhibitors found in seeds. We consider this problem later.

We assume that embryo blocks are chemical. Blocks in the seedcoat and membranes are simple and well understood in comparison with blocks within the embryo. It is perhaps even misleading to suggest that the embryo blocks are chemical, although our increasing understanding of growth and metabolism indicates that most growth phenomena result from chemical processes.

We must be careful, however, not to assume that the embryo blocks are necessarily caused by growth-inhibiting chemicals. They may result equally from a deficiency of some essential compound. The effect of afterripening might then be to permit the accumulation of the missing compound to the level that would permit germination. When seed of the loblolly pine (*Pinus taeda*), for example, is kept 2 weeks at a low temperature, some substance apparently accumulates that permits germination when the seed is stimulated by light.

Many investigators believe that inhibitors cause embryo blocks. Their evidence is not always sound, because it is extremely difficult to isolate and identify an inhibitor. It cannot be isolated until an active compound can be measured outside the plant. Since its chemical properties cannot be known until after isolation, some plant response, or bioassay, must be used for measurement.

The best test for an inhibitor would be to inhibit afterripened seeds of the kind from which it was isolated. But how can one be sure that a compound will enter the undamaged embryo? To overcome this difficulty, investigators frequently test isolated compounds by their effect on cell elongation in isolated sections of stem tissue. But what evidence is there that a germination inhibitor acts by directly blocking cell elongation?

Even the isolation of an inhibitor is not direct evidence that it actually functions as an inhibitor in the seed. When a chemical is extracted, it is torn from its normal location and form in the cells.

Cyanide, a powerful (and deadly to animals) inhibitor, is a common constituent of many seeds. It is an obvious candidate for a compound that can control germination. In the embryo, however, it occurs in a chemical complex known as emulsin, a glucoside. In this form it has no growth-inhibiting properties. Free cyanide is formed only when the cells are damaged. Many investigations have failed to give adequate evidence that cyanide actually functions as a germination inhibitor.

There is a rigorous test that should be used to decide whether an extracted compound functioned in the seed as an inhibitor. The true inhibitor should change in quantity parallel to changes in the physiological condition of the seed. If the seed is strongly blocked, a germination inhibitor should be present in high concentration. As the block is removed, the concentration of inhibitor should decline to a minimum when germination is most prompt. If afterripening is reversed by high temperature or lack of oxygen, the concentration of inhibitor should increase.

WITH THE present state of our knowledge, we can conclude that growth-inhibiting chemicals may very well control germination. They are not the only possible mechanism, however.

Much more intensive research will be required to establish their nature.

CHANGES in cellular organization exemplify a type of mechanism that has not yet been investigated enough as a possibility for controlling germination.

Modern biology recognizes that cells of animals and plants are similar in that they contain large numbers of complex chemical compounds. The compounds are not distributed at random within the cells.

They exist in definite chemical and physical combinations in parts of the cell, such as mitochondria and microsomes, which are too small to be seen with ordinary microscopes. Even powerful electron microscopes can only suggest how they are arranged.

We know that the processes of respiration, photosynthesis, and protein synthesis depend on such structures.

In the seed, is it possible that germination may fail because the compounds within these structures are incompletely or improperly joined? We have no direct information yet on this possibility, but we should not ignore it.

Many uncertainties and unknowns exist in our understanding of the mechanism of germination blocks.

What, in fact, do we know?

We know that we can distinguish between blocks that seem to yield easily to removal and those that require much more strenuous efforts. Light, for example, stimulates the germination of many seeds, and this same mechanism controls other plant growth responses, including flowering.

We know that the light reaction results from a pigment that may absorb either red or far-red light. Although the pigment has been isolated from seedlings, we do not know how it is coupled to germination.

We know that other factors also can stimulate germination. Virginia runner-type peanut seeds (*Arachis hypogaea*) are blocked at maturity. They germinate within 48 hours if exposed to air containing a minute amount of ethylene gas.

Some kinds of seed respond to environmental factors much more sluggishly. They do not seem to require a true stimulus. Time is important; the essential processes are slow. This is the case with low temperature.

We know that low temperature is required to remove the blocks in many seeds. This may require a few days to several months. High temperature can regenerate the block.

Since chemical reactions depend on temperature, increasing in rate with increasing temperature, we assume that temperature must influence one type of chemical reaction differently than does another. The specific reactions involved are completely obscure, however. Why low temperatures should be required is difficult for us to understand.

Interaction between blocks is common. Blocks that can be removed by stimuli (such as light) and blocks that can be removed by long exposure to low temperatures may be interdependent. Artificially applied chemicals can interact with light and temperature.

We know that these interactions exist. We know that germination is controlled by "blocks." It seems reasonable therefore to visualize germination proceeding by a number of alternate pathways. These pathways may be closed by blocks imposed and removed by various environmental conditions. Some of the pathways are temperature sensitive. Some are light sensitive. Some can be controlled by applied chemicals. Some cannot be.

The idea of alternate pathways is not unique.

Biochemistry has shown that chemical reactions in cells and organisms are brought about by enzymes. The rate of activity of these enzymes is controlled by many factors, including temperature. We do know that a cell may have several pathways of producing or utilizing a required chemical. These are alternate pathways of synthesis or destruction.

Are these also alternate pathways of germination? This question cannot now be answered, but we strongly suspect that the answer is yes.

Why bother with these complexities of mechanism? Are they important? Are they worth the time and energy spent in studying them? The answers to these questions must be yes.

Understanding in a scientific sense leads to control. Control of germination is of enormous practical importance. Think of agriculture without weeds!

We recognize that germination is a critical stage in the life of each plant. Natural mechanisms exist that control germination. An understanding of these mechanisms would provide us with the scientific basis upon which control of germination could be based.

With this knowledge we might cause, or prevent, germination at will. We also could probably control the storage life of seeds.

There is another reason for understanding the mechanism of germination. Scientists since 1930 have come to recognize that all cells, whether they are bacterial, insect, plant, or human, are essentially the same. Blocks to growth are not unique to plants; they are known to exist in many, if not all, organisms.

An understanding of the mechanisms of germination blocks in seeds could contribute to a larger understanding and control of growth in the other organisms.

BRUCE M. POLLOCK *is Leader of Vegetable Seed Investigations for the Crops Research Division of the Department of Agriculture. He has done postdoctorate research in the Cytochemical Department of the Carlsberg Laboratory in Copenhagen, Denmark, and was associate professor of biological sciences and horticulture at the University of Delaware.*

VIVIAN KEARNS TOOLE *is a plant physiologist doing research on seed physiology in the Vegetables and Ornamentals Research Branch, Crops Research Division, Agricultural Research Service. She holds degrees from the University of North Carolina and the George Washington University.*

Problems and Rewards
in Improving Seeds

JOHN H. MARTIN AND S. H. YARNELL

THE NUMBER of acres that are planted to a variety of a crop may depend on the availability and cost of its seed.

The point is important and as simple as 1–2–3: Some farmers buy low-priced seed although they know it is inferior. The cheap seed often makes a poor crop. Seed can be produced at lowest cost when a heavy-yielding variety is planted.

Here are some examples:

Soybeans largely replaced cowpeas for hay and green manure purposes because soybeans give higher yields and the seed costs less.

Denton sorgo is an excellent sweet variety, but it was never popular because the heads bear few seeds.

Scarborough No. 7 broomcorn produces excellent hurl fiber, but the heads have short seed branches. Yield of seed therefore is low, and the cost of its seed is high. Other strains of Scarborough that have poorer hurl fibers but are better seed producers are preferred by most growers of broomcorn seed.

Tift sudangrass and Narragansett alfalfa did not attain the popularity they deserved because the seed yields were lower than those of other varieties. Seedgrowers are reluctant to produce such varieties because the slightly higher price received is insufficient to offset the loss from lower yields of seed.

Birdsfoot trefoil is sown on a smaller acreage than it would be if its harvested seed yields were larger. Yields of seed of birdsfoot trefoil, lupines, reed canarygrass, and some other crops are low mainly because the seeds shatter as they ripen, although other seeds on the plants are not yet mature.

GOOD QUALITY of seed therefore is important in maintaining the popularity of a crop variety.

Club kafir was a productive grain sorghum in Kansas when the field stands were adequate, but its soft seed, which favored seed rots, often produced thin stands and replanting often was necessary. Club kafir therefore was never popular with farmers.

Other crop varieties suffer from seed rots or seedling blights, which interfere with stand establishment.

Hybrid sorghum, which has largely replaced open-pollinated varieties in the United States, often produces better stands than the open-pollinated varieties, chiefly because of greater seedling vigor. This is important when seedbed conditions are unfavorable because of cold soil or the formation of a crust.

Yogo winter wheat is popular in Montana and Wyoming because it was bred particularly for resistance to extreme cold. It also has the capacity to germinate in a drier soil than do other varieties, a characteristic that was recognized after Yogo was widely grown on farms in the drier parts of the West.

Soft, starchy seeds of corn and sorghum are more subject to mechanical injury and to consequent rotting when planted in cool soil than are harder seeds, but they are less likely to require grinding before they are fed to livestock.

Inbred line WF 9 is used in producing a large proportion of the hybrid seed corn planted in the Corn Belt. It is a particularly popular seed parent because it produces a large percentage of medium-flat seed. Seed of this size and shape brings the highest price for planting.

THE SIZE and vigor of a seedling are associated closely with size of seed. In fact, a direct logarithmic relation often exists between weight of seed and the dry weight of the seedling.

Large seeds also permit a seedling to

emerge from deeper sowing. Larger seeds thus are particularly important in small-seeded species of forage legumes and grasses. Such seeds must be sown shallow so the seedlings can come up, but then the upper layers of soil may dry out before the seedling is established and the stand may be lost. Large seeds can be sown deep enough to permit the seedling roots to reach moist soil before the upper soil layer is dry.

Because large seeds in tomatoes, cucumbers, okra, eggplant, and watermelon are objectionable to consumers, little attempt may be made to breed varieties with larger seeds to enhance their value for planting.

Seed improvement of crops such as beans, peas, and sweet corn, whose seeds are eaten by people, must give full consideration to food quality as well as suitability for planting.

Temporary dormancy is a desirable characteristic in oats, sorghum, sweet corn, and other crops that are subject to field sprouting in the shock or on the standing stalk before the ripe seed is threshed.

TEMPORARY dormancy is particularly helpful for natural reseeding of crimson clover and other winter annual legumes that mature and drop their seed in early summer. The seedlings that emerge in midsummer quickly perish from the heat, but the ones that come up in the fall usually survive.

On the other hand, dormancy is a handicap in northern winter wheat regions where the crop is sown soon after harvest.

Durum wheat intended for spring sowing often shows a poor germination in laboratory tests for several months after harvest. This dormancy makes it difficult to determine seed quality until shortly before the season for sowing.

Some seeds of certain strains of Hubbard Market and Grand Rapids lettuce remain dormant so long that they do not germinate until several months after harvest.

The presence of many hard seeds that do not germinate promptly in forage legumes such as alfalfa, sweetclover, and true clovers has imposed difficulties in establishing stands. Hard seeds sometimes are desirable, however, because they retain their viability and may germinate later to reestablish a stand.

Hard, or corneous, seeds of cotton, corn, and sorghum are more resistant to seed rots than are the softer seeded varieties of those crops.

Seed of many grasses, particularly native species, bear awns, hairs or long chaff, which prevent the seeds from passing through the seeding equipment readily.

Home gardeners often have poor stands of lettuce because most of the seed was covered with soil after planting. Certain varieties of lettuce require light for germination, and the buried seeds remain dormant. This light requirement could be eliminated by breeding.

CERTAIN biennial crops, such as sugarbeets and garden beets, and vegetable crops, such as cabbage, celery, lettuce, onion, and spinach, may tend to bolt and produce seed during the crop season. Such plants use food and energy to produce a seedstalk so that the root or top is not worth harvesting. It is essential to breed slow-bolting varieties of these crops, but the plants must be able to bolt during the seed-producing season.

The tendency to bolt under a given environment is controlled by hereditary factors, and the desired bolting characteristics are thus subject to improvement by breeding and selection.

Length of day or temperature or both determine the time at which a plant will bolt and flower. The hereditary makeup of the plant determines its response to light and temperature, but treatment with a chemical like gibberellic acid also may induce the plant to bolt.

THE FOREGOING indicates some of the problems of producing seed, and some of the many accomplishments in improving seed.

One of the achievements is the breeding of the monogerm sugarbeet seed, which eliminates the need to thin the beets by hand. It came about 60 years after its need was recognized. Several varieties and hybrids of monogerm sugarbeets are now in production.

They are descendants of one weak plant that had a single seed in each seedball. It was found in western Oregon in 1948. Plant breeders transferred this monogerm character to productive sugarbeets by crossing, selection, and backcrossing.

Five varieties of crimson clover—Dixie, Autauga, Auburn, Chief, and Talledega—were selected for hard, dormant seed characteristics that permit the natural establishment of stands in the fall from seed that was dropped in early summer.

IMPROVEMENT in seeds of forage and turf grasses by State and Federal breeders has resulted in varieties with better quality of seed or higher yields of seed.

The improved varieties produce as much forage or more than the unimproved ones. Nordan crested wheatgrass, released in 1953, produces more seed, and the seeds have fewer awns than the unselected type. Its larger seed provides greater seedling vigor. Two other strains of crested wheatgrass with large, awnless seeds were developed also at Mandan, N. Dak., but had not been released in 1961.

Two strains of intermediate wheatgrass, selected in Idaho, appear to have high yields of seed and are nearly free from awns and pubescence. Another selection made in South Dakota offers some improvement in yield of seed.

The Vinall variety of Russian wildrye yields more seed than the unselected type. The use of Russian wildrye has been restricted by its low yield and high price of seed.

The Penncross variety of creeping bentgrass, released in Pennsylvania in 1954, produces vigorous plants for putting greens from direct seeding. Tualatin tall oatgrass, released in Oregon in 1940, produces high yields of seed because of its resistance to shattering and to smut.

Butte, Trailway, and Coronado sideoats grama have good yields of large seed, from which grow vigorous seedlings. Butte and Trailway were released in Nebraska in 1958. Coronado was released in Oklahoma in 1955.

The Georgia Selection and Lamont rescuegrasses are good seed producers because they are resistant to smut. Lamont was released in Mississippi in 1957. Lancaster and Lyon smooth bromegrass, which were released in Nebraska in 1950, give high yields of both seed and forage. Lyon also has improved seed quality and strong seedlings. Caddo switchgrass, released in Oklahoma in 1955, gives heavy seed yields if conditions are favorable. Tifhi bahiagrass, released in Georgia in 1957, shatters less than other strains of bahiagrass; more seed thus can be harvested.

Selection for low seed dormancy in green needlegrass has been effective.

SOME DIFFICULTIES have been encountered in efforts to improve the seeds of forage legumes.

Selection for increased percentage of hard seed in a variety of Persian clover has been partly successful. Selection for increased percentage of hard seed of legumes in Canada sometimes has reduced plant vigor.

Attempts to cross introduced large-seeded annual species of sweetclover with domestic species have not yet succeeded. A large-seeded sweetclover has been introduced from Turkey, however.

The vigor of birdsfoot trefoil seedlings has been increased by selection. Because they, like the unimproved type, are susceptible to root rots, however, it has been difficult to establish good stands in warm climates. Selection for reduced shattering and for a prostrate plant type has been partly successful.

A yellow lupine with nonshattering pods has been found, but this character is still lacking in commercial lupines for forage. Some lupine selections made in Georgia bear certain genetic markers that would permit the identification of a variety and a determination of its purity in the field. Such markers are greatly needed in many forage crops in order that the purity of improved strains can be maintained.

IMPROVED VEGETABLE seeds include Ferry's Round Dutch cabbage and Great Lakes lettuce. They are outstanding products of selection for resistance to bolting. Ferry's Round Dutch was selected to permit heading and eliminate bolting after periods of cold weather. Great Lakes was selected to permit heading during periods of warm weather, when most varieties of head lettuce bolt.

Genetic safeguards against loss from premature bolting are essential. It is possible to breed strains that will bolt and flower only under unusual conditions. Often, therefore, they produce no seed. An individual cabbage plant selection may or may not flower after the usual cold treatment of 2 months at 37° F.

The yield of commercial seed of Great Lakes and other slow-bolting varieties of lettuce was low until better seed-producing selections were developed.

CERTAIN CHARACTERS, such as nonshattering of seed, appear to have been developed during domestication because the wild forms of many crops drop their seeds as soon as they are ripe. Nonshattering of garden lettuce is of utmost importance in the commercial production of seed. The wild *Lactuca serriola*, which depends for its existence on shattering of the seed, differs in this respect from garden lettuce by only a single dominant gene.

Most breeding of vegetables is concerned with the yield and the eating,

preserving, and shipping qualities of the part of the plant that is consumed. Seed fields may contain individuals having such characters as heavy growth, numerous flowers, or large fruits, which favor high yields of seed. Selection for high yield of seed must avoid any concurrent selection of undesirable market types. The two breeding objectives must therefore be coordinated.

The areas producing vegetables for market and for seed often are widely separated, with different growing conditions, a fact that tends to complicate the breeding and maintenance of seed stock.

In melons, squash, and pumpkin, in which the fruit is eaten but the seeds discarded, the consumer may wrongly think that large seed is an indication of coarse texture of the flesh. Large seeds may also detract from the appearance of cut watermelon fruit. In general, seeds of medium size are preferred. Many think that a black seed gives a pleasing contrast to the red flesh of the watermelon, although a dark-brown seed also is considered acceptable. A dark seed may also be used as an indication of a desirable stage of maturity.

Seeds of tomatoes, cucumbers, eggplants, and peppers are eaten incidentally. They must be unobtrusive. A tough seedcoat may be objectionable in the slicing cucumber and in "seedless" watermelons. In the latter, the seeds abort because the plants are sterile triploids, the result of crossing normal diploid watermelons with special tetraploid strains that have the double number of chromosomes. The best seedless varieties produced thus far have been developed by doubling the chromosome complement of small-seeded, small-fruited varieties. The undeveloped coats of the aborted seeds are inconspicuous and are eaten with the melon flesh. Work on large-fruited varieties is in progress.

IN CROPS grown for their seed, the size and shape of the seed must conform to accepted standards. The seed varieties of lima bean may differ in size and shape, such as the large, thick seeds (potato type) and medium to small thin seeds (sievas). The latter is simple dominant to the former type. Differences in seed size among the thin sieva limas may result from complementary action of nonallelic genes.

Shape of seed is important in sweet corn. A relatively narrow, deep kernel is preferred for both fresh consumption and canning. Sweetness and tenderness are even more important.

COLOR OF seed is important. Most commercial requirements are met by using only few of the rich assortment of colors and patterns that are available among the breeding stocks in the world.

In beans, the colors are in the seedcoat. Colored seed generally has given better germination and vigor than white seed, which canners prefer. Small amounts of color develop in the seed of colored sorts at a very early stage. Some of the color is released during processing, and the liquid gets a murky appearance. Because a clear liquid is preferred, much work has gone into the breeding of white-seeded varieties that germinate as well as those with colored seed.

Most sweet corn is yellow or white. The yellow color results from xanthophyll, cryptoxanthin, and carotene in the endosperm. The carotene gives added nutritive value compared with white corn. The yellow color varies, depending on the genes present, from pale yellow to deep orange. The color usually deepens for each gradation as the kernels mature. Most sweet corn hybrids are a light yellow, which avoids the appearance of overmaturity, although the deeper yellows supply larger amounts of carotene. Another vitamin, niacin, ranges from 18 to 62 micrograms per gram of air-dry kernel. Selection for higher niacin content should prove effective.

Green cotyledon is preferred to yellow cotyledon in garden peas and in lima beans, especially the smaller sievas. The desire to avoid the appearance of overmaturity is also a factor favoring the selection of green cotyledon. The degree of maturity of green seeds is difficult to detect by visual inspection, and such lima beans sometimes are overripe when harvested.

The inheritance of seed color and pattern often is rather complicated.

The anthocyanin colors depend for their expression on a few "basic" genes, which can be suppressed by a dominant inhibitor. The depth and shade of color result from a number of independent genes that complement each other. On this complex are superimposed the genes for pattern, whose effect often is affected by the point of seed attachment. Color and pattern are useful in the identification of seed as to variety.

Tenderness of the seedcoat is important for any crop whose seeds are consumed. Tenderness often is associated with thin seedcoats, and thickness increases with maturity. Comparisons should be made at equivalent stages of maturity, as determined by content of dry matter. The puncture test is not so accurate as weight determination. In sweet corn, the tenderness of the pericarp is inherited on a multiple-factor basis.

TESTS FOR sweetness, consistency, and flavor also are essential in selecting sweet corn for improved quality.

Success in selection for high germination and vitality of white-seeded beans suggests that the color genes are not primarily involved but are linked on the same chromosome with other genes that affect viability of the seed. Once the linkage is broken, the white-seeded beans germinate and grow as well as the colored.

Some lines of sweet corn produce a good stand early in the season while growing conditions are still unfavorable. This means that such lines germinate and grow well at relatively low temperatures and resist the attack of soil organisms that cause decay. Tests

that try to reflect such conditions are
the basis for selection.

Seed dormancy is valuable in moder-
ation, but it may be disastrous in either
extreme.

Total lack of dormancy means premature germination before the seed
matures properly. Many genetic factors can be responsible for premature
germination in sweet corn. Sometimes
the supplemental effects of two or three
recessive factors are required. Some of
these genes affect the plant adversely.

Dormancy results from a physiological influence of some part of the seed
on the embryo or some condition
within the embryo itself. In cabbage,
this influence is concentrated in the
seedcoat. Individual seeds vary as to
the degree or length of dormancy under conditions that are favorable for
germination.

Dormancy that is unduly extended
interferes with normal crop procedures. Some lettuce may even remain
dormant until vitality is lost.

LONGEVITY of seed is an important
consideration in the selection of desirable lines. Certain homozygous recessive characters reduce the vitality
of corn seed after a relatively short
time.

Seeds of cool-weather crops that are
planted in late summer must be able
to germinate at high temperatures.
Four varieties of head lettuce—Imperial 456, Imperial 17, Imperial 101,
and Great Lakes—germinate better at
79° than do Imperial 44 and Imperial
D. All germinate better at this temperature than does Imperial 615.

Seed defects of snap beans have been
greatly reduced in recent years through
breeding. So-called hard seeds, while
normal in appearance, are undesirable because they lack ability to
absorb moisture readily when planted.
This delays germination to the detriment of production. Hard seeds also
require more cooking. Differences
among individuals and breeding lines
in this respect permit its elimination
through selection.

Split seedcoat occurs in lima beans,
snap beans, and soybeans. Soybeans
also have a netted cracking of the seedcoat. All such defects result from the
presence of recessive genes. Cracking
of the seedcoat after wrinkling occurs
in the concentrated Fordhook variety
of lima bean. Fordhook 242 is little
affected.

Deformity of the cotyledons in snap
beans can be minimized by selection.
This and other defects contribute to
difference between varieties with respect to the amount of thresher injury,
which has been greatest in the newer
high-quality varieties, such as Top-
crop and Wade. White-seeded varieties usually appear to be more susceptible to thresher injury than those
with colored seed, but the exceptions
hold promise for the development of
improved new white-seeded varieties.
Differences in the amount of thresher
injury have also been found among
varieties of lima beans.

Yield of seed among the seed-con-
sumed crops has received much attention. In sweet corn, it is related to
number of rows and number of kernels
per row, but from a practical standpoint the desirable ear size is largely
determined by fresh market requirements. An ear just above medium size
is preferred to one that is either larger
or smaller.

A high yield of seeds is important in
such crops as peas, black-eyed peas,
field beans, and lima beans. The most
effective method of increasing their
potential yields has been to breed varieties that are resistant to diseases.

JOHN H. MARTIN *has been a research
agronomist of the Agricultural Research
Service for 46 years. His experience, in addition to research in crop breeding and crop
production, includes the cleaning, testing,
and merchandising of seeds.*

S. H. YARNELL *is geneticist in charge
of the Regional Vegetable Breeding Laboratory of the Agricultural Research Service,
Charleston, S.C. From 1930 to 1947 he was
head of the Horticultural Department of the
Texas Agricultural Experiment Station.*

Breeding for Food, Feed, and Industrial Uses

G. F. SPRAGUE

MOST of the cultivated species of crop plants have been modified by breeding procedures to increase their usefulness as food, feed, and industrial products.

Let us begin our survey with wheat, the cereal of major importance among those grown primarily for food.

Wheat was brought into the North Atlantic coastal area by the several groups of colonists. All the groups brought varieties characteristic of their points of emigration. Diverse types thus were available. The ones best adapted to the new country persisted.

The first introductions were supplemented by additional introductions made by the successive waves of immigrants. Some came to have major importance: Red Lammas in Virginia; Mediterranean, in the southern Corn Belt; Purple Straw, in the Southeast; White Australian, on the west coast; Turkey, in Kansas, Iowa, and Nebraska; and the durums, in Minnesota, North Dakota, and South Dakota.

The improvement of wheat has followed the sequence of introduction, selection, and hybridization.

Most of the older varieties were gradually replaced by newer combinations, which in turn were replaced by still newer developments. The result has been the development of higher yielding types better adapted to the environment of the area of their culture.

The major improvement has been in resistance to various production hazards. These include greater resistance to hessian fly, green bug, and other insects; a greater winter hardiness; stiffer straw; and a higher resistance to smuts and rusts.

Covered smut has been particularly bothersome in the Pacific Northwest, where it is a soilborne parasite. Sources of resistance are available now to all of the physiologic races of importance.

Achieving resistance to stem rust has been more of a problem. As resistant types have been developed and become established commercially, new forms of rust to which commercial varieties of wheat are susceptible have arisen by mutation, hybridization, or other means.

New sources of resistance have had to be located, and such resistance has had to be incorporated into commercially acceptable types.

The use of newly discovered sources of resistance and the newer breeding refinements afforded by chromosomal substitution techniques offer promise of still further improvements. Much remains to be done in clarifying host-parasite relationships and establishing the genetic and chemical basis for physiological specialization.

Dwarf wheats, developed in the Pacific Northwest, appear to have a much higher yield potential than varieties in commercial use in 1960. Plant breeders have started to transfer the dwarf characteristics to wheats adapted to other sections, but the work had not progressed sufficiently in 1961 to assess the value of this development.

POTATOES may have been introduced in early colonial times. They were grown in New Hampshire as early as 1719. Breeding work during the next 100 years was limited. New varieties began to be developed from seed about 1840. Most of the important varieties were developed from true seed.

Cultivated potatoes are tetraploid—that is, they possess four basic chromosome sets. Most varieties initially had a high degree of male sterility. Male fertile varieties and selections have been developed. Polyploidy—three or more repetitions of the basic chromosome set—is favorable or at least is not disadvantageous under conditions of asexual propagation. The presence of extra chromosome sets, however, complicates breeding and genetic studies.

Considerable progress has been made nevertheless in developing varieties that possess satisfactory resistance to such diseases as scab, early blight, and fusarium wilt, certain types of virus, and late blight.

There remains the task of combining all these qualities and other desirable attributes, such as adaptation, yielding ability, and cooking qualities, into commercially acceptable types.

A few diploid seedlings—plants with two sets of chromosomes—are found in some seedling progenies. Exploratory work has begun to determine whether breeding operations can be conducted at the diploid level. If this can be done, all breeding operations should be simplified. The main deterrent appears to be a high degree of male sterility and the lack of a satisfactory technique for resynthesizing tetraploids.

SUGAR has become one of the cheapest of our common foods—thanks to a combination of breeding improvements, improved cultural practices, and improved extraction and refining techniques. Sugar is produced from both sugarcane and sugarbeets in the United States.

Cane has been grown for hundreds of years. Even the primitive tribes of today maintain a wide variety of recognizably different types, which undoubtedly arose largely by natural hybridization and selection.

When the culture of sugarcane expanded to commercial proportions, the types utilized were naturally occurring wild types or selections made by primitive man.

Following the usual pattern, diseases became of increasing importance as culture became more extensive. At first, to combat disease, one variety was substituted for another. The first sugarcane breeding stations were established in Java and Barbados in 1886. Previously there had been some question as to whether sugarcane could be propagated by seed.

Three species have been used for sugar production in various parts of the world—*Saccharum officinarum, S. spontaneum,* and *S. barberi.* Improvement has been done by crossing desirable varieties within *S. officinarum,* or by crossing *S. spontaneum* or *S. barberi* with *S. officinarum,* followed by nobilization and selection. Nobilization consists in backcrossing to the "noble" canes, *S. officinarum.*

Various virus diseases, red rot, and root rot have been the major diseases. Considerable success has been achieved in developing resistant types. Sugarcane is a high-order polyploid (probably octoploid).

In plants that reproduce exclusively by seeds, the individuals that have a greater or fewer number of chromosomes than typical tend to be eliminated by natural selection. This relationship does not hold if the individuals are propagated vegetatively. This is the situation in sugarcane, and chromosome numbers may be 80 to 160.

A measure of the progress that has been made is that the yield of dry sugar per acre has increased more than 1,000 percent since 1844.

Approximately one-fourth of the sugar consumed in the United States comes from sugarbeets. This crop is of recent culture and may be considered as the direct contribution of plant breeding.

A German chemist demonstrated in 1749 that the sugar from beets and the sugar from cane are identical. The first factory for the commercial extraction of sugar from beets was built about 1800. Extensive breeding work with sugarbeets was conducted in Germany and France, from which we imported seed until about 1930.

The European varieties were susceptible to curly top virus and cercospora leaf spot. The continuance of the sugarbeet industry required that varieties resistant to these two diseases be developed. The development of U.S.

Number 1 (resistant to curly top) and the demonstration of the feasibility of the overwintering method of seed production provided the start of a domestic sugarbeet seed industry based on locally developed varieties.

Marked progress has been made since 1930 in the development of varieties adapted to the important producing areas and combining high yields of sugar with resistance to the worst diseases.

Major developments in production practices have lowered labor requirements. Machinery has been developed for the mechanization of harvesting operations and for the "shearing" of seed to reduce the seedball to a single-seeded condition. This reduced the labor requirements for thinning. The discovery and utilization of the monogerm type followed.

Both cytoplasmic and genic sterility exist in beets. These types of sterility differ in their mode of inheritance. Their utility in plant breeding lies in the fact that both types are male sterile. The male-sterile plants can be used as female parents in the production of hybrid seed and the commercial utilization of hybrid vigor without the cost and volume limitations that would be involved in the production of hybrid seed by hand pollination. Considerable progress has been made in developing and evaluating the necessary stocks.

EARLY research to improve tomatoes was done primarily by private breeders and seed companies. Considerable work has been done since 1910 by public agencies to develop varieties resistant to disease. Marglobe was one of the most important of the first wilt-resistant types. Progress has been made in developing special types for canning and for growing in greenhouses. F_1 varietal hybrids have become available for home and market gardens.

Because the hybrid seed is produced by hand pollination, the cost is too great for extensive commercial utilization. A number of genetic male-sterile types are available. They may be used eventually to simplify production of hybrid seed and to permit the commercial utilization of hybrid vigor.

Most of the varieties of peas grown in the United States were introduced from England. They were not well adapted to our climatic conditions, and we had to develop adapted types that would fill different requirements for canning and for the home and market gardens.

Progress has been made in developing varieties having the growth habit and features of pods and seed the two outlets require and in combining these with resistance to wilt, a serious disease of peas.

One of the first major improvements in green beans was the reduction in pod fiber—the so-called stringless varieties. Diseases later became of major importance, and attention was directed toward the development of resistance to anthracnose, bacterial blight, rust, and mosaic.

Regional adaptation and the differing requirements for market gardens and canning have complicated the breeding problem, but progress has been made.

Of the several types of lettuce, the "crisp head" type is the one usually offered for sale. Once it was grown mostly in the Western States. Varieties resistant to mildew, brown blight, and tip burn have been bred.

Until about 1940, the head lettuce grown in the East was primarily of the "butter head" type, but consumer demand led to a shift to the "crisp head" type. Seed of this type was produced only in California, and the varieties developed for the West were poorly adapted to eastern conditions. Breeding programs were started in the East in the late 1920's, and a number of acceptable "crisp head" varieties have been developed and released.

Improvements in vegetables thus involve other attributes than greater yield and resistance to disease. Another goal has been to increase the range of adaptation of a crop. In some instances, as in lettuce, that can be solved by the development of several varieties of the desired type, each adapted to some specific set of soil and climatic conditions.

Preferences of consumers for fresh, frozen, or canned vegetables impose requirements that the plant breeder also must consider.

CORN, first among the feed grains, is native to the Americas. It was an important crop of the Indians before the first voyage of Columbus. By 1700, both flint and "gourd seed" dents were being grown, but we know little about the varieties that were developed and grown between 1700 and 1850. Mass selection was the major breeding procedure for developing new varieties. Some varietal hybridization was practiced, perhaps to produce new populations from which new varieties could be developed.

The experimental basis for hybrid corn was laid by the early work of G. H. Shull at the Station for Experimental Evolution in Cold Spring Harbor, N.Y.

His studies indicated that there was a marked loss in vigor upon inbreeding but that when inbred lines were crossed some of the resulting hybrids were superior to the parental varieties. He visualized the commercial use of this hybrid vigor, but he did not explore the possibility further.

Following Shull's early work, a number of experiment stations conducted studies on the inbreeding of corn. The consensus appeared to be that the inbred lines obtained were too weak and low yielding to make the commercial use of hybrids feasible.

Then came the development of the "double cross" by D. F. Jones, of the Connecticut Agricultural Experiment Station. This development placed the burden of commercial seed production upon vigorous, high-yielding, single-cross parents, rather than the weak inbred parents previously visualized.

Thereafter inbreeding and hybridization studies were undertaken on a greatly expanded scale by the Department of Agriculture, the State experiment stations, and private seed companies. Important contributions in the development of both theory and practice were made by each group before hybrid seed was first offered for sale in the late 1920's.

It was estimated that 0.3 percent of the corn acreage was planted to hybrid seed by 1933. The utilization of hybrid seed has increased rapidly since that date and exceeded 95 percent of the acreage in 1960.

Adapted hybrids are now available for all sections in the United States where corn is of importance.

The use of hybrids has affected production directly and indirectly. The increased uniformity and resistance to lodging of hybrids have fostered more harvesting by machines. Hybrids have made the use of larger quantities of fertilizers economically feasible. The total production of corn has increased steadily on fewer acres at lower costs.

The use of cytoplasmic sterility—failure of pollen production presumably conditioned by the cytoplasm and transmitted only through the female parent—to facilitate the production of hybrid seed has increased since 1956. Perhaps more than half of the seed produced for the Corn Belt in 1960 involved the utilization of this procedure. The use of cytoplasmic sterility should reduce the hazards of seed production but will not reduce the cost.

CORN also has industrial uses.

The Department of Agriculture in 1941 established Utilization Research and Development Divisions in Wyndmoor, Pa., Peoria, Ill., New Orleans, La., and Albany, Calif. A major assignment was to develop new industrial outlets of agricultural products and crop residues. They have been responsible for many developments.

There is, however, another approach to increased industrial use of agricultural crops—the genetic modification of a particular crop to fill some special industrial need.

The development of waxy corn is an example of the possibilities of genetic modification.

Waxy corn, introduced from China in 1907, has a form of starch different from that of normal corn. The starch from waxy corn has pasting and viscosity properties like those of tapioca. Before the Second World War, about 175 thousand tons of tapioca starch were imported from the Dutch East Indies annually. This source of supply was lost, and the culture of waxy corn was started to fill this important need.

Double-cross hybrids having the waxy-starch characteristics were developed, and production began in 1943. Production has increased steadily since then. More than 1 million bushels of this type have been milled annually since 1950.

Work has been started to develop high-amylose corn. Types are available in which the starch has 70 to 80 percent of the straight-chain component, amylose.

Somewhat higher percentages are desired by industry. If such types can be developed, amylose starch would find an important outlet in the production of films and fibers.

Amylose starch has properties somewhat like those of cellulose, and its utilization in paper is a possibility. If it works out, the annual consumption of this type of corn could be several million bushels annually.

Sorghums are used for forage, sirup, and grain. Grain sorghums have become a major feed grain.

Sorghums have been introduced from various areas. Those of African origin have proved to be most useful. Before we had hybrids, the production of grain sorghums was concentrated in the Plains States. The varieties once grown were tall and hard to harvest, but the double dwarf, or combined-height, types came into use after 1920 and nearly replaced the taller kinds.

A genic male sterile was discovered in 1936. Plans were developed to utilize it to produce hybrid seed. It proved to be unsatisfactory, and others were found and investigated. Before the genic sterility was in extensive commercial use, a cytoplasmic sterile strain was discovered that proved to be more adaptable to commercial production of hybrids.

The first hybrids utilizing this sterile source were available for commercial planting in 1956. The utilization of hybrid sorghum has progressed faster even than hybrid corn. About 70 percent of the grain sorghum acreage was planted to hybrid seed in 1960.

Alfalfa is a widely grown and valuable hay crop. Colonists brought alfalfa (lucerne) from Europe. Much later it was introduced into California from Chile. Alfalfa was grown all over the United States by 1900.

Modification of the crop at first was almost entirely by natural selection. Northern common types had fall dormancy and the ability to persist through cold winters. The important varieties that were developed through introduction and selection during the early period were Grimm, Baltic, Cossack, and Ladak.

Wendelin Grimm emigrated to Carver County, Minn., in 1857, bringing seed of alfalfa from his native Germany. The original importation was not winter hardy, but seed from surviving plants were saved year after year, and so Grimm, a winter-hardy variety, was developed. It became one of the most widely distributed varieties in the northern sections until bacterial wilt attacked it.

After scientists determined the nature of bacterial wilt, alfalfas from Russian Turkestan, northern India, western China, and northwestern Iran were found to have some resistance. A few resistant plants also were found among some adapted varieties.

State and Federal alfalfa-breeding programs were enlarged and coordinated to concentrate on wilt resistance and other breeding problems.

From this work have come such improved varieties as Ranger, Buffalo, Atlantic, and Vernal. They represent marked improvements in disease resistance and adaptation to the areas for which they are recommended. These new varieties could be called synthetics, because they were produced by recombination of individually selected and tested clones, or inbred lines.

Many research workers have set as their ultimate goal the production of hybrid alfalfa.

Pioneer work in the breeding of grasses in the United States was that of W. M. Hays with timothy at the Minnesota Agricultural Experiment Station. Improvement work began later at several stations. Selection was the primary breeding technique, but precautions were not taken to prevent cross-pollination. A number of improved varieties were distributed, but most of them were adapted to only a limited area.

Rust has been one of the major diseases. It has been relatively easy to isolate and select resistant types of timothy. Because timothy usually is grown for hay with alfalfa or clover, types are needed that will be ready for cutting when the legume is ready. Varieties like Shelby and Marietta nearly fill the requirement.

Types especially adapted for pasture use have been sought. Progress has been made in isolating prostrate types, but seed supplies have been inadequate because of low yields of seed.

The work with timothy has been done almost entirely by evaluating and propagating clones, but the work with other species of grass has attempted to utilize hybrid vigor more completely.

In types such as bromegrass and orchardgrass and reed canarygrass, clonal selection has been followed by the recombination of a relatively small number of selected clones into a synthetic. The level of hybrid vigor in such material would be greater than the vigor of the parent clones.

Pensacola bahiagrass contains about 20 percent of plants that exhibit self-incompatibility. Such plants when self-pollinated set less than 2 percent of seed. When grouped in pairs, seed sets as high as 90 percent may be obtained.

This method of hybridization has been used to produce Tifhi-1. This F_1 hybrid has produced 69 pounds more beef per acre per year than an unimproved variety that was used for comparison. The same breeding procedure could be used with several other perennial pasture plants.

Buffalograss is dioecious—that is, the staminate and pistillate flowers are borne on separate plants. This phenomenon has been used to produce the F_1 hybrid Mesa. Seed fields are prepared by vegetatively interplanting selected clones of the two dioecious parents in the seed fields.

Gahi-1 pearl millet is a hybrid composite made from the random interpollination of four selected inbred lines. The seed produced represents a combination of F_1 hybrid seed and selfed or sibbed seed—the result of interpollination among plants of the same parental line. The nonhybrid seed is selectively eliminated, through competition, in heavy seedings, and an essentially pure stand of hybrid plants remains.

Yields obtained by this procedure have exceeded those of the parental check by more than 50 percent.

Cytoplasmic male sterility has been discovered in pearl millet. This will provide an alternative procedure for the production of hybrid seed.

As work with the various forage species progresses, growing emphasis may be placed on procedures that permit wider utilization of hybrid vigor.

THE MAIN SPECIES of cotton grown in the United States are sea-island and Egyptian (*Gossypium barbadense*) and upland (*G. hirsutum*).

Sea-island is outstanding in length and quality of fiber, but its production has been limited to South Carolina, Georgia, Florida, and the islands near South Carolina. Wilt became a problem in parts of this area about 1895.

Erwin F. Smith, of the Department of Agriculture, determined the cause of the disease. Resistant varieties were developed. Before resistant types of the upland could be developed, the production of cotton had to be abandoned in many areas in the Southeast.

The boll weevil, first found in Texas in 1892, moved eastward and did so much damage that the late-maturing, long-staple types could not be grown profitably. Early efforts of plant breeders were devoted to the development of productive early types, which tended to escape serious damage. Fiber qualities, particularly length, were sacrificed for earliness.

After productive early varieties were available, greater attention was directed toward increasing the length of the fibers.

Varieties of Egyptian cotton were introduced into the irrigated sections of Arizona and southern California in 1903, but as a group they were poorly adapted. Selection, however, was continued, and improvement in earliness and productivity was gradual.

In 1908 two types differing from normal were found and increased. One of them was later named Yuma. A selection from Yuma was later named "Pima," which continues to be important in the Salt River Valley of Arizona.

Cotton often is cross-pollinated. The extent varies with varieties and the number of pollinating insects. This chance hybridization has provided the variability that permitted the isolation of the many different varieties.

Controlled hybridization also has been used to produce new, variable populations, in which further selection could be practiced.

The breeding methods most commonly used have been mass selection or the selection of individual plants. When pollination is not controlled, neither leads to a high degree of uniformity. Thus variability was a factor that permitted the rapid change in varieties when wilt and the boll weevil became serious.

The commercial utilization of first-generation hybrids of cotton has been suggested by many workers. Four methods have been proposed: Interplanting of the desired parents, with cross-pollination to be effected by bees; controlled hand pollinations; the use of genetic or cytoplasmic sterility; and induced male sterility induced by chemicals (gametocides).

For various reasons, only the use of gametocides has been tried on a commercial scale. Further developmental work is required before this method of producing hybrid seed can be considered entirely satisfactory.

Soybeans have been grown in China for several thousand years, but only 50 thousand acres were grown in the United States in 1907. Then the crop was used largely for forage.

The possibility of utilizing soybeans as an oilseed crop was visualized about 1920. Mills were built, and by 1929 there had developed a considerable demand for high-oil, yellow-seeded varieties.

Some of the leading varieties in 1929 were Illini, Dunfield, Mukden, and Scioto, which were direct introductions from the Orient or selections from such introductions.

It became apparent that various combinations of the desired attributes could not be obtained readily by a direct selection. Between 1930 and 1940, hybridization (followed by selection) or hybridization and backcrossing (followed by selection) became the standard breeding procedures.

Most of the varieties released since 1940 were developed following controlled hydridization.

Breeding of soybeans has been effective in isolating types superior in yielding ability, resistance to lodging and shattering, adaptation to suit various requirements as to maturity, and resistance to disease.

Yielding ability seems to be conditioned by relatively few genes, because transgressive segregation—types that exceed the normal range of the two parents—for yield has been observed in the progeny of many crosses. Resistance to lodging and shattering are required for satisfactory harvesting by combines.

Few of the original introductions

were adapted to the Northern States. Varieties having a suitable daylength response are now available. Evidence of the importance of this development is that in Minnesota soybeans were grown on 97 thousand acres in 1938 and on 3.1 million acres in 1958.

The percentage and quality of oil are under genetic control but are subject to some environmental modification. Oil content has been increased through increased yields and a higher oil content of seed. Many of the newer varieties are superior in oil content to their parental strains. Much soybean oil is used in the manufacture of shortenings, margarine, and paints.

The protein in soybean varieties ranges from 35 to 50 percent. Oilmeal, the residue after the oil is extracted, is an important protein concentrate for feeding livestock. The protein concentrate also has many industrial uses, including the making of plastics and adhesives.

Increased emphasis has been devoted in the last few years to the breeding of new varieties with a higher percentage of protein.

In the early years of production in the United States, soybeans were relatively free of diseases and insect pests. Several diseases and the root knot nematode have become more bothersome in recent years. This development has been so new that the genetic basis for resistance is still undetermined in several instances.

The production of varieties that have adequate resistance to all of the major diseases remains a task for the future.

EFFORTS to improve ornamental plants have varied with time and the method of propagation.

At first probably no more was involved than the selection of the more attractive types that grew wild and their transfer to cultivated conditions.

Further progress depended on the type of propagation used. The rose, one of the most ancient of cultivated flowers, is an example. Several wild species are involved. Most of them are confined to the North Temperate Zone. During the 16th century, propagation was largely by cuttings, and only a few varieties were cultivated. Some 21 double varieties were cultivated in Europe by 1800.

Now the total number of varieties of rose probably would be close to 20 thousand. This big increase has come about by hybridization and the evaluation of the resultant seedlings.

The development of large numbers of new varieties in other forms also depends on the evaluation of seedling progenies. The development of new types under vegetative propagation is limited to the recognition and maintenance of chance bud sports.

The breeding of flowers and ornamentals has been done largely by amateurs, with some participation by private seed firms and public agencies. Some of the work undoubtedly has suffered from a lack of understanding of genetics, yet the most modern techniques sometimes have been used. I give several examples.

Stock, *Mathiola incana*, has both single- and double-flowered forms. Doubleness, the desired type, is conditioned by recessiveness for a single gene. The double-flowered forms are sterile and must be propagated from heterozygous singles, which yield only 25 percent of double-flowered plants.

In one such strain, a mutation occurred that kills all of the pollen grains carrying the mutant gene. When the pollen lethal is linked with the gene for single flowers, approximately 50 percent of the plants produce double-flowered plants. Still later a trisomic type, called "slender," was discovered. Trisomics are $2n+1$ types, in which one chromosome of the complement is present in triplicate. The extra chromosome involved in "slender" is the same one that carries the gene for doubleness. Because of the unequal fertility of gametes carrying the extra chromosome, the selfed progeny of the slender type yields approximately 90 percent of double-flower plants. Furthermore, the single-flowered plants can be recognized in the seedling stage and discarded. Thus, although the desired double type cannot be propagated directly by seed, genetic techniques have made it possible to increase the frequency of doubleness from 25 to approximately 100 percent.

Colchicine is an effective agent for doubling the chromosomes in many plant forms. Such doubled chromosome forms, called tetraploids, have larger flowers and usually a sturdier form of growth.

Colchicine treatment has been used to produce tetraploid forms of many of the annual flowers, such as snapdragons, marigolds, and petunias. Tetraploid forms in vegetatively propagated types, such as forsythia and lily, have also been produced.

Crosses between tetraploids and diploids yield triploid progeny, which are sterile. Where seed propagation is required, triploid forms must be propagated anew each generation. Where vegetative propagation is possible, desirable triploids may be maintained indefinitely. The tiger lily and certain varieties of cannas and day lilies are triploids which are propagated vegetatively.

In plants propagated by seed, species hybridization has played an important role in improvement. Roses, dahlias, gladiolus, amaryllis are common flowers that involve extensive species hybridization in their ancestry.

The limit to the usefulness of species hybridization is determined by the percentage of seed set and the viability of such seed. Viable seedlings often can be obtained from otherwise sterile crosses by use of embryo culture. In this method, young embryos from developing seeds are dissected out and transferred to an appropriate nutrient media. Embryo culture has been used extensively in the breeding of iris.

G. F. SPRAGUE *is leader in charge of Corn and Sorghum Investigations, Cereal Crops Research Branch, Crops Research Division, Agricultural Research Service, Beltsville, Md.*

Fundamental Procedures in Breeding Crops

S. L. EMSWELLER

THE IMPROVEMENT of farm and garden crops undoubtedly began in prehistoric times after man abandoned his nomadic habits and settled in more or less permanent quarters.

Evidence has been found in graves and caves in many parts of the world of a slow, steady improvement in the quality of crops people have grown since the dawn of history.

We feel sure that they have always carried forward some sort of selection of the better plants for seed.

Man's native curiosity must have led individuals in every group in every age to save seed from the plants in their plots for planting the next year, even though they knew nothing as to how seeds are formed and how plants inherit their features.

The Arabs were the first people to recognize sex in plants. They knew they had to plant a few male trees in their date gardens in order to get dates.

After all those centuries of living, when crops were good, and starving, when they were not, and not doing very much about it, the breeding and improvement of plants came to have a scientific basis when the experiments of a monk in Austria became known.

Gregor Johann Mendel (1822–1884), a botanist, entered the order of Augustinians at Brünn when he was 21 years old. In the monastery garden he grew peas year after year and made crosses between the different types (tall × dwarf, yellow seed × green seed, and such).

He noted and recorded the characteristics of size and color and how each persisted or failed in each succeeding generation of peas. After 22 years of experimenting and observing, he read a paper before the members of the Natural History Society of Brünn, in which he told how traits of peas were transmitted.

His discovery, known as Mendel's Law, explains the inheritance of many characters in animals and plants from their parents. His hearers failed to understand the importance of his findings. This small group should not be censured too severely—an outstanding botanist of the period also failed to appreciate Mendel's epochmaking work.

Father Mendel's paper collected dust on the shelves of the Brünn library until 1900, when three botanists in other countries discovered his paper, confirmed his results, and opened a new world of knowledge.

A PLANT produces seed in one of four ways.

The flowers of some plants are so formed that the stigma is never exposed and receives only its own pollen. Such plants, called self-pollinizers, include peas, beans, and wheat.

A second group of plants set no seeds or only a few seeds unless pollen from an unrelated plant reaches the stigma. They are called self-incompatible and include members of the cabbage family and some species of tobacco and lilies.

A third type sets seeds from its own pollen (self-pollination) or pollen from another plant (cross-pollination). Corn, onions, and celery are examples.

The fourth type has some plants that are male and some that are female. Seeds are formed only when male plants are present to furnish pollen. Spinach, asparagus, hops, and hollies are examples.

It is essential in all plant breeding work to control pollination.

Self-pollination is no problem with wheat, beans, and peas, in which the anthers and stigma are in close contact and are shielded within the flowers so that only their own pollen can function.

If they are to be cross-pollinated, however, their own anthers—the male organ—have to be removed before they shed pollen, and the stigma—the female organ—has to be protected for some days after pollen from another plant is applied to them.

The same procedure is necessary—in plant breeding, that is—with plants that have open flowers and are naturally cross-pollinated.

Pollination by hand is slow and laborious. Small, delicate flowers frequently are injured, and seeds are not obtained.

In nature, the pollination of many flowers depends on insects, which carry pollen on their legs and bodies as they move from flower to flower. Plant breeders now use insects to make cross- and self-pollinations by placing flies and bees in cages where plants are isolated to protect them from undesired pollens.

In the Netherlands I saw breeding work with cabbage, in which the plants were grown in small, screened cages with bumble bees as pollinators. The Dutch investigators discovered there were two types of female bees. One soon tried to escape from the cage and did not live long in captivity. The other lived contentedly in the cage. The contented bees were found to be diseased; the disease made them sterile and lacking in homing instinct. They flew low over the ground for short distances, settling and creeping in between plants or into little holes. They were easily captured in insect nets and were much calmer than healthy individuals.

THE PLANT BREEDER has available several methods of obtaining seeds for the improvement of crops: Mass selection, self-pollination and progeny testing, the combining of desirable plant characters by hybridization, and the use of hybrid vigor.

Improvement by means of induced polyploidy also has been tried but needs to be explored more thoroughly.

Mass selection was in general use during the 19th century and had considerable value in developing varieties of some plants. It consists in selecting uniform plants of the desired type for seed production. The selected plants are planted in an isolated plot or under cloth or screened cages to insure that undesired pollen will not reach them. When a crop is grown from seed of the selected plants, the best individuals are again selected, and the process of isolation is repeated.

Successive repetitions of this procedure result in a gradual improvement of the variety, since only superior plants are used each year to produce the succeeding generation.

The method is no longer in general use in plant breeding, but seedsmen use it to maintain a high degree of uniformity of stock seeds from which the main crop of seed will be produced.

Self-pollination with progeny testing is a vast improvement over mass selection. Mendel showed that a plant, although it seems identical to others, may carry hidden characters that show up only in some of its seedlings.

Self-pollination of a plant is inbreeding. It reveals the hidden characters of the parent plants and demonstrates their value for breeding.

Selfed—self-pollinated—seed can be obtained only on plants that are self-compatible. Wheat, rye, and barley are examples. They produce seed without pollen from other flowers because their flowers never fully open and expose the stigma to other pollens.

Onions, corn, celery, and carrots bear fully opened flowers and cross-pollinate readily. If their own pollen reaches the stigma, they also set selfed seed. These plants, unless isolated, set a mixture of selfed and crossed seed.

Plants may be isolated in a number of ways. A cloth or a cage of wire screen may be placed over the plant. The flower may be enclosed in a paper bag or small cloth or wire cage. The object is to keep the flowers protected from visits of pollen-bearing insects and from windblown pollen.

Lettuce is both self- and cross-pollinated. Selfing is assured by using cloth bags tied to the stem of the plant below the flowers and to a stake above them.

A variety of any seed-propagated plant is valuable only when it comes true to type. A breeder can determine trueness only by growing a number of seedlings from selfed seed in a progeny test and observing them for uniformity. A plant that is fairly pure (homozygous) for many characters, will produce uniform progeny. A plant not pure (heterozygous) will produce variable progeny.

The breeder selects the best plants from the most uniform progeny and self-pollinates them in succeeding years until he gets the degree of uniformity he wants. When that point is reached, he isolates all the plants of the selected progeny in a large cage or in an isolated plot far from other similar plants so they can form seed only from selfing and interpollinations. If the progeny obtained from this mass planting is satisfactory, the line may be considered established.

Complete self-incompatibility in crop plants is not common. Some groups, such as cabbages and radishes, are only slightly self-compatible, and pure breeding lines of such plants are difficult to obtain.

O. H. Pearson found that seeds were produced if flowerbuds of cabbage were artificially opened and their pollen applied to the stigma. Seed is produced also on self-incompatible radishes by bud pollination.

Cabbage plants of the same variety will cross-pollinate if they are not too closely related.

Onions and some crops lose vigor after a few generations of inbreeding. With such crops it is probably unwise to continue self-pollinations beyond a few generations. Varieties made uniform by inbreeding can then be mass planted for seed production.

Plants, such as asparagus and holly, that have separate male and female individuals present a problem.

With asparagus, where yield is of primary importance, it is necessary to obtain production records of male and female plants for a number of years if the best potential parents are to be chosen. It is also desirable to test the combining ability of each male with all the female plants. Such a program takes a long time. It probably explains why there are relatively few named varieties of asparagus, compared to the many in most other crops.

Several plant breeders have attempted a different way to breed asparagus. Various investigators discovered that male asparagus plants outyield female plants.

W. W. Robbins and H. A. Jones, of the University of California, learned that an occasional perfect flower, with both male and female organs present, was borne on a male plant. Male plants of this type seldom occur. Later, C. M. Rick and G. C. Hanna determined the mode of inheritance of sex in asparagus and showed it was controlled by a single genetic factor.

The factor for maleness was found to be dominant and was designated by M. Femaleness was designated by m. When females were crossed with males, one-half of the progeny was male (Mm) and one-half was female (mm). It was reasoned that selfing perfect flowers on male plants should produce one-fourth MM to one-half Mm to one-fourth mm. This has proved to be the case, and J. Sneep of Holland obtained all male plants that are MM and these can be planted with female mm plants to produce hybrid seeds that will all be Mm. All seedlings therefore have the male characteristics. By testing with various female plants, breeders hope to develop all male plants of superior quality.

Hybridization makes it possible to combine the desirable characters of two plants. Hybrids are produced by the crossing of plants of different genetic constitution. Hybrids may be made between varieties, and some can be made between species. When cross-pollinations are made, the seed parent should be protected from receiving undesired pollens. Removing the anthers is not necessary if the plant is completely self-incompatible. The anthers of self-compatible flowers, in order to eliminate self-pollination, should be removed before pollen is shed. The stigma of each flower should be protected from contact with undesired pollens.

Plants that are naturally cross-pollinated by insects or windblown pollen are usually heterozygous for some characters. It is hard for the seedsmen to keep such varieties pure. It is not feasible to isolate the plants within any sort of cage when the seed crop is grown on a large scale. Seedsmen resort to isolation by separating cross-compatible varieties at distances too far for windblown pollen and insect transference of pollen. Such precautions are not necessary for crops that are naturally self-pollinated.

When two heterozygous plants are crossed, the seedlings will be variable, depending on how heterozygous the parents were. Much time can usually be saved in plant breeding if relatively homozygous plants are used as parents.

Plants may be made homozygous by making successive self-pollinations. Some plants are made fairly true after a few selfings. Others may require seven successive self-pollinations—or even more.

If hybrid seedlings are both self- and cross-compatible, seeds may be obtained by self-pollinations, by intercrossing, or by backcrossing to each parent. If the hybrids are self-incompatible, seeds are produced only from cross-pollinations and backcrosses.

The seedlings obtained by crossing two plants are the F_1 hybrid generation. If F_1 plants are self-pollinated or two of them are crossed, the seedlings are the F_2 generation. The progeny of a self-pollinated plant is the first inbred generation. When hybrids are crossed to either parent, the seedlings obtained are called backcrosses.

The hybrids obtained by crossing two plants may be of little value even though the parents possessed desirable characters. Subsequent generations from the hybrids must be obtained in order to get new desirable combinations of the parental characters. The plant breeder should select as parents for each succeeding generation the plants that are closest to his objective.

A plant may be undesirable in every respect except in resistance to a certain disease. If it is crossed to a more valuable, although susceptible plant, the hybrids may be susceptible or resistant. It is advisable in such instances to use the backcross method of breeding.

If the hybrids are resistant, the best plants among them should be backcrossed to the susceptible parent. The resulting progeny will contain both resistant and susceptible plants.

By making successive backcrosses to the susceptible parent—using in each generation only the superior resistant plants as one parent—the breeder can transfer resistance from one variety to another.

If the first-generation hybrids are all susceptible, backcrossing to the susceptible parent is advisable even though resistance has not appeared in the hybrids. Some of the plants of the first backcross generation should then be self-pollinated if possible or crossed with sister plants. The progeny obtained will produce both resistant and susceptible plants. The best resistant plants should be backcrossed to the original susceptible parent. This procedure will eventually yield desirable plants that are resistant to the disease in question.

Hybrid plants often are more vigorous than either parent. Hybrid vigor is utilized in the production of some crops. The outstanding example is hybrid corn.

Hybrid seed is available in cabbage, cantaloup, castorbean, corn, cucumber, eggplant, onion, pearl millet, petunia, snapdragon, sorghum, spinach, squash, sugarbeets, tomato, and watermelon.

HYBRIDS, to be useful, must be uniform in growth, quality of product, and high yield.

When two varieties of any crop plant are crossed, the hybrid may or may not exhibit hybrid vigor. If the varieties are homozygous, the hybrids will be uniform, the degree of uniformity depending on how pure the parents were. The vigor of hybrids between different plants of the same variety or species varies greatly.

The method now used generally to develop hybrids is to obtain homozygous lines by inbreeding and then to make all possible crosses between them to test their combining ability. Desirable inbred lines that are obtained are kept isolated to maintain their genetic purity. The producer of hybrid seed then makes the appropriate cross-pollinations, and the seed he sells, although it produces a good crop, will not produce uniform seedlings because of its hybridity.

Only corn and onions are now grown on a large scale from hybrid seed. The others are used so far by home gardeners, but as better methods of obtaining hybrid seed are developed, other crops are certain to be produced by this method.

Hybrid seed is more difficult to produce than ordinary seed. The method of making cross-pollinations varies with each crop, and the considerable hand labor required makes the seed rather costly.

Hybrid corn is relatively easy to produce because the male and female flowers are on separate parts of the same plant, and one can be removed without disturbing the other. The corn tassels, borne on the top of the corn plant, produce the pollen. A plant that is detasseled can set seed only if pollen is supplied from another source.

Hybrid corn seed is produced by planting six rows of the seed-bearing parent bordered on each side by a row of the pollen-bearing parent. A ratio of one row of pollen parent to three rows of seed-bearing plants is in general use. The tassels of the six rows are removed, and all seed set on them will be hybrid.

A large seed field may have many blocks of plants arranged in this manner. Such fields are kept isolated according to regulations established by the States where hybrid seed is produced. The distance required between plantings of different lines varies with the size of the field. In all instances, a certain number of rows of the pollen parent must be planted around the entire field. These rows intercept pollen blown in from other sources and also the pollen from flying insects that work over these plants.

Most hybrid seed is produced by hand crossing. This involves removing the anthers (emasculation) of all flowers to be crossed before pollen has been shed and keeping such flowers protected from insects and windblown pollen. The small, fragile flowers of some plants are easily injured and are difficult to isolate under bags. Emasculation and pollination are carried on in greenhouses for some plants, such as snapdragon and petunia.

The utilization of male sterility to produce hybrid onion seed has stimulated a search for the same character in other plants. Plants that are male sterile do not need to be emasculated.

A male-sterile plant of the variety Italian Red was found by H. A. Jones in the onion-breeding plots of the University of California at Davis in 1925. Viable pollen was not produced on the flowers of this plant, and all seed set on it originated from pollen from other plants.

The male-sterile character had to be introduced into inbred onions in order to produce a wide range of onion hybrids, uniform in shape, color, and other characters.

Male sterility is inherited as a recessive gene. Two types of cytoplasm are involved. When the gene for male sterility is present in a plant with normal cytoplasm, the plant produces normal pollen. The male-sterile gene functions only in the presence of a sterile type of cytoplasm, and viable pollen is not formed. Hybrid onion seed can be produced by planting a male-sterile variety with a normal variety that furnishes pollen.

The male-sterile gene has now been incorporated into many onion varieties, and hybrid onions are widely grown. The male-sterile bulbs are planted in four rows with a row of bulbs of the pollen parent on each side. Bees and flies carry pollen to the male-sterile plants, and all their seed is of hybrid origin.

The time of blooming varies with different onions. The pollen parent bulbs are planted a week or two earlier, depending on their flowering date. This insures that pollen will be available when the male-sterile plants come into flower.

The same general type of cytoplasmic male sterility as occurs in onions has been found in sugarbeets, carrots, corn, millet, orchardgrass, pepper, petunia, sorghum, tobacco, and wheat. Hybrid petunias are produced with male-sterile lines. Research has begun with beets, carrots, and other crops.

Plant breeders are aware of the potential possibilities of this method of producing hybrid seed. Undoubtedly male sterility will be discovered in other crops.

Polyploid plants are ones that have multiples of their basic chromosome number. Plants with twice the basic number are called diploids. Those with three sets of chromosomes are triploids. Those with four sets are tetraploids.

There are known instances of spontaneous doubling of the chromosome numbers of a primrose and of the poinsettia.

Some of our finest ornamental plants and many of our fruits are polyploids. Until about 1910, practically all varieties of garden iris were diploids. Larger flowered seedlings began to appear about this time in the plots of iris breeders. These large-flowered seedlings were named, and in 1943 the chromosome number of 109 of these new varieties was determined; 108 were tetraploid. One was a triploid.

The new varieties of poinsettia originated as bud sports and were propagated because of their superior characters. These new varieties have been found to be tetraploids.

The discovery in 1937 that colchicine would double the chromosome number of plants gave plant breeders the opportunity of exploring the possible usefulness of tetraploidy in improving crop plants.

Research workers found that the immediate results were not promising. Tetraploids of seed-propagated crops are highly sterile, especially those of normally self-pollinated crops. The tetraploids of many plants were inferior to the diploids, and some of the early enthusiasm regarding induced tetraploidy subsided. It was not generally recognized that induced tetraploids should be considered as raw material for continued breeding and selection.

MANY ORNAMENTAL plants are propagated from cuttings (asexual propagation), and fertility is not important in them. In fact, practically all asexually propagated ornamentals do not come true from seed because of their heterozygosity.

Induced tetraploids of such plants have shown some promising results. Several species of *Lilium* have been made tetraploid and are coming into use in gardens. A tetraploid forsythia produced by colchicine treatment at the Arnold Arboretum, Boston, Mass., bears larger flowers of a deeper golden color.

Tetraploid carnations from colchicine have sturdier stems and larger flowers. A few tetraploid carnations are on the market.

Induced tetraploids usually flower later than their diploids and produce fewer flowers per plant.

This was the situation in lilies, but after 15 years of continued breeding and selection, early blooming and floriferous tetraploid lily seedlings were developed. There has been a re-arrangement of the genes in these lilies, and late blooming and lower flower production have been eliminated.

Colchicine-induced tetraploids may be useful in breeding when one parent is diploid and the other is tetraploid.

In cranberry, there are three species: two are diploid and one is tetraploid. All attempts to cross the tetraploid with the diploids failed. The chromosomes of the diploid varieties were doubled, and some of these induced tetraploids were crossed with the tetraploids. These crosses are leading to new and improved varieties of cranberries.

Hybrids between species are usually sterile. The chromosomes of the two species, although able to form a new plant, cannot form functional pollen and egg cells. Doubling the chromosome number of such hybrids usually produces fertile plants that may lead to developing new varieties. Such sterile hybrids have spontaneously produced branches with fertile flowers. The branches have the double number of chromosomes.

Polyploid sugarbeets have been produced in Sweden and Japan. The tetraploids with 36 chromosomes were inferior to the diploids with 18 chromosomes, but when they were crossed with diploids, they produced useful triploids with 27 chromosomes. Swedish plant breeders have reported that after a long period of breeding and selection, useful strains of tetraploid sugarbeets are being obtained.

A triploid watermelon from Japan is available. It was developed by crossing colchicine-induced tetraploids with diploids. The cross is successful only with the tetraploid as seed parent. The triploid watermelons are seedless. They have a thin rind and high content of sugar.

THE PLANT breeder now has many techniques and tools to work with. The accomplishments of the past half century are many, but will probably be far exceeded as newer and more improved methods are devised.

S. L. EMSWELLER *entered the Department of Agriculture in 1935. He is leader of Ornamentals Investigations. He came from the University of California, where he received his doctor's degree in 1932.*

Propagation of Crops
Without True Seeds

AUGUST E. KEHR, FRED P. ESHBAUGH, AND
DONALD H. SCOTT

MOST of the plants in our fields and gardens usually are grown from true seeds. Many other plants must be propagated in another way.

To do that, we cut small sections of living stem or root tissue from the parent plant. We handle the cut sections in one of several hundred different ways. In due time we have new plants exactly like the original ones. This seedless method of increasing plants is asexual, or vegetative, propagation, which is essentially the development of entire plants from buds.

Plants so grown are literally and actually "chips off the old block." They therefore have the qualities of the original plant.

We use vegetative propagation for two basic reasons.

First, some plants do not commonly produce seeds and hence must be propagated vegetatively. The seedless grape is one example. Another is garlic. No one in this country has ever produced true seed of garlic, although its near relative, the common onion, almost always is grown from seed. Other plants that produce flowers but seldom, if ever, a seed are horseradish, pineapple, some palms, sugarcane, some bamboos, bananas, and certain sterile hybrid plants. Still other plants, such as the common ground-ivy (*Hedera helix*), rarely produce flowers. Vegetative propagation is the most economical way to increase them.

The second reason is that many seed-bearing plants do not breed true—that is, seedlings that grow from their seeds do not closely resemble the parents. We could plant seeds of the Delicious apple, or Peace rose, or Meyer zoysia grass, and get seedlings that definitely are apples, roses, and zoysia grasses, but we would lose the identifying characteristics that made the originals famous. In short, when we buy new plants of the Delicious apple or another named variety, we want them to be identical with the parent plants and with each other to the extent that we can distinguish no differences in them.

Our sole purpose in propagating named varieties of many plants—woody ornamentals, tree fruits, small fruits, grasses, ornamental perennials, white potatoes, sweetpotatoes, bulbs—is to keep intact the variety features that we prize.

Valuable breeding stocks of alfalfa and other field crops often are maintained vegetatively to insure the exact genetic makeup in the resulting seed and thus prevent the unavoidable change that occurs when they are increased by true seeds.

We choose and plant named varieties of certain plants in our fields, gardens, and orchards primarily because we know they have certain desirable features, but the only way we can be reasonably certain of getting plants absolutely true to variety name is by propagation of stem or root tissues of the original parent plant.

VEGETATIVE PROPAGATION has its limitations.

For the same reason that it is a highly desirable means of maintaining the status quo in a variety, the usefulness of vegetative propagation is restricted to this purpose, and consequently it cannot be used to develop new varieties of plants. It is always necessary to resort to sexual reproduction in order to obtain true seed with which to develop new varieties of crops that commonly are propagated vegetatively.

To create a new variety of white potato, for example, we must allow the potato plant to grow, form flowers, pollinate the flowers, and then allow the seedballs to develop. Occasionally when weather conditions are suitable and the seedballs are formed naturally, the event is so unusual that many gardeners are bewildered to see "small tomatoes" growing on their potato vines.

Improvement of plants that normally are propagated vegetatively by pollination and formation of true seed is exceedingly slow. For white potatoes, about 1 million seedling plants must be grown in order to obtain one selection worthy of being named as a new variety. From that point onward, it must be maintained vegetatively.

New forms or varieties of plants can appear naturally—but very rarely!—in vegetatively propagated plants as the result of sports. Another name for sports is mutations. Sports and mutations are plants or parts of a plant that abruptly show a noticeably different appearance from the rest of the plant.

Such a change, if it is the result of a true mutation, may be maintained by vegatative means once it has occurred.

Examples of changes in a sport or mutation are a deeper red in a red apple, an unusual color or shape in a flower, a different leaf color in a shade tree, double flowers instead of singles, and similar noticeable changes.

For some unknown reason, mutations, which, as we said, are rare in most plants, occur so often in some sweetpotatoes that it is difficult to maintain a variety unchanged even by vegetative propagation.

WHEN WE increase plants by vegetative reproduction, our aim is to stimulate the growth of buds on "borrowed" roots and stems or to encourage the formation of entirely new buds and roots from primordial—first-formed—tissue.

There are essentially two types of buds of importance in vegetative propagation—true and adventitious buds.

A true bud is a growing point that usually is formed at the base of a leaf and along the stem of a plant.

True buds occasionally may remain inactive and are made active only by some unusual stimulus. For example, an apple tree, if cut, may grow new shoots from the stump when the inactive true buds are stimulated to grow.

True buds may develop into leaves, flowers, or stems. Inactive true buds are "reserves" and function only when active true buds are killed or removed or do not grow for some other reason.

Adventitious buds are formed from embryonic or undifferentiated tissue cells in the roots, stems, or leaves. Given the proper stimulus, these cells form buds that in turn may form either roots or sprouts, depending on their location.

Theoretically, any living cell in the plant may be stimulated to form a bud and ultimately a new plant. In fact, fully developed carrot plants have been grown experimentally from a single root cell of a carrot.

Such development, however, usually is easiest from the cambium (a soft formative tissue just under the outer bark, which is the growing layer in most stems); the pericycle (undifferentiated cells surrounding the central cylinder); or rarely from phloem tissue (the tissue in which food materials are transported within the plant).

Adventitious buds in a sense are emergency buds, which insure the perpetuation of the plant when it is in danger of dying for lack of true buds.

The structure of the plant largely determines the method of vegetative propagation that we can use. Thus in propagating plants classified as monocots—pineapple, sugarcane, and bamboo, for example—it is difficult or impossible to stimulate adventitious buds. We achieve vegetative increase by stem tillers or offshoots or from inactive or latent buds at the nodes of the stems.

In the plants classified as dicots, bud formation is not so restricted because the cambial and other undifferentiated tissues are distributed more widely. It is rather easy therefore to stimulate the growth of adventitious buds in most dicotyledonous plants.

True stems are used oftenest in asexual propagation methods. They include cuttings, grafting, and budding. Other modified stems are used—tubers, stolons, rhizomes, tillers, bulbs, and corms.

Stems differ from true roots in certain basic ways. We all know that roots always grow down toward the center of the earth, but stems, even though they are underground tend to grow upward. The distinction between roots and stems that is of greatest importance in vegetative propagation is that stem buds are formed on the surface while roots have no surface buds.

Bud growth from roots is adventitious and is always initiated from the internal tissue.

VEGETATIVE PROPAGATION may be applied to both underground and aboveground parts.

Belowground parts would include roots, tubers, stolons, rhizomes, tillers, bulbs, corms, and mycelium. (Mycelium is the threadlike vegetative growth of fungi that develops underground more or less as roots do for most plants. In mushrooms mycelium is commonly called spawn.)

Aboveground parts involve stems for cuttings, layering, grafting, and budding.

Plants often are increased directly from true roots by two primary methods, root suckers and cuttings of whole roots.

A true root sucker is formed when an adventitious bud develops from the internal root tissue and continues growing into a stem. Root suckers are sometimes produced naturally near the base of the parent plant and form dense, close-knit clumps, which easily can be lifted and separated.

In plants like the raspberry, the root suckers occur at some distance from the parent plant, and we get new plants merely by cutting the connecting roots.

Two variations of the usual root-cutting method are used commercially—induced suckering and undisturbed whole-root cutting.

Induced suckering is useful in species that rarely produce root suckers. By this method, suckers form in response to partial girdling or cutting of an exposed root in such a way that the partly severed root receives some nutrients from the parent plant.

Undisturbed whole-root cutting merely goes one step further. The exposed root is severed completely, and the cutoff portion is left in the soil.

Polyethylene plastic film has recently come into common use for rapid rooting of softwood and hardwood cuttings. Methods employed are simple.

Cuttings are prepared in the usual way in lengths of 2 to 6 inches, depending on the material to be propagated. The stem is cut off at an angle of 45 degrees just below a node. One-half to one-third of the lower leaves are removed. Unusually large leaves are cut back to one-half their length to save space and reduce loss of moisture.

Cuttings must be kept fresh and turgid from the time they are removed from the plant until they are placed in the rooting medium. Freshness may be preserved by placing cuttings in a polyethylene bag or between layers of damp paper or cloth. Cuttings root more quickly if they are treated with a rooting compound—such as Hormodin #2 or #3—before they are inserted in the rooting media.

Single cuttings may be rooted by placing a small amount of damp sphagnum moss in a square piece of plastic. The cutting is inserted in the moss, and the plastic film is pulled up around the stem and tied. The bundle is then placed in a situation where there is good light, such as a window sill or screened porch.

Under favorable conditions, rooting should be accomplished in 2 to 5 weeks, depending on the species. Such house plants as African-violets, gardenia, begonia, coleus, and peperomia may be handled in this way with little care and space.

In rooting larger numbers of cuttings with the aid of plastic film, a moist medium of equal parts of sand

and peat gives good results. The mixture is placed in clay pots or shallow wooden trays or packed in plastic bags. After cuttings have been inserted in the medium, the tops of bags are closed and held tightly with rubber bands. Clay pots are enclosed in polyethylene film held tightly by rubber bands. Flats are sealed by tucking the plastic under the base of the flat. If tall cuttings are being rooted, the plastic canopy may be held above the cuttings by a light frame of wire or wood.

A technique of rooting cuttings under a fine mist has been developed. It is particularly for commercial propagators, but adaptations are of interest to home gardeners.

Four conditions are necessary to operate a mist system successfully: An adequate supply of fresh water under pressure; perfect drainage of the rooting medium within the propagating bed; proper types of nozzles; and propagating beds or frames, 3 to 4 feet wide, constructed of wood, concrete blocks, or brick.

The length of bed depends on the size of the operation. Ordinarily one nozzle will cover an area of 10 square feet. Nozzles may be placed 3 to 4 feet apart in the center of the bed. Usually they are mounted 12 to 16 inches above the bed. If the mist is to be intermittent rather than continuous, there must be electric controls and timing devices.

Under mist systems, cuttings root best in porous mediums, such as sand and peat, vermiculite, perlite, and clean sand. Drainage is provided by 2 to 3 inches of coarse gravel placed under the rooting mediums. Water may be supplied from pipes above the bed or brought up through the bed from pipes inside or below the bed. Types of nozzles in use vary in capacity and design. Under most conditions a discharge capacity of 1 or 2 gallons of water an hour gives good results.

Home gardeners may wish to operate a simple mist system out-of-doors during the summer. One or two nozzles connected to a hose may be operated manually during daylight hours to provide good rooting conditions. The bed should be protected with a plastic shield around the sides. The shield should be of sufficient height (about 18 inches) to contain most of the mist within the enclosure. A hinged plastic cover may be provided to fit over the top of the frame. It is necessary to provide ventilation on warm days by raising the cover a few inches and opening one side or end of the plastic shield. Cuttings for mist propagation are prepared in the same way as are those to be rooted in plastic-enclosed pots or wooden trays.

Plants may be air layered by cutting a deep gash into the stem, wrapping the wound with moist sphagnum moss, and then covering them with polyethylene plastic to keep the moisture in. This method is successful for plants that are hard to root by other methods.

THE SWEETPOTATO, a true root, is propagated mostly by root suckering.

Sound, medium-sized roots are laid on a loose bed and covered with an inch or two of sand or sandy loam. Sometimes the roots are cut lengthwise; the cut surface is treated with a fungicide to prevent rot and placed downward, so that the plant-producing surface is uppermost.

The young root suckers, 3 to 5 inches high, are pulled off in 4 or 5 weeks, and others emerge to take their places. Three or four crops of sprouts may be obtained from each "mother" root. The sprouts are true root suckers in that they originated from adventitious buds in internal tissue of the roots.

Sweetpotatoes also root readily from stem cuttings, a method that we discuss later.

Whole-root cuttings, by which new plants can be produced from short pieces of root, are used more commonly than root suckers.

With root cuttings, an adventitious bud may be initiated from callus tissue at the proximal end of the root (root end nearest the parent plant); or from tissue near the proximal end of the plant (as in horseradish); or from tissue anywhere along the root (raspberry).

The root cutting furnishes all nourishment to the young plant until it becomes self-sufficient. The original root cutting often becomes a part of the new plant, but it may also function solely as a source of nourishment.

One should mark the tops and bottoms of root cuttings to avoid planting them upside down. Horseradish roots when inverted (that is, when the proximal end—the end that normally was the stem end—is planted downward) will grow and develop stems from the proximal end and roots from the other end. Growth is retarded, though, and the resulting roots are small and unsalable. Growers who make root cuttings therefore cut the upper (proximal) end square and the lower (distal) end oblique. Root cuttings thus marked can be properly placed when they are planted in the field.

Curly aspen, a forest tree whose wood is valued as a veneer for furniture, must be reproduced vegetatively or the wood will be similar to that of ordinary aspen.

Shipmast locust grows fast and is straight, but it must be propagated from root cuttings in order to retain those special qualities. In fact, it seldom produces viable seed.

Smilax, oriental poppy, halesia, amelanchier (shadbush), and shepherdia are examples of plants often propagated by root cuttings.

Some root tissues do not commonly form adventitious buds. Dahlias and peonies, for example, have large, fleshy storage roots, which will not grow unless a bud from true stem tissue is attached. Such propagations are not true root cuttings, but, strictly speaking, are stem cuttings with attached nonregenerative storage roots.

ALTHOUGH the storage organ of the white potato is formed underground, it is really stem tissue, because it has true buds (eyes), which grow from the surface layers.

The eyes of white potato are formed only during the early stages of growth in much the same way as buds form along the stem of a woody plant. If the eyes are removed mechanically, the tuber usually will not grow. (The sweetpotato, a root, produces adventitious buds after the root is fully grown.) Consequently, when plants are propagated by cuttings from a tuber, care must be taken to include at least one eye or bud on each seedpiece.

Tubers are used to propagate white potatoes and Jerusalem-artichokes. Blocky seedpieces weighing 1.5 to 2 ounces and having two eyes or more are desirable. These may be cut and planted immediately, but if the soil is overly dry or wet, they may first be healed. The process of healing of the cut surface of a potato is called suberization. Suberization occurs in about 7 to 10 days at 60° to 70° F. and a relative humidity of about 85 percent.

Potato seed that has been precut at the farm where it was grown is suberized during transit in railroad cars equipped to provide suitable temperature and moisture. The seed arrives at its destination ready to be planted.

Sometimes potato "eyes" are marketed for seed. They really are small seedpieces, cut to include the eye and a small part of the storage tissue. Because seedpiece eyes weigh little, they are desirable for a special garden trade. They are usually cut and packed in fine sawdust or similar material for suberization and subsequent mailing. Eyes are not recommended for the commercial production of potatoes.

The tubers of other tuberous plants, including gloxinias and tuberous begonias, may be cut before planting (again with an eye in each piece), but they usually are planted whole.

STOLONS, rhizomes, and tillers are stem structures that frequently grow under or near the ground surface in more or less specialized patterns.

Usually we call it a rhizome if the stem tissue remains partly underground and occasionally sends up leafy shoots from the upper surface and roots from the lower surface. Examples are the German iris and canna.

The crown roots of asparagus and lily-of-the-valley usually are considered to be rhizomes. Usually they are semi-fleshy, thickened storage stems, unlike stolons or runners, which are usually slender, aboveground stems that most frequently take root at or near the tip.

Most persons are familiar with the stolons, or runners, of strawberries, which represent the commonest means of propagating this important crop. Stolons also are utilized to increase named varieties of many important lawn grasses, including St. Augustine, zoysia, bermuda, and bent grasses.

Somewhat distinct are tillers, or off-sets. They are stem sprouts that usually come from the underground axils of the lower leaves. In general, tillers arise at the base of the parent plant and form a cluster or clump of plants.

Tillers represent the only means of propagation for certain monocots, which, because of their lack of a continuous cambium layer, cannot be budded, grafted, or grown from cuttings. The date palm, which does not breed true from seed, for example, can be propagated only by tillers that develop near the base of the parent.

Propagation of new plants by means of rhizomes, stolons, and tillers is probably the most easily accomplished of all the methods of asexual propagation. One need only transplant the rooted plants, which are readily separated from the parent plant. Commercial nurserymen find this method relatively slow and cumbersome.

A BULB is a thickened fleshy bud. Usually it grows underground. It has specialized storage parts, which provide a convenient means of vegetative propagation. The onion, lily, hyacinth, tulip, and narcissus are known as bulbous plants.

If there are continuous rings of scales around a central growing point or axis (as in the onion, tulip, hyacinth, and narcissus), the bulb is known as a tunicated bulb.

Bulbs that have individual scales attached to the axis in a rather loose manner (somewhat like ruffled feathers on a chicken) are known as scaly bulbs. The lily is a scaly bulb.

True bulbs increase by division by breaking up into a number of smaller parts, which, in a few years, develop into a bulb of flowering size. During the time of maturing, bulbs also form offsets, or small bulbils or bulblets, which appear outside of the protective sheath (as tulip and hyacinth).

Some plants form new bulbs every season of growth, as tulips do. Others, like narcissus and hyacinth, grow new tissues around the old bulb to increase in size and later may divide or split into new bulbs. Propagators generally agree that bulbs originating from offsets are more vigorous or thrifty than those formed from divisions.

The planting of bulbs is regulated in part by the size of bulb, seasonal conditions, species, and such other factors as the type and drainage of soil.

Tulips and lilies may remain in the soil year after year, but stronger plants and better blossoms will result from frequent digging, sorting, and resetting of the largest and strongest bulbs. The average gardener is best guided by the planting and cultural directions recommended by the distributor.

THE CORM is not a true bulb but often is called such in commercial trade.

A corm is a thickened underground stem that contains nodes and internodes, as in gladiolus, crocus, and related types.

When it is properly planted in the fall or spring, a corm thickens its leaf blades above the old corm to begin the formation of a new one. Cormlets start to form at the base of the new corm during the flowering period. The old corm becomes detached or decays, and the new corm formed above the old one may be encircled by cormlets, which, if separated and planted, will usually produce flowering-size corms in 2 or 3 years.

Gladiolus corms generally are dug in

the fall after the flower stalks have died and are placed in dry storage until planting time the following spring or early summer.

Crocus is usually fall planted and may be left in the soil more than one season. The corms have to be replanted at intervals of 2 or 3 years, however, as new corms formed on top of old ones tend to produce plants that are too shallow for good flowering.

THE MUSHROOM plant grows underground in the form of fine fungus threads, called mycelium. Spawn is made by culturing the mycelium on a solid medium, usually rye-grain. Mushroom growers inoculate their beds by broadcasting pieces of spawn over the surface. The mycelium grows into the beds from each piece of spawn.

Unlike the roots of green plants, however, the growing strands of the many separate "root systems" soon fuse with each other.

Strains of spawn are improved by testing and selecting cultures made from single spores and from strains that develop during mycelial growth. The differences between strains grown from single spores are due to genetic segregation in the mushroom. The growing mycelium is usually rather stable, but new strains sometimes arise spontaneously. Presumably they are due to mutations.

REGENERATION by cuttings is basically a form of bud propagation.

The modern use of rooting compounds, mist systems, plastics, and improved rooting media has increased the range of plants that may be propagated profitably by this means.

A cutting may be made from any part of a plant from the root to the growing tip.

We can list three general classifications of cuttings: Cuttings from stems; cuttings from growing or soft wood or semihardwood; and cuttings from ripened or mature wood.

Growing-wood cuttings may be prepared from soft or hardened wood.

The length of cuttings may vary with the length of stem between nodes. Cuttings usually contain two to five buds. The upper end of the stem is cut off on an angle just above the topmost bud, and the lower end is cut off just below a bud. Plants that often are propagated from soft growing tips include coleus, salvia, verbena, geranium and viburnum.

Semihardwood from healthy plants often is used for cuttings. A rule-of-thumb method of testing for proper condition of wood is through a bending test. If the wood snaps readily and does not remain bent and springy, it is considered acceptable for use. Cuttings of this type are usually taken during the summer after the period of flowering. Plants of commercial importance that are propagated from semihardened wood include the azalea, camellia, osmanthus, ligustrum (privet), and lonicera (honeysuckle). Many plants can be propagated from soft or semihardwood cuttings.

Hardwood cuttings are taken from well-ripened, mature stems collected after the leaves have fallen. Many plants of the nursery trade are propagated from cuttings taken in late fall and winter. Among them are the grape, rose, spirea, arbutus, tamarix, and euonymus.

Boxwood, most conifers, and some of the broad-leaved evergreens are rooted successfully from cuttings taken in late December and January.

Whole leaves and leaf sections are used to regenerate some of the house and conservatory plants, such as African-violet, gloxinia, rex begonia, and peperomia.

For plants like gloxinia and peperomia, the entire leaf is used. It is inserted upright in moist sand to the depth of the petiole (leafstalk).

Rex begonia is propagated from leaf sections, each of which has a basal portion of the midrib. The sections are inserted upright in sand. Another way is to sever the main veins and place the entire leaf flat upon the rooting medium.

A complete, mature leaf of the African-violet is removed from the parent plant by cutting it near the crown to avoid leaving a stub. The cutting may be rooted in water, sand, peat moss and sand, sphagnum, or vermiculite. Adventitious buds and roots form at the base of the petiole.

IN GRAFTING, one inserts a part of one plant into or upon another in such way that they become united and continue to grow. The cambium layer of each part must unite with the other.

The part with established roots is called the stock or understock. The shoot portion of the desired variety is called the scion.

Graftage is a term applied to scion grafting, inarching (or grafting by approach), and bud grafting.

There are limits within which successful unions may be accomplished, but the range is greater than one might expect. Plants having true bark cambium and pith, known botanically as exogenous plants, may be grafted. Good results may be expected, in general, within the same genera, quite frequently within the same family, and less frequently between different families. Grafts between species are sometimes called heteroplastic grafts.

Interesting examples of heteroplastic grafts include white sweetclover (Leguminosae family) grafted on sunflower stock (Compositae) and geranium (Geraniaceae family) on smoking tobacco (Solanaceae family). Cowpeas can be grafted on tomatoes, clover on geranium, and tomato on geranium.

Pears are grafted on quince rootstocks to produce dwarf pears. Lilacs may be grafted on ligustrum. Plums are often grafted on peach rootstocks.

There is an almost limitless number of successful heteroplastic grafts.

Of the several kinds of grafts, the most used are whip (or tongue) grafts for joining scion and root; veneer grafts (for joining scions to growing plants); and inarching (to unite two growing plants).

A whip graft is prepared by inserting a fitted scion into a notched rootstock in such way that the growing cambial tissues or cambium of the scion and root are alined so closely that they may grow together. The scion may be matched to one side of the root only and does not need to correspond in diameter to that of the root which is often larger. After fitting the scion and root together, the graft is tied with waxed grafting cord or a rubber or plastic grafting band.

A veneer graft is prepared by cutting out a small section of the stock and replacing it with a fitted scion. The graft is tied in the same manner as the whip graft.

Inarching, or approach grafting, is accomplished by removing a small piece of bark from each of two scions that are growing on their own roots (as would be the case of two potted plants), joining the two cut surfaces together, and tying them with waxed cord. It provides a convenient means of maintaining the scion in fresh condition when the uniting process is expected to be somewhat slow.

Stocks for grafting are selected to obtain certain objectives. The propagator may be seeking such desirable characteristics as root vigor, disease resistance, transplantability, or maybe dwarfness.

Whip grafts are usually prepared from dormant scions cut from the past season's growth. The scions are stored until midwinter or until they are ready for grafting. Stocks are dug in the fall after the leaves have fallen and are placed in storage until needed.

Veneer grafts may be made in the summer or winter, depending on species and suitable scions. Most conifers are grafted in winter. Most hollies and yews are grafted in early spring.

IN BUDDING, one inserts a single bud into an incision beneath the bark of a stock. It usually is done while the stock is growing in the nursery row and when the bark parts easily from the underlying wood tissues.

The budder may desire to do his budding in the early spring by inserting buds that were formed the previous season. He usually chooses periods in the summer or very early autumn and uses buds that were formed on wood that grew the same season.

Previous-season buds, especially roses, are stored as "bud sticks" over winter and are thus available for use in the spring before new buds are available.

Buds can be attached to stocks in a number of ways.

Shield budding is the commonest and perhaps the easiest method. Bud sticks are selected from the vigorous shoots. They are scions with leaves and buds attached, except in the case of budding in early spring where leaves have been removed for storage or by freezing.

Leaves are removed by cutting the petiole off at the base of the leaf. A short stub is left by which to hold the bud during insertion.

Bud sticks are prepared at the time of budding, if possible, and must be kept moist by wrapping in damp cloth or several thicknesses of damp paper or moss. Stocks in the nursery row are made ready by removing leaves and small branches, which may hinder the work of the budder. If a few leaves are left to shade the bud, there is less danger that it will dry out before a union is effected.

A successful budder is a careful workman. He uses a sharp, clean knife. He cuts through the bark only at a point as close to the soil as possible and makes a T-shaped incision in the stock. He folds the bark on both sides of the vertical cut back to make room for inserting the bud. A bud surrounded by bark (and sometimes a small bit of wood beneath) is removed in the form of a shield from the bud stick and is inserted into the T-shaped incision of the stock. If the bud is a bit too long, it is cut to fit in such manner that the bark of the stock will fold over the bark of the shield. The bud is held in place by wrapping with a rubber strip or raffia, starting just below the bud and

increasing tension around the stock above the bud until the area of incision is well closed. Five turns around the stock, if well placed, will hold the bud.

Stocks 1 to 3 years old or more are used for budding, depending on species and conditions. As a rule, 1-year wood is easiest to handle. The top of the stock is removed the following spring when the bud has started to make growth. Sometimes, when the bud grows slowly, the top of the stock is removed in spring to force growth of the inserted bud.

Many fruits, including the peach, cherry, plum, and (in some localities) apple and pear, are propagated by budding. Many ornamentals, including field-grown roses, are budded in summer.

IN LAYERING, we remove plant parts that have been stimulated to produce roots while they are still attached to the parent plant. Some plants tend to form natural layers. Others may be induced to produce roots from aboveground parts by artificial means.

Layering is done easily by covering stems or side shoots of a plant with a suitable medium, such as moist sand or soil. Some plants, like the gooseberry, are layered by removing a greater part of the top growth and mounding the plant with soil. Roots will strike along the buried stems. With some plants, one has to pin the stem to the soil with pegs or hold them in place with a brick or stone after the stem is covered.

Raspberries are propagated easily by pegging the tips to the soil while the plant is growing vigorously.

Grapes, clematis, and other vining plants may be increased by looping a stem or cane so that it comes in contact with the soil in several places. The stem has to be pegged tightly at each point of contact. Rooting is often stimulated by cutting notches or rings or by twisting the stem at the point it touches the soil.

A PROBLEM in vegetative propagation is the need to maintain vigor and prevent the degeneration of stocks.

Degeneration is any disorder that reduces the vigor or productivity of plants during subsequent series of propagations.

The use of a part of an established plant for starting new plants may result in degeneration of the stock if the established plant suffers from certain diseases, insects, nematodes, or abnormalities.

Nowhere do the expressions "like father, like son" or "a chip off the old block" apply more exactly than in vegetative propagation. For the "chip" to be healthful, the "block" must be healthful.

Preventing degeneration, or running out, of vegetatively propagated stocks is highly important in the cultivation of crops that are vegetatively propagated.

Degeneration may result from infection by diseases (virus, fungus, bacteria), by genetic mutations, by infestation with nematodes and insects, or by varietal mixtures.

Virus diseases and genetic mutations probably are the most fearsome causes of degeneration in plants, as they are irreversible and usually are difficult to detect and identify. Once a plant is infected with virus, all plants propagated from it are usually infected. Most viruses weaken plants. A virus is a transmissible infectious agent, too small to be seen by a compound microscope, that multiplies within the cells of a suitable host.

Some mutations are inconspicuous. Others are spectacular, as when leaves become streaked or variegated. Variegated (for example, Blakemore strawberry with June yellows) plants are frequently unproductive and worthless.

Viruses may be spread by the handling of infected material and by insects and nematodes. The most important operation in the production of some crops may be to prevent the spread of viruses during propagation of plants. That usually requires rigid control of insect vectors by using insecticides or by isolating plants from sources of disease.

We cite strawberries as an example of how degeneration is avoided in a vegetatively propagated crop, although peaches, potatoes, chrysanthemums, lilies, and other crops could be used as examples.

Strawberries are vegetatively propagated by runners (stolons). Each runner plant is like its mother plant. Any diseases the mother plant has may be passed on to the runner plants. Aphids, cyclamen mites, two-spotted mites, and nematodes, all harmful to the plants, are passed along from plant to plant during propagation.

Aphids are particularly harmful. Some kinds carry viruses and in a few days may cause untold damage by spreading virus from a nearby field of infected plants into virus-free stocks.

Most viruses in strawberries cause a weakening and degeneration of the stocks without any distinctive foliage symptoms in plants of cultivated varieties. Indexing is grafting a part of one plant to part of another plant that is very sensitive to virus. Only by indexing to *Fragaria vesca*, a wild species of strawberry, was the presence of viruses established.

Shortly after the Second World War, investigators discovered that most stocks of strawberries in the United States were infected with viruses, as shown by indexing to *Fragaria vesca*.

The discovery led to an extensive search for the most vigorous plants of each variety. They were indexed, and some were found free of virus. The virus-free plants were propagated, first by research investigators and then by commercial nurserymen, under conditions that would insure substantially virus-free stocks. The new plants then were distributed to growers.

Certain precautions to prevent reinfection by viruses were taken by nurserymen during the propagation of the substantially virus-free stocks. These included isolation at a considerable distance from other strawberry stocks and applying an insecticide (malathion) frequently to control aphids.

Some States with large strawberry

industries have adopted regulations governing the production of virus-free plants based on the principle of periodic replacement of stocks with new virus-free plants. Each State maintains indexed virus-free stocks in screenhouses to furnish new stocks to the nursery industry. Thus they prevent degeneration from virus diseases.

Parasitic fungus diseases can devitalize nursery stocks. If the fungus is soilborne, such as *Verticillium*, control may be difficult.

Chrysanthemum stocks infected with *Verticillium* can be freed of the disease by removing rapidly growing tips, rooting them in sterile sand or soil, and growing them in field plots free of *Verticillium*. Contaminated soil can be freed by fumigating with chloropicrin or methyl bromide by modern machine methods.

Modern fungicides can be used to reduce or eliminate some devitalizing airborne fungus diseases and thereby avoid degeneration of nursery stocks. Cyprex is effective against cherry leaf spot, a disease that severely weakens and stunts cherry trees in the nursery, but it cannot be used on trees bearing fruit.

Captan effectively controls leaf spot and leaf scorch of strawberries and prevents weakening of the stocks. Strawberry plants free of the trouble, if grown in isolation, remain free indefinitely.

Crown gall is widespread and especially troublesome in nursery plantings. Infected plants are unsalable. The organisms spread quickly by cultivating and pruning tools and by persons who handle the plants. Control is difficult and consists mainly in treating soil with antibiotics, such as Terramycin, and applying methods of sanitation. Avoidance of alkaline soils is helpful. The detection of incipient infections is difficult. Dipping nursery stocks in antiseptic solutions that will not harm the plants may be helpful.

Degeneration of nursery stocks usually occurs following severe infection from nematodes, the tiny eel-like worms that live on the tops or roots of plants. The stunting and leaf malformations caused by nematodes feeding in the tops of plants usually are conspicuous enough that infected plants can be eliminated by diligent roguing. Incipient infections are difficult to detect, and stocks may be contaminated sufficiently to cause degeneration when the nematode population increases over a period of several months. Sanitation is the chief control unless all plants are infected. Completely infected plants sometimes may be freed of nematodes by subjecting dormant plants to a flash hot-water treatment that kills the nematodes without seriously damaging the plants.

Two general types of soilborne nematodes are parasitic on plants. One type spends its life in direct contact with the soil and feeds on roots from the outside. The other type spends most or all of its life within roots.

The former can be eliminated from plants by thorough cleansing of the root system. The latter require special treatments, such as hot-water treatment or rooting aerial parts of plants in disinfected sand or soil.

Fumigation of soils to rid them of nematodes is an important part in preventing degeneration of stocks.

AUGUST E. KEHR *is Assistant Branch Chief of the Vegetables and Ornamentals Research Branch of the Agricultural Research Service. Before entering Government work, he conducted research in the Department of Horticulture at Louisiana State University. In 1954 he became horticulturist in charge of the Government Research Program of Potato and Onion Improvement at Iowa State University.*

FRED P. ESHBAUGH, *horticulturist, became Superintendent of the U.S. National Arboretum in 1954. He joined the Department in 1944 as nursery manager of the Soil Conservation Service at Manhattan, Kans.*

DONALD H. SCOTT *is leader of the Small Fruit and Grape Investigations of the Crops Research Division, Agricultural Research Service. His principal field for many years has been the development of new and improved varieties of small fruits.*

THE

PRODUCTION

OF SEEDS

ↂↂ

Producing Seed of Hybrid Corn and Grain Sorghum

JOHN M. AIRY, L. A. TATUM, AND J. W. SORENSON, JR.

AFTER 26 years or so of research, the first commercial hybrid corn seed for sale to farmers in any quantity was produced in Iowa in 1926.

Hybrid corn was planted on about 1 percent of the corn acreage in the Corn Belt in 1933 and on almost 100 percent in 1955. The wide adoption of high-yielding hybrid strains in 1938–1945 led to an increase of 15 to 20 percent in the average yield of corn in the United States.

The development of hybrids of grain sorghum followed discoveries of male-sterile characteristics in 1935 and later. Farmers accepted grain sorghum hy-brids more quickly than they did corn hybrids. The first commercial seed field was planted in 1955. Nearly 70 percent of the acreage in 1960 was planted to sorghum hybrids.

The use of hybrid seed requires the production of new seed each year; the use of seed from farmers' fields of a hybrid would result in a loss of 15 to 20 percent in yield in the succeeding crop because of the reduction of hybrid vigor from inbreeding. An extensive business has been developed to supply the need.

Farmers need 10 million to 12 million bushels of seed corn and 1.5 million to 2 million bushels of sorghum seed each year. Large amounts of capital, labor, and technical knowledge are required of the specialized seed producers, which may be small farm-type operations or corporations. Some of the corporations conduct research on methods, develop inbred lines, produce and test hybrids, produce seed in their own plants, and sell directly to farmers. Much of the hybrid corn seed is produced by such firms.

CULTURAL practices for growing seed of corn and sorghum are similar in many respects.

Fields for seed are in high-yield areas that have fertile soil and favorable conditions of temperature and moisture.

Some corn seed is produced in irrigated areas, but much is produced in parts of the Corn Belt where normal rainfall is adequate.

Small amounts of grain sorghum seed are produced in humid areas, but more is produced west of the Corn Belt in irrigated areas where grain sorghum is a regular crop.

Before we had hybrids, seed usually was grown in areas where the variety was adapted. Seed fields for producing hybrid seed may be grown elsewhere, however, and the seed will be as well adapted as if grown locally. This is possible because hybrids are crosses of specific and uniform inbred lines, which change little or not at all when they are grown in different geographic areas or a different climate.

Potential yield in seed fields, weather risks (such as drought, high temperatures, hot winds, and hail), length of season, maturity of the hybrid parents, date of freezing temperatures, isolation from undesirable varieties, freight costs to the planned market, and other economic factors influence the decisions as to where to locate seed fields.

Seed of hybrids for the South, however, is grown in the South, and seed for the North usually is grown in the Corn Belt. Seed of corn hybrids for farthest northern areas often is grown 200 to 400 miles south of the area where it is best adapted to reduce risk of a freeze before harvest and to increase the size of the seed.

Regional limitations from south to north are not so great for most grain sorghum hybrids as for corn. Seed intended for Nebraska thus can be grown in Texas, or much of the seed for Texas can be grown in Nebraska.

Much of the seed is produced by farmers under contract with seed companies. The seedsmen pay certain costs, such as for the parent seedstock furnished to the growers and for the detasseling operation. High yields are thus mutually advantageous, and improved practices are applied to a greater degree than on the average farm. Some seed companies employ specialists who advise the growers on cultural practices.

It is important to get a stand of the correct number of plants to the acre. Heavy stands affect the size of the seeds and also the yield if drought and heat ensue.

An adequate supply of each fertilizer element is important for uniformity throughout the field, high-quality grain, early maturity, and the most profitable yields. Growers test the soil carefully before they apply fertilizers.

The use of herbicides varies with community and need. The use of 2,4-D to control broadleaf annual weeds in corn is common. The preemergence application of several newer chemicals controls both broadleaf and grassy annual weeds.

Weedkillers must be used with caution on grain sorghum for seed because the small, shallow-planted seedlings are susceptible to injury.

Many growers treat soil with insecticides—as spray or granules by broadcast or row application—against wireworms, rootworms, white grubs, seed corn maggot, seed corn beetle, cutworms, and others. Spray or granule applications to the growing plants are used to control the corn borer, corn earworm, corn leaf aphid, armyworm, sorghum webworm, grasshopper, and chinch bug.

Control of weeds in corn is important for maximum yields but is not important in obtaining weed-free seed.

Weed control in grain sorghum is essential in order to produce seed that is practically free of weed seeds and entirely free of seeds of noxious weeds. Sometimes a grower has to resort to hand operations to control weeds.

SEED FIELDS for corn usually are 40 rods from other corn of the same type and color. This distance sometimes is reduced when extra male rows are planted for added pollen production along the side of the field next to one on which corn is being grown for feed.

Fields of different types of corn (like white and yellow or sweet corn and field corn) must be at least 80 rods apart. Seed fields of waxy or other special endosperm types and special plant types, such as dwarf corn, have to be at least 40 to 80 rods apart to avoid contamination.

All volunteer plants within the field and in fence rows or lots within the isolation distance must be removed before the seed parent flowers.

Early planting is preferred in order to gain early maturity in the fall and to have the corn at safe moisture levels in the event of an early freeze. Germination of grain with moisture levels of 35 to 40 percent may be reduced in a few hours by temperatures of 26° to 28° F. Germination of the grain at a moisture content of 30 percent and less may escape injury.

Early planting in the Corn Belt increases the need to use chemicals to control corn borers.

Differences in maturity may require different planting dates for the seed parents and the pollen parents so that the silk emerges at the same time the pollen is shed. Because the difference in planting dates may be 2 or 3 weeks, problems in tillage may arise. Control of weeds by chemicals may be especially helpful in such instances.

Heat units are often used as an aid in estimating when to plant the delayed seed parent. A heat unit is the number of degrees the average daily temperature exceeds a base—usually 50° F. for corn—near the low temperature at which growth occurs. Thus, with an average temperature for the day of 62°, 12 heat units occur.

Records from special nursery plantings give comparable data as to the heat units to flowering and silking for the different seed parents when they are planted at the same time. Such records tell whether the two parents will nick at flowering time or, if not, how much the early parent must be delayed in date of planting. With a difference of 100 heat units, it is necessary to delay planting the early parent until 100 heat units have occurred.

The system is not infallible. In seasons when May temperatures are well above normal, the delay may require 10 to 20 percent more heat units than normal. Similarly, in cool seasons, the number of heat units required will be fewer than normal.

Seed fields usually are planted in alternating strips of two rows of the pollen parent and six rows of the seed parent. Extra pollen rows are planted on the sides of fields or across the ends, as may be needed for mechanical convenience (to make it easier to use machinery on odd-shaped fields, for example) or for border rows as protection against nearby corn.

DETASSELING of corn is the removal of the tassel from each plant of the female seed parent at the proper stage of growth but before pollen is produced. The tassel on an individual plant may be pulled during a period of 6 to 18 hours. Because plants differ in time of tasseling, however, the time in which a field is detasseled may be from 5 to 10 days.

Crews must patrol each row four to seven times during the season and must go over the fields every 24 to 48 hours. The workers walk or ride through the field. They remove the tassel by a gentle upward pull and drop it to the ground. This procedure does not reduce the grain yield very much.

Detasseling crews often include girls, women, and boys who are available for part-time summer work. Adults are sometimes hired on a contract arrangement that allows them to detassel on a piecework basis. They get higher hourly wages than the younger workers.

Standards for detasseling vary somewhat by producer and by State certification agencies. In general, detasseling must be done so that not more than 1 percent of the tassels are shedding pollen in any one day. The total cumulative shedding for any three inspections must not exceed 2 percent. These tolerances are met without difficulty, except in bad weather.

Heat units are used in estimating the acreage that may require detasseling on any given date. The projection of date of flowering, using heat-unit data, thus gives the detasseling date for each field and an acreage total by date, even though fields were planted at different times and the hybrids vary in heat units they require for flowering. Such estimates are approximate. The heat-unit differences among varieties are sufficiently consistent so that the projection of acreage by varieties from the planting date base will give good estimates of acreage to detassel on succeeding dates during the season. The number of heat units required differs between seasons, but adjustments for this variation from normal can be made at intervals before the detasseling season so that the accuracy of estimates increases with the season.

THE USE of male-sterile seed parents avoids some detasseling of corn.

Plant breeders have developed special strains of inbred lines in corn and sorghum in which the male flower does not develop normally and does not produce pollen. With a double cross, as is common in corn, the female (or ear seed parent) also can be male sterile. Thus a male-sterile female seed parent grown in alternating rows with a normal male-fertile line of corn as a source of pollen will cross naturally and produce hybrid seed on the rows of male-sterile type.

Some strains of corn do not produce pollen because of inhibiting factors in the cytoplasm—the protoplasm, exclusive of the nucleus. The cytoplasmic-sterile factor is bred into the seed-parent inbred line of the seed-parent single cross. This single cross cannot produce pollen. When the sterility-inducing cytoplasm is introduced into some lines, it is necessary also to breed out genes that can counteract the sterility. The breeding and testing techniques for making seed by the cytoplasmic-sterile method are complex.

Cytoplasmic-sterile female corn that is crossed with the normal male produces double-cross hybrids that are essentially the same as those produced by detasseling methods, except there may be sterility in the double-cross plants in the farmers' fields.

The cytoplasmic-sterile method involves planting part of the seed-parent acreage to the normal parent, which requires detasseling, and part to the cytoplasmic-sterile parent, which does not require detasseling, and then effecting a satisfactory blend of the seed from two female types.

The blend may be made by growing the corn in separate fields, sizing— screen separations according to width, thickness, and length of kernel—the lots separately, and making a known blend of the different sizes. This method usually is more expensive, and it requires additional facilities. More commonly, the seed field is planted in alternating strips of about 12 rows of the regular seed parent and 12 rows of the cytoplasmic-sterile seed parent when the field blend is to be made on a half-and-half basis.

A modification of the male-sterile method may make unnecessary the blending with nonsterile seed and thus eliminate detasseling in the production of certain corn hybrids.

This method involves the planting of all rows of seed parent to the cytoplasmic-sterile type and the use of restorer lines in the male. The restorer line restores fertility and causes the seed sold to farmers to produce pollen. The method has considerable promise, but more investigation is needed to produce good lines that also have appropriate cytoplasmic-sterile and restorer characteristics.

Ear corn from seed fields is harvested and dried on the ear to 12-percent moisture before shelling. Harvest begins at 30- to 35-percent moisture in the grain, when the plant has attained physiological maturity and maximum production of dry matter in the grain.

Harvest may begin at 40-percent moisture in cool, slow seasons to reduce the chances that part of the crop may be damaged in germination from severe early freezes. Four to 8 hours of exposure to temperatures of 25° to 28° may reduce germination of seed containing more than 30 percent of moisture. Slow maturity in the fall usually occurs in years with abnormally low temperatures in June.

Small amounts of seed corn are harvested with combines or picker-shellers at a 12-percent moisture level in some places like the Central Valley in California and parts of the South.

Drying facilities for ear corn make early harvest possible and enhance the quality of the seed by avoiding damage from freezing, reducing insect damage, and arresting the development of ear rot organisms. Early harvest avoids picker losses of 5 to 7 bushels an acre, compared to harvest at low moistures safe for cribbing.

The seed fields are harvested with mounted two-row cornpickers modified by removing the pegs from snapper and husker rolls, releasing the pressure on ear-retarding units at the husker rolls, and driving squarely on the row at slow speed. With these precautions, corn of high moisture can be harvested without serious damage to the kernels at the butt end of the ears.

Special facilities for handling seed corn have been built throughout the Corn Belt. The crop is received from the seed fields at harvest. Drying, sizing, cleaning, and preparation for delivery to the customer follow. The facilities may cost 200 thousand dollars.

A small plant may have a drying building of four or more bins that hold 5 thousand bushels of ear corn at one fill. Its air blowers and furnace are big enough to dry this quantity. Plants that have drying capacities of 15 thousand to 30 thousand bushels are common.

The plants are equipped with conveyors, elevators, storage bins, warehouses, cleaning machines, and handling facilities so as to provide a continuous operation. As harvest progresses, the drying bins are filled five to seven times in one season.

The operations before drying are picking, trucking, and unloading; taking samples; and running the corn over huskers to remove husks, silks, and trash and over sorting belts to remove offtype and moldy ears. High-moisture ears may be removed, especially if there has been a freeze of 28°.

Corn must be harvested from the field no faster than it can be dried at the plant. Intermediate storage is not possible, because the germination of ear corn of high moisture may be reduced by heating if it is held in bulk without ventilation. There is no damage if drying starts within 24 hours after picking in the field.

Shelling, sizing, and cleaning are done with equipment supplied by manufacturers who service the industry. Shellers, elevators, and conveyors are operated at slow speeds to reduce damage from mechanical handling. Bins are shallow. Devices are used to reduce abrasion as the grain is dropped into bins. Such care is necessary because seeds damaged mechanically may give a weak germination if extremely wet, cold soil conditions prevail in the spring.

Modern plants provide good storage facilities. Seed stored in bulk bins are aerated properly to prevent migration of moisture and the development of mold during storage.

Large warehouses are required once the finished seed is put in bags. Some warehouses are air cooled for summer storage so that the maximum temperature is 50° and relative humidity is 55 percent.

Because tonnages are large, mechanical handling methods are used. Some plants use fork trucks for transporting boxes of bulk grain and transporting and warehousing bagged seed on pallets.

Equipment for sizing and cleaning

requires an investment about equal to that required for drying facilities. Sizing and cleaning usually begin as soon as shelled corn is available after drying and is completed in February, so that the seed can be distributed for spring planting.

The kernels are sized according to width and thickness to give uniform sizes that will fit the cells of planter plates. Special machines are used to remove the short kernels—length sizing—so that the seed will be more attractive and planting will be more accurate. Grade is often taken to mean the same as size, but there is little difference in productivity of seeds of different sizes.

Gravity cleaners, which separate corn according to weight, use a combination of vibration and air flotation to remove cracked, moldy kernels and light kernels. Special aspirators are used if air cleaning is sufficient.

Fungicides are added to protect the seed against various micro-organisms in the soil, which may cause seed rot during cold, wet weather. Fungicides in use for corn and grain sorghum are almost exclusively organic fungicides. Thiram or captan is their active ingredient.

Producers seldom add insecticides to corn seed. A few apply dieldrin to the seed to give protection against insects like the seed-corn maggot and grape colaspis and partial protection against wireworms.

A commoner practice is for the farmer to add an insecticide to the seed at planting time. Some insecticides must be added only at planting time because seed is damaged by prolonged contact with them or because they lose their effectiveness after several months. Methoxychlor or malathion is added sometimes to the fungicide to give protection against insects in storage.

A cold-test germination technique has been developed as a measure of quality in corn seed. The seed is placed in soil for 6 to 8 days at temperatures of about 50°. The samples then are transferred to warm chambers for germination. The test approximates damage to seed during cold, wet field conditions. As it is a biological test and conditions cannot be fully standardized, it is not suitable as a legal requirement. There is a high correlation between field stands under cold, wet conditions and such tests.

GRAIN SORGHUM seed fields require isolation from other sorghum. Isolation needs to be a minimum of 40 rods from other types of grain sorghum and 60 rods or more (usually 1 mile) from forage sorghums, hegari, sudangrass, and broomcorn.

Extra pollen rows often are planted along the sides of the field, but the separation from other fields is not reduced. Volunteer plants or outcrosses of forage types must be removed if they occur in nearby fields of grain sorghum, since distance requirements for forage types are more than for the grain types.

Because dwarf types of grain sorghum carry recessive genes for height, effective isolation is necessary to give seeds free of tall outcrosses. Broomcorn, sudangrass, sorghum almum, forage sorghums, silage sorghums, and certain grain sorghum varieties, as hegari, therefore are serious sources of contamination, and seed fields should be separated as far as possible from them. Outcrosses to some of these crops also have unwanted brown seeds.

Johnsongrass will cross with grain sorghum occasionally. Such outcrosses are particularly conspicuous and objectionable. Special isolation is essential where johnsongrass occurs. An isolation distance of one-half mile or more is desirable.

Seed of grain sorghum must be produced on land where sorghum did not grow the preceding year—some growers prefer 2 years to assure against volunteer offtype plants in the field.

A sorghum occurring as weed patches in many fields, especially in parts of Kansas, is identified variously as "chicken corn" or wild sorghum or

Sorghum drummondii. It is taller than grain sorghum and has black heads because of the dark color of the glume. Seed must not be grown on or near badly infested fields.

Weeds must be controlled in seed fields so that weed seed will not be harvested with the grain. Seed cleaning, however, removes most weed seeds except those of johnsongrass, bindweed, morning-glory, and some others.

Standards of purity provide that no seeds of noxious weeds and not more than 0.05 percent of common weeds be present.

The production of hybrid seed of grain sorghum utilizes a cytoplasmic male-sterile female or seed parent and a restorer line as the male or pollen parent. Thus none of the heads in the female rows should produce pollen.

The rows require patrolling to remove any plants with heads showing fertility. Grain sorghum flowers are complete, and normally about 90 percent are self-fertilized.

Because detasseling, as with corn, is not possible in grain sorghum, a male-sterile method is required to produce hybrids of grain sorghum.

A genetic-sterile method was used to produce the first commercial seed of the hybrids distributed in 1956, but it was discontinued.

Hybrids of grain sorghum are of such recent origin that many seed-production practices still are not proved. Practices that were considered all right in 1961 very likely will be improved with increasing specialization in the production of more expensive seed. Longer experience may reveal that particular sections and techniques produce seed of better quality.

Locality is important. Northern areas, such as Nebraska, South Dakota, and Iowa and parts of Missouri and Kansas where johnsongrass is not common, have little difficulty in producing seed free from outcrosses to johnsongrass or sorghum almum types. Where the growing season is short, as in Nebraska, Iowa, and South Dakota, however, the seed must be early in maturity and harvested early in the fall to avoid frost damage.

Irrigated land is the most suitable for seed production, because ample soil moisture insures uninterrupted growth, maximum yields, and a minimum of pollen production in the male-sterile parent. Furthermore, harvest may be hastened, and fields may mature more uniformly because irrigation can be stopped at the proper time.

Weathering and discoloration of sorghum seed and sprouting in the head are hazards, especially in the more humid areas. Germination in the head may occur during damp autumn weather. Production in regions of high risk of frost damage may require a harvest method in which the heads are removed from the plants and dried in large driers, much as the ears of corn are removed from the plants and dried.

Production of sorghum seed in the Southwest has advantages: A long, frost-free season; low humidity at harvesttime; high yields and large seeds; harvesting with combines; the need to dry only in certain seasons; nearness to the market; and low seed costs.

The greatest hazard in southern localities is outcrossing with johnsongrass, sorghum almum, or forage types. Care in selecting isolated fields in places with a minimum of offtype sorghums can insure pure seed.

Seed set is more difficult in sorghum seed than in corn. The sorghum plant is sensitive to changes in heat, moisture, and length of day.

Kafirs react differently from milos. Seed fields with good seed set usually give seed that is low in outcrosses.

The planting of 4 rows of the pollen parent alternating with 12 rows of the seed parent is most convenient mechanically, although the 2-and-6 combination is followed in southwestern Iowa.

With the 4-and-12 combination, a 4-row planter can be used where the parents are planted on different dates. A self-propelled combine can gather readily the four rows of the pollen parent before the seed crop is harvested.

The proper timing of planting parents with different flowering dates sometimes is difficult. Low frequency of outcrosses is expected when the parents nick at flowering and a large part of the female florets are pollinated in a few days.

Hybrids requiring different planting dates for the parents need increased isolation and careful attention at planting time. Extra pollen rows around the field may improve seed set, especially at the ends and on the side of prevailing winds.

When seed set is low and temperature and humidity are favorable, the female florets may remain fertile for a long period after the male-row pollen has been shed. The risk of outcrossing then is high. This risk is greatest with adequate rain and mild temperatures.

We need some method whereby we can end the period during which the stigmas in the female florets are receptive to pollen.

In roguing seed fields of grain sorghum to remove offtype or undesirable plants, it is necessary to pull up the entire plant instead of merely removing the heads, because late tillers and side branches may flower and produce seed. In irrigated fields or in humid areas, precautionary measures are necessary to prevent uprooted plants from again taking root in the moist soil.

Both pollen rows and seed rows are rogued carefully. The male requires special care to reduce the amounts of undesirable pollen in the field. In female rows, fertile and offtype plants must be removed before they shed pollen.

Offtype plants may differ from the majority in such traits as height, head type, color of anthers and plants, and presence or absence of awns.

Most dwarf types tend to produce mutants toward tallness in ratios of about 1 to 1,000 plants. They are removed as offtype. Plant breeders have started work to develop types without tall mutants.

Plants that show evidence of pollen fertility in the cytoplasmic-sterile parent are removed as the anthers emerge. Some pollen is shed, because the anthers must emerge before the plants can be identified. Frequent patrolling of the rows during pollinating time therefore is necessary to reduce self-pollination, which would produce non-hybrid seed, which yields less than hybrid seed and sometimes gives offtype plants in the farmers' fields.

Certification standards for tolerances on fieldwork vary. An example: The maximum tolerance is not more than 1 definitely offtype plant per 2 acres; not more than 10 doubtful offtype plants per acre; no head smut; not more than 1 head in 100 with kernel smut; and no uncontrolled areas of field bindweed, hoarycress, Russian-knapweed, or johnsongrass. If field inspection shows evidence of hedge bindweed, morning-glory, or velvetleaf, special measures must be taken in connection with inspection of the grain.

Most producers of hybrid seed have followed a practice of making special harvests from their seed fields during October to get representative samples of seed for planting in winter observation plots in Mexico, Florida, Jamaica, or southern Texas. Such winter plantings usually mature sufficiently to determine purity before the seed is to be sold. The seedsman thus can withhold undesirable lots.

MOST SEED of grain sorghum is combined at moisture levels of 13 percent and less. Drying therefore is not needed. Aeration may be needed in some areas if such combined seed is stored in bulk.

Some seed is harvested at 16- to 18-percent moisture and then dried to a maximum moisture content of 12 percent in batch or continuous-flow driers.

An important consideration in determining the maximum air temperature for drying seed is the time required for drying, because it determines the length of time the seed remains in contact with heated air.

A maximum air temperature of 95° is recommended for drying deep depths (3 to 6 feet) of seed of 16- to 18-percent moisture. In tests in Texas, an air temperature of 120°, with the seed exposed to the heated air for 2.5 hours, was not injurious to the germination of seed dried in thin columns 10 inches thick. A maximum air temperature of 110° is normally recommended.

Even though seed is cooled as a part of the heated-air drying operation, the temperature of the seed is usually above normal when it is placed in storage. It should be stored in bags therefore, or some provision should be made to cool seed after it is stored in bulk. A practical and economical method of doing this is with an aeration system that uses a motor-driven fan to move small amounts, one-tenth to 1 cubic foot of air per bushel a minute, of air through the stored seed.

Another procedure is to harvest heads at moisture levels of 25 percent in the grain, dry with air at a temperature of 110°, and thresh with a reduced number of concaves in the thresher.

Sizing and cleaning seed of grain sorghum requires less equipment than for corn, because the small seed does not require sizing. The necessary operations include scalping, to remove large grains; screening out the extremely small grains; and screening and air cleaning to remove weed seeds. The clean product is given fungicide protection (with thiram or captan) and then weighed and packaged in 50-pound bags, ready for delivery.

JOHN M. AIRY *is the production manager of Pioneer Hi-Bred Corn Co., Des Moines, Iowa. He has had experience in producing seed of hybrid corn and sorghum and has conducted research on many problems.*

L. A. TATUM *is Chief of the Cereal Crops Research Branch, Crops Research Division, Agricultural Research Service, Beltsville, Md. He has done research with cereal crops.*

J. W. SORENSON, JR., *is professor of agricultural engineering at Texas Agricultural and Mechanical College, College Station, Tex. He has conducted research on engineering problems encountered in harvesting, drying, and storing field crops.*

Seeds of Oats, Barley, Wheat, and Rice

HARLAND STEVENS AND JOHN R. GOSS

THE GOOD farming practices that are needed for a successful cereal crop are the same whether the crop is grown for feed or seed.

The seeds of small-grained cereals can be produced on nearly all soil types that are well drained and relatively productive.

All cereals yield more seed if they are planted in a well-prepared seedbed that has 2 or 3 inches of mellow surface soil. The surface should be slightly rough to guard against soil movement by water or wind. A good seedbed will help the young plants to emerge promptly and vigorously and compete with weeds. Oats make good growth with less preparation of soil than wheat, barley, and rice.

The first step in the successful production of cereal seed is careful selection of the seeds to be planted. Unadapted seed can be expensive to the farmer.

Carelessness in selecting seeds may mean that the oat field is full of wild oats, a field of winter wheat contains much rye, red rice comes up in a cultivated rice field, or noxious weeds abound in a planting of any of the small cereals.

The production of seeds of small cereals for farmers or seed producers in other areas is not a large enterprise. It is usually a specialty of occasional growers, who are the only ones who should grow a variety not adapted to their own sections. Most growers grow seed adapted to the area in which they are grown.

In some seasons of bad weather or

sudden changes in crop acreages, sizable amounts of seed are moved into areas of short supply.

Spring wheat and barley survive in the mild winter climates of the Deep South and the Pacific coast, but plantings in the fall under more rigorous climatic conditions generally end in a poor crop or none.

The hardier winter wheats and barley, if spring planted, will not head or will produce low yields. The buyer must know the variety he buys and its adaptation.

A REGULAR seed producer should plant only adapted varieties, certified to be true to variety and free of noxious weeds and disease. Because the cost of producing seed is much more than the cost of producing cereal grains for feed or food, a grower of seed must plant the best seed he can get. If he grows a crop to maturity and it then fails to meet seed standards, he may realize only the actual cost of production.

Seed should always be treated with a fungicide to guard against smut and other seedborne diseases. Where loose smut is a problem in wheat or barley, only smut-free seed should be used unless the producer has access to equipment for adequate treatment with hot water.

The most reliable source of seed is the certified, registered, or foundation seed recommended and labeled by the experiment station or crop improvement association of the grower's area.

The income per acre from cereals grown for seed is considerably higher than that of those grown for grain and will more than compensate the grower for the extra labor and the higher cost of production.

CEREALS should follow a cultivated crop whenever possible, because that helps to control weeds. Cereals planted for seed should never be planted on land containing noxious weeds. Since it is impossible to clean a field contaminated with mixture of other cereals by roguing, such crop rotation as will leave the fields free of that type of volunteer is imperative.

Little cross-pollination occurs in cereal crops, and isolation is not necessary, but there must be an alleyway between two crops wide enough to enable harvesting without mixture.

In the eastern, southeastern, and Corn Belt areas, it is quite easy to grow any one of the spring cereals immediately following a cultivated row crop. Oats are commonly planted in the Corn Belt the season following a crop of corn.

In sections where winter barley and oats are raised, either may follow cotton. If the winter cereals are to follow a cover crop of lespedeza or other legumes, the field should be plowed at least a month before seeding time for the development of a firm seedbed. Disking or other shallow cultivation is needed to complete preparation of the seedbed.

In the drier parts of the Great Plains, to produce a seed crop of winter wheat without mixtures of volunteer small grains requires planting on land on which grass or a legume crop has been grown.

If spring cereals have to be planted following a summer fallow, a satisfactory crop usually can be produced by a spring cultivation late enough to destroy volunteer grain and weed seedlings before planting.

Wherever corn or sorghum are grown and harvested for ensilage, winter wheat can be seeded without danger of serious mixtures. Summer fallowing is usual every other year in the western sections and the drylands of the Great Plains.

Seed production of cereals usually follows a row crop in the Southwestern States. Two crops of the same species of cereal should not follow one another in the production of seed, except when a certified variety is grown on a field that was used the preceding year to produce certified, registered, or foundation seed of that same variety.

Successful yields have been had in many sections by planting in rows spaced far enough apart to allow cultivation. That practice may be used if unfavorable weather makes it necessary to plant a cereal crop on land that will be quite weedy.

A GOOD METHOD of weed control is through crop rotation and cultivation. If the land is known to contain quite a lot of seeds of any weeds—as often happens following a noncultivated legume crop—cultivation shortly before planting usually destroys enough of the germinated weed seeds to allow the grain to germinate and grow fast enough to control the situation.

It is good farming practice to control weeds in fence rows, turn rows, levees in irrigated fields, and other places where there is little or no plant competition. If an unavoidable condition lets a heavy stand of small weeds germinate and emerge at about the time the grain does, working the field with a rotary hoe or a spike-tooth harrow sometimes helps.

If cereals are planted without being used as a companion crop to legumes or grass, fields can be sprayed with 2,4-D or other chemical sprays for killing weeds. This should be done just before the crop is in the boot stage, which is just before the stems elongate and expose nodes. Because oats and rice are more susceptible to damage after the seed heads start to emerge from the boot, the time of application is extremely important.

If a field of cereals has many large weeds at maturity, spraying with 2,4-D will dry the weeds so that the crop can be combined and stored without damage from excessive moisture. Good farm practices are better than chemicals for the control of weeds.

The grower of cereals is familiar with the recommended rates, dates, and depths of seeding for his area and their modification for his use.

It is quite handy, however, to have a simple method of checking the rate of seeding of his drill: Put the drill in gear and drive a short distance on hard ground. Seeding rate for oats at one-fourth bushel per acre at spacings of 6, 7, or 8 inches will be 1.2, 1.4, and 1.6 kernels per foot, respectively. Wheat will be 2.0, 2.3, and 2.7 per foot. Barley will be 1.7, 2.0, and 2.3 per foot. For example, if 2 bushels of oats are considered a correct seeding rate in a 6-inch drill, there should be 7.2 kernels per foot, which would show a correct calibration.

When cereals are grown under irrigation, soil moisture should be sufficient at seeding time so that the growth will shade the ground by the time of the first irrigation.

SEEDING CEREALS with a grain drill is the most satisfactory method of planting for seed production. It assures a uniform seeding at the proper depth. It puts the seed in moist ground, assures uniform emergence of good stands, and gives the crop a good start in the competition with weeds.

The grower should have some equipment with which to clean a drillbox thoroughly between varieties of cereals planted for seed. A vacuum cleaner may be the easiest to use. Cleaning can be done by running the drill until the seedbox is practically empty and then blowing out the last few kernels from each cup with compressed air. That can be done with a small hand bellows.

If it is suspected that the last crop seeded by a drill contained smut-infected seed, it may be advisable to wash the drill with a solution of a seed-disinfectant chemical.

The drill most commonly used in the United States is the single disk drill with row spacings of 6, 7, or 8 inches.

A hoe-type opener with spring release is sometimes used on rocky land in place of the disk opener. When seeding cereals for seed production with this type of drill, a good practice is to close one or two of the center drill cups in order to facilitate roguing of mixtures from the field.

A GOOD CROP rotation is necessary in all areas for maximum production of seed or grain.

Excellent yields of wheat for food and feed have been produced on well-fertilized land planted to a wheat crop for 3 years. The grower of seed, however, cannot plant wheat or other cereals more than 1 year in succession.

How much fertilizer to apply on cereal crops depends on the soil and the rotation system. The producer of cereal seeds is concerned with fertilizer, as it influences the total yield and viability. Barnyard manure or commercial fertilizers usually are more profitable when they are applied to a high-income crop in a rotation.

If the cropping system involves only cereals or one cereal and fallow, barnyard manure must be applied at least one season ahead of the planting for seed production so that weed or other cereal seeds can be destroyed before the seed crop is planted.

There is little evidence that the various forms of fertilizer show significant differences in yields. The farmer therefore should buy the form that is most economical and feasible for him to use. In many instances he can apply the fertilizer with a fertilizer attachment to his grain drill and thus save the cost of a separate operation.

As the total income anticipated per acre for seed is more than that of grain for other commercial purposes, slightly higher rates of fertilizer may sometimes be justified.

Cereal crops grown in areas of high rainfall or under irrigation can profitably utilize heavy applications of commercial fertilizer.

Rates of nitrogen fertilizer as high as 120 pounds of actual nitrogen to the acre have given profitable yield increases on new soils of low fertility where ample water was available.

Cereal crops planted following sorghum require considerably higher rates of fertilizer than when they follow corn. Grass seed fields leave an unusually heavy root crown residue and require exceptionally high applications of nitrogen to aid the decay of the residue and leave enough nitrogen for a crop. If the preceding crop is a broad-leaved plant and has been heavily fertilized, high yields of cereals can be produced with the fertilizer carryover.

Wheat will utilize more nitrogen fertilizer than barley, oats, and rice. When cool weather follows planting of small cereals, 20 to 30 pounds of actual nitrogen plus phosphate are recommended to carry through a period when plant nutrients are not readily available.

Accurate dates and rates of application are available from experiment stations and extension services.

THE FIRST TIME a seedgrower starts a roguing crew in the field he will become aware of the value of leaving a walkway in the field from which they can operate.

Seldom are single-tillered plants produced in seed production. The primary tiller invariably heads earlier and grows taller than secondary tillers. A roguing crew should be trained to examine carefully and remove the complete plant, because the later tillers will not grow tall enough to be easily observed.

There are three periods when mixtures can be observed more readily than at others: When the head or panicle is just emerging from the boot (mixtures of earlier maturing grains are easily recognized); when plants are just headed and before lodging is likely (offtypes, particularly bearded cereals, are easily recognized); and when a field is mature (mixtures of differences in color or head position, such as curved neck, can be spotted and taken out if lodging is not serious).

Many seedgrowers find it advisable to have the roguers just ahead of the harvesting equipment where mixtures can be observed readily and are easy to get at.

Walking through a ripe grainfield, even though walkways or alleys have been provided, is difficult and destroys a considerable amount of grain by shattering.

Practically never is it possible to grow a cereal crop for seed without roguing the mixtures of offtypes or other cereal contaminants. When the cereal has been planted in rows of 12 inches or more apart, roguing often can be done without walkways.

HARVESTING the seeds is as important as raising the crop.

Improper methods and poor adjustment and operation of harvesting equipment can result in contamination of the seed, excessive losses, and low germination.

Only a small acreage of grain now is harvested with a binder and threshed with a stationary threshing machine. The combine has taken their place.

Collected samples of cereals for storage experiments show practically all seeds to have a quite high count of organisms on the surface. When grain is stored with a moisture content above 12 percent, the air is often humid enough in a sizable pile of grain to start most organisms to grow. This growth will tend to create a considerable rise in temperature and, if the bin is not carefully checked, may mean serious damage to the germination of the stored seed crop. If a careful check shows a rise in temperature, it may be well to remove the grain from the bin and run it through a cleaning mill before putting it back.

Unless adequate drying equipment is available, seed grain should not be threshed until it can be stored safely at a moisture content near 12 percent.

If grain is combined directly from the field and a device for testing moisture is not at hand, moisture can be estimated in the following way: Barley should be ripe and dry enough that kernels bitten with the teeth will snap and appear chalky inside. Oats are ready to combine 7 days after they first appear to be dry and ripe. Wheat can be tested by grasping the base of the head between the finger and thumb of one hand, placing the point of the head against the palm of the other hand, bending it slightly, and rotating it rapidly. At least three-fourths of the heads tested should shell out.

The moisture content of standing rice usually is tested by devices to determine when to begin harvesting milling rice. The same practice should be followed for harvesting fields of rice seed.

Considerable experimental evidence indicates that when rice and small grains are cut or threshed at contents of moisture of seed greater than 20 percent, there is a reduction in the percentage of seed that will germinate.

Men at the Texas Agricultural Experiment Station recommend that seed rice be harvested when the moisture content is 18 percent or less.

WHEAT SHOULD NOT be harvested above a kernel moisture of 20 percent in order to maintain a high germination. This is a recommendation of William H. Johnson, of the Ohio Agricultural Experiment Station, after 3 years of experiments on the combine harvesting of wheat. The same recommendation applies to the harvesting of barley and oats for seed.

When it is necessary to dry a seed crop artificially, the temperature of the drying air should not be greater than 110° F. The independent relation between relative humidity of the drying air and the reduction in germination in small grains has not been established. It is known, however, that the loss of germination tends to increase as air of lower humidity is used to dry the grain.

THE POSSIBILITY of contamination of the harvested seed with other crop and weed seeds can be greatly reduced by thoroughly cleaning all seeding, harvesting, and seed-handling equipment before seeding or harvesting operations are started.

A portable source of compressed air is helpful in cleaning seeding equipment, combine harvesters, stationary threshers, grain elevators, binders, and windrowers.

Seeder or drill boxes and their seed metering units, as well as the tubes and boots, must be cleaned thoroughly to remove seeds of other crops before planting the seed field. All sieve and canvas drapers should be removed from the harvesting machinery and cleaned.

Opening inspection doors and elevator boots and running each piece of machinery empty at rated speed is helpful in removing seed lodged in and around moving parts.

The equipment can be washed with water when compressed air is not available. Attention must be given to the lubrication of bearings immediately after washing.

The seedgrower should always have a copy of the operator's manual for his make and model of combine or stationary thresher. His machinery dealer should be able to supply it. The operator must understand the operation and adjustment of the machine if he expects to harvest the maximum amount of high-quality seed.

The germinating quality of harvested seed is closely related to the amount of cracked, broken, and internally damaged seed. Cylinder speed is normally the main cause of this type of damage. The use of grain blowers to handle the harvested seed also is a factor.

THE ACCOMPANYING table lists a range of cylinder speeds and concave adjustments that will give adequate threshing without excessive damage to the seed.

The peripheral speed of the cylinder depends on the cylinder diameter and cylinder shaft speed. The larger the cylinder, the slower the shaft needs to turn for a given peripheral speed.

When the cylinder speed is given in feet per minute, the required cylinder r.p.m. (revolutions per minute) can be computed by dividing the cylinder peripheral speed by the product of 3.14 times the cylinder diameter in feet.

THE GERMINATING quality of the harvested seed can also be seriously reduced by grain blowers. That is a result of the same type of damage that is caused by excessive cylinder speed. The impeller shaft speed of the grain blower should be checked and adjusted, if necessary, to the speed recommended by the manufacturer for the particular application.

Feeding the grain blower at considerably lower than the rated handling rates can also result in damage to the grain even when the blower is operated at the proper speed.

The speed of the cylinder and the clearance between the cylinder and concave bars (or the number of rows of teeth in the concave and the overlap between cylinder and concave teeth) should be such that an occasional seed remains in the head and there is little cracked grain in the seed when it is harvested.

The open, bar-type, concave grate should be open to allow maximum separation of seed from the straw at the concave—except when harvesting a seed crop that is difficult to thresh and the straw breaks up badly. Then part or all of the grate should be closed to reduce the amount of chaff going over the shoe as well as increase the threshing action of the cylinder.

INCREASING the cylinder speed or overlap between the cylinder and concave teeth, reducing the clearance between bar-type cylinders and con-

Crop	Cylinder speed, f.p.m. (feet per minute)	Cylinder-concave clearance (inch)	Rows of teeth in concave
Barley (6-row varieties)	4,800 to 5,600	¼ to ½	2 to 4
Barley (2-row varieties)	3,200 to 4,000	¼ to ½	2 to 4
Wheat	4,500 to 5,500	⅜ to ⅝	2 to 4
Oats	5,000 to 6,000	¼ to ⅝	2 to 4
Rice	3,800 to 4,800	¼ to ⅝	3 to 6

caves, or increasing the number of teeth in the concave will all increase the amount of threshing.

An increase in cylinder speed, however, will increase rapidly the amount of damaged seed, even if there is adequate clearance for the seeds in the cylinder.

Increasing the number of teeth in the concave or reducing the cylinder concave clearance generally will not noticeably increase the amount of seed damage until the minimum clearance is about the same as the largest dimension of the seed.

Spike-tooth cylinder teeth should be centered on the concave teeth, and worn cylinder bars or bent concaves should be replaced, so that a uniform clearance is maintained between the cylinder and concave bars.

Better bearding of varieties that have suffered from hot weather or lack of moisture during the seed-forming period can be accomplished by reducing the clean grain sieve opening and thereby returning a high percentage of the seed to the cylinder for re-threshing.

THE COST and time spent in growing and harvesting a seed crop make it quite expensive. It would be foolish to ruin it by using poor equipment to unload it into granaries.

A wind elevator operated with too much pressure can cause enough mechanical injury to make the crop worthless for seed purposes. Damage also may result if auger equipment is run at excessive speeds. The operation of such equipment should be thoroughly checked. A trial run should be made before they are used.

HARLAND STEVENS, *an agronomist engaged in cereal research, Cereal Crops Research Branch, Agricultural Research Service, has been stationed at the Branch Experiment Station, Aberdeen, Idaho, since 1931.*

JOHN R. GOSS *is an agricultural engineer in the Agricultural Engineering Department, University of California, Davis.*

Our Sources of Seeds of Grasses and Legumes

HUGO O. GRAUMANN

SEVERAL hundred varieties of grasses and legumes comprising more than 125 species have economic importance in the United States.

They differ in performance and in their requirements as to soil and climate. At least one variety is adapted to each use and to each particular site or location. Grasses and legumes therefore are an important part of the cropping system on nearly every farm.

Permanent stands of grasslands, including hayland, pastures, and ranges, comprise about a billion acres in the United States.

The various species are grouped as perennials, biennials, and summer and winter annuals. The longer lived species generally have the widest range.

Alfalfa is most widely grown of all cultivated forage species, primarily because of the success of plant breeders in developing numerous varieties that differ markedly in growth response, cold endurance, and persistence.

We estimate that 8 to 10 percent of our grasslands are planted each year to replace acreages on which either a grass crop has passed maturity or is plowed under as a phase of crop rotation. For replanting those acreages and seeding other land, nearly 1 billion pounds of seeds are needed annually.

A highly specialized seed-production industry is essential to assure domestic supplies of seed that have the specific superior genetic characters that differentiate the recommended varieties one from another.

Several developments have caused shifts in the regions of seed production.

Many meadows and hayfields that had been sources of seed of local strains of grasses and legumes were put under the plow in the war years and planted to cereal and feed grains. The mechanization of many farming operations and economic problems changed many agricultural practices. Specialization in corn, soybeans, wheat, and other cash crops grew. Soil conservation practices caused some shifts in the use of land. Increasing numbers of livestock meant that many of the remaining meadows once used for both forage and seed were set aside for pasture and hay only. The demand for forage seeds of improved varieties has grown.

Imports of legume and grass seed before 1930 were relatively large. For several years we imported annually 40 million pounds of alfalfa and red clover seed. One year we imported 11 million pounds of alsike clover.

At one time, practically all the bahiagrass used in the South was imported. Our need now for this species is met almost entirely with domestic seed of improved varieties, which are superior in winter hardiness, persistence, and yield.

The total imports of forage seeds has dropped since 1930, primarily because of substantial increases in the domestic production of seed. Nevertheless, relatively large amounts of seed of sweetclover, crimson clover, birdsfoot trefoil, fescue, and orchardgrass were imported from overseas in 1960.

Most of the grasses and legumes available to farmers before the Second World War were the result of importations or seed increases of locally adapted types selected from introduced or native materials. Varieties were uncommon. The production of grassland seed was a minor enterprise on many farms.

Local customs dictated most of the production practices. The preferred or best adapted crop usually was grown, primarily for forage and soil conservation; when the weather was favorable, a seed crop was produced and harvested from a meadow or hayfield.

In those instances where varieties existed, little effort was made to maintain foundation planting stock and to minimize the chances of genetic contamination from cross-pollination with other varieties growing nearby. The characteristics of ecotypes and varieties therefore kept undergoing change from one generation to another. This gave rise to an increasing number of local strains, which were superior to imported seed.

Whereas seed once was a byproduct, a trend started about 1948 to plant exclusively for seed production. Such enterprises, to be most profitable, must take close account of the requirements as to climate, soil, and management of the variety.

Winter annuals usually do best where winters are relatively mild.

Some summer annuals are adapted to the South and others to northern latitudes. A generally favorable climate for most perennial species is characterized by winter conditions with near-freezing to freezing temperatures at night; a relatively rain-free growing season of 180 to 200 days; and clear, sunshiny days, with optimum daytime temperatures during set and development of seed ranging from about 75° F. for the cool-season grasses to approximately 95° for most perennial legumes.

Pollinating insects, such as bees, are essential for most legumes. These insects are relatively inactive on cloudy days and at temperatures below 70°.

The length of day required for flower initiation varies among and within species. The cool-season grasses and northern-adapted alfalfas and clovers usually blossom most profusely and according to schedule in the more northern latitudes under conditions of low night temperatures in spring and long, warm or hot days in summer.

As these grasses and legumes are moved south (into regions of shorter days) for production of seeds, many plants in normal populations of given varieties are retarded in both initiation and profuseness of flowering, particularly if night temperatures in spring are not low enough to fulfill the variety prechilling requirements for flower initiation. The unwanted genetic shifts that result cause changes in the characteristics of a variety.

GREAT PROGRESS has been made in breeding improved grasses and legumes since 1940.

The development of new varieties with disease resistance and tolerance to a greater range of temperatures and improved management technology have permitted the extension of some species of legumes and grasses into new regions and soils previously unsuited to grassland agriculture.

The growing interest in grassland farming meant that the demand for forage seeds could no longer be met by the older methods of producing seed from hayfields. The total yield of seed had to be increased and greater care had to be taken to guard against genetic shifts caused by effects of daylength, temperature effects, and outcrossing to other varieties and sorts.

Seed production had to advance from a minor to major farm enterprise.

The success of such an enterprise rests on proper management—row planting with proper isolation of fields, timely irrigation, forcing plant growth to flower when temperatures are favorable, adequate control of insects and weeds, satisfactory pollination, and timely harvest. Farmers who were willing to make seed production a primary business achieved success.

Production shifted to new sections. Bluegrass, alfalfa, and the bentgrasses are examples.

Kentucky and parts of adjoining States before 1920 produced more than half of the seed of Kentucky bluegrass harvested in the United States. Insect damage to old fields and declining soil fertility caused a shift to Missouri, Iowa, Nebraska, South Dakota, and North Dakota, which in 1960 produced more than 80 percent of our seed of Kentucky bluegrass.

Frequent summer rains in the Corn

Belt and farther east, and sustained demand for hay were deterrents to the production of alfalfa seed. The primary sources of seed were the Great Plains and Intermountain regions, and until recently seed production was considered mostly a byproduct of hay production even in those sections. The production of alfalfa seed has mushroomed since 1945 in the West, where water for plant growth can be controlled by irrigation.

The bentgrasses once were important in pastures in the eastern New England States and later in turf plantings. For many years the seed was harvested in late summer from pastures that were grazed in spring and early summer. The seed, however, came to have so many weed seeds that bentgrass seed harvested from the established areas became unsuitable for lawn, golf courses, and other turf.

Similarly, bentgrass seed harvested from natural stands in the coastal sections of Oregon became unsatisfactory because of large numbers of seeds of other grasses and perennial weeds. Ergot and the nematodes, furthermore, caused sharp declines in yield and serious contamination of seed.

New seed fields therefore were established in inland irrigated valleys of Oregon. More than 90 percent of our bentgrass seed was grown in the noncoastal areas of Oregon in 1960.

The expansion of seed production in the West has doubled our output of alfalfa seed since 1945. Most of the expansion was in new irrigated seed-producing areas in the West, particularly in Washington and the Central Valley of California.

Just before the war, California, Oregon, and Washington produced less than 7 percent of our alfalfa seed; 15 years later, they produced well over 50 percent of the crop.

California alone produced more than 47 million pounds of certified Ranger alfalfa seed in 1955—about four-fifths of the annual production in the United States in 1930–1939.

Substantial amounts of seed of red

clover are still harvested from hay-fields and pastures in the eastern half of the country, but the dependable production of certified seed from new varieties now comes from the West.

Oregon and Idaho have produced a great deal of alsike clover since 1930. Total production of alsike seed declined by one-third since 1935, due largely to a drop in acreage and production in the Corn Belt, where the draining, liming, and fertilizing of wet and acid soils (which alsike clover likes) led farmers to shift to other, more productive forage crops.

Whiteclover seed is produced mainly in Wisconsin, Alabama, Mississippi, Louisiana, Idaho, and Oregon. The center of production of Ladino clover seed is California.

Oregon produced one-third of all crimson clover seed harvested in the United States in 1958–1959. The remaining two-thirds came from South Carolina, Georgia, Tennessee, Alabama, Mississippi, and Arkansas, where crimson clover is an important winter cover crop. We import sizable amounts of seed of crimson clover.

The production of lupine seed is confined to the Southeastern States, where the temperatures are favorable. The production of vetch seed is of economic importance in Arkansas, Oklahoma, Texas, California, Idaho, Oregon, and Washington. Austrian winter peas are produced in the Pacific Northwest. These winter annual legumes are grown for soil cover and green manure in the South Central and Southeastern States.

SOME EXPANSION of production of grass seed has occurred in regions outside the area where grass is used primarily for pasture, soil conservation, and turf, but the shift has been less pronounced.

Production of noncertified seed of orchardgrass has been centered in Kentucky, Virginia, and Missouri. Most of the certified seed of improved varieties of orchardgrass is grown in the West.

The western part of the Corn Belt continues to be the primary source of noncertified and certified bromegrass seed. A few other States have limited acreages of improved varieties of bromegrass for seed.

The production of timothy seed has declined since 1940. Most of it is harvested from pastures and meadows in the Corn Belt.

Nearly all redtop seed is harvested in Illinois and Missouri.

Production of red and chewings fescue is limited to Oregon, Washington, and Idaho. Tall fescue seed is produced primarily in Oregon, Kentucky, Tennessee, Missouri, South Carolina, Georgia, and Alabama.

The production and use of carpet-grass and dallisgrass seed in the Southeast has declined sharply since 1950 because of the vegetative plantings of more than 1 million acres of coastal bermudagrass and the growing popularity of improved varieties of bahia-grass, much of the seed of which we get from the Southern States.

Sudangrass, a summer annual forage grass, is grown in nearly all States. Its seed comes mainly from dryland or irrigated fields in the Southern Plains States westward to California.

Most pearl millet seed is produced under irrigation in New Mexico, Texas, and Arizona. It is used mainly in the Southeastern States.

The production of ryegrass seed is a highly specialized enterprise in Oregon.

Plantings of Merion bluegrass for seed are mostly in Oregon, Idaho, Washington, and California.

Crested wheatgrass and closely related species are best adapted to the northern Great Plains and Intermountain States to the west for the production of seed.

THE NATIVE GRASSES are well adapted to the Great Plains.

Until about 1950, most of the seed was harvested from wild stands, which usually included mixtures of species. Increasing acreages have been devoted since then to growing certified seed of more than 15 new varieties of 7 species. They are grown primarily in Nebraska, Kansas, Missouri, Oklahoma, Texas, Colorado, New Mexico, and California.

The primary values of grasses and legumes are for pasture and hay, soil conservation, and turf. Management for those uses usually precludes seed production. Management for both forage and seed production results in a costly and hazardous farm operation. Climatic conditions best suited for forage production and cropping practices conducive to good soil conservation often are unfavorable for the production of seeds.

Production of seed therefore has become specialized and has moved westward to places where the climate is more favorable for seed set, curing, and harvest.

Unlike some other crops, the seed of many improved grass and legume varieties is produced far from the areas of use. Along with this development, increasing numbers of grassland farmers in the Central States and East have found it good business to shift from byproduct seed production to more profitable crops and cropping practices.

These developments mean that the specialized grower will have to continue to be aware of the needs of those who buy and plant his seeds.

He needs to keep himself informed about changes in agricultural programs, new varieties, their adaptation and use, demands, seed-yielding capacity, safeguards in seed production, and the replacement of old varieties by the new.

HUGO O. GRAUMANN *is Chief of the Forage and Range Research Branch, Crops Research Division, Agricultural Research Service. He studied crop breeding at Oklahoma State University and the University of Nebraska. Dr. Graumann taught and did research at the former institution and began his research with the Agricultural Research Service at the latter university in cooperation with the Nebraska Agricultural Experiment Station.*

The Production of Grass Seeds

GEORGE A. ROGLER, HENRY H. RAMPTON, AND M. D. ATKINS

THE GROWERS of seed aim to grow good seed of species and varieties that are in demand and to achieve economical production.

They know that it is easier to grow clean seed than to clean it up after harvest, and that once the seed reaches maturity they can do little more to improve its innate quality.

The best seedgrowers are specialists. Seed production is their main farm enterprise. They have made many technological advances in the art of growing seeds.

Research workers, in studies of effects of environment and cultural practices on the life history of the grass plant, are changing this art into a science.

Some sections have become outstanding in the production of seeds because of conditions that favor low cost of production or a superior quality of seed or both.

Among the conditions are choice of crops; suitable soils; favorable growing seasons; ample supply of water; absence of objectionable weeds; warm, dry seasons for curing and harvesting seed; and the use of correct cultural and management practices.

Some seed is harvested from native grasslands, primarily in the Great Plains. The practice developed from the demand for seeds of the native grasses for converting croplands to grass and improving rangelands. Such seed harvests are sporadic. They occur only when seasonable moisture conditions are unusually favorable, but it is not uncommon to obtain several million pounds of seed annually in this way. No attempt is made to encourage development of seed by cultural or management practices.

Another source is the pastures of tame grass of the subhumid and humid areas of the Midwest, South, and East. They sometimes are fertilized and managed for seed production, but their primary use usually is for pasture or hay. A seed crop is taken when the seed appears to be more valuable than the forage.

A third source, the most dependable and the one we discuss in this chapter, is the grass crops grown primarily for seed.

Two BROAD GROUPS of grasses are based on their season of growth.

Cool-season grasses grow actively at cool temperatures, develop rapidly in the spring, are more or less dormant during periods of high temperature and drought in summer, and recover active growth in the fall.

Most of the perennials among them have good winter hardiness. They flourish in the northern half of the United States.

They include the fescues, wheatgrasses, bluegrasses, bromegrasses, orchardgrass, timothy, ryegrasses, bentgrasses, and redtop.

The seedgrowers of the Pacific Northwest and Intermountain regions give special attention to perennial and common ryegrass; red, chewings, and tall fescues; bentgrass; Kentucky bluegrass; orchardgrass; and several wheatgrasses.

The wheatgrasses, smooth brome, and Russian wildrye are grown in the northern Great Plains.

Warm-season grasses make their maximum growth during the summer.

They start spring growth about 3 weeks after cool-season grasses and cease growth with the first hard frost in the fall. They are predominant in the southern sections, where the long growing seasons have high temperatures and precipitation in summer.

Much seed is produced in the High Plains of western and southern Texas, and in western Oklahoma, Kansas, and Nebraska.

Some of the grasses in commercial production are buffelgrass, blue panicum, King Ranch bluestem, Caucasian bluestem, big sandbur, Arizona cottontop, plains bristlegrass, green sprangletop, sideoats grama, blue grama, little bluestem, sand bluestem, big bluestem, switchgrass, indiangrass, sand lovegrass, and bermudagrass.

THE ADAPTATION of a crop to its environment is reflected in its development and its yield of seed.

Warm-season grasses, for example, are not grown successfully in the Pacific Northwest, where the climate favors the cool-season grasses. Species and variety adaptation often is less limiting to the grower of grass seed than to the forage producer, however, because his crop is grass seed, which may be used elsewhere.

When seed is produced under special culture and management, environment often is less restrictive. Seed therefore may be produced in one area for use in another.

Quality is a watchword of the farmer who specializes in growing grass seed.

The factors that mean quality in the seed he plants and the product he sells usually rank so: Genetic or varietal purity (Is it true to type?); mechanical purity (Is it free from inseparable seeds of other crops and weeds that cannot be economically controlled in the field and from undue quantities of inert matter?); germination (Will the seed produce vigorous healthy seedlings?).

To attain those standards, the grower must plant seed stock of high quality. He must select land that is sufficiently isolated to minimize cross-pollination from other fields and is free from weeds and other crops that are highly competitive or have seeds that are inseparable from the sown crop.

Grasses vary in adaptability to different soil conditions, but all respond in seed yields to the soil factors that favor the complete development of plants.

The most important conditions are adequate depth of soil to permit abundant development of roots; favorable drainage and supply of moisture; aeration, nutrient-supplying ability, and tilth of soil; and topography.

THE SEEDBED should have the proper moisture, temperature, tilth, and fertility to stimulate germination, rapid emergence of seedlings, and quick establishment of the stand.

Methods of preparing the seedbed for sowing grass seeds vary with soil type, climate, time of sowing, kind of grass, and the grower.

A plowed, well-tilled, and firm seedbed usually is prepared just before the planting.

If fertilizer or soil amendments are used, they may be mixed into the soil or applied in bands with the seeding.

Seed fields often are established in the Great Plains in the standing stubble of the previous crop. The stubble helps to control blowing soil, catches snow, reduces evaporation, and provides a firm surface.

MAXIMUM SEED production of most grasses can best be attained with wide-spaced rows—24 inches or more apart. Exceptions are stoloniferous species, such as buffalograss and bermudagrass, and low-growing bunchgrasses, such as blue grama and perennial ryegrass.

Wide-spaced rows result in cleaner seed, higher yields, better control of weeds, more economical use of fertilizer, and longer productive life of stands. They also permit a lower seeding rate and the stretching of limited or high-priced stock seeds of new varieties.

Row culture affords better utilization of limited moisture. Under irrigation, row planting facilitates furrowing and gravity irrigation.

Most row spacings are 24 to 48 inches apart, depending on the seeding, cultural, and harvesting equipment available; type of grass; and the grower's preference.

Row spacings up to 84 inches have been used successfully for Russian wildrye in the northern Great Plains.

Perennial grasses usually yield more seed when sown at rates lower than the optimum for forage production. The most effective seeding rates vary, naturally, with size of the seed. The amount for cultivated rows is one-half pound to 4 pounds an acre, and 2 to 16 pounds for close drills (6 or 7 inches).

Rhizomatous, sod-forming perennial grasses, such as smooth brome and intermediate wheatgrass, present special problems in the control of the plant population because they are vigorous spreaders. This habit results in dense growth, which is known as sod binding, and a rapid decline in yields of seeds.

Sod binding often can be delayed and seed production of some sod-bound grass often can be restored by providing adequate nitrogen, postharvest burning, and reducing the plant population by mechanical renovation.

Annual grasses, such as common ryegrass and sudangrass, usually respond in yields to heavier sowing rates, or about the same as for forage production. When the soil moisture is limited, the seed fields of sudangrass often are sown at lower rates in rows.

A DRILL should be used for planting. It has several advantages. The rate of sowing can be controlled more accurately. The seed is distributed more evenly. Seed can be covered at a uniform depth. Seedings can be made in wide-spaced rows. Fertilizer attachments can be used to place the fertilizer in bands beside or below the seed.

The fluted feed grain drill, modified to sow at the desired intervals, is popular. Drills for beets or beans, corn planters, and shop-built seeders frequently are used for sowing rows and are superior to a grain drill.

Many seedgrowers in the southern

Great Plains use a specially built, two-row, tractor-mounted planter.

It is equipped with cotton boxes (for light, trashy, or awned seed) and vegetable boxes (for small, free-flowing seed). It has double-disk furrow openers, with depth-control bands, and heavy press wheels. All are important features of a planter unit.

Chaffy, fluffy, or heavily awned seeds are sometimes mixed with free-flowing material of a similar weight, such as rice hulls, to aid in getting the seed through a drill.

SOWING too deep causes many failures to get stands of grass. Seeding equipment therefore should have accurate devices to control depth.

Desirable sowing depths vary with the type of soil, kind of seed, depth to moisture, and the season of seeding.

For quick emergence of seedlings, the seed must be placed in moist soil—but that does not mean seeding so deep that the seedlings cannot emerge.

In general, bentgrass and Kentucky bluegrass should be seeded no deeper than one-fourth inch; the fine fescues, timothy, and most warm-season grasses, no deeper than one-half inch; and smooth brome, wheatgrasses, ryegrass, tall fescue, meadow fescue, orchardgrass, and tall oatgrass, no deeper than 1 inch.

Greater depths are permissible on light soils. Shallower sowings are advisable on heavy soils.

Fertilizer, especially nitrogen applied at seeding time, often helps in the establishment of grass seedlings.

Broadcasting is not a good way to apply fertilizer to newly seeded rows. When the fertilizer is banded about 1 inch below the seed or below and slightly to one side of the drill row, the seedlings make better use of the fertilizer, less goes to the weeds, and the establishment of the grass is hastened and improved.

Companion crops are not recommended generally. Stands almost always are better when grass is sown without them. The rapid growth of companion crops places the slower developing grass seedlings at a serious competitive disadvantage for light, nutrients, and the moisture, especially when the field is not irrigated.

Seeding with a nurse crop at half the normal rate may be justified when protection from erosion by water or wind is needed.

The best date of planting may depend somewhat on the rainfall and temperature pattern.

Warm-season grasses are commonly planted in the spring 2 to 4 weeks before the time one expects seed-germinating temperatures. They can be planted successfully in midsummer with frequent irrigation.

Warm-season grasses are planted in spring or early fall in the far South.

Cool-season grasses usually are planted in early spring or early fall in the Great Plains and the Intermountain region. Late-fall plantings are made occasionally.

In the Northwest on unirrigated lands, spring seeding—as soon as a firm, fine, weed-free seedbed can be prepared—is generally best.

If weeds are numerous, a few weeks of fallow will destroy several crops of weed seedlings.

Late spring sowing of the small-seeded grasses, such as bluegrass, is risky without irrigation. There is less risk with smooth brome and other large-seeded species. A well-managed spring seeding usually requires a minimum of weed control and produces a seed crop the following year.

On irrigated lands, late spring or summer seedings made before September 1 on weed-free land require little effort for weed control and usually make a seed crop the next year.

Fall seeding of grasses presents problems in weed control in places where winter annuals grow in abundance. A seed crop the following year seldom is produced from fall seedings. One notable exception is annual or common ryegrass, which normally is sown in the fall and produces its seed crop the next year.

THE PRODUCTION OF GRASS SEEDS

Fall is a good time for seeding cool-season grasses in the Great Plains, where winter annuals are not a serious problem.

Managing the stand of seedlings is of utmost importance in the rapid establishment of seed fields.

If water is available, irrigations should be frequent enough to keep the soil moist and light enough to prevent erosion or silting. With sprinkler irrigation, the problems attending the furrow method are reduced. After the grass seedlings are well established, irrigations may be of lower frequency and longer duration.

If the new grass plant is to develop rapidly, weeds should be controlled during the first year. Wide-row seedings can be weeded by cultivation and spraying. Some handwork may be needed.

The early cultivations should be done with great care to avoid covering or uprooting young grass seedlings. Injury to the roots of the young plants can be lessened by cultivating no deeper and no oftener than is necessary to kill the weeds.

When seedlings have four or five leaves, 2,4-D may be used to control broad-leaved weeds.

Removing the leaves of young grass retards its development. Clipping to prevent seed formation and reduce the topgrowth of weeds therefore is not a good substitute for cultivation or hand weeding but is better than no control at all.

Pasturing of seedling grass in lieu of clipping should be carefully controlled. Livestock will destroy seedlings by pulling out and trampling them.

Insects and diseases seldom are serious problems on new seedings of grass, although slugs, cutworms, and wireworms are sometimes destructive in the West. Grasshoppers may require control measures, especially in the Great Plains.

Damping-off organisms of seedlings may cause losses in stands—usually minor but occasionally severe in some sections.

THE MANAGEMENT of established grass for highest yields of seed requires that the grower fit his production practices to the needs of the grass plant during the different phases of its growth.

Grasses go through a regular seasonal cycle, in which temperature and daylength are vital influences in their development.

All grasses do not follow the same seasonal pattern. At a given geographical location, however, this rhythmic process is repeated each year with minor deviations due to variations in the environment.

The seed crop of most perennial cool-season grasses begins the fall prior to harvest. Sometime before the emergence of the seed heads in the spring, the head is initiated as an almost microscopic group of rudimentary flowers from vegetative tissue in the basal part of the shoot or tiller. The length of time between initiation and emergence varies with the kind of grass. After the seed crop has matured, the tiller that bears seed next year will arise and gain enough vigor during the rest of the growing season to become ready to form floral parts.

The tiller usually produces a seed head the following year if it has a minimum specified number of leaves for the species by a certain date.

Yields of seed the following year usually are lower when new tillers are restricted in number or reduced in vigor by fall drought, lack of fertility, and excessive defoliation by insects, disease, pasturing, clipping or late burning.

Conversely, the presence of many tillers in condition to form floral parts, followed by vigorous growth, favors high yields of seed.

The time of initiation of the floral shoot in our important cool-season perennial grasses is known definitely in only a few geographical areas. Length of day largely determines when initiation of flowers takes place.

More research is needed to give a clear picture of the development cycles of grasses as they occur under different environments. The work already done, however, is of great value in understanding the responses of the species studied to various environmental factors and has resulted in improved management practices.

FERTILIZATION with nitrogen is one of the seedgrower's most effective means of stimulating abundant and vigorous growth of fertile tillers and increasing yields.

The amount and time of application is determined by the fertility level of the soil, the kind of grass, the manner in which plant residues are handled, and the amount of available water.

All grasses may not respond alike to time of fertilizer application.

Such grasses as Kentucky bluegrass and tall fescue, which go through floral initiation in the winter, respond to split applications of nitrogen in the fall and early spring and give better yields of seed.

Grasses that reach floral initiation in the spring make less efficient use of nitrogen applied in the fall than nitrogen that is applied in the spring.

Warm-season grasses respond best to nitrogen when it is applied soon after growth begins in the spring and (in the case of grasses that produce more than one seed crop) immediately after the harvest of each crop.

An annual application of 30 to 40 pounds of nitrogen to the acre usually is enough in areas of limited rainfall where there is no irrigation.

In more favorable areas and under irrigation, 60 to 200 pounds of nitrogen are applied annually. The higher rates usually are applied in split treatments to old stands or in localities where moisture is plentiful.

Phosphorus and potassium, the other major nutrients, generally do not limit production on western soils, but their use will increase as cropping depletes natural fertility. Phosphorus may be advantageous under some conditions to improve strength of the straw or to make more effective use of nitrogen.

The lack of sulfur and boron limit production on a few western soils.

Irrigation is needed for consistently high yields in most areas.

With lengthening days and rising temperatures of spring, grass should begin to grow vigorously. If lack of soil moisture limits growth, irrigation should be given as needed to carry fertilizer into the soil and sustain strong growth.

Plentiful moisture is needed during pollination and while the seed is filling. Most growers of grass seed apply nitrogen fertilizer heavily in the spring. Losses of nitrogen by leaching often result from overwatering. Uneven use of water results in uneven development and maturity.

When the seed crop nears maturity, irrigation usually is withheld to promote uniform ripening.

Irrigation may be needed in the late summer and fall to stimulate formation of abundant new shoots and build up food reserves in the overwintering plant tissues. Where irrigation of crops of grass seed is not usually needed, abnormal fall drought sometimes limits the formation of new shoots. Irrigating to relieve this condition will bring about the fall development required to produce a high yield of seed in the next crop.

Pastured or harvested aftermath of cool-season grass crops after a seed crop has been removed is a valuable byproduct. The combination of production of both seed and livestock can be efficient and profitable. Yields of seed are not affected adversely by removal of the aftermath following seed harvest.

With warm-season grasses, there is little opportunity for pasturing, because they mature seed in midsummer or late summer near the end of their seasonal growth.

WEEDS must be controlled if the seed crop is to be of high quality.

The use of good seed and special care given to establishment of a full initial stand do much to solve the problem of weeds in the established stand.

Chemical weedkillers, such as 2,4-D,

have simplified and reduced the cost of weed control, but they have not eliminated the need for using clean land, cultivating row seedings, and hand roguing to produce seed of high quality.

DISEASES have become increasingly destructive.

Blind seed disease is severe on perennial ryegrass when recommended cultural control methods are not practiced.

Ergot affects most grasses grown for seed.

The grass seed nematode affects chewings fescue and bentgrass.

Dwarf bunt injures the first seed crop of many grasses but spring sowing gives good control.

Leaf rust and stripe rust are especially injurious to Kentucky bluegrass.

Orchardgrass is subject to severe injury by a number of leaf diseases that are most active in the spring.

In Oregon, afterharvest burning is an important part of the recommended control program for blind seed, ergot, nematode, rust, and some other leaf diseases. Large propane burners sometimes are used to supplement the field burn to destroy disease inoculum where there is doubt that the field burn was adequate.

THE GRASSHOPPER was among the first recognized insect pests of grasses.

The sod webworm works on the basal parts of the grass plant and may be destructive to the fine fescues and Kentucky bluegrass.

Silvertop has a possible relationship to thrips and is destructive to seed crops of most perennial grasses.

Other commonly destructive insects are the Banks grass mite, aphids, mealy bugs, cutworms, stem maggots, and meadow plant bugs.

Afterharvest burning is an aid in controlling the sod webworm, silvertop, meadow plant bugs, thrips, mites and others.

Pesticides also are effective against certain insects.

Field mice sometimes are destructive in grass crops. Heavy populations have practically killed out grass fields. Such infestations are destructive to crops in general, and areawide control with poison baits is required.

THE REMOVAL of crop residues after harvest is important in maintaining maximum yields of grass seed. Development of seed stalks and yields of seed are improved if the grass aftermath is removed.

Since harvesting with a combine has become general, considerable quantities of loose straw must be removed from the field. Shredding with a rotary mower or chopper and attempts to incorporate the material into the soil have been unsatisfactory where the residue is heavy.

Many growers windrow the straw and bale it for livestock roughage or bedding and pasture the aftermath.

In some places, postharvest burning to remove crop residues is increasing. This method has some practical merits. It is cheap and has value in the control of some injurious insects and diseases. Injurious insects and diseases usually increase when crop residues are not removed.

Preharvest crop conditioning with desiccants—chemical sprays that kill and cause quick drying of the exposed plant parts—may be used before direct combining of the standing crop.

The method appears to be practical only under conditions of high temperature and low humidity and on open erect grass stands. The most commonly used material is DNBP, a dinitro spray. Application is by airplane at rates of 1 to 3 pints in 10 to 15 gallons of weed oil per acre. The crop should be ready to combine within 3 to 5 days after treatment.

Chemical injury to grass seeds and reduction in germination may occur from use of a desiccant. Injury to tall fescue and Kentucky bluegrass seeds has been observed. Seeds of sudangrass and blue panicgrass are tolerant because of their heavy, waxy hulls.

When to harvest is a problem that confronts all seedgrowers. In every grass seed field, as maturity approaches, there are grass plants in different stages of seed ripening. On every grass plant also are seeds in various stages of maturity, especially in humid weather and when fields are irrigated.

The mature seed shatters in many grasses so that it may be lost on the ground if it is left too long. It is not practical therefore to leave the crop unharvested until all of the seeds are ripe.

The grower's question of when to harvest is decided by estimating when he can get the most mature seed without excessive loss by shattering of the earliest seed.

Grass seeds may reach physiological maturity or attain maximum dry weight before the head appears ready to harvest. Higher yields may be possible because of reduced shattering loss with earlier harvesting than is generally practiced. In general, grass seed is likely to be physiologically mature when it has passed the milk stage and is in soft-to-medium dough.

Direct combining of the standing seed crop and bulk handling of the seed do not mean earlier harvesting when facilities for quickly reducing the moisture in seed, which may average 35 to 45 percent, are limited.

Newly harvested seed of high moisture content will heat and mold, and losses in germination and good appearance will occur if it is left in the bulk for just a few hours.

Early harvesting is generally practiced only when the crop is windrowed and allowed to cure in the field before combining.

Indeterminant seed maturity is a problem with a number of warm-season grasses. Harvest generally is delayed until there is some shattering from the tips of the inflorescence. Then harvest must be completed in a few days. At that stage, most of the seed has reached a maturity that will give good germination.

We do not know exactly when the growing of grass seed became a distinct enterprise in the United States. Orchardgrass, timothy, and Kentucky bluegrass probably were the first grasses to be harvested for seed.

The first known commercial production of seed of orchardgrass occurred possibly before 1850 in Kentucky. Timothy seed was a sizable crop item in Illinois in 1877. Stripping seed from bluegrass pastures in Kentucky was a well-established practice in 1900. Smooth bromegrass seed was harvested in Kansas about 1895. It is not known if any of these early plantings were made primarily for seed production rather than for forage with only intermittent seed harvests at opportune times.

We do know that much of our domestic production of grass seeds came as byproducts in the early part of this century. The actual planting of grass fields for the primary purpose of growing seed crops seems to have begun on sizable scale between 1910 and 1920. Expansion was gradual until the 1930's, when the effects of drought and the need for soil-conserving practices brought increased demand for grass seeds and stimulated seed production.

The names and doings of pioneers in important undertakings always are of special interest. We list a few men who we know pioneered in growing grass seed.

The first commercial harvest of orchardgrass seed, possibly before 1850, was said to have been at Goshen, Ky.

Edwin C. Johnson of Portland, Oreg., grew seed of common ryegrass before 1900. Smooth bromegrass seed was first harvested about 1895 by the Achenbach brothers of Washington, Kans., and Charlie Jeanerette of Madison, Kans.

Dr. E. B. White of Leesburg, Va., and Robert N. Legard of Hillsboro, Va., began producing seed of orchardgrass shortly after 1900. They found it to be a good cash crop that required little labor, and growing the seed soon became popular in northern Virginia.

Among the first growers of perennial

ryegrass seed, about 1920, was J. E. Jenks of Tangent, Oreg. Max Heinrichs, a German immigrant, specialized in growing seed of smooth bromegrass, tall fescue, and crested wheatgrass near Pullman, Wash., before 1930.

APPARENTLY the first commercial grass seeding in cultivated rows was made in 1927 with crested wheatgrass by Leroy Moomaw of Dickinson, N. Dak. Neal and Sam Parker of Creston, Mont., also made commercial plantings in rows in 1932, as did Walter Holt of Pendleton, Oreg.

Howard Wagner of Imbler, Oreg., followed with row culture within a short time, but special recognition is due him for the high standards of seed quality he maintained in his crops of crested wheatgrass, fescues, bentgrass, bluegrass, and native grasses.

Commercial culture in rows of native grasses of the Great Plains was begun with switchgrass and sidcoats grama about 1942 by Clyde Dennis, Larned, Kans.

Among others who followed him were H. W. Clutter of Garden City, Kans., and Harold Hummell of Fairbury, Nebr. Pioneers in the commercial harvest of bluegrama, buffalograss, and bluestem seed from native grass lands were Tom Munger, Enid, Okla.; Bob Hartley, Vinita, Okla.; and Glen Miller, Lincoln, Nebr.

GEORGE A. ROGLER, *a research agronomist, since 1936 has done grass breeding and pasture and range management research at the Northern Great Plains Field Station, Mandan, N. Dak.*

HENRY H. RAMPTON *is a research agronomist in the Department of Agriculture and is stationed at Oregon State College, Corvallis. He has conducted research on seed production of small-seeded grasses and legumes since 1938.*

M. D. ATKINS *has been Washington field plant materials technician for the Great Plains States with the Soil Conservation Service, Lincoln, Nebr., since 1956. Previously he was plant materials technician for Kansas and Oklahoma.*

Producing Seeds of the Legumes

M. W. PEDERSEN, L. G. JONES, AND T. H. ROGERS

SEVERAL botanical features are a bane and a boon in the production of seed of the legumes.

The growth of legumes generally is indeterminate—growth continues from the terminal and axillary buds while flowering and formation of seed are both in progress. Mature seed therefore is ready to harvest on the lower part of the plant while new flowers are still forming at the top. The decision as to when to harvest always is arbitrary. Cutting too late permits ripe seed to shatter to the ground and be lost. Cutting too early means an excessive amount of green, shriveled seed.

In some species, such as the trefoils, the pods open and the seed drops as soon as it is ripe. In others, special equipment is needed to remove the pods from the seeds. Strawberry clover is unique in that it has an inflated calyx, which lets it float on water. Such characteristics sometimes may complicate the harvesting.

The size of the seed—about 3 thousand seeds in a pound of field peas to about 2.5 million in a pound of large hop clover—affects many of the cultural practices, especially the rate and depth of planting and methods of harvest.

Most of the small-seeded legumes have hard seed and so cannot take up water promptly. The proportion of hard seed varies in species. The percentage of hard seed of most species is reduced by aging. In harvesting and cleaning operations, some of the seeds are scratched. The seedcoats of some species, such as sweetclover, are so hard that scarification is necessary before the seed will germinate.

Longer lived species tend to spread. Whiteclover and kudzu spread by stolons. Rambler and some other varieties of alfalfa spread by creeping roots. Crown vetch, Kura clover, big trefoil, and zigzag clover spread by rhizomes.

All of these species, except alfalfa, spread vigorously and are hard to maintain in rows for seed production. Cultural practices are affected.

The seed of many legumes need to be inoculated. Bacteria must be applied to the seed to insure the development of the symbiotic relationship in which nitrogen from the air is fixed in the plant. The inoculum varies from one species to another. Most seed dealers can supply the proper inoculum with seed that requires it.

The variability of legumes applies to genera, species, varieties, and to plants within varieties. Cultural practices for the production of legume seeds have distinctive features for each species.

PERENNIAL legumes include alfalfa (*Medicago sativa*), red clover (*Trifolium pratense*), alsike clover (*T. hybridum*), white or Ladino clover (*T. repens*), birdsfoot trefoil (*Lotus corniculatus* and *tenuis*), Kura clover (*T. ambiguum*), strawberry clover (*T. fragiferum*), zigzag clover (*T. medium*), sericea lespedeza (*Lespedeza cuneata*), big trefoil (*Lotus uliginosus*), crown vetch (*Coronilla varia*), and kudzu (*Pueraria lobata*).

ALFALFA for seed usually is planted on a firm, well-prepared seedbed in spring or fall, depending on the location, at a seeding rate of two-thirds to 4 pounds of seed per acre in rows 22 to 40 inches apart or as much as 15 pounds per acre in solid stands.

M. W. Pedersen and associates at Logan, Utah, used a four-dimensional scheme to explain the relationship between density of stand and production of seed. The space between rows and the distance between plants within the row are the first two dimensions.

Plant height is the third dimension. Pollination is the fourth.

The best plan probably is to space the plants equally within and between rows on about 2-foot centers. From a practical standpoint, however, it is better to have enough plants in the rows to crowd out weeds and volunteer alfalfa plants. A greater stand density can be tolerated if the plants are short and if pollination is rapid. Generally, however, seed setting is better on thin stands.

At Logan, Utah, the best yields have been obtained on 24-inch rows planted at 1 pound of seed per acre. The average annual production in a 4-year period was 211 pounds of seed per acre from a stand planted in 8-inch rows at a rate of 12 pounds of seed per acre, and 385 pounds from a stand planted in 24-inch rows at a rate of 1 pound of seed per acre.

When the forage stand was thinned, the yield of seed was increased to a level equal to or better than that from a stand that was originally thin. For example, a yield of 183 pounds of alfalfa seed per acre was obtained from a dense stand in 1955, compared to 427 pounds when the stand was thinned to 12-inch hills in 24-inch rows.

In the Delta area of Utah, thicker stands were better. In California, 40-inch rows planted at about 1 pound of seed per acre have given good results.

Solid-seeded stands often have given good results, but only when pollination was good. Much of the alfalfa seed is produced on stands that are utilized for both hay and seed.

At Logan, the yield of seed from the first crop is nearly twice the second, but about one-half of the seed produced in the State nevertheless is grown on the second crop. Governing factors include the relative values of hay and seed, date of the first frost, synchronization of bloom with the activity of pollinators, and weeds.

Fertilization with phosphorus is necessary in many sections. An application of 200 pounds of triple superphosphate often is used when the need is established.

Scientists at the Utah Agricultural Experiment Station noted, however, that seed yield of alfalfa dropped when the soil phosphorus content exceeded 17 parts per million. This depressing effect would probably be most apt to occur when stands are dense, irrigation is excessive, and pollination is slow.

Until more exact information is available, caution should be exercised in the application of phosphorus for the production of alfalfa seed.

Potash and such minor elements as boron, zinc, sulfur, and molybdenum also are required in some places.

The results of several years of study of irrigation in the production of alfalfa seed in Utah showed that when the root zone contained 15 inches of available water when flowering began, no benefit was derived from additional irrigation. When the soil contained only 7 inches, however, irrigation following full bloom was considered to be of value.

An advantage of 22 percent for furrow irrigation over sprinkler irrigation for alfalfa seed production also was reported.

Weeds must be controlled. If the seed is to be certified, the volunteer alfalfa plants (plants developed from shattered seed of the harvested crop) must also be killed.

Cultivation is done by row machinery, spring-tooth harrows, disk harrows, and tillers. Once a stand is established, it is necessary sometimes to cultivate across the rows to kill volunteer plants and weeds in the row.

Scientists at Oregon State College reported the effective use of diuron [3-(3,4-dichlorophenyl)-1, 1-dimethylurea] and IPC [isopropyl N-phenylcarbamate] or CIPC [isopropyl N-(3-chlorophenyl) carbamate] for the over-winter control of weedy annual grasses and broad-leaved weeds. A combination of dalapon and 4-(2,4-DB) [4-(2,4-dichlorophenoxy) butyric acid] was also suggested for establishing weed-free stands. EPTC [ethyl N,N-di-n-propylthiolcarbamate] was suggested as a preplanting treatment.

Contact weedkillers of the Dow general type [dinitro ortho secondary butylphenol] can also be used on established stands.

Harmful insects must be controlled without killing a disproportionate number of beneficial ones. Many beneficial and harmful insects are present in alfalfa.

Serious pests include the alfalfa weevil (*Hypera postica*), lygus bugs (*Lygus* species), pea aphid (*Macrosiphum pisi*), clover seed chalcid (*Bruchophagus*), spotted alfalfa aphid (*Therioaphis maculata*), and spider mites (*Tetranychus*).

A treatment of DDT (dichloro-diphenyl-trichloroethane) or dieldrin in the bud stage followed by toxaphene in the bloom stage controls lygus bugs. Demeton can be added to control mites and aphids.

One to five colonies of honey bees per acre are needed for pollination if enough native pollinators are not present to pollinate the crop.

Harvesting can be done by combining from cured windrows or from the standing crop. If combined direct, a defoliant spray (such as a dinitro product of the Dow or Sinox-general type) often is applied.

RED CLOVER is grown in all sections of the United States where there is sufficient rain or irrigation.

A fine, firm seedbed is essential to good stands of red clover. The surface should be firmed by settling by irrigation or rain, cultipacking, or rolling before seeding.

A medium soil of the loam, sandy loam, or clay loam type is preferred. Alkaline and extremely sandy soil should be avoided.

Red clover is planted between September and November and in February in California. In other areas, it is planted in the spring and late summer except in the Southeastern States, where fall plantings are made.

Broadcast seeding requires 10 to 20 pounds per acre; 8 to 10 pounds is enough when drill seeded. One or two pounds make satisfactory stands in row plantings. Spacings from 20 to 30 inches result in maximum seed yields in row plantings.

Tests in Minnesota indicated that red clover in 18-inch rows, planted at a rate of 2 pounds of seed per acre, and broadcast stands, planted at 4 pounds per acre, were superior to stands in 18-inch rows planted at a rate of 4 pounds and 36-inch rows planted at 1 or 2 pounds per acre.

Investigations in Kentucky led to recommendations of fall plantings, broadcast at the rate of 6 pounds of seed per acre.

The seed should be sown at a depth of about one-half inch or less.

Seeding rates are usually 8 to 10 pounds when drill seeded and 10 to 12 pounds per acre when broadcast. Red clover commonly is seeded in established stands of small grain or in grain stubble.

Inoculation is often necessary. Red clover will thrive only if enough legume bacteria are present. These may be lacking in soils where true clovers (*Trifolium*) were not grown a year or two previously.

Red clover needs more moisture than alfalfa. For maximum yield of seed, the plants should be kept growing vigorously throughout the growing and seed-setting period.

The border or furrow methods are satisfactory for applying irrigation water to red clover. Sprinkler irrigation may have limited use. Repeated wettings may promote deterioration of the heads and lead to shattering after the seed heads begin to mature.

Clipping is not generally recommended in the West, although clipping may help control weeds, diseases, and insect pests. If clipping is necessary, it should be done at about the time of the first bloom. The first crop is always clipped or grazed in the Midwest. The highest yields were obtained in Kentucky when the first crop was cut about June 1.

Because the red clover flower is prac-

tically self-sterile, cross-pollination is essential for a commercial seed crop. Two hives of domestic bees per acre usually are enough in the West. Better yields are obtained with three to four colonies per acre in the Midwest. They should be placed in the field when the plants begin to bloom.

Fertilizers often increase yields. Phosphorus, potash, and sulfur should be applied if they are deficient in the soil.

Two insects that must be controlled if seed of red clover is to be produced satisfactorily are the clover seed midge (*Dasyneura leguminicola*) and the clover seed chalcid.

Other pests that may cause damage include lygus bugs, grasshoppers, armyworms (*Prodenia*), spider mites, and clover root borer (*Hylastinus obscurus*).

Land relatively free of weeds should be used for producing seed of red clover. Cultivation generally is the most economical way to kill weeds where it is possible, as in row plantings. In excessively weedy, close-drilled or broadcast stands, it may be necessary to use herbicides or pull the weeds by hand. If weedy winter annual grasses are a problem, pelleted or granulated IPC—isopropyl N-phenyl-carbamate—is effective. In California, the IPC material should be applied on wet soil in December and January when the soil is cold.

Harvesting methods are similar to those for alfalfa, except that red clover is not usually combined standing and is harder to thresh.

ALSIKE CLOVER is used in hay and pasture mixtures in the eastern half of the United States and in the higher elevations of the Western States. It is especially useful in wet meadows and acid soils where other clovers do not thrive.

Like red clover, alsike is a perennial that generally behaves as a biennial.

The seedbed for alsike clover should be firm, uniform, and well drained. Fall and spring plantings are common in the Klamath Basin of Oregon. It usually is seeded in early spring in the colder regions. It may be broadcast, drill seeded alone, or drill seeded into established stands of small grain in early spring or grain stubble in the fall.

Broadcast plantings take 8 to 12 pounds of seed; 6 to 8 pounds is adequate when it is drill seeded. Alsike generally is grown in solid stands.

Under irrigation, the management of water is important. Alsike seedlings are slow to establish roots and require an abundance of water. The soil should not be allowed to dry to a depth greater than 1 to 2 inches until 2 or 3 weeks before harvest.

Alsike clover will thrive only if proper bacteria are present. Its seed should be inoculated when it is planted for the first time in a field.

Alsike plantings usually respond to phosphorus or sulfur or both in the Klamath Basin. Applications of 300 to 400 pounds of single or ordinary superphosphate at planting time may increase yields of seed.

The best yields are produced on early growth. Cutting back to condition stands for seed production therefore is poor management.

Pollination requirements are similar to those of Ladino whiteclover.

The major pests of alsike are the clover seed weevil (*Miccotrogus picirostris*), the clover root curculio (*Sitona hispidula*), and several species of lygus bugs. The pea aphid and clover aphid (*Anuraphis bakeri*) may also require control.

Rodents, field mice, and gophers often are problems in seed fields. Excellent control of field mice has been obtained by using toxaphene, which is applied in water at the time the field mice are feeding on the plants above the ground.

Harvesting is done much as with alfalfa, but alsike seed is small and shatters if it is not handled carefully.

LADINO CLOVER will do best on heavier clay or loam soils. It does well on shallow soils underlain by a tight clay layer or hardpan, even if the restricting layer is within 12 to 18 inches of the soil surface. Ladino clover does not thrive on saline soil. Seed production is seldom successful on deep, open, friable, fertile soils, because plants fail to produce an abundance of seed heads unless they are irrigated frequently.

Ladino clover grown for seed requires irrigation every 7 to 12 days during the 60 to 80 days required to set a seed crop. Careful preparation of the land to provide economical and uniform application of water and to facilitate other cultural operations is essential. The border system of land preparation is in general use.

A fine, firm seedbed is recommended. The surface should be firmed by cultipacking, rain, or irrigating before seeding.

Seeding can be done in September or November or in February. Spring seeding is preferred if fields are foul with winter weeds.

The rate of seeding is 4 to 6 pounds per acre when broadcast or drill planted. The seed should be covered to a depth of one-fourth inch or less.

Inoculation of Ladino seed is recommended, particularly on new lands not previously in clover.

The production of seed in stands or pasture plantings will benefit from liberal applications of phosphorus and sulfur if the soil is low or deficient in those elements. New seedings of Ladino in California respond to nitrogen, phosphorus, and sulfur. Many growers broadcast 200 pounds per acre of 16–20–0 and 100 pounds of agricultural sulfur before seeding new stands.

Grazing or mowing seed fields in late April or early May helps control weeds. On stands of seedlings, dinitro selective sprays are effective against young broad-leaved weeds. The dinitro selective sprays should be used with extreme caution in seedling Ladino if the air temperature is above 75° F.

In established fields, when properly used, 2,4-D (2,4-dichlorophenoxyacetic acid) has proved effective against such troublesome weeds as dock, buckhorn, plantain, chicory, and dodder.

When 2,4-D is used, time of application, type of material to be used, and the rate of the application are important.

In irrigated areas, fields sprayed with 2,4-D should be kept well watered for 3 to 4 weeks following treatment.

Weedy grasses, particularly winter annual species, can usually be controlled by applying granulated or pelleted IPC. The IPC material should be applied when the ground is wet and cold.

Because daylength affects flowering of all whiteclover and may influence setting of seed, the time of cutting back or grazing preparatory to seed production is important.

The recommended time to condition the stand for Ladino seed production in California is May 5 to 20. The regrowth of plants to full bloom requires 25 to 30 days. Therefore seed setting would start about June 30 to July 20 and continue to August 20 or September 10. Harvest is 15 to 20 days later.

Ladino clover plants are extremely variable. Locality, time of seed setting, and plant differences may affect the genetic composition of strains or varieties that are grown under different environments.

E. H. Stanford and his coworkers at the University of California studied the effects of harvest dates and location on the genetic composition of the Syn. 1 generation—the first generation produced by the interpollination of a group of plants in isolation—of Pilgrim Ladino clover.

They concluded: "Parental clones of Pilgrim Ladino clover differ in their seed-producing ability. The relative amounts of seed produced by individual clones varies with harvest dates and areas of production. Pollen contribution of individual clones also differs. If genetically uniform lots of breeder seed are to be produced, they must be produced under similar environmental conditions."

Daylength also governs the area where seed of Ladino clover can be grown. South of about 32° north latitude the daylength is too short to promote profuse formation of flowers.

Investigations in California indicated that time of harvest in relation to cutting back is important. Tests showed these yields: 180 pounds per acre, when harvested in 52 days after cutting back; 280, in 66 days; 298, in 75 days; 407, in 96 days; 380, in 110 days; 298, in 120 days; and 280 pounds in 130 days.

The loss of seed, as indicated by harvests after 110 days of production, were due to deterioration of pedicels, heads, and pods, which led to shattering of seed, dropping of heads and pods, and germination of seed after irrigation.

The flowers must be cross-pollinated. Wind and rain are not effective carriers of pollen. Bumble bees and many other wild bees are useful and effective, but usually there are so few of them that one cannot rely on them for effective pollination. Honey bees therefore generally are used. An average of 1 or 2 strong colonies to the acre is enough for complete pollination.

Lygus bugs, grasshoppers, cutworms (*Chorizagrotis auxiliaris*), armyworms, and spider mites (red spider) must be controlled to produce Ladino seed.

The crop is ready to cut when about 90 to 95 percent of the seed heads are brown and the flower stems have started to dry (usually 90 to 110 days after cutting back). The crop is usually harvested by one of three methods—direct combining, following spray curing; combining from the windrows; and by stationary threshers.

To cure, Ladino is cut as close to the ground as possible. The mower is equipped with a curler to windrow, or a side-delivery rake is used for windrowing following mowing. Sometimes it is dried in the swath and windrowed at night before threshing. Desiccation or chemical curing also is used. Curing usually takes 4 or 5 days.

THE SEED HABITS of birdsfoot trefoil are such that sometimes much seed is lost.

The seed ripens unevenly. The ripe pods pop open, and seed shattering may lead to a complete loss of the crop.

Localities that have relatively cool summer temperatures and moderately high daytime humidity (40 to 60 percent) are best suited to seed production. Seed is produced in Oregon, California, North Dakota, Minnesota, Iowa, Vermont, and New York.

A firm seedbed is essential. Seed fields should be relatively free of weeds.

Birdsfoot trefoil is normally seeded in California in October and November or in February. The stand then becomes established under normal rainfall over most of the area.

Seeding in standing water on flat lands that are irrigated by contour checks is fairly common. Successful stands are obtained throughout late summer and early fall by this method. After the land is prepared for irrigation, the field is flooded. The seed is broadcast on the water from an airplane. The land is flooded for about 48 hours. By that time, the seedcoat has been ruptured, the cotyledons have emerged, and the primary root has begun to develop. As the water is drained off, or seeps into the soil, the primary root is anchored in the mud. If the water is held too long, the seedlings may be driven to the levee by the wind.

Trefoil generally is seeded in spring in colder parts of the country. The recommended rate of seeding is 3 to 5 pounds per acre drill seeded to a depth of one-fourth inch or less.

Inoculation is essential in places where trefoil has not grown previously. Trefoil bacteria do not occur naturally in most soils.

Soil moisture should be controlled. Irrigation should be frequent enough to keep the ground moist throughout the period of seed setting and ripening. Frequent irrigation also helps to maintain a canopy of new growth above most of the seed pods and to keep the humidity high to reduce seed shattering. Trefoil stands grown for seed on soils low in phosphorus, potash, and sulfur will often benefit from liberal applications of fertilizer containing them.

Birdsfoot trefoil, like alfalfa, responds to thin stands. In replicated tests with row-planted stands of Viking trefoil, rows spaced 6 to 24 inches apart produced 30 to 60 percent more than stands planted by broadcasting. Seed shattering increased sharply in the 24-inch, row-spaced stand.

Weedy grasses, particularly winter annual species, usually can be controlled by applying granulated or pelleted IPC, which should be applied when the ground is wet and cold. Many broad-leaved weeds can be eliminated by spraying with 4-(2,4-DB). The spray should be applied before the trefoil is cut back to start seed production.

Daylength influences blossoming and may influence setting of seed. The time of clipping back preparatory to seed production therefore is important. The recommended time to cut back in California is May 1 to 15; in Oregon, May 25 to June 5.

Regrowth to full bloom requires 30 to 35 days. Seed setting would then start about June 20 and continue to August 1 to 10. Harvest is 20 to 30 days later.

Pollinators are essential during the entire seed-setting period. If wild bees are scarce or absent, one or two strong hives of honey bees per acre should be furnished.

The first crop is usually used for seed in nonirrigated areas. Harvest follows about 25 to 30 days after full bloom.

Harmful insects and mites, such as lygus bugs and stink bugs (Pentatomidae), must be controlled.

We know of no completely satisfactory method of harvesting trefoil. Direct combining after spray curing can be done under ideal conditions. Mowing and drying in the swath for 8 to 24 hours before combining has been a successful method. Mowing and windrowing to cure and threshing from the windrow is commonly used. Mowing trefoil at night and curing it on a hard surface has been tried.

Curing in shocks and bales to be threshed by stationary harvesters and other methods have been tried, but we cannot give a good, general recommendation. •

BIENNIAL yellow and white sweetclovers are grown mainly for grazing and soil improvement. Planting practices are like those for alfalfa.

According to Samuel Garver and T. A. Kiesselbach, who worked in Nebraska, the first year's growth can be grazed or mowed for hay, but grazing gives better seed production the following year.

About 6 inches of stubble or growth should be allowed to remain for the winter. Higher seed yields are obtained when the second year's early growth is not grazed or mowed. Some of the varieties grow so tall if they are not grazed, however, that it is advisable to graze them so that the harvesting machinery can handle the growth. About 10 inches of stubble should be left to insure regrowth.

Thick stands should be avoided when sweetclover is grown for seed. The yield on dry land is reduced because of excessive competition for soil moisture. The seed yield on wetter lands is reduced because of excessive shading.

At least one plant per square foot is required to control weeds and is considered suitable for drier sites for seed production. If there is enough soil moisture, two or three plants to the square foot is better.

Sweetclover is quite drought tolerant when it is established, but it requires favorable moisture conditions in the early stages of seedling development. Moisture is needed for the companion crop as well as the sweetclover. There should be enough soil moisture the second year to provide a good vegetative growth, but drier weather favors flowering, seed formation, and harvesting.

Sweetclover requires readily available calcium. It can grow with lower levels of soil phosphorus than alfalfa. Weeds are normally controlled by

the companion crop in sweetclover the first year. A spring-tooth harrow or similar tool can be used to control annual weeds in the spring of the second year if they are troublesome.

It is sometimes necessary to control the sweetclover weevil (*Sitona cylindricollis*). Dieldrin can be used for this purpose.

Bees at the rate of two or more colonies per acre must be provided for pollination.

Combining from windrows is a satisfactory method of harvesting.

SUMMER ANNUAL legumes include Korean and striate lespedezas (*L. stipulacea* and *L. striata*), velvet bean (*Stizolobium deeringianum*), cowpea (*Vigna sinensis*), alyceclover (*Alysicarpus vaginalis*), crotalaria (*Crotalaria*), and hairy indigo (*Indigofera hirsuta*).

Lupine, vetches, field pea, and Hubam sweetclovers are summer annuals in the North, although fall seeding of peas with oats is practiced on the Pacific coast.

The summer annuals generally are planted in the South from January to March and harvested in the fall.

LESPEDEZA is planted in early spring by drilling or broadcasting with pasture mixtures or grain at the rate of 25 to 30 pounds of unhulled seed per acre. The stand is maintained indefinitely by volunteering.

A crop of hay usually is cut or the stand is pastured until about July 15. If it is pastured and a dense growth persists or weeds are present, mowing may be worthwhile. The seed yield is greater if a hay crop is not taken, however. The crop should not be mowed if the lower leaves are firing or dying. Live buds should be left below the mowing line.

Lespedeza does well on a wide range of soil conditions, but responds favorably to lime on acid soils and to mixed fertilizers, particularly phosphorus, on deficient soils.

Dodder, the major weed problem in lespedezas, is controlled by burning.

There are no severe problems of insect pests or pollination.

Kobe lespedeza, a late-maturing strain of *L. striata*, generally is combine harvested from windrows. The Korean can be harvested standing.

THE *Trifolium* genus of winter annual legumes includes berseem (*T. alexandrinum*), large hop (*T. campestre*), small hop (*T. dubium*), rose (*T. hirtum*), crimson (*T. incarnatum*), Persian (*T. resupinatum*), and lappa (*T. lappaceum*) clovers and subclover (*T. subterraneum*).

The *Medicagos* include spotted burclover (*M. arabica*), California burclover (*M. hispida*), and little burclover (*M. minima*), button clover (*M. orbicularis*), and black medic (*M. lupulina*).

The *Melilotus* genus includes sourclover (*M. indica*), Hubam, Israel, and Floranna sweetclover (*M. alba annua*).

Also included are rough pea (*Lathyrus hirsutus*), lupine (*Lupinus* species), Austrian winter pea (*Pisum arvense*), and vetch (*Vicia*).

The last three species and Hubam sweetclover are grown as summer annuals in the northern parts of the United States and as winter annuals in the Pacific coast region, west of the Sierra Nevada and the Cascade Mountains and in the lower South.

Hairy vetch is the only one of the vetches that is winter hardy enough to be used as a winter annual in the North.

Winter annual legumes usually are planted in the South from August to November and harvested in June and July, about the same time as the small grains.

Although annuals, the small-seeded species ordinarily maintain themselves by reseeding, the key to which is their percentage of hard seed.

Common crimson clover does not normally reseed because of its low percentage of hard seed, but varieties such as Dixie do reseed, because they have a higher proportion of hard seed.

Cultivating or disking the soil after harvest sometimes helps to plant the volunteer crop.

It is common practice (except among specialized seedgrowers) to graze the crop until about a month before normal flowering time. The yield of seed may be reduced thereby, but sometimes such grazing helps to control weeds.

The tall-growing species, such as lupines, peas, and vetches, require no special management and produce more seed if they are not grazed or clipped.

CRIMSON CLOVER is seeded in the fall alone in an open, established, short grass sod or with oats or barley.

The crop can be grazed until early in March in the southern sections before it is allowed to go to seed.

Usually 10 to 20 pounds of inoculated seed are planted per acre.

Crimson clover will require fertilization with phosphorus, potassium, and sometimes boron in the South, but too much fertilization for seed production should be avoided in order to avoid excessive growth and damage from crown and stem rotting organisms.

One colony of honey bees per acre should be provided for pollination.

The clover head weevil (*Hypera meles*), lesser clover leaf weevil (*H. nigrirostris*), seed chalcid, pea aphid, and other insects may be problems.

Crimson clover sometimes is combined standing, but usually it is combined from windrows.

THE VETCHES require cool temperatures for best development. In the Southern and Pacific States, they usually respond as winter annuals and mature in late spring and early summer. In the North, where winters are severe, they usually act as summer annuals and mature late in summer or fall.

Species vary in winter hardiness. Hairy vetch is the most winter hardy and the only variety recommended for fall planting in the North. Hungarian, woollypod, and smooth vetches will stand a temperature of o° F. without snow protection. Of the common vetches, Willamette, the most winter hardy, tolerates temperatures down to 10° without injury. Bitter, purple, and Monantha vetches are less hardy than Willamette vetch.

Vetches generally do not require a particular soil, but some varieties are better adapted to certain soil types than others. All varieties do well on rich loam. Hairy vetch, smooth, Monantha, and woollypod vetches do well on poor, sandy soils. Hungarian vetch is well suited to heavy, wet soil where other varieties fail to thrive.

A moderate supply of moisture is necessary for vetches. None tolerates drought.

Little or no seedbed preparation is used when vetches follow cultivated crops. The seed is usually sown broadcast and disked in. When seeded in ricefields, the seed is broadcast by airplane into mud following drainage preparatory to harvesting the rice. Disked seedbeds are used in the Pacific Northwest when vetch follows cultivated crops or spring-seeded small grains.

In the Northern and Eastern States, where hard freezes occur, all cultivated vetches, except hairy vetch, should be sown early in spring. Hairy vetch may be sown in August and early September. In the Pacific coast region, west of the Sierra Nevada and Cascade Mountains, vetches can be sown in the fall. Seedings also are common in September and October in the Cotton Belt.

Seeding rates vary according to variety and locality. Hairy, smooth, narrowleaf, and woollypod vetches require 20 to 30 pounds; Hungarian, Monantha, and the common vetches, 30 to 50 pounds; and Bard and purple vetches, 60 to 70 pounds to the acre.

The seed is broadcast or drill planted. Drill-planted stands are preferred for seed production. The depth of planting, which varies with the soil type and the amount of surface moisture, usually ranges from 1.5 to 3 inches.

Vetch grown for seed often is sown in pure stands. Hay stands usually include a companion crop of oats, barley, or rye.

On soils deficient in phosphorus, sulfur, or potash, vetches grown for seed, hay, or cover crops will respond to liberal amounts of those elements.

Inoculation is essential to the growth of all vetches.

To grow vetches for seed requires little special management. If it grows fast and is not clipped or grazed, it tends to smother weeds.

Diseases and pests are few. The vetch bruchid (*Bruchus brachialis*) was a serious threat to the vetch seed industry in Oregon in the 1940's. DDT effectively controlled it.

Honey bees and bumble bees like to visit vetch blossoms. The structure of the vetch flower is adapted to cross-pollination, and visits by pollinators are essential for maximum seed set.

To harvest seed of hairy, smooth, woollypod, and other shattering vetches, the plants must be cut as soon as the lower pods are fully ripe.

The nonshattering species, such as purple and Hungarian vetches, are allowed to ripen 80 to 95 percent of the pods before cutting. An important point in growing vetch for seed is to handle the crop quickly and as little as possible to avoid seed shatter.

FIELD PEAS are grown like small grain; in fact, a mixture of oats and peas sometimes is used in growing seed.

Peas for seed are seeded in the fall or spring, depending on locality. The crop is fall seeded in September to early November in the Pacific coast region. Often winter oats is a companion crop. In the irrigated section of Idaho, Washington, Montana, and Oregon, peas are planted alone in early spring.

With a companion crop, the rate of seeding is 80 pounds of peas and 40 pounds of oats. For irrigated plantings made in spring the seeding rates are 80 to 100 pounds of pea seed per acre. The crop is usually drill seeded and covered to a depth of 1.5 to 3 inches.

Field peas prefer an abundance of lime and often respond to liberal amounts of sulfur. Sulfur in the form of gypsum is used at rates of 100 to 150 pounds per acre in western Oregon. The elemental sulfur is used at a rate of 50 pounds per acre on irrigated lands.

Field peas are subject to bacterial blight, leaf blotch, downy mildew, anthracnose, and root rot. The growing of peas on different fields that are rotated helps to reduce the incidence of disease.

Insects that infest peas are the pea weevil (Bruchus pisorum) and pea moth (Laspeyresia nigricana). The pea aphid has been destructive in some years. Good control of the pea weevil can be had by dusting with DDT before the eggs are deposited.

Field peas should be cut for seed as soon as the pods are mature and the seed is firm. Peas may be windrowed or bunched for drying and threshed directly from windrows.

Threshing is usually done with an ordinary grain combine. The adjustment of threshing equipment should be such as to eliminate cracking, chipping, and breaking of seed.

M. W. PEDERSEN *is a research agronomist in the Forage and Range Research Branch of the Crops Research Division of the Agricultural Research Service. Since joining the Department of Agriculture, he has been engaged in plant breeding and seed production research.*

L. G. JONES *is a specialist in the Department of Agronomy, University of California, Davis. He has done research since 1946 in problems of seed production, irrigation, and harvesting methods. In 1951, at the request of the International Bank for Reconstruction and Development, he served on a mission to Iraq to undertake a general review of the country's economic potentialities and make recommendations for a development program.*

T. H. ROGERS *is Head of the Department of Agronomy, University of Georgia, Athens. Formerly he was professor of agronomy, the Alabama Polytechnic Institute, and agronomist in the University of Kentucky.*

Harvesting the Seeds of Grasses and Legumes

JESSE E. HARMOND, JAMES E. SMITH, JR., AND JOSEPH K. PARK

IT IS NOT easy to harvest the seeds of grasses and legumes. Many methods and special machines are needed, and they get only a part of the seed.

Several factors are involved—variations in the size, weight, and maturity of the seeds; plant types; the height and spacing of the plants; the growing season; and time of harvest.

Some examples: Velvet bentgrass has 10,800,000 seeds to a pound; field peas have only 1,800. Subterranean clover may bury its seed in the topsoil; sudangrass will grow to 8 feet tall. Vetch seed is large and dense; the Arizona cottontop has a light, fluffy seed, covered with short, white hairs.

The seeds of some species ripen evenly; the slender gramagrass has seed in all stages from the bloom to maturity, from June until frost.

Some seed plants are grown in solid stands. Others may be sparsely spaced in rows. Some kinds have a single stem; others grow in a clump.

A survey by research engineers in the Department of Agriculture disclosed that a farmer might be harvesting less than one-half of the seeds he produced—33 percent of the crimson clover crop as pure live seed; 23 percent of the subterranean clover; 65 percent of the Alta fescue; 53 percent of the hairy vetch; 46 percent of the alfalfa; 25 percent of birdsfoot trefoil; and 40 percent of the Ladino clover.

To combat such heavy losses of seed, improved machines and methods are being developed continually. Some of them we consider here.

THE COMBINE, developed to harvest cereal grain crops, has been modified to handle small seeds and is the chief machine used in harvesting crops of grass and legume seed. All the different types of combines have been used, tractor drawn and self-propelled, with cutting mechanisms 6 to 18 feet wide. Small harvesting machines save more seed than the larger ones.

Modifications of the combine include a speed control for the cleaning air fan; baffles for air distribution; rubber-covered angle bars in place of a spike-tooth or rasp bar cylinder and concave; special sieves for the combine cleaning shoe; a variable speed control for the threshing cylinder; a sheet metal pan under the chaffer tailing extension; and check curtains behind the threshing cylinder.

The weather, the stage of seed maturity, and the kind of seed crop determine the alterations necessary.

Rubber-covered angle bar cylinder and concave often are used to thresh crimson clover seed, which is hard to remove from the pod yet damages easily.

The size and shape of the openings of the special sieves on the combine cleaning shoe accommodate a particular seed. For example, a 24 by 24 wire mesh screen is recommended for redtop seed. The adjustable sieve can be regulated to accommodate many seed sizes. To handle dallisgrass, the sieve is set one-half open and the cleaning air is shut off. With the variable cylinder speed control, the cylinder speed can be increased to handle seed, like crimson clover, that is hard to thresh. It can be reduced to handle seed that is easy to thresh.

The metal pan under the tailing extension keeps seeds, stems, and leaves from falling into the return elevator and being rethreshed. Check curtains back of the cylinder deflect the discharging material down to the rack so that the seed can be shaken out of the straw and on to the shoe for cleaning.

Rubber rolls may be mounted ahead of the threshing cylinder for crushing seed pods in crops like alfalfa and flax. For threshing alfalfa, the cylinder speed can be reduced as much as 1,000 revolutions per minute; there is less damage to seed, and the percentage of unthreshed seed is no higher.

Four-way automatic leveling devices are used in hillside combining to keep the threshing and cleaning mechanism level while operating on the side of a hill. Without the leveling, the material would crowd to the low side of the cylinder, rack, and the cleaning shoe, thereby causing cylinder chokage, inefficient separation of the seeds from the straw, a slow forward speed, and greater loss and damage of seeds.

A vertical sickle at the end of the cutterbar cuts the tangled crop and separates the cut and uncut standing crop, so that there is less chokage and seed shatter in crops like vetch. The rotary screen cleaner, mounted in the discharge of the combine grain bin auger, screens out dirt and small seeds of weeds before the seeds go into the sacker.

Lift fingers on the cutterbar raise a low-growing crop or a down crop above the sickle so it can be cut. A vacuum attachment under the combine can be used to reclaim shattered seed from the ground.

Special cutterbars, like the lespedeza bar, have more and smaller ledger plate guards and cut the crop near the ground. The double sicklebar has no guards, and both the top and bottom sickles reciprocate to cut heavier and greener crops without chokage.

Special reels can be used, like the tined reel, which lifts down crops, or the wind reel, which blows the crop into the cutterbar, instead of the revolving reel, which causes shattering

Special gears reduce the forward speed of the combine without lowering the speed of the threshing and cutting mechanism. The possibility of cylinder chokage and overloading the rack and shoe is less.

As THE CROP gets drier, the seed shatter more easily, but the setting o the concave clearance can be wider and the threshing cylinder can be operated at slower speed.

When the moisture is high, the cylinder speed is increased and the clearance is lowered to thresh the seed.

In direct combining, the standing crop is cut and immediately run through the combine to free the seed from their pods and separate them from the straw. When crop conditions, maturity of seed, and weather permit, direct combining is desirable. It requires less labor and equipment.

In windrow combining, the crop is cut and gathered into swaths or windrows to field cure. A pickup attachment on the combine lifts the cured crop from the windrow and feeds it into the combine, which threshes and separates the seed from stems and leaves. Windrow combining is used usually on crops whose seeds shatter before the plant and seeds are dry enough to combine and store.

To ANALYZE the operation of a combine, we recommend several steps:

Adjust the threshing cylinder speed and clearance to the crop that is being harvested.

Regulate the forward speed of the machine so that the crop will not overload the threshing cylinder, rack, and shoe.

Make a test run and analyze the operation by considering the combine in four sections—feeding, threshing, separating, and cleaning—and observe the operation of each part.

The feeding section consists of reel, divider, cutterbar, and feeding mechanism. The reel should hold the crop upright, while the sickle makes the cut, and then lay the straw gently on the draper. The reel speed should be 10 percent faster than the forward movement of the machine. The reel height should be adjusted so the slats contact the straw just below the seed heads. The cutterbar knives and ledger plates should be sharp and in register.

The threshing section consists of a threshing cylinder and concaves. The discharging of unthreshed heads over the rack is caused by a low cylinder speed or excessive concave-cylinder clearance. Broken seeds are due to too high a cylinder speed, too little concave-cylinder clearance, or the return of threshed seed to the cylinder by the tailing return auger.

In setting the threshing cylinder, adjust the cylinder-concave clearance to one and one-half times the thickness of long seed or one and one-half times the diameter of round seed.

If excessive straw breakage is observed, increase the concave-cylinder clearance.

Adjust the cylinder speed so the seed is rubbed or knocked out of the seed pods or heads. Then gradually reduce the speed until some of the heads are unthreshed.

At this point, slowly raise the cylinder speed until only an occasional unthreshed seed head is found. Most of the occasional unthreshed seed is immature or partly filled seed.

The separating section consists of the beater cylinder, check curtains, and straw rack. Threshed seed in the straw discharge is due to overloading the rack, too slow a speed, or a worn check curtain.

Slow down the forward speed of the combine to prevent overloading.

Increase the rack speed to shake seed out of straw and renew the check curtain if the cylinder is throwing the seed over the rack.

The cleaning section has the fan, grain return, chaffer sieve, chaffer extension, and shoe sieve.

Excessive air blows seed over the chaffer sieve and out the back of the combine. Too large a volume of material also prevents seed from coming in contact with the sieve and dropping into the seed pan.

Adjust the cleaning air so the material is slowly agitated over the chaffer sieve. Precise air adjustment is required on light grass seed. For some grasses, the fan discharge is completely closed. The shoe sieve opening should be as large as possible without getting excessive straw and trash in the clean grain.

On grasses that are easy to thresh, the concave-cylinder clearance is widened to reduce the straw breakage, and the chaffer extension is blanked off by placing a piece of sheet metal under the bars to prevent material from being returned to the cylinder for rethreshing and possible damage.

IF A CONVENTIONAL grain binder is used to cut and bundle the seed crop, the bundles are shocked and left in the field to cure. The bundles are then threshed in a stationary thresher or a combine.

In dew areas, cutting and binding are done usually in early morning, while the humidity is high. After a curing period, the bundles are threshed in the afternoon when the sun has lowered the humidity.

To reduce seed losses, the binder often is altered by removing every other reel slat and installing catch pans under the binder deck and beneath cracks between the canvas and elevator to catch the shattered seed. Since the binding-shocking-threshing method involves a number of operations and takes more work and equipment, it is being abandoned, even though it may save more seeds than other methods.

IN SEED STRIPPING, the ripe seed is removed and the plant is left growing. A number of native grasses in the Great Plains, which cannot be harvested satisfactorily by any of the conventional methods, are stripped. Many kinds of shop-made strippers are in use.

Even under the best operating conditions, seed stripping is an inefficient way of harvesting seed; the stripped seed must be cured or dried before cleaning and storing.

A widely used machine is the bluegrass stripper, which removes the ripe seed with a ground-driven, spike-tooth cylinder so mounted that the revolving cylinder rakes off the mature seeds and discharges them into a seed hopper as the machine is pulled through the field.

The hopper lid is opened periodically, and the stripped seed is removed for curing and processing. Sometimes several bluegrass strippers are drawn by one tractor.

The pneumatic-type stripper in general use is a tractor-mounted machine in which an airblast directed at the seed heads blows the seed into a receiving head equipped with a rotating spiked drum and a scrubbing screen. The air current from the nozzle and the revolving drum convey the light seed through the air duct and into a burlap bag.

HEADERS are machines that clip the plants just under the seed heads and gather the material in a catch pan. The seeds are cured in piles and later are threshed.

Combines equipped with a wheel-mounted trailer box are used in harvesting some of the native grasses, like the bluestems, in the Great Plains. The heads are threshed by the combine. The tailings are caught in the trailer box, dumped in piles, and left to cure. The straw is then rethreshed to recover a large proportion of the seed that would have been left in the field.

THE FORAGE harvester that is used to harvest green forage often is used to harvest subterranean clover and the light seed of several of the Great Plains grasses. The practice is to let the seed mature and use the unit to chop the forage and blow it into trailing wagons. The finely chopped material of the native grasses is cured and planted. For subterranean clover, the chopper is run as close to the ground as possible to pick up free seed burs. The harvested material is then threshed with a combine.

The chopper is used to harvest Arizona cottontop, needlegrasses, feather bluestems, and Texas bluegrass. The seeds and chopped forage can then be planted with a picker wheel-type cotton planter. Harvesting big cenchrus with the chopper reduces the time required to hammermill the seed

COMMON METHODS OF HARVESTING GRASS, LEGUME, AND SEED CROPS

Crop name, common and botanical	Binder	Combine Windrow	Direct	Stripper	Remarks
Alfalfa (West and North Central States). (*Medicago sativa*)	x	x	x	.....	Windrowing is the most common practice.
Bentgrass............... (*Agrostis*)	.....	x	x	.....	Weather conditions permitting, direct combining yield better.
Bermudagrass............ (*Cynodon dactylon*)	.....	x	x	.....	
Bluegrass, Kentucky...... (*Poa pratensis*)	.....	.....	.....	x	Small areas are often hand stripped.
Bluegrass, Merion........ (*Poa pratensis*)	x	x	.....	.....	
Bluestem, big and sand... (*Andropogon geradi* and *A. hallii*)	x	.....	x	.....	Seed from combine should be cured several days before being sacked.
Bluestem, cane–......... (*Andropogon barbinodis*)	.....	.....	.....	x	
Bluestem, King Ranch.... (*Andropogon ischaemum*)	.....	.....	x	x	
Bluestem, little.......... (*Andropogon scoparius*)	.....	.....	x	x	
Bristlegrass, plains....... (*Setaria macrostachya*)	.....	.....	x	x	
Bromegrass, field......... (*Bromus arvensis*)	.....	.....	x	.....	It is necessary to deawn seed to facilitate cleaning.
Bromegrass, smooth...... (*Bromus inermis*)	x	.....	x		Direct combine, unless crop badly lodged.
Buffalograss............. (*Buchloe dactyloides*)	.....	x	x	.....	Requires special beater mounted in place of sickle for direct combine.
Canarygrass, reed........ (*Pholaris arundinacea*)	x	x	x	.....	When direct combined, the seed must be dried immediately.
Cenchrus, big*.......... (*Cenchrus myosuroides*)	.....	.....	.....		
Clover, crimson.......... (*Trifolium incarnatum*)	.....	x	x	.....	Sometimes double threshed.
Clover, Ladino........... (*Trifolium repens* var.)	.....	x	x	.....	
Clover, red.............. (*Trifolium pratense*)	.....	x	.....	.....	
Clover, sub............. (*Trifolium subterraneum*)	.....	x	.....	.....	
Cottontop, Arizona*..... (*Trichachne californica*)	.....	.....	.....		
Cowpea................. (*Vigna sinensis*)	.....	x	x	.....	
Dallisgrass.............. (*Paspalum dilatatum*)	.....	x	x	.....	Direct combining starts when a few spikelets have shattered and most are brown.
Fescue, chewings......... (*Festuca rubra* var. *commutata*)	.....	x	x	.....	To direct combine, harvest when seed are in the hard-dough stage.
Fescue, tall............. (*Festuca arundinacea*)	x	x	x	.....	Check for seed heating when direct combining.
Grama, blue........ (*Bouteloua gracilis*)	.....	.....	x	x	Combine in hard-dough stage. Windrow before full maturity.
Grama, sideoats......... (*Bouteloua curtipendula*)	.....	.....	x	x	

*Forage harvester can be used.

Crop name, common and botanical	Binder	Combine Windrow	Combine Direct	Stripper	Remarks
Hardinggrass (*Phalaris tuberosa* var. *stenoptera*)	x				
Indiangrass (*Sorghastrum nutans*)	x		x		
Lespedeza, annual (*Lespedeza striata*)		x			Some farmers mow and stack the hay for threshing at a later time.
Lovegrass, sand (*Eragrostis trichodes*)			x		
Lovegrass, weeping (*Eragrostis curvula*)	x		x		Make two runs with stripper.
Lupine (*Lupinus* species)		x	x		Windrowing should be done while seed are in medium- to hard-dough stage.
Meadow foxtail (*Alopecurus pratensis*)	x		x		Harvest as soon as seed will thresh; dry immediately.
Oatgrass, tall (*Arrhenatherum elatius*)	x		x		
Orchardgrass (*Dactylis glomerata*)	x		x		Combine within a 3-day period following seed ripening or seed will be lost by shattering.
Peas, field (*Pisum sativum arvense*)		x			
Redtop (*Agrostis alba*)	x	x	x		When combine harvested, cure immediately.
Ryegrass (*Lolium* species)	x	x	x		To direct combine, the field should be uniformly ripe, free from green weeds.
Soybean (*Glycine max*)			x		
Sprangletop, green (*Leptochloa dubia*)			x		
Sudangrass (*Sorghum sudanense*)	x		x		Usually seed do not ripen uniformly for combining; most of the seed crop is cut with a binder.
Sweetclover (*Melilotus* species)		x	x		Seed obtained in combining direct must be dried before hulling and cleaning.
Switchgrass (*Panicum virgatum*)	x		x		Combined seed should be dried to prevent heating.
Timothy (*Phleum pratense*)	x		x		Binders used little in large timothy producing areas.
Trefoil, birdsfoot (*Lotus corniculatus*)		x			After first seed sets begin shattering, cut when humidity is high or morning dew is on the plants.
Vetch, hairy (*Vicia villosa*)		x	x		Seed saved in windrow-combining justifies extra operation. In direct combining, fill sack only two-thirds full; let dry in field.
Wheatgrass, crested (*Agropyron cristatum*)	x	x	x		Harvest should begin at stiff-dough stage to reduce shattering.
Wheatgrass, western (*Agropyron smithii*)		x	x	x	Combined and stripped seeds should be allowed to cure before sacking.
Wheatgrass, slender (*Agropyron trachycaulum*)	x		x		Heavy shatter losses occur when direct combining.
Wildrye, Canada (*Elymus canadensis*)	x		x		To combine, use only partial width of cut.

burs to remove spines. This procedure is necessary before the burs can be planted.

The suction seed reclaimer is used as another combine attachment. It sucks shattered seeds from the ground during the harvesting operation and feeds them to the combine for threshing along with the incoming crop. The reclaimer recovered an average of 68 percent of the shattered seed in harvesting crimson clover. Eighty-nine percent of the seed was recovered in subterranean clover. The machine reclaimed only 11 percent of the shattered seed in birdsfoot trefoil, where the small, round, dense, naked seeds were beneath the stubble.

Tractor-drawn or self-propelled windrowing machines are 8 to 16 feet wide. They consist of a cutterbar and a draper conveyor that delivers the straw to the center or to one end.

Another type is the tined windrower, which consists of a series of metal tines—each one progressively longer—fastened to the back of the mower cutterbar so that the material being cut rolls into a continuous roll as the mower moves through the field.

The wheel windrower consists of two tined wheels mounted behind the mower cutterbar so that they come in contact with the ground and slowly rotate and gently fold the outer edges of the cut material toward the center to form a swath.

The width of material cut and put into the windrow should be about the same as the width of normal cut of the combine that is to be used to thresh the seed. Swathing the straw for the seed to cure is a method used to harvest seed crops such as bentgrass, alfalfa, bermudagrass, Merion bluegrass, buffalograss, and many others.

CHEMICAL SPRAYS may be used to hasten the curing of standing seed crops. They make it easier to combine a crop before the seeds shatter excessively.

Chemical curing has been effective in reducing cost and losses in the harvesting of seed in sunshine areas where the temperature is moderate to high. The chemicals give uncertain results in areas where cool nights, heavy dews, fogs, and cloudy days occur. For example, in the Willamette Valley of Oregon, a treatment may be worthless one time; the next time the chemical will dehydrate the leaves, seed pods, and stems enough so that the standing crop can be combined without damaging the seed or the roots. In California, where the temperature is higher and the humidity is lower, nearly all the alsike clover is chemically cured and direct combined with the aid of chemical sprays. The practice is used on Ladino clover, alfalfa, red clover, birdsfoot trefoil, sudangrass, Alta fescue, and orchardgrass.

The advantages are many where chemical dehydration and direct combining can be practiced. It saves the labor and equipment required to windrow a crop. The loss of seed caused by cutting, windrowing, and the pickup operations are saved by direct combine harvesting.

The rapid development of new agricultural chemicals has led to the appearance of many unproved desiccants on the market. To prevent the possibility of poor seed production, one should use only the chemicals that have been tested and recommended by agricultural experiment station specialists or county agents.

TIMING the harvest is important.

Tests in the Willamette Valley have shown that a day's delay in harvesting may result in severe loss of seed due to shatter. As an extreme example, yields of birdsfoot trefoil were found to be reduced about 25 percent over a 4-hour period of hot, sunny weather after several days of cool weather.

A 3-year study was made at the Oregon Agricultural Experiment Station of the effect of mowing time on the amount of pure, live seed collected in the combine grain bin. It showed that proper timing could increase by 75 percent the seed saved of crimson clo-

188   YEARBOOK OF AGRICULTURE 1961

ver, 36 percent of Alta fescue, and 60
percent of subterranean clover.

Early harvest does not work on all
seed crops, however. In the same test,
the take of pure live seed of birdsfoot
trefoil was reduced substantially by
early harvest. The first seed set was beginning to shatter before the germination of harvested seed was high enough
to meet the requirements of State and
interstate seed laws.

Enough nutrients were left in the
windrowed straw of crimson clover for
the seed to finish maturing. The result
was the largest amount of seed, the
highest germination, and the lowest
percentage of damaged and shriveled
seeds.

Records were kept of the appearance
of the stems, the leaves, the floret, the
seed, and the moisture content of the
seed. Color pictures were used as
guides to pinpoint the time to harvest
a crop for maximum yields. Only the
seed moisture at the time of cutting
was a true indication of the time to
windrow the crop each year.

Results of research studies indicate
that a seed is at its peak in quality at
maturity and that it should be harvested immediately in order to get the
highest percentage of quality seed.
Seeds start deteriorating immediately
upon reaching maturity, and all man
can do is to retard the change by regulating the time and method of harvest
and treatment after harvest.

JESSE E. HARMOND *is Head of the
Small Seed Harvesting and Processing Sec-
tion, Agricultural Engineering Division,
Agricultural Research Service. He began re-
search in agricultural engineering in the
Department in 1939. He established the
Seed Cleaning Research Laboratory on the
campus of Oregon State College in 1953.*

JAMES E. SMITH, JR., *is field plant materials technician for the Soil Conservation
Service in Texas, stationed at Temple, Tex.*

JOSEPH K. PARK *is an agricultural engineer in charge of research in the harvesting
of small seed, conducted by the Department
of Agriculture and Clemson Agricultural
Experiment Station, Clemson, S.C.*

Producing Seeds of Cotton and Other Fiber Crops

BILLY M. WADDLE AND REX F. COLWICK

FOUR LARGE companies produce the
cotton seed that is used on 90 percent
of the planted acreage in the Southern
and Southeastern States.

The rest of the acreage in that part
of the Cotton Belt is planted with seed
produced by public agencies and by
several companies that primarily serve
their own immediate districts.

In some parts of the Cotton Belt,
particularly in Texas and Oklahoma,
a large percentage of the planting seed
is produced by companies that supply
seed for local needs.

Most of the planting seed in the Far
Western States is produced by selected
growers under the supervision of the
grower-owned cooperative organizations, which control conditions rigidly
under the supervision of seed-certifying
agencies. They make the planting seed
available to the producers at prices
slightly above costs.

Public agencies conduct the breeding programs in the Western States.
When the new varieties are developed
and proved, small amounts of early-in-
crease seed lots are made available to
the organizations of cotton seed growers. They increase the seed through the
steps of foundation, registered, and
certified categories and distribute the
seed to the growers. In each State, except California, the controls that guarantee purity are under the direction
of the State's official seed-certifying
agency.

The seed-distributing agency in
California is grower owned and works
closely with the breeders at the U.S.
Cotton Field Station at Shafter in the

development and distribution of pure seed to the growers of the San Joaquin Valley. The organization is its own certifying agency. Small amounts of selfed seed are furnished the distributors by the field station. The subsequent increases and sales are controlled by the distributors. Technical supervision in the maintenance of pure seed is furnished by station officials. The result is the production and maintenance of adequate supplies of high-yielding, pure seed of highest quality at a relatively low cost.

Different procedures are used by the seed companies and public agencies in their improvement programs.

One is the pedigree method, which uses inbred lines for composite mixtures, in which inbred lines and the composites are tested for yield and fiber quality.

Another is the selection of numerous open-pollinated plants in pure seed fields and subsequent elimination of undesirable types by yield and fiber tests. The best strains are kept for final increase.

A third procedure is the selection of limited numbers of individual plants from chosen fields of registered or foundation plantings. Such selections are also screened vigorously by strain and fiber tests to give the best stocks.

After the extensive selection and testing phases of the programs have produced the variety or varieties judged to be superior in one or more attributes, the seed-increase program is inaugurated, and the variety is released.

Most of the seed companies utilize a number of similar features in their variety-increase programs. Three steps are usual.

Foundation seed is produced from breeder seed or parent seed. Care is taken to maintain the proper isolation from other varieties and types of cotton—cotton is easily cross-pollinated by bees and other insects—and to assure that no contamination results from volunteer plants in the field. Great care is exercised to prevent the mixing of seed when it is harvested, ginned, and bagged.

The increase phase from the foundation seed is generally known as registered seed and goes through essentially the same procedures as for the production of the foundation seed, except that the requirements for isolation and amount of contamination are not quite so rigid as in the earlier phase.

The final stage is known as certified seed and may be produced for 1 or 2 years, depending on the practices of the seed-certifying agency in a given State. Certified seed usually composes the bulk of planting seed stock for the producers.

In all stages of the work to multiply the seed of a variety, close supervision is maintained by the Crop or Seed Improvement Association to assure varietal purity and the best possible seed for cotton producers.

The responsibility of the seed-certifying agencies in most of the States where cotton seed is produced for planting in the Cotton Belt is to assure purity and germinating ability of the seed. The Crop Improvement Association approves applications from growers to produce seed in the certification program and inspects the fields for proper isolation and possible contamination by weeds and offtype cotton plants. Sometimes an association may supervise the ginning of the cotton and the bagging of the seed.

All seed companies and associations engaged in producing and selling pure seed utilize the services of official seed-testing laboratories.

The laboratories determine the germination percentage (which must not be below a specified minimum), the percentage of impurities in the form of seeds of other crops and weeds; inert matter; and the total percentage of pure seed.

The farmer who buys approved varieties of seed that have been tested by an approved laboratory and carry the label of the Crop Improvement Association therefore is assured of the best possible seed.

In the South and Southeast, the seed companies commonly make contracts with dependable farmers for seed for use by the industry. The contract growers agree to produce the seed under the restrictions and controls of the official certifying agency to guarantee varietal purity.

The production of pure seed by the small companies of Texas and Oklahoma for their own localities usually is confined to the company landholdings, and contractual arrangements are not common.

In the grower-owned seed organizations of California, New Mexico, and Arizona, contracts are made with the farmers to produce the pure seed under stipulated conditions of land cleanliness, isolation, and approved production practices. The seed organizations supervise the contracts.

The production of pure seed in all regions of the Cotton Belt is processed by one-variety gins or by gins that are thoroughly cleaned before the ginning of pure seed. This practice further assures a minimum of risk of seed mixtures and is considered one of the prime requisites in the production of pure seed.

In ginning, the cotton is subjected to a minimum amount of machining. A loose seed roll is used to avoid mechanical damage.

Delinting—the removal of seedcoat hairs and short fibers that remain after ginning—is common throughout the Cotton Belt. Chemical delinting, mechanical delinting, and flame delinting are used.

Chemical delinting uses concentrated sulfuric acid (with later washing in water) or hydrochloric acid gas (later neutralized by soda ash). Chemically delinted seed is used mainly in the western irrigated part of the belt. Commercial acid-delinting plants are in all the Western States.

Mechanical delinting is performed by the same type of machinery that is used by the cotton oil mills to remove seed fuzz before the crushing of the seed. The use of mechanically delinted seed is common throughout the belt, but it is less popular in the Western States than the acid-delinted seeds.

Flame delinting has gained some popularity. It removes some of the seed fuzz. Some large producers in the South use it to remove any patches of fuzz on machine-delinted seed.

The use of delinted cotton seeds allows a more precise seeding rate, which aids in planting to a stand and more rapid germination. Another advantage is the ease with which the delinted seed is graded by gravity grading machines. The light, immature seed can be removed; the quality is improved thereby. Fuzzy seeds also are gravity graded, but the process is not so effective as with delinted seeds.

Fungicides are applied to the seeds before planting to destroy or remove seedborne disease organisms. The treatment is recommended for all planting seed in the Cotton Belt. In the slurry method, the seeds are treated with a water-fungicide mixture.

Fuzzy (nondelinted) seed may be treated by dust applications of the appropriate fungicide, but slurry treatments are also used. Delinted seeds are treated easily by the slurry method.

In localities where the pink bollworm is a problem, quarantine regulations have been established to help prevent its spread. Seeds sent from an area of pink bollworm infestation to another area must receive appropriate treatment to assure bollworm-free seeds in the shipment. Steam sterilization treatment of all cotton seeds is practiced in Arizona. Extreme care is necessary to prevent damage by overexposure to heat and steam. Methyl bromide gas or other approved treatments may be used in other States.

Cotton seeds and the attached fiber (seed cotton) are harvested by hand or machine. About 50 percent of our cotton crop is harvested by hand. The worker grasps the seed cotton and picks it from the bur or snaps the bur containing the fiber and seed from the stem. The seed cotton is placed in a bag or basket and carried to a wagon or trailer. When the trailer is fully loaded, it is taken to a cotton gin, where the seeds are separated from the lint by ginning.

The procedure in machine harvesting is like hand harvesting, except that the machine replaces human hands in the removal of the seed cotton from the plant. The two machine-harvesting methods are picking and stripping. Mechanical picking by spindle machine removes only the lint and seed from the plant. The burs, unopened bolls, and plant are left intact. Mechanical stripping removes the burs, bolls, and some leaves and stems from the plant. Stripping is necessarily a once-over operation and must be conducted after frost or defoliation.

Mechanical picking by spindle machine can be done several times as the crop matures. It is often possible therefore to obtain more uniformly mature seed from mechanical picking than from once-over stripping. The Far Western States harvest up to 90 percent of the crop by this method.

Hand snapping and machine stripping are practiced chiefly in the western parts of Texas and Oklahoma, where about 30 percent of the United States crop is grown. Picking by hand or spindle machine is practiced in the rest of the Cotton Belt.

The precautions to be observed in harvesting to maintain high quality are generally like those needed to maintain the quality of the cotton fiber. Timing the harvest when the cotton is fully and uniformly mature is first. Clean harvesting with a minimum amount of such material as grass, leaves, and plant bark permits minimum handling and cleaning in the gin. It reduces the possibility of mechanical damage from excessive machining of the fiber.

To reduce leaf trash in the harvested cotton, the leaves often are removed from the plant or killed by the application of a chemical in spray or dust form. The chemicals that remove the leaves from the plant are called defoliants. Those that kill the leaves on the plant are called desiccants. Defoliation is practiced primarily to aid mechanical picking. Desiccation is used chiefly to facilitate stripping before frost.

Cotton should not be harvested while it is wet from dew or rain. If seed cotton is stored in the trailer or elsewhere at a moisture content of 12 percent or more, heating will occur and damage the seed and fiber. Damp cotton requires more processing in the gin and exposes the seeds to more mechanical damage.

The time of harvest of the cotton crop may affect the quality of seed. In parts of the irrigated West where it is more efficient to harvest only one time by mechanical harvester, it is necessary to defoliate before the first killing frost or to wait until after frost for the single harvest.

For the production of the best seed, it is necessary to harvest the first part of the crop before first frost to assure that all seed saved for planting will be fully matured. Therefore the practice of hand harvesting the early-season crop for planting seed is common in some places. The agencies handling cotton seed will not accept seed harvested after frost except in an emergency.

In the rain-grown areas of the Cotton Belt, adverse weather may lower the quality of the seed. Excess rain in the early or midpart of the harvest season may be harmful. In years of bad weather, such as 1957, substandard seed may be accepted from necessity. Most of the larger companies operate at enough different locations to counterbalance this problem in most years, unless unusual weather occurs generally over large areas.

If the seed is suspected of having poor quality following excessive rainfall, some checks are available to the seedsmen. A preliminary free-fatty acid test of the seed may be used to pinpoint germination potential. Excessive free-fatty acid is an indication of low quality, and this advance information can be of value to the seedsman in saving his planting seeds.

The storage of seed with excess moisture because of rainfall just before harvest may result in the lowering of seed quality or the destruction of the seed. Most distributing organizations have proper storage bins, including facilities for drying moist seed with forced air.

All of the varietal maintenance and production programs we have discussed are efficient and successful. If the farmer plants genetically pure seed of the variety or varieties recommended for his soil and climatic conditions, he is sure he has the best possible seeds.

THE PRODUCTION of planting seed of leaf and stem fiber crops is on an experimental basis in the United States. There is no large commercial production of fiber crops other than cotton in the Nation. Flax and hemp are no longer produced for fiber in this country, but seed stocks of the best varieties that have been developed by research agencies are maintained.

Kenaf has shown some promise of being a good substitute for jute in the event of emergency needs. Considerable research on this crop has led to varieties that are high yielding and resistant to some of the major diseases that attack the crop. The seed can be harvested with machines, but the acreage is so small that only limited amounts of seed are maintained.

Other fiber crops—sansevieria, ramie, phormium, and jute—are propagated vegetatively. Research in mechanizing the propagation, growing, and harvesting of some of them is carried on by public agencies.

BILLY M. WADDLE *became Assistant Branch Chief of the Cotton and Cordage Fibers Research Branch, Crops Research Division, Agricultural Research Service, at Beltsville, Md., in 1958.*

REX F. COLWICK *became Head of Cotton Harvesting Investigations of Harvesting and Farm Processing Branch, Agricultural Engineering Research Division, at State College, Miss., in 1959.*

Producing and Harvesting Seeds of Oilseed Crops

J. O. CULBERTSON, H. W. JOHNSON, AND L. G. SCHOENLEBER

THE LEADING oilseed crops grown in the United States are soybeans, peanuts, flaxseed, safflower, castorbeans, and sesame. A large amount of oil is obtained from cottonseed, but cotton is a fiber crop, and we do not consider it here.

The seeds and oil from them have many uses.

Soybean oil is used in margarine, shortening, paints, varnishes, and other industrial products. Although soybeans are generally classified as an oilseed, the monetary value of the protein, or meal, equals or exceeds that of the oil.

Peanut oil is used for edible purposes.

Nearly all linseed oil from flaxseed goes into the manufacture of paints, varnishes, and linoleum.

Safflower oil is used primarily as a drying oil, but an increasing amount is being consumed in edible products.

The major uses of castor oil are as a drying oil and for hydraulic fluids.

Nearly all the sesame grown in this country is consumed as whole seed.

The harvested acreages of soybeans, peanuts, and flax in the United States in 1960 were about 23.6, 1.5, and 3.3 million acres, respectively.

Safflower acreage has been rising steadily, and about 300 thousand acres were grown in 1960. Castorbean acreage in 1960 was about 30 thousand, and that for sesame, 10 thousand.

The same general cultural practices that produce the best yields of high-quality seed for industrial uses also produce the best seed for planting.

The control of weeds is important in the production of all the oilseeds and is especially important in the production of planting seed. The presence of seed of noxious weeds may cause otherwise good planting seed to be rejected for certification and is sufficient cause for a farmer to refuse to buy uncertified seed. Weeds may also reduce yields and cause difficulties in harvesting. Weed seeds similar in size and weight to the harvested oilseed make further cleaning difficult and expensive.

Chemical weed control has given excellent results with flax and appears promising with peanuts, safflower, sesame, and soybeans. Current recommendations about materials and rates should be obtained locally.

Special aspects, if any, of final preparation of the seedbed are discussed for specific crops in the following sections. It is assumed that basic procedures of early seedbed preparation will be followed before the final preparation.

All oilseed crops are normally self-pollinated, but enough natural cross-pollination occurs to be troublesome when different varieties are grown close together. Safe distances between different varieties vary with the crop.

The isolation of fields intended for seed is treated in a later chapter.

THE LENGTH of days and nights is the primary factor in the flowering and maturing of soybeans.

Each variety has rather specific photoperiod requirements for flowering. Varieties are adapted to the photoperiods of rather narrow latitudinal belts running east and west. A variety grown north of its area of adaptation flowers and matures too late. One grown too far south flowers and matures too early. The most successful production is normally obtained from varieties that utilize the full growing season but mature before frost.

Soybeans do best on fertile, well-drained soils, but they are tolerant of a wide range of soil conditions. They are highly susceptible to salt damage in saline soils. Soil conditions determine

their need for fertilizer and lime. Soybeans require relatively large amounts of phosphorus, potassium, and calcium and a pH of about 6.0 for maximum yields.

The soybean, a legume, can be produced successfully without nitrogen fertilizers if it is properly nodulated. Planting seed should be inoculated unless the bacteria are known to be present in the soil. Some growers inoculate the seed every year. Others do not inoculate seed if a well-nodulated crop has been grown on the field within the previous 4 or 5 years. Inoculum prepared specifically for soybeans should be used. It can be applied following chemical treatment of the seed.

Soybeans are normally planted, cultivated, and harvested with equipment used in the production of other crops. The primary consideration in preparation of the seedbed is that weeds should be destroyed immediately before planting.

Most soybeans in the United States are planted in May or June in rows 36–42 inches apart at a rate of about one viable seed per inch of row (40–60 pounds to the acre). Row spacings of less than 36 inches often give increased yields in northern areas; the amount of the increase depends on variety, location, and growing conditions.

Planters should be fitted with soybean plates to prevent serious injury to the seed.

Cultivation with a rotary hoe, drag harrow, or similar implement should begin as soon after complete emergence as necessary to control weeds. Subsequent cultivation may be done with row cultivating equipment.

All seeds on a soybean plant mature at about the same time. At the time the seed matures, leaves soon drop off and the stems dry. The final maturing process is so rapid that chemicals applied early enough to hasten the harvest date reduce the yield.

Harvesting is done with a combine harvester. The moisture in the seed should be 14 percent or less, unless the seed is to be dried artificially.

Mechanical injury increases as the moisture content of the seed drops. When seed moisture goes below 10 percent, cracking of the seedcoat and injury to the embryo are more likely to occur in threshing.

Moisture content of seeds and pods may change enough during the day to necessitate adjustments in the speed of the combine cylinder. Cylinder speed should be just fast enough for proper threshing action.

Soybean seed should be combined as soon after maturity as possible to reduce chances of weather damage. Rain and high temperatures after maturity cause rapid deterioration in quality of the seed. Some varieties withstand such conditions better than others, but long periods of warm, rainy weather will damage the seed of all.

Several seedborne diseases affect soybeans, but none need be of serious concern to the seed producer. They are so widespread in the established production areas of the United States that there is little likelihood of seriously increasing their distribution on seeds.

PEANUTS grow their seeds underground. Light-textured soils that do not bake are best. Large amounts of nitrogen, potash, or organic matter are unfavorable. Peanuts grow best on soils with a pH of 6.0 to 6.5 if enough lime is available for normal development.

Peanuts should be planted in a deep, firm seedbed when the soil is thoroughly warm. Planting machines that have seed boxes using slow-moving slant plates and seed cells of the proper size should be used to reduce injury to the tender seeds and seedcoats.

Recommended planting rates range from 35 pounds an acre for small-seeded varieties planted in 36-inch rows to 96 pounds an acre for large-seeded varieties planted in 24-inch rows.

Proper disposal of debris from previous crops before planting operations and careful cultivation to prevent covering leaves, stems, or plants help reduce the incidence of stem rot and enhance yields. Some hand hoeing may be required to remove weeds near the plants.

Numerous diseases and several nematodes may attack peanuts, but relatively few are likely to be serious. They include seedling diseases; heat canker; leaf spot; southern blight; various root, peg, pod, and seed rots; black pod; and concealed damage within the seed.

Two vital factors in sections where peanuts are widely grown are an adequate (but not excessive) supply of soil moisture from the onset of heavy flowering until about 2 weeks before digging, and a generous supply of readily available calcium in the top 3 or 4 inches of the soil where the pods are developing.

Without enough calcium in the fruiting zone of the soil, the seeds may abort, or their development may be impaired at any stage until shortly before full maturity.

Drought accentuates the adverse effects of calcium deficiency in the fruiting zone on seed development. Large-seeded varieties seem to be harmed more by such a deficiency than those with smaller seeds.

Two-thirds of the peanut crop now is cured in the windrow for several days to 2 weeks or longer. The rates at which peanuts dry or cure in different positions in the windrow vary. During warm, sunny periods, seeds in pods that are exposed to direct sunlight may dry too rapidly, become hard, have impaired viability, lose their seedcoats, and have a high percentage of breakage on shelling. Seed pods at the bottom of the windrow may become overrun with molds in warm and rainy weather.

The seed peanuts of the highest quality are cured slowly in moderate to cool temperatures. Curing in carefully constructed stacks usually can be expected to give better seed peanuts than curing in windrows.

Harvesting peanuts to insure seed of high quality begins with digging operations. Proper digging, shaking, and loose windrowing to remove all soil from the vines help provide the uniform drying conditions essential for satisfactory combining.

The peanuts should be picked carefully with the picker or combine, which should be operated at the slowest feasible rate. The plants should be fed into the machine at a uniformly moderate rate. With proper adjustments, the recently developed combination carding-cylinder-stemmer combines harvest properly cured, windrowed peanuts with little damage to the seed.

Peanut seeds are among the most delicate that the grower handles. The shelling operation is a violent one. Few seeds come through it uninjured; 2 to 15 percent of the seed may be split in shelling. Others will have ruptured seedcoats, and one or both of the cotyledons may be partly broken away from the embryonic axis. Pieces of the cotyledons of some are broken off. Those that appear to have seedcoats intact often are bruised.

Factors that reduce damage in shelling are freedom from foreign material, such as sticks, stones, and woody pieces of the peanut plant; use of a grid of the proper size for the peanuts to be shelled; operation of the sheller at a moderate speed; and shelling at a time when the moisture of the seeds is about 8 percent.

FLAX grows best on fertile soil that produces good crops of small grain or corn.

Results from commercial fertilizers have been uncertain, but often fertilizer has increased yields of flax in the same places where it has benefited small grain. Heavy rates of nitrogen stimulate growth of weeds and may do more harm than good to flax.

The seedbed should be firm and well packed below the surface inch and free from large clods. Flax competes poorly with weeds. As many weed seedlings as possible should be destroyed when the seedbed is being prepared.

Flax normally is sown early in the spring in the North Central States. It may be sown from November to January as a winter crop in California, Arizona, and Texas.

About 35 pounds of seed are sown per acre in the drier sections. This may be increased to 56 pounds in more humid areas or for production under irrigation.

Losses from rust, wilt, and pasmo have been spectacular at times, but present varieties have a high degree of resistance to rust and wilt and considerable tolerance to pasmo. Two virus diseases, aster yellows in the North Central States and curly top in California and Texas, have been serious on a few occasions.

Seed of flax should be harvested as soon as it is mature. Maturity is judged by the color of the seed bolls rather than the stems. Flax is considered mature enough to harvest when 90 percent of the bolls have turned brown. In cool, wet years, some varieties may still have green stems when the seed is mature.

Late flowers often fail to set seed in the north-central region. Seeds that develop from late flowers are immature when growth ends and are lost in harvesting and cleaning. Harvest therefore should not be delayed in the hope of getting a bigger yield from late flowers.

On the other hand, flax may be induced by extra fertilizer and irrigation to form two or three consecutive sets of seed when it is grown as a fall-sown crop in the Southwest. Quality of seed normally is not lowered by the delay in harvest in the Southwest.

Nearly all flax, whether for seed or market, is harvested with a swather followed by a pickup combine as soon as the straw is dry enough to thresh. The weather between swathing and combining affects quality. Rain on the swath may cause weathering and discoloration of the seed and allow parasitic fungi, which may later reduce the viability, to grow on the seed.

Extra care needs to be given to threshing flax, especially when it is to be used for planting seed. The seedcoat is injured easily during threshing, especially if the seeds are very dry. It may be advisable to reduce cylinder speed slightly, as the seeds become progressively drier during the day. Sometimes seeds of better quality may be produced if threshing or combining is discontinued during the middle of the day, when the humidity is low.

The most important cause of poor germination of flax seeds is directly associated with a mechanical injury. Farmers' seed lots have been found to contain 10 to 50 percent of cracked seed. The cracks may be microscopic scratches or major cracks that nearly sever the seed. Bruises that are hard to see also may reduce germination.

If mechanically damaged seeds germinate at all, the seedlings are usually malformed. Disease organisms may enter the seeds through the cracks, rot the seeds, and prevent germination. Chemical treatment of damaged seeds usually increases emergence of seedlings.

A yellow seedcoat is associated with natural splitting of the seedcoat over the germ end of the seed. Yellow seeds crack more easily in harvesting and threshing than brown seeds. Such injury permits disease organisms to enter and damage the seed before the seedling can emerge.

The use of a chemical seed treatment frequently is more effective with yellow- than the brown-seeded varieties of flax.

SAFFLOWER is a member of the thistle family. All cultivated varieties have spiny leaves and seed heads, but complete mechanization of production spares one the discomfort the spines can cause.

Soils suited to the production of small grain are satisfactory for safflower.

Commercial fertilizers have increased yields under irrigation and in sections where rainfall is plentiful but not excessive. The use of too much nitrogen, however, may cause heavy growth of weeds.

Safflower on nonirrigated land is seeded with a grain drill at about 20 pounds of seed to the acre. If irrigation is used, it is best to plant on beds 40 inches from center to center with two rows 14 inches apart on each bed.

The highest yields of safflower are produced under irrigation or on subirrigated land following a crop of rice. Too much soil moisture, particularly after a period of stress, can cause considerable damage from root rot. Irrigation should not be excessive at any time.

Safflower may be planted as early as November as a winter-sown crop in the Southwest. Spring sowing may extend from February in California to early May in Montana.

Weed control is important. One should try hard to destroy seedlings in preparing the seedbed. The rotary hoe has been effective in reducing weed growth when the weed seedlings are small and the safflower plants are growing vigorously. Cultivation with ordinary cultivating equipment is satisfactory when the crop is grown in rows.

The most serious diseases of safflower are rust, root rot, and leaf spot. Use of disease-free seed, treatment with a volatile mercury fungicide, and crop rotation will reduce losses from rust. Root rot may be kept low by frequent light irrigation. Seed treatment and crop rotation have been effective in the control of leaf spot.

Careless handling of the combine at harvesttime may result in damaged seed, but safflower is less easily damaged than sesame and flax. Fewer concave and cylinder teeth are required than for small grain. The teeth of cylinder and concave should just mesh. Rub- or bar-type cylinders should be adjusted to about one-half inch clearance with the concaves.

Safflower threshes more slowly than barley and wheat. The speed of the combine should be adjusted so that a minimum of seeds are cracked in the threshing.

Safflower for seed should be combined promptly when the heads turn brown and the seeds are hard. Wet weather after maturity may cause germination in the head and encourage the growth of disease-producing organisms, which lower germination.

CASTORBEANS are grown in cultivated rows on fertile soils, such as are suitable to cotton, corn, and grain sorghum. The seedbed should be well prepared and firm.

Often it is advantageous to use more fertilizer than with the other oilseeds. The fertilizer rates and formulations that are best for corn, cotton, and grain sorghum generally are best. An additional application of nitrogen may be required if the plants show stunting or yellowing during the growing season.

Castorbeans are planted in the spring after the soil is warm and danger of frost is past. Planting rates vary with the size of seed, but are generally from 10–15 pounds per acre.

Weed control in castorbeans is similar to that in corn, grain sorghum, and other tall-growing row crops. Ordinary cultivators are used.

Castorbeans have relatively few serious diseases in the areas of commercial production. *Alternaria* leaf spot, bacterial leaf spot, and *Alternaria* capsule mold are the most serious.

Alternaria leaf spot and bacterial leaf spot may be controlled partly by the use of resistant varieties. Sufficient fertilizer, especially nitrogen, seems to reduce the loss from *Alternaria* leaf spot. We know of no practical control of *Alternaria* capsule mold. The disease may be avoided by restricting the crop to irrigated areas of low humidity.

Row-crop planters used on other crops are suitable for planting castorbeans. They should be equipped with planter boxes that have special seed plates of proper cell size. The plates should rotate slowly to prevent seed breakage and a buildup of oily residue on the plates. Residue buildup that may occur over a period can be controlled best by adding a little coarse cornmeal or similar material in the seedbox with the castorbean seeds.

Careful planting to obtain a uniform stand promotes the uniformly shaped plants that are the most desirable for harvesting.

Castorbeans normally are harvested and threshed in a single operation with a machine specially built for the purpose. A header attachment has been designed that will convert one make of small grain combine into a castorbean harvester.

Castorbean harvesters are two- or four-row machines. Some are self-propelled. Others are mounted on tractors. All employ the same methods of harvesting and hulling the castorbeans. The capsules are knocked from the plants by rotary knockers, which strike the stems of the plants a few inches above the ground.

The capsules fall into conveyors, which carry them to scalpers to remove sticks and leaves. The capsules are then passed through a huller device to remove the hulls from the seeds. Machines that have no scalpers move the capsules directly to the huller. This device consists of two rubber-covered disks (one stationary and one rotating), two rubber-covered rotating cylinders, or a rubber-covered cylinder and rubber concave to remove gently the hulls from the fragile seeds.

Cleaning is done by blowing the hulls and immature seeds from the sound seeds. Proper adjustment between the rubber hulling surfaces is essential so that all capsules are separated and hulls removed.

With reasonable care, one can harvest and hull castorbeans that are relatively free from mechanical damage.

Once the castorbean seed is hulled, it must be handled carefully to prevent breakage or seed injury. Frequent handling and harsh treatment with conveyors cause breakage. Conveyors with clearances more than the dimensions of the seed are best suited for loose seed.

The castorbean plant is indeterminate in its growth habit and continues to set new spikes until harvest. Mature seed, fully formed green seeds, and partly developed green seeds are all present at the same time. The green leaves must be removed and green capsules allowed to dry before harvesting. Usually frost is allowed to kill the plants, or chemical defoliants may be used. About 2 weeks are required between frost or defoliation and the time the plants are dry enough to harvest.

Immature seeds may seem to be of good planting quality. If they are pressed between the thumb and forefinger, however, the seedcoats break with a distinct popping sound, and the seeds are found to be only partly formed. These seeds are known as pops, and have little value as planting stock.

Seed that has a low weight per bushel but appears good in other respects contains a high percentage of pops and usually will not be satisfactory for planting. Recleaning the seed with a gravity table or a strong airblast, or both, should remove the lightest seed and improve the value of the seed for planting.

Castorbeans are poisonous to people and animals. Precautions must be taken to prevent mixing the seeds with food or feed crops.

SESAME does best on fertile, well-drained soils of medium texture with a neutral reaction.

Commercial fertilizers suitable for cotton are satisfactory for sesame on the same soil.

The seedbed should be mellow, warm, and moist.

Sesame seeds are small. One pound contains about 150 thousand seeds. The seedlings emerge from the soil quickly when conditions are favorable, but the small plants make slow growth at first.

It is harder to establish a good stand of sesame than some other oilseed crops. The crop requires a warm soil and warm weather. A cool period after planting may destroy the stand. A heavy rain after planting may compact the soil and prevent uniform emergence. Replanting may be necessary then.

Sesame is normally planted about 1 pound per acre in rows 36–42 inches apart. Vegetable planter boxes are used. Ordinary cultivating equipment used for corn, cotton, and grain sorghum may be used to control weeds.

The small, rather soft seeds are easily damaged in harvesting, particularly threshing.

Two types of sesame are grown. One is dehiscent—that is, the capsules open when dried after maturity, and the seeds spill out. This type requires little mechanical work to remove the seeds from the capsules.

The other type has indehiscent capsules, which are difficult to thresh.

Since little effort is required to remove the seeds from dehiscent capsules, the cylinder on the combine may be set as far as possible from the concave. Slow cylinder speeds of not over 500 revolutions a minute for 21-inch cylinders, 580 for 18-inch, or 700 for 15-inch cylinders should be used. A slower speed may be used if all the seed is removed. The threshing surface may be increased to at least double the standard area by increasing the number of cylinder bars, concave bars, or both. Tailings should be returned directly to the shakers and not the cylinder.

Undesirable seeds, such as seeds of johnsongrass, that are harvested with sesame are extremely difficult and expensive to remove. Every effort should be made to eradicate johnsongrass plants before harvest.

Considerable success has been attained in breeding indehiscent varieties that do not shatter their seeds at maturity. Although indehiscent varieties available in 1961 were not widely grown, improved varieties may be developed that will have acceptable yield and quality of seed and can be grown by complete mechanization.

Threshing indehiscent varieties is more difficult than for dehiscent varieties and requires extra care. The plants are cut and windrowed with standard machinery. Most sesame is grown under irrigation, and the windrows are placed on the rows and not in the irrigation furrows, where pickup would be difficult and seed damage from rainwater standing in the furrows might occur. The plants should be dry and brittle before combining is attempted. This may be 2 or 3 weeks after windrowing.

The capsules of nonshattering varieties are hard. The seeds are soft and easily damaged. Even microscopic cracks in the seedcoat can reduce the viability of the seeds.

Cylinder speeds should be reduced below the requirements for small grain or sorghum to approximately 500, 580, or 700 revolutions per minute for 21-, 18-, or 15-inch cylinders, respectively. As for dehiscent sesame, the threshing surface should be doubled by adding additional cylinder bars, concave bars, or both. Cylinder clearance should be set to one-eighth inch. Unthreshed capsules should be returned to the cylinder.

Indehiscent seeds sustain more mechanical damage than dehiscent seeds. A rough estimate of damage can be obtained if 100 seeds are examined for injury. If fewer than 20 percent have injuries, one can assume the combine is doing an acceptable job. Both sides of each seed should be examined.

A number of serious diseases of sesame are carried on the seed. Some measure of control can be attained by producing seed free from disease and by proper seed treatment. If seed free from seedborne diseases is sown on ground not in sesame for several years and if the harvested seed is protected from weather and mechanical damage, the danger from seedborne diseases will be diminished.

J. O. CULBERTSON is Leader, Industrial Crops Investigations, Oilseed and Industrial Crops Research Branch.

H. W. JOHNSON is Leader, Soybean Investigations, Oilseed and Industrial Crops Research Branch, Beltsville, Md.

L. G. SCHOENLEBER is Leader, Special Crops Harvesting and Processing Investigations, Harvesting and Farm Processing Research Branch, Stillwater, Okla.

New Ways With Seeds of Sugarbeets

DEWEY STEWART

THE OLD method of producing seeds of sugarbeets was to grow vegetative plants one season, store them over winter in pits or field trenches, and reset them in the field the second year to let them seed.

Because it took so much work, the production of the seed cost more in this country than in Europe, and for many years the American beet sugar industry relied on the European sources of seed.

Research workers of the New Mexico Agricultural Experiment Station and the Department of Agriculture demonstrated in the 1920's that excellent yields of seed could be had in the southern part of New Mexico if the sugarbeet were grown on the seasonal schedule of a winter annual—a plant from fall-sown seed that blooms and fruits the following spring.

The new method—the winter-annual method—was developed by J. C. Overpeck and his coworkers. It greatly reduced labor requirements and permitted complete mechanization of the field operations. It met the need for homegrown seed of disease-resistant varieties.

Seed was grown by the winter-annual method on 62 acres in 1932. More than 12 million pounds of sugarbeet seeds were produced on about 7 thousand acres in 1937.

The winter-annual method proved to be successful also in the Virgin River Valley of southern Utah, the Salt River Valley of Arizona, the Willamette River Valley of Oregon, and southern California.

We produced enough seeds for our needs and for export to Europe during the Second World War. More than 10 million pounds were shipped overseas in 1947, but the seed became a small item of foreign trade as soon as the European countries could reconstruct their own seed establishments.

THE SUGARBEET and other cultivated varieties of *Beta vulgaris* produce two to five or more flowers in dense clusters. The flowers cohere at the base and grow together during maturation to form glomerate fruits, which usually comprise as many seeds as there were flowers in the cluster. The dry, hard fruits are the "seed" of commerce and often are referred to as glomerules, seedballs, or multigerm seed.

The first fruits formed on the spikes of the flowering sugarbeet are the largest. The size of fruit and the number of seeds per fruit get smaller toward the end of the branches. The fruits formed on the tips usually are single seeded.

Investigators have found sugarbeet plants that have a single flower in each axis of the entire inflorescence.

These plants produce single-seeded fruits, or monogerm seed. This characteristic is inheritable, and monogerm varieties of sugarbeets have now been developed.

The sugarbeet is a biennial plant and normally requires two seasons for the growth of seed plants.

When the sugarbeet is grown for sugar, only the vegetative phase of growth—a rosette of leaves and the fleshy taproot that yields the sugar—is desired.

The reproductive phase of growth, with the production of seedstalk and flowering branches, can be induced in vegetative plants by cool temperatures. This temperature effect is called thermal induction.

Length of day, or photoperiod, also influences the growth and development of the sugarbeet, and the effect of temperature and light as an impulse to reproductive development is referred to as photothermal induction.

The temperatures that favor reproductive development in sugarbeets are fairly well established. Temperatures above 70° F. favor only vegetative growth. With proper nutrition and protection from hazards, the sugarbeet can be grown vegetatively for several years. Temperatures near freezing greatly reduce metabolic activity and have low inductive effect. The most effective range of temperatures for thermal induction is 45° to 55°.

Most commercial varieties of sugarbeets require 90 to 110 days of exposure to inductive temperatures for reproductive development. In a district suited to the production of sugarbeet seed by the winter-annual method, therefore, the winters must be mild to permit survival of the plants, but the period of cool temperatures must be long enough to supply the photothermal induction required for reproductive growth the following spring.

If the sugarbeet is grown for sugar in a region where the photothermal effect is just on the threshold of inducing reproductive development, some of the plants will shoot seedstalks. A few may produce seeds. These precocious plants are bolters.

Bolters reduce yield and quality and increase the amount of trash to be handled in the field and at the factory. Varieties that resist bolting have been developed for use in northern regions and in southern districts where spring weather supplies high dosages of photothermal induction.

Breeding work to develop sugarbeet varieties usually is conducted in the region where the varieties will be used for sugar production. The level of bolting resistance established in the basic strains is maintained through seed produced in a manner that forces all parental plants into reproductive development. The district chosen for commercial seed production by the winter-annual method must supply the photothermal requirements bred into the variety.

Bolting-resistant varieties are grown chiefly in the Willamette Valley and in other regions that have relatively long, mild winters. Commercial seed of varieties of ordinary bolting resistance can be produced farther south.

As long as the breeder knows the photothermal requirement of the elite—foundation—seed and chooses the proper district for commercial seed production, no great change in the level of bolting resistance should result from one generation of increase by the winter-annual method.

Photothermal requirements for reproductive growth can be established rather precisely in varieties through breeding. It is important to maintain this varietal characteristic in the commercial seed supplied to the grower.

THE BOLTING resistance of a variety has definite bearing on regional adaptation for production of sugar and on the district in which seed can be grown by the winter-annual method.

If seed of a bolting-resistant variety is produced in a district where winter conditions do not force all plants of the population into flowering and seeding, there will be a natural selection toward a lower level of inductive requirement.

We can illustrate the remarkable manner in which different levels of photothermal requirement determine regional adaptation of varieties of sugarbeet and the choice of seed for planting by referring to the Imperial Valley of California and the Salt River Valley of Arizona.

The Salt River Valley has the largest acreage of sugarbeets for seed in the United States. This district, centering around Phoenix, in 1948 produced more than 11 million pounds of seed, with a germination of 93 percent, on about 3 thousand acres. With a lower demand for seed in later years, the production has leveled off at about 5 million pounds annually. All the seed is produced by the winter-annual method.

The Imperial Valley, which is ap-proximately 250 miles west, 40 miles south ($\frac{1}{2}$° latitude), and 1,200 feet lower in elevation than Phoenix, produces more than 100 thousand tons of sugar annually from roots grown on approximately 40 thousand acres. The acreage is grown as a winter crop.

The sugarbeet is fall sown in both the Salt River Valley and the Imperial Valley. A considerable acreage is planted concurrently in September.

The products harvested from the sugarbeet in the two valleys are strikingly different, however.

The production of sugar in the Imperial Valley and seed in the Salt River Valley depends wholly on a level of bolting resistance that has been established and maintained in the varieties. Because of bolting, the seed produced in Arizona would be undesirable in the Imperial Valley. Conversely, varieties adapted to that region could not be grown by the winter-annual method in Arizona.

THE DEVELOPMENT of the sugarbeet, largely during the second half of the 19th century, attracted wide attention, because it was a sugar plant that could be grown in temperate climates. The desire for self-sufficiency in sugar led to the introduction of the sugarbeet in our pioneer West, where land for crops was plentiful but where sugar was scarce and expensive. Seed of the sugarbeet was imported from Europe along with machinery and technical knowledge as well.

European varieties suffered great losses in the irrigated districts west of the Rocky Mountains because of curly top, a virus disease. In districts east of the Rockies, leaf spot and root rot caused heavy losses in yield and reduced quality.

It became evident during the 1920's that European varieties were susceptible to American diseases of the sugarbeet and that disease-resistant varieties were essential to a continuation of a competitive industry in this country.

The first American variety with distinctive characteristics to reach commercial status was US 1, a curly top resistant variety that was introduced in 1933. The urgent demand for seed of US 1 was a major incentive to the establishment of the seed enterprise.

Other varieties were developed soon by the Department of Agriculture, State agricultural experiment stations, and plant breeders employed by beet sugar companies.

Disease-resistant varieties were available for our major sugarbeet districts as early as 1940. Seed of American varieties have been used almost exclusively in this country since then. The dependence of the American producer and processor on homegrown seed of disease-resistant varieties made the seed enterprise an integral part of our beet sugar industry.

HOMEGROWN SEED of adapted varieties has contributed greatly to high yields of roots.

The acreable yield of sugarbeet roots averaged about 10 to 11 tons during the decades European seed was used in this country.

Beginning with the introduction of homegrown seed of American varieties, the yield of roots has increased steadily. The national average since 1952 has been no less than 16 tons. The crop of 1959 averaged 18.8 tons an acre.

This achievement cannot be attributed entirely to homegrown seed of improved varieties. Homegrown seed of resistant varieties has lessened the disease hazards of the past and brought a stability of crop performance that encourages the grower to apply improved field practices.

The crop averaged approximately 800 thousand acres annually for several decades before the Second World War. The recommended rate of drilling was 15 to 20 pounds to the acre, but the 20-pound rate was more general. Our annual seed requirement for many years therefore was 16 million pounds.

The acreage in sugarbeets has increased since 1950 to the limits permitted by production quotas established under the Sugar Act. The allotment for 1960 was 1 million acres. Despite the increase in acreage, however, the seed requirement has declined because of the practice of using a lower planting rate to obtain a seedling stand more readily thinned by machine.

Machine harvesting of sugarbeet roots became a general practice during the war, but dense, clumpy stands of seedlings obtained with multigerm seed prevented mechanization of thinning and weeding. The pressing need for a reduction of labor requirements focused research on the seed.

The first accomplishment in the research was the development of a method of milling seedballs to produce small segments and possibly single-seeded units. If the product from milling, known as segmented seed, was planted at a low rate, a sparse stand was obtained that facilitated thinning.

SEGMENTED SEED was an accomplishment in the direction of reducing labor requirements, but there were several objections to the milling operations: Approximately one-half of the seed was wasted as fragments and chaff. A significant percentage of the embryos were injured. Seedlings did not emerge normally from damaged embryos. Milling did not reduce fully all seedballs to single-seeded segments.

Segmenting has been replaced by another milling operation. The seedballs, after screening to a desired size, are passed between two horizontal steel disks, one of which rotates. The mechanical action of the disks rubs the corky tissue from the seedballs and reduces them to a fairly uniform shape and size.

This type of milling, known as decorticating, processing, or rubbing, is preferred generally to the more severe method of segmenting, because less seed is wasted and the embryos suffer almost no injury.

Commercially processed seed consisting of 30 to 40 percent single-seeded units is widely used at a recommended planting rate of 4 to 6 pounds to the acre. Stands of seedlings can be obtained with processed seed (if properly drilled) that greatly reduce the labor requirements of thinning and weeding.

Segmenting and processing of seedballs were desperate efforts to produce by machine a seed type that was not obtainable as a natural growth of the sugarbeet plant. Although harvesting of sugarbeets had been fully mechanized, it was still necessary, despite reduced labor requirements with segmented and processed seed, to transport many extra workmen into sugarbeet districts each spring to perform the jobs of weeding and thinning. The discovery of a plant which produced monogerm seed therefore was a major advance.

MONOGERM SEED has further fashioned the plant to meet the producer's agronomic and economic problems. Its advantages were recognized 50 years ago, and plants producing single-seeded fruits were diligently sought by investigators. But inheritable monogermness in the sugarbeet was not available in this country until its discovery in 1948 by V. F. Savitsky, a collaborator of the Department of Agriculture, employed by the Beet Sugar Development Foundation.

Reports from the Soviet Union have indicated that the monogerm character was under investigation in that country more than a decade earlier.

Monogerm seed was available for trial plantings in some districts as early as 1956, but not until 1958 was the new seed used on extensive acreage.

Monogerm varieties have not been developed for all districts, and the acreage cannot be determined accurately. The seed produced one year, however, may be taken as an indication of the varieties that will be planted for sugar production the following year. Monogerm seed amounted to 11.4 percent of the seed crop in 1957, 24.8 percent in 1958, and 25.4 percent in 1959. Fall plantings in 1959 indicated a marked increase in production of monogerm seed for 1960.

Commercial monogerm seed was largely hybrid by 1960—that is, single-cross, three-way cross, or double-cross.

Practicable methods of producing hybrid seed evolved from the fundamental research by F. V. Owen, a geneticist of the Department of Agriculture, on male sterility in the sugarbeet.

His findings concerning the cytoplasmic and genetic factors that condition sterility of pollen have supplied tools for the production of commercial hybrid seed of both monogerm and multigerm sugarbeets.

Pollen-fertile lines (the so-called type "O") that do not restore pollen production in the offspring when crossed with pollen-sterile lines carrying cytoplasmic factors for sterility are basic parental material for the production of hybrid seed. Backcrossing the type "O" parent to the male-sterile offspring in recurring generations produces a male-sterile equivalent of the line.

Male-sterile equivalents of type "O" lines may be hybridized with complementary pollinators to produce a vigorous F_1 (first generation following a cross) for use as single-cross commercial seed. However, male-sterile F_1's, which are obtained if the pollinator is type "O," are being used also as the chief seed bearer in the production of broad-base hybrids.

Male-sterile F_1's are widely used in the production of three-way commercial hybrids, including US H2 and other hybrids developed by J. S. McFarlane, a geneticist of the Department of Agriculture.

In usual practice, the seed of the male-sterile F_1 is mixed with the seed of the pollinator to give a blend consisting of about 10 percent of the pollen parent in the planting stock and presumably about the same ratio of pollen-fertile plants in the seed field.

The commercial crop contains a low percentage of seed that is not hybrid. At greater cost, however, a completely hybrid crop can be obtained if the pollinator is planted in separate rows and removed from the field before harvesting the hybrid seed produced on the male-sterile parent.

The multigerm pollinators were employed in the production of commercial seed of monogerm hybrids before 1960. Seeds of parental sorts, usually a monogerm male-sterile F_1 and a multigerm pollinator, were blended to give the desired ratio of pollen-fertile plants in the seed field.

The large multigerm seedballs were removed by screening. Then the commercial seed was processed to give the desired size and quality. The seed planted by the sugar producer contained a low percentage of fruits that were not monogerm, but the lack of complete purity with respect to this trait was not considered objectionable.

The use of multigerm lines as pollinators in the production of commercial monogerm hybrids made possible further utilization of the disease-resistant multigerm breeding material that has been developed in long research.

Furthermore, utilization of the established multigerm sorts as pollinators made available commercial monogerm seed of productive hybrids in a much shorter period of breeding than would have been possible with the requirement that both parents be newly developed monogerm sorts.

The fact that the commercial monogerm hybrid obtained by the method outlined would produce multigerm seed and many male-sterile plants if grown to the fruiting stage is of no concern to the sugar producer, since he obtains a new supply of hybrid seed for each crop of roots.

The ultimate goal has been the employment of only monogerm parents in the production of hybrid seed, but multigerm pollinators will continue in use until there is a great wealth of disease-resistant monogerm lines that display a high level of ability to combine.

THE SEED must be of high quality if the full laborsaving advantages are to be realized from the use of monogerm varieties.

In the determination of quality, a multigerm seed was counted as having germinated if it produced a single sprout. Thus a high germination percentage could be obtained with a seed sample in which the actual seed set was low in relation to the number of flowers incorporated in the glomerate fruits.

THE LOW germination percentage of some monogerm lines was a matter of much concern, but the percentage values were higher than formerly obtained with multigerm seed when the basis of evaluation was the number of sprouts in relation to the number of flowers.

Fortunately, the germination of commercial monogerm seed has greatly improved through selection. By proper cleaning and processing, a commercial product of high quality and germination has been made available to growers.

Monogerm seed makes possible single-plant hills along the row. If the drilling rates are right, stands of seedlings can be obtained that are readily thinned by machine or rapidly singled with a long-handled hoe. Monogerm seed should make possible a saving of 50 percent in labor requirements for weeding and thinning.

Some agronomists—the more optimistic ones—have directed their experimental programs with monogerm varieties toward seeding rates that will give an emergence stand approximating the final stand left to grow for root production.

Weed control in the seedling stage is accomplished by selective herbicides and harrowing; in later stages of growth, by timely cultivation. Hand labor usually is not required for this method of production, because harvesting has been fully mechanized.

Actually, a small, commercial acreage of sugarbeets is being grown with complete mechanization of all field operations. Thus the visionary goal of two decades ago appears to be attainable through the use of monogerm seed and the application of improved field practices.

Field practices for seed production by the winter-annual method have been fairly well standardized. The seed is planted in August and September. The row width is usually 20 or 24 inches. The planting rate is 15 to 17 pounds per acre. The seedling stands are not thinned.

Varietal purity is maintained in the commercial varieties of sugarbeets by the separation of seed fields. If the varieties are similar in certain major characteristics, such as disease resistance, the separation of seed fields need not be greater than one-half mile. For stock seed and elites, especially the sorts that involve male sterility, seed fields should be separated by at least 2 or 3 miles, depending on terrain and climatic conditions.

Curly top, a virus disease, is a major hazard to seed production in the Southwest if susceptible varieties are grown. Virus yellows occurs in all major seed-producing districts and is a threat to production and quality. The combined attack of curly top and virus yellows is extremely damaging. The control of these diseases depends on the control of the insect carriers.

The seed is harvested by machine. In some districts, the harvesters are equipped with front cutting bars, which operate both horizontally and vertically. They cut a wide swath through the tall, bushy plants and draw the mass into a windrow. The windrow, when dry, is picked up by traveling thresher, which separates and sacks the seed and returns the large stems and leaves to the field.

Seed is produced by the seedgrower under contract with a sugar company or a seed company that acts as an agent for sugar companies. The sugar company placing an order for seed production furnishes the elite seed or foundation stock. The seedgrower is paid on the basis of clean seed of acceptable quality.

Processing and grading of seed to give a uniform product of a desired quality are performed by the sugar companies after the seed has been moved from the centers of production.

The seed is usually treated with a fungicide, and sometimes with an insecticide, before packaging for sale to growers.

MARKETING of sugarbeet seed in this country is almost exclusively through sugar companies.

A stipulation in the contract between the sugar producer and the processor requires that the seed planted must be obtained from the sugar company buying the roots. A small amount of sugarbeet seed is used to grow a root crop for cattle feed, and seed for this and other purposes can be obtained also from firms handling seeds of field and garden crops.

New strains and varieties of sugarbeets developed by the Department of Agriculture are released through the Beet Sugar Development Foundation under a memorandum of understanding that covers procedures whereby breeder seed and parental lines of hybrids are increased and enter into commercial seed production for the use of growers.

Varieties and strains arising from the breeding programs of individual sugar companies are recognized as their exclusive property.

The production of sugarbeet seed in this country in 1950–1960 was about 10 million pounds annually. It was grown on slightly more than 3,500 acres. The crop value to the grower was approximately 400 dollars an acre. The farm value of the sugarbeet seed crop was about 1.5 million dollars.

Sugarbeets are grown as a source of sugar in 22 States. Returns to growers amount to more than 200 million dollars annually.

DEWEY STEWART *became Head, Sugar Beet Section, Crops Research Division, Agricultural Research Service, in 1955, and Leader of Sugar Beet Investigations in 1960. He has been engaged in sugarbeet research in the Department of Agriculture since 1925.*

Producing and Harvesting Tobacco Seed

JAMES E. MCMURTREY, JR.

THE FIRST step in producing a satisfactory crop of tobacco is to use good seed that is true to type. The grower often can save his own seed to advantage, if he wants to.

Before topping is done, he should go over the tobacco field carefully to pick out desirable seed plants. When he has decided on the ideal type of plant, he should select the plants that conform to this type for producing seed.

One plant produces about one-half ounce of viable seed (about 150 thousand seeds), which is enough for 100 square yards in seedbed area and, if conditions are favorable, enough seedlings to plant 2 to 5 acres.

THE TOBACCO flower tends to be self-fertilized, because the pollen normally is discharged by the anthers soon after the flower opens and may fall on the stigma. The advantage of selecting good seed plants is lost if crossing with other types takes place.

Crossing can be prevented by covering the flower head with a 12- to 16-pound-size manila paper bag, manufactured with waterproof glue. The small leaves and branches just below the flower head itself should be removed. The seed pods or any open blossoms that have formed must be removed before the bag is placed in position.

It is usually desirable to treat the seed head with a suitable insecticide, such as 10-percent DDT dust, at the time of covering with the paper bag to control bud worms. The mouth of the bag is fastened securely to the stalk immediately below the flower branches by a string or other suitable method.

The bag must be adjusted from time to time to accommodate the growing flowers and maturing seed pods. The amount of seed produced under a bag generally is less than the amount produced on unbagged plants.

THE PRODUCTION of certified tobacco seed has been developed so that growers can get seed of most familiar varieties of most types.

Certified seed has been grown by regular seedgrowers under the supervision of the State agricultural experiment stations and crop improvement association of a State to see that the necessary precautions have been followed to insure that it is uncontaminated and true to the variety. Many growers prefer to obtain their seed from these sources.

The certified seed is produced from foundation seed, which is usually produced under bags by the tobacco breeder. If the grower or producer of certified seed plants a pure strain of seed of only one variety, he does not have to save seed under a bag if he grows it in a field that is adequately isolated from fields of other varieties.

He must take into account his own fields and his neighbors'. The extent of the isolation depends on the number of pollinators, such as hummingbirds, hawk moths, bees, and other visitors to tobacco flowers.

Unrestricted crossing may explain the idea that a variety "runs out" soon after it is introduced into a new area—it becomes the native type. More crossing occurs between adjacent plantings (2 to 10 percent) than among isolated plantings. In most States, 440 yards is considered adequate, but twice that distance is desirable; even that may not always prevent cross-pollination.

The amount of viable seed that can be expected is 150 to 300 pounds an acre, depending on the variety, season, soil, and methods of culture.

The methods used for growing seed are those commonly employed for the production of commercial leaf tobacco. Where the leaves are harvested by priming, a smaller yield of viable seed can be expected.

Where the seed heads are trimmed—that is, some of the lateral branches are removed—the amount of good seed usually is less.

When the seeds are mature—the seed pods turn brown—and have dried somewhat, the seed heads may be cut off and hung in a cool, dry place to air-dry. Sometimes it is well to do the drying in a heated barn, starting at 75° F. Once the seed has become loose in the pods, the temperature can be raised to 90°. Heating too rapidly or to higher temperatures lowers the ability to germinate.

The pods are crushed by hand or some other suitable method when the seeds are thoroughly air dried. The hulling process is followed by screening and the use of suitable blowers to remove the broken seed pods, dust, light seed, and other foreign matter.

Tobacco seed must be protected at all times to avoid destruction by birds, mice, rats, and insects. It should be stored only at a low moisture content (about 7 percent) and in airtight containers at a temperature not above 70°.

The germination should be tested before seeding. A satisfactory germination is 80 percent or better. Properly stored seed of good germination can be expected to be satisfactory for use for up to 5 years. It should be tested each year as to germination before it is planted.

For each acre of tobacco, the grower seeds 50 to 100 square yards of seedbed. That usually provides extra plants as a safety factor. Failures in the plant bed may be due to insects, diseases, inadequate moisture, and freezing.

The total acreage of tobacco grown in the United States, about 1.5 million acres, requires about 375 thousand to 750 thousand ounces of seed, when the crop is seeded at the rate of 1 ounce to 200 square yards of seedbed.

The varieties used for growing the flue-cured type are derived from the Orinoco group, such as Hicks. In places where black shank is a problem, Vesta 5, S.C. 58, N.C. 73, and N.C. 75 may be grown. Where both wilt and black shank occur, Dixie Bright 101 and Coker 187 can be grown.

Among the most popular burley varieties are Kentucky 16 and Burley 2. Burley 11A, 11B, and Burley 37 can be grown where black shank is a problem. Burley 21, which has resistance to wildfire and mosaic and black root rot and gives good yields of high-quality leaf, is popular.

Varieties used for growing the Maryland type belong to the broadleaf and medium broadleaf groups, such as Wilson's and Catterton's Broadleaf and Robinson's Medium Broadleaf.

The broadleaf or seedleaf, Havana seed, and Cuban variety groups are used for growing cigar tobacco. There are numerous strains of the Pryor group, which are used for growing fire-cured and dark air-cured tobaccos, such as Madole, a typical fire-cured variety. Yellow Pryor and One Sucker are grown for the dark air-cured type.

The tobacco flower tends to be self-pollinated, but self-pollination is not sufficiently assured to make protection unnecessary when pure seeds are desired. The actual amount of natural crossing has been found to vary from season to season and from location to location and with the degree of isolation. Three years of systematic tests in 1956, 1957, and 1958, in which two marker-carrying gene varieties planted adjacently and at distances of one-twentieth, one-tenth, one-fourth, and one-half mile, showed most crossing in adjacent plantings, and the greatest distance did not always prevent crossing.

JAMES E. McMURTREY, JR., *joined the Department of Agriculture in 1917, when he was appointed as an assistant in tobacco investigations. He is now Leader of Tobacco Investigations, Crops Research Division, Agricultural Research Service. Dr. McMurtrey holds degrees from the University of Kentucky and the University of Maryland.*

Growing Vegetable Seeds for Sale

LESLIE R. HAWTHORN

MEN WHO grow vegetable seeds for sale engage in a specialized and highly competitive farming operation.

They compete to maintain superior strains of most standard varieties and to develop new varieties. Most of the large vegetable seed companies have well-qualified staffs to develop and maintain stock seed, from which is produced seed for the market, mostly by farmers who have contracts with the companies.

The producers of vegetable seeds must know the cultural requirements of the vegetables they are growing throughout the life of the plants, not just until they have reached an edible stage. As a food crop, a biennial such as carrot or onion, for example, requires but one year of growth, but as a seed crop it requires two. On the choice between leaving a biennial in the ground over winter or storing it in a cellar may depend the yield and quality of the seeds harvested the following year.

The growers must know whether their crops are self- or cross-pollinated and, if the latter, whether insects or wind carry the pollen. On such facts depend the necessary isolation distances between fields.

Harvesting seeds differs with different vegetables, both in the method of cutting or the picking of the crop, as well as in the operating speed of the threshing machine. Seeds of fleshy-fruited vegetables like tomatoes are extracted—often with variations of food-processing equipment—rather than threshed, as dry seeds are.

This explains in part why the saving of home garden seed is normally not so simple or satisfactory as it might seem. Experienced seedsmen can grow seeds of good type and true to name for less cost than the home producer, who has a small planting and faces hazards of cross-pollination from nearby plantings of which he may be unaware.

VEGETABLE SEEDS are grown in many States, but most seed acreage is in the West, mainly because of the climate.

Dry air and lack of rain during summer and fall, when many seed crops mature, facilitate the harvesting and threshing. In some western irrigated areas, absence of rain throughout most of the growing season favors the production of disease-free seeds—a tremendous advantage, particularly with beans and the cabbage family.

The largest variety of vegetable seeds is produced in California, where a wide range of climatic conditions within a relatively short distance enables seedsmen to supervise diverse crops from a central place.

Cabbage and closely related crops and garden beets and spinach thrive best in a cool, marine-type climate, and seed production is concentrated in the Pacific Northwest, particularly around Puget Sound.

Beans, peas, sweet corn, melons, squash, carrots, onions, lettuce, turnips, radish, and other dry-seeded crops are grown in various interior places in the Western States.

Seed acreages of tomatoes and sweet corn are common in the North Central and Eastern States.

Pimiento pepper, eggplant, watermelons, okra, and edible cowpeas are grown for seed in the Southeast and South.

FEWER THAN 200 thousand acres a year are planted for vegetable seeds in the United States. About 85 percent of this acreage is required for three large-seeded crops—garden peas, garden beans (including limas), and sweet corn. Thirty-five small-seeded vegetables take the rest—fewer than 30 thousand acres in some years.

About 200 million pounds of vegetable seed may be grown some years, and about 1.4 million pounds are imported. Most of this seed is used in the commercial production of vegetables valued at around 1,111 million dollars.

Peas and green beans are grown for seed almost entirely in the West in localities where the atmosphere is dry. Soil moisture, with one notable exception, is mostly supplied by irrigation.

The exception is in the Palouse areas of northern Idaho and eastern Washington, where most of the seed of smooth-seeded garden peas is grown. Since the irrigated sections of southern Idaho have large acreages of beans and peas, Idaho accounts for the greatest production. Plantings are also common in eastern Washington and in California.

Peas and beans, which are self-pollinated legumes, are grown for seed in much the same way.

Peas are hurt by severe frost, but they should be planted as soon as that danger is past, for they produce higher yields of seed in cool weather.

Beans are sown after all danger of frost is over.

Both crops require at least moderate fertility, but in general they are not fertilized when they are grown for seed. Both require a fair amount of irrigation, but peas usually respond more favorably to additional water.

All but the dwarf varieties of peas usually are sown with a grain drill at rates of 200 to 250 pounds to the acre.

Dwarf peas and all varieties of beans are planted in rows 20 to 30 inches apart, depending on the variety and the equipment that has to be used for other crops in the rotation.

Peas are commonly harvested for seed in midsummer. Beans are harvested in late summer and early fall.

Unlike many cross-pollinated plants, plantings of peas and beans need little isolation. Accidental crossing can take place, however. In the production of stock seed, varieties planted side by side commonly are separated by one or two rows of corn or sunflower. Such barriers help to prevent chance crossings and mixtures at harvesttime.

Roguing—the removal of offtype plants—is done in fields of stock seed. That and a program of rigid control of the quality of stock seed largely eliminate the need to rogue the market-seed crops of peas and beans.

Because both crops are naturally self-pollinated, pure lines can be built up from single plants of the right type. It is essential in such a program that true-to-type plants be selected to protect a variety from gradual change.

Peas and beans are harvested when pods are nearly dry. Pea vines in the Palouse are allowed to dry completely. Then they are combined directly on the stump. A harvesting machine cuts the dry plants close to the ground and elevates them immediately to the threshing cylinders. The seeds are collected in suitable containers—usually large boxes, each of which holds 3 thousand pounds of seeds. All that is done in one operation.

Peas and beans in irrigated areas are commonly cut and windrowed and then allowed to cure until they are dry enough to thresh. The seeds are less likely to be injured if they still have a moisture content of 12 to 15 percent.

Threshing machines especially developed for peas and beans have two or more spike-tooth cylinders or rub bars and a pair of rubber rollers. To avoid serious injury, especially to beans, cylinder speeds should not normally exceed 350 revolutions per minute.

Lima beans are handled much like green beans but require a longer growing season. The climate should be warm, but excessively high temperatures or extremely dry air are undesirable, because they may cause excessive blossom drop and therefore low yields.

Large-seeded lima bean seed consequently is grown usually in southern California, where length of season and temperature are favorable and the air usually is somewhat more humid than it is farther inland. Some of the small-seeded lima beans are grown in Idaho.

Cowpeas, or southern peas, have climatic and cultural requirements like those of lima beans. Seed is grown in the Southern States and California. The "black-eyed pea" of commerce is a variety of cowpea.

SWEET CORN, another large-seeded vegetable, is grown in much the same way as field corn.

Corn does best on productive soils with abundant moisture and when the average monthly temperature is about 70° F. A season of at least 120 days is required for seed production. Dry weather during harvest is desirable.

About 80 percent of all sweet corn produced in 1960 was F_1 hybrid. About 80 percent of all hybrid seed is grown in southwestern Idaho. Some, notably open-pollinated varieties, are grown in the Corn Belt, Connecticut, New York, and California.

The wide use of hybrid varieties has revolutionized the growing of sweet corn for seed during the past several decades. The F_1 hybrid is a cross between two inbred lines. A hybrid must be superior to open-pollinated varieties in one or more characteristics, such as yield, uniformity, and quality, to warrant release as a variety.

The seed breeder today has to know how to develop inbreds and to test their combining ability with perhaps hundreds of others. He also must know how to maintain the satisfactory inbreds over the years and how to produce profitably the market seeds from them.

When a gardener uses seed of hybrid sweet corn, he has to buy new hybrid seed each year if he expects to maintain the yield and quality of the ears he is accustomed to producing. As seed saved from a hybrid crop does not reproduce another crop of the same high yield and quality as the seed from which it was grown, a grower can hardly afford to use such seed. The seed trade therefore requires a large amount of hybrid seed each year. That demand has led to the highly specialized business of growing such seed.

Methods and times of planting, cultivation, and weed control with sweet corn are practically identical with those used in the production of seed of field corn, whether open pollinated or hybrid. Similar distances of isolation need to be observed. Methods of harvesting and curing sweet corn seed and the use of special drying plants also resemble the practices followed in producing field corn seed.

Seed of popcorn is produced in much the same way as that of sweet corn.

FLESHY-FRUITED vegetables present a special problem because at harvest the seed is wet, rather than dry. These vegetables include several related crops—tomatoes, peppers, and eggplants, and some unrelated vine crops—cucumbers, melons, squashes, and pumpkins.

Seed of tomato, pepper, and eggplant is produced in a number of States, but mostly in areas in which they are grown also for processing.

Considerable tomato seed is produced in connection with the processing of tomatoes in some eastern and north-central localities, but many planters prefer to obtain seed that is produced apart from any food-processing operation.

A moderate soil fertility, a uniform supply of soil moisture, mean summer temperatures of 70° to 75°, and a long frost-free season of 4 to 6 months favor high yields of fruit and seed. A grower obtains an average of 6 to 15 pounds of tomato seed from each ton of fruit.

As tomatoes are primarily self-fertilized, the isolation of seed fields presents no difficulty. Because bumble bees sometimes visit tomato flowers and may cause some crossing, a distance of at least 50 feet is desirable between varieties. Greater distances should certainly be planned where stock seed is produced.

Only plantings of stock seed of tomatoes normally are rogued. Offtype plants should be removed before they flower to prevent any chance of cross-pollination. If too many of the fruits on a plant fail to meet established requirements, the entire plant should be removed.

A grower harvests tomato fruits for seed much as he would harvest fruit for market or processing, except that it does not matter if the fruit is overripe, cracked, or injured.

When extraction of seed is the main concern, the fruit is dumped directly in the field into a mobile seed extractor, which cuts the fruit and separates most of the seed and juice from the mass of pulp and skin.

The seed which is surrounded by a mucilaginous sheath is separated from both the sheath and the juice by an acid treatment, or fermentation, in which the pulp and juice ferment for about 2 days in large vats, preferably at temperatures around 75° to 80°. A lower temperature takes more time. Stirring hastens the disintegration of the tissues surrounding the seed, which settles to the bottom. The pulp and other material float to the top, where they can be removed.

In the acid method, about 2 gallons of hydrochloric acid are added to each ton of juice and pulp. The seed separates from the pulp in 15 to 30 minutes. Little equipment is needed, but a disadvantage is that the bacterium that causes canker disease is not killed, as it is by the fermentation process. The seed therefore has to be treated with 0.8-percent acetic acid if there is danger of bacterial canker.

Regardless of the method of extraction, the tomato seed must be washed thoroughly in shaker washers or in a sluiceway before it can be dried. Sun drying in screen-bottom trays is common in the West. Drying in heated, moving air is commoner in the East. Further processing is sometimes necessary to break up clumps of seeds and remove light seeds.

The production of seeds of pepper and eggplant resembles that for tomato. Both crops need greater isolation than tomatoes, as they are often cross-pollinated by honey bees and other insects. Between two varieties of the same type, one-fourth mile is enough, but the distance between the sweet and pungent types of pepper should be much greater.

THE CULTURE of the vine crops (cucumbers, cantaloups, watermelons, squashes, pumpkins) for seed parallels the culture required for market production. Seed acreages are scattered through many States.

Cucumbers and squashes, because of their cooler climatic requirements, are planted generally in Michigan and Oregon and other Northern States.

Seed acreages of watermelons exist all the way from Kansas and Texas to Florida. California and Colorado produce seeds of all the vine crops.

The vine crops require fertile soils with a good organic content and a good moisture supply, but moisture should not be excessive. Fields in the West usually are irrigated.

Honey bees are essential for pollination and high yields in vine crops.

Cucumbers, cantaloups, and watermelons belong to different botanical species and hence do not cross with each other.

Varieties of squashes and pumpkins belong to four botanical species of the genus *Cucurbita*. Crosses may occur among some of them. The need for isolation therefore depends on the species to which a variety belongs—not on whether it is a "squash" or a "pumpkin."

This diagram indicates the crosses that can or cannot occur:

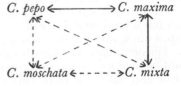

Species joined by a solid line do not cross, but crossing may occur between species connected by a broken line.

Although nearly all the winter squashes are in *C. maxima*, summer squashes and pumpkins are found in *C. pepo*, *C. moschata*, and *C. mixta*.

The producer therefore has to know the species to which his varieties belong to determine proper isolation distances. If a cross may occur easily, the crops should be at least one-fourth mile apart. A much greater distance is desirable if stock seed is being grown. F_1 hybrid seed of cucumber and squash now is produced commercially. The male parent is planted in a row after every third to fifth row of the female parent, from which the seed is harvested. Every morning workers carefully remove all the male flowers from the seed plants. As in the production of hybrid seed of sweet corn, the seedsman has to develop and find satisfactory inbreds—populations that have been self-fertilized for several or even many generations—and test their ability to combine with other inbreds.

Growers should rogue all vine crops fairly early and at least twice. If all plants that are obviously offtype can be removed before they flower, considerable contamination (through pollination) of seeds on other plants is prevented. The removal later of all plants with any offtype young fruits reduces greatly undesirable cross-pollination between late opening flowers.

At harvest, the vines of cucumbers and squashes often are dead and actually may have been frosted before the fruit is gathered. Cucumbers, muskmelons, and watermelons are juicy enough to be handled by equipment and methods like those used for tomatoes. Fermentation is commonly used for the final separation.

With winter squash—mostly *Cucurbita maxima*, but some *C. moschata*—which has a hard rind, the fruits often are split open, and the seed is scooped out. Fermentation of squash seeds should be avoided, as the process may discolor and injure the seed. Pulp and seed are gradually separated by lightly rolling, raking, and similar action.

All vine seed has to be washed thoroughly (as suggested for tomatoes), but often vine seed needs also some screening and fanning to eliminate dry parts of pulp and seeds of subnormal size. Methods of drying vine seeds are similar to those for tomatoes.

SEEDS OF LETTUCE, endive, salsify (vegetable oyster), chicory, dandelion, and globe artichoke are produced almost entirely in the Western States, particularly in California and Idaho.

Areas with rain-free harvest seasons are preferred, for rain may cause shattering and delay normal maturity. Lettuce may be planted early in the spring or in the fall and winter if the climate is suitable. Fall planting and overwintering are feasible in some northern areas, especially if a snow cover lasts all the winter. Such a method is not practiced generally by commercial seedgrowers, even though it enables one to harvest seed from late varieties as early as July or August.

Lettuce is sown on raised beds in rows 20 to 22 inches apart or in single rows 22 to 30 inches apart. Plants are thinned to stand 8 to 12 inches apart. Growers rogue lettuce before or during the market stage of development.

Extreme isolation is unnecessary because lettuce is mostly self-fertilized. A distance of 25 feet between plantings of market seed may be satisfactory, but a distance of several hundred feet is preferable between fields of stock seed. Because wild lettuce (*Lactuca serriola*) crosses readily with cultivated lettuce, all wild lettuce should be removed in and near seed fields.

One difficult task in growing seed of the crisp-headed varieties is to remove or open up the head, so that the seedstalk can develop normally. Some growers cut them open with knives.

Another way is to hit the head downwards with the palm of the hand and then lift it off; the central core with its growing point is left intact.

Timing is important with any of these methods. Deheading should be done just as the heads reach full size and before the core within has begun to elongate.

Lettuce seed is harvested in several ways. One is to shake the seed into containers from plants. Standing plants sometimes are threshed with a combine. The first method, repeated at weekly intervals, gives maximum yields, but is feasible only when labor is cheap. Combining saves labor but saves less seed and makes necessary the immediate drying of the threshed material to avoid discoloration of seed and reduction in germination.

Intermediate methods of harvesting involve cutting the plants by hand or with machines and windrowing them to cure before threshing.

SPINACH is an annual of the same botanical family as the garden beet, which is a biennial.

Planted early in the spring, spinach produces seed the same year, but as it is winter hardy, it is also sown in the fall in some localities; then the seed is harvested the following year.

Spinach is unique among vegetables because it has four types of plants: Extreme males; vegetative males; monoecious plants (those which have both male and female flowers); and female plants.

Extreme male plants are small. They bolt early. They are undesirable therefore in a market or home-garden crop. Because these characteristics can be transmitted to seed-bearing plants when crosses occur, growers try to rogue out all extreme male plants.

Monoecious plants are the most common type. For production of F_1 hybrid seed, lines are desired that consist of pure male and pure female plants. The males are rogued out of the female parent line as they become recognizable.

Spinach flowers are borne in clusters in the leaf axils. They are small and lack petals and so are rather inconspicuous. Male flowers produce pollen which flies into the air like dust, when the flowers open and the plant is jarred. A completely female plant produces no pollen.

The pollen of spinach is small and may be carried far by wind. Varieties should be isolated by 1 mile at least, especially in the direction of the prevailing wind. Advantage should be taken of any natural barriers, such as stands of tall trees.

The seedstalks are cut when the late-maturing ones begin to turn yellow. The entire crop dries in windrows. Then it is threshed with a pickup combine.

Spinach is one crop with which fairly high cylinder speeds may be used in threshing.

THE COMMON type of radish, sprouting broccoli, mustard, and Chinese cabbage are annuals in the large cabbage family. Each differs from the others as a vegetable, but methods of producing their seeds are much alike.

The acreage devoted to the production of radish seed often exceeds that of any other member of the cabbage family, including cabbage itself.

All are sown early in the spring in northern sections. They can be planted in the fall in southern areas, as for lettuce. Isolation to prevent cross-pollination by pollen-carrying bees between varieties of any one kind should be about one-fourth mile for market, and 1 mile between stock seed plantings. All should be rogued in their vegetative state. For the production of stock seed of radish, the roots are usually dug, rogued for type, and replanted.

The crops are cut and windrowed when a noticeable proportion of the pods have turned yellow. When dry, they can be threshed with a pickup combine. Threshing radish often is facilitated by having a pair of rubber rollers in the machine to help crush the pods, because radish pods do not split lengthwise as do those of the other cabbage members.

SEED PRODUCTION of the biennial vegetables is more complicated because they have to be carried over into the second year.

The cabbage family includes the largest collection of biennial vegetables. Many of them, including both leaf and root vegetables, can be grown for seed either by seed-to-seed (that is, overwintering the plants in the field), or by storing the crop under cover during winter. Market seed is generally produced by the first method, and stock seed by the latter.

The cabbage family is pollinated by insects. Satisfactory isolation between the different members and between varieties is one of the most difficult and complicated in the seed industry. That is because cabbage, cauliflower, collard, kale, kohlrabi, brussels sprouts, and the annual sprouting broccoli all belong to the same botanical species, *Brassica oleracea.*

Furthermore, cabbage alone falls into distinct varietal groupings based on head shape, season, and foliage color. Cross-pollination between any of these varietal types or any of the other vegetables within the botanical species inevitably gives rise to noticeable offtype plants. To avoid such crossing, seedsmen try to maintain for market seed production minimum isolation distances, which range from one-eighth mile to 1 mile depending on the kinds of vegetables involved. For plantings of stock seed, a distance of several miles is preferable.

When seed is to be grown from cabbage that is to be stored over winter, the crop is grown the first year much as it would be for market, except that the time of planting must be adjusted so that the head matures just ahead of winter.

The crop is rogued as the individual plants are lifted from the ground. The outer leaves are removed from the head. Plants that meet varietal requirements are placed in storage in a single layer on shallow shelves to reduce losses from decay. Storage temperature should be just above 32°. Relative humidity should be high to prevent dehydration of the cabbage. The crop is replanted in the spring.

In seed-to-seed production, seedbeds of the late varieties are planted first, beginning about May 15, and the early varieties last, about July 15. Plants are transplanted in August to the seed fields in which they overwinter. Highly selected stock seed is essential, as the plants never produce fully mature heads and no opportunity comes to rogue the crop critically. The plants also need some protection from freezing and thawing, even in the Puget Sound area. After roguing is completed, therefore, soil is thrown against the plants so that only the upper part is visible. The partly buried plants can withstand temperatures of 5° to 10°.

Seedstalks develop during the second year if interrelated factors (low temperature, chiefly) have been satisfactory. A cross-cut—two cuts at right angles to each other—may have to be made in heads of cabbage overwintered in storage to allow the head to burst and the seedstalk to develop.

When a good proportion of the pods of all these cabbage-type crops have turned yellow, the seedstalks are cut individually and piled in windrows, where they may cure one to several weeks before threshing. When dry, the crop threshes easily, and cylinder speeds should not be higher than is necessary. As the seeds of all the crops in the cabbage family are similar, seedsmen take care to avoid mechanical mixtures.

Of the cabbage-type crops, cauliflower has the most exacting climatic requirements. These include uniformly cool and relatively humid atmospheric conditions, without danger of subfreezing temperatures.

AMONG THE other biennial crops are a number of fairly important vegetables. They are not related botanically, but they are root or bulb crops and are grown for seed by similar cultural methods. They are carrots, onions, garden beets, turnips, and many related crops of less importance.

Seed of all of them is produced either by root (or bulb)-to-seed or seed-to-seed methods.

In the former, which is consistently used for production of stock seed, the crops are grown the first year in much the same way that they are grown in a garden or for market. With all except onions, time of planting has to be delayed somewhat so that the roots reach marketable size just before winter storage. Medium-sized roots (or stecklings, as they are called) and medium-sized bulbs are preferred to large ones. Storage temperatures should be about 40° for all these crops. Relative humidity should be high, except for onion, for which low humidity is preferable.

WHEN seed is grown by the seed-to-seed method, planting has to be done so that the crop goes into the dormant winter season when the edible root or bulb is only partly developed. Onions should not have formed bulbs. If the crops are developed too far, they are more subject to decay during the winter; if they are underdeveloped, they are more likely to be killed by freezing and thawing during the fall or spring.

Experiments in Utah have shown that moderate or even infrequent irrigation is associated with high seed yields of carrots, the fibrous roots of which extend down 5 feet or more.

In 1946–1950, carrot stecklings were set out for seed production in experiments in which three soil moisture conditions (high, medium, and low) and various spacings were studied simultaneously. Soil moisture stress was recorded periodically by means of gypsum blocks to depths of 5 feet.

The onion, which is shallow rooted, usually responds to fairly frequent irrigation with high yields, but even under low soil moisture conditions, a spacing as close as 9 inches between seed-to-seed rows may triple the yield normally expected when rows are 30 inches or more apart.

Seed yields of onions, turnips, and garden beets often are higher when moderate amounts of nitrogen have been included in the fertilizer.

ALL THESE crops, except beets, are pollinated by insects, so that varieties of each vegetable need to be isolated from others at least by one-fourth mile and much farther when the colors of the roots are different—white-rooted and yellow-rooted carrots, for example.

The pollen of garden beets, like that of spinach, is carried so easily by the wind that varieties should be separated about a mile for market seed and twice that or more for stock seed.

As garden beets cross easily with Swiss chard, sugarbeets, and stock beets, the distance between them should be at least 2 miles.

Through the development of male-sterile onions (plants that produce no viable pollen), many hybrid varieties of this vegetable are being grown. Some production procedures are similar to those followed in growing seed of hybrid sweet corn. Several rows of male-sterile plants, from which the hybrid seed is harvested, are planted for each pollen row. A good supply of honey bees is essential for satisfactory yields. To avoid mechanical mixtures, the seed of the pollen rows should be removed before the hybrid seed on the other rows is harvested.

In all production of onion seed, the seed heads have to be handpicked and cured before threshing. Some growers cure the heads on canvases or in trays exposed to the sun. Others dry the crop indoors in a stream of warm air.

The plants of carrot and beet are pulled and windrowed when a good proportion of the seeds have turned brown. Turnip is pulled when the pods are turning yellow or a few have dried. Curing may require 4 or 5 days or much longer, depending on the weather and the maturity of the crop when it is harvested. A combine with pickup attachment is suitable for all three. In some dry localities, where turnip matures during July, the crop can be combined like grain as it stands in the field without too much loss from shattering.

LESLIE R. HAWTHORN, *horticulturist, Vegetables and Ornamentals Branch, Crops Research Division, Agricultural Research Service, is stationed at Logan, Utah, and conducts research in the production of vegetable seed in cooperation with the Utah and Idaho Agricultural Experiment Stations.*

The Commercial Production
of Seeds of Flowers

HOWARD BODGER

SEEDS OF some 1,500 varieties of flowers are available to amateur gardeners in the United States. The major part of the acreage on which they are grown is devoted to producing about 750 of them. The value of the seeds is about 2.5 million dollars. Five genera produce seed crops valued at more than 100 thousand dollars each.

The acreage for flower seeds thus comprises small plantings of many crops—an acre of this, half an acre of that. By usual farming standards, it is manicured acreage that requires the best level, irrigated land.

The income per acre is two to five times that of beans, for example, but costs of production are correspondingly higher. More than 40 percent of the cost is for field labor, which must be of such manual skill that good work approaches a craft status.

Each species of flower grown for seed has its own planting time, culture, problems of pollination, and harvesting technique, but there is one basic requirement for good seed production: A mild climate with little rain during the growing and harvesting seasons. The United States industry therefore is concentrated in California.

Less favorable conditions result in uncertain and usually lower yields and germination percentages, although colder climates are suitable for some annuals and many perennials. Colorado, Oregon, Washington, Texas, Illinois, Indiana, Ohio, New York, New Jersey, and other States produce some seeds of flowers.

To engage in the production out-doors of rowcrop flower seeds, by far the largest poundage of the industry, the flower-seed farmer should have ability, prime acreage, a source of skilled labor, and a suitable climate. Greenhouse production is independent of location, having its own "California" climate tailormade, but it is an entirely different business.

The growing of flower seeds in the United States dates from the early 1800's. The experience and planting stock came from Europe at first. The industry was well established in New York State by the time California came into production about 1880, but the advantages of drier climates had shifted most of the production west by the First World War, and the United States became a major producer of flower seeds. By 1949 five firms, all in California, were growing 75.6 percent of the crop value of the Nation.

The structure of the industry is one of farmers selling to wholesalers, who then sell to retailers, since only 6.3 percent of the sales represent retailing by the farmer. The wholesalers themselves, however, are major producers of what they sell. They operate their own farms and contract only in areas or on crops that are not suited to their organization.

The reasons therefor lie in the nature of the crops of flower seeds.

Many of the kinds represent highly hybridized strains, on which elite (or foundation) planting stock must be planted anew each year—not crop seed planted back. The wholesaler almost invariably produces this stock himself, on his own farm, which incorporates research breeding work and trial grounds, to keep pace with the rapidly changing technology of the industry.

Elite strains require planning and supervision to insure their pedigree and uniform cultural practices to insure the maximum salable crop. Buyers have specific standards of varietal purity and germination in mind when they buy, which is not on a daily bid basis but on annual contract, usually in advance. The wholesaler has to deliver seed of these standards, grown under his supervision.

GENERALLY SPEAKING, most annuals require as much time between first flowering and good seed production as they need from planting to the first flush of bloom. Species that can be grown for flower production in short-summer locations almost anywhere in the world are not necessarily seed crops in those locations.

Quick-blooming, tender annuals, such as zinnias, need 6 frost-free months for seed formation, although a light frost does not harm the harvest. Others require 8 to 11 months.

Half-hardy annuals may be started before all danger of frost is past and summer harvested, but even with them the requirement of a long spring season eliminates many hard-winter locations from consideration for reliable production.

Few places in the world have the Mediterranean climate needed to grow the variety of flower crops of a major seed producer. California is high on the list. Planting there is continuous from November to May (one species following another on the schedule), and harvesting extends from June to December. Spring-blooming annuals are usually the first in and off, but stocks, for example, need a season of 11 months.

Rain is beneficial before flowering. Rain later encourages fungi in the seed head and reduces the yield. Rain on the mature seed lowers germination percentages. Nevertheless, most sections of semiarid climate, even in latitudes where frost is not a problem, may not be suitable for seed farms because high summer temperatures also reduce yield of seed of all but a few annuals.

PRODUCTION in California is mainly in the cool Lompoc, Santa Maria, and Salinas Valleys for this reason, but zinnias and others (basically of Central American origin) may be cropped in the Los Angeles area and on the edges of the hot inland valleys.

Biennials and perennials are grown in cold-winter areas for seed production but even they do best in a mild climate. When they are grown in California, they are handled as 2- or 3-year plantings because, without killing frosts, both plants and their diseases are rampant.

All crops in California require extensive irrigation during the summer. A common practice is to withhold the water at the end of the season to encourage rapid and uniform maturing of the seed crop. Ditch irrigation is general. Overhead systems are used seldom.

Flower-seed farming has its special problems, and those who can master them tend to be seed farmers year after year.

The plants usually grow so slowly, for example, that weed control is a major problem. Chemical weedkillers are popular, but the man with a hoe is still the mainstay. Most fields need complete hand weeding three times or more a season; sometimes it is combined with thinning in drilled crops. Petunias and many others usually are transplanted to the field by hand, because mechanical transplanters cannot handle such small, fragile seedlings.

MECHANICAL mixing of harvested plants is prevented by alternating plantings of species to be harvested at different times of the year.

Special field-labeling techniques are used to identify lots going through the cutting and threshing process to avoid seed mixing. Mixed lots are nearly worthless in an industry where high prices are paid only for pedigreed seed.

The many small plots of closely related kinds on one farm mean that one crop may be unintentionally cross-pollinated by another of the same species, rendering the resulting seed virtually useless.

Unintentional fertilization by "foreign" pollen is insidious because there is no visible mixing.

Pollination is, however, what makes the wheels go in the seed business. The high acre yields of sweetpeas in California, for example, are partly due to the constant winds, which jostle the flowers of this strictly self-pollinated species. In most other kinds, self- and cross-pollination are accomplished by insects, which cannot distinguish between several named colors of sweet alyssum, for example, so that such plantings must be isolated from each other. Strict isolation by as much as one-fifth mile sometimes is necessary.

When the grower lays out two fields of different colors or of double- and single-flowered varieties, he must consider the result of a possible cross: Which condition will be dominant in the result? Perhaps he can turn this into an advantage; maybe he will get a new kind of flower or one that the competition cannot reproduce. Hybrid marigolds are an example. All such decisions require the skills of a geneticist.

The emphasis on varietal purity is not solely the concern of flower men in the seed industry, but only they set out deliberately to produce mixed varieties. Only in flower seed can a mixture of colors of one kind be a salable or even highly desirable product. Many times this mixture is blended of named colors in the warehouse, according to formula, but field-grown mixtures are the rule when named colors have not yet been trued up or when there is an advantage to controlled cross-pollination of colors, such as added vigor in the final product.

Because the crop will be sold long before a check sample can be flowered next year, every result of this cross-pollination must be predicted in advance: Does one color outyield the others? Then adjust the planting formula to reflect this. Does a cross between red and white yield all-red, all-white, or some of each (perhaps even intershades)? Then make sure to plant enough of the recessive color to assure many self-pollinations of that color. Does one color mature earlier than another? Then choose the har-

vesttime carefully, or one color will dominate the mixture because of this factor.

FOOD AND FIBER crops of survival interest to man have been grown for so many centuries that their climatic adaptability is great; even those grown for their seeds produce the same under similar conditions. Flower crops, being primarily of esthetic interest, are latecomers in the selection process and still retain many preferences for a specific environment and no other.

Flower-seed farmers have learned that climates, even microclimates, must be charted carefully. The economic benefit of finding the right location for a crop in California, for example, can easily outweigh the advantage of much lower wages and costs of growers of the same item in other countries.

In the 1940's, for example, the seed yield of larkspur was trebled by moving the crop a distance of 8 miles.

Precipitation in these two places, Lompoc Valley and the adjacent Santa Rosa area, was the same; humidity was a few points drier; and the temperatures perhaps averaged four degrees higher in Santa Rosa. The result was that the new area produces the major part of our larkspur seed. In the competitive flower seed industry, the search for new microclimates is continuous, and wholesalers keep detailed records on each production area, new and old.

Visitors to the flower farms are amazed that much flower seed is harvested and threshed by machinery of the sort used for grain. Even the fine seed of petunia is handled so. Hand picking or cutting saves more seed, but high labor costs and the need for speed dictate mechanical methods whenever possible. Crops are harvested occasionally with a combine, but much more commonly the plants are cut and windrowed until they can dry to a moisture content suitable for machine threshing.

The diversity of crops leads to several cutting methods. Nasturtiums may be windrowed on the ground. Species with seed heads that shatter at a touch must go onto large canvas sheets.

The stems of petunia plants are so sticky that, even though the seed shatters out of the capsule, a significant amount of it adheres to the stem and can be saved if the whole plant is put on sheets to dry. Only early-rising visitors see the cutting operation, which is carried out when the morning dew is on the plants to avoid loss of the dry seeds. The drying period varies according to the weather, but usually is 10 to 20 days. Rain at this time is catastrophic.

Regardless of the trend toward mechanization, a major part of harvesting is still handwork, either in preparation or finishing. In perennials such as delphinium, several handpickings precede the final cutting because the plants have a long flowering period and seed production is continuous.

Zinnias are commonly handpicked, and the flower heads must be flat rolled preparatory to threshing, as the seeds stick tenaciously to the central cone.

RECLEANING is basically the same operation as in the rest of the seed industry. Fanning mills, specific gravity separators, disk and roller separators, and occasionally flotation are used.

The difference with flower seeds lies in the multiplicity of small lots, which necessitate short machine runs and scrupulous cleaning of the machinery between each run. The high wholesale value makes for extreme care and elaborate recordkeeping. The dimensions of the recleaner's job can be illustrated by the fact that more than 4 million petunia seeds weigh a pound (sometimes worth as much as 100 dollars); a pound of sweetpea seeds has about 500 seeds, worth perhaps 70 cents. Screens, sieves, disks, and such to handle all shapes and sizes are essential.

RELATIVE AIR humidity has an important bearing on the curing of flower seed in the field. Generally speaking, the lower it is, the better. One of the reasons why production is concentrated in California is that normal drying may be accomplished entirely under natural conditions, and California seed is famous for its high initial germination and long keeping qualities. Up to 1958, practically no artificial drying machinery was used in the industry; then it was introduced to extend the already excellent keeping qualities of the California product.

A large part of United States production is processed to the optimum moisture content for long-term storage and sealed in moisture-vapor-proof containers so that retailers in "wet" climates can count on the vigor, vitality, and keeping qualities of the seeds as originally harvested.

THE GREATEST change in the American flower seed industry since the Second World War is the expansion of greenhouse production. It stems from the application of the F_1 hybrid principle to give garden and florist plants tremendously greater vigor and productivity.

Petunias are the most important greenhouse crop of flower seeds in dollar value. The reason is that some colors (scarlet and coral) and forms (doubles and 100-percent large-flowered singles) can be had only as hybrids grown in the greenhouse. The essence of the production of F_1 hybrid seed is the development of unique parent strains for use in a specific and controlled cross. The research work involved is such that only well-organized seed firms are in a position to initiate or contract production. The crop requires a supervisor with the equivalent technical education of the flower breeder.

Production is under a glass or plastic cover. Plastic is used in summer or the whole year in California. Usually even the ventilators are screened to keep out insects that might bear contaminating pollen. The sanitary precautions to prevent disease are formidable.

The seed parent (female) is pot or bench grown. The anthers and stamens of each flower are removed before it opens. The procedure is called emasculation. The pollen parent is grown elsewhere, and its pollen is gathered when it is ripe.

The pistil of the seed parent is receptive about a week after emasculation, and pollen from the male parent is applied to fertilize the flower. In 6 weeks the seed capsule has matured. Then it is harvested by hand.

Production is continuous on each plant, which may produce hundreds of flowers during its useful life. (Petunias and antirrhinums, or snapdragons, are first-year-blooming perennials, but disease and forced seed production result in a useful plantlife of only 5 months.)

Production is measured in ounces per thousand plants. Few of the dozens of varieties on the market reach a production rate of 100 ounces a year or more, but the value of that amount exceeds 10 thousand dollars at wholesale.

The problems in this type of seed production may center around disease (which is always a danger with pot-grown plants weakened by forced seeding), pollen contamination, plant nutrition, temperatures, humidities, light intensities, and the growth or productivity quirks of parent lines seemingly identical with their sisters. Labor availability and utilization, effective supervision, and the ever-present concern with product quality are more akin to manufacturing than to farming.

AN INSPECTION of seed catalogs and the advertisements of retail seedsmen indicate the drive that flower seed producers have to produce new, unique, and improved varieties every year.

Some notable contributions have been made by amateurs—for example, McKana's aquilegia, which won an All-America award—but the main body of this work is carried on by the wholesalers, large and small, of flower seeds. A large company will budget up to 5 percent of its annual income to research work.

The introduction of new varieties before the Second World War depended primarily on line selection, a method still basic, particularly in maintaining the highly bred standard strains. The typical novelty developed in this way used to require about 10 years from idea to finished product.

Improved techniques, which yield more than one generation in a year, and better knowledge of the behavior of the plant material have cut the development time to an average of 5 years. The F_1 hybrid technique, however, not only in petunias and antirrhinums but in a widening array, including marigolds and zinnias, has increased the number of new items marketed each year.

People who grow flower seed form a rather exclusive "club" (350 of them in 1960), whose initiation may be complicated but whose education is likely to be one of the broadest in agriculture. Independent people with a lively interest in many things and skills are drawn in, not particularly to get rich (although salaries totaled 900 thousand dollars in 1960), but because competence is widely respected in the industry and pride of craftsmanship is strong. Many new cultural, chemical, and genetic techniques, which eventually find application in the seed trade as a whole, are pioneered by the workers in this small, highly skilled industry.

More than 25 million American families plant flower seeds each year, for a total of many millions of hours of gardening pleasure. Some of them may give little thought to whether the seeds are better than what their parents planted. The flower seed people, however, give the matter a lot of thought: Most of them do indeed love flowers, but not uncritically; they are dedicated to producing the very best strains, and next year they will be better than that.

HOWARD BODGER, F. R. H. S., *is vice president, Bodger Seeds Ltd., a director of the All-America Selections program, a trustee of the Los Angeles State and County Arboretum, and a director, Southern California Horticultural Institute.*

Collecting and Handling Seeds of Forest Trees

PAUL O. RUDOLF

SOME 50 million acres in the United States (exclusive of Alaska and Hawaii) need to be planted to trees because they are not restocking naturally with desirable forest trees; because they are eroding, idle, or unprofitably used; because farmers' fields, animals, or buildings need protection from wind; and because the United States is going to need all the timber we can grow.

This tremendous undertaking will require more than 25 thousand tons of seeds of forest trees. To insure that this program gets the best possible start, we must apply the best knowledge we have about collecting, extracting, storing, and using the large quantities of forest tree seeds needed every year.

Although more than 600 species of woody plants are useful for conservation planting in the United States, about 130 species make up the bulk of the seed trade. Furthermore, some 25 species, mostly conifers, account for about 90 percent of the area planted and seeded. Even this smallest group presents a variety of problems in collection, extraction, and handling.

THE COLLECTING of forest tree seeds in the United States is largely from wild stands, but increasing quantities are being gathered in plantations.

Beginning in the 1950's, some seed has been collected in seed production areas—high-quality stands specially treated to foster heavy production.

Just being established, primarily in the South, are seed orchards made up of vegetatively propagated material representing selected superior trees. More and more of our seeds of forest trees are expected to come from these special stands and orchards.

Much of the supply in the United States is collected by private individuals, most of whom are independent operators. The greatest users of the seeds in this country, however, are the public forestry agencies, although there is a growing use by forest industries and commercial seed dealers.

Both the public and industrial agencies usually buy unextracted cones or fruits from the small private collectors.

The progressive collector of seeds of forest trees will scout out desirable collection areas in advance. He can get some early estimates at the time of spring flowering, but he should check the crops in the summer after the fruits are well developed, keeping in mind these points:

1. Confine collections wherever possible to trees above average in one or more of these qualities: Growth rate, stem form, crown and branching habit, resistance to damage, and seed production. Stands with a high proportion of superior trees are especially desirable for seed collections. Where areas of seed production or seed orchards are available, collect from them.

2. Obtain written permission of landowners before making any collections on their land.

3. Where available, utilize the regional tree seed-crop reporting services to locate collecting areas. In any event, estimate production from actual counts of fruits on representative trees or small sample plots well distributed over the collecting area.

4. Test for soundness of seeds in each locality and on individual trees before collection.

5. Label each sack, before it leaves the collecting ground, to show species; exact locality of collection (including approximate elevation); day, month, and year of collection; and any special merits of the parent stand (as "seed production area," superior stand, or "seed orchard").

Chances are best for getting seeds high in germinability and keeping qualities if they are collected when they are ripe and before they have suffered deterioration on the tree or on the ground.

Experienced collectors judge the ripeness of fruits by their fullness, size, color, degree of "milkiness" of the seeds, hardness of the seedcoat, their attractiveness to animals, or some combination of these factors. More precise indices are desirable.

For some pines and spruces, ripeness can be determined more accurately by the floatability of freshly picked cones in suitable test liquids, some of which are linseed oil for eastern white pine and blue spruce; SAE 20 motor oil for loblolly, longleaf, and slash pines; turpentine for white spruce; half linseed oil and half kerosene for Jeffrey and ponderosa pines; and kerosene for red and sugar pines.

For many tree species, the best time to collect is when the first seeds begin to fall naturally. Large-scale operations must begin sooner than that, however, to avoid substantial losses of good seed.

The best time for seed gathering varies for each species from season to season and place to place. As a guide, the general season is known for a great many species including some that can be collected in two seasons, as follows:

Spring: Aspens, cottonwoods, most elms, red maple, silver maple, poplars, and the willows.

Summer: Cherries, chokecherries, Douglas-firs, red maple, mulberries, Siberian pea-tree, and the plums.

Fall: Most ashes, beeches, most birches, boxelder, catalpas, cherries, Douglas-firs, firs, hickories, junipers, most larches, black locust, maples (except red and silver), Osage-orange, pecan, most pines, plums, spruces, sweetgum, sycamores, walnuts, white-cedars, and yellow-poplar.

Winter: Some ashes, yellow birch, boxelder, catalpas, Osage-orange, black spruce, Norway spruce, sycamores, and walnuts.

Any season: Jack pine (except in the southern part of its range), lodgepole pine (except on the eastern side of the Cascade Mountains), Monterey pine, and sand pine.

Forest tree seeds commonly are gathered from standing trees. Collectors usually climb tall trees and detach the seeds or fruits by picking, cutting, or knocking them off. They handpick or flail off the seeds of small trees onto cloths from the ground or ladders.

Sometimes felled trees provide a cheap source, but the collector must gather seeds only from desirable trees cut after the fruits have begun to ripen.

The amount of seed produced per tree varies widely between species and from year to year. It is influenced also by the age, size, and health of the seed trees. Within any age or size class the dominant, widely spaced or open-grown trees usually produce the most seed if they receive adequate pollination. In good years a good seed tree may produce the following bushels of cones: Tamarack, 0.75; black spruce and eastern hemlock, 1; jack pine, ponderosa pine, red pine, and slash pine, 1 to 1.5; European larch and white spruce, 2; white pine, 5; and sugar pine, 5 to 7.

Some collectors gather squirrel-cut cones from the ground, but these fruits may not be adequately ripened. Collectors 30 or 40 years ago often obtained conifer cones from squirrel hoards in the Lake States and the West, but this is a rare practice today, except in the Pacific Northwest.

Fleshy fruits should not be crushed or dried more than superficially. Others should be spread out and dried partly before shipment. The fruits should be processed or extracted as soon as possible after collection.

SEEDS OF MANY TREE SPECIES must be separated from the fruits and cleaned of fruit parts or debris to prevent spoilage, conserve space and weight, and facilitate handling and sowing.

They fall into three groups as concerns extraction:

1. Tree seeds readily extracted from dry fruits, such as cones (baldcypresses, cypresses, firs, larches, pines, spruces, white-cedars); conelike clusters (yellow-poplar); pods (Kentucky coffeetree, honeylocust, locust); or capsules (aspens, cottonwoods, poplars, willows).

2. Dry fruits with seeds surrounded by a tightly adhering fruit wall, such as the nuts (chestnuts, oaks), and samaras (ashes, elms, maples, yellow-poplar).

3. Seeds of fleshy fruits, such as drupes (cherries, dogwoods, plums, walnuts), and multiple or collective fruits (mulberries, Osage-orange), and berrylike conelets (junipers).

Seeds of the second group are seldom extracted from the fruits because that is either unnecessary or very difficult. Those of the first and third groups are separated from the fruits by drying, threshing, tumbling, depulping, fanning, or sieving.

The simplest method of drying is to spread the fruits in shallow layers so that there is free circulation of air around each fruit. Where the climate is dry, drying may be done in the open. Where the climate is damp or the amount of fruit is great, it usually is done under a roof.

Protection from rodents and birds often is necessary to prevent serious seed losses during drying.

Some cones do not open readily and must be heated artificially in special kilns. These kilns provide the highest dry heat (usually between 100° and 150° F.) that the seeds can stand without injury, and these predetermined safe limits must not be exceeded.

Two general types of kilns are used for extracting seeds from cones—simple convection and forced-air kilns. The first is the oldest, cheapest, and simplest to operate. The second is more complicated and expensive but more efficient.

Recommended temperatures and schedules in convection kilns for several pines are: Jack pine, 2 to 4 hours at 145° to 150°; loblolly and slash pines, 6 to 48 hours (usually 8 to 10) at 120°; longleaf pine, 12 to 72 hours at 120°; ponderosa pine, 3 hours at 120° or less; red pine, 24 to 72 hours at 130° to 140°; and Scotch pine, 5 to 24 hours at 130°.

In forced-air kilns, comparable schedules are 8 to 16 hours at 115° for longleaf pine, 5 hours at 170° for red pine, and 4 to 8 hours at 130° for Scotch pine.

Seed of the following genera and species usually are extracted by air or kiln drying: Aspens, baldcypresses, chestnuts, cottonwoods, cypresses, Douglas-firs, elms, hemlocks, incense-cedar, larches, the pines, poplars, sequoias, spruces, sweetgum, sycamores, thujas, white-cedars, and yellow-poplar. Normally kilns are necessary for the hard-to-open cones of these pines: Bishop, jack, knobcone, lodgepole, Monterey, pond, and sand.

After drying, the cones are tumbled in revolving screened cages or drums to shake out and separate the seeds.

The separation of seeds of many dry fruits from the bunches, pods, or capsules in which they grow requires flailing, treading under foot, or treatment in agricultural threshing machinery or special apparatus, such as a macerator, hammermill, or mixer.

Threshing or screening commonly is required to extract seeds of the alders, American beech, Kentucky coffeetree, firs, hickories, honeylocust, black locust, Siberian pea-tree, eastern redbud, and walnut.

Some small fleshy fruits are dried whole, but the seeds of most fleshy or pulpy fruits must be extracted promptly to improve germination and to prevent spoilage. Small lots can be cleaned by hand methods, but larger lots should be processed mechanically.

Seeds of the following genera usually are extracted by depulping the fruits: Cherries, chokecherries, junipers, mulberries, Osage-orange, plums, tupelos, and yews.

Fruits that require mashing or soaking before cleaning (such as those of the cherries, mulberries, Osage-orange, plums, or yews) usually should not be allowed to ferment. An experienced operator, however, can use slight fermentation to make the process easier.

Seeds that require no extraction are produced by the ashes, basswoods, birches, elms, hackberries, oaks, and yellow-poplar. Some of them, however, need to be freed of chaff or trash. In addition, some of the small fleshy fruits, such as those of the common chokecherry and Russian-olive, often are dried without extraction.

CLEANING IS NECESSARY sometimes to eliminate chaff, trash, adhering fruit parts, or empty seeds and to facilitate seed storage and handling.

Often cleaning is combined with extraction, or a combination of methods may be required. Many seeds can be cleaned satisfactorily by running them through screens, either dry or with running water.

Most conifer seeds have wings that must be removed by hand rubbing, beating or trampling in sacks, moistening and raking, or treatment in dewinging machines or macerators. Treatment must be done carefully to avoid injury to the seeds. Unfortunately no mechanical dewingers yet devised are entirely satisfactory, yet hand methods are too expensive for large-scale use. Dewinging damage therefore is one of the major causes of low-quality seed.

Wings, light chaff, or empty seeds usually are removed by fanning. Most conifer seeds require this treatment in addition to dewinging. Large lots usually are run through standard agricultural or specialized seed fanning or cleaning mills. Some skill is needed to remove the debris but not good seeds.

Flotation in water is the most effective means of cleaning the seeds of most pulpy or fleshy fruits, but is not satisfactory with the junipers, because their seeds float. Sound seeds usually sink, but poor seeds, skins, and pulp either float or sink more slowly. The extracted seeds should be dried promptly after wetting.

The yield of cleaned seeds per 100 pounds of fruit as usually collected is called the extraction factor. It is necessary to know this factor and average viability of the seeds to determine the amount of fruit needed for specific sowing or market requirements.

The average extraction factor varies by species and within species as shown below. Some are so variable that they overlap into two or more groups:

1 to 5: Douglas-firs, hemlocks, incense-cedar, larches, mulberries, Osage-orange, pines, spruces, thujas.

6 to 10: Cottonwoods, firs, sweetgum, American sycamore.

11 to 20: Paper birch, chokecherries, cherries, shellbark hickory, Siberian pea-tree, plums, redwood, Russian-olive, white-cedars.

21 to 40: American beech, yellow birch, boxelder, butternut, catalpas, Kentucky coffeetree, cherries, shagbark hickory, shellbark hickory, honeylocust, junipers, black locust, plums, eastern redbud, Russian-olive.

41 to 60: Baldcypress, boxelder, Kentucky coffeetree, elms, mockernut hickory, Norway maple, sugar maple, oaks, pecan, Russian-olive, black walnut, yellow-poplar.

61 to 80: Ashes, basswoods, boxelder, hackberry, bitternut hickory, mockernut hickory, pignut hickory, sugar maple, oaks, pecan, yellow-poplar.

81 to 100: Bitternut hickory, pignut hickory, black maple, red maple, sugar maple, oaks, pecan.

STORAGE OF FOREST TREE SEEDS usually is necessary for a few months up to several years.

Frequently seeds are extracted in the fall and held over winter, although those of species like longleaf pine and the white pines often are sown soon after extraction and cleaning, and white oak acorns must be sown immediately after gathering.

Seeds of some species often must be held for several years because good seed crops occur infrequently.

Storage methods should be used that will maintain high viability. This is a simple matter for some species. It is difficult for others. For many, suitable storage practices are not yet known. With proper storage, seeds of many trees can be kept reasonably viable for 5 to 10 years, and those of a few species have been kept for several decades.

Seeds of the following forest trees can be kept satisfactorily by the oldest and simplest method of storage—in sacks or sealed containers at air temperatures: Basswoods, Kentucky coffeetree, black locust, and Siberian pea-tree.

Seeds of many trees, however, keep best at low temperatures in sealed containers. Temperatures between 32° and 41° have given good results, but recent research shows that seeds of several conifers keep better at 0° to 23° than at higher temperatures. At 0°, sealing of the containers appears to be unnecessary and perhaps undesirable.

Before storage, seeds of most conifers should be dried to a moisture content below 8 percent of ovendry weight. Seeds best stored cold and dry include those of the ashes, some aspens, birches, cypresses, Douglas-firs, elms, firs, hackberries, hemlocks, honeylocusts, junipers, larches, black locust, maples (other than silver), Osage-orange, pines, some poplars, eastern redbud, sassafras, sequoias, spruces, sweetgum, sycamore, thujas, white-cedars, yellow-poplar, and yews.

Several other forest trees also have seeds that keep best at low temperatures but at a moisture content above 35 percent. Included are: Beeches, buckeyes, American chestnut, hickories, silver maple, oaks, and walnuts. Many of these seeds can be stored for a few months by mixing them with one to three times their volume of moist peat moss, sand, exploded mica products, or chopped sphagnum moss and placing them in a refrigerator or holding them over winter in the ground under a mulch.

Although they can be stored dry and cold, yellow-poplar seeds have been kept for 8 years without loss in viability by placing them in layers alternated with sand in pits dug in the nursery.

Spring-ripening seeds, such as those of the red and silver maples, often are sown soon after collection in the spring to avoid storage losses. For the same reason, the seeds of many of the fall-ripening species are fall sown.

The short-lived seeds of some aspens and poplars can be kept for several months in sealed containers either under a partial vacuum or with a relative humidity of the air of less than 20 percent.

PRETREATMENT IS NEEDED to overcome the seed dormancy common to many tree species. Such seeds fail to sprout even when exposed to favorable conditions of temperature, moisture, oxygen, and light unless they are first given special treatment.

Of some 400 species of woody plants studied, 33 percent have seeds that are commonly nondormant, 7 percent have seeds with impermeable coats, 43 percent have seeds with internal dormancy, and 17 percent have more than one kind of seed dormancy.

Among the species that require softening of the seedcoat are most of the legumes, including Kentucky coffeetree, honeylocust, and black locust.

Species that usually require cold, moist treatment or fall sowing to promote prompt germination include most alders, most ashes, baldcypresses, beeches, most birches, most buckeyes, cherries, American chestnut, Douglas-fir (coast form), firs, hackberries, hemlocks, hickories, junipers, most larches, most maples, mulberries, black oaks, some pines (especially the white pines), plums, sassafras, some spruces, sweetgum, sycamores, tupelos, walnuts, white-cedar, and yellow-poplar.

Seeds that often require either a combination of seedcoat softening and cold moist treatment or sowing soon after collection in the late summer or early fall are those of black ash, baldcypresses, basswoods, some junipers, Osage-orange, Digger pine, whitebark pine, eastern redbud, and yews.

A tree species may have both dormant and nondormant seeds or those with more than one kind of dormancy. Unless there is time for tests before sowing, however, dormancy must be assumed and the best treatment given for the suspected condition.

TESTS SHOULD BE MADE to determine seed quality, a necessary basis for specifying the rate at which seeds should be sown to produce a certain number of usable seedlings. Such tests usually concern genuineness, purity, number of seeds per pound, moisture content, and viability.

THE RATE OF SOWING in the nursery and for direct seeding in the field is determined from laboratory tests, as modified by local experience.

Nursery and field germination of forest tree seeds usually is 50 to 80 percent of laboratory germination (in the South it may be 95 percent or higher), but further losses normally occur after germination.

The number of usable seedlings produced per 100 viable seeds sown, therefore, usually ranges from 10 to 60 for conifers and varies even more widely for broadleaf species.

Averages run below 10 for the aspens; 10 to 15 for paper birch, yellow birch, eastern cottonwood, American elm, Russian mulberry, northern white-cedar, and yellow-poplar; 16 to 20 for Japanese larch and redwood; 21 to 30 for American basswood, chokecherries, black locust, Osage-orange, eastern redbud, and Russian-olive; 31 to 40 for boxelder, catalpa, cherries, rock elm, hackberry, eastern hemlock, European larch, Siberian larch, most maples, Siberian pea-tree, plums, most spruces; 41 to 60 for baldcypress, Kentucky coffee-tree, Douglas-fir, honeylocusts, bur oak, pecan, some pines, eastern red-cedar, and tamarack; 61 to 80 for some ashes, American beech, most pines; and 81 to 100 for most oaks and walnuts.

IMPROVEMENT of seed handling is an activity of a number of agencies.

The Food and Agriculture Organization of the United Nations is urging all collectors of tree seeds to supply information on the origin of their seed and has developed a reporting form for that purpose.

Several Federal, State, and industrial forestry agencies have begun to collect most of their seeds from high-quality stands and selected trees. Some have established seed production areas or seed orchards. These and related activities will help to provide more and better forest tree seeds for the forestation of those 50 million acres in the best and the quickest way.

PAUL O. RUDOLF *is a research forester in the Division of Forest Management Research, Lake States Forest Experiment Station, maintained by the Department of Agriculture in cooperation with the University of Minnesota at St. Paul. He has been staff specialist in artificial forest regeneration and forest tree improvement there since 1931 and is the author of numerous publications on those phases of forestry. Mr. Rudolf holds degrees in forestry from the University of Minnesota and Cornell.*

For further reading:

Baldwin, H. I.: *Effect of After-Ripening Treatment on Germination of White Pine Seeds of Different Ages.* Botanical Gazette, volume 96, pages 372–376, illus. 1934.

Flemion, F.: *Further Studies on the Rapid Determination of the Germinative Capacity of Seeds.* Contribution Boyce Thompson Institute, volume 11, pages 455–464. 1941.

Isaac, L. A.: *Cold Storage Prolongs the Life of Noble Fir Seed and Apparently Increases Germinative Power.* Ecology, volume 15, pages 216–217. 1934.

Kaylor, J. F., and Randall, L. R.: *Methods of Collecting, Stratifying, and Planting Black Walnuts in Indiana.* Indiana Department of Conservation, Forestry Bulletin, No. 12, 8 pages, illus. 1931.

Maki, T. E.: *Significance and Applicability of Seed Maturity Indices for Ponderosa Pine.* Journal of Forestry, volume 38, pages 55–60, illus.

Stoeckeler, J. H., and Jones, G. W.: *Forest Nursery Practice in the Lake States*, U.S.D.A. Handbook 110, pages 1–17, illus. 1957.

Wakeley, Philip C.: *Planting the Southern Pines*, U.S.D.A. Agricultural Monogram 18, pages 26–56, 65–67, 215–216, illus. 1955.

Woody-plant Seed Manual, U.S.D.A. Miscellaneous Publication 564, 416 pages. 1948.

Production of Seeds

of Forest Trees

P. E. HOEKSTRA, E. P. MERKEL, AND
H. R. POWERS, JR.

TWO MILLION acres of forest land were planted with tree seedlings, for which about a thousand tons of seeds from a multitude of species had been collected, in the winter of 1959.

In 1985 or thereabouts we shall know the results, but until then we cannot be sure whether the trees will be tall and straight or crooked and runty. We are not sure because the genetic quality of most of the seed was not known. In fact, the pine species probably were of a low grade because the seed collectors got much of it from low and bushy trees that they could climb more easily than taller, better trees.

It is too bad that only a few people were concerned about tree seed, that forests were left to regenerate themselves, that harvested trees often were replaced by undesirable species, that new stands were sparse or failed to come up. Many people considered it farfetched even to think about controlling the quality of the seeds.

The situation has changed quickly and radically. Forestry practices have been intensified in a hundred ways. The planting of forest seedlings has mushroomed, and millions of acres are being planted. Foresters see the need and the opportunity for improving the planting stock.

It is not easy to do so. To provide superior tree seed in the needed amounts takes time. The task is to achieve large-scale production of the best possible seed as quickly as possible. Selection of good trees as parents,

breeding stock from them, and testing the progeny will produce forests of better trees that grow much faster than they do today. In the meantime, landowners have had to settle for seed that is only a little better.

The most efficient way yet devised to produce large amounts of genetically superior seed is to make a seed orchard, a plantation of genetically improved trees that is intensively managed to produce large seed crops.

We have no production figures of seed orchards in the United States, because they are too young to produce seeds in quantity. Two American natives, loblolly pine (*Pinus taeda*) and slash pine (*P. elliottii*), produced 43 and 25 pounds of viable seeds per acre at 20 years of age in Australia. From that, we assume that an acre of seed orchard should produce enough seeds each year to plant at least 200 acres in the United States.

To ACHIEVE genetic improvement, a number of steps must be taken before the seed orchard can be planted.

The heritable characteristics of the parent trees must be defined. Improvement of growth rate, tree form, and wood properties generally is the aim.

Sometimes special features are emphasized, such as resistance to blister rust in white pine (*Pinus monticola*, *P. strobus*), high yield of oleoresin in slash pine, or drought resistance in loblolly pine that is to be grown in some parts of Texas.

The next step is rigorous and careful selection of parent trees within the range of the species that is to be propagated. Selections are grouped by geographic races of the species if the existence of such races is known or suspected. Geographic races have been indicated in loblolly pine, Scotch pine (*P. sylvestris*), white ash (*Fraxinus americana*), green ash (*F. pennsylvanica*), black cottonwood (*Populus trichocarpa*), slash pine, shortleaf pine (*P. echinata*), and longleaf pine (*P. palustris*). Most species with a wide physiographic range may contain two or more races.

The next step is tests to determine how much genetic improvement the selected parents provide. The tests involve breeding the selections and observing the growth rate, form, and wood properties of the resulting progeny. If the young trees do well, the parents are accepted as breeding stock.

To save time, this step may be postponed until the seed orchard is established. Progeny tests can then be made while the orchard is growing up, and unsatisfactory parents are removed as the results of the tests become available.

The final step is vegetative propagation of the parents and planting in the seed orchard. Grafting is the most widely adopted propagation method for establishing a seed orchard, but air layering or rooting of cuttings can be used.

We know little about the relationships between rootstock and scion in the coniferous species. Genetic and physiological incompatibility between the two sometimes cause abnormal growth, imperfect union at the point of grafting, and death. Until the causes of incompatibility are better known, most workers use random nursery seedlings for grafting stock.

The seed orchard should be in a place where there will be no damage from wind, snow, and ice. Soil fertility and internal drainage should be excellent. The area should be easily-accessible to facilitate intensive management, which requires expensive equipment and skilled labor.

The orchard should be isolated from contaminating pollen sources. For southern pines, for example, an isolation strip at least 400 feet wide is recommended. The isolation strips could serve as pasture or cropland or they could be planted to trees of a commercial species that does not hybridize with the orchard trees.

The size of the seed orchard has a bearing on its efficiency even though the strip can be made productive.

B. J. Zobel, at North Carolina State College, calculated that a square seed orchard of 4 acres surrounded by a 500-foot isolation strip occupies 40 acres in all. He recommended that seed orchards be made as large as circumstances permit. The Georgia Forestry Commission, following this reasoning, started a 325-acre orchard for slash pine and loblolly pine.

The orchards contain a number of plants propagated from each parent tree, which constitutes a clone—a group of plants derived from a single individual by grafting, for example.

We have no firm experimental evidence on the minimum number of clones necessary for adequate cross-pollination. Most European workers give a range of 9 to 50 clones. Dr. Zobel reported that most seed orchards in the Southeastern States contain 15 to 25 different clones on each acre.

Clones should be arranged in a random pattern to permit statistical analysis of clonal differences. Two plants from the same clone should have at least two other plants in between to reduce pollination within the same clone.

Spacing should be wide enough to allow good development of tree crowns and rate of growth. Final spacings of 20 x 20 feet to 30 x 30 feet are recommended. The wider spacing is for the large-crowned species. For slow-growing conifers with narrow crowns, initial spacing may be 15 x 15 feet, to make sure that the pollen production, which is low at the start, will be used more efficiently.

Spacing can be increased by removing every other tree when the trees become crowded.

A permanent sod cover in the seed orchard prevents erosion, but it competes with the trees for moisture and nutrients. It probably is best to clean-cultivate the whole area or around the base of the trees during the years that they grow rapidly in order to conserve moisture.

Irrigation may be feasible when moisture is critical.

Nutrient levels in the soil may be improved by applications of fertilizer and the use of leguminous cover crops.

The best system of orchard management must be worked out for each species and soil region.

Seed collection would be simplified if the orchard trees could be kept at a maximum height of 25 to 30 feet. Pruning to achieve that and to develop rounded, bushy crowns would be simple in hardwoods but does not offer much promise for conifers. Severe pruning to limit the height may reduce seed production of coniferous species because most of the cones are found in their upper parts.

TREE SEED ORCHARDS in the United States produced a small amount of seed in 1961. It will be at least 1970 before the orchards will add much to the supplies of seed of some species. Fewer than 500 acres of tree seed orchard had been established in 1961, but the area was being expanded rapidly, notably in the Southeast.

T. O. Perry and Wang Chi Wu, at the University of Florida, estimated that 6 thousand acres of orchard will supply all of the slash and loblolly pine seeds needed. We have no estimates of this kind for other species.

Seed orchards in North America in 1961 included such species as slash pine, loblolly pine, shortleaf pine, eastern white pine, western white pine, ponderosa pine (*P. ponderosa*), red pine (*P. resinosa*), Douglas-fir (*Pseudotsuga menziessi*), noble fir (*Abies nobilis*), and hemlock (*Tsuga heterophylla*).

The parents in only two of the seed orchards had been progeny tested—a small experimental slash pine seed orchard near Lake City, Fla., for high yield of oleoresin, and a shortleaf seed orchard near Union, S.C., for resistance to the littleleaf disease.

Seed orchards will produce large quantities of seed efficiently, although genetic improvement may be slight at the start. They have practical advantages over random collection of seed from natural stands. Large amounts of seed can be collected with less effort and at the proper time. Seed yields per bushel of cones will be greater because of better cross-pollination. Seed orchards, above all, afford good opportunities for stimulating and protecting abundant cone crops through intensive management practices.

SEED-PRODUCTION areas can serve until seed orchards come into production. They are good natural or planted stands of seed-bearing age, which have been thinned to provide the best possible growing space for the remaining trees.

As a rule, not more than 30 to 40 of the best formed trees are left after one or more cuts. Genetic improvement by this practice is uncertain, but since it insures that seed comes from the best trees, it is an improvement over random seed collection without any control over the source of seed. This type of control is important because poor form can be inherited. One southern pine tree, whose poor form can be passed on to the next generation, may produce enough seeds to plant 30 to 40 acres.

Several thousand acres have been converted to seed-production areas for slash pine, loblolly pine, red pine, eastern white pine, western white pine, ponderosa pine, sugar pine (*P. lambertiana*), and Douglas-fir. The total area in seed-production tracts is being extended rapidly over the whole Nation. The most rapid expansion is taking place in the pine belt of the Southeast.

MANY FACTORS influence the production of forest tree seed. In most species, 3 to 6 months elapse between flowering and seed ripening. In the pines, however, fertilization takes place a year after pollination, and the seed ripens in the fall of the second year.

Each species exhibits a rather well-defined pattern of seed production throughout the life of a tree. The age at which flowering starts and the span of productive years vary sharply among the species. Vigorous trees with large crowns, however, produce the largest crops for a given age and species.

Seed crops from the same tree fluctuate from year to year, partly because of weather. Heavy rainfall during pollination may wash a great deal of pollen to the ground and so reduce pollination to much below the normal. Late frosts and strong winds can cause a considerable loss of flowers. Available moisture when flower primordia—the first flower cells—are being formed is important.

Most forest trees bear seed in cycles. A good crop may occur at intervals of 2 to 10 years, depending on the species. Between good years, crops are much lighter and sometimes fail completely. One reason may be that food reserves stored in the stem are exhausted after a bumper seed crop and a number of years are needed to replenish these reserves.

Trees vary also in their inherent fruitfulness. Some trees do not produce a good seed crop even under the most favorable circumstances, while others consistently rank high.

Some of the factors can be manipulated to cause premature flowering, stimulate heavy seed production, and lessen the year-to-year fluctuation.

The time at which flower primordia are first differentiated in the bud determines when stimulation treatments can be applied most effectively. Female flowers start to form during August or during September in *Pinus*, *Taxus*, and *Pseudotsuga*. Male flowers in these genera generally are initiated several weeks before their female counterparts. Environmental and inherent factors, however, cause considerable variation within a species.

Heavy thinning—release—generally increases seed production in well-stocked stands. Longleaf, loblolly, and slash pine bear two to three times as much seed several years after release increases the growing space, moisture, and nutrients for each tree. Single trees with no competition from neighboring trees or other vegetation produce the largest seed crops.

The highest seed production per acre, however, requires a closer spacing than for maximum production per tree. Maximum seed production per acre for slash pine, for example, can be obtained with spacing about 25 x 25 feet.

Release cuttings to develop seed-production areas can best be applied before the stand reaches pole size. The remaining trees can then maintain large crowns and high vigor. If release is delayed too long, the trees will not respond.

Fertilization generally raises seed production of forest trees and causes slash pine (and perhaps other trees) to start bearing seed at an earlier age. One to two pounds of commercial fertilizer per inch of diameter (at breast height) applied around each tree will promote health and vigor and thus benefit seed production.

White oak (*Quercus alba*), sugar maple (*Acer saccharinum*), beech (*Fagus grandifolia*), loblolly pine, slash pine, sugar pine, and Douglas-fir have responded to single applications of commercial fertilizers, and their seed crops have increased twofold to fivefold. No firm recommendations can be made, however, as to amount and type of fertilizer until nutrient requirements for each species have been determined. Fertilizer ratios can then be calculated on the basis of deficiencies shown by soil analysis.

Stem injury, which retards the normal phloem transport of organic food substances, stimulates production of seed of a number of forest trees. Stems may be girdled or banded. A girdle is made by removing a strip of bark and cambium in two semicircles or a spiral around the tree. Wire or metal strips can be used to band the tree; this treatment, however, may be less effective than girdling. Longleaf pine, slash pine, loblolly pine, red pine, and Scotch pine have yielded two to three times a normal cone crop after they were girdled.

Seed stimulation by means of stem injury should be used with caution, because this type of treatment may become harmful in the long run. Repeated wounding may kill the trees by weakening them too much or by making them more susceptible to damage from insects and diseases.

Root pruning, a less injurious treatment, stimulates production of seed. Careful pruning may be repeated without much damage. Root pruning combined with fertilization is most likely to increase yields in seed orchards with a minimum risk to the trees.

SEVERAL DISEASES attack flowers, fruits, and cones of forest trees. Seed losses from disease can become serious on conifers. As far as we know, damage to hardwoods usually is slight.

Among the cone rusts that occur on various conifers, the one that attacks slash and longleaf pines is the most important. It is caused by the fungus *Cronartium strobilinum* and destroys annually nearly 20 percent of first-year slash pine cones. The fungus infects the female flowers. As the infected flowers grow into a cone, they swell to several times natural size and in late spring turn to a bright yellowish-orange color. Diseased cones as a rule are heavily attacked by cone moth (*Dioryctria*) larvae, and in turn serve as a source of further insect infestation of neighboring healthy cones. Practically all diseased cones are shed by late summer.

Evergreen oaks, particularly live oak (*Quercus virginiana*), and the runner oaks (*Q. pumila* and *Q. minima*) are alternate hosts to the fungus. It is advisable therefore to establish seed orchards of slash pine north of the range of these alternate hosts.

Weather conditions greatly influence the severity of cone rust. Some years are more favorable than others for the buildup of the disease on the evergreen oaks. There also appears to be a direct relationship between heavy infection and long periods of high relative humidity and rainfall.

Ferbam, a fungicide, has given good protection against cone rust. It can be applied with an orchard sprayer in January and February, when flowers of slash pine are susceptible to infection. The most effective time to spray seems to be just before or immediately after each 18-hour (or longer) period when the relative humidity exceeds 85 percent. Delay of only a day or two may mean a complete loss of protection.

Other cone rusts are similar in many ways to the one we described. *Cronartium conigenum*, for instance, infects cones of Chihuahua pine (*Pinus leiophylla*) in Arizona and New Mexico. The fungus kills up to 50 percent of the cones on groups of trees and up to 90 percent on single trees. Alternate hosts are *Quercus emoryi* and *Q. hypoleucoides*. *Melampsora Farlowii* infects cones of eastern hemlock (*Tsuga canadensis*). Infected cones turn yellow and die.

Chrysomyxa pyrolae infects cones of black spruce (*Picea mariana*), blue spruce (*P. pungens*), Engelmann spruce (*P. engelmannii*), Norway spruce (*P. abies*), red spruce (*P. rubens*), and white spruce (*P. glauca*). Infected cones turn yellow and produce no seed. Alternate hosts are species of *Pyrola* and *Moneses*.

Among diseases that affect the seed crops of deciduous trees are a blight (*Taphrina*) and powdery mildew (*Erisiphe aggregata*). Both damage female catkins of alders (*Alnus*). The blight *Taphrina pruni* causes plum pockets on wild plum.

MANY INSECT pests prey on the flowers, fruits, and cones of most commercial forest trees in North America.

Insect depredations are nearly always completed by the time seed is extracted; rarely is seed damaged during storage. Dynamics of insect populations coupled with seed crop fluctuations result in considerable variation of seed losses in successive years, among stands of the same tree species, and even between neighboring trees.

The average extent of insect damage,

however, is large enough to cause concern to managers of seed orchards and seed-production areas.

The seedworm *Laspeyresia youngana* can infest as much as 79 percent of the cones on white spruce and Sitka spruce (*P. sitchensis*) in Alaska.

Up to 64 percent of the seed in cones of white spruce (*P. glauca*) can be destroyed by the fly larva, *Pegohylemyia anthracina*, in Saskatchewan and Ontario. This insect appears to do more damage when the white spruce cone crop is small.

Surveys in California have shown cone moths (*Dioryctria*) to damage 17 to 73 percent of Douglas-fir cones.

Seed chalcids (*Megastigmus*) in the same State have destroyed as much as 21 percent of Douglas-fir seed.

A beetle, *Conophthorus lambertiana*, can destroy 25 to 75 percent of the cone crop of sugar pines over large areas in the West.

The white pine cone beetle (*Conophthorus coniperda*) in 10 years destroyed more than 95 percent of the white pine cone crops on the Massabesic Experimental Forest in Maine.

Cone moth larvae damage 10 to 60 percent of maturing slash and longleaf pine cones in many seed-production areas in the South. Two species of pine seedworms have infested up to 90 percent of the slash pine cones in some localities of north Florida and destroyed as much as half of the seed in damaged cones. A small sucking insect, *Gnophothrips piniphilus*, has killed up to 20 percent of the slash pine flower crop in Florida.

The major insect pests that affect seed of forest trees belong to four large orders—the beetles (*Coleoptera*), the moths (*Lepidoptera*), the flies (*Diptera*), and the wasps (*Hymenoptera*). Nearly always are the insects in the larval stage when they destroy seeds.

Seed chalcids, seedworms, and acorn weevils feed almost exclusively within seeds. The *Conophthorus* beetles, *Barbara* moths and *Dioryctria* moths · feed throughout the cone. The *Conophthorus* beetle, attacking coniferous trees, bores an egg gallery in the cone axis about the time cones start their second year of development. Developing larvae then proceed to destroy internal scale and seed tissues. Cone moths produce more than one generation in the South. Their larvae feed on pine flowers, cones, vegetative buds, shoots, and tree trunks at different times throughout the year.

To protect seed crops from insect damage in seed orchards and seed-production areas, we must have detailed knowledge of their life histories and habits. Much of this essential information is still lacking. Results from several tests with insecticide sprays indicate, however, that chemical control can give at least partial protection to seed crops.

A measure of protection of sugar pine cones from the cone beetle has been obtained by application of 2 pounds of DDT in 2 gallons of diesel oil sprayed from a helicopter. First- and second-year cones of slash and longleaf pine in the South have been protected from cone moth larvae with a 0.5-percent water emulsion of benzene hexachloride, applied by hydraulic sprayer or mist blower.

During the period of establishment, seed orchards may need protection from insects other than those attacking seeds or cones. Grafts of southern pine, for instance, need protection from the beetle, *Pityopthorus pulicarius*, which bores in at the graft union and kills the scion. Monthly sprays with benzene hexachloride or DDT, applied until the graft union heals over, have controlled the insect. Pine tip and shoot moths hinder the development of young planted pine in many parts of the country. These insects can be controlled in newly established seed orchards with emulsions of DDT or benzene hexachloride.

P. E. HOEKSTRA, *a research forester;* E. P. MERKEL, *an entomologist; and* H. R. POWERS, JR., *a plant pathologist, are employed at the Southeastern Forest Experiment Station of the Forest Service.*

Seeds for Rootstocks of Fruit and Nut Trees

L. C. COCHRAN, W. C. COOPER, AND
EARLE C. BLODGETT

THE PRINCIPAL fruit and nut trees grown commercially in the United States (except figs, tung, and filberts) are grown as varieties or clonal lines propagated on rootstocks.

Almost all the rootstocks are grown from seed. The resulting seedlings then are either budded or grafted with propagating wood of the desired variety. This practice has come about chiefly because the improved varieties of these fruits and nuts do not come true from seed and are not easily propagated on their own roots from cuttings.

Seedlings used for rootstocks generally are easy to grow. Experience has taught us which scion-rootstock combinations are suitable and how to produce good nursery trees.

Growing fruit and nut trees on rootstocks rather than on their own roots has many advantages.

Some of the desirable horticultural varieties have more vigor when they are grown on vigorous rootstocks. Some varieties on their own roots are susceptible to root-infecting, disease-causing organisms and nematodes, root- and crown-infesting insects. Some are intolerant to salt, drought, alkali, and poorly drained soils. The cold hardiness of some varieties can be increased by topworking them onto the framework of cold-hardy varieties.

Many varieties produce fruit of better quality and are more productive on suitable rootstocks than they are on their own roots. By a choice of rootstocks, some fruit and nut crops can be grown in areas otherwise not suitable.

In instances where rootstocks have solved problems for one crop, their use has led to calamity in another.

An example is the sour orange. Because of its adaptability to heavy soils, resistance to foot rot, relatively high resistance to cold, and production of good crops, the sour orange has become widely used throughout the world as a rootstock for sweet oranges.

The tristeza virus, which destroys sweet orange trees growing on sour orange roots, got a foothold in South America. It spread and killed millions of trees and almost wiped out the industry. The tristeza virus has now become universal there, and the industry is being reestablished only by the use of tolerant rootstocks, such as Cleopatra mandarin, sweet orange, Rangpur lime, and rough lemon.

Many factors, some of which are changing continuously, determine the suitability of rootstocks. Likewise, new information is being developed constantly, and new and better rootstocks become available to meet the need.

A GOOD ROOTSTOCK is one on which the desired variety of fruit or nut makes a good graft union and on which it is long lived, yields well, grows relatively fast, and fruits early. It must be reasonably compatible with the top variety.

If the rootstock variety is vigorous and the top variety is thoroughly compatible on it, the resulting tree tends to grow fast, is large, and often comes into fruit late. Such overvigorous combinations sometimes result in reduced quality or yield of fruit.

On the other hand, when the rootstock and top are not thoroughly compatible, the tree is likely to be dwarfed. Such incompatibility is often the result of failure of suitable formation or function of the phloem at or near the bud union. The phloem is the tissue that contains the food-conducting tubes in the bark through which the elaborated food made in the leaves flows to the roots to nourish them. Because of reduced nutrition, the roots are dwarfed, and there is a corresponding dwarfing of the tops.

The reduced function of the phloem at the bud union leads to an accumulation of elaborated food in the tops, that in turn causes earlier maturation of fruiting wood and earlier fruiting.

Nurserymen have made use of such partial incompatibility directly or with interstocks to produce dwarf trees, which fruit correspondingly at an earlier age.

Other desirable features claimed for dwarfed trees are cheaper and easier control of pests; lower cost of pruning, thinning, and harvesting; and higher quality and better color of fruit.

The problem in producing dwarf trees is to find combinations that allow enough of the normal functions to go on so that the trees will have the desired size; not be subject to winter injury, malnutrition, and disease; and be productive of good fruit.

A ROOTSTOCK seed parent should produce seedlings that are uniform in size, vigor, and the qualities which make a seedling a good rootstock.

Preferably a rootstock seed parent should be self-fertile so that it can be grown in isolated blocks and thereby prevent hybridization and variability in the seedlings. The fruits and seeds should all mature at the same season to permit machine harvesting. If the seeds are in fleshy fruits (such as cherries and plums), the fruit should be a freestone to allow easier removal of the fruit flesh.

The trees that are sources of seed should be productive. The seeds should give a high percentage of germination.

THE SEEDS of fruit-tree rootstocks have to be harvested, stored, and handled in different ways.

Some cannot be dried or allowed to ferment in the juice of the fruit. Some need afterripening before they will germinate. Some remain viable in a dry condition for several years.

Because citrus seed soon loses its vitality if it becomes too dry, it is usually extracted from fresh fruit by hand, washed free of pulp and juice, surface dried, and planted immediately. If it is to be stored, the washed seed should be dipped in a 1-percent solution of 8-oxyquinoline sulfate, surface dried, and placed in a polyethylene plastic bag and kept in cold storage at 38°–40° F. Such treated citrus seed can be stored many months with only a slight decline in viability.

SEEDS of peach, apricot, cherry, and plum should be extracted from fresh fruit and preferably washed free of fruit parts and juice as soon as possible. These stone-fruit seeds lose their ability to germinate if they are allowed to ferment in fruit juice or fruit pomace. Viability is severely reduced if left in fermenting juice even for 24 hours. On the other hand, properly dried and cured seeds of peach, plums, and apricot may be kept 4 years or more in a cool, dry storage with little loss in viability.

Cherry seeds generally are more sensitive to drying. After harvest they should be thoroughly washed, surface dried, and kept in a cool, moist storage until they are ready for planting or placed in storage for afterripening. In some sections, cherry rootstock seeds are planted directly in the nursery in the fall. Some growers prefer to hold them in a mixture of moist peat and sand in a cold storage and plant them in the spring. Cherries need approximately 110 to 120 days at 40° for best germination.

Mazzard and mahaleb cherries are the commonest rootstocks for sweet cherries. Some cherries are grown exclusively on mahaleb. Seeds of both mahaleb and mazzard do not remain viable as long as peaches and apricots.

Seeds of apple, pear, and quince mainly are harvested from local varieties at processing plants, washed, surface dried, and stored in cool, moist storage. Sometimes they are planted immediately directly in the nursery row.

Almonds can be air dried. They will

retain their viability for several years in common dry storage.

Pecan seeds are harvested and planted immediately in the fall or they can be stratified in moist sand until they germinate when they are planted in the nursery row.

No entirely satisfactory rootstock has been found for the Regia or Persian walnuts. *Juglans hindsii*, the northern California black walnut, Regia seedlings, and Royal and Paradox hybrids are all used. The seed is stored over winter in a cool, moist place and planted in the spring.

MANY TREE seeds need a rest or afterripening period before they will germinate.

Generally speaking, seeds with a hard shell or pit require more rest than those with a softer shell or without a shell.

Most soft or fleshy seeds that do not stand drying usually will grow almost immediately as soon as they are put in a suitable environment for germination.

Most seeds acquire their needed rest period or chilling requirement only when placed under proper environment. Most varieties of peach need 100 to 120 days in a moist substrate, such as a mixture of moist peat and sand at 40°, to give maximum germination.

A few seeds will germinate after 60 days, and the percentage increases with time. Peach seeds can be held at 32° for several months after their rest period has been satisfied without germination, but will germinate immediately if the temperature is raised.

Moisture is as important as cold in the afterripening process. Most deciduous seeds in temperate climates will receive more rest than they need if they are planted directly in the nursery row and allowed to obtain their chilling from natural exposure. Freezing is not necessary but usually is not harmful unless it is severe.

Apricots, almonds, cherries, and plums can be afterripened in the same way as peaches.

Some plums, especially *domestica*

species, require much more chilling than most peaches. The myrobalan plum, *Prunus cerasifera*, requires about the same chilling as peaches.

Mahaleb cherries require slightly more than peaches, up to 125 days, and some mazzard cherries may require even more.

Apricots and almonds require only 50 to 60 days for afterripening.

Pears and apples require only 6 weeks or less.

In general, the seeds cannot be dried after they have had their rest period without losing their viability.

Seeds of some fruits, such as peaches and cherries, will continue to grow if removed from fruits at maturity and placed in a proper environment without drying. No chilling is needed for such seed unless they are allowed to stop growing, in which case they will require chilling before growth is resumed.

FEW DISEASES are spread in or on seeds used for rootstocks. Most important are virus diseases.

No viruses are known to be carried in citrus seeds, although most of the commercial citrus trees throughout the world are infected with virus. Some of the viruses, like psorosis, produce violent and devastating symptoms. Others are latent unless the variety is topworked on a sensitive rootstock. Citrus varieties and species that produce asexual seeds can be reconstituted free of virus by merely growing seedlings, which are propagated.

The prunus ring spot virus can pass from parent through seeds to seedling in peach, cherry, and certain plums. Very likely it is seed-transmitted in other species. It also may be spread to seedling progenies of virus-free trees that are pollinated with pollen from infected trees. The viruses of peach necrotic leaf spot, prune dwarf, and sour cherry yellows are transmitted in peach and cherry seeds.

Several bacterial diseases are spread on rootstock seeds. The crown gall organism, *Agrobacterium tumefaciens*, is widely present in many soils and is carried in water. Seeds that are allowed to come in contact with contaminated water will carry the organism with them. The crown gall organism, a wound parasite, commonly infects young seedlings whose cotyledons are torn as they emerge from the seedcoat. Incipient infections develop with the seedling and often form large galls at the crown. *Prunus* seeds also can become contaminated with the organism that causes bacterial canker, *Pseudomonas syringae.*

THE CLIMATE, soils, salinity of water, pests, diseases, and conditions under which citrus is grown are so varied that no one rootstock is satisfactory for all citrus trees.

The various kinds of citrus respond differently on the same rootstock. Some grow better on one, and others on another. The adaptability of sour orange to heavy soils, its resistance to foot rot, and production of good crops of high-quality fruit has made it a first choice in many areas for oranges and grapefruit. Where tristeza virus has become established, however, it cannot be grown.

Rough lemon produces large trees with good yields on the light, sandy, ridge sections of central Florida and in many other areas with similar soils and climates. It is tolerant to tristeza. It is about as susceptible to foot rot as sweet orange and produces fruit with low solids.

Citrus macrophylla is the most tolerant of boron of any citrus rootstock and produces good crops of lemons in high-boron soils, but it is only moderately tolerant to chlorides and is tender to cold.

The trifoliate orange, *Poncirus trifoliata*, is deciduous and sufficiently hardy that it will grow as far north as Boston. It is not deciduous in warm climates and is only slightly more cold hardy than sour orange. Sweet oranges and certain mandarins grow well on it and produce good crops if they are free of the exocortis and other viruses that stunt trees on it. It is salt sensitive and therefore cannot be used on salty soils.

Rangpur lime has proved to be a good rootstock, well adapted to the soils and climates of some areas, but is severely damaged if the top variety is infected with the rangpur lime disease virus—a virus related to exocortis.

Cleopatra mandarin is a good prospect for replacing sour orange because of its tolerance to foot rot and tristeza, its reasonable adaptability to heavy soils, its salt tolerance, and its ability to produce good quality in grapefruit and sweet orange. In some sections, trees on it are slow to come into bearing and do not grow so rapidly or bear so heavily as on some of the other rootstocks.

Some of the citranges (trifoliate × orange hybrids), such as Troyer, have shown excellent promise in some areas but, like its trifoliate parent, is salt sensitive. Carrizo citrange has shown resistance to the burrowing nematode in Florida. Other selections and hybrids of trifoliata have shown resistance to the citrus nematode.

Citrus is somewhat by itself with respect to rootstocks because of the large number of distinct genera on which it will grow and the striking responses a single variety will produce when grown on closely related species and varieties.

Through hybridization, new rootstocks can be tailored for individual varieties, soils, and resistance to pests. Extensive work to develop better stocks is underway in Florida, Texas, and California.

Most of the seed used for citrus rootstocks in the United States is obtained from trees grown specifically for seed production. Growers specify varieties—even individual strains of varieties—that they know will give good uniformity, vigor, and performance.

STONE FRUITS show considerable mutual grafting affinities, but many combinations are not satisfactory for commercial use.

Peach is used widely as a commercial rootstock for apricots, plums, almonds, and some other prunus species. Peach, however, does not do well when the combination is reversed and it is grown as the top on rootstocks other than peach.

Seedlings of the Lovell peach are the commonest rootstock used for peach. Seedlings of Muir also have been widely used but have become hard to get. The wide use of these varieties is due partly to availability of seeds. Because both varieties have been used for drying and for jam, seed is saved easily and dried at the time of processing. Lovell seedlings are preferred by nurserymen over other varieties because they are more uniform, less bushy, and easier to bud.

Peach nursery stock used to be grown almost exclusively on Tennessee or Carolina naturals—escaped semiwild peaches, which descended from seed introduced by early Spanish settlers in the Southeastern States. Because of lower cost, ample supply, and good performance, Lovell has largely supplanted naturals as a source of seed.

The increasing recognition of damage to trees on peach rootstock by nematodes, particularly the root knot nematodes, has heightened interest in nematode tolerant stocks. Bokhara, Yunan, and Shalil, introduced from China and India in the 1920's, showed some resistance to the root knot nematodes, but seedlings have had variable amounts of infection. Orchards on some selections of Shalil have been severely damaged by crown rot in California.

Several nematode-resistant peach rootstocks have been introduced. Stribling's Nursery at Merced, Calif., introduced a patented variety under the name S–37. The Del Rancho Fortuna Nursery at Delano, Calif., introduced Rancho Resistant in 1956. The Department of Agriculture released FV–234–1 for trial in 1959.

S–37 has proved to be more resistant than Shalil, Bokhara, or Yunan, but it segregates in resistance and growth habit. Some seedlings are weak and weeping in habit.

Rancho Resistant appears to be resistant to the *acrita* strain of the root knot nematode but not to *javanica*. The heritage of FV–234–1 is unknown. It was selected by J. H. Weinberger at Fort Valley, Ga., from seedlings from a lot of seed obtained from an importer as *Prunus davidiana*. As it resembles a true peach, it may be a hybrid. It is resistant to the *acrita* strain, but about one-fourth of the seedlings develop small galls when exposed to *javanica*. We have no evidence, however, that *javanica* is able to reproduce on them.

There is a growing demand for nematode-resistant and virus-free seed stocks of peach. To supply the demand, orchards are being planted specifically for seed production. Seeds from them very likely will replace the seeds that have been available as a byproduct of processing industries.

The viability of peach seeds varies from year to year. We do not know why. Seed lots with high viability retain their viability if kept dry for several years. Some nurserymen hold over and use seed from such good germination years in order to assure good stands of seedlings.

Peaches have never been successful commercially on rootstocks other than peach. They are more compatible with apricot than with plums and almonds. Before nematode-resistant peach rootstocks were available, some peach orchards were grown on apricot rootstock. Such trees were somewhat dwarfed and were generally shorter lived than on peach.

Peaches grown on certain strains of St. Julien and Damson plums are more dwarfed and shorter lived than on apricot.

Dwarf peaches are standard varieties grown on the sandplum, *Prunus besseyi*.

PLUMS are less demanding than peaches as to rootstocks. Most plums appear to do well on peach as a rootstock. About 50 percent of the commercially grown plums are on peach. The European plums seem to be less suited to peach than the Japanese. Imperial prune appears to be more resistant to bacterial gummosis on peach than on myrobalan plum.

French prune tends to bear earlier and produce larger fruit on peaches than on myrobalan. Italian prune in the Pacific Northwest is commonly grown on peach rootstock.

Plums will also grow on almond and apricot rootstocks. A number of French prune orchards are on apricot roots. A few varieties of plum, such as Beauty, Gaviota, El Dorado, and Duarte, make weaker unions on apricot than on peach. Some plums have trouble on almond roots.

Myrobalan and marianna plums, *P. cerasifera*, are widely used as rootstocks for plums. The most of the myrobalan is propagated from domestic or imported seed. Some orchards are grown on myrobalan 29C selected in California, a vegetatively propagated myrobalan clone that is tolerant to nematodes and armillaria root rot. Marianna 2624, a similarly vegetatively propagated clone, also developed in California, is gaining favor.

ABOUT HALF of the apricots and almonds are grown on peach rootstock. The rest are on seedling apricot and almond, respectively. Seed of Royal or Blenheim from fruit-drying yards are the commonest sources of apricot seedlings.

Formerly the seeds of the bitter almond, commonly used as a pollenizer in almond orchards, was used as a source of seeds for almond rootstock, but the variety Texas probably is most commonly used now.

Almond is losing favor as a rootstock for almonds in heavy and poorly drained soils because they appear to be more susceptible than peach to crown rot.

SWEET AND SOUR cherries are grown chiefly on mahaleb, *P. mahaleb*. Mazzard, *P. avium*, is preferred in some areas.

The seeds of mahaleb are harvested from seedling orchards grown entirely for seed purposes. New varieties, known as Russian and Turkish mahaleb, have been tested and have proved to be more vigorous and winter hardy and appear very promising.

Mazzard seeds used to be obtained from pollinator trees in western orchards and from wild native trees in the eastern States. Improved strains of the so-called "silver bark" mazzards, imported from Germany by the Geneva branch of the New York Agricultural Experiment Station, appear promising. Because the ring spot, sour cherry yellows, and prune dwarf viruses are seedborne, scientists began work to establish virus-free orchards as sources of seed. Some seed of both rootstocks still are imported from Europe.

MOST OF the apples in the United States formerly were propagated on French crab, a cider apple grown in France. More recently, seedlings of domestic varieties, such as Delicious, Winesap, Jonathan, Rome Beauty, and York, have become widely used.

In places subject to low winter temperatures and sudden drops in temperatures, the practice of double working to produce trees with cold-hardy trunks is increasing. The use of partially incompatible trunk sandwiches—interstocks between the variety top and the seedling rootstock—to produce dwarf trees has become popular, but most dwarf trees are produced by growing varieties directly on dwarfing stocks, like the East Malling and Malling Merton series. Apples are grown commercially only on apple rootstocks and appear to grow equally well on seedlings of most commercial varieties.

PEARS are grown mostly on domestic Bartlett seedlings. The early pear plantings in the United States were almost entirely on French pear seedlings. Since 1920 or so, most of the pear stock was grown on oriental pear understock from seed brought from

Asia. They produced vigorous trees, and were liked in the nursery because of some resistance to fire blight and woolly root aphis and freedom from leaf troubles. The association of hard end and black end of the fruit with oriental rootstock discouraged their use, and no oriental stock is used in the commercial pear orchards of western States.

PEAR DECLINE, a new disorder that has devastated pear orchards in the western States, has been associated with oriental rootstocks and has brought about renewed interest in pear rootstocks.

The Angers quince propagated vegetatively is used as a dwarfing stock for pears, but there is wide variation in behavior of varieties grown directly on quince. Bartlett normally does not do well on quince. In areas where blight is bad, blight-susceptible pears are grown on trees composed of seedling roots, Old Home, or other blight-resistant variety trunks on which the desired varieties have been top-worked. If planted deep, the Old Home often forms roots above the bud union with the original seedling.

The Persian walnut, *Juglans regia*, is grown mostly on the northern California black walnut, *J. hindsii*. Regia seedlings, Royal and Paradox hybrids (*J. hindsii* × *J. nigra*), and (*J. hindsii* × *regia*) have been gaining in popularity because of black line, a disorder in which the bark dies at the bud union on trees of Persian on *J. hindsii*. Regia and its hybrids appear to be more resistant to the meadow nematodes.

PECANS are grown almost entirely on domestic pecan seedling rootstocks. Seed from scab-resistant varieties with medium-size nuts, such as Curtis and Stuart, are preferred, because the seedlings in the nursery are less affected by scab and make more vigorous trees.

The small, native western nuts produced out of the heavy scab area are apt to be highly susceptible to scab and should be avoided.

TUNG is grown mostly as seedlings directly on their own roots. Seed should be collected as first-generation seed from clonally propagated varieties that have progeny performance records as to production, oil yield, vigor, and cold hardiness. Seedlings of Folsom, Lampton, and LaCrosses come true to the parent type. Lampton is probably the most widely used seed parent.

Filberts are grown from layered cuttings and thus are on their own roots. Trees are mounded and new plants are obtained from the suckers that grow from the base of the tree and root in the mound.

Figs are nearly all grown on their own roots. Cuttings are made of dormant 1- to 3-year-old wood, which is buried until it is well calloused. Then it is planted in the nursery row and later in the orchard. Some varieties have shown greater vigor and nematode resistance and are used as rootstocks for other varieties.

L. C. COCHRAN, *Chief, Fruit and Nut Crops Research Branch, Agricultural Research Service, studied horticulture and plant pathology at Purdue and Michigan State Universities. He did research at the University of California before joining the Department of Agriculture in 1941. He has published many papers on the ills of fruit trees, particularly in the field of virus diseases.*

W. C. COOPER *is plant physiologist in charge of citrus and subtropical plants production investigations, Crops Research Division, Agricultural Research Service, Orlando, Fla. He holds degrees from the University of Maryland and California Institute of Technology. His research field has been with citrus rootstocks and citrus nutrition.*

EARLE C. BLODGETT *holds a dual position of plant pathologist with the Washington Department of Agriculture and the Washington Agricultural Experiment Station. He holds degrees from the Universities of Idaho and Wisconsin. He has done research work on diseases of fruit trees, with particular reference to diseases of nursery stock.*

Pollination of Seed Crops by Insects

GEORGE E. BOHART AND FRANK E. TODD

IN A PLANT that is adapted for self-pollination, the male spores often are transferred from the anther of the plant to its stigma by gravity or movement of parts within the flower.

If the floral parts are so arranged as to prevent or limit sharply the ability of the plant to pollinate itself, the pollen has to be transferred by such external agencies as wind and insects in order for fertilization—the union of the sex cells—to take place.

Plants adapted for cross-pollination—that is, the transfer of the pollen from a different plant—depend entirely on external agencies.

Many plants are adapted for both self- and cross-pollination in different flowers or at different periods in the life cycle of the flower. For such plants, cross-pollination usually results in more seeds of better quality, but automatic self-pollination is insurance that some seeds will form even if external agencies fail.

Plants with specific adaptations for automatic self-pollination are almost always self-fertile—that is, the sperms and eggs of the same plant are compatible. Self-fertility is also present in some plants that depend on external agencies for pollination.

Many plants that are adapted primarily for cross-pollination are more or less self-sterile. They must have external agents of pollination and external sources of pollen to produce seeds in any quantity.

Plant breeders in the past often selected plants for breeding for their self-fertile, self-pollinating characteristics.

Varieties developed from such selections tend to remain true to type, and they do not depend very much on external agents of pollination. Their principal drawback is the loss of hybrid vigor. The more recent emphasis on inherent yielding capacity has led to reinvestigation of many self-pollinated crops to determine the advantages and possibilities of growing hybrid seed.

WIND, BIRDS, and insects are the main external agents of pollination. Birds are of little importance to commercial crops, especially in temperate regions.

Wind is the principal pollinating agent of corn and other grasses, coniferous trees, nut trees (except almonds), and a scattering of other crops (for example, castorbeans, spinach, and beets).

Most other plants are self-pollinated or insect pollinated, or both. Peas, beans, tomatoes, and lettuce are examples of plants that produce good crops of seed without help from external agents of pollination.

WE GIVE a partial list of seed crops that require insect pollination or at least benefit from it. Not included are ornamentals, medicinals, and most spices, many of which are also insect pollinated. The stars indicate crops in which insect pollination usually increases yields of seed but is not essential for commercial production.

Leguminous crops:
alfalfa
clovers
  alsike
  crimson
  white
  Ladino
  red
  *strawberry
  Egyptian
sweetclovers
  yellow
  white
  Hubam
  sour
trefoils
lespedezas (bush)
vetch (hairy)

*horsebean (broad-
  bean)
*lima bean
Cruciferous crops:
cabbage
brussels sprouts
cauliflower
collards
broccoli
kohlrabi
kale
turnip
mustard
rutabaga
radish
Chinese cabbage
rape

Cucurbitaceous crops:	Umbelliferous crops:
cucumber	carrot
cantaloup	parsnip
watermelon	celery
citron	celeriac
squashes	parsley
pumpkin	Solanaceous crops:
Malvaceous crops:	*eggplant
*cotton	*peppers
*okra	Miscellaneous crops:
kenaf	*flax
Allium crops:	sunflower
onion	buckwheat
leek	asparagus

Some plants in the list (onion, for example) produce no seeds without insects. Others, like cotton, produce nearly as many seeds without insects as with them, but varieties within species often vary in this respect. Most are somewhere between these extremes.

When the production of hybrid seed is developed for more crops, the list will be increased, because nearly every crop that is not pollinated by wind requires insects for the production of hybrid seed.

Many thousands of kinds of insects visit flowers. Nearly all of them can pollinate at least a few plants. Most of them, because of small size, scarcity, specialized food habits, or for other reasons, however, are unimportant as crop pollinators.

A large variety of insects visit umbelliferous flowers, but even on these flowers, which are general in their pollination adaptations, a small percentage of the visitors accomplish most of the pollination.

The honey bee is by far the most important insect pollinator. Indeed, for commercial crops in temperate regions it is more important than all other species combined. It occupies this preeminent position by virtue of a number of valuable qualifications.

Because it produces honey and beeswax, the honey bee is maintained at a high population level in many agricultural areas. It can be readily increased and moved to satisfy pollination requirements. It is widely adapted and successfully fends for itself in most parts of the world.

As a species, it visits an extremely wide variety of flowers—wider than any other insect. As an individual on a single foraging trip, it usually confines itself to one species of plant.

It is large enough and hairy enough to accumulate many grains of pollen and to touch the stigma in most of the flowers it visits. Because it must store enough pollen and nectar to carry the larval and adult bees through the winter and other dearth periods, it is unusually industrious in its flower-visiting habits.

But as one might expect, the honey bees are not always fully dependable pollinators. Because they generally seek the richest sources of pollen and nectar, they may neglect the crop requiring pollination and go to richer food sources that are blooming at the same time.

Honey bees sometimes visit seed crops for nectar alone. On many crops, nectar collectors are less efficient pollinators than pollen collectors. An individual honey bee usually works within a small radius after it starts foraging. This presents a problem in the production of hybrid seeds when a grower wants to use as few pollen parent plants as possible.

Although the honey bee is probably the most important pollinator of every crop in our list, other species have a valuable supplementary role. On a few crops, such as alfalfa and cotton, other species of bees may be more efficient individual pollinators. On a few crops (carrot and squash), other insects sometimes are more abundant.

WILD SPECIES of bees rank next to honey bees as pollinators of seed crops. Relatively few of the many kinds are sufficiently abundant on seed crops to be of great importance. The principal advantage of most wild bees is that they visit flowers primarily for pollen and have no tendency to take the nectar without effecting pollination.

Bumble bees usually are excellent pollinators of the crops they visit, but a few of the shorter tongued species cut holes in the bases of red clover and vetch flowers and in that way prevent pollination.

Wild bees usually have a much narrower range of hosts than honey bees. If the favored host is a crop that requires insect pollination, the reduced competition from the other plants is beneficial.

Many wild bees ignore cultivated crops, preferring a narrow selection of native plants. Most wild bees are non-social and require large areas of un-cultivated land to develop effective populations. Some solitary bees, like the alkali bee, however, are gregarious and can build up immense numbers in a few acres of ground.

Insects other than bees are important on only a few of the seed crops in the list.

Flies of various families and sphecid wasps are important pollinators of um-belliferous and *Allium* crops and to a lesser extent of cruciferous crops. Such insects generally can be considered abundant only when all species are combined. They are usually most abundant on small seed fields sur-rounded by uncultivated terrain.

WILD BEES can be encouraged by providing them with nesting sites, maintaining suitable bloom through-out their nesting season, and protect-ing them from insecticides.

In sections where farming is intensive and wasteland is scarce, it may be im-possible to increase populations of most species of wild bees to a practical level.

The best opportunities for successful management are with highly gregari-ous ground-nesting species or ones that nest in timber or wooden structures. Specific studies have been limited to alkali bees, bumble bees, and leaf-cutting bees.

The green-banded alkali bees are the chief pollinators of alfalfa in the North-western States. They concentrate their nests in moist, bare, alkaline soils, usu-ally developed from irrigation seepage.

In many places where suitable soil conditions can be developed with little difficulty, growers are beginning to realize the possibilities and take ad-vantage of them.

It is possible to create artificial nest-ing sites when natural soil conditions are unfavorable. This can be done by installing a plastic film a few feet be-low the soil surface to retain the mois-ture and placing a layer of gravel above the film to transport the water laterally. Water added through verti-cal pipes leading to the gravel layer rises through the overlying soil to the ground surface. Finally, enough salt is added to the soil to control vegeta-tion and aid in maintaining moisture at the surface.

Building and maintaining sites for alkali bees is a growing development in Oregon, Washington, and Idaho.

Colonies of bumble bees rarely ex-ceed 100 individuals. It is impractical, therefore, to attempt "bumble beekeep-ing" for pollination, except in enclo-sures, such as greenhouses. They can probably be encouraged best by pro-viding them with spring and early fall forage (for example, hairy vetch and red clover) and suitable conditions for nesting. Permanent areas of bunch-grass make good nesting sites for some species. Rock walls and well-drained holes in banks are attractive to others.

Because bumble bees usually select abandoned rodent nests for their domi-ciles, studies should be made to de-termine the practicability of alter-nately encouraging and controlling certain species of rodents.

Leaf-cutting bees are stout, gray-colored bees that often nest in beetle holes in timber or in hollow- or pithy-stemmed plants. The nurseryman is only too familiar with the circular and oval pieces these bees cut from the leaves of roses and other nursery stock. Although there are recommended methods for destroying them, the good they do as pollinators warrants their protection instead.

Leaf-cutting bees in Saskatchewan have been conserved and increased by growing alfalfa seed in narrow strips through aspen and cottonwood forest land. The bulldozed timber from the cleared land is piled along the margins of the surrounding forest so that the bees can nest in the burrows made by invading beetles. People in Utah and Oregon have observed that any holes drilled into the walls of outbuildings attract many leaf-cutting bees.

The introduction of foreign pollinators is a step for the future. Most of our seed crops were introduced from other continents. Some of them undoubtedly are pollinated in their homelands by specially adapted species of bees. For example, none of the many species of wild bees that pollinate alfalfa in its central Asian homeland occurs on this continent. Some of them would probably do well here.

Investigations have been started in Utah and California with a view to establishing the feasibility of introducing them into the United States.

MOST LEGUME flowers are adapted for visitation by bees. Honey bees are the most important pollinators of the legumes, but some problems have arisen with their use, especially on red clover, alfalfa, hairy vetch, and Ladino clover.

For most of the legumes, the pollination problem is simply one of knowing how many bees are needed and then placing enough good colonies in or next to the fields to achieve the desired density.

One bee to the square yard appears to be enough for most legume crops. At that level, the beekeeper can usually make a satisfactory honey crop if nectar secretion is normal. Yields of sweet-clover seed apparently continue to increase as bee densities increase to 10 or 15 bees per square yard. Sweet-clovers yield both pollen and nectar in good amounts, especially in the Northern States, and such population densities are not incompatible with good crops of honey.

The problem in Ladino clover is one of low nectar secretion. Beekeepers, therefore, are reluctant to pasture their bees on it without a substantial subsidy.

ON RED CLOVER, honey bees insert their proboscis straight into the flower throat and thus trip the pollination mechanism. They trip the red clover flowers readily to obtain pollen, but they find it difficult to reach the nectar unless it is high in the corolla tube. Nectar collectors consequently may avoid a field that is not secreting heavily or suddenly leave it when the secretion slows down.

Studies have been made on the value of flowers with short corolla tubes and of long-tongued bees, but without definite results.

Various research workers in Russia have claimed success with training honey bees to visit the red clover by feeding them sirup scented with red clover. Similar attempts in other countries, however, generally have been unsuccessful.

The best results with red clover are obtained in the Northwest, where competing sources of pollen and nectar are not too abundant, and warm, dry conditions favor the secretion of nectar. Favorable conditions occasionally result in good yields in the Central States, where most of the red clover is grown.

Bumble bees are especially fond of red clover, and most species do an excellent job of pollinating it. A few short-tongued species cut holes at the base of the corolla tube to secure nectar. Subsequent visitors, including honey bees, learn to search for these holes to the neglect of normal flower visitation.

When bumble bees were introduced into New Zealand about 60 years ago, satisfactory yields of clover seed were produced for the first time. One of the three species introduced was a hole cutter, which partly negated the advantage gained.

HAIRY VETCH presents difficulties similar to those of red clover. It is attractive to honey bees, but in Texas, where much of the seed is grown, nectar secretion is erratic. When the nectar is low in the corolla tube, honey bees often use a side approach, thus circumventing pollination. If they use the direct approach under the same conditions, they usually split the corolla tube, although this may not be harmful.

Even if nectar secretion is good, they may spend most of their time searching for holes previously cut in the corolla bases by bumble bees. Since hairy vetch is highly attractive to many kinds of long-tongued wild bees, small fields surrounded by wild land are usually well pollinated.

ALFALFA has several unique pollination problems.

Honey bees generally do not favor alfalfa as a pollen source. When they visit it for nectar, they soon learn to visit the flowers from the side to avoid the pollination mechanism. However, nectar collectors accidentally trip a few of the blossoms they visit this way. Even nectar collectors can set a good crop of seed if sufficiently abundant on the field for a long time.

Honey bees in North America tend to pollinate alfalfa more efficiently toward the Southwest. In this direction, the percentage of pollen collectors and the accidental tripping rate of the nectar collectors increases.

Two or three bees per square yard can do a fine job of pollination in southern California, but 8 or 10 are required in northern Utah. High yields of alfalfa seed from pollination by honey bees are rare in Washington and Canada.

Most species of wild bees that visit alfalfa do so for pollen. They therefore pollinate it efficiently. They usually are too scarce to be reliable, however. An exception is the alkali bee of the Northwest, which in favorable areas is responsible for exceptional yields year after year.

CRUCIFEROUS CROPS vary from self-sterile to partly self-fertile, but they are nearly incapable of pollinating themselves. Thus they require insects for commercial production of seeds. They are usually attractive to honey bees and provide good supplies of both nectar and pollen.

They are visited also by many kinds of wild bees and several families of flies, all of which probably serve as pollinators.

The small domestic acreage of cole crop seed (*Brassica oleracea* varieties) is centered in the Puget Sound area of Washington, where honey bees are not very abundant but where syrphid and muscoid flies abound.

Turnip, radish, and mustard seed arc grown in sunnier parts of the Western States and are probably well pollinated by honey bees, although the honey produced is not generally favored by the beekeepers. In Canada, where rape seed is produced, honey bees are effective pollinators, and rape is a good source of nectar for honey production.

UMBELLIFEROUS CROPS are self-fertile. Automatic self-pollination is not extensive, however, since it must take place between rather than within florets. Their umbels attract a wide variety of insects and are almost equally attractive to bees, wasps, flies, and beetles. Bees and some of the larger, hairier wasps and flies are the most valuable, although usually not the most abundant, pollinators.

Honey bees visit carrots for both pollen and nectar, but alfalfa and sweet-clover offer strong competition. Carrot honey is not considered desirable for the market, and some beekeepers try to avoid it.

ALLIUM CROPS are moderately self-fertile but require insects for either cross- or self-pollination.

Onions attract many insects, but fewer than carrots, and many of the smaller and less hairy visitors transfer almost no pollen.

Pollen-collecting honey bees rank among the most efficient pollinators, but nectar collectors apparently avoid the stamens to a large extent.

For good pollination by honey bees,

onions should not be grown adjacent to a good pollen source, like yellow sweetclover.

CUCURBITACEOUS CROPS require insect pollination. The squashes are native to America and are pollinated by several kinds of wild bees, besides honey bees. The best pollinating species are restricted to squashes and gourds, but their efforts are largely unappreciated since they forage only in the early morning.

Cantaloups, watermelons, and cucumbers are from the Old World, and are attractive principally to honey bees in this country. The practice of renting bees for the pollination of cantaloup and watermelon is increasing, particularly in southern California and Arizona.

COTTON, the principal malvaceous crop, is self-fertile and largely self-pollinating. Some varieties produce as much seed without insects as with them, but others yield up to 25 percent more when they are insect pollinated.

There is considerable interest among cottongrowers in developing a hybrid seed industry, which, of course, would make insect pollinators mandatory.

Honey bees visit cotton flowers for nectar only, but when the flowers are not too wide open, the nectar-gathering bees transfer pollen satisfactorily. Many of the bees visit extrafloral nectaries, and often it is necessary to "saturate" the field with bees to force enough of them to visit the blossoms.

THE TOMATO FLOWER is unattractive to most domestic species of pollinators and has structural adaptations to insure self-pollination. Consequently seed of first-generation hybrid tomato is produced by emasculating and hand pollinating the flowers.

Suitable male-sterile lines of tomatoes have been developed, but pollinators are not attracted to them in sufficient numbers to set much seed. In their Peruvian homeland, tomatoes are attractive to their natural pollinators, and native varieties of tomato are structurally adapted for cross-pollination.

Male-sterile lines probably could be used for the production of first-generation hybrid seed if they were grown in the country of origin or if the natural species of pollinators could be established in this country. The problems involved may be difficult to overcome, but when we consider that hybrid tomato seed produced in California by hand pollination cost 200 to 300 dollars a pound in 1961, the effort seems to be justified.

THE HONEY BEE can be considered as a tool in the grower's hands for increasing seed production. Natural pollination is like natural soil moisture and fertility—it is there for the using, but it usually requires supplementation.

"How many colonies do I need?" is the question most often asked by growers of seed.

A reasonable answer is almost impossible to give for growers who have little control over the total acreage in bloom or the total number of colonies within flight range of their fields.

A more practical question is, "How many bees per square yard do I need?"

Before the research worker can give an answer for the crop in question, he must determine four things: The number of flowers per day requiring pollination; the number of visits required per flower; the working speed of honey bees; and the seed-setting capacity of the plants. The efficiency and abundance of the wild pollinators present should be included in the calculation of the number of honey bees needed for a particular field.

The grower can work toward the calculated optimum population on the field by continually increasing the number of colonies, reducing competing sources of bloom, and making his field more attractive to bees.

Some seed crops give a clear indication of the adequacy of pollination by the speed with which the flowers wilt. For crops like alfalfa, in which flowers appear progressively along the stems and racemes, an appearance of full bloom is a sign of inadequate pollination.

Colonies should be distributed throughout the field if the acreage is large. Although honey bees sometimes fly long distances to forage, most of them range within a few hundred feet of their colonies if plenty of attractive bloom is available within that radius.

Furthermore, if colonies are placed within the field, flight to other fields is lessened, and the bees conserve time and energy. Very likely two-tenths of a mile is a good spacing for groups of colonies in large seed fields.

Strong colonies should be used for pollination. The percentage of field bees available for pollination and the possibility of obtaining surplus honey are better with strong colonies than weak ones.

Progressive movement of colonies into a field insures that some bees will be present to pollinate the first flowers and reduces the danger of mass orientation to other sources. If the full number of colonies is brought to the field when it begins to bloom, many of the bees are likely to locate other sources of bloom and remain faithful to them for long periods. The introduction of colonies to the field should be scheduled to the blossoming cycle of the crop.

COOPERATION among beekeepers and seedgrowers and community action are the twin keys to the pollination of seed crops by honey bees.

Cooperation by the grower usually takes the form of providing locations for apiaries and exercising care in the use of insecticides.

If the number of colonies needed exceeds that which the beekeeper considers best from the standpoint of a honey crop, he will expect supplemental income in the form of rental or a percentage of the seed crop.

The success of a grower's relationship with the beekeeper usually hinges upon cooperation throughout the community. Honey bees range far from their colonies—sometimes several miles. If the neighbors use insecticides carelessly, the bees and their pollination services suffer, to the detriment of both parties in the cooperative agreement.

If the neighbors raise seed and do not enter into cooperative agreements with beekeepers, they benefit from pollination provided by the cooperating parties and provide nothing in return. That obviously is economically unsound.

Growers of alfalfa seed in California have formed what amounts to pollination districts, in which the seedgrowers in an area deal with a pollination coordinator, who contracts for a specific number of colonies to be placed in the fields according to a predetermined time and space schedule. Applications of insecticides follow a careful program supervised by entomologists working for the growers under the guidance of the California Agricultural Experiment Station.

This arrangement, which approaches the ideal, seems to be working out to the satisfaction of all concerned. In other areas where only a few members of the farming community have participated, little progress has been made toward consistently good pollination by honey bees.

GEORGE E. BOHART *and* FRANK E. TODD *are members of the Entomology Research Division, Agricultural Research Service. The former is in charge of the Bee Culture Laboratory at Logan, Utah, and the latter of the Bee Culture Laboratory at Tucson, Ariz. The research work of these stations is carried on with the cooperation of the agricultural experiment stations of Utah and Arizona, respectively.*

For further reading:
   Bohart, G. E.: *Insect Pollination of Forage Legumes.* Bee World, volume 41, number 3, pages 57–64; and number 4, pages 85–97. 1960.
   Hambleton, Jas. I.: The Honey Bee as a Pollinating Agent, *The Hive and the Honey Bee,* chapter XVII, pages 423–446, edited by Roy A. Grout. 1949.

Insecticides and Honey Bees

FRANK E. TODD AND S. E. MCGREGOR

PEOPLE who grow seed crops have a double problem with insects: Many of the crops must be pollinated by bees, which are highly sensitive to insecticides. Harmful insects, though, must be controlled, usually by the use of the pestkillers.

An experiment with alfalfa, which is typical of such crops, was conducted by Frank E. Todd, Frank V. Lieberman, and John W. Carlson in 1949 at the U.S. Department of Agriculture Legume Seed Research Laboratory in cooperation with the Utah State Agricultural College at Logan, Utah. There were 24 plots, each 12 by 24 feet, in the experiment. Each plot was covered by a 6-foot-high plastic screen cage to control pollinators.

Harmful insects were controlled on a series of plots of growing plants, but not on another comparable series. Bees were excluded from some of the plots and were provided on others. The seed was harvested in due time.

The plots that had neither bees nor insect control produced only 5 pounds to the acre. Those on which insects were controlled and had no bees yielded 15 pounds. Those with bees but no insect control produced 31 pounds. Plots where both bees and insect control were provided yielded 321 pounds of seed an acre.

To protect the pollinators while controlling the harmful insects requires considerable knowledge of both groups as well as of the flowering habits of plants and the toxicity of the insecticides to bees.

The harmful insects are relatively permanent residents in a field. They remain, feed, and multiply in it as long as conditions are favorable for them. They damage the plant in obtaining food for themselves. They attack various parts of it and at different stages of its growth.

Bees visit the plant only when it is in flower, and even then they seek only its nectar and pollen. The plant usually is benefited by their visits. The bees spend the night in the hive and visit the field only during daylight hours to collect food for the colony.

Bees usually are not harmed when insecticides are applied to plants not in flower. Even when the plants are flowering, materials having short residual action can be applied during the hours bees do not visit them.

THE BEEHIVE is like a miniature, isolated airport on which many tiny planes converge from all directions. Its prosperity is determined by its traffic, as all food and supplies must be flown in. Its radius of operation is only a mile or so. The effect of an application of insecticide within this area of operation could be compared to the effect of a hurricane. All planes in flight may be downed or seriously damaged, and even the airport itself may be destroyed. But just as airports operate under proper control in regions where hurricanes occur, so may colonies of honey bees survive in areas where insecticides are applied if proper precautions are taken.

Rearing a field bee, like training a pilot, requires time—about 6 weeks. Half of this time is spent as a larva or immature bee. The remainder is spent as a young adult bee devoted to hive maintenance or "ground crew" duties.

The best pollination service is derived from a strong colony. It should have enough bees to form a cluster over about 20 brood combs. It should also have sufficient brood of all stages and stores of pollen and honey to maintain this strength during the period its services are needed for pollination.

Just as the licensed pilots represent

only a small part of the airport personnel, so do the field bees represent only a small part of this entire unit. They are the ones upon which both grower and beekeeper depend. They are also the first to be exposed to insecticides and often the only ones killed. The loss of this group of bees can make the difference between a strong colony and an inadequate one.

The bees that are seen flying or visiting flowers are part of the colony's field force of perhaps 20 thousand fliers that gather food for the colony. They are at least 3 weeks old and have a normal life expectancy beyond that of 10 to 15 days, but they are continually being replaced if egg laying by the queen is uninterrupted.

A considerable number of them have regular flight schedules as water carriers. A few others scout the range for new food sources. When they find new foraging areas, they return to the hive and communicate to unemployed food gatherers the scent of the source plant, its direction, and distance from the hive.

These recruits fly directly to the area. Each of them confines its foraging activity to the indicated plant species on only about 10 square yards. This tiny theater of operation is visited repeatedly, sometimes for days, until the food becomes exhausted. The bee then awaits recruitment in the hive by another scout.

When insecticides destroy these field bees, the flow of food to the colony is cut off. Colony routine is disorganized. Productiveness is reduced. The area where the insecticide was applied is neglected until rediscovery by scout bees and the recruitment of a new field force. This may take only a few hours (if an insecticide with low residual effect was used) or several days (if it was an insecticide having long residual action, because the latter continues to kill searching scout bees).

The greatest concentration of fliers is near the hive. Direct applications of insecticides over the hives, therefore, can cause the greatest destruction.

Even applications of materials to plants unattractive to bees and not over hives may cause heavy mortality if the flight pattern of the bees is through the dust or spray cloud.

An application of insecticide anytime the bees are working on the field usually kills the bees it touches.

If the material is slow acting, the flier limps back to crashland at the hive, and a litter of other dead bees accumulates around it.

If the material is fast acting, the flier crashes in the field and is heard from no more. No external evidence of damage may be seen at the hive except that flight dwindles and ceases.

Some materials kill the "ground crew" also. When that happens, the ventilating and cooling systems are disrupted, the brood is neglected, and it dies. If the colony survives this onslaught, a week or months may be required to restore normal conditions. During this time the colony may superficially appear normal, but it is a useless unit to the seedgrower and the beekeeper.

KNOWLEDGE of the flowering habits of crop plants is useful in timing applications of insecticide to avoid the destruction of pollinators.

Some plants produce only pollen. Others produce both pollen and nectar. The grasses (corn, sorghum, bermudagrass, and johnsongrass) are of the first type. They usually yield pollen until about 10 a.m., after which they are unattractive to bees. Insecticides applied to these crops at other times of the day should destroy no pollinators.

The flower of the cantaloup or muskmelon exemplifies one that produces both pollen and nectar and is open only a single day. It opens early in the morning and is attractive to bees through the forenoon. The safest time to apply insecticides to this crop would be after the flowers begin to wilt and close during late afternoon or evening. Other plants in this group are watermelons, cucumbers, squash, and pumpkin.

The cotton flower opens a few hours after sunup and may be visited by bees throughout the day. Although it is open only 1 day, the extra-floral nectaries on the plant are functional for several days and may attract bees early in the morning. Often the highest bee population may be found in cottonfields then. Usually there are only a few bee visitors in late afternoon, but the best time to treat cotton would be at night.

Another type of flowering is exemplified by alfalfa on which a single floret may be open for a week unless the stigma and anthers are released from the keel of the flower, or "tripped," by bees. Bees do not usually visit alfalfa until 2 or 3 hours after sunup. Pollinators therefore would not be exposed to direct contact with any insecticide that is applied early in the morning.

The flowering habits of other plants may be similarly utilized to reduce insecticide losses.

When agricultural chemicals are to be used around bees, the choice of the least harmful material becomes very important.

Materials may be grouped into three classes according to their effect on bees:

Materials highly toxic to bees.

Materials that kill bees not only at the time of application but may kill those that visit the field for several days after treatment. (If these materials are used, the bees should be removed from the area.) The group includes such materials as arsenicals, aldrin, BHC, chlordane, Diazinon, Dibrom, dieldrin, Dimethoate, EPN, Guthion, heptachlor, lindane, Metacide, methyl parathion, parathion, Phosphamidon, and Sevin.

Materials that kill bees primarily on contact. (These materials should not be applied when bees are visiting the field.) This group includes malathion, Phosdrin, sabadilla, and TEPP.

Materials moderately toxic to bees. (These materials may be used with limited damage to bees if applied during the hours bees are not visiting the field.) This group includes cryolite, DDT, endrin, isodrin, Perthane, tartar emetic, TDE, Tedion, Thiodan, toxaphene, and Trithion.

Relatively nontoxic materials. (These materials have no effect on bees, or kill only on direct contact. With normal precautions they can be used at any time without serious damage to bees.) This group includes fungicides, hormone weed sprays, defoliants, allethrin, Aramite, chlorbenside, Delnav, demeton, Dilan, Dipterex, ethion, methoxychlor, Neotran, nicotine, ovex, Phostex, pyrethrum, rotenone, ryania, schradan, silica gel-78, sulfur, and Sulphenone.

With such an array from which he may choose, the grower can usually select a material that is safe for bees. If he needs one of the more toxic materials to control certain pests, he can take the proper precautions to prevent damage to his pollinators.

In general, this relative toxicity of pesticides to honey bees probably applies equally to native (wild or solitary) bee pollinators. For example, alkali bees (*Nomia*) are highly susceptible to parathion but not to toxaphene. Our knowledge of native bees is limited, but the indications are that any protection given to honey bees would tend also to protect them.

We know of no practical way to repel bees from an area to be treated. If a material could be found that would "black out" the area for bees during the danger period, serious loss to the bees might be prevented.

Likewise, no attractant has been found to lure the bees into an area where their pollination services are desired or to pull them away from treated areas.

The development of either a repellant or an attractant, or both, would be of value in reducing losses of bees by insecticides.

SEVERAL STATES have attempted to solve the problem of bee poisoning through legislation.

California, with its broad interests in

seed production and fruit growing, makes special endeavors to protect bees through local enforcement of agricultural laws. Pest control operators are required to obtain permits and to operate under strict conditions set up by county agricultural commissioners. This close supervision, which covers both time of application and materials applied, has reduced poisoning of bees in the State.

Despite such precautions, damage to colonies still occurs. For example, the pesticide may drift from an unattractive field onto one attractive to bees or even into the apiary itself and cause damage. Such damage may occur from simultaneous applications of materials to more than one field.

The extent of the loss may depend on the time it occurs. The colony may lose its field force at the end of the flowering season, with no economic loss to the beekeeper. The same number of bees lost earlier in the season could render the colony valueless to both grower and beekeeper for the remainder of the year. Both the source and the extent of damage therefore usually are difficult or impossible to establish legally.

Contracts between the seedgrower and the beekeeper who provides pollination service should (and usually do) contain clauses concerning the use of insecticides. They define what insecticides may be used, how they may be applied, and provide for financing of the moving of bees if highly toxic materials must be applied.

A community approach to the problem has many advantages, particularly in concentrated seed-growing sections where bees are an economic necessity. As bees cannot be confined to a particular crop or field, the improper use of insecticides can reduce production of neighbor seedgrowers. Community education can be undertaken to focus attention on the problem. If the area is of sufficient size, an entomologist may be employed to supervise pest control with due regard to the protection of pollinators. Where

large ranches are engaged in seed growing, the protection of pollinators often is handled in this way.

Education and cooperation offer the best solution to the protection of pollinators. Seedgrowers do not intentionally kill their pollinators, but the pertinent points may not be widely understood.

They are:

Choose the material least harmful to bees.

Make applications during the hours bees are not visiting the field.

Avoid making applications directly over colonies.

Consider all hives within one-half mile of the field.

When highly toxic materials are used, remove colonies from the area before the application is made.

When these essentials are followed, the "miniature airport," the beehive, usually hums with activity, and the prospects are brighter for a good harvest by both the seedgrower and the beekeeper.

FRANK E. TODD *became Head of the Bee Culture Laboratory, Tucson, Ariz., in 1950. He joined the Department of Agriculture in 1931 to do research on honey bees. He served successively as the Senior Apiculturist and Assistant Division Leader at Beltsville and Head of the Legume Seed Research Laboratory at Logan, Utah.*

S. E. MCGREGOR *entered the service of the Department of Agriculture in 1936 at Baton Rouge, La., where he did research on bees. Later he worked in Arkansas, Wisconsin, and Texas before he joined the Bee Culture Laboratory in Tucson.*

For further reading:
Anderson, L. D. and Atkins, E. L., Jr.: *Effects of Pesticides on Bees,* California Agriculture, volume 12, number 12, pages 3–4. 1958.
Growing Alfalfa for Seed in Utah. Utah Agricultural Experiment Station Circular 125.
Johansen, Carl: *Bee Poisoning—a Hazard of Applying Agricultural Chemicals.* Washington Agricultural Experiment Station Circular 356 revised. 1960.
Todd, Frank E. and McGregor, S. E.: *The Use of Honey Bees in the Production of Crops,* Annual Review of Entomology, volume 5. 1960.

Some Insect Pests of
Important Seed Crops

F. V. LIEBERMAN, F. F. DICKE, AND
ORIN A. HILLS

THE HARMFUL insects that seek food and shelter in forage legumes, grains, and sugarbeets must be controlled if crops of seeds are to be produced profitably.

Modern chemicals have made it reasonably easy to prevent much of the damage they inflict, particularly when the crop leavings are not to be used as feed. For controlling others, we rely on helpful farm practices and resistant varieties. Parasites, predators, and the diseases that attack the insects often help.

Most of the harmful insects attack the plants when they are in the vegetative, or growth, stage. Controlling these root and foliage feeders is the first order of business in protecting a seed crop, for a healthy plant with normal growth is the best foundation for successful seed production. In fact, in combined effect the insects feeding on the roots, leaves, and stems often are responsible indirectly for most of the loss in yield and also reduce the quality of seeds.

Different conditions over the country influence the choice of chemical treatment. The stage of development of an insect and the particular pest complex present at the time of treatment also must be considered.

County agricultural agents give advice on the insecticides to use and suggest the dosage that gives good control. They also know the restrictions placed on the use of various chemicals to protect the health of people. Some of our most effective insecticides must not be used on a seed crop if they leave a residue on any part (chaff, straw, stalks, leftover seeds) that is to be fed to livestock.

Some insects that feed on plants in the early stages of development, like the beet leafhopper (*Circulifer tenellus*) and the green peach aphid (*Myzus persicae*) on sugarbeets, carry plant diseases.

The insects that feed on the buds, flowers, or seeds can more truly be called seed-crop pests. Many are the same ones that earlier fed on the stems or leaves or, in another developmental stage, on the roots. They are best controlled therefore before they directly attack the fruiting parts.

Some destructive insects specifically seek the buds, flowers, or seeds. They ordinarily cause damage out of proportion to their numbers and their feeding. Their damage is often swift or hard to detect. Some are thought to inject toxins into the plants. Controlling them is further complicated by the need to protect pollinating bees from destruction while they are visiting flowering fields or flying to and from their hives or nests.

EVERYWHERE where seed alfalfa is grown, the lygus bugs must be controlled. Their tremendous importance was first shown by C. J. Sorenson at the Utah State Agricultural Experiment Station before 1932. Growers of alfalfa seed generally did not regard them as their chief tormentors until after DDT was developed, and the great benefit of their control was demonstrated. Now they are recognized as the chief pests of seed crops of alfalfa and sugarbeets. They do great damage in cotton, other legumes, and a number of vegetables.

Three species of the genus *Lygus*, *L. hesperus*, *L. elisus*, and *L. lineolaris*, are important. The last is sometimes called the tarnished plant bug. The lygus bugs are pale-green to reddish- or dark-brown sucking insects about three-sixteenths inch long. Their young are yellowish or bluish green. The adults insert their eggs into the top growth of plants they attack.

No distinction is made in a control program among the *Lygus* species. We do know, however, that differences exist in their relative abundance from place to place and from crop to crop. *L. lineolaris* is the common species in the eastern half of the United States. *Hesperus* dominates in the Southwest, but on seed sugarbeets *lineolaris* is equally abundant. *L. elisus* tends to be most abundant in the Northwest. Within these regions, the composition of the lygus bug population on cultivated crops may vary considerably; often it is influenced locally by the abundance of various wild host plants.

The damage the several species do also varies. *L. hesperus* and *lineolaris* favor the seeds of alfalfa and sugarbeets and can do more damage to them than *elisus*, which prefers to feed on the buds and flowers.

Lygus bugs live and feed on many kinds of crops, weeds, and native vegetation. The adults are strong fliers and have an uncanny knack of seeking out alfalfa at just the right time to lay their eggs so that hatching begins when the first buds appear. The bugs have been known to destroy 99 percent of the potential crop in a field of alfalfa by blasting the flower buds as fast as they are formed. When not enough of them are present to prevent flowering, they will feed on the blossoms and cause most of them to drop. Then they suck the juice from the seeds.

DDT was first tried against lygus bugs in 1944. The results on alfalfa were spectacular. In Utah, for example, a DDT-treated plot yielded 24 times the amount of seed produced on an untreated check plot. Soon all producing areas were utilizing DDT to control lygus bugs. Yields started an upward climb. The average yield was tripled by 1956. A part of the gain was due to better control of other insect pests, better crop management, and increased use of honey bees for pollination. But the lygus bug had to be checked before such gains could be registered.

During the late 1930's, when the large-scale production of seed of sugarbeets was getting started in this country, growers were troubled by the occurrence of a high percentage of nonviable seedballs. The corky balls would contain two to four seeds; all would be dead; but the grower might not know that until harvesttime.

At first the dead seed was attributed to adverse weather, insufficient water, or alkaline soil—factors that do cause seed embryos to abort. But researchers of the Department of Agriculture questioned that the severe losses were caused entirely by soil or moisture conditions. They suspected insects.

At Phoenix, Ariz., in 1938 various harmful insects found in seed beet fields were caged alone on developing seedballs. Then the balls were dissected to appraise any damage done. It was learned that the same three species of lygus bugs that damage seed alfalfa were the main offenders. Both adults and the nymphs inserted their mouthparts through the balls and into the seeds, drawing out the sap and destroying the embryos. The nymphs and the female adults of all three species damaged more seeds than the males.

Additional cage tests showed that the greatest amount of damage done to the beet seed crop by lygus bugs was to the soft, newly formed seeds. Little or no damage was done to the crop before or after this stage.

Efforts to develop an insecticide treatment that would kill the bugs before the crop of beet seed attained the soft-seed stage were rewarded when DDT was tested. By application of DDT, growers could consistently produce good yields of good seed.

MOST CHALCIDS are beneficial insects and destroy many common pests. A few chalcids attack crops.

One species destroys the seeds of alfalfa and certain clovers and trefoils. It is a tiny, black wasp that lays its eggs singly in their seeds. It does not attack any other part.

No differences were observed for many years among the chalcids in alfalfa, clovers, and trefoils.

A. N. Kolobova, a Russian scientist, in 1950 demonstrated that chalcids raised on alfalfa would not lay eggs on clover, and vice versa.

Now we know that there are at least three biological races of legume seed chalcids. One infests alfalfa and other *Medicago* species. One develops on red clover and other *Trifolium* species. A third lives on birdsfoot trefoil and other *Lotus* species. They are all called the clover seed chalcid (*Bruchophagus gibbis*).

This pest has attracted special attention in California since 1957. Kern County has a relatively new certified alfalfa seed industry. It started in 1949 when the seed supply of certified varieties was short, and it was learned that seed of new varieties could safely be grown outside their region of adaptation. Good crop and pollination management and insect control provided excellent yields. As it was a new area, chalcid damage was not a problem at first. By 1957, however, the clover seed chalcid was cutting deeply into yields of seed despite good practices conducive to its control, and it became clear that better control measures were urgently needed. Greatest hope lies in new systemic insecticides or in the development of resistant varieties. Research workers undertook studies of both.

Each egg of the variety of seed chalcid that lives on alfalfa is laid inside a partly developed seed of alfalfa or burclover. The newly hatched larva gradually devours the contents of the seed, pupates, and changes to an adult wasp. The wasp chews its way out through the seedcoat and the pod. It leaves a hole in each.

One to several generations may develop, depending on the latitude and altitude of the area, each season. The winter is spent as full-grown larvae within the hollowed-out seedcoats.

These infested seeds are the source of infestation for the new year wherever they may be—in cleaning plant or warehouse, in the thresher, on the ground, or on volunteer or other uncut plants that have gone to seed.

Control measures recommended in 1961 were based on destroying as many of the larva-bearing seeds as possible. To do so, one should clean all seed carefully and destroy or use the cleanings, prevent seed from forming on volunteer plants, clear the field after harvest, work all chaff into the soil, and, if necessary, provide moisture to encourage the growth of fungi present in the soil that will kill the overwintering larvae in the seeds.

STINK BUGS, particularly the Say stink bug (*Chlorochroa sayi*), occasionally cause great damage in the West to alfalfa and sugarbeet seed crops as well as to small grains.

An outbreak of stink bugs usually depends on unusually good conditions for their development in the uncultivated areas. During wet years on the deserts, a lush growth of host plants can produce a huge population. The adults fly to cultivated areas, often far away, when the desert plants dry up. They usually attack grains first, but may fly directly to alfalfa or sugarbeets. They suck the sap from the immature seeds and have been known to destroy excellent seed sets completely. In sugarbeet fields they can damage mature seed and may even do damage after the seed growth is cut and windrowed.

Of the many organic insecticides that have been used to kill stink bugs, toxaphene, benzene hexachloride, and dieldrin are particularly effective.

More than one application may be necessary, because the adults move about freely and the migration may be prolonged. Nymphs are seldom a problem, because eggs laid by the migrating adults usually are heavily parasitized or hatch after the crop is harvested.

TIMING the crop is the most successful cultural method used against insects.

It is used in the production of clover seed to control the clover seed midge (*Dasyneura leguminicola*). This is a tiny, delicate, mosquitolike fly that has a bright-red abdomen. It lays eggs on or near the flower heads of clover crops, principally red clover. The newly hatched larvae wriggle into the unopened flowers. They suck the sap from the ovaries and keep the ovules from developing. The seed crop may be heavily damaged or destroyed.

Development of the clover midge is closely correlated with weather and is particularly dependent on rainfall. Three generations are produced each year in the Northwest. The seed crop is grown from May to August; it is the summer generation of midges that damages it.

Control is effected by timing the appearance of the flower heads so that the midges find few suitable heads on which to lay their eggs.

Pasturing the field in the fall after the seed crop is harvested or in the spring before the seed growth is started will prevent most midges of the fall or spring generations from finding suitable flower heads. In consequence, the summer generation of midges will be small, and little damage will be done to the seed crop.

Clipping the spring hay growth for mulch about May 20 times the seed growth so that neither the spring nor summer generation midges find suitable flower heads.

If a hay crop is raised first, cutting and removing it promptly from the field in early June will kill most of the mature spring-generation larvae in the crop as well as time the blooming of the seed crop so that most summer-generation midges will have disappeared before the flowers become attractive for midge oviposition. It is important to remove the hay promptly because the mature spring-generation midge larvae, needing the moisture to move, will leave the flower heads for the soil and develop into adults if enough rain falls on the hay.

Another midge, *Dasyneura gentneri*, closely related to the clover seed midge, attacks Ladino and alsike clovers. It is less important than the clover seed midge, and no control has been developed.

Two tiny weevils frequently ruin seed crops of clovers. *Tyshius stephensi* is mainly a pest of red clover. *Miccotrogus picirostris* attacks white, alsike, and Ladino clovers. Both are gray and long beaked.

Like most weevils, they hide in winter in field trash or in heavy vegetation nearby. They become active in spring near their winter quarters. Often they feed on such plants as dandelion and wild strawberry. Later, when clover comes into bloom, the weevils move into the fields and feed upon the flowers. They lay one or two eggs in each young pod they encounter. Larvae hatching from these eggs devour most of the ovules. Both adults and larvae feed on the developing seeds, eating irregular holes into or through them. The larvae cause the greater damage.

DDT controls the seed weevils. The treatment must be applied after most of the weevils are out of hibernation but before many eggs are laid—about the time that 20 percent of the first set of blooms have turned brown.

Two other weevils, *Hypera nigrirostris* and *H. meles*, attack the heads and seeds of various clovers. The latter is particularly damaging to crimson clover seed in the Southeast. The larvae of both feed on the flowers, ovules, and growing seeds. The adults cause lodging of the heads by feeding on the stems. Control can be obtained by an early season application of aldrin, dieldrin, or heptachlor in granulated form.

THE VETCH BRUCHID is a little weevil that hollows out the seeds of hairy vetch. It ruined the production of hairy vetch seed in several Eastern States and then found its way into the Pacific Northwest and Midwest. It does not damage other vetches very much.

The bruchids lay eggs on the seed pods just after they are formed. Worms hatch from the eggs and bore into the pods from the underside of the eggshell without exposing themselves. They enter the green seeds and devour the contents. Each larva takes one seed. Each bruchid produces about 100 worms. They usually are abundant on hairy vetch and may destroy most of the seeds.

To control these weevils, a single application of DDT just as the pods begin to form is recommended. Because the bruchids congregate on the vetch for egg laying at that time, most of the seeds thus are protected. Bruchids survive in dry vetch seeds for months, but they do not feed on them.

MOST PRODUCERS of hybrid corn seed now have a well-planned insect-control program, which includes preventive measures, superior hybrid varieties, and insecticides.

Prominent among the pests of corn is the European corn borer (*Pyrausta nubilalis*). It is the larva of a moth that ordinarily has two broods or egg-laying periods annually in the major production sections of dent seed. The fully developed larvae are about an inch long. The first brood is more serious in causing loss of yield and chaffy seed in early planted corn. Early hybrids of sweet corn are subject to severe ear damage.

Planting early is a preferred farm practice in the production of dent corn seed. This practice facilitates processing the crop and is a safeguard against fall weather hazards. Well-timed applications of DDT, endrin, heptachlor, or toxaphene granules and DDT and endrin sprays can be depended on to control borers.

Late-planted or late-maturing corn is more likely to be damaged by the second brood, which becomes established in July and August. Worm survival is high on such corn, and about 50 percent of the infestation develops on the ear. Invasion of the shank and internodes above the ear cuts off the flow of nutrients to the ear. Direct injury to the kernels, with subsequent introduction of molds, lowers the yield and quality of seeds and makes costly hand culling necessary in the processing operation. Insecticides directed to the ear zone have given satisfactory results in protecting the ear against second-brood infestation.

Inbred lines have varying resistance to borers. It commonly is referred to as first-brood early leaf-feeding resistance. At least three resistant lines are required in a commercial hybrid to achieve effective resistance. Resistant hybrids are recommended and available for certain localities in the Corn Belt.

ANOTHER SERIOUS corn pest is the corn earworm, *Heliothis zea*. This moth larva destroys kernels and introduces molds to the ear. It is also known as the cotton bollworm and tomato fruitworm. It is a pest every year in the South, where it has several generations, and periodically in the North, where it may have only one or two generations. The moths are attracted to the fresh corn silk for depositing eggs. As the young larvae hatch, they begin feeding on the silks and gradually penetrate to the kernels.

The fall armyworm (*Laphygma frugiperda*) has feeding habits like those of the corn earworm on corn, but is of much less importance in the major areas of seed production.

Corn varieties differ in the husk qualities that protect the ear against damage by earworms. Through many years of selection, good husk protection is typical of southern varieties. Loose husks, characteristic of varieties in the Corn Belt, enable earworm larvae to damage the surface of the ear out of proportion to the actual grain destroyed.

For sections of the Central and Eastern States where seed is produced, early planting is desirable to avoid seed injury. Intermediate plantings are desirable in Southern States to avoid early and late season peaks in ear damage.

The rice weevil (*Sitophilus oryza*), which often follows earworms, enters the ears through holes the earworms make. Poor husk coverage and damage by birds or rodents late in the season also expose ears to field infestation by the rice weevil. Such infestation of standing corn is the principal source of populations that develop during storage.

Both adults and larvae of the rice weevil injure the kernels. Besides feeding, the adults eat out a cavity, usually one to a kernel, in which to lay each egg. Eggs laid in kernels that have higher than 65 percent moisture do not hatch. The larvae devour most of the contents of the kernels and then pupate within them. Adults emerge from the kernels a few days later, and the new females soon begin to lay eggs. The infestation may thus increase rapidly.

Entomologists at the Louisiana Agricultural Experiment Station reported that when harvest of corn is delayed in the South, up to 90 percent of the kernels may become damaged in the field. The rice weevil causes most of this loss, but other pests of stored grain, particularly the Angoumois grain moth (*Sitotroga cerealella*), cause some.

THE CORN LEAF aphid (*Rhopalosiphum maidis*) sometimes becomes a problem in seed production. It is known to overwinter only in warm climates on small grains and wild grasses. On corn, the colonies of small, green, soft-bodied plant lice escape observation in the early stages of development down among the whorl leaves. The farmer and seedsman usually see heavily infested plants, which have a sooty or reddish appearance, at about tasseling time or later. Then the damage has been done and plants often are partly or wholly barren.

Some inbred lines of corn are subject to barrenness. Other lines are attacked only lightly and show little effect on yield. Insecticides, as they have been used against the aphids, have not prevented barrenness.

Pollination in corn sometimes fails as a result of persistent feeding on the emerging silks by certain insects. The commonest are adults of the northern corn rootworm (*Diabrotica longicornis*), the southern corn rootworm (*Diabrotica undecimpunctata howardi*), the Japanese beetle (*Popillia japonica*), and several species of grasshoppers. All are attracted to fresh silk and congregate in their feeding long enough to interfere with pollination.

The sap and fungus beetles (*Glischrochilus q. quadrisignatus* and species of *Carpophilus*) often infest corn. These little black beetles are attracted to fermenting plant wounds, such as the entrance holes of the corn earworm and the European corn borer in corn. Sometimes they enter ears with loose husks without the aid of these worm tunnels.

The beetles will displace and even incidentally kill borers in the ear or stalk. They may lay eggs on the decaying plant tissue. The larvae of *Carpophilus* beetles sometimes hatch and feed among the kernels. Adults usually feed in worm-damaged areas and cause ear rot molds to spread. Their net effect on seed corn sometimes is considered beneficial because their presence causes the more destructive earworms and corn borers to abandon their burrows.

THE SORGHUM MIDGE (*Contarinia sorghicola*) is the most important insect in grain sorghum in the Gulf States. The gnatlike flies deposit their eggs in the flowers. On hatching, the gray or red maggots begin to extract the contents of the developing seed. Heavily infested heads have a blighted appearance. Multiple generations result in high seasonal populations. Johnsongrass and sudangrass are important hosts of the midge in the spring before sorghum heads appear. They also harbor puparia over winter.

A recommended control measure is to dust the heads with DDT. In controlled pollination work, paper bags treated with a streak of aldrin give protection against the sorghum midge as well as the corn leaf aphid and the corn earworm, which attack sorghum when they are unusually abundant.

The earworm in particular is a corn pest that is becoming more of a problem on grain sorghum. Eggs are deposited on the leaves before heading and later on the peduncle and head. Feeding on leaves is comparatively minor. The larvae do most of their feeding on the developing grain; they devour kernels, sever lateral branches of the panicles, and create conditions for development of mold. Half of the seed often is destroyed.

THE SORGHUM WEBWORM (*Celama sorghiella*) is the moth stage of a somewhat flattened, hairy, greenish caterpillar, which sometimes attacks sorghum in the more humid areas. Newly hatched caterpillars feed on the flowers. When about half grown, the worms shift to the seeds and hollow out the kernels one by one. They spin a light amount of silk to attach themselves to the plant when they are ready to molt or when disturbed. Sometimes the worms become abundant enough to cover the heads. Half the crop may be destroyed.

The full-grown caterpillars spin cocoons on the plant and pupate. The whitish moths that emerge from the cocoons dart about at night from plant to plant, laying their eggs one at a time on the sorghum heads. Because damage becomes more severe as the season progresses, early planting is suggested as a means of keeping down loss. The worms overwinter only on host plants; it is possible therefore to reduce populations by plowing under the crop leavings in the fall and burning off nearby areas of johnsongrass, the principal host plant of the webworms, early in the season before sorghum attracts them.

THE ENGLISH GRAIN aphid (*Macrosiphum granarium*) and the apple grain aphid (*Rhopalosiphum fitchii*) feed on developing seed of small grain and cause blasting of heads. Both species attack the leaves in the fall and spring before active head growth. Reproduction is greater in cool weather.

Parathion, methyl parathion, and tetraethyl pyrophosphate are used to control aphids. These materials are highly poisonous and should be used strictly according to directions.

INSECTS have caused little damage to rice in California.

In the Southern States, the rice stink bug (*Oebalus pugnax*) has been responsible for serious annual losses. Rice stink bugs overwinter, feed, and multiply on grasses and migrate to rice when it begins to head. They suck the juices from the developing seeds. Their feeding produces empty seed or pecky rice—kernels that have discolored spots, which appear when the seed contents are only partly consumed.

Another sucking bug (*Paromius longulus*) causes damage similar to that of the rice stink bug but is of less economic importance.

The common chinch bug (*Blissus leucopterus*) has been observed in some places to cause direct damage to developing rice heads by invading fields after they are drained. The bugs feed on the plants at the nodes and under the leaf sheaths, and often cluster heavily just below the panicles, blasting them.

Aldrin, dieldrin, and toxaphene are used against the rice stink bug and chinch bug.

DDT AND the outstanding insecticides that have since been developed and marketed solved some of the vexing problems of insect control that faced seedgrowers one or two decades ago. There are indications, however, that these chemicals have not provided permanent solutions. Some insects that were remarkably well controlled in the 1940's developed measurable tolerances for DDT and several others.

Most of this resistance to insecticides in seed production has occurred in the Southwest. In the Salt River Valley of Arizona, sugarbeet seed of low quality reappeared in 1953. Experiments there in 1954 demonstrated that the residual action of DDT was no longer great enough to kill the nymphs of the lygus bugs that hatch after the DDT is applied.

Similar results were encountered in various localities on alfalfa and cotton. In Kern County, Calif., entomologists of the University of California found that lygus bugs taken from alfalfa seed fields became progressively more difficult to kill with DDT as the crop matured. By the end of the seed-crop period, the lygus bugs in seed fields were three to five times more tolerant of DDT than those in hayfields. They also found indications that nutrition may influence this change in susceptibility to DDT.

In later years, insect resistance to DDT has been met with additional applications or by substitution of other insecticides that provide better control.

In sugarbeet seed crops, for example, a second application of DDT or an application of toxaphene, benzene hexachloride, and dieldrin have been used.

Toxaphene, which kills better than DDT in warm weather, was substituted successfully on alfalfa for a time, but later in some localities tolerance for toxaphene also appeared.

Other insecticides under development in 1961 may meet this deficiency.

F. V. LIEBERMAN *joined the Entomology Research Division of the Agricultural Research Service in 1929 as a scientific aid. Since his graduation from Iowa State University in 1936, he has studied western forage insect problems in Colorado, Utah, Montana, California, and Arizona.*

F. F. DICKE *is an entomologist with the Entomology Research Division and associate professor of zoology and entomology at Iowa State University. He joined the Department in 1927 and has been engaged in research on the biology and control of insects on cereal and forage crops.*

ORIN A. HILLS *is Leader of Western Vegetable Insect Investigations of the Department of Agriculture, at Mesa, Ariz.*

Insects, Viruses, and Seed Crops

ORIN A. HILLS, KENNETH E. GIBSON, AND W. F. ROCHOW

MANY serious plant diseases are due to viruses that insects carry. Some of the viruses may be transmitted in other ways, but the diseases would have little importance without insect vectors.

Sometimes a single species of insect is the carrier. Sometimes many different insects, usually of a related group, are to blame.

The aphids are the worst. The green peach aphid exists everywhere, is not overly particular about the plants it feeds on, and is said to transmit more than 50 plant viruses.

One reason therefor is that it is active. One winged aphid can spread more disease than a whole colony of comparatively inactive wingless forms.

Leafhoppers, next to the aphids in destructiveness, also are active. Often they feed for a comparatively short time in one locality and then move on, spreading disease as they go.

A plant unsuitable as a breeding host or even for food of a particular insect is not safe from a virus the insect may be carrying. Plants susceptible to the disease but unfavorable to the insect may be damaged more than a plant the insect likes better. The green peach aphid, for example, carries several mosaic-type diseases of muskmelons. It does not like muskmelons and cannot live long on them. It moves quickly over a field, sampling the plants and spreading disease as it goes.

Several hundred virus diseases are spread by insects.

One group of them is nonpersistent,

because the vectors can continue to transmit the virus only a short time, often only a few minutes.

A second group is called persistent, because the vector generally can transmit the virus for a long time—often as long as the insect lives.

Nonpersistent viruses usually are transmitted by the aphids and can be acquired by the insects after a short feeding time on an infected plant.

Beet mosaic virus can be picked up by certain aphids after feeding only 10 seconds. Leafhoppers or aphids that transmit most persistent viruses may have to feed for several hours or more before they can acquire a virus of the persistent type.

At least part of the explanation for these differences in feeding time lies in the fact that nonpersistent viruses infect most of the tissues of a plant and that aphids can easily acquire virus by feeding in the outermost cells. Persistent viruses often seem to be restricted to the phloem, and a longer feeding time is required to penetrate into this internal tissue.

Aphids that have acquired a nonpersistent virus usually can transmit it immediately. A leafhopper or aphid that has acquired a persistent virus usually is unable to transmit it for a time that varies with each specific case—a few hours to many days. This period before the vector becomes infective may be the time needed for the persistent virus to penetrate the gut, enter the blood, and be injected into the plant along with saliva during feeding. The delay also may be due to the time needed for the virus to multiply in the insect vector.

Another difference between the nonpersistent and persistent viruses is the effect of fasting on transmission. Aphids that have not been allowed to feed for some time before they reach a plant infected by a nonpersistent virus are more efficient vectors than are aphids that had been feeding continuously. Furthermore, fasting after feeding on the infected plant may prolong the time during which an aphid carrying a nonpersistent virus is infective. Fasting has little effect on the transmission of persistent viruses.

These effects have been noted mostly in experimental work, but the observations are of practical as well as fundamental importance because the winged insects undergo periods of fasting in nature.

Viruses of the nonpersistent group sometimes are transmitted by many different aphid species. Western celery mosaic, a nonpersistent virus, has been transmitted by 17 species of aphid.

Viruses of the persistent group usually have more specific vector relations. Sometimes only one insect species may be the vector.

Viruses of the nonpersistent group generally have been transmitted experimentally from plant to plant by mechanical sap inoculation, although it is quite clear that transmission of these viruses by aphids involves more than mere mechanical contamination of mouthparts.

Differences between the nonpersistent and persistent virus-vector relationships have practical applications.

Because aphids can transmit nonpersistent viruses for such a short time, plants that are the source of these viruses obviously must be near the crop fields. Insects may acquire a persistent virus at great distances from the fields, however, and still cause infection when they feed.

Diseases caused by the nonpersistent viruses sometimes may be controlled by breaking the succession of crops necessary to maintain the virus. Such a succession will not affect the maintenance of persistent viruses, since they can be retained for long periods by the insect. Because a persistent virus may even overwinter in its vector, the insect does not have to feed on source plants before it can infect new crop plants at the start of the next growing season.

THE CURLY TOP virus, transmitted by the beet leafhopper (*Circulifer tenellus*), is an example of a persistent virus that affects some important seed crops. This disease was a serious menace to sugarbeets in the Western States before 1900. Before long, the occurrence of curly top was associated with outbreaks of the beet leafhopper. Now we know that curly top is transmitted solely by this insect species. Many vegetable crops, ornamentals, and seed crops are affected.

The beet leafhopper breeds on weeds in deserts and semiarid wastelands and moves from them to cultivated crops. Some 40 thousand square miles in the drier sections of southern Arizona are breeding areas of the insect. When rainfall is sufficient to maintain the annual herbaceous plants on which it breeds, astronomical numbers are produced. When winds and weather conditions are right, the leafhoppers migrate some 500 to 600 miles from southern Arizona to the agricultural areas of eastern Utah and western Colorado.

Many other breeding areas exist in all Western States. In outbreak years, movements of beet leafhoppers cover most of the agricultural land west of the Rocky Mountains. Some of the weeds on which the beet leafhopper breeds serve as reservoirs of the curly top virus. The virus is of the persistent type. It remains in the body of the insect and during migration plants far from the breeding area are infected.

CURLY TOP limits the production of garden beans for seed in the arid or semiarid regions of the West. This is true in south-central Idaho, but, because other conditions are favorable to the crop, about 80 percent of the national requirement of seed beans is grown here.

The disease is most severe on beans when the plants are infected in the crookneck, or seedling, stage. The problem is therefore particularly serious in Idaho, since the emergence of the bean plants frequently coincides with spring migrations of beet leafhoppers from breeding areas in deserts and wastelands.

Oddly enough, the leafhopper does not like beans. It cannot live long on the plants and does not breed on them. During migration, however, the insects feed briefly on the plants and transmit curly top.

Large acreages of garden beans are grown in Idaho for seed and for commercial dry beans. Some varieties are highly resistant to curly top, but none of the varieties of snap beans grown for seed is resistant to curly top. Some are extremely susceptible to curly top. Others may be less so, but in years of heavy infestations, all the seed varieties suffer heavy losses.

Research and control efforts have been directed primarily into two channels—chemical and cultural practices and development of resistant varieties through an extensive breeding program.

Chemical and cultural control practices involve the beet leafhopper in its desert and wasteland breeding areas as well as in cultivated crops.

Chemical seed treatments, leaf sprays, and dusts are applied directly to the susceptible crops. The aim of the chemical control in the breeding areas is to reduce the extent of the migration into cultivated lands. Applications of insecticides as seed treatments or as foliar dusts or sprays to crops susceptible to curly top are intended to kill the beet leafhoppers soon after they appear and so reduce the spread of curly top.

Chemical control of the beet leafhopper in its breeding area has been practiced in southern Idaho since 1949 in years when the numbers of the leafhoppers, as measured by a spring survey, threatened destruction of cultivated crops.

For control, an oil solution of DDT is applied at the rate of 1 pound per acre to desert and wasteland areas where there are heavy concentrations of the spring nymphal brood. The application is made before the insects have matured as winged adults.

Work was started in southern Idaho in 1958 to reseed some of the large desert breeding areas with suitable perennial range grass. Russian-thistle, the worst summer host plant, is eliminated by the competition of the perennial range grasses when the grass becomes well established. About 87 thousand acres were reseeded, primarily with crested wheatgrass by 1960.

Systemic insecticides also have been used. They are used as seed slurry treatments, seed soaks, foliage sprays, drenches, and dips. These toxicants move from the point of application through the growing plant, and may be effective against insects for several weeks after application.

In laboratory experiments at Twin Falls, Idaho, curly top in garden beans was reduced materially by spraying the plants with systemic insecticides combined with juice from sugarbeets highly resistant to curly top.

The climate of southern Arizona is ideal for the production of seed of sugarbeets, and about 60 percent of the Nation's crop is grown here. The seed-producing areas, however, are close to large desert breeding grounds of the beet leafhopper, and curly top has been a problem. Because of the extent of the breeding grounds surrounding the beet-seed-producing areas, desert control is impractical or impossible.

Some of the varieties grown are resistant to curly top, but as a large percentage of the seed is for use in areas where the beet leafhopper is not a problem, varieties susceptible to the disease also are grown. Even varieties resistant to curly top are damaged in the early stages of development.

The beet seed crop in southern Arizona is subject to two seasonal migrations of the beet leafhopper from the surrounding desert. One occurs in the fall and one in the spring. Inoculations of beet plants with the curly top virus after seedstalk development starts in the spring have little effect on the seed crop. On the other hand, curly top inoculations from fall leafhopper migrations may produce disastrous results. Severely affected plants do not produce a seedstalk at all. Less severely affected plants may produce a small seedstalk but little seed. The yield drops. The disease does not affect the viability of the seed very much.

Early fall migrations of beet leafhoppers into the fields of seed beets cause greater damage than later migrations, because smaller plants are more susceptible to the disease than larger plants and fields of small plants are more attractive to the insects.

The beet leafhopper prefers an open, sunny environment, and as the soil surface becomes shaded with the beet foliage, the field is less attractive to the insects. Usually fewer than 10 percent of the leafhoppers from the southern Arizona breeding areas are curly top infective, but if they stay in the field the virus is rapidly passed through the beet plants to the noninfective insects, and the disease spreads rapidly.

Since fall migrations of beet leafhoppers are of comparatively short duration and growth of the plants is rapid, control is necessary only for 3 or 4 weeks. DDT dusts or sprays are effective, but because there is too little foliage to hold the insecticide, control is sometimes difficult on young plants, which are most susceptible to curly top.

Here the new systemic insecticides, such as phorate or Di-Syston, which are translocated within the plant, are of special value. By treating the seed with them, the cotyledons and first pair of leaves of the sugarbeet plants become so toxic to the leafhoppers that one feeding will kill them and protection is afforded until the plants reach the four-leaf stage, when there is enough foliage to hold a DDT dust or spray.

VIRUS YELLOWS, or beet yellows, is caused by the aphidborne beet yellows virus. It generally is considered nonpersistent. The ability to transmit usually does not last more than 1 or 2 days.

The disease has been recognized for many years in Europe, but it was not reported in the United States until 1951, and was first discovered in sugarbeets grown for seed in Arizona in 1955.

The appearance of the disease was accompanied by losses in yield of seed. Studies to determine more definitely its effect on the crop and possibilities of treatment were commenced in 1956.

The green peach aphid (*Myzus persicae*) was known to be an efficient vector of beet yellows and was also recognized as a pest of the sugarbeet seed crop in Arizona. Before the appearance of virus yellows, feeding damage alone was negligible unless the insect became exceedingly numerous. Flight trap records as well as population studies and observations on known host plants showed that few of the insects survived the southern Arizona summers. The first winged forms appear in late September and early October. Flights continue in low numbers throughout the winter, but wingless forms constantly increase in the beet fields. Many winged forms develop in the fields by March, and large numbers are flying in March and April.

Knowledge of reservoirs of the beet yellows virus is incomplete, but because the aphids do not usually retain the virus more than 48 hours, the source must be within a 2-day flight range of the insect and probably the more important reservoirs are local. Beets that have escaped cultivation or fields not plowed up after seed harvest are likely sources. The virus also has been recovered in a low percentage of trials from Australian saltbush along ditch banks within the cultivated area.

It appears that a low initial infection occurs with the influx of aphids in October, November, and December. Virus is spread from them by the large numbers of winged forms during late February, March, and April. The buildup of wingless forms in winter might be relatively unimportant if they are controlled before the winged forms appear in early spring.

Experiments were made in which plots were inoculated with virus yellows by artificial infestations of infective green peach aphids on different dates. They showed that the greatest reductions in yield resulted from early inoculations. Later inoculations gave progressively less damage. Infestations with infective aphids when the plants were blooming also resulted in a lower percentage of germinating seed.

MANY CEREAL crops are affected by virus diseases.

A leafhopper (*Endria inimica*) transmits a persistent virus that causes a disease of wheat called striate mosaic because of the chlorotic dashes or streaks that occur along veins of infected leaves in the early stages.

Wheat striate mosaic virus was first found on wheat in South Dakota in 1950.

No serious losses are known to be a result of striate mosaic, but the disease is severe on some wheat varieties and is considered to be of potential importance. The virus has been transmitted by means of the leafhopper to oats, barley, and some native grasses.

Wheat striate mosaic virus has a latent period in its vector. Ten to 14 days elapse between the time the leafhopper begins to feed on an infected plant and the time it can transmit virus to a healthy plant.

Leafhoppers then may continue to transmit the virus for a month or two. This long period of persistence of the virus in its vector means that leafhoppers could acquire virus from infected plants in the summer and carry the virus over directly to fall-sown wheat. Since infected plants can survive the winter, the disease cycle can be continued during the next growing season.

Another virus disease of wheat, wheat streak mosaic, is transmitted not by an insect but by the wheat curl mite (*Aceria tulipae*). This disease was known for some time. The vector was discovered in 1953. It was an important discovery, as mites were not generally recognized as vectors.

The wheat streak mosaic disease is particularly severe in Kansas and other Midwestern States, although the virus exists in other localities in the United States and Canada. Leaves of infected wheat plants develop yellow streaks, the plants wilt quickly, and the yield is much less than normal.

Conditions that existed in Kansas in 1958 illustrate the factors that are important in a severe outbreak of the disease. The cool, wet summer of that year encouraged growth of volunteer grain and also favored multiplication of the mites that live on volunteer grain as well as on native grasses. Because many of the grain plants and the grasses were infected with the wheat streak mosaic virus, it was picked up by great numbers of the mites. When the winter wheat began to grow early in the fall, the mites, which were blown about by the wind, transmitted virus to many of the young wheat plants. So many plants were weakened by infection that the wheat crop in Kansas in 1958–1959 was reduced by more than an estimated 46 million bushels.

A three-pronged approach has been recommended to Kansas wheatgrowers to reduce damage caused by this mite-transmitted virus. Elimination of nearby volunteer wheat and native grasses a week or two before seeding will destroy the source of virus inoculum. Seeding at the latest recommended date will mean the shortest possible time in the fall for the mites to transmit virus to the wheat. The use of resistant varieties will further reduce losses caused by the virus.

Corn stunt occurs in the San Joaquin Valley of California, the Rio Grande Valley of Texas, and Mexico. Symptoms include bud proliferation, successive tillering, chlorotic spots and streaks on leaves, and general stunting of the plants. The disease is caused by a virus transmitted by the leafhopper (Dalbulus maidis).

It has not been transmitted mechanically from plant to plant, but it has been transmitted by means of fine needles to the leafhopper vector. This technique was used to prove that corn stunt virus multiplies in its insect vector as it does in the plant. This discovery proved that the virus persisted in the vector.

Two distinct strains of corn stunt have been studied. A strain prevalent in Texas can immunize the leafhopper vector against a strain prevalent in Mexico. The immunized insect cannot transmit the other strain of the virus nor support its multiplication. The strain from Mexico will neither prevent multiplication of the strain from Texas nor prevent its transmission by the vector. Although one other case of cross-protection between virus strains had been demonstrated in leafhoppers, this was the first known case of unilateral protection.

The significance of this unilateral protection in the vector was brought out by the discovery that a parallel unilateral protection occurred in the corn plant. These findings provide a tool to identify and classify viruses that are difficult to study by the usual methods.

Barley yellow dwarf virus is a persistent, aphidborne virus that sometimes causes considerable reduction in seed production of several small grains. Oats and barley are most severely affected, but wheat and many other grasses also are susceptible.

Infected plants develop diffuse yellow blotches on leaves and have heads in which little or no grain develops. Barley yellow dwarf virus was not discovered until 1951 in California, but the disease may have been present for many years.

Yellow dwarf of oats (also called red leaf) was the worst oat disease in the United States in 1959. Yield reductions were particularly heavy in parts of the Midwest and Northwest.

Many different strains of the barley yellow dwarf virus exist in nature. Some cause a more severe disease than others and infect certain grasses that are not infected by others, although all strains of this virus have a very wide host range among grasses. Another kind of variation among strains of barley yellow dwarf virus involves the aphids that transmit it.

Transmission by aphids is the only known means of spread of this virus, but about six species may be vectors.

Research on the relations between the virus and its aphid vectors has revealed an unusual type of virus specialization, called vector specificity. Some strains of the virus are transmitted by one aphid species. Other strains are transmitted by other species. This specificity between the virus strain and its vector is the only way we know to differentiate the virus strain involved.

Breeding disease-resistant varieties appears to offer the most hope at present for control of barley yellow dwarf, but the presence of so many strains of the virus may make it difficult to develop varieties that are resistant in all areas and under all conditions of fluctuation in aphid populations.

Hoja blanca, or white leaf, disease of rice was first found in the United States near Belle Glade, Fla., in 1957. Rice plants with symptoms of the disease also have been observed in Mississippi. A similar disease in other rice-growing areas of the world is known to be caused by a virus transmitted by leafhoppers.

The leafhopper (*Sogata orizicola*) has been reported as an important vector in Cuba. Since this leafhopper has been collected in Florida, it is thought to be the vector that was involved in the minor outbreaks of the disease that have occurred in the United States.

Hoja blanca was considered a potential threat to the rice crop in the United States before the disease was found in this country. It was found in Panama as early as 1952, but was of minor importance. It was first reported in Cuba in 1954 and increased rapidly in importance in that country. The disease also occurs in Venezuela, Colombia, Surinam, Costa Rica, El Salvador, Guatemala, and Dominican Republic.

Symptoms of the disease include narrow, longitudinal white leaf stripes, nearly white leaf blades, or mottled leaves. Diseased tillers are dwarfed. Floral parts are absent or sterile if present. Normal tillers may be found on diseased plants.

The Department of Agriculture has tested many rice selections for resistance to the disease since 1957 by planting cooperative nurseries in Cuba and Venezuela. A fairly large number of the selections tested were resistant to hoja blanca. Many of the resistant selections came from Japan, China, or Korea. If the disease should become serious in the United States, use of resistant varieties may be a means of control.

These examples are only a few of the known plant virus diseases transmitted by insects or mites to seed crops. There are many other maladies of unknown causes which some day may be attributed to insect-borne viruses.

ORIN A. HILLS *became Leader of Western Vegetable Insect Investigations of the Department of Agriculture, at Mesa, Ariz., in 1960. He first entered the service in 1929 as an entomologist in Oregon, where he conducted studies on the beet leafhopper in desert breeding areas. These studies were continued in Colorado during 1934–1938. Since 1938 he has been in Arizona conducting research on insects affecting cantaloups, lettuce, and sugarbeets grown for seed.*

KENNETH E. GIBSON *became Head of the Twin Falls, Idaho, laboratory of the Entomology Research Division in 1957. He first entered the service of the Department of Agriculture in 1927. Mr. Gibson has done research on aphids as vectors of potato leaf roll and on the beet leafhopper as the vector of curly top, as well as the chemical control of wireworms and the western bean cutworm.*

W. F. ROCHOW *joined the Department of Agriculture in 1955 as a plant pathologist. He is engaged in research on viruses infecting cereal crops. Previously Dr. Rochow spent a year in the Virus Laboratory of the University of California. He holds degrees from Franklin and Marshall College and Cornell University.*

Diseases that Seeds Can Spread

K. W. KREITLOW, C. L. LEFEBVRE,
J. T. PRESLEY, AND W. J. ZAUMEYER

SEEDS can spread plant diseases from a neighbor's farm to yours, from one State to another, and from a distant country to the United States.

Some disease pests may survive for years, safely lodged on or in a seed or on bits of stem or leaf mixed with the seeds.

Many seedborne diseases we cannot recognize when we examine the seeds, and we cannot detect them when we incubate them. Only by inspecting the growing crop can we be sure that the seeds are free of viruses, bacteria, and fungi, organisms that cause disease and are called pathogens.

Most seedborne parasites do not affect germination immediately. They do not kill the seeds but multiply on emerging seedlings, which may then succumb to the disease. Some seed lots that show high germination in tests are nearly destroyed when they are planted under conditions that favor development of the organisms they carry.

The control of seedborne diseases begins with the seed. It is easier and cheaper to eliminate a pathogen from a few pounds of seeds than to attempt to spray or dust entire fields of growing plants.

Some pathogens can be eliminated or their range of occurrence can be reduced by treating the seed with suitable chemical compounds, hot water, or fumigants. Seed-cleaning equipment can remove many lighter, disease-infected seeds and fragments of diseased plant parts carried with them.

Some seedborne diseases are not so prevalent in regions of low rainfall and relatively high temperature during the growing season. Seeds produced under such conditions usually are free of many of these destructive, disease-causing bacteria and fungi. The commercial production of seed of certain vegetable, ornamental, and forage crops therefore has been shifted from humid areas of the East and Midwest to irrigated, semiarid western areas.

Careful inspection and weeding out of diseased plants in fields destined for seed production greatly reduce the incidence of seedborne diseases.

Although hundreds of pathogens are known to be seedborne, effective control measures have eliminated some and reduced the incidence of others to the point where they are troublesome only occasionally.

We discuss here the seedborne diseases that occur oftenest or have special significance.

SOME OF THE worst diseases of vegetable crops are seedborne. In most instances, no varieties resistant to seedborne diseases have yet been developed. For some, no chemical seed treatment gives satisfactory control. The vegetable grower therefore should make every effort to plant disease-free seeds.

Most of the seeds of beans and peas used by processors, market gardeners, and home gardeners before 1925 were produced in New England, New York, and Michigan. Frequent rainfall and high humidity there favor development of the three most important seedborne diseases of beans—anthracnose, common bacterial blight, and halo bacterial blight, which are incited by *Colletotrichum lindemuthianum*, *Xanthomonas phaseoli*, and *Pseudomonas phaseolicola*, respectively. The environment is ideal also for the two major seedborne diseases of pea, ascochyta blight, caused by *Ascochyta pisi*, and bacterial blight, caused by *Pseudomonas pisi*.

Before western-grown seeds came to be used, losses from the three bean diseases in some years amounted to 30 or 40 percent of the crop, and severe outbreaks of ascochyta blight and bacterial blight of peas often were reported in the East and the Midwest. These diseases reduced yields and impaired the quality of the canned product.

Although bean seeds grown in the Western States are free of anthracnose, they are not free of the bacterial blight organisms in some years.

The bacterial blight diseases frequently are widespread in Nebraska, Colorado, Wyoming, and Montana and occur infrequently in California and southern Idaho.

Rain, hail, and high humidity following storms, which are responsible for the spread and development of the bacterial blight organisms, occur much less frequently during the growing season in parts of Idaho and California than in the other States. Consequently the production of seed of snap beans now centers in those sections. Seed of most of the bush types is grown in Idaho and that of the pole types in California.

Weather conditions in the Columbia Basin of Washington also are unfavorable for the development and spread of the three bean diseases, but curly top, a virus disease that kills beans of susceptible varieties, is widespread there. Since no garden varieties have yet been developed that resist curly top, no seed of garden beans is produced in the Columbia Basin. Several varieties of dry beans resistant to curly top are grown there.

The most important seedborne virus diseases of beans are common bean mosaic virus and a strain of it referred to as the New York 15 virus. Most of the varieties of snap and dry beans now grown are resistant to these two viruses, and the losses they once caused have been reduced. Certification of seed fields of dry beans also has been effective in reducing seed transmission of viruses in the few susceptible varieties still grown in 1961.

Most of our pea seed originates in southern Idaho, the Palouse section of northern Idaho, and the Columbia Basin. Ascochyta blight and bacterial blight rarely occur there because of low rainfall.

As practically all the bean and pea seeds of the market and processing varieties used in the United States now are grown in a few of the Western States, anthracnose and the bacterial blights of snap beans and ascochyta and bacterial blight of peas have been reduced to minor importance throughout the country. These diseases caused severe and widespread damage to both crops in the 1930's and cost the American farmer millions of dollars each year in crop losses.

Lima beans grown in the South and East sometimes are affected by two seedborne diseases—bacterial spot, caused by *Pseudomonas syringae*, and stem anthracnose, caused by *Colletotrichum truncatum*. These diseases differ from bacterial blight and anthracnose of snap and dry beans.

Most of our seeds of lima beans are grown in California, where the environment does not favor the development of these diseases and they are not known to occur. Even though disease-free seed is used, stem anthracnose sometimes causes severe losses in the South and in some of the Eastern States. The causal fungus may overwinter on lima bean refuse and infect a crop the following year if the environment is ideal for the development of the disease and strict crop rotation is not practiced.

Seed of cabbage, cauliflower, rutabaga, and turnip, like seed of beans and peas, once were produced commercially in the East and Midwest. Because of the destructiveness of two seedborne diseases—black rot, caused by the bacterium *Xanthomonas campestris*, and blackleg, caused by the fungus *Phoma lingam*, both of which spread and develop only in humid, rainy weather—production of seeds was shifted to the Pacific Coast States. Because of low rainfall during the time these vegetables are growing in the seedbed and as transplants in the field, the organisms causing the two diseases do not become established.

Bacterial canker of tomato, a seedborne disease caused by *Corynebacterium michiganense*, is found in fieldgrown tomatoes from New Jersey to California and in several Southern States. The disease can be controlled by fermenting the seed and pulp for 72 hours before extraction. Soaking freshly extracted seed in acetic acid is also effective. Inspection and certification of seed fields has greatly reduced the importance of the disease.

Another seedborne bacterial disease, angular leafspot of cucumber, caused by *Pseudomonas lachrymans*, occurs mainly in humid regions. Seed grown in arid parts of the interior of California usually is free of the organism.

Late blight, *Septoria apii-graveolentis*, a destructive foliage blight of celery, affects the seeds and is widely distributed by this means. Since the fungus in infected seed usually dies before the seed loses viability, 3-year-old seed is recommended as the most effective control measure.

Lettuce mosaic virus causes considerable damage in the coastal valleys of California and losses in all parts of the United States. Fewer than 1 percent of the seeds are infected with the virus; the disease therefore causes little damage unless the virus is transmitted by aphids from infected seedlings or weeds to lettuce plants.

No resistant varieties are available but losses from the disease are being reduced by roguing diseased plants from seed fields and producing seed in fields free from wild lettuce species and other weeds infected with the virus. Isolation of seed fields from other lettuce fields is also recommended.

Many of the most destructive diseases of oilseed crops are seedborne. They occur primarily in the more humid regions of the United States with the possible exception of bacterial blight of cotton, which is most severe in semiarid areas. Because of climatic requirements and for economic reasons, much of the total oilseeds are produced in humid sections where rainfall is moderate.

The production of soybeans in the South Central and Southeastern States has increased. This shift of production from the North Central States has accentuated the seedborne disease problem in this crop. Such diseases as purple seed stain, target spot, wildfire, and bacterial pustule, caused by *Cercospora kikuchii*, *Corynespora cassiicola*, *Pseudomonas tabaci*, and *Xanthomonas phaseoli*, respectively, are more prevalent and destructive in the South than elsewhere.

Other seedborne diseases of soybean, such as brown spot, frogeye, downy mildew, and bud blight, caused by *Septoria glycines*, *Cercospora sojina*, *Peronospora manshurica*, and the tobacco ringspot virus, respectively, are hazards. Varieties of soybeans resistant to several of the important seedborne diseases are available and are usually recommended for areas where these diseases occur.

The gradual shifting of the center of cotton production toward the Southwest has increased the problem of bacterial blight, caused by *Xanthomonas malvacearum*.

Although the seedborne diseases anthracnose and wet weather blight, caused by *Colletotrichum gossypii* and *Ascochyta gossypii*, are largely controlled by the use of chemical seed protectants, diseased crop residues frequently are the source of new epiphytotics.

Resistant varieties are available that provide practical control for the seedborne diseases fusarium wilt and bacterial blight, which are caused by *Fusarium oxysporum* f. *vasinfectum* and *Xanthomonas malvacearum*. Destruction of diseased crop residues and thorough treatment with chemical seed protectants control most seedborne diseases of cotton.

Ohio and Kentucky led in the production of flax before 1900. Production has shifted since to Indiana, Illinois, Iowa, Minnesota, and North Dakota. This shift was caused partly by the injurious effects of flax wilt in the older cultivated lands. Wilt, rust, and pasmo caused by *Fusarium oxy-*

sporum f. *lini*, *Melampsora lini*, and *Septoria linicola*, respectively, are perhaps the most important diseases of flax in the United States.

Another seedborne disease that is widely distributed and occasionally destructive is anthracnose (*Colletotrichum lini*). Although losses from seedborne diseases may be spectacular, in recent years such losses have been smaller in flax than in many other crops. Resistant varieties give adequate control of wilt, rust, and pasmo, while chemical seed treatment is effective in controlling anthracnose and seedling blight.

Although commercial production of peanuts is concentrated in the Southern and Southeastern States, where conditions are favorable for the development of many disease-producing organisms, there are no seedborne diseases of economic importance. The practice of planting only shelled peanut seed and the use of chemical seed protectants has largely eliminated seedling disease problems.

Production of safflower is confined to the arid and semiarid parts of the United States. Leaf spots and molding of the seed before harvest in the humid areas have been factors limiting production. The only serious seedborne disease of safflower is rust caused by *Puccinia carthami*. Use of volatile mercury compounds as seed protectants has given satisfactory control.

The production of castorbeans also is concentrated in areas of relatively low rainfall because of leaf spot diseases and molding of the capsules, which frequently cause half of the crop to shed before harvest in humid areas. The seedborne disease organisms *Alternaria ricini*, *Sclerotinia ricini*, and *Xanthomonas ricinicola* occasionally cause damage, but they are satisfactorily controlled by chemical treatment of seeds.

Sesame is grown mostly in the northwestern part of Texas, eastern New Mexico, and western Oklahoma. The only seedborne disease of consequence is bacterial leaf spot, which is caused by *Pseudomonas sesami* and is controlled by soaking the seed in bactericidal solutions before planting.

MANY of the bacteria that cause diseases in cereals and grasses are seedborne. Some, such as bacterial wilt of corn (*Bacterium stewartii*), are restricted largely to one host. Others, such as the halo blight of oats, caused by *Pseudomonas coronafaciens* var. *atropurpureum*, and bacterial blight, caused by *Xanthomonas translucens*, occur widely on cereals and grasses.

The bacterial diseases occur most frequently in areas where high humidity or wet weather occurs during the time heads are forming. Bacterial infection in cereal and grass seeds usually is confined to the hull, however; the bacterium that causes wilt of corn can penetrate deeply beneath the seedcoat.

Bacterial diseases are best controlled by growing available resistant varieties. They can also sometimes be controlled by treating the seeds with bactericides.

Numerous fungi are seedborne in cereals and grasses. Some of the commonest, such as species of *Alternaria*, are weakly pathogenic. Among the most destructive are species of *Helminthosporium*, *Fusarium*, and *Diplodia*. The *Helminthosporium* and *Fusarium* fungi are the commonest seedborne root rotting pathogens. Sowing infected seed results in seedling blight, root rot, and lowered yields. Striking differences exist in the prevalence of these fungi in different seasons and in different localities. Seed of wheat, oats, and barley with 10 to 25 percent of *Helminthosporium* and *Fusarium* infection is fairly common some seasons, and seed lots containing more than 50 percent of infected seed are not uncommon.

Species of *Helminthosporium* frequently incite kernel blights of cereals and grasses. *Helminthosporium teres* causes net blotch and kernel blight of barley. *H. sativum* causes a kernel blight of barley, wheat, and grasses. Diseased kernels turn dark brown or almost black, notably near the germ end. The condition is sometimes called black point.

A similar disease incited by *H. avenae* occurs on oats and several related grasses. Most of the commercial varieties of oats are moderately resistant.

Victoria blight of oats, incited by *H. victoriae*, nearly eliminated several high-yielding, rust- and smut-resistant varieties of oats in 1946 and 1947. The disease is primarily a seedling and culm trouble, but infected seeds spread the pathogen. Resistant varieties are available. Treating seeds with organic mercury fungicides frequently reduces seedling losses from helminthosporium diseases.

Fusarium head blight or scab, a seedborne disease of wheat, barley, rye, and some grasses, occasionally is damaging. The disease occurs most frequently in the humid and subhumid eastern and central Corn Belt. Flower infection occurs, and diseased heads turn straw colored or light brown. Frequently a pinkish mold growth develops, and kernels have a rough scabby surface. Diseased grain is weakened in germination and contains compounds poisonous to humans and pigs. No highly resistant varieties of wheat, rye, or barley are available. Treating seed with organic mercury compounds helps to control seedborne infection.

Seed infection is less common in hybrid corn than in open-pollinated varieties, partly because most hybrids contain lines selected for disease resistance and the artificial drying of most hybrid seed corn checks the spread of initial disease infection.

Among the most destructive seedborne diseases of corn are ear and stalk rots, which are incited by *Diplodia zeae* and species of *Gibberella*. Diplodia ear rot is most prevalent in the warmer, more humid regions and in seasons when June and July are dry and August and September are wet. Hybrids that have loose husks, which expose the ear tip, or have upright ears show a high incidence of diplodia ear rot. Hybrids that dry quickly usually are less diseased than those that dry slowly.

The gibberella ear rots are more prevalent in the northern and western Corn Belt. Wet weather at silking time favors infection of the ears. The fungi often gain entrance to the ear through channels made by earworms and corn borers. Some varieties that develop breaks in the seedcoat enable fungi to gain access for infection.

When seeds infected with either *Diplodia* or *Gibberella* fungi are planted in cold soil, they decay or the seedlings die before emergence. In warmer soils, seedlings usually emerge but are stunted because the roots rot.

Ear and stalk rots are best controlled by planting disease-resistant hybrids, treating seeds with recommended fungicides, and rotating crops.

The smut fungi are among the most important seedborne organisms of cereals and grasses. Smuts that attack all or parts of the heads generally destroy the seeds. Leaf and stem smuts only occasionally affect the heads, but often they suppress the formation of seeds in diseased plants.

Head, kernel, and leaf smuts infect cereals and grasses by spores, which lodge in or on seeds of healthy plants. During threshing operations, smut spores from infected plants coat the surface of healthy seeds. Seed and smut spores germinate simultaneously, and young seedlings become diseased.

Treating the seeds with fungicides destroys adhering smut spores. Crop rotation also aids in controlling the smut diseases. Where resistant varieties are available, they should be grown to prevent infection by spores in the soil.

Loose smut of wheat, barley, and some grasses differs from most other smut diseases in that it is flower infecting and incites a deep infection in seeds. The disease occurs widely in humid and subhumid areas and is less common in dry areas. Because of the deep-seated infection, treatment with fungicides is ineffective, and diseased seed must be treated by immersion in hot water or by steeping in warm water and storing for a period under anaerobic conditions.

Ergot of cereals and grasses, not strictly a seedborne disease, is important because flower infection induces sterility. In infected heads, seeds are replaced by fungus sclerotia that are harvested with the seeds or fall to the ground where they germinate and infect plants the next season. Because ergot infection spreads from grasses to cereal crops, neither crop rotation nor the use of ergot-free seeds completely controls the disease. No varieties of cereal grains are resistant to ergot, but some resistance has been found in forage grasses like dallisgrass.

Most grain and grass nematode diseases are associated with soil infestation, but several are seedborne. They include the white tip disease of rice, which occurs in Louisiana, Arkansas, and Texas; the nematode disease of wheat and rye, which occasionally is troublesome in the Southeastern States; and the grass seed nematode, which exists mainly in the Pacific Northwest.

In each disease, nematode larvae infest the growing point and are carried upward as the plant grows, ultimately infesting the grass or grain head.

White tip disease of rice differs from the others in that the nematode larvae are seedborne on the surface of the kernels or under the hull, and they do not induce formation of a gall that replaces the grain.

In the nematode diseases of grain and grass seed, kernels are replaced by one or several galls in each head. The galls are filled with nematode larvae that are very resistant to drying, low temperatures, and chemicals.

The nematodes can remain alive in dry galls for 10 years or more. Because of their longevity and resistance to ordinary treatment, nematodes can be spread in the screenings, on threshing equipment, in floodwater, and with the seeds.

White tip disease of rice is controlled by seeding grain in water. Infested seed can also be treated with nematocides and fumigated with methyl bromide.

The grain and grass seed nematode diseases are controlled by sowing seed from noninfested fields, by removing galls with specific gravity separators, by treating infested seed in hot water, and by growing nonsusceptible crops in infested fields.

The grass seed nematode in chewings fescue has been controlled in some fields by burning straw and stubble following seed harvest.

Barley stripe mosaic or false stripe is one of the few virus diseases of cereals and grasses known to be seedborne. Infection has resulted in reductions in yield of 75 percent in wheat and 64 percent in barley. The disease is controlled by growing resistant varieties and by treating seeds with hot water.

Many diseases are seedborne in forage legumes, but it is difficult to evaluate their importance because many of the legumes are perennials and diseases attacking them occur in epidemic proportion in nearby fields and on uncultivated plants growing in fence rows or along roadways.

In most fields, airborne contamination largely nullifies the benefits derived from planting disease-free seeds. The only practical solution to the problem is to sow adapted, disease-resistant varieties where available.

Blackstem diseases of alfalfa, clovers, and vetches induced by *Ascochyta* spp. are among the most prevalent and destructive seedborne troubles of these crops. Heavily infected alfalfa fields have yielded 30 to 50 percent of diseased seed. Inspection of random alfalfa seed samples has revealed that 1 to 40 percent of the seeds are infected by the blackstem fungus. Blackstem severely restricts seed production if infection occurs during the flowering and seedset period. Seed infection can be reduced by treatment with fungicides.

Some diseases occur infrequently or are locally important. They usually reduce seed production and may be spread to uncontaminated fields with the seed. An example is blackpatch, a fungus disease of red clover and several other legumes. During wet seasons, heavy infection by this fungus reduced seed yield up to 50 percent in fields of red clover in West Virginia. Treating seed with fungicides was only partly successful in controlling the disease.

The bacterial wilt disease of lespedeza is seedborne and is widely distributed. Reductions of 30 to 50 percent in forage yield have been recorded in Missouri. The disease occurs chiefly in annual lespedeza. Some experimental strains of plants are more tolerant than others, but no resistant varieties are available. Only seeds from disease-free fields should be planted.

Several diseases are seedborne in lupines. During wet seasons, the fungi that cause anthracnose (Glomerella cingulata) and brown spot (Pleiochaeta setosa) attack plants and often infect the seeds.

In northern Florida and southern Georgia, the incidence and destructiveness of seedborne virus diseases is one of the major factors limiting seed production of sweet yellow lupine. Blue and white lupines are damaged less severely. Incidence of the diseases can be reduced by planting seed from disease-free fields. No resistant varieties were available in 1961.

Stem nematodes perhaps are introduced into new areas on seed or in plant debris carried with the seed. The stem nematode disease of alfalfa and red clover is most serious in the Western States, but infested fields have been reported in New York, Virginia, and North Carolina. Only seed from noninfested fields should be planted. One should avoid moving soil or irrigation water from infested to noninfested fields. Volunteer plants should be destroyed when a field is plowed. Nonsusceptible crops should be grown for at least 3 years. Lahontan and Nemastan, which are resistant varieties of alfalfa, should be grown in the West.

MANY DISEASES of ornamentals are seedborne and cause serious losses, but much of the seed is grown in Western States, where the dry weather during seed formation and harvest favors the production of disease-free seed. Some bacteria, fungi, and viruses attack ornamental plants grown for seed. They exact a toll in loss of seed yield and poor stands.

The heterosporium disease of nasturtium, incited by Heterosporium tropaeoli, is internally and externally seedborne in up to 93 percent of the seed. Infection occurs in maturing fruits when humidity is high. The fungus survives in seeds for at least 3 years. Stem lesions develop in seedlings from infected seeds, and the fungus multiplies and spreads to adjacent plants. The disease is controlled by treating seeds in hot water.

The alternaria disease of zinnias, caused by Alternaria zinniae, may be seedborne. The disease occurs oftenest in the humid Eastern States, where it causes spotting of blossoms, leaves, and stems. Treating seeds with a fungicide to reduce the hazard from seedborne inoculum is suggested. Field and garden sanitation should be practiced, because the fungus may overwinter in the soil.

Fusarium wilt, caused by Fusarium oxysporum f. callistephi, is the most serious disease of China aster. It causes damping-off of seedlings, a wilt of mature plants, and decay of flowers in storage. Seeds presumably become contaminated with spores during threshing. Spores can also be carried on debris mixed with the seed.

The seedborne fungus is even more destructive in steamed soil and is thus more severe in greenhouses and seedbeds. Soil once infested with the fungus is ruined for growing susceptible varieties of asters. Seeds therefore must be treated with mercury-containing fungicides before planting them in noninfested soil, but seed treatment does not protect seedlings growing in infested soil. Varieties possessing some resistance to fusarium wilt are available and should be grown in infested soil.

Erwinia phytophthora, the organism that causes bacterial crown, stem, and bud rot of delphinium, is carried in seeds. Development of the disease is favored by excessive soil moisture. The crop should be irrigated with the least amount of water required and water should be applied in furrows somewhat distant from the rows. Treating seeds in hot water is helpful.

A bacterial blight of garden stock, *Mathiola incana*, caused by *Phytomonas incanae*, has occurred since 1933 in plantings for seed production in the coastal areas of California. The principal damage has been a serious reduction in seed production in some years. In home gardens and commercial cutflower enterprises, many plants may be killed or severely stunted. Since the organism is seedborne, seedlings are often infected and killed. Under humid conditions the disease may spread rapidly from the infected seedlings to neighboring plants. The disease can be controlled by treating seeds in hot water.

K. W. KREITLOW *is research leader for forage crop disease investigations in the Forage and Range Research Branch, Agricultural Research Service, Beltsville, Md. He received degrees from the University of Minnesota and Louisiana State University. He has investigated forage disease problems since 1941.*

C. L. LEFEBVRE *is Assistant Director for Plant Science Programs in the State Experiment Stations Division, Agricultural Research Service, Washington, D.C. He is a graduate of the University of Minnesota and Harvard University. He joined the Department in 1937.*

J. T. PRESLEY *is research leader for cotton pathology investigations in the Cotton and Cordage Fibers Research Branch, Agricultural Research Service, Beltsville, Md. He received degrees from the University of Maryland and the University of Minnesota. Since 1935 he has devoted the major part of his time to cotton diseases.*

W. J. ZAUMEYER *is Leader, Bean and Pea Investigations, Vegetables and Ornamentals Research Branch, Agricultural Research Service, Beltsville, Md. He is a graduate of the University of Wisconsin.*

Seed Treatments for Control of Disease

EARLE W. HANSON, EARL D. HANSING, AND W. T. SCHROEDER

SEED treatments are used to prevent or reduce losses from diseases caused by organisms associated with seed or present in the soil.

Such organisms are associated with seeds in several ways. They may be mixed with seed in the form of sclerotia, smut balls, nematode galls, and infested plant parts. Pathogens may be present in or on seeds.

Treating infested seeds with chemicals or with heat greatly reduces the incidence of many seedborne pathogens. Seed treatment is used also to protect healthy seed against soilborne organisms, notably *Pythium*, *Fusarium*, and *Rhizoctonia*, which cause seed rots, preemergence damping-off, and seedling blights of many crops.

Some treatments kill organisms mixed with the seed or on its surface. Some destroy pathogens within the seeds. Others kill or retard the activity of soil organisms near the planted seeds.

Mechanical, physical, and chemical methods are used.

The mechanical method is designed to remove infectious materials mixed with seeds. Seeds should be thoroughly cleaned before seeding. Mechanical treatment does not kill pathogens within a seed. It does not remove all organisms from the surfaces of seeds or protect them against soilborne organisms. Mechanically treated seed therefore often requires further treatment.

Physical methods are used primarily to kill pathogens deep in the seeds. Some pathogens, such as those that

SEED TREATMENTS FOR CONTROL OF DISEASES

cause loose smuts of wheat and barley, can be inactivated in no other way.

Physical methods include hot-water and water-soak treatments and ultraviolet, infrared, X-ray, and other kinds of irradiation. Dry heat has been tested. Only the hot-water and the water-soak treatments have been shown to be practical. Physical methods do not protect seeds against soilborne organisms; they are effective against pathogens on or in seeds.

The hot-water treatment was the most commonly recommended physical method before 1950, but it never has been used extensively because of difficulties in exactly controlling temperature and duration of treatment; there is little margin of safety. Adequate supplies of steam or hot water, accurate thermometers, water tanks or vats, and drying facilities also are required. The method has been used mostly for disinfecting small lots of seed and batches of small-seeded crops that require low seeding rates per acre. Procedures differ with the crop and to some extent with the pathogen.

Various modifications of a water-soak method have been developed since 1950. They are safer and less critical in their requirements than the hot-water treatments. They have been used mostly for controlling loose smuts of wheat and barley but are effective against some other pathogens.

In all water-soak treatments, the seeds must be soaked in water at least 2 hours and subsequently kept under anaerobic or near anaerobic conditions for one or more days. In some instances the seeds are soaked for 64 hours in water at approximately 72° F. and then dried. Sometimes the seeds are soaked for only 2 hours, and then placed in airtight containers at 80° for 48 hours before being dried.

Other effective modifications differ in the temperature used and duration of the treatment. The higher the temperature, the shorter is the time required. Varieties of crops differ considerably in their sensitivity to injury from soaking for long periods. The

possibility of injury is reduced by adding 1 percent of common salt or 0.2 percent of Vancide 51 to the water in which the seeds are soaked.

Chemical treatments are the most commonly used method of treating seeds. Many excellent chemicals are available. They may be organic or inorganic, mercurial or nonmercurial, and metallic or nonmetallic.

Organic fungicides are used more than inorganic ones, but the latter are preferred for some purposes. Fungicides may be applied as dusts, liquids, or suspensions. Equipment is available for using them. Recommended dosages vary with the fungicide, the crop, the length of the storage period after treatment, and sometimes with the method of application. The use of excessive amounts of fungicides may injure the seed, waste the chemical, and make the handling and sowing of treated seed disagreeable and even dangerous. The use of less than the recommended amount of fungicide hampers disease control and may cause loss in yield and quality of crop.

Volatile fungicides usually are used at lower dosages than nonvolatile materials and are most effective when the treated seeds are stored for at least a few days before planting.

All dry fungicides present hazards. Special precautions are necessary. All dusts are harmful to people if they are inhaled over long periods or in excessive amounts. Seed fungicides are even more dangerous because all of them are poisonous. The extent of the hazard depends on the amount of dust inhaled, the toxicity of the chemical, the length of the period of exposure, and the person's sensitivity.

When treating large quantities of seeds, particularly over a period of many days, artificial ventilation should be provided to collect and exhaust the dust from the treating room. Workmen should wear clean filter masks over the nose and mouth. A special mask must be used against volatile chemicals. If the fungicides are applied wet, this special equipment may not be necessary, but one must not inhale the chemicals or their fumes. The chemicals should not come in contact with the skin. If a worker does get them on him, he should wash himself promptly with soap and water.

Originally wet treatments involved soaking the seeds in a water solution of a fungicide for a prescribed time, after which the seeds were removed and dried before they could be used or stored. Farmers never liked the method, because it took time, much work, and extra space in the granary for drying. Seeds that were not dried properly were hurt.

Today wet treatments are applied mostly by the slurry method or by quick-wet procedures, in which no drying is necessary because the treatments add less than 1 percent of moisture to the seeds.

In the slurry method, the seeds are completely coated with a thick suspension of the chemical in water. The suspension is applied by a special machine, a slurry treater. Because this method eliminates flying dust during treating, it is safer and less disagreeable for the workmen. More accurate and uniform dosages of chemical can be applied by it to most kinds of seeds.

In the quick-wet method, a concentrated solution of a volatile fungicide is added to the seeds and thoroughly mixed with them. Panogen 75 and Ceresan 75 are examples of fungicides applied in this way. The use of volatile liquid fungicides has increased greatly since 1950, especially for treating small grains, sorghum, cotton, flax, and rice.

Pelleting is another method of applying chemicals. It is used mostly as a protectant against soil organisms and as a repellant against birds and rodents. It has been particularly valuable for treating seeds of pine and other conifers but is used to some extent for treating seeds of other crops, notably onion for the control of smut.

Still other methods are used. For instance, the best method of destroying the pathogen that causes bacterial canker of tomato is to ferment the

seeds and pulp at about 70° for 72 hours before extraction. Storage of seed for one or more seasons destroys some pathogens—for example, the fungus that causes late blight of celery and the virus causing tobacco mosaic in tomato.

It is outside our scope to discuss seed treatment for the control of insects, but we should point out that insecticides are applied to the seeds of many crops and that the efficiency of the fungicide may be affected by the insecticide used.

Insecticides also increase the need for fungicide treatment, since they tend to predispose seeds and young seedlings to attack by soil fungi. Compatible fungicides and insecticides such as captan-dieldrin and thiram-dieldrin are available.

Some manufacturers package insecticide-fungicide mixtures, and the combination is applied as a single treatment. Others market the insecticide and fungicide separately, and the materials are applied separately as a dual treatment.

All seeds containing chemical dusts should be placed in closely woven bags (10 ounce or heavier) to reduce sifting of the chemical during handling and shipment. This is particularly desirable when chemicals are applied at high rates to smooth-surface seeds. If the seed is to be offered for sale, it must be labeled to indicate that it has been treated and is unfit for food or feed.

The ideal fungicide would be highly effective in disease control; harmless to the seed, even at higher than recommended dosages; economical to use; easy to apply; relatively nontoxic to people; noncorrosive to machinery; adapted to use in planting equipment, so as not to interfere materially with uniform seed flow; stable for relatively long periods; and relatively harmless to animals that may consume the treated seeds. No chemical in use in 1961 met all these requirements.

The choice of treatment depends on the crop, the nature of the disease problem, the condition of the seeds, the relative cost and availability of acceptable fungicides, the availability of treating equipment, and the weather conditions expected after seeding.

Crops differ in their responses to seed treatment. Some benefit more than others. Some are more sensitive to injury than others. That is true also of different lots of seed of a species. It is essential to know which diseases are to be controlled and whether the pathogen is located in or on the seeds or in the soil.

Only seeds of high quality should be planted. They should be thoroughly cleaned, cured, and dried before treating. Cracked, damaged, and old seeds sometimes benefit more from treatment than good seeds, but treatment should not be expected to substitute for good seeds. Even good seeds may benefit from a protectant.

When soil and weather conditions after seeding are unfavorable for rapid germination and development of seedlings, treatment of seeds will often mean the difference between a good and a poor stand. When growing conditions are favorable for the host, there may be no apparent benefit from treatment. Since the weather cannot be foreseen several weeks in advance and treating costs are low, however, many crops are treated every year as insurance against losses. Corn and sorghum are examples of such crops.

The treatments have been standardized to a remarkable degree, and recommendations for controlling diseases in specific crops can be made that are applicable over wide areas. Nevertheless, a grower will do well to consult his agricultural experiment station for the best fungicides for his situation.

CORN is extensively treated. Almost all of the seed of hybrid corn is treated chemically to prevent seed rots and seedling diseases.

The nonmercurial organic fungicides, principally captan and thiram, are used most. They are applied as dusts or slurries. Captan is superior at low dosages and on old seed, especially when conditions after planting are unfavorable. Both chemicals give adequate protection to good seed when applied at recommended rates. Dieldrin can be combined with either captan or thiram if protection against soil insects is needed and such combination treatments are used commonly in some States. Heavy insect infestations, however, can be controlled best by soil treatment.

Sorghum also is almost always treated to control kernel smuts, seed rots, and seedling blights. Both mercurial and nonmercurial organic fungicides are used. Among the proprietary mercurials, Ceresan (M, 75, 100, or 200), Panogen (15 or 42), and Chipcote (25 or 75) rank high.

Of the nonmercurials, captan and thiram formulations have given superior results. Dieldrin often is added to the nonmercurials. Insecticides are less often combined with mercury compounds, although aldrin has been used with Panogen. Nonmercurials are replacing the mercurials for sorghum.

WHEAT is treated to control bunt, loose smut, seed rots, and seedling blight.

Organic mercury compounds, such as Ceresan (M, 75, 100, and 200), Panogen (15 and 42), Chipcote (25 and 75), and various Ortho LM Seed Protectants, are recommended generally for bunt control when the pathogen is not present in the soil. Ceresan M, 100, and 200; Panogen 42; Chipcote 25; and Ortho LM Seed Protectant (concentrate) are applied in slurry-type treaters. Ceresan 75, Chipcote 75, Panogen 15, and Ortho LM Seed Protectant should be applied in a direct-type treater. Ortho LM Seed Protectant (dry) may be used either as a slurry or a dust.

If the pathogen is present in the soil, the seeds should be treated with HCB, which is sold under the trade names of No Bunt, Smut Go, Sanocide, and Anticari. It is a wettable powder suitable for use as a dust or slurry.

Soil surface treatments with HCB (10 pounds to the acre of a 40-percent formulation) have been effective in reducing dwarf bunt in the Pacific Northwest. Seed treatment does not control dwarf bunt.

Loose smut can be controlled only by a hot-water or water-soak treatment. The hot-water treatment is: Soak the cleaned grain in water at 60° to 70° for about 4 hours; preheat it in water at 120° for 1 minute; treat it in water at 129° for exactly 10 minutes; plunge it into cold water immediately to cool; and dry it rapidly at not more than 100°.

The water-soak method we have already discussed. Some workers feel that it is less dependable for wheat than it is for barley. Perhaps further modifications will give better results.

Seed treated with either the hot-water or the water-soak methods should receive an additional treatment with a fungicide, such as captan or thiram, to protect it against soil organisms.

The seedborne pathogens that cause seed rots and seedling blights are killed by the mercurials ordinarily used for controlling bunt, the hot-water treatment, or the water-soak method. They are not controlled by HCB. The mercurials are not very effective against soilborne organisms.

BARLEY diseases that respond to seed treatment are covered smut, loose smut, intermediate loose smut, stripe, seed rot, and seedling blights. Loose smut is controlled by hot-water or water-soak treatments like those described for wheat.

The standard hot-water method for barley is: Soak the seed in water at 60° to 70° for 5 or 6 hours; preheat it in water at 120° for 1 minute; treat it in water at 126° for 13 minutes; cool it; and dry it.

The water-soak method is effective against loose smut and is replacing the hot-water method because it is safer and easier to use. All of the organic mercury compounds used on wheat will control covered smut, intermediate loose smut, stripe, and the seedborne pathogens that cause seed rots and seedling blights of barley.

OATS are treated with the same organic mercury compounds recommended for wheat and barley. These fungicides are effective against loose smut, covered smut, helminthosporium blight, seed rots, and seedling blights.

Rye, a minor crop in the United States, is not generally treated. The organic mercurials used for wheat are effective against bunt, stalk smut, and the various seedborne pathogens that cause seed rots and seedling blights.

Rice stands can be improved by treating seeds with captan or thiram dusts or slurries. These fungicides protect the germinating seeds against soilborne pathogens. Organic mercury compounds are recommended if the seed is known to be infected with *Helminthosporium, Piricularia*, or other seedborne fungi. Seeds that contain nematodes should be fumigated with methyl bromide. Exposure to a concentration of 1.25 pounds per 1,000 cubic feet of space for 12 to 15 hours kills the nematodes without injuring the seeds.

SEED OF COTTON is treated to protect the plant against angular leaf spot, anthracnose sore shin, seed rots, and seedling blights. The seed usually is delinted before it is treated. Delinting is done mechanically by reginning or chemically by acid treatment. The method of delinting may influence the choice of fungicide.

Organic mercurials, such as Ceresan (M, 100, and 200) and Panogen 15, generally have been most effective against seedborne pathogens.

The nonmercurials, such as captan and Dow 9–B, are superior against soil organisms.

In some localities in the Cotton Belt, the application of a fungicide or a mixture of fungicides as a spray or dust into the seed furrow and the covering soil at planting has helped to reduce preemergence and postemergence damping-off by reinforcing the effect of seed treatment and by providing a treated zone through which the seedlings can emerge.

FLAX seed commonly is cracked and damaged in the threshing. Cracks develop in the seedcoat during maturation in some of the yellow-seeded varieties. The cracks let many fungi enter that rot the seeds or cause seedling blights.

Organic mercury compounds, such as those used for wheat, are recommended for flax. They also kill the seedborne pathogens. They may be applied as liquids, dusts, or slurries. Heavier dosages are required for flax than for most field crops because fungicides do not readily adhere to the smooth seedcoats and because flax seeds have more surface area per bushel. Wet treatments cause some gumming of the seeds because of the mucilaginous nature of the coat.

Nonmercurial organics, such as captan, have not been widely used for flax, but they are effective against soil organisms.

SUGARBEETS should be treated with a good protective fungicide like captan, thiram, Dexon, or dichlone to control seed rots and damping-off.

Organic mercury compounds are effective against seedborne pathogens but are less satisfactory against the soil organisms.

Sugarbeets usually are treated with dusts rather than slurries or liquids.

YIELDS of soybeans are rarely increased by seed treatment unless poor seeds are used or weather conditions after planting are especially unfavorable. Captan, thiram, and chloranil are the best fungicides when treatment is required.

Organic mercurials are sometimes injurious.

Treatment of peanut seed is a profitable farm practice, especially when machine-shelled seed is used. It reduces seed rotting and improves stands.

Recommended chemicals include thiram, chloranil, and 2-percent Ceresan applied as dusts.

SMALL-SEEDED FORAGE legumes, such as alfalfa, clovers, sweetclovers, vetches, lespedezas, and trefoils, usually do not respond to seed treatment under field conditions. Occasionally small increases in stand are obtained, but they have not been reflected in increased forage yields.

Treatment may be helpful on *Pythium*-infested muck soils and under certain other special conditions where it is hard to establish a stand. Captan and thiram are among the most effective and safest seed fungicides for these crops. Copper and mercurial fungicides may cause severe injury.

The many species of forage grasses differ in disease problems and their responses to treatment. Losses from seed decay and damping-off can be reduced by the use of a protectant such as captan or thiram. Damaged seeds usually benefit more from treatment than sound seeds.

Some grasses, such as sudangrass, are injured oftener in threshing than others and therefore are more responsive to seed treatment.

Smuts—common on millets, slender wheatgrass, Canada wildrye, and sudangrass—can be controlled by treatment with any of the organic mercury compounds suggested for sorghum and the small grains.

MANY VEGETABLES benefit from seed treatment.

Damping-off and seed rots are particularly bad in vegetable crops. They can be controlled to a considerable extent by seed treatment. Treatment also is effective in preventing the introduction of seedborne pathogens into new areas.

Asparagus seeds are treated for control of damping-off with the mercurials Calogreen or Ceresan M, applied as dusts at the rates of 4 ounces and ⅛ ounce, respectively, per pound of seed.

Beans (lima, green, or dry) usually

are treated with a combination fungicide and insecticide as a dust or a slurry. Captan or thiram in combination with dieldrin or lindane have been used.

Beets, spinach, and Swiss chard should be treated with a protectant, such as captan, thiram, or dichlone, to prevent rotting and preemergence damping-off. These crops are also subject to postemergence damping-off, which cannot be controlled adequately by seed treatment.

Carrots often are treated with a combination fungicide-insecticide dust to control damping-off and to reduce damage from the first generation of the carrot rust fly. A nonmercurial organic fungicide, such as dichlone or thiram, is used, together with an insecticide such as lindane. Seeds that are to be used for seed increase should first be given a hot-water treatment to make sure that they are free of the bacterial blight organism.

Celery seeds usually are soaked in hot water (118°) for 30 minutes to destroy the organisms of early and late blights. Seeds 2 years old or older need not be treated. Protectants are sometimes used in addition to the hot-water treatment, but we have little evidence that they are beneficial.

Crucifers, such as cabbage, cauliflower, broccoli, and brussels sprouts, are subject to diseases caused by organisms that are internally seedborne. Disinfection with hot water is generally necessary, but procedures vary. At a temperature of 122°, some States recommend a 30-minute soak for all of these crucifers.

Other States recommend 20 minutes for cauliflower and broccoli and 25 minutes for cabbage and brussels sprouts. After the seed has been disinfected, it should be treated with a protectant, like captan or thiram, to reduce stand losses caused by soil organisms.

Radishes, rutabagas, turnips, kale, kohlrabi, and mustard are other crucifers that benefit from seed protectants.

Seeds of cucurbits, such as cucumbers, muskmelons, watermelons, and squashes and pumpkins may be disinfested with mercuric chloride if the organisms causing anthracnose or angular leaf spot are suspected.

The procedure consists in soaking the seeds for 5 minutes in a solution of 1 ounce of mercuric chloride in 7.5 gallons of water, thoroughly rinsing them in running water, and drying. A protectant should be used afterwards. Captan or thiram, alone or in combination with an insecticide such as lindane or dieldrin, are beneficial, especially on the larger seeded cucurbits.

Onion seeds may be protected against decay by materials like captan or thiram, but the primary purpose in treating onions is to give protection against the soilborne smut fungus. Pelleting the seeds with thiram or captan has largely replaced the old standard formaldehyde-drip method. An insecticide, such as aldrin, may be included in the pelletant to control maggots.

Peas are treated with a protectant to control seed rots and seedling blights. Chloranil formerly was used, but captan and thiram, alone or in combination with an insecticide, have largely replaced it. The rate of seed flow through the drill is retarded somewhat by both captan and thiram, so that a compensatory change in seeding rate must be made or graphite added as a lubricant at the rate of 1 ounce per bushel.

Seeds of tomato, eggplant, and pepper often require disinfectant treatments as well as protectants. They can be disinfected by soaking them in hot water (122°) for 25 minutes. Immediately afterwards, the seeds should be plunged into cold water, drained, and spread out to dry.

Pepper seeds sometimes are disinfected in a mercuric chloride solution instead of in hot water. The procedure is to soak the seed for 5 minutes in a solution containing one-fourth ounce of mercuric chloride in 5.5 gallons of water, rinse thoroughly in running water, drain, and dry.

Some States require that tomato seed be treated with an organic mercurial, such as Ceresan M, before plants are certified for export. Seeds treated with mercurials should not be treated again with other chemicals as this may cause injury. Protectants are beneficial to seed treated with hot water or not previously treated.

GREAT QUANTITIES of apple, pear, cherry, peach, plum, and lesser quantities of almond and apricot seeds are sown each year. It is common practice to soak the seeds in water for several hours before planting, but treatment with a fungicide is uncommon. Occasionally damping-off causes losses in stand. The losses could be reduced by the use of a good protectant.

SEEDS OF many kinds of ornamental plants benefit from treatment. Some large producers of flower seeds use treatments to reduce losses from seed rots and damping-off.

Thiram, captan, chloranil, and Semesan are commonly used. They usually are applied as dusts. Hot-water and chemical-soak treatments also are used to eliminate seedborne pathogens. Little of the packeted seed sold to home gardeners is treated.

Seeds of China aster sometimes are treated with a mercuric chloride or Semesan-soak treatment to prevent the introduction of wilt organisms (*Fusarium* and *Verticillium*) into clean soil. Treatment will not control wilt if the soil is already contaminated.

The standard treatment for wilt is to soak the seeds for 30 minutes in a 1:1000 mercuric chloride solution, which can be prepared by dissolving one 7.5-grain tablet of mercuric chloride in a pint of water. Treated seeds should be rinsed immediately for at least 5 minutes in running water and then dried for 24 hours at room temperature.

Instead of mercuric chloride, seeds may be treated in a 0.25-percent Semesan solution (two teaspoons of Semesan to 1 quart of water) for 30 minutes. Either treatment also helps to reduce the incidence of *Septoria*, *Ascochyta*, and other seedborne pathogens that incite leaf spots.

Stock seeds infected with the bacterial blight organism should be given a hot-water treatment, which consists of soaking it for 10 minutes in water at 129°–130°, plunging it in cold water to cool, and then drying it. A plastic screen bag makes a good container for submerging the seed during treatment, because it permits instantaneous contact of all the seeds in the bag with the hot water and facilitates quick and easy drainage. Timing is important. Stock seeds also may benefit from a protectant.

Sweetpeas frequently are treated with captan, thiram, or chloranil to prevent seed rots and seedling blights.

Zinnia seed is sometimes soaked in hot water (125°) for 30 minutes to kill seedborne *Rhizoctonia solani*, a fungus that causes damping-off.

SEEDS OF FOREST TREES frequently are treated before sowing in nurseries to control seed rots and preemergence and postemergence damping-off. Most of the pines, Norway spruce, and concolor fir are treated routinely. Thiram and captan are commonly used. Other chemicals are sometimes added to protect against insects, birds, and rodents.

Hardwoods and some of the large-seeded southern conifers like loblolly (*Pinus taeda*) and slash pine (*P. caribaea*) can be protected by simply dusting the seed with thiram or captan. The conifers with smaller seeds (more than 20 thousand seeds to the pound) usually are pelleted.

Dosages of fungicides vary with the species to be treated and the chemical used. Lower dosages are required for large-seeded than for small-seeded species and for seed sown in the spring than for fall-sown seed. Approximately twice as much captan as thiram is needed. For red pine (*P. resinosa*) 4 ounces of 50-percent thiram or 8 ounces of 50-percent captan per pound of seed commonly are recommended.

In pelleting, an adhesive, such as
methyl cellulose, Dow Latex 512–R,
or Flintkote Asphalt-Emulsion C–13–
HPC, is required, and this must be applied first to the seed.

The amount of sticker required per
pound of seed depends upon the size of
the seed, the sticker to be used, and
the amount of dust to be fixed to the
seed. To apply 4 ounces of fungicide
per pound of red pine seed, 2 fluid
ounces of 4-percent methyl cellulose
are required. If 8 ounces of fungicide
are to be used, 3 ounces of the sticker
are needed. The next step is to apply
the fungicide. If an insecticide is to be
used it should be added at the same
time. When a repellant is to be incorporated into the pellet, it should be
added last—just before the seed is to
be removed from the mixer.

EARLE W. HANSON *joined the Depart-
ment of Agriculture in 1937. From 1937 to
1946 he was employed by the Division of
Cereal Crops and Diseases of the Bureau of
Plant Industry, Soils, and Agricultural
Engineering to do research at the Minnesota
Agricultural Experiment Station on the
diseases of hard red spring wheats and
to cooperate in the development of disease-
resistant varieties of wheat. Since 1946 he
has been employed jointly by the Crops
Research Division of the Agricultural
Research Service and the University of
Wisconsin to investigate diseases of forage
crops.*

EARL D. HANSING *has degrees from the
University of Minnesota, Kansas State
University, and Cornell University. Since
1940 he has served as a plant pathologist at
Kansas State University and has conducted
research on cereal and forage diseases.*

W. T. SCHROEDER *is a graduate of the
Universities of Idaho and Wisconsin. From
1941 to 1943 he served as plant pathologist
for the Green Giant Co. of LeSueur, Minn.
He moved in 1944 to the New York State
Agricultural Experiment Station of Cornell
University at Geneva, where he is a professor
in the department of plant pathology and
conducts research on the control of vegetable
diseases through fungicides and disease resistance.*

The Control of Weeds
in Seed Crops

W. C. SHAW AND L. L. DANIELSON

THE SEQUENCE of events that occurs
when cultivated fields are abandoned
is well known. Without the efforts of
man, an abandoned cultivated field
eventually will be occupied by the
climax vegetation characteristic of the
geographical area.

The fundamentals of plant ecology
emphasize that plant successions always occur in the direction of the
climax vegetation rather than toward
the growth of more economic crop
plants. Weeds such as crabgrass, pigweed, ragweed, and lambsquarters
represent the first step in the plant
succession away from economic crops
toward the climax vegetation.

In our efforts to produce economic
crops, we attempt to utilize fully all
available technology to stabilize and
balance the vegetation at a highly productive level and to prevent the occurrence of plant successions to the climax
vegetation. We attempt to delineate
and eliminate or correct the limiting
factors in the production of economic
crops.

One of the most important places to
start is with the control of the weeds,
which compete directly for all production factors and most critically for
those that are limiting.

Seeds of weeds often are disseminated
in crop seeds. The use of weed-free
crop seeds is a sound starting place for
an effective program to control weeds.
Regardless of the effectiveness of weed-
control practices, weed-control programs are relatively ineffective unless
the program is accompanied by efficient weed-control practices in crops

grown for seed production and weed-free seeds are available to farmers.

Weeds are among the greatest contributors to production costs on American farms. Losses due to weeds have reached an estimated 4 billion dollars annually.

Weeds compete with crops for water, light, and mineral elements. One plant of common mustard (*Brassica kaber*) requires twice as much nitrogen, twice as much phosphorus, four times as much potassium, and four times as much water as a well-developed oat plant. Ragweed (*Ambrosia artemisiifolia*) requires three times as much water as corn to produce a pound of dry matter.

The reduction in yields of seed crops and quality caused by weeds is influenced by the composition and the density of the weed population, the length of time the weeds are allowed to grow in competition with crop plants, and soil and environment.

Numerous investigations on weed-crop competition in the production of soybeans, corn, rice, small grains, vegetables, forage plants, and other crops grown for seeds indicate that weed competition is most serious during the first 30 days after they emerge. The emergence of weeds should be prevented, or they should be controlled immediately after emergence for maximum reduction of competition.

The competitive effects of barnyard-grass (*Echinochloa crusgalli*), a serious weed in ricefields, are illustrated by results from studies in Arkansas in which average yields obtained from heavily infested rice sprayed with the herbicide, isopropyl N-(3-chlorophenyl) carbamate [CIPC] at 4, 6, 8, and 10 pounds per acre were 85, 90, 94, and 96 bushels per acre, respectively. The yield of rice on untreated check plots averaged 56 bushels per acre.

WEED SEEDS are disseminated by wind, water, animals, and people.

Many weed seeds have modifications and adaptations for dissemination by one or more methods. For example, the seed of Canada thistle resembles a parachute and can travel long distances through the air. Many weed seeds will float for indefinite periods and may be carried long distances by water. Irrigation canals and ditches are important means of disseminating weed seeds in irrigated farming areas.

Wild and domestic animals assist in the dissemination of weeds. The seeds of many weeds pass through the digestive tract of animals without impairment of viability.

Weeds may be disseminated by mass means of modern transportation. Weed seeds are often transported in the packing about trees; in soils and of gravel used in construction; in refuse or mud; on the wheels of vehicles; in soil adhering to plows, cultivators, and other farm tillage implements; in threshing machines, harvesting combines, hay balers, and portable seed cleaners; and on tires of automobiles and airplanes.

The prevention of the introduction and spread of weeds and weed seeds is important. Preventive methods include the use of weed-free crop seeds.

The viability of weed seeds in screenings of grain or hay can be destroyed by grinding or ensiling before they are fed to livestock. The viability of weed seeds in manure should be destroyed by thorough fermentation before it is used on farms. Livestock should not be permitted to move from weed-infested areas directly to uninfested areas. Grain drills, harvesters, cleaners, hay balers, and other farm machinery should be cleaned before moving from infested areas. The use of gravel, sand, and soil from areas known to be heavily infested with weeds should be avoided. Nursery stock should be inspected for the presence of weed seeds, tubers, and rhizomes of perennial weeds. The banks of irrigation ditches, fence corners, fence lots, roadsides, railroad rights-of-way, and other uncropped areas should be kept free from weeds.

THE METHODS of control include mechanical techniques, such as hand hoe-

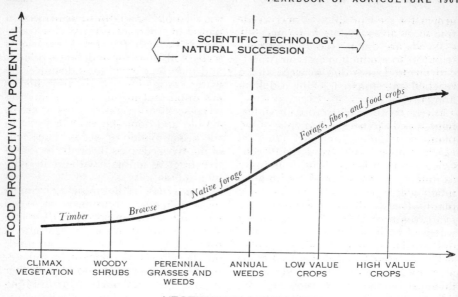

The relationship of plant ecology to control of weeds.

ing, tillage, mowing, flooding, burning, and smothering; cultural methods, such as crop rotation and crop competition techniques; biological methods, which involve the use of insects, plant diseases, and other organisms to control weeds; and chemical methods, including the use of selective and nonselective herbicides as foliage and soil applications. A well-balanced program of weed control should make maximum effective use of hand, mechanical, tillage, cultural, biological, and chemical methods.

Increased emphasis has been given the use of herbicides. We are now entering an era in agricultural production in which various forms of energy are used to control weeds and to control insects and diseases and for crop protection in many ways.

The chemical energy of herbicide molecules is a reservoir out of which must come our most efficient weed-control practices for the future. There is increasing evidence in weed-control techniques that mechanical equipment

will be used more and more in the future to transport chemical energy. The herbicides will be the sources of energy and perform the work rather than the machine with which they are applied.

This does not imply that the need for mechanical equipment will be reduced. It means greater emphasis on the specificity and accuracy of equipment in placing the chemical energy in the exact amount, in the exact place, and at the exact time for the chemical to perform its maximum work.

CHEMICAL methods include the use of herbicides as soil-incorporated preplanting, preemergence, and postemergence treatments; directed postemergence treatments; band applications immediately over the row; and soil sterilization.

Herbicides offer almost unlimited opportunities in versatility and completeness in the control of weeds.

To use herbicides most effectively, one should know their nature and properties, sites and mechanisms of action, metabolic fate in plants and soils, and the effects of environment on their performance.

Herbicides may be classified on the basis of their mode of action and use. The selectivity of herbicides is relative and depends largely on the rate of application and the stage of growth of plants.

The number of different types available for use on farms makes it possible to control a wide variety of specific weeds and a broad spectrum of weed populations in the various weed-crop situations.

Herbicides kill weeds by inhibiting essential processes in plant growth, such as respiration, photosynthesis, transpiration, and mitosis (an important process in cell division) or by preventing the biosynthesis of elements essential to the growth of plants.

2,2-Dichloropropionic acid [dalapon], a selective, systemic herbicide used for the control of grasses, inhibits the enzymatic synthesis of pantothenic acid, a vitamin B essential to the growth of plants. When dalapon inhibits the biosynthesis of this essential metabolite in treated plants, they are seriously damaged or killed.

Some herbicides may kill plants by interfering with mitosis and other reproductive processes in plants. Compounds such as CIPC cause abnormal chromosome behavior in plants.

Herbicides may also kill plants by preventing the normal function of essential processes in plant growth. For example, 2-chloro-4,6-bis(ethylamino)-s-triazine [simazine], a new herbicide very effective as a preemergence treatment for the control of weeds in corn, kills plants by inhibiting the efficiency of the chloroplasts to function in the process of photosynthesis. Treated plants are thus inefficient in the production of sugar and starches, which are essential to their growth.

The selective action of herbicides is determined by the molecular structure of the herbicide, the anatomy and morphology of plants, and the physio-logical and biochemical processes in plants, as effected by environmental and edaphic (soil condition) factors and the interaction of these factors as they influence the concentration of the herbicide reaching the site of action in plants at any given time.

Many factors influence the selective action of herbicides—the structure, volatility, formulation, amount applied, amount intercepted by the leaves or soil, amount retained on the leaf, amount penetrating the plant, the time and rate of absorption, the efficiency of absorption, the amount and efficiency of translocation, and the metabolic fate of herbicides in plants and soils.

The growth habit of the plant, including the nature of the leaf surface—whether or not it is smooth, waxy, or pubescent—the angle and width of the leaf, and the location and activity of growing points, influences the selectivity of herbicides. Other factors, such as placement of the herbicide, size and age of plants at the time of application, and environmental conditions before and after application also influence selectivity.

The fundamental basis for the selective action of herbicides is nevertheless the amount of the herbicide reaching the site of action in the plant at any given time.

Herbicides applied to plants or directly to the soil may be absorbed by the soil, deactivated by chemical reactions in the soil, decomposed by soil micro-organisms, dissipated by volatilization, deactivated by photochemical reactions, leached through the soils below the root zone, and absorbed by plants and metabolized to inactive metabolic products.

Inactive chemicals may be applied to plants and metabolized to herbicidally active compounds. The chemical 4-(2,4-dichlorophenoxy) butyric acid [4-(2,4-DB)] is not active as a herbicide. When this chemical is applied to certain weeds and crops, however, it is metabolized from 4-(2,4-DB) to 2,4-dichlorophenoxyacetic acid [2,4-D].

Weeds and crops capable of beta-oxidizing 4-(2,4-DB) to 2,4-D will be killed, while plants not capable of effectively beta-oxidizing 4-(2,4-DB) are not killed.

The metabolic fate of simazine in plants is opposite to that of 4-(2,4-DB). When simazine is absorbed by the roots of corn, it is metabolized to a nonphytotoxic chemical. Corn therefore shows considerable tolerance to simazine. On the other hand, many important weeds do not metabolize the simazine to an inactive chemical. These weeds are highly susceptible to the herbicide and are easily controlled.

Weeds and crop plants play a significant role in the selective action and fate of herbicides in plants. Thus, crop plants and weeds possess the capacity to metabolize herbicides to inactive metabolites, as illustrated by the conversion of simazine by corn, or to perform the opposite function, to convert an inactive chemical into an active herbicide, as in the case of the conversion of 4-(2,4-DB) to 2,4-D.

These fundamental discoveries have made it possible to develop a herbicide such as simazine for use as a preemergence herbicide to control weeds in corn grown for seed production, and to utilize 4-(2,4-DB) for the selective control of a wide variety of broad-leaved weeds in alfalfa, red clover, whiteclover, canning peas, flax, and other crops grown for seeds.

The herbicides are applied as soil-incorporated preplanting, preemergence, postemergence, and soil-sterilant treatments for the control of weeds grown for the production of seeds. Herbicides also may be used alone, in mixtures, and in combination with cultural and mechanical methods of weed control.

Alfalfa grown for seed production is an example of how herbicides are used to control weeds in seed crops. Ethyl N,N-di-*n*-propylthiolcarbamate [EPTC] may be applied as a soil-incorporated preplanting treatment for the control of broad-leaved weeds and annual grasses in alfalfa. The

herbicide is applied to the surface of the soil and disked thoroughly to incorporate it. Alfalfa is usually seeded 1 to 10 days after the soil-incorporated preplanting treatment with EPTC. EPTC, when soil incorporated, gives good control of weeds without injury to alfalfa.

Herbicides may also be used as preemergence treatments for weed control in alfalfa grown for the production of seeds. Several compounds have shown promise for this use. 3-(3,4-Dichlorophenyl)-1,1-dimethylurea [diuron] applied as a preemergence treatment has been effective in many areas.

EFFICIENT and economical chemical methods are available for a number of horticultural crops.

Preemergence applications of 4,6-dinitro-*o-sec*-butylphenol [DNBP] control annual broad-leaved weeds and weed grasses in field beans, pole beans, green beans, lima beans, mung beans, broadbeans, and edible soybeans without injuring the crops. Postemergence applications of DNBP applied when canning peas are 3 to 8 inches tall have been used widely for the control of important broad-leaved weeds in this crop. Band applications are used to cut the cost of the herbicide, and the middles between the rows are cultivated.

Weeds in sweet corn can be checked with preemergence applications of simazine. Preemergence applications of N-1-naphthylphthalamic acid [NPA] control annual weed grasses and certain broad-leaved weeds in cantaloups, cucumbers, watermelons, and pumpkins.

Annual grasses, chickweed (*Stellaria media*), and henbit (*Lamium amplexicaule*) are controlled in leaf, salad, and cole crops with a combination of 2-chloroallyl diethyldithiocarbamate [CDEC] and CIPC.

Stoddards solvent, a petroleum fraction, is effective as a postemergence spray on small, annual, broad-leaved weeds and weed grasses in carrots, parsley, dill, and fennel. Late-season annual weed grasses in tomatoes and peppers can be controlled with CIPC, applied following clean cultivation at lay-by.

Soil-directed sprays of a mixture of CIPC, DNBP, and fuel oil emulsified in water provide excellent control of many growing annual broad-leaved weeds and weed grasses under the trees in apple, peach, pear, and nut orchards and under the arbors in vineyards. This combination of herbicides also provides a continuing control of weeds for several weeks by killing germinating weed seeds.

Soil fumigants such as methyl bromide, sodium-N-methyldithiocarbamate [SMDC] and 3,5-dimethyltetrahydro-1,3-5,2H-thiodiazine-2-thione [DMTT] are effective in controlling annual and perennial broad-leaved weeds and weed grasses in vegetable plant beds. These chemicals are applied after the soil is plowed and disked. Crops are planted after a predetermined waiting period.

All herbicides should be used with proper caution until experience has shown that they are suitable for the particular crop variety, weed problem, climatic conditions, soil composition, and cultural methods of the farm on which they are to be used.

FOR THE MOST efficient control of weeds in crops grown for seeds, a combination of cultural, mechanical, biological, and chemical methods should be used when possible.

The control of weeds in rice grown for seeds may be used as a good example of the necessity for using multiple methods of weed control. Annual and perennial grasses, sedges, broad-leaved weeds, and aquatic weeds constitute serious problems in the production of rice.

Cultural methods of weed control in rice include the use of weed-free seeds of adapted varieties, efficient land preparation, crop rotation, an efficient fertilizer program, and hand pulling of weeds. Adequate land leveling, combined with proper construction of levees to permit a uniform depth of irrigation water, is essential. Seeding rice in water reduces infestations of barnyardgrass. Germination of barnyardgrass is inhibited while the rice grows well under such conditions. Judicious flooding of rice when it is in the seedling stage also reduces weeds. Barnyardgrass may be partially controlled by flooding early to a depth of 4 to 6 inches for 2 to 3 weeks.

Repeated cultivations in the spring at intervals of 1 to 3 weeks before seeding rice usually reduce barnyardgrass and other weeds. The last cultivation is usually shallow, so that viable weed seeds will not be brought near the surface of the soil. Seeding the rice on a roughly prepared seedbed to discourage germination of weed seeds is also employed.

The time of applying phosphate is important because phosphate stimulates the growth of barnyardgrass and other weeds when applied before seeding rice in a dry seedbed. Competition of weedy grasses can be reduced by applying phosphate to a crop other than rice in the rotation or by delaying application until just before the rice is flooded for the first time.

Time of applying nitrogen to fields of rice infested with weedy grasses is also important. Barnyardgrass and other weeds are stimulated by the application of nitrogen before seeding of rice. When rice is infested with barnyardgrass and other grasses, delaying nitrogen applications until heading of the barnyardgrass reduces competition with the rice. If nitrogen is applied while the grass is vegetative, barnyardgrass consumes most of the nitrogen, and the competitiveness of the grass with the rice is enhanced. When grass infestations in rice are high, yields of rice have been almost doubled by delaying applications of nitrogen until heading of the barnyardgrass.

Chemical methods of weed control in rice are used in combination with and supplemental to the cultural practices. CIPC is used for the control of barnyardgrass and other grasses in rice in certain areas, while several of the

ROTATION OF DIFFERENT HERBICIDES ON THE SAME CROP [1]

| Year | Crop sequence | Chemical weed-control treatments | |
		Preemergence	Postemergence
First..............	Corn..............	Simazine..............	2,4-D
Second...........	Corn..............	CDAA+2,3,6-TBA.....	2,4,5-T
Third.............	Corn..............	Atrazine..............	2-(2,4-DP)
Fourth...........	Snap beans........	DNBP...............	

[1] Hypothetical rotations used to illustrate the principle of keeping maximum pressure on the weed population by the use of a series of herbicides which differ in their effectiveness in controlling various weed spectrums. This procedure reduces the chance that a species that is tolerant to a specific herbicide will become dominant. It also reduces the chance of an accumulation of herbicide residues in the soil.

THE USE OF VARIOUS HERBICIDES ON ALL CROPS IN A ROTATION [1]

| Year | Crop sequence | Chemical weed-control treatments | | |
		Preplanting	Preemergence	Postemergence
First............	Corn............	EPTC........	Simazine......	2,4-D
Second..........	Peanuts.......	....	Sesone........	DNBP
Third..........	Cotton........	....	Diuron........	Ipazine
Fourth..........	Soybeans......	EPTC........	PCP..........	

[1] See footnote of the first table.

THE USE OF DIFFERENT HERBICIDES ON SEVERAL HORTICULTURAL CROPS IN A ROTATION [1]

| Year | Crop sequence | Chemical weed-control treatments | |
		Preemergence	Postemergence
First..............	Snap beans........	DNBP.................	
Second...........	Sweet corn........	Simazine..............	2,4-D
Third.............	Cantaloups........	NPA.................	NPA
Fourth...........	Spinach...........	CDEC+CIPC........	

[1] See footnote of the first table.

phenoxyalkylcarboxylic acids such as 2,4-D,2-methyl-4-chlorophenoxyacetic acid [MCPA], 2,4,5-trichlorophenoxy-acetic acid [2,4,5-T], and 2-(2,4,5-trichlorophenoxy) propionic acid [silvex] are used for the postemergence control of broad-leaved weeds and sedges.

The weed-control methods that are being developed for the control of weeds in rice exemplify an outstanding example of maximum utilization of cultural and chemical methods for efficient weed control in the production of this seed crop and crops grown in rotation with rice.

Numerous investigations indicate that the composition of the fertilizer, the time of application, and the placement in relationship to the crop seeds are critical factors in weed control in crops grown for seeds. Fertilization, irrigation, and other cultural practices should be employed in such a manner as to insure maximum benefits to the crop plants and minimum benefits to the weed population.

WEEDS are a total farm liability and all crops on the farm are subject to their competition.

The cost of controlling weeds in

individual crops undoubtedly appears high because only the current crop is considered—rather than the total weed problem in all crops grown on the farm.

Too often producers of crop seeds approach the problem of controlling weeds in crops only when the weeds are present in the current crop. In order to obtain a better balanced and more efficient weed-control program, farmers must be encouraged to use chemical weed-control methods in all crops. Greater emphasis must be placed on the necessity of supplementing this program by the rotational use of herbicides on all tolerant crops throughout the rotation in combination with various cultural and mechanical weed-control practices. Farmers should rotate different herbicides on the same crops grown continuously and learn more about the efficiency of rotating different herbicides on different crops throughout the rotation.

The rotation of herbicides on the same crop and on different crops throughout the rotation enables the grower to prevent undesirable ecological shifts in the populations of weeds. Using herbicides throughout the rotation illustrates the principle of keeping maximum pressure on the weed population by the use of a series of herbicides which differ in their effectiveness in controlling various weed spectrums. This procedure reduces the chance of a species that is tolerant to a specific herbicide from becoming dominant and spreading.

THE ROTATION of herbicides and the use of herbicides on all crops in the rotation also reduces the chance of an accumulation of herbicide residues in the soil. Residual-type herbicides can be rotated with those possessing little or no residual problems.

The potentialities for more efficient weed control in crops grown for seeds seem almost unlimited if herbicides could be developed for use in all crops and the weed problem is considered a total liability to the entire farm.

Herbicides must also be used in mixtures and in combination with mechanical and cultural practices for greater efficiency.

For example, herbicides are not available which will selectively control Canada thistle in growing tomatoes. However, a herbicide such as 4-(2,4-DB) can be effectively used to control Canada thistle in alfalfa and 2,4-D can be used to control it in corn. While herbicides are not available for the control of all weeds in all crops without causing any injury to the crop, herbicides are available which can be used for a wide variety of weed problems if the herbicides are used on all crops in a rotation which will tolerate herbicides.

FARMERS know that thorough preparation of the seedbed, followed by clean, efficient, shallow, timely cultivation, has an important place in weed control. It has been established, too, that there are no substitutes for adapted varieties that are properly fertilized and managed.

However, knowledge is needed of the value of the rotational use of herbicides, the use of mixtures of herbicides, the use of herbicides in combination with effective cultural and mechanical practices, and the multiple uses of herbicides in crop rotations, just as they have learned the value of rotating crops, the use of good varieties, clean seeds, and sound fertilizer practices.

Surveys indicated that in 1959 farmers used more than 100 million pounds of herbicides on approximately 50 million acres of agricultural land at an estimated cost of 150 million dollars. The herbicides applied on this acreage were developed for commercial use since 1950.

W. C. SHAW *is Leader, Weed Investigations, Agronomic Crops, Crops Research Division, Agricultural Research Service.*

L. L. DANIELSON *is Leader, Weed Investigations, Horticultural Crops, Crops Research Division, Agricultural Research Service.*

The Seeds of

Wild Flowers

P. L. RICKER

OUTSIDE the city limits is a bounty of Nature for all to enjoy. A bounty free, colorful, rewarding. A bounty that gives and gives and wants only protection against destruction. A bounty all the more precious in a civilization of pavements, machines, noise, economics.

It is the bounty of wild plants. It is a large bounty: Probably about 20 thousand species of trees, shrubs, and herbaceous—nonwoody—plants in the United States are classified as wild. About 15 percent are well-established species that came from other countries or escaped from cultivation. Most of them are herbaceous. A goodly number have leaves and flowers so attractive that many persons want to grow them in home gardens, along roadsides, and in other suitable places, large and small.

Some natural difficulties, which pertain also to cultivated plants and involve the age-long adaptation to a particular soil, the amount of moisture, sunlight, heat, and so on, are encountered when one tries to domesticate the wildlings. Growing them is worth the effort, however.

Knowing that, many persons want information about sources of seed of wild flowers.

There are a few dealers in seeds of wild flowers, but not all of them have a large number of species. Their catalogs usually give directions for cultivation. A list of them may be obtained from the U.S. National Arboretum, Washington 25, D.C.

Small packets of seeds of wild flowers sell for 25 to 50 cents each. Packets of mixtures for broadcasting may sell for 2 or 3 dollars an ounce. Many of the seeds are so small that an ounce may contain 1 thousand or more.

Dealers sometimes find that the high cost of time, labor, and travel to collect a large amount and variety of seeds from the wild often makes such work unprofitable unless they use seeds first to establish gardens, where their collecting can be done at small cost.

Wild flower enthusiasts will get a great deal of pleasure from collecting their own seed. Many beautiful nonweedy species may be found along roadsides, and particularly secondary roads, and adjoining fields near pastures and wooded areas.

SEEDS mostly can be collected about a month after the flowering period. Each kind, with stem and often basal leaves to help identify the species, should be placed in an envelope or paper bag of an appropriate size. On the envelope also, as a guide to proper planting, should be the date and place of collecting; the type of soil, whether dry, moist, or wet; and details of the surroundings, whether open or dense woods and the predominant type of tree growth.

Seed capsules and pods, if few, can be stripped from the stems. The seed in them can be crushed out by hand or on a newspaper on a table by light pounding with a small block of wood.

For a larger amount of seeds, the threshing is best done by light pounding in a large paper or cloth bag, in which they were collected. The seeds will fall to the bottom of the bag and most of the coarse material can be removed readily.

For further cleaning, a series of sieves 10 by 10 by 2 inches (or larger, if needed) is easily made with ¼-inch wood frames. Screen material may be obtained from hardware stores in galvanized, copper, or brass wire, in a mesh of 4, 8, 12, 16, 20, and 30 wires to the inch.

For cleaning, the sieves are stacked with the No. 30 mesh at the bottom and the No. 4 at the top. For shaking seeds through the sieve, these stacks should be held together with an easily loosened, strong cord or strap. Coarse material in the top sieve should be removed. Any uncrushed capsules or pods in the sieve should be placed on a newspaper on a table and the seed crushed out of them. The same is done with each succeeding smaller sieve.

The seeds of most wild flowers vary so in size that seeds may be found in sieves of two or three sizes. Often seeds in the smallest sieve may be immature and will give less good germination than the larger seeds. For home use, however, they may be mixed with the larger ones.

One who collects seeds should not overlook those with fleshy coverings. The covering can be removed by soaking the seed in warm water for 10 or 15 minutes. Then the seeds are placed in a sieve with a mesh smaller than the seeds. The coating is scrubbed off with a stiff-bristled or wire brush. This process is not required in Nature, as the covering naturally disintegrates after planting.

Keeping a collection of samples of all seeds of wild flowers one obtains is an interesting hobby. One becomes familiar with the many types of seed found in some families and often with two or three types of seed in a genus.

Small seeds are best kept in straight-walled glass vials ⅜ by 1¾ inches in size with cork stoppers. The Latin name of the species should be printed on ½- by 2-inch gummed labels with the date and place of collecting and reference to the herbarium specimen, if one keeps a herbarium. The label should be pasted around the top of the vial. The vials are kept in shallow boxes about 11 by 17 inches that have 4 rows of 25 cardboard partitions. Larger seeds are placed in larger vials in deeper boxes that have 54 or 26 compartments. The larger seeds may be kept loose in boxes with 18 compartments.

A large collection of seeds of mostly native plants in the United States is

that of the Department of the Interior, Patuxent Wildlife Research Center, at Laurel, Md. It has about 7,500 species. Particular attention is given species that are used as food by birds and game.

Scientists for many years conducted extensive studies on the food preferences of birds, as indicated by an examination of their stomachs. From this and other sources, a large catalog of plants whose seeds are food for birds was compiled. Among them are a number of attractive wild flowers, although most are seeds and fleshy fruits of shrubs and trees. Seeds of small-flowered and abundant weedy plants, grasses, and grasslike plants supplied a large proportion of bird food.

The Wild Flower Preservation Society of Washington, D.C., also has a large collection of about 5 thousand species. It stresses the more attractive flowered herbaceous ones, and probably has at least 2 thousand species that are not in the Patuxent collection.

MOST WILD seeds ripen and fall to the ground about a month after flowering. Those that are light or have wings or hairy appendages are blown some distance by the wind before falling.

A few species, particularly of annuals or biennials, like the daisy-fleabane and fringed gentian, may germinate and develop leaf rosettes in the fall.

Seeds of wild flowers in most temperate regions require one winter in the ground before germinating. If they do not get the right conditions of moisture and temperature to germinate the following spring, they may go dormant and not germinate until conditions are right—maybe another year or two.

Some wild flowers are difficult to establish if the roots are disturbed in transplanting. The seeds of such species should be planted in a small, tough, fiber paper pot, which is to be placed in the ground in the spring when the seedlings are 3 or 4 inches tall or long.

When seeds are broadcast along roadsides that are covered with more aggressive vegetation, the seedling plants may be choked out. The same may happen if they are broadcast in woodland areas.

Much better results will be obtained if the ground is cleared and a good seedbed is prepared. Along some roadsides in Texas, the State highway department has obtained good results by mowing areas of attractive flowers just before the seed is fully ripe and spreading this material along roadsides not too thickly covered with other vegetation.

For home gardens it is best to sow the seed of wild flowers in the fall in about 3-inch-deep boxes of soil, which are placed in glass and lath-covered cold frames. Seedling plants can be transplanted in the spring when they are about 3 or 4 inches tall.

SOME WILD FLOWERS have a marked preference for soils that are loamy or sandy, dry to damp or wet, acid to alkaline, and open to dense woodland conditions. When you collect your own seeds, these conditions of natural growth should be noted on your package.

Inexpensive soil-testing sets are available that give a list of soil preferences for 500 species of plants. In time, you should learn to tell the soil reaction from the plants growing there. Areas of pine, fir, spruce, hemlock, rhododendron, mountain laurel, and oak vary from slightly to strongly acid, depending on the decomposed leaves.

Some books on the cultivation of wild flowers list the soil preferences of many species.

A list follows of some of the more popular and attractive flowered species across the country. Some have been photographed on a glass slide ruled into square millimeters (a millimeter being approximately one twenty-fifth of an inch), so that one can determine the size of the seed before enlargement. Brief descriptions of some seeds not illustrated are given with common names when they exist in the standard manuals of botany. The photographs appear at the end of the first picture section.

Seeds of most wild flowers of the six geographic areas given below grow well in the average conditions of soil, light, and moisture of each area and habitat of each species, unless otherwise noted or given in catalogs and books on the subject.

NORTHEASTERN SPECIES

Meadow anemone (*Anemone canadensis*). The plants prefer damp thickets or meadows and in gardens should have partial shade. The seeds are thin, broadly oval, and about 4 x 4 mm. They have a curved beak as long as the seed.

Wild columbine (*Aquilegia canadensis*). The plants prefer wooded or open rocky areas. In some of its range, blossoms appear from spring to late fall. They do well in partly shaded gardens. The elliptic or pear-shaped seeds are glossy black and about 2 mm. long.

Butterfly-weed (*Asclepias tuberosa*). The seeds are thin, brown, pear shaped, and about 5 x 7 mm. long and have a tuft of about 20 mm. white hairs at the top for distribution by wind. The plants eventually develop a large, spindle-shaped root 2 to 3 feet deep in the ground.

Marshmarigold (*Caltha palustris*). A native of wet meadows, open woods, and swamps which in the garden must have similar conditions. In a small water garden the 1 x 2.5 mm., elliptic to pear-shaped, brown seeds should be planted a quarter of an inch deep in the wet margin, or in a pot that can be kept constantly wet until ready for transplanting.

Dwarf-cornel (*Cornus canadensis*). A cool mountain woods, acid soil plant that cannot be grown in gardens away from such areas. Seeds, ovoid, buff, about 2 x 3 mm. in a 5–6-mm. bright red fleshy fruit.

Pink ladyslipper (*Cypripedium acaule*). The seeds are 1.5–2 mm. long, straight or curved, colorless, and hairlike. They have no food supply, as most seeds do. They can be grown only in the laboratory in sterilized glass flasks on culture media. They are borne in ovoid, three-valved capsules about the size of a walnut and contain 30 thousand or more seeds. When ripe, the pods open along the valve edges, and the wind may carry the seeds considerable distances. Probably not 1 seed in 10 thousand falls on a suitable place to germinate. The plants require very acid soil and are almost impossible to grow in gardens.

Trailing-arbutus (*Epigaea repens*). The minute oval-oblong reddish-brown, finely pitted seeds are borne on a waxy receptacle about the size of a pea, enclosed in a membranous capsule that is covered with short, stiff, glandular hairs. The ripe capsule splits into five parts, which turn back to expose the seeds. Within a short time, a line of ants will be found carrying the waxy material, with the seeds, into their nests as food for their young, and it may be a long time before the seeds are returned to the surface.

Trout-lily (*Erythronium americanum*). The plants are found in moist to dry open woodlands. The seeds are pale brownish, pear shaped, and about 3 mm. long. The first year, the plants develop a small bulb with a small, narrow leaf. Each succeeding year to the seventh, when they flower, they develop larger and deeper rooting bulbs with larger leaves. *E. hartwegii* and several similar species found in the Rocky Mountains, the Cascades, and Sierras are difficult to establish in the East. Some of them have flowered from seeds in 2 years.

Wintergreen (*Gaultheria procumbens*). Seeds are somewhat pear shaped, reddish brown, and about 1 mm. long. The plants may be grown in an acid soil that is rich in humus.

Closed gentian (*Gentiana andrewsii*). The seeds differ markedly from the next species in that they have thin, oval seeds about 1 mm. long, surrounded by a whitish 1 x 2 mm. wing. It is the easiest gentian to grow, but it prefers a damp soil.

Fringed gentian (*Gentiana crinita*). The 0.5–0.7 mm. oblong, angular-tubercled seeds ripen in capsules the latter half of October. They should be sown at once in a damp, low meadow. They cannot be grown in gardens. The seeds and flowers are similar to those of the Rocky Mountain *Gentiana elegans*.

Wild geranium (*Geranium maculatum*). The dark, ovoid seeds, 2–2.5 x 4 mm., are borne on the lower end of stiff, strap-shaped fruit segments. When ripe, the straps curl up abruptly and may throw the seed several feet.

Beach pea (*Lathyrus maritimus*). The seeds are spherical, smooth, dark brown, and about 5 mm. in diameter. A sea beach plant, it has typical pea-like pods and can be grown only under natural conditions.

Tigerlily (*Lilium superbum*). The seeds are thin, brown, oval, about 5 mm. in diameter, and surrounded by a papery, triangular wing about 8 mm. wide. The plants eventually develop a scaly bulb, which in old plants may be 2 feet or more deep in the ground.

Cardinal flower (*Lobelia cardinalis*). A plant of low, wet ground and swamps. The ovoid to oblong, tubercled seeds, 0.7 mm. long, should be sown only in moist soil.

Oswego-tea (*Monarda didyma*). It prefers moist, open thickets and woods but does well in garden soil. The seeds are oval, light to dark brown, and about 1–1.5 x 2 mm. in size.

Rosebay (*Rhododendron maximum*) and related eastern and northwestern species, including azaleas, as well as most other plants of the Heath family, have small, slender seeds. For germination, fill a shallow pot with sandy wood's mold from under oak trees or laurel bushes, wet down, and allow to settle over night. Sow seeds thinly and cover with a thin layer of sphagnum moss rubbed through a 16-mesh sieve, cover with glass, and protect from direct sunlight.

Golden ragwort (*Senecio aureus*). Seeds are linear and about 3 mm. long. An equal tuft of hairs is at the top. This, the similar *S. smallii*, and several southern species are among the earliest flowers of the Composite family. It is well adapted to gardens, but most seed heads should be cut before they are ripe to prevent too much spreading.

Large - flowered trillium (*Trillium grandiflorum*). A plant of rich woods and thickets, it grows well in partly shaded gardens. The reddish-brown, ovoid, 2 x 3 mm. seeds have a conspicuous hilum (point of attachment) on the edge at one end. The plants bloom in 5 to 10 years.

Blue violet (*Viola papilionacea*). This is typical of several common, blue-flowered species that develop normal 1 x 2 mm. seeds in a two-valved capsule; other seeds come from inconspicuous, nonopening flowers and ripen at the base of the stems.

The birdsfoot violet (*Viola pedata*) requires dry, acid soil and is difficult to establish in gardens.

Southeastern Species

Yellow jessamine (*Gelsemium sempervirens*). An attractive, yellow-flowered vine with an oval 4 x 5 mm. seed at one end of a 4 x 10 mm. membranous wing for wind dispersal.

Purple gerardia (*Gerardia purpurea*). The seeds are pear shaped or irregularly angular, 1.3 mm. long, and dark brown and are in an ovoid, pointed, 2-celled capsule up to 7 mm. long. The plants are parasitic on grass roots.

Puccoon (*Lithospermum canescens*). The seeds are turnip shaped, pale, glossy, 2 x 3 mm. and have a short, conic hilum at the top.

Passionflower (*Passiflora incarnata*). This is an attractive, purple-flowered vine, whose flower parts bear a fancied resemblance to a cross and crown. The seeds are about 4 x 6 mm., dark brown, ovoid, and netted veined.

Scorpionweed (*Phacelia bipinnatifida*). The plants grow in rich, open woodlands and require partially shaded garden conditions. The seeds are dark, wedge shaped to angular, and about 2 x 3 mm. in size.

Meadowbeauty (*Rhexia mariana*). It prefers damp and sandy to peaty areas.

The seeds are pear shaped and about 0.3 mm. long.

Rosepink (*Sabatia angularis*). The plants grow in open woods and fields. The seeds are oval-oblong, pitted, and 0.4–0.7 mm. long.

Firepink (*Silene virginica*). The plants grow in open woods, thickets, and dry rocky or sandy slopes. The seeds are globular, 1.3 mm. in diameter, and finely tubercled.

Goatsrue (*Tephrosia virginiana*). These are plants of dry, acid soil. The 2 x 4 mm., buff-colored seeds have a conspicuous hilum at the middle of one edge.

Aarons-rod (*Thermopsis caroliniana*). These plants of wooded mountain areas grow well in gardens. The seeds are buff, ovoid, and 2 x 4 mm. in size. They have a conspicuous hilum on the edge near one end.

Prairie and Plains Species

The prairie and plains area is characterized by a deficiency of rainfall, increasing progressively towards the west and south. Most plants of this area are not well adapted to eastern and far western conditions, but some of them can occasionally be induced to grow in other areas, notably in rock gardens, if one provides sandy and gravelly conditions.

In the southwestern plains and often in adjoining desert areas of low annual rainfall, one may occasionally see miles of a 3-foot-wide hedge of a single weedy species, like sweetclover, along paved highways, often accompanied in the background by many plants of less weedy species. This growth may occur a short time after a sudden, heavy downpour and is caused by the heavy runoff from the paved road.

Farther away from paved roads in these areas, unusual heavy rainfall, such as happens once in 5 to 10 years or longer, will produce an almost unbelievable riot of color, in which flowers of the Composite family often predominate. This will give a good idea of what one might do experimentally

with seeds of wild flowers of the area
by following a dry spell with brief but
copious watering.

Sandverbena (*Abronia fragrans*).
Seeds are about 3 x 7 mm. in size and
tapering; the sides are fluted and
reticulate veined.

Pasqueflower (*Anemone pulsatilla* var.
wolfgangiana). The seeds are slender,
about 4 mm. long, silky, and sharp
pointed at the base. They are borne at
the base of a 30-mm., short, feathery
awn.

Poppy-mallow (*Callirhoe involucrata*).
The seeds are semicircular, wedge
shaped, about 4 mm. long, and thinner
at the side of attachment. The surface
often is reticulated.

Indian paintbrush (*Castilleja lindheimeri*). The seeds are brownish, pear
shaped, about 1.5 mm. long, and
netted veined. The many species across
the country are parasitic on roots of
grass or shrubs.

Purple cactus (*Coryphantha vivipara*).
The ovoid seeds are reddish brown,
minutely pitted, about 1 x 2 mm., and
borne in green, fleshy receptacles.

Plains-gentian (*Eustoma russelliana*).
The seeds are oval, about 0.2 mm.
long, and finely pitted.

Bindweed-heliotrope (*Euploca con-
volvulaca*). The buff, spherical, two-
parted seeds are about 2 mm. in
diameter.

Bluebonnet (*Lupinus texensis*). The
seeds are buff to grayish, quadrangu-
lar, and about 5 x 6 mm. in size.

Blazing-star (*Mentzelia decapetala*).
The seeds are thin, oval, and about 3
mm. long. They have a narrow wing.

Wild four-o'clock (*Mirabilis nycta-
ginea*). The buff, oblong, pear-shaped
seeds, about 2 x 5 mm. in size, are
covered with short, stiff, spreading
hair.

Fern-leaf evening-primrose (*Oenothera laciniata*). The seeds are light
brown, pear shaped, and about 1.3
mm. long.

Pricklypear (*Opuntia polyacantha*).
The pale, oval seeds are about 5 mm.
in diameter and have a depressed
center and margin.

Large-flowered beardtongue (*Penstemon grandiflorus*). The seeds are buff,
oblong-angular, pitted, and about 2 x
3 mm. in size. This species has pink,
40-mm. flowers and is one of the largest flowered and more easily grown
over a wider area than most of the 250
American species. The few eastern species are mostly white to pale pink or
bluish. In the southwestern plains and
desert area, several are bright red.
Most of the others are of a purple
color. Some at high altitudes are deep
blue or tend to become pale when cultivated at low altitudes.

Texas-sage (*Salvia coccinea*). The
seeds are oblong, angular or bowed,
and about 2 x 3 mm. in size.

ROCKY MOUNTAIN SPECIES

Sego-lily (*Calochortus nuttallii*). The
seeds are oval, about 3 mm. long, and
surrounded by a transparent coat, 1
mm. wide.

Sulphurflower (*Eriogonum umbellatum*). The seeds are dark or light,
spindle shaped, angular, and 1 x 4 mm.
in size.

Skyrocket (*Gilia aggregata*). The seeds
are buff and oblong-angular or bowed
and 1 x 4 mm. in size.

Panicled bluebell (*Mertensia paniculata*). Similar far-western species are
plants of rich, damp, open woods but
also grow well from seeds in partially
shaded gardens if kept well watered
until seedlings are established. The
oblong-angular seeds, about 3 x 5 mm.,
of the eastern *M. virginica* produce a
carrotlike root 1 to 2 inches long, and
do not flower until the second year.

Stemless locoweed (*Oxytropis lamberti*). This and several related purplish
species are found from mountain slopes
to the plains and prairies. The seeds
are dark brown, about 2 x 2 mm., and
notched on the hilum edge.

Shrubby cinquefoil (*Potentilla fruti-
cosa*). One of the species that is found
in many places from East to West and
in some Eurasian countries in both
wet and dry-rock areas. It will grow
in average garden soil. The seeds are

pear shaped, brown, and about 0.5 x 1 mm. in size.

Spiderwort (*Tradescantia scopulorum*). This and many other species prefer damp or wet places. Some, like the eastern *T. virginiana*, have been cultivated over a wide range and do well in partial shade and average garden soil. The seeds are ovate to oblong, light to dark brown, and about 2 x 3 mm. in size. The hilum is depressed and transversally ridged around the seed.

Globe-flower (*Trollius laxus*). It and the smaller white-flowered western marshmarigold (*Caltha rotundifolia*) prefer wet mountain meadows. The flowers are creamy to bluish tinted. The seeds are oval, dark brown, and about 0.5 x 2 mm.

SOUTHWESTERN SPECIES

Century-plant (*Agave americana*). The seeds are thin, black, pear shaped, and about 7 mm. in diameter.

Pricklepoppy (*Argemone mexicana*). The seeds are brown, nearly spherical, 2 x 2 mm. in size, and reticulate; they have a small, obtuse, projecting hilum.

Barrel cactus (*Ferocactus wislizeni*). The seeds are in a small, fleshy receptacle; are black, pear shaped, 1.5–2 mm. in size; and have a slight projecting hilum.

Blanketflower (*Gaillardia pulchella*). The dark, turnip-shaped seeds are 2–2.5 mm. long and have a fringe of 1.5-mm. stiff hairs at the base and top, surrounded by a membranous collar that has bristly teeth.

Small-flowered gaura (*Gaura parviflora*). The seeds are buff, 2.5 x 7 mm. in size, smooth, four angled, and tapering at both ends.

Pincushion cactus (*Mammillaria hemisphaerica*). The oval or pear-shaped, tubercled seeds are about 1 mm. long.

Fishhook cactus (*Thelocactus uncinatus*). The seeds are black, spherical to ovoid, and about 1 mm. long.

Spanish-bayonet (*Yucca baccata*). The black, pear-shaped seeds are about 11 mm. long.

PACIFIC STATES

Firecracker plant (*Brodiaea ida-maia*). The seeds are black, oblong, and angular and 2 x 4 mm. in size.

Tall clarkia (*Clarkia pulchella*). The plants are annuals. The pear-shaped to oblong, dark-brown seeds are about 1 x 1.5 mm. in size.

Springbeauty (*Claytonia linearis*). The seeds are glossy black and disk shaped and about 2 mm. in diameter. The very similar appearing eastern *C. virginica* and various other species develop a small bulb 4 to 6 inches deep at the end of a slender, fragile stalk.

Chinese-houses (*Collinsia bicolor*). The plants are annuals and prefer a partly shady situation. The seeds are ovoid and brownish and about 1 x 2 mm. in size. They are hollowed from one side.

Wallflower (*Erysimum asperum*). The seeds are cylindric, pale reddish-brown, about 1 x 1.5–2 mm. in size, often swollen or slightly winged at one end, and borne in a long, four-sided pod.

California-poppy (*Eschscholtzia california*). The plants are annuals. The dark-brown, subspherical seeds, about 1.5 x 2 mm., are finely roughened.

Summer's-darling (*Godetia amoena*). The plants are annuals. The seeds are brown, ovoid to pear shaped, and about 1.3 mm. long.

Baby-blue-eyes (*Nemophila insignis*). The seeds are ovoid to oblong, pale brown, about 1 x 2 mm., and coarsely roughened. The plants are annuals.

Owlclover (*Orthocarpus purpurascens*). The seeds are narrowly elliptic, about 1 mm. long, and surrounded by a slightly larger roughened membrane. The plant is parasitic on grass roots.

Prostrate verbena (*Verbena prostrata*). The seeds are linear-oblong, light to dark brown, about 1 x 2 mm., and transversely and longitudinally ridged.

P. L. RICKER *retired in 1948 after many years of service as a botanist in the Crops Research Division, Agricultural Research Service. As president of the Wild Flower Preservation Society, he is widely known as a leader in the conservation of wild plants.*

THE

PROCESSING

OF SEEDS

฿฿฿฿฿฿฿฿฿฿฿฿฿฿฿฿฿฿฿฿฿฿฿฿฿฿฿฿฿฿฿฿฿฿฿฿฿฿

Why and How

Seeds Are Dried

N. ROBERT BRANDENBURG,
JOSEPH W. SIMONS, AND LLOYD L. SMITH

HIGH MOISTURE in seeds during storage is one of the chief reasons that they lose their ability to germinate.

The moisture affects the respiration rate of seeds and the micro-organisms that at moisture levels above 20 percent may produce heat rapidly enough to kill seed or start fires in a seed mass. Some seeds suffer mechanical damage in handling and processing if their moisture content is too high.

Molds tend to grow in moist lots of seed, particularly when the seed is cracked or damaged and they can enter and grow even more easily. Insect damage also is related to seed moisture, but most of the weevils and insects cannot breed properly at levels below about 8 percent and tend to die out. When fumigation is used to control insects, the danger of seed injury is increased by high levels of moisture in the seed. Finally, damp seeds tend to stick together and interfere with proper feeding and operating of processing equipment.

Seeds therefore must be dried if their processing and storage are to be satisfactory. People always have dried seeds—in former times by the heat of the sun and now by artificial means, as well.

Drying basically is simply the evaporation of moisture.

Every liquid at a given temperature has a definite vapor pressure, which tends to produce vaporization. The moisture in a seed exhibits such a pressure. Water vapor in the atmosphere exerts a similar pressure.

The drying of seeds can take place only when vapor pressure of the seed moisture is greater than the resisting vapor pressure of surrounding air. The rate of drying drops as the differential of vapor pressure lessens. Drying will stop when a balance is reached between the vapor pressures. The seed moisture at this point is called the equilibrium moisture content of the seed at that atmospheric condition.

Moisture to be removed in drying is associated with the seeds in two main ways.

Surface moisture occurs on the outer surface, and the air readily absorbs it under proper conditions.

Internal moisture is distributed throughout the inner parts of the seed. Its removal involves capillary action or diffusion of the moisture to the surface, where evaporation can take place.

The many ways of drying seeds can be classed as natural or artificial.

Natural drying takes place with typical atmospheric air moving naturally around damp seed spread on trays, canvas, floors, or fields.

Artificial drying uses heated or unheated air that is forced mechanically through a drier.

All drying operations involve some movement of air through the seed. In normal vaporization, each seed tends to become surrounded by a film of saturated vapor, which obstructs heat transfer and limits the evaporation of moisture. Air movement, if nothing more than a gentle breeze, is needed to replace this wetted air continuously with drier air so the drying process can go on.

ARTIFICIAL DRYING can be done with heated or unheated air, dehumidified air, or a partial vacuum. In each, the particular air condition facilitates drying when used in conjunction with a movement of forced air through the seed. Heating air raises its saturation point and creates a thirsty medium that absorbs moisture readily.

An example: Air at 65° F., which contains 46 grains of water vapor per pound of dry air, represents a condition called 50 percent relative humid-

ity, because the air is holding 50 percent of the maximum water vapor it can hold (92 grains) at that temperature. If the same air is raised in temperature to 95°, its moisture-holding capacity increases greatly, and the resulting relative humidity is only 19 percent. This characteristic of air is important in drying, because the moisture content of a seed varies according to the relative humidity of the air.

The use of heated air assists drying also by heating the seed and thereby its contained moisture. The resulting rise in temperature stimulates the diffusion of internal moisture to the surface and increases vapor pressure of the liquid, thus encouraging vaporization.

Another form of artificial drying employs air that is dehumidified chemically or by refrigeration. Dehumidified, or dried, air can dry seed readily because some of the water vapor has been removed from it and its moisture-absorbing tendency thereby is increased.

Actually, since vapor pressure of the atmosphere decreases with a drop in its moisture content, the vapor pressure of liquid to be removed becomes more effective in causing evaporation. The use of dehumidified air is especially helpful when seed is to be dried to a relatively low content of moisture.

Certain chemicals that have a strong affinity for moisture are used to dry air in dehumidifying systems. Silica gel, for example, can pick up moisture from air in amounts up to 30 percent of its dry weight. When it will hold no more moisture, it can be reactivated for further use by drying at 250°–350°.

Other common drying agents are calcium chloride, activated alumina, and anhydrous calcium sulfate.

An alternate method of dehumidifying air is to employ refrigeration to drop air temperature below its dewpoint—where moisture begins to condense. This will reduce the moisture-holding capacity of the air and remove surplus vapor, which can then be withdrawn from the system.

Vacuum drying is another way to remove moisture from seeds. It, like dehumidified air, usually is used in special situations where seeds must be dried to a very low moisture content.

Vacuum drying is somewhat like drying with dehumidified air in that the vapor pressure of the surrounding atmosphere is reduced so seed moisture can vaporize more readily. When the total pressure in a vacuum-drying chamber is lowered, the component of this pressure due to vapor is reduced proportionately. In vacuum drying, the heat for evaporation must be supplied mainly by conduction or radiation, since there is little air available for heat transfer by convection.

In drying by infrared heat, the seed, rather than the air, receives special attention. Radiant heat rays from infrared lamps will pass through air without warming it and be absorbed by the seed. The result is an increased temperature of seeds, which hastens movement of internal and surface moisture to the surrounding air. A feature of this method is its speed, especially when seeds are dried in a thin layer.

Artificial drying has advantages. It permits earlier harvest and reduces chance of loss from bad weather.

Early harvest and artificial drying usually provide larger yields of seed with fewer losses from overripening and shattering. Early harvest also tends to lower damage from insects and birds. Despite morning dews, harvesting can begin earlier in the day. Artificial drying means less worry—because natural drying is not dependable every year—and cuts labor costs and seed damage.

Artificial drying also has limitations in time, which reflect such considerations as mold growth in moist seed, possible drop in vigor of seeds, casehardening of seeds, and seed damage. All these conditions depend on time, temperatures, and moisture levels during the drying.

Molds are most active in atmospheres of high relative humidity and at temperatures of 80°–100°. Even when suitable drying conditions reduce the moisture to about 15 percent, mold can still grow in some lots of seed. At that level also, seed respiration may be active, so that vigor and ability to germinate may decline.

A short drying period tends to combat molds and drop in vigor, but too fast drying has its dangers. During rapid drying, the seedcoats of some seeds will shrink or split and become impermeable to moisture, even though inner portions of the seed remain wet. This condition, called casehardening, can prevent complete drying, produce hard seed, and allow disease organisms to enter easily.

High temperatures in fast drying may injure seed that is moist. Free surface moisture can be removed safely at high temperatures, because rapid evaporation extracts heat from the seeds fast enough to keep the actual temperature of seeds depressed to the wet bulb temperature of the drying air. As the moisture of the seeds drops to 30 percent or lower, however, the supply of moisture for evaporation is less readily available and actual seed temperature will increase. High temperatures can injure seeds in this moisture range; for safety, temperatures of drying air should not exceed 90°–110°.

So, with regard to safe drying time, it is important to find the proper balance between too rapid drying (with resulting casehardening or seed injury) and too slow drying (with deterioration of the seed).

THE TOTAL DRYING time for any seed is influenced by its initial and final moisture content, its drying rate, the rate of airflow, and the temperature of the drying air.

The higher the moisture level, the greater the time needed to reach the desired dry condition. The drying rate of seed also affects this time for drying. Most seeds have a fast drying rate at high contents of moisture, but have an increasingly lower rate as they approach the final, desired moisture con-

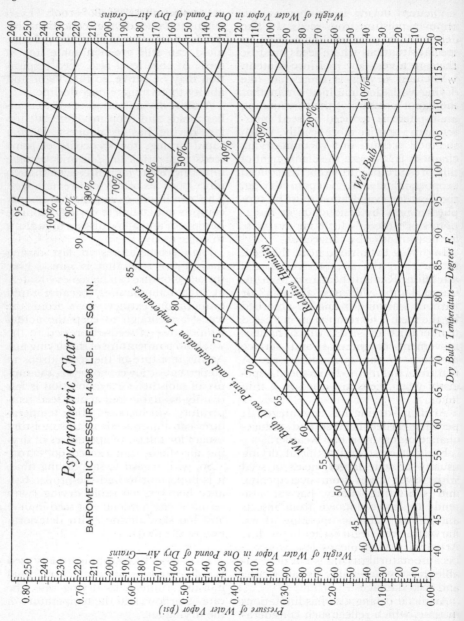

tent. Considerable time may be required to remove the last 1 percent of moisture.

The final moisture content for safe storage of seed is 4 percent to 14 percent, depending on the kind of seed, the type of storage, and the anticipated storage period. Lower moisture levels generally are desirable for longer storage times and confined storage conditions.

Airflow rate, too, can influence drying time. If an extremely low airflow rate is used, the drying air can become saturated before completing its passage through the seed, and no further drying with that air can occur. Drying then is limited by the airflow rate through the seeds, and greater airflow will lower the drying time.

On the other hand, as airflow increases, a point is reached at which the air is absorbing all the moisture that is made available to it. Beyond that point, additional airflow does not reduce drying time, because rates at which moisture diffuses from the inner parts of the seed to the surface are the main controlling factors.

A rule of thumb that can be used to determine drying time is that about 0.3 percent of the moisture can be removed per hour with an airflow rate of 5 c.f.m./bu.—cubic feet per minute per bushel—at 110°. This drying rate varies with different seed, temperature, and the initial moisture. The hourly rate will be less if the initial moisture content is low and if the drying air is unheated or at temperatures below 110°.

Recommended minimum airflow rates for drying seed with unheated air under average conditions are: For seed with 25 percent moisture, 8 c.f.m./bu.; 22 percent moisture, 6.5 c.f.m./bu.; 18 percent moisture, 4.5 c.f.m./bu.; and 15 percent moisture, 3 c.f.m./bu. Generally, airflow rates greater than 8 c.f.m./bu. are not economical with unheated air because more power is required at the higher rates and no appreciable increase in drying rate can be obtained.

When seed is dried with heated air in bin-type barn driers, the airflow rate for light seed should be at least 3 c.f.m./bu. and at least 5 c.f.m./bu. for heavy seed. Uneven drying between bottom and top of the batch will be minimized if the seed depth in the bin is not excessive.

Most commercial driers use greater airflow rates and heated air. Rates usually vary between 20 and 40 c.f.m./bu. A uniform drying of seed is possible with those rates and the seed depths often used in commercial units.

MAXIMUM RECOMMENDED DEPTHS IN FEET FOR DRYING VARIOUS SEED AT DIFFERENT INITIAL MOISTURE CONTENTS (WITH UNHEATED AIR)

Seed	Moisture content			
	25	22	18	15
Crimson clover...	2	2.5	3	4
Fescue..........	3	3.5	4.5	5.5
Grain sorghum...	4	5	6	7
Lespedeza, Kobe..	4	4.5	5	6
Lespedeza, Sericea.	2	2.25	2.5	3
Lupine..........	7	8	9	10
Oats............	4.5	5	6.5	8
Rescuegrass......	7	8	9	10
Soybeans........	7	8	9	10
Wheat..........	3.5	4	5	7

THE DEPTH of seed and the resulting static pressure—resistance to airflow through seed—alters the power needed to produce a given airflow rate in bin-type driers. All seed offers some resistance to airflow according to its size, shape, moisture content, and weight.

To illustrate: One foot of seed of alfalfa or sericea lespedeza in a bin offers a resistance to airflow of about 0.66 inch of water (static pressure) at 5 c.f.m./bu., but 4 feet of soybeans or shelled corn have the same static pressure. Another example: Shelled corn at that airflow rate exhibits a static pressure of 0.35 inch of water for a depth of 2 feet and 3.37 inches of water for a depth of 8 feet.

Static pressures also vary with the airflow. Shelled corn, again, has a static pressure of 0.35 inch of water for a depth of 2 feet at 5 c.f.m./bu., but the same depth at 20 c.f.m./bu. has a static pressure of 1.01 inches of water, or nearly three times as much.

Static pressures have less importance in commercial continuous-column or tower-type driers. Usually the seed depth that air must penetrate is only 6 to 16 inches in this type of drier. Also, the total air delivery of a commercial drier cannot be changed in many instances. About the only variation in the rate of airflow is the one due to small differences in static pressures of various seed types.

STATIC PRESSURES ENCOUNTERED AND ESTIMATED QUANTITIES OF SEED THAT CAN BE DRIED

Seed	Air rate per bushel c.f.m.	Seed depths ft.	Static pressure [1] in. water	Maximum quantity that can be dried per fan horsepower [2] bushels
Alfalfa.....	5	1	0.66	960
		2	1.93	330
	10	1	1.09	290
		2	3.75	80
Blue lupine.	5	2	.32	1,990
		3	.41	1,550
		4	.56	1,140
		6	1.15	550
		8	2.25	275
	10	1	.29	1,100
		2	.42	760
		3	.74	430
		4	1.10	270
		6	2.83	110
		8	3.65	85
	20	1	.35	470
		2	.75	210
		3	1.60	100
		4	3.05	50
Clover, crimson...	5	1	.52	1,225
		2	1.39	460
		3	2.95	220
	10	1	.82	390
		2	2.65	120
Fescue, Kentucky 31..	5	1	.37	1,720
		2	.77	830
		3	1.51	420
		4	2.45	260
	10	1	.51	625
		2	1.35	240
		3	3.04	100
	20	1	.80	200
		2	3.05	50
Kobe lespedeza.....	5	1	.33	1,930
		2	.59	1,080
	5	3	1.06	600
		4	1.81	350
		6	4.03	160
	10	1	.42	760
		2	1.00	320
		3	2.14	150
		4	3.93	80
	20	1	.62	260
		2	2.09	75
Oats.......	5	2	.47	1,350
		3	.82	780
		4	1.29	490
		6	3.01	210
	10	1	.36	880
		2	.77	410
		3	1.63	200
		4	3.05	100
Oats—Con.	20	1	0.51	310
		2	1.65	100
Rescuegrass.	5	2	.33	1,930
		3	.46	1,380
		4	.65	980
		6	1.21	525
		8	2.25	280
	10	1	.29	1,100
		2	.44	720
		3	.73	430
		4	1.25	250
		6	3.01	100
	20	1	.34	470
		2	.75	200
		3	1.63	100
		4	3.05	50
Sericea lespedeza.....	5	1	.66	960
		2	1.93	330
	10	1	1.09	290
		2	3.75	80
	20	1	2.00	80
Shelled corn.	5	2	.35	1,820
		3	.52	1,225
		4	.77	825
		6	1.63	390
		8	3.37	190
	10	1	.30	1,060
		2	.51	625
		3	.97	330
		4	1.73	185
		5	2.85	110
	20	1	.38	420
		2	1.01	160
		3	2.41	65
Soybeans...	5	2	.33	1,930
		3	.43	1,480
		4	.62	1,025
		6	1.25	510
		8	2.33	270
	10	1	.29	1,100
		2	.44	720
		3	.70	450
		4	1.29	250
		6	3.19	100
	20	1	.35	470
		2	.77	200
		3	1.72	90
		4	3.25	50
Wheat......	5	1	.33	1,930
		2	.59	1,080
		3	1.06	600
		4	1.85	340
	10	1	.42	760
		2	1.05	300
		3	2.11	150
	20	1	.65	240
		2	2.25	70

[1] Static pressure includes 0.25 in. allowance for loss from duct friction.

[2] Airflow (c.f.m.) per horsepower based on formula

$$c.f.m. = \frac{\text{Static efficiency}}{0.000157 \times \text{static pressure}}$$

with static efficiency in this case assumed at 50 percent.

LITTLE CAN be done about temperature when seed is dried with natural or unheated air. Relative humidity of the air therefore becomes a key point. The most economical drying with unheated air is accomplished when the atmospheric relative humidity is below 70 percent.

An example of the importance of relative humidity: If the drying air reaches 100 percent saturation during its passage through the seed, air at 80° and 40 percent relative humidity will have about twice the drying potential of air at 80° and 70 percent relative humidity.

Temperature, although not controlled, also can influence natural-air drying because the maximum moisture that air can hold depends on its temperature. Using the similar assumption as above that air becomes completely saturated, air at 80° and 50 percent relative humidity again will have about twice the drying potential of air at 60° and 50 percent relative humidity.

When heated air is used for drying seeds, the drying temperature usually should not exceed 110°. Some seeds, such as peanuts and certain vegetables, are dried at 90° to 100°. If the temperature sensitivity of a given type of seed is not known, it is wise to select the drying temperature according to the moisture level of the seed.

This schedule is safe for a number of field and vegetable seeds: 18 to 30 percent moisture content, 90°; 10 to 18, 100°; under 10 percent, 110°.

FORCING AIR in one direction only through the seed mass is practiced in nearly all drying with unheated air and in most drying with heated air.

Often much usable heat is lost in heated-air drying because the heated air travels through the seed mass once and is then exhausted to the atmosphere. This is particularly true in commercial driers, in which high rates of airflow are used to obtain fast drying and a uniform, final moisture content. Simple construction of the seed-holding bin and of the air distribution system is an advantage possible with this method of air handling.

Two-way or reverse-airflow drying is practiced by reversing the direction of air movement through the seed mass during part of the drying operation. It makes for a more uniform moisture in the seed mass, and high airflow rates are unnecessary. The drying time and operating costs are reduced slightly.

The chief disadvantage is that the fan must be detached, turned around, and reconnected, or extra ducts and tight construction must be provided at the top of the seedbin. An extensive practice in drying seed corn in the ear is to pass the same air successively through several bins. Drying efficiency is greater because better use is made of the heat.

BOTH HEATED and unheated air have advantages and disadvantages.

When one plans for drying facilities, he should determine first if atmospheric conditions in his locality permit satisfactory drying with unheated air. He can get this information from agricultural colleges.

If atmospheric conditions are satisfactory for unheated-air drying, the final choice will rest mainly on the amount of seed to be dried and the time available for drying.

Drying by heated air can be done regardless of weather, and the drying time is short, usually from a few hours to less than a day. A high drying capacity per fan horsepower may be obtained, because of the faster drying. Among the disadvantages are higher costs of equipment and maintenance, fuel expense, some fire hazard, and the need for close supervision.

Equipment and maintenance costs are lower when unheated air is used; there is no fuel expense and no fire hazard. Little supervision is required. Success, however, depends on weather conditions. The time required for drying usually is several days to several weeks, and more space is needed to dry the same amount of seed than with heated air.

SOME SEED is dried and stored in the same bin. It is common when drying is done with unheated air, but heated air sometimes is used.

Drying in storage is commonly called a batch-type operation, as the entire batch is dried without moving the seed. A simple bin with perforated floor can be used for supporting the seed in the bin. The perforated floor is elevated above the floor of the building to provide a fan or drier-outlet connection to the space between these floors. Air forced into this space flows upward through the perforated floor and the seed mass. The floor of the building and foundation walls of the bin must be reasonably airtight to prevent excessive loss of drying air. The perforated floor may be supported on concrete blocks, laid flat side up. One should allow one block for each 50 bushels of storage capacity.

A system of lateral ducts branching from the main or central duct often is used in place of a perforated floor. The ducts rest on the floor of the building, and the main duct is connected to the fan or drier. The duct systems usually are less expensive than the perforated floor with supports. Bins with perforated floors are somewhat easier to unload, although the ducts are made in lengths that can be easily removed as the bin is emptied. Factorymade metal ducts are available, or ducts may be built of lumber.

WHEN ATMOSPHERIC AIR is used for drying, a slight increase in air temperature can improve drying, especially during damp or cold weather.

The use of supplemental heat at times may mean the difference between success and failure in maintaining high quality of seeds.

Special units—supplemental heaters—are available. They are usually designed to provide a maximum rise in air temperature of 10°. They often have humidistats that shut them off when the relative humidity of air is below 60 or 70 percent. Many of the heaters burn liquefied petroleum or natural gas, weigh little, and are relatively inexpensive.

Solar heat sometimes is used to dry

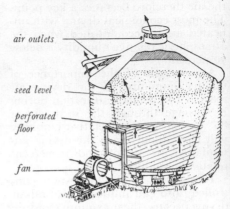

Drying in Bin with Unheated Air

seed. Fairly simple designs of solar collectors have been developed, but they need further study. The primary disadvantage of heat from the sun is that it is not available in large amounts during rainy weather, when it is most needed. Collected solar heat can be stored for limited periods, but the cost of storing it probably exceeds the cost of commonly used fuels.

In heated-air drying, the seed is usually dried in a special bin, chamber, column, or tower, and then transferred to other buildings for storage. Stationary batch-type facilities are used mainly on farms, but may be used in custom and commercial drying. Portable, rubber-tired units are available. They can be pulled by tractor or truck to different locations.

The continuous-type drier—generally a large, stationary unit—is used most commonly in commercial drying. In most of them, the seeds move downward by gravity during the drying process and are discharged at the bottom of the tower, where they are elevated into the storage or processing plant. Sometimes more than one pass through the drier is required to reduce the moisture content to the desired level. The continuous unit is often called a self-contained drier because it holds the seeds during drying and has the built-in features of heater, fan, con-

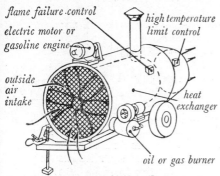

flame failure control

electric motor or gasoline engine

outside air intake

high temperature limit control

heat exchanger

oil or gas burner

Portable Indirect-fired Heating Unit for Drying Seeds

trols, and, often, elevating and unloading mechanisms.

Another drier type consists of a rotating drum, which lifts the seeds and drops them continuously through a heated air supply.

Fans used with unheated air must be designed to operate against the resistance encountered in forcing air through the seed mass. Suitable fans include the centrifugal, propeller, and axial types.

The horsepower requirements for operating seed-drying fans vary considerably. The power depends on the design and size of the fan, operating conditions, the amount of air delivered, kind and moisture of the seeds, and depth of seeds to be dried.

Only one control is essential in drying with unheated air—a switch to turn the fan on and off. Automatic operation of fans can be had at low cost by means of a humidistat, which permits the fan to operate only when the relative humidity is below a desired level. A relay usually is required with the humidistat.

Operating the fan during loading of the bin will help to blow out some of the chaff and other foreign matter and may help keep the seed cool.

The fan should be operated continuously for most seed (except during long rainy periods) until the moisture is down to about 17 percent (wet basis).

Exact humidistat settings to obtain greatest efficiency in drying seeds further to safe storage moisture content cannot be stated, because they vary with the temperature and kind of seed.

Generally, for summer drying, the humidistat must be set so that the fan will operate only when the relative humidity is below 70 percent. With the air temperature around 80°, this setting is needed to obtain reasonable efficiency in drying to 13 percent (wet basis). Drying to 11-percent moisture will require additional operation of the fan when the relative humidity is below 50 percent. This also applies to fall drying with temperatures no lower than 50° to 55°.

Drying is extremely slow at temperatures below 50°, and an even lower humidistat setting is required. The fan should be operated two or three times a day, at least 15 minutes each time, during long periods of rainy weather if the moisture in the seed exceeds 15 percent. This will help the seed cool and prevent overheating.

HEATERS for driers are direct fired or indirect fired.

In the direct-fired type, the combustion gases go directly from the burner into the drying airstream and thence into the drying bin. The efficiency in the use of the fuel can be more than 90 percent.

Direct-fired oil-burning heaters are somewhat less safe than the indirect-fired type, because the oil burner may release particles of hot soot if it is not properly adjusted. Most gas-fired driers are of the direct-heat type. Because particles of hot soot do not form with gas, the danger of fire is less.

The indirect-fired type has a heat exchanger with a smokestack. It is like a house furnace in operation. The efficiency of this type usually is not more than 65 or 70 percent, as some of

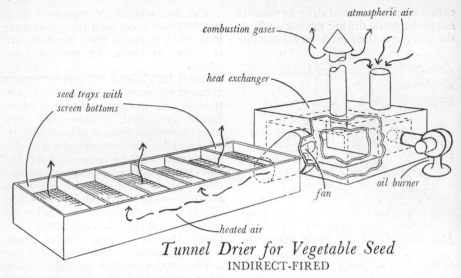

Tunnel Drier for Vegetable Seed
INDIRECT-FIRED

the heat escapes through the smoke-stack. Oil is the commonest fuel. Coal, coke, natural gas, and liquefied petroleum gas also are used.

Fan requirements for heated-air drying are about the same as for unheated air. The fan, when mounted in a drier, however, usually delivers less than the manufacturer's rating because of additional resistance encountered. Some allowance should be made for this added resistance in predicting the horsepower requirements for different situations and seeds.

DRIERS come in various sizes. The small farm driers burn 1 to 5 gallons of fuel oil an hour, or the equivalent in another kind of fuel. The larger units burn 10 to 15 gallons an hour. Commercial driers usually burn much more.

Farm driers generally have electric motors of 3, 5, or 7.5 horsepower and fan sizes to fit the motors. Fans also can be driven by gasoline engines or by tractors from the power takeoff or belt pulley.

The size of drier a farmer needs will depend mostly on how much seed he must dry in an hour, the kind of seed, the first and final content of moisture, and the season.

A burner capacity of about 1 gallon of oil an hour (or its equivalent in other fuels) should be figured for each 75 to 100 bushels of heavy seed in the bin. This will provide reasonably efficient operation at a drying air temperature of 110°. To get efficient operation in drying lighter seeds, proportionately larger batches are needed. One gallon an hour, for example, should be allowed for each 125–150 bushels of oats in drying at 110°.

The smallest driers on the market usually are rated at 3 horsepower.

Generally it is wise to have a drier larger than one estimates for several reasons. Drying small seeds requires considerably more power than large seeds for the same depth. Drying at the minimum recommended rate of airflow is slow; within limits, higher rates reduce the time of drying appreciably. The higher rates also result in a more uniform moisture content. At the minimum specified rate, a big difference between driest and wettest layers will occur, and much of the seed will be dried more than is necessary for safekeeping. The producer will

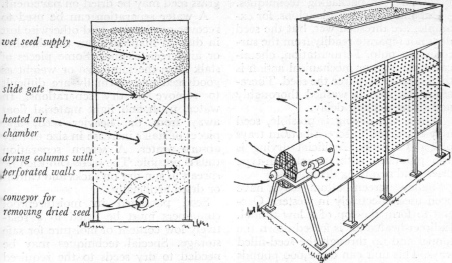

wet seed supply

slide gate

heated air
chamber

drying columns with
perforated walls

conveyor for
removing dried seed

Column Seed Drier Equipped with Direct-fired Heater

lose money in selling the overdried
seeds because of the extra loss in
weight.

The drier should be of a size that will
let it keep up with the rate of harvesting. Rather than install too large
a drier, however, a farmer may well
start harvesting a few days earlier, if
possible, and so spread harvesting over
a longer period.

The burner should be cut off when
drying is completed. The seed should
be cooled before it is stored by running
the fan at least one-half hour. A few
drying bins or units for holding the
seed during the drying process have
cooling sections, an arrangement that
loses no drying time in the cooling
process.

The requirements for a good heated-
air drier are:

It must be built substantially of
proper materials—for example, special
heat-resisting metals are needed in
combustion chambers to give long life.

It must be firesafe. Combustible materials should not be used where
temperatures exceed 165°. Combustion
chambers on direct-fired driers should
have air intakes covered with screen

of ½-inch mesh to keep out trash.
Direct-fired driers that burn oil or
coal should have a corrosion-resistant
screen of ¼-inch mesh or some other
device to keep burning particles out
of the drying bin. Complete control
of combustion and high temperature
is essential.

It must have an easily adjustable
heating unit to provide good regulation from 50 percent to 100 percent of
rated capacity.

It must deliver amounts of air for
each horsepower of the motor as follows: 3,000 c.f.m. at ½-inch static
pressure; 2,000 c.f.m. at 1-inch static
pressure; and 1,000 c.f.m. at 2-inch
static pressure.

It must operate under all ordinary
weather conditions.

It must have overload and low
voltage protection on electric motors.

Safety standards have been developed by the National Fire Protection
Association. Many insurance companies require that drying installations
meet these standards.

SPECIAL DRYING is needed for some
seeds because of unusual harvesting,

processing, or packaging techniques. Cucumbers and muskmelons, for example, are threshed wet, but the seed does not separate readily from the surrounding pulp. Fermentation, chemical treatment, or mechanical action is then used to help free the seed. Thereafter, the seed is washed thoroughly and dried without delay.

Where sun drying is possible, seed may be spread in screen-bottom trays placed on racks. Artificial drying is also practiced with various bin-type driers and revolving drum units.

Shallow screen-bottom trays have been used effectively in western Oregon to form the top of a low tunnel. Indirect-heated air is forced down the tunnel and up through the seed-filled trays. This unit can dry 2,000 pounds of cucumber seed in 6 to 8 hours. Seed of consistently high quality is produced, even though drying air temperatures are relatively high—125°–130°—while free-surface moisture is present on the seed and 100°–120° during the rest of the drying process. Usual recommendations place 100° as the maximum safe temperature while cucumber seed is wet and 110° as the seed becomes drier.

The seeds of watermelon, pumpkin, tomato, and other fruits also require washing in their processing and are later dried like cucumber seed.

WATER can be helpful at times in processing seeds that normally are handled dry. Honeydew, secreted by aphids, sometimes coats seeds, like red clover or alsike clover, and causes them to stick together. Washing with water tends to remove the honeydew; afterwards the seed must be dried. If weather permits, the seed can be spread to dry on large, paved areas, like unused airport runways or roads. Occasional raking or agitating assists drying.

This large-area method is also practiced for many grasses that need drying after harvest. Seed of bluegrass is dried on flat roofs of buildings. Reed canarygrass is spread on dry lakebeds. Rye-grass seed may be dried on pavement.

A water separation can be used to recover good onion seed otherwise lost in discard material from the thresher or air-screen cleaner. Some pieces of stalk have the same size or weight as good seed and normally are difficult to remove in dry separations. In water, trash and light material float away from the heavier seed, and pieces of stalks increase in size as they absorb water. A screen separation thus is possible. The seeds can then be spread to sun-dry on racks and canvas or dried artificially.

Seed packaged in moistureproof containers must be dried to a relatively low content of moisture for safe storage. Special techniques may be needed to dry seeds to the required moisture levels (about 4 percent to 8 percent, depending on the seed) without using damaging temperatures. Recirculation of dehumidified air through bins is practiced successfully for this purpose with some vegetable and flower seed.

THERE ARE many ways of drying harvested seeds, but all are aimed at one goal—to help provide seeds that grow vigorously when planted. Drying, whether natural or artificial, must lower the moisture content of seeds so that, through efficient storage, good seeds are available for their important place in agriculture.

N. ROBERT BRANDENBURG *is an agricultural engineer in the Harvesting and Farm Processing Research Branch, Agricultural Engineering Research Division, Agricultural Research Service. He is stationed at Oregon State College in Corvallis.*

JOSEPH W. SIMONS *is principal agricultural engineer, Livestock Engineering and Farm Structures Research Branch in the same Division. He is stationed at the University of Georgia in Athens.*

LLOYD L. SMITH *is an agricultural engineer, Transportation and Facilities Research Division, Agricultural Marketing Service. He is stationed at the University of Georgia.*

Equipment for Cleaning Seeds

LEONARD M. KLEIN, JAMES HENDERSON, AND ABRAHAM D. STOESZ

SEED as it comes from a field is never pure. Mixed with it are seeds of weeds and other plants. They have to be separated after harvest so as to get pure, live crop seeds for replanting.

Seed from each crop is basically different in physical makeup from the others and can be identified easily. The differences—in size, shape, weight, surface area, specific gravity, color, electrical properties, texture, stickiness, and pubescence—can be measured or sensed by mechanical devices, called separators, which cull unwanted seeds from wanted ones on the basis of one or more of those physical differences.

Seed separators also remove dirt, leaves, stems, and chaff. Cleaning reduces the bulk to be handled and stored and removes moist material that may cause heating in storage. All seed crops, whether of grasses, legumes, grains, vegetables, flowers, fibers, trees, and shrubs, require some cleaning.

In the usual sequence through a processing plant, seeds first go through a precleaning operation. It may include scalping, the removal of material coarse enough to be easily separated by screens; hulling, a completion of the field threshing operation; and scarifying, the scratching of hard-coated seed so that moisture can enter it when it is planted. The processing of seeds of native grasses and other seeds that have awns and appendages usually requires additional precleaning to remove awns and beards.

The seed is then processed on an air-screen cleaner, in which the bulk of the foreign material is removed by screens and air.

The final separation is made on one or more finishing machines, which generally separate only one type of contaminating seed from the desired clean product.

Specific gravity separators will divide seeds according to their weight and size.

Indent disk and cylinder separators will remove long seeds from short ones.

Pneumatic and aspirator separators will separate seeds that present a different resistance to airflow.

Velvet roll separators remove smooth seeds from rough seeds.

Spiral, inclined draper, timothy bumper mill, vibrator, and horizontal disk separators divide seeds according to their shape.

Electronic separators sense a difference in the electrical properties of seeds.

Magnetic separators and the buckhorn machine separate rough or sticky-surfaced seeds from smooth seeds.

Color separators divide the light-colored seed from the dark ones.

SEEDS FROM a thresher or combine brought to a cleaning plant may contain a great deal of trash, green leaves, green weed seeds, and insects. Because of the moisture in the leaves and weed seeds, the seeds cannot be safely stored, or efficiently handled, or accurately cleaned until most of the foreign material has been removed. Many seed-cleaning plants therefore separate the foreign material immediately with a machine called a scalper.

Scalpers are of many types. One consists of a reel of perforated metal screen, which is inclined slightly and turns on a central shaft. Seeds fed into the higher end tumble inside the reel until they drop through the perforations, but longer and larger trash continues through the reel and is discharged separately. Another type of scalper makes the same type of separation with a single, flat, perforated screen, which is mechanically shaken.

The two types are simple devices

intended to remove only large trash. Because some seeds are mixed with small weed seeds as well as large trash, many seedsmen prefer a more complete precleaner to a simple scalper. It is a simple air-screen seed cleaner that makes a separation of light chaff and dust with a controlled air current, a separation of large trash over a large-hole screen, and a separation of small foreign material through a small-hole screen. Most scalpers are arranged to make the air separation before the seeds reach the screens.

Scalping, or rough cleaning, has certain advantages: The mechanical handling is facilitated. Subsequent seed flow is more even. The time required for artificial or natural drying is reduced. Succeeding machines can have a higher capacity.

After scalping, many kinds of seeds can be cleaned without any further preprocessing, but others may require hulling or scarifying.

Hulling is the removal of an outer coat or husk.

Scarification is scratching the seed-coat.

The hulls of some seeds are impermeable to water, and the seeds will not germinate promptly unless the outer coat or husk is removed before the seed is planted. Some legume seeds are hard and must be hulled or scarified if they are to absorb water and sprout promptly and evenly.

Hullers and scarifiers usually abrade the seeds between two rubber-faced surfaces or impel seeds against roughened surfaces, such as sandpaper. The severity of the abrasion or impact must be controlled accurately to prevent damage.

Seeds of a high moisture content are harder to hull or scarify than seeds with less moisture. Because a huller or scarifier adjusted for moist seeds may damage dry seeds, the moisture content usually is determined before hulling or scarifying and the necessary adjustments are made.

Some kinds of seeds that maintain viability for long periods after being hulled and scarified can be processed immediately after harvest and stored until the following season. Others that lose viability quickly can be hulled and scarified shortly before planting time. Hulling and scarification may be performed separately or jointly, depending on the presence of unhulled or hard seed or both.

Some seeds that may require hulling are bermudagrass, bahiagrass, buffalograss, and Korean, Kobe, common, and bicolor lespedeza.

Some seeds that may require scarification are wild winter peas, hairy indigo, alfalfa, crotalaria, subclover, and suckling clover.

Some seeds that may require both hulling and scarification are sweetclover, sericea lespedeza, crownvetch, black medic, and sourclover.

Many native grasses, small grains, and other plants produce seed units that have awns, beards, hairs, glumes, and other appendages, which make them difficult to handle in processing and planting operations because they tend to interlock and cause undesirable clustering. They can be removed by a precleaning treatment, which improves their flow properties, cleaning characteristics, and quality of the seeds.

Especially troublesome awned grasses are species of *Stipa*, or the needlegrasses, and species of *Elymus*, or wildrye. In other grasses, like the bluestems and gramas, hairy appendages make the seeds fluffy and bulky.

After scalping to remove excess straw and trash, several mechanical actions may be employed to remove awns and appendages. These include a high-speed thresher, the hammermill, a debearding machine, and a tumbling pebble mill. All employ a vigorous abrading action and must be operated carefully to insure little damage to seed and maximum removal of awns.

High-speed threshing or rethreshing of the seed to remove awns without too much seed damage is done by running the once-threshed seed material through the thresher or combine a second time at a high cylinder speed.

A concave setting of minimum clearance and a reduced airblast gives best results. Complete removal of awns by threshing is controlled by closing the seed pan screen so that only deawned seeds drop through into the seed auger. The tailings screen must be opened enough to allow the awned seeds to drop into the return auger and be rerun.

THE COMMONEST type of machine used successfully for deawning and debearding is the farm hammermill. The results depend on cylinder speed, size of the screen openings, rate of feed, and condition of the crop. The speed of the hammermill best suited for pretreating is about 50 percent of that used in normal grinding operations—600 to 1,400 revolutions a minute. Long, thin seeds need a slower cylinder speed to avoid loss through breakage. Excessive hammer speed will mutilate, crack, or groat the seeds. If the speed is too slow, awns will not be removed.

Openings in the screen must be slightly larger than the deawned seeds. Oversized screen openings will pass a high percentage of seeds with awns. If the openings are too small, the seeds will be damaged and capacity reduced. Those with slots instead of round openings will handle slender seeds with less breakage.

The mill should be fed to full capacity so the hammers will rub and roll the sufficiently trimmed seeds through the openings. When feeding is reduced, the cushioning effect is also reduced and more seeds will be damaged. Seed moisture should be held within close tolerances. Awns on moist seeds often are limber and will not break off easily; cracking damage results in lowered germination if the seeds are too dry.

The following steps should be followed in adjusting the hammermill:

First, choose a screen with openings slightly larger than the deawned seeds.

Second, start the cylinder at slow speed—fill the mill and keep it full.

Third, examine the seeds after a short trial run. If the appendage removal is incomplete and no damaged seeds are found, advance the cylinder speed about 100 revolutions per minute. Be careful to avoid cracking or otherwise damaging the seeds.

Fourth, repeat the third step until the most trimmed seed is obtained with the least breakage. Small seeds that come through untrimmed should be rerun through a screen with smaller openings.

Seeds of the following species have been successfully processed in a hammermill: Native grasses like bluebunch wheatgrass, blue wildrye, Canada wildrye, Siberian wildrye, the gramas, the bluestems, the needlegrasses, and tame species like tall oatgrass, bulbous barley, squirreltail, alfilaria, and virgins-bower.

Debearding machines, used to precondition grasses, have a larger capacity, are simpler to operate, and damage the seeds less than hammermills.

Debearding machines have a horizontal beater with arms rotating inside a steel drum. The arms are pitched to move the seeds through the drum. Stationary posts, adjustable for clearance with the arms, protrude inward from the drum.

These machines rub the seeds against the arms and against each other. The time the seeds remain in the machine is varied by regulating a discharge gate. The degree of action is determined by the processing time, beater clearance, and beater speed.

A debearding machine has been used to remove cotton webbing from Merion bluegrass, which was 98 percent pure when it was cleaned properly. The debearder also is used to clip seed oats, debeard barley, thresh whitecaps in wheat, break apart grass seed doubles, remove awns and beards, hull some grass seeds, and polish seeds.

Another precleaning unit that is effective in removing seed hairs and fuzz is the tumbling pebble mill. It has a drum rotating about a shaft inserted

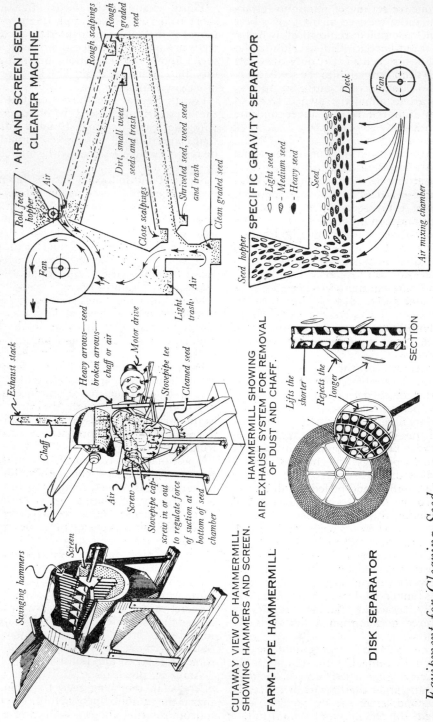

AIR AND SCREEN SEED-CLEANER MACHINE

Rough scalpings
Rough graded seed
Roll feed hopper
Air
Fan
Dirt, small weed seeds and trash
Close scalpings
Shriveled seed, weed seed and trash
Clean graded seed
Light trash Air

SPECIFIC GRAVITY SEPARATOR

Deck
Fan
⊃ – Light seed
⊕ – Medium seed
● – Heavy seed
Seed
Seed hopper
Air mixing chamber

Exhaust stack
Heavy arrows—seed
broken arrows—chaff or air
Motor drive
Chaff
Stovepipe tee
Cleaned seed
Air
Screw
Stovepipe cap-screw in or out to regulate force of suction at bottom of seed chamber

HAMMERMILL SHOWING AIR EXHAUST SYSTEM FOR REMOVAL OF DUST AND CHAFF.

Swinging hammers
Screen

CUTAWAY VIEW OF HAMMERMILL. SHOWING HAMMERS AND SCREEN.

FARM-TYPE HAMMERMILL

Lifts the shorter
Rejects the longer
SECTION

DISK SEPARATOR

Equipment for Cleaning Seed

off center at opposite ends. The mill is loaded with seed and smooth, half-inch pebbles and turned at a slow speed until the rubbing action of the pebbles rolls the fuzz from the seeds into small, round balls. The mixture of pebbles, seeds, and matted fuzz is then run over a scalper to remove the pebbles. The pebble mill is used for removing cobwebby hairs from bluegrass and similar seeds.

Some seeds like black grama, which have fine, flexible, hairlike awns that do not break off when run through a hammermill or debearder, lend themselves to differential burning. The seeds are dropped through a flame, and an instant flashing of awns takes place. The burn exposure must be short to avoid damaging the seeds by excessive heat. Seeds of black grama that were deawned in this way were cleaned and seeded easily.

SEEDS of some native grasses of the Great Plains need little processing.

Arizona cottontop, for example, is harvested by heading and then is fine chopped in a hammermill or similar unit. The seed material is reduced in size, and special planting equipment can distribute it without removal of the fuzz or additional cleaning. The same treatment is given other grasses, such as tanglehead, *Trichloris* species, and cane bluestem.

A green forage harvester is used in Texas wintergrass to harvest and chop the seed material for planting in one operation. With grasses such as big cenchrus and Argentine wintergrass, both of which require precleaning to remove spines and awns, the forage harvester is used for the harvest and does part of the job otherwise required of the hammermill in processing.

Some seeds with cottonlike stylets, such as Texas bluegrass, defy processing with hammermills, debearders, and similar devices or planting with regular grass drills. A new development is pelleting. All plant material, including seeds, stems, leaves, and trash, are mixed with a binder, like cornstarch, silvicon, or krilium, and water and extruded through a quarter-inch hole in a die. Pellets made with cornstarch can be planted easily with a corn planter or cotton planter. Silvicon-binder pellets crumble and can be planted easily with a range seeder.

ALMOST EVERY KIND of seed must be cleaned over an air-screen cleaner before any other separations can be attempted. Many kinds can be cleaned completely on this machine and made into a finished product. The air-screen cleaner therefore is known as the basic equipment in cleaning plants. In this unit, screens take advantage of a difference in size and shape, and moving air senses a difference in surface area and density in seeds so that a separation can be made.

A seed mixture, directly from the combine or from any of the precleaning units, flows by gravity from a hopper to the feeder, which meters it into an airstream. Light, chaffy material is blown out, and the remaining seeds are distributed uniformly over the top screen. In a typical operation of a four-screen machine, the top screen scalps or removes large material. The second screen sizes or drops particles smaller than the seeds. The third screen scalps the seeds more closely. The fourth performs a final grading. The graded seeds then pass through a second airstream, which lifts light seeds and chaff into the trash bin while dropping the plump, heavy, crop seeds into a clean chute.

Top screens have openings larger than the seeds to be cleaned. Bottom screens have openings smaller than the seeds. The size of air-screen cleaners varies from the small, two-screen farm model to the modern precision unit, which is so arranged that several top and several bottom screens can be used in one cleaning operation.

Large cleaners, used in commercial seed-cleaning plants, subject seeds to as many as seven screens and three air separations in one pass through the

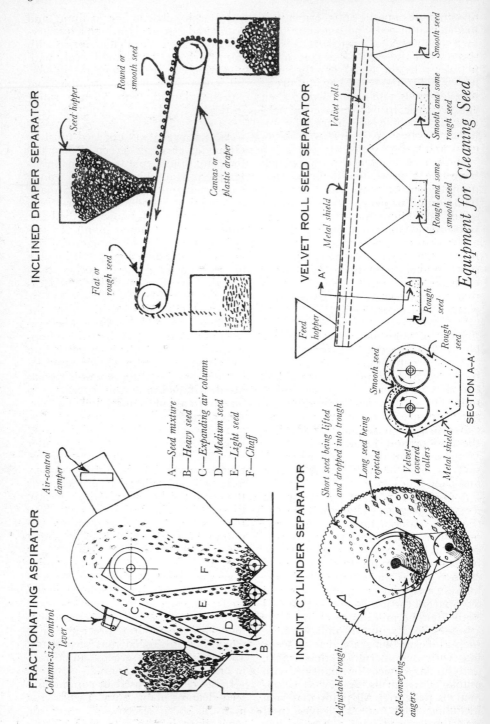

INCLINED DRAPER SEPARATOR

Seed hopper

Round or smooth seed

Flat or rough seed

Canvas or plastic draper

FRACTIONATING ASPIRATOR

Column-size control lever

Air-control damper

A—Seed mixture
B—Heavy seed
C—Expanding air column
D—Medium seed
E—Light seed
F—Chaff

VELVET ROLL SEED SEPARATOR

Feed hopper

Metal shield

Velvet rolls

Rough seed

Rough and some smooth seed

Smooth and some rough seed

Smooth seed

Smooth seed

Rough seed

Velvet covered rollers

Metal shield

SECTION A–A'

Equipment for Cleaning Seed

INDENT CYLINDER SEPARATOR

Short seed being lifted and dropped into trough

Long seed being rejected

Adjustable trough

Seed-conveying augers

machine and have capacities up to 6 thousand pounds of seeds an hour.

The air-screen cleaner uses perforated metal or wire mesh screens. The perforated metal screens are available with round, slotted, or triangular openings. Round-hole sizes range from 0.039 to 1.250 inches in diameter; slotted holes, from 0.039 by 0.500 to 0.375 by 0.750 inch; and triangular, from 0.078 to 0.187 inch in length of each side.

Screens of wire mesh are woven with square or rectangular openings in sizes that range from 0.0117 to 0.286 inch.

Air-screen cleaners with two top screens generally have one round-hole screen and one slotted. The first bottom screen should be slotted; the second should have round, square, or triangular holes.

Each screen is slanted at a slight angle to cause the seeds to roll or slide downward over the openings. The pitch of each screen is adjustable to facilitate accurate separations.

The mechanism that shakes the screens can be adjusted to shake them slowly or rapidly. The experienced operator can adjust the screen shake so the seeds will slide smoothly over the screen or be agitated by the screen motion, as may be required.

The rate of feed can be adjusted to keep the screens operating at nearly full capacity. The airflow in each air separation is usually regulated by means of dampers in the air ducts.

Commercial cleaners have cleaning brushes that travel under the screens to prevent seed from lodging in its openings. Some have mechanical screen bumpers to assist in dislodging seed.

Seeds that have been cleaned with a precision air-screen machine are ready for planting or further processing, depending on the kind and amount of remaining contaminant. Some weed seeds and particles of foreign material are so near the same size, shape, and weight as the crop seeds that they cannot be separated with the air-screen cleaner. One or more finishing separators are then used.

THE SPECIFIC gravity separator senses a difference in density or specific gravity of seeds to make a separation. It was developed to separate ore from clay or dirt and to grade ore in arid mining districts.

The gravity separator employs a flotation principle. A mixture of seeds is fed onto the lower end of a sloping perforated table. Air, forced up through the porous deck surface and the bed of seeds by a fan, blows the lightest material to the top and stratifies the seeds in layers according to density. An oscillating movement of the table "walks" the heavy seeds in contact with the deck uphill, while the air "floats" the light seeds downhill. The seeds traveling to the edge of the table range from light at the lower end to heavy at the upper end. The discharge can be divided into any number of density fractions.

The deck is the heart of the gravity separator. Deck coverings of linen, plastic, woven wire, and perforated metal have been used to distribute air uniformly beneath the seeds. A closely woven covering gives best results for small seeds, such as those of bentgrass. Large seeds, like corn and soybeans, require a coarse weave or larger opening. The covering materials must stand abrasion. Decks are furnished lint-free air that will not clog their openings.

Several adjustments are available to match machine performance to seed mixture and separation requirements. Feed rate is critical and should be adjusted to provide an even supply and a uniform covering of the deck at all times.

Airflow through the deck should be adjusted to allow heavy seed to stay in contact with the deck while moving light seeds up through the seedbed. An oversupply of air causes mixing while an inadequate supply will not stratify the light seeds at the top.

The tilt of the deck is adjustable. The inclination should be great enough that light seeds will flow down to the lower end. The oscillation rate of the table should be fast enough so that

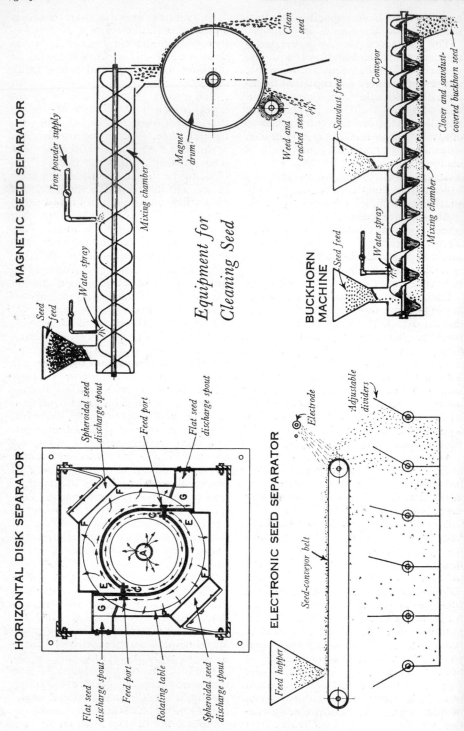

Equipment for Cleaning Seed

MAGNETIC SEED SEPARATOR

Iron powder supply

Water spray

Seed feed

Mixing chamber

Magnet drum

Weed and cracked seed

Clean seed

Sawdust feed

Conveyor

Clover and sawdust-covered buckhorn seed

BUCKHORN MACHINE

Water spray

Seed feed

Mixing chamber

HORIZONTAL DISK SEPARATOR

Spheroidal seed discharge spout

Feed port

Flat seed discharge spout

Flat seed discharge spout

Feed port

Rotating table

Spheroidal seed discharge spout

ELECTRONIC SEED SEPARATOR

Electrode

Adjustable dividers

Seed-conveyor belt

Feed hopper

heavy seeds in contact with the deck will move to the upper end.

The gravity separator will separate seeds of the same size but of different densities. It will also separate seeds of the same density but of different size. It will not separate a mixture of sizes and densities. For example, a sized mixture of dirt, seeds of wild geranium and crimson clover, and gravel may be separated. The geranium and weevil-eaten clover will be discharged at the low side of the deck, rocks and dirt at the upper side, and good crimson clover seeds in the middle.

The indent disk and indent cylinder separators take advantage of a difference in seed length to make a separation. Both types use pockets or indentations to lift short seeds from a mixture and reject long seeds.

The indent disk separator consists of a series of disks revolving together on a horizontal shaft inside a close-fitting housing. Each disk has many pockets or cups on each face. As the disks revolve through a seed mixture, the recessed pockets lift out short seeds and drop them in a trough at the side of the machine. Rejected long seeds are conveyed through the disk spokes to the end of the machine and discharged through the tailings opening.

When seeds or material of varying lengths are to be removed or graded by length, the mixture first encounters disks with small cups and then disks with cups progressively larger from inlet to discharge. When only one separation is required, many disks with the same size of indent are used in a machine to increase capacity. Removable vanes attached to the spokes of the disks serve to move seeds through the machine, agitate them, and bring them in contact with the cups.

Size and shape of the disk pockets are the important variables. Disk pockets are made in two basic shapes with many sizes for each.

The "R" pocket derives its designation from "rice" and was designed to remove broken rice grains from whole grains. The lifting edge, being flat, will lift out cross-broken or flat seeds and reject round seeds.

The "V" pocket derives its name from "vetch" and was designed to remove round seeds. The round lifting edge tends to reject tubular or elongated seeds. Disks with other letter designations are designed for specialized separations.

Other important adjustments are disk speed and rate of seed flow through the separator. Disk speed is adjusted to obtain proper emptying of the pockets. Speed too slow or too fast will allow seeds to leave the pockets before the proper discharge point. The seed level in the machine and the rate of discharge may be controlled by removing or adding vanes attached to the disk spokes or adjusting the height of the discharge gate. Adjustments within the machine make it possible for liftings from the various disks to be either discharged or returned to the head of the machine for further recleaning.

The indent disk separator can be used to lift vetch from oats or wheat and crimson clover from ryegrass and fescue seed. Small particles such as seed of dodder, dock, sorrel, or plantain can be separated from fescues and ryegrasses.

INDENT CYLINDER separators perform separations on the same basis as indent disk separators—that is, on a difference in seed length.

The indent cylinder separator has a horizontal rotating cylinder and a movable separating trough. The inside surface of the cylinder has small, closely spaced, semispherical indentations. When a seed mixture is introduced into one end of the cylinder, short seeds are lifted by the combined effect of fitting into the indents and centrifugal force. Near the top of the rotation, they drop into an adjustable trough inside the cylinder. A spiral conveyor in the bottom of the trough moves the lifted material to the end where it is discharged. Usually the cylinder is slightly inclined, so that rejected long seeds will flow in the cylinder to the discharge end by gravity.

Cylinders are available with indents of many different sizes, but all indents in one cylinder are of the same size. The cylinder is changed when a different size of indent is required.

Two adjustments for obtaining the desired separation are cylinder speed and position of the adjustable trough. With indent cylinder separators, centrifugal force helps hold the seeds in the pockets and thus affects the distance traveled before dropping out. Cylinder speed is adjusted therefore to lift seeds nearly to the top of the arc. Excessive speed will not allow seeds to drop from the indents. A speed that is too slow will not lift short seeds from the mixture. The separating edge of the adjustable trough should be positioned to catch the desired fraction of the dropping seed.

The indent cylinder separator can make separations, such as sloughgrass from meadow foxtail, long barley from oats, and dock or sorrel from orchardgrass or fescue. The cylinder can also be used for sizing oats and rice and grading hybrid corn by length.

Pneumatic and aspirator separators use the movement of air to divide seeds according to their terminal velocities. This refers to the velocity of air required to suspend particles in a rising air current. Density, shape, and surface texture affect resistance of a particle to airflow.

When a seed mixture is introduced into a confined rising airstream, all particles with a terminal velocity less than the air velocity will be lifted. Seeds with higher terminal velocities will fall against the airflow.

Regulation of the air velocity, the most important variable, can be adjusted by changing the speed of the fan or the size of the air inlet.

In a pneumatic separator, the fan forces air through the machine by creating a pressure greater than atmospheric. In an aspirator, the fan is at the discharge end and induces a vacuum, which allows the atmospheric pressure to force air through the separator.

One type of aspirator separator is the scalping aspirator. A rough separation is made when a seed mixture is dropped into a rising air column that has a velocity slightly below the terminal velocity of the heavy, plump seeds. The leaves, trash, and light seeds rise with the air and are deposited in an enlarged settling chamber. The denser, plumper seeds fall through the incoming air into a receiving bin below.

Another type of aspirator is the fractionating aspirator. When a seed mixture is introduced into the lower end of an expanding air column, heavy seeds fall against the airflow, and light seeds are lifted. Air velocity through the expanding column lessens and gradually drops out seeds with lower terminal velocities. Each outlet along the column receives a lighter fraction of seeds; the mixture thereby is separated into several divisions.

Pneumatic separators can make many precise separations, such as lifting seeds of meadow foxtail from seeds of Alta fescue.

The velvet roll separator classifies seeds according to a difference in texture of seedcoat. The separator consists of two parallel, inclined, velvet-covered rolls in contact with each other. They revolve outwardly. An adjustable shield conforms to the rolls and is held just above them. When a seed mixture is fed onto the upper end of the rolls, the smooth seeds travel downhill between them and are discharged at the lower end. Rough-coated seeds, caught in the velvet, take a bouncing path between shield and rolls and are thrown over the sides. The discharge from the side of the rolls is caught in several divisions. The roughest seeds are ejected first.

Several adjustments are available to obtain the desired separation. The clearance between rolls and shield should be great enough to allow all seeds to pass freely. The rate of feed is adjusted to allow all seeds to come in contact with the rolls. Angle of incline of the rolls may be increased if the surface texture difference of the seeds is great. The speed of the rolls should be increased to discharge all rough-coated seeds over the side of the rolls.

Many pairs of rolls are mounted one above another to gain capacity. The unit is sometimes called dodder roll, because it often is used to remove rough-coated seeds of dodder from smooth legume seeds. Other common separations are dirt clods from beans and clovers, seeds of timothy from seeds of alsike clover, and unhulled from hulled lespedeza.

THE SPIRAL SEPARATOR makes a division of seeds according to shape or the degree of its ability to roll. The separator resembles a stationary, open-screw conveyor standing on end. A mixture, fed onto the spiral at the top, slides or rolls down the inclined surface. The fast-rolling seeds gain speed and are thrown by centrifugal force into an outer housing, which directs them to a chute below. The sliding or slow-rolling seeds remain on the inner inclined surface and enter a second chute at the bottom.

The spiral separator has no moving parts. The only adjustment is the rate of feed, which should be light enough so each seed may act independently. Increased capacity is gained by placing several spiraled surfaces in the same housing. The chief disadvantage of the spiral is lack of flexibility. Often a different diameter or incline is desired to match a range of seed samples. This device is less versatile than other seed cleaners, but it is simple, inexpensive, and quite useful in a seed-cleaning establishment. The spiral is used to separate rape, vetch, and soybean seeds from wheat, oats, and rye-grass; whole vetch from broken vetch; and crimson clover from rape and mustard seeds.

THE INCLINED DRAPER separator senses a difference in shape and surface texture to separate seed on an inclined plane. A mixture to be separated is metered onto the center of an inclined draper belt traveling in an uphill direction. Round or smooth seeds, which roll or slide down the draper faster than the draper is traveling up, drop off and are caught in one hopper. Flat and rough-coated seeds are carried to the top of the incline and dropped into a second hopper.

Belts with different degrees of roughness may be used as the draper. A rough canvas belt is used when rolling tendencies of the seed are predominant. A smooth, plastic belt may be employed when sliding action is desired for the lower fraction. Other important variables are feed rate, draper speed, and angle of incline.

The rate of feed should be slow enough to allow each seed to act individually. The draper speed may be varied to simulate a shorter or longer length of incline. The angle of incline is set to assure rolling or sliding of the desired lower fraction.

To gain capacity in commercial operations, many belts are used one above another in a single machine. Typical separations made by the inclined draper separator are seeds of crimson clover from grass seeds and vetch seeds from oats.

THE HORIZONTAL DISK separator takes advantage of differences in shape and surface texture to determine whether seeds slide or roll when subjected to centrifugal force.

Seeds, confined to the center of a flat rotating disk by a stationary circular plastic fence, are metered to the outer part of the disk through adjustable outlets. Centrifugal force causes round or smooth seeds to roll or slide off the disk. Irregular or rough seeds remain on the disk and are raked off into a different hopper.

The rate of feed through the outlets is adjusted so that each seed moves independently. The horizontal disk is similar to the spiral separator, but it is more selective because it has a disk speed control that can change the pro-

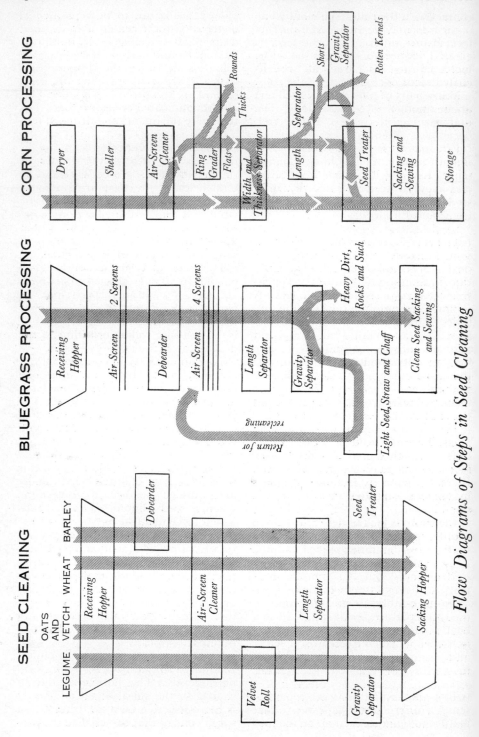

CORN PROCESSING

Dryer — Sheller — Air-Screen Cleaner — Ring Grader — Rounds — Thicks — Flats — Width and Thickness Separator — Length Separator — Shorts — Gravity Separator — Rotten Kernels — Seed Treater — Sacking and Sewing — Storage

BLUEGRASS PROCESSING

Receiving Hopper — Air Screen — 2 Screens — Debearder — Air Screen — 4 Screens — Length Separator — Gravity Separator — Heavy Dirt, Rocks and Such — Clean Seed Sacking and Sewing — Light Seed, Straw and Chaff — Return for recleaning

SEED CLEANING

OATS AND LEGUME VETCH WHEAT BARLEY

Receiving Hopper — Debearder — Air-Screen Cleaner — Velvet Roll — Length Separator — Gravity Separator — Seed Treater — Sacking Hopper

Flow Diagrams of Steps in Seed Cleaning

portions of seed retained or thrown off.

An added capacity is obtained by mounting many disks on a single vertical shaft. The horizontal disk separator will separate dodder seeds from alfalfa, curly dock from red clover, and other mixtures in which one seed has a greater tendency to roll or slide than another.

ELECTRONIC separators divide seeds on the basis of differences in their electrical properties. The degree of separation depends on the relative ability of seeds in a mixture to conduct electricity or to hold a surface charge.

Electronic or electrostatic separators have been used for many years to separate minerals, but their application to seeds is relatively new. Their use offers the possibility of making separations that have been difficult or impossible with conventional equipment.

A thin layer of seed is conveyed on a belt through a high-voltage electrical field, where it is given a surface charge. This charge is like the one that is picked up by a comb passed through the hair.

As the belt rounds a pulley, seeds that have quickly lost their charge fall in a normal manner from the belt. Seeds that are poor conductors and slow to lose their charge adhere to the belt and fall off gradually. Dividers in the drop path can then be positioned to collect any fraction of the distribution desired.

Among the many adjustments are feed rate, belt speed, electrode position, voltage, and divider position. Preliminary research has been conducted to determine the effect of these variables, but much is still to be learned. The moisture content of the seeds is important, because the ability of a seed to conduct electricity is affected by changes in its moisture.

Some of the separations that have been made with commercial electronic separators are seeds of watercress from rice, leaf material from raisins, chaff from ground coffee, ergot from bentgrass, and johnsongrass from sesame.

Experimental units have separated seeds of bachelor's-button from Alta fescue and ryegrass and seed of curly dock from red clover.

MAGNETIC SEPARATORS take advantage of the surface texture and stickiness of seed to make a separation.

A seed mixture and a proportioned amount of water and finely ground iron powder are mixed in a screw conveyor or other mixing device. In the presence of moisture, the powder will adhere to rough, cracked, and sticky seeds. When the mixture is fed onto the top of a horizontal revolving magnetic drum, smooth or slick seeds that are relatively free of powder fall from the drum in a normal manner. Rough-textured or sticky seeds, coated with iron powder, are attracted by the magnetic drum and stick to it until they are removed by a rotary brush or a break in the magnetic field.

The degree of successful cleaning depends largely on the extent of the difference in seedcoats; the proper proportioning of water, iron powder, and seed; and the thoroughness of the mixing operation.

The magnetic separator is excellent for removing seeds of weeds like dodder, buckhorn, plantain, and mustard from alfalfa and clovers. Dirt and cracked seeds may also be removed from them. Hulled johnsongrass can be separated from alfalfa by using an emulsified oil with the water to help the grass seeds pick up and hold the powder.

The buckhorn machine is a special unit designed primarily to remove buckhorn plantain from seeds of legumes, such as crimson clover, alfalfa, and red clover.

Normally the buckhorn plantain and the legume seeds are so similar in size, shape, weight, and surface texture that many of the buckhorn cannot be completely removed by the air-screen cleaner, gravity separator, or other common cleaning machines.

The buckhorn seed has a mucilaginous surface, which becomes sticky when dampened and will pick up finely ground sawdust. Thus a larger, rough-surfaced, less dense seed unit is formed. Smooth legume seed will not take on any of the sawdust.

A buckhorn seed mixture and a sufficient amount of water and sawdust are mixed in an auger or continuous-type paddle stirrer. The enlarged buckhorn seeds then can usually be removed with an air-screen cleaner. The specific gravity or the velvet roll machines may be used to complete the separation if necessary.

The timothy bumper mill separates seeds on the basis of a difference in shape. It is a special machine developed to remove weed seeds.

The timothy seed mixture is fed onto the lower corner of the upper end of a small rectangular metal plate, which is inclined slightly in both directions but more in the lengthwise direction.

A back-and-forth movement of the plate, parallel with its short side, is smooth in one direction but is stopped with a bump in the other. Round timothy seeds roll downhill lengthwise of the plate between bumps and fall off the end. Irregular-shaped seeds are gradually bumped uphill across the plate and fall off the side.

In the commercial machines, many plates are suspended in two identical frames, which are bumped together simultaneously. With proper adjustment of feed rate, bump intensity, and plate inclination, the timothy bumper mill will separate alsike clover, Canada thistle, sorrel, ryegrass, quackgrass, and other seeds from timothy.

The vibrator separator is a newer machine that makes a division of seed on the basis of a difference in shape and surface texture.

As in the timothy bumper mill, the seed mixture is fed near the center of the upper end of a rectangular deck inclined both sideways and endwise. The deck is activated by an electromagnetic vibrator. Flat or rough seeds climb to the high side of the deck. Round and smoother seeds roll, tumble, and slide to the low side.

The endwise tilt induces both seed fractions to travel to the discharge end, where they drop off and are kept separate by dividers.

The tilt of the deck may be adjusted both sideways and endwise to provide a wide range of deck inclinations. Decks can have various textures, ranging from smooth metal to rough sandpaper, depending on the seed components that are being separated. The intensity of vibration can be regulated by a rheostat controller in the electrical circuit. To increase capacity, multiple decks may be mounted in a rigid frame and powered by a single vibrator. A properly adjusted vibrator separator removes seeds of curly dock from crimson clover, dogfennel and hedgemustard from timothy, rippleseed plantain and ergot from bentgrass, dodder and lambsquarters from carrot seeds, and sweet vernal grass from ryegrass.

The color separator separates the seeds on the basis of a difference in color or brightness.

One type of machine picks up the seeds on a series of suction fingers and carries them past a phototube, where they are judged for color or brightness and ejected into separating containers one at a time.

Color separators are practical for larger seeds, like those of beans and peas. They have not been used for smaller seeds because of the low capacity involved in scanning the particles individually.

MANY FACTORS should be considered in designing a seed-cleaning plant.

Handling and cleaning the seeds should be possible without mixing or damaging and with a minimum of equipment, personnel, and time.

The seed separators, elevators, conveyors, and storage bins should be arranged so seeds can flow continuously from beginning to end, yet flexible enough to bypass a machine or return part for recleaning.

Other factors to be considered are kinds of crop seeds to be cleaned, kinds of contaminating crop and weed seeds, volume of seed to be handled, method of handling (bulk or sacks), type of conveying system (pneumatic or mechanical), and location of shipping and receiving facilities.

The commonest plant layout is the multistory design, in which machines are placed in a vertical processing line and seed flows by gravity from one to another. This arrangement requires a high, reinforced structure and many workers to operate equipment on the several floors.

Single-story plants are increasing in popularity because of the emphasis on reduced cost of structures, less labor, varietal purity, and the need for special processing of certain crops.

There is no all-purpose machine that will remove all the objectionable material from the different kinds of seed.

Each unit in a cleaning sequence is employed to make a specific separation. The machines used and their arrangement in the processing line depend on the crop being cleaned, the condition of the crop (partly or completely hulled); the type of other materials present (rocks, sticks, stems, leaves, dirt, weed seed); the size of the contaminating material compared to the crop; and the proportions of each in the mixture.

When a seed lot to be cleaned arrives at a processing plant, a sample is first analyzed to determine which machines to use and the best flow pattern through the plant. Combined seed ordinarily requires one or more precleaning treatments.

If the seed lot includes a high percentage of large trash, green leaves, green weed seeds, or insects, it is first rough cleaned on a scalper. If a large percentage of the seed is unhulled, it is often necessary to hull the entire lot.

A lot containing hard seed may be scarified during the precleaning sequence or some time after cleaning is complete, depending on its ability to maintain viability after processing. Many grains and most grasses are given a debearding or deawning treatment with either the hammermill or

debearder. Many native grasses require special treatment to remove troublesome appendages.

After precleaning, most of the remaining contaminants are removed with an air-screen cleaner. Some lots, with a minimum of excess material, may be finished by this machine, but most will need further processing with finishing machines to make first quality seed. This unit is also capable of accurate sizing for thickness and width with the selection of proper screens.

The finish cleaning may be accomplished by many machine arrangements, but an indent disk or cylinder usually is next in line. These units separate weed seeds that are different in length and also may be used to divide the lot according to size.

The specific gravity separator will next split off light and heavy contaminants with most of the cut being usable seed. The "middlings" or mixture fractions may be rerun on another gravity separator or a different type of machine for further cleaning.

Further processing will depend upon the characteristics of the specific contaminant remaining. Rough weeds are removed by the velvet roll; seeds of irregular shape by the spiral or inclined draper; and seeds with rough or mucilaginous surfaces by the magnetic or buckhorn machine.

The separator selected generally is the one that will remove the most contaminating materials with the smallest loss of crop.

Manufacturers have developed outstanding seed-separating equipment, but the knowledge and skill of the operators remain most important.

LEONARD M. KLEIN *is an agricultural engineer, Harvesting and Farm Processing Research Branch, Agricultural Engineering Research Division, Agricultural Research Service, Corvallis, Oreg.*

JAMES HENDERSON *is sales manager of A. T. Ferrell & Co., Saginaw, Mich.*

ABRAHAM D. STOESZ *is head plant materials technician, Plant Technology Division, Soil Conservation Service.*

Special Processing and Treatment of Seeds

LAURENCE H. PURDY, JESSE E. HARMOND, AND G. BURNS WELCH

MOST agricultural seeds need some kind of processing to make them easier to handle.

The processing may remove or change some objectionable structure or give specific information about the seed lot or protect the seeds from pests.

It may be done for a specific purpose on a particular type of seeds (for example, delinting of cotton), a group of closely related seed types (scarification of legumes), or a large number of seed types (seed treatment).

This processing is done after cleaning and separating have made sure that a particular lot is pure as to variety.

The value of special processing is illustrated by results from the use of delinted cotton seed. One ton of undelinted seed will plant 60 acres. One ton of undelinted seed gives 1,700 pounds of delinted seed, which will plant about 210 acres, allow more uniform plantings, be free of certain lintborne pathogens, and permit better coverage with chemicals.

The treatment with chemicals to control certain seedborne and soilborne diseases, such as damping-off, or seed decay, and some smut diseases, is another form of special processing.

Indeed, the application of effective chemicals to seed of wheat is the only control of common wheat bunt when resistant varieties are not available or have broken down.

The use of ineffective chemicals on seed, which is like planting untreated seed, accounts for large losses of crops.

In the Pacific Northwest, for example, a comparison of hexachlorobenzene and a mercury fungicide to control soilborne common bunt of wheat was made by planting alternate drill strips with seed treated with each material across a grower's field. An average of 16 percent of bunt developed in strips planted with seed treated with hexachlorobenzene; 65 percent of bunt developed with the mercury fungicide. A yield of 55 bushels an acre was obtained from the strips treated with hexachlorobenzene. Losses due to the use of the ineffective mercury fungicide were 50 dollars an acre.

SEED OF COTTON still has a small amount of lint or fuzz on the surface after ginning. The fuzz makes it hard to plant because the seeds stick together and do not flow easily.

Mechanical delinting is like ginning. Saws in the delinting equipment are closer together and have finer teeth. Lint is cut as close as possible to the seed without breaking the hull. A small amount of fuzz is left on mechanically delinted seed.

The seeds, metered by a fluted roller, enter the roll box, in which a float revolves them so that the saws come in contact with all seeds. A saw cylinder, with more than a hundred fine saws, is under the roll box. Saws project a short distance into the roll box through narrow slots and cut the lint from the seeds. Cut lint is removed from the roll box by the revolving saws. A large brush behind the saw cylinder brushes lint from the saw teeth. Lint is blown to the separator, or condenser, where it is separated from the airstream and rolled into large rolls or pressed into bales.

Flash—or flame—processing removes more of the fuzz left on mechanically delinted seed. Flash furnaces have a vertical duct with butane burners in the side of the duct at the bottom. Seeds are metered onto a vibrating conveyor, which feeds them into the furnace at the top. They usually pass through two furnaces operated at 2,400° F. to insure removal of lint.

Thereafter the seeds pass over an air-screen cleaner, which removes immature seeds and foreign material.

Chemical delinting removes all lint by an acid.

In what is called the dry process, hydrochloric acid and sulfuric acid are mixed to form a gas, which is piped into a revolving tank. A reaction between gas and fuzz on the seed in the tank causes the fuzz to crystallize. Heat hastens the reaction. Then the seeds are dumped into a revolving perforated cylinder, which removes the crystallized lint. An air-screen cleaner removes immature seeds and foreign material after all the lint has been removed. Anhydrous ammonia neutralizes acid on the seeds in a revolving tank.

In a wet process, an acid solution is applied to seed until the fuzz is crystallized. The seeds are rinsed to remove crystallized fuzz, and the acid is neutralized. Then they are dried and passed over a cleaner, which removes immature seeds and foreign material.

MULTIPLE GERMS and irregularities in size, shape, and density have made accurate planting of sugarbeet seeds difficult. New methods and machinery enable us to get seeds of more uniform size and fewer germs in a seedball.

The first attempt to get single-germ seeds was to cut them in a machine that had a vertical carborundum wheel and a metal shear bar, between which the seeds passed. The segmenting process injured the seeds, so that germination often was poor and seedlings were damaged. Less drastic methods were sought.

Decortication involves the use of two units. One has a metal bur plate above a rough, horizontal stone. The other is a neoprene pad mounted above a smoother horizontal stone. Whole seeds are fed into the bur machine through the top and pass between the bur plate and the revolving stone. This process reduces the size of seed units by removing outer corky parts of the seedballs, which then pass between the pad and its revolving stone. Here more of the corky portion of the seedball is removed, and the number of germs in the larger seedballs is reduced further. The mixture of seeds and dust is separated by a cleaner and grader. Seeds are then delivered to a gravity table or aspirator to remove light or incomplete units.

Decorticated seeds have a greater density than whole seeds and about one-third the volume of the whole seeds. Decorticated seeds also are smoother and more uniform in size and are more easily planted than whole or segmented seeds.

Decorticated seeds are superior to segmented seeds in all respects except degree of singleness. When germination is less than 50 percent, better stands and higher percentages of single plants are obtained with decorticated seeds than with segmented seeds. The work of singling, or thinning, is cut by 25–30 percent when decorticated seeds are planted.

SOME HARD SEEDS are scarified—scratched—to break their impermeable layer of surface cells, which form a moisture barrier. Unscarified seeds of this type do not readily absorb the moisture needed for germination.

Legumes, asparagus, and okra usually contain a high percentage of hard seeds, which do not give a uniform stand if their seedcoat is not broken.

Scarifying can be done in several ways—by buffing after treatment with a special oil; treating the seeds with acid or heat; irradiating them electrically; and abrading them mechanically.

Scarification has to be done with little damage to the seeds.

The industry mostly uses mechanical scarification. The acid method is used more extensively on seeds of cotton.

Irradiation has been used experimentally on corn, cotton, some vegetables, and legumes.

Mechanical scarifiers pass the seeds over some abrasive surface, such as sandpaper, or a carborundum stone. Airstreams separate hulls and chaff.

One machine has a stationary disk and a rotating disk. Seeds fed into the center of the top disk fall on the rotating disk. The seeds travel outward and strike abrasive paper at an angle that removes hulls and breaks the outside layers. A jet of air removes the hulls, dust, and light stems.

In another huller-scarifier, seeds are fed into the center of a rotating distribution disk, which throws the seeds outward, where they strike a carborundum stone ring. The seeds drop through a funnel to a second rotary distributor and abrasive stone. The dust and chaff are separated from the seeds in a cyclone separator.

In a rotary drum-type scarifier, seeds are drawn into the drum and moved through it by air. The seeds are hulled and scarified when they strike segments of carborundum stone embedded in the drum surface. Hulls are removed by a suction fan. The severity of scarification can be regulated.

The machines have capacities up to 100 bushels an hour.

SAMPLING EQUIPMENT used to obtain correct and representative samples of seed lots generally are simple devices. One automatic type is run by an electric motor.

Commonly used samplers for grain in bags and in bulk are probes or sleeve-type triers of brass or aluminum tubing. They have a hollow inner tube with slots or compartments and an outer tube, or sleeve, with a like number of slots. Bagged grain usually is sampled with a six-slotted, 30-inch probe 1 inch in diameter. Small seeds, such as clover, are sampled with smaller probes.

A probe for bulk grain has 11 compartments separated by partitions in the inner tube. The probe is inserted in the grain, and the inner tube is turned a half turn to allow the grain to enter the compartments. Another half turn closes the compartments. The tube is withdrawn, and the sample is removed. Grain from each compartment is inspected separately.

A representative sample of grain is obtained by probing the bulked grain in five or more places. Seven or more places are probed to get a representative sample of flax.

Bulked grain that is being loaded aboard ships can be sampled with a spout sampler, or pelican. It is used to cut the stream of grain at frequent and regular intervals to assure the collection of a correct and typical sample. The pelican, a leather basket, is attached to a pole 8 to 10 feet long. Samples obtained with it are later reduced in size by running the sample through a sample divider.

A probe, designed for sampling corn in cribs, is inserted between the boards of the crib. Corn is shelled from the ears by rotating and rocking the handle of the probe. Shelled corn falls into the opening of the probe. A true sample can be obtained by repeated probing of the crib.

A semiautomatic sampling device, operated manually, is used to collect samples from seed cleaners. It is activated by pulling a rope or chain at the work-floor level. When collecting the sample, a small cup is turned to allow seeds to enter the cup at the discharge of the cleaner. The sample falls to the floor through a pipe attached to the sampling device.

A power-driven, automatic device obtains samples from the stream of grain in the elevator head at timed intervals. Its hinged cover is connected to the power source so that the cover opens and closes to receive the grain. When open and collecting a sample, the holes in the 3-inch pipe are exposed to the stream of grain. Grain that enters the holes falls to a divider, which sends half of the sample to the work floor. The other half is returned to the elevator leg.

Automatic samplers for elevator belts with one to four rows of cups can be obtained that operate on the same motor but open alternately.

IRRADIATION of seeds as a practical method for inspection can be done with compact X-ray equipment adapted to grain inspection. It requires little technical skill and a minimum of preparation of the sample. Other methods used in grain inspection require considerable time of highly trained personnel, and test results often are inconclusive.

Radiographs of grain samples for inspection are easily interpreted and give rapid results on the degree of internal infestations of insects. They can also be used to determine the amount of checking in rice, the effectiveness of fumigations, and the selection of grain for processing.

Irradiation of seed is the treating of seed electrically to increase its water absorption and reduce the count of hard seeds.

Irradiation is accomplished experimentally in two ways.

One is to place seeds in an evacuated glass tube and to apply about 1,000 volts to electrodes on the tube ends, so that there is a 10- to 50-milliampere current flow. The current flow causes gases in the tube to glow and act on the seeds. This is called a glow discharge treatment.

The other method is to subject the seeds to high frequencies using radio-frequency equipment.

An irradiated cotton seed, placed in water, sinks within a few seconds. A nonirradiated cotton seed will float 24 hours or longer before it absorbs enough water to sink.

Irradiation tests of seeds of alfalfa, corn, cotton, and red clover indicate that the treatment speeds up their water absorption, reduces the count of hard seed, and improves germination.

Irradiation tests offer some possibilities for sterilization. A mixture of turnip, red clover, and mustard seeds was treated. The germination of the turnip seeds was destroyed, but the germination of the red clover and mustard was apparently normal.

BLENDING seeds of a single variety may compensate for variations in germination, purity, and appearance, which are due to differences in soil fertility, weed infection, soil moisture, and time of harvesting.

This mixing process ordinarily is done after the seeds have been cleaned.

One method is to use several tanks, which are filled successively. The tanks are opened simultaneously into another tank or elevator. The operation is repeated until the desired uniformity is obtained.

To blend several lots of different purity or germination to any desired purity or germination, each lot is first blended to uniformity within itself and placed in a tank. The bottom of each tank is opened enough to meter out the desired amount of seeds that is needed in the finished product. The seeds from the various tanks can be discharged in a screw conveyor or similar device for thorough mixing.

Batch-type mixers are used for blending small lots. The vertical screw type, which was developed for mixing feed, is used in small seed-cleaning plants. Manufacturers have made improvements for cleaning and inspection.

Drum-type mixers tumble the seeds until they are mixed. Another type has a stationary drum, which has revolving paddles inside for mixing the seeds. The batch-type mixers are good for blending within a given batch. When several batches are to be blended, the work should be supervised so as to get all the batches uniform.

Pelleting has been tried with many kinds of seeds with varied degrees of success. Equipment has ranged from cement mixers to pharmacists' pill-coating machines.

Pelleting can be done by compression and coating in a rotary drum.

In the compression machine, seeds are placed in a recess. A water-soluble paste is forced around them. The pellet is formed as the molds are moved together. This method reduces germination and retards emergence of seedlings.

The rotary drum has replaced it. Seeds are placed in a rotating drum and alternately mist-sprayed with a liquid binder and fogged with a dust.

Dust adheres to the moist seeds and forms a sphere when the seeds roll around in the drum. Repeating the spraying and dusting gives a uniform spherical-shaped pellet.

Pelleting regulates the size of seeds for precision planting by machine and by hand, reduces the amount of seeds required to plant, and cuts the work of thinning crops.

Nontoxic insecticides, fungicides, inoculants, lime, coloring matter, animal and bird repellants, and fertilizer can be added to the coating. The pellet can be of a color so that birds and small animals cannot recognize the seed. It is said to be the first time man has consistently outwitted the crow. Pellets of flower seeds can be made of the same colors as the bloom to help gardeners arrange color patterns.

Pelletized seeds cost more and weigh two to five times more than ordinary seeds. In small seeds, in which pelleting seems most advantageous, a piece of inert matter may form a pellet without a seed, while some pellets may contain more than one seed.

More moisture is required to germinate pelleted seeds, since the pellets must be dissolved. Delayed and irregular emergence may occur if moisture is limited.

Some seeds that have been pelleted successfully are those of pepper, cauliflower, lettuce, cabbage, tomatoes, parsley, celery, carrots, onions, sugarbeets, table beets, melons, corn, legume, and some grasses.

Pelleting of small, irregular-shaped seeds is favored by vegetable producers because their uniform size makes them easier to plant by hand or with a precision planter.

Decortication and the development of the monogerm sugarbeet seeds have meant that pelleted seeds of sugarbeets are used only in trial plantings.

SEEDS in plastic rolls and tapes are new. Grass, vegetable, and flower seeds have been used in them.

The seeds are metered at the desired rate on a water-soluble plastic tape or fibrous mat, which is coated with water-soluble adhesive that holds the seeds in position. The planting area is worked to form a good seedbed, and on it the tape is unrolled with the seeds down. Rain or irrigation water dissolves the adhesive. The seeds are uniformly distributed over the planted area. The tape reduces soil erosion, movement of the seeds by water and wind, and the loss of moisture through evaporation. It shades the tender sprout from the sun. The tape is a mulch as it dissolves.

Seeds of turf grass are embedded in rolls 24, 30, and 36 inches wide. The 30-inch width seems easiest to handle.

The tape is useful particularly on steep banks and highway shoulders, where seeds are not easily held. Mixtures of lawn seeds can be metered by machines on a tape to give a uniform mixture in a lawn.

Flower seeds are placed on narrow tapes and wound on a plastic reel, like transparent household tape. The tape is unrolled and cut to the desired length for planting. With the seeds down, it is placed in a trench and covered with a thin layer of soil. Some flower seeds can be purchased on tapes three-eighths of an inch wide and of different lengths.

Seeds also are glued to paper grids and fibrous mats. Mixtures of turf seeds treated with disinfectant can be purchased on fiber mats in rolls that measure 100 to 5,000 square feet.

Flower seeds are also placed in fibrous mats or bats, which are called "roll-out-gardens." Some cut-flower or dwarf edging mixtures are available in mats that are $\frac{1}{8}$ inch thick, 8 inches wide, and 144 inches long. The mat is unrolled on top of a loose seedbed and covered with a one-fourth-inch layer of topsoil and then watered. Cut-flower mats are available with seeds of asters, babysbreath, larkspur, marigolds, petunias, snapdragons, and zinnias. Dwarf edging mats contain sweet alyssum, poppies, marigolds, petunias, mignonette, and portulaca.

Small, plastic-covered cartons are available in which seeds have been placed in vermiculite. Holes are punched in the recesses of the plastic cover of the carton, and it is watered. After 24 hours, the cover is removed, and the vermiculite is kept moist. When plants emerge, they may be thinned. The carton can be used as a window box, or the plants can be transplanted. Flower and vegetable seeds are planted in the cartons—aster, carnations, dahlia, pansy, petunia, tomato, pepper, and others.

Inoculants, insecticides, pesticides, and fertilizer can be placed on the mat or tape along with the seeds to simplify gardening. Color is added to the mat or tape so it will absorb or reflect heat.

ANOTHER PROCESS is the adding of bacteria of the *Rhizobia* species to seeds of legumes to help them convert atmospheric nitrogen into protein and transfer nitrogen from air to soil. The bacteria encourage the formation of nodules on the roots. Nitrogen is stored in nodules and used by the plant as needed. Not all soils contain the correct kind of bacteria.

It has long been a practice to add bacteria to a new field or inoculate seeds to be planted. Specific bacteria can be purchased commercially for use on specific groups of seed—the alfalfa, clover, soybean, pea and vetch, cowpea, bean, and lupine and serradella groups.

Birdsfoot trefoil, big trefoil, Dallas or "Wood's" clover, black locust, crownvetch, foxtail dalea, hemp, sesbania, lead plant, trailing wild bean, and Siberian peashrubs need specific strains of bacteria.

Seed inoculation often is done on the farm, usually on the day before seeding. The seeds and inoculant may be mixed in a bucket or tub. Large amounts can be mixed in the back of a truck. Small concrete mixers have also been used to mix large amounts.

Various binders and carriers—such as powdered skim milk, sirup, and finely ground peat—have been used in mixing.

THE SLURRY seed treater is suitable for applying the seed inoculant, but it can handle only small lots of seeds at a time and it must be cleaned thoroughly before it is used for inoculating seeds.

For certain legumes, the inoculant is placed in the seedbed at the time of planting. Inoculants mixed with a granular carrier can be applied with the fertilizer attachment on the planter. If it is in a liquid carrier, the inoculant is placed in the plow furrow with an attachment for applying liquid fertilizer.

Alfalfa seeds treated commercially can be held from one planting season to the next before the bacteria lose viability. In this new process, bacteria in water are applied to the alfalfa seeds in a seed treater. Air is removed from the coated seeds in a vacuum. Bacteria are forced under the seedcoats when the vacuum is released.

This "noculized" process was welcomed by the seed industry as a major advance that saves time, effort, and messy work. Major seedhouses have installed machinery for the process. Seeds of alfalfa so treated were planted on more than a million acres in 1959, the year after the process was born.

EQUIPMENT used for processing flower seeds includes a stationary thresher, a table model of the air-screen machine, a laboratory blower, and a specific gravity separator.

Conventional seed-cleaning equipment is used for sweetpea seeds. Vines are cut and left in a windrow to dry. Then they are lifted from the windrow and threshed with a combine that has a windrow attachment. Threshed seeds are cleaned on an air-screen cleaner to remove straw, leaves, weeds, and other large materials. The seeds are passed through another airstream that removes light trash. Light or shriveled seeds are removed with a specific gravity separator.

HAND LABOR is used often in producing and processing seeds of the new petunia hybrid. The seeds are planted by hand. Seedlings are transplanted by hand. Pollination, cultivation, harvesting, threshing, and packaging are done by hand. These seeds have sold for 7 thousand dollars a pound wholesale.

Seeds of petunia, salvia, primroses, marigold, zinnia, nasturtium, and many other flowers are harvested by hand, dried, and then processed in stationary threshers of many sizes up to field combines. Small air-screen and gravity separators and some handpicking are used in processing them.

Seeds of foxtail, snapdragons, asters, and similar flowers are cut before the seeds reach the shattering stage with a special swather that deposits the seeds on a canvas, where they are left to dry. The seeds are covered with canvas at night to protect them.

These seeds are cleaned after drying on the air-screen blower and gravity separators. Low-temperature, forced-air driers are used to reduce the moisture content to a safe level.

Flower seeds usually are processed in small volumes on small equipment, because only small amounts of seed are used each year. Many types of flower seeds lose vitality when they are stored more than a year. Seeds of some flowers that are properly dried and stored at moderate temperatures and humidities can be kept several years.

FUNGICIDES used to be applied in wet treatments, but the practice was unsatisfactory.

The development of dry-dust treatment was a big advance. Copper carbonate, introduced into the United States about 1920, mostly replaced the wet treatments as a control measure for many cereal diseases, especially stinking smut or bunt of wheat. Various types of equipment were developed for its application, notably a hand-operated, barrel-type treater, in which the seeds and the dry fungicide were mixed by a tumbling action.

Continuous-type dust treaters were developed and used many years. They have a fairly high capacity in bushels of seed treated per hour, but the problems, discomforts, and dangers involved in treating, handling, and planting dust-treated seed were many.

These objectionable features were overcome to a certain extent with the introduction of organic mercurials formulated as wettable powders for application in slurry-type treaters.

In it, the fungicide is mixed with water to form a thick, soupy suspension. Slurry machines are equipped with an adjustable hopper to control the flow of seeds into the machine, a slurry tank with a mechanical agitator to stir the mixture constantly, a positive seed and slurry metering device, and a short mixing auger that mixes the fungicide slurry and seeds and also moves the treated seeds to the discharge spout of the machine.

Slurry machines with output capacities up to 600 bushels of treated grain an hour are available. They usually are powered by small electric motors. Seeds of cereal grains, legumes, grasses, and vegetables can be treated in the basic machine. It can be modified as to seed hopper and mixing auger to treat delinted or fuzzy seed of cotton.

Special treaters have been developed for the application of concentrated liquid fungicides and insecticides directly to seed without water dilution. Two such treaters are available. One is of a rotating drum type; the other, a mist type.

The former has an adjustable seed hopper, which regulates the flow of seed into the machine; a small fungicide reservoir, from which the fungicide is metered into the machine; a storage drum of fungicide connected to the machine through a series of hoses and a centrifugal pump; a positive seed and fungicide metering device; fingerlike tubes at the drum inlet, which dispense the fungicide to the seed; and an inclined mixing chamber, whose adjustable baffles regulate the time the seed is retained.

Some models of the drum machine can treat up to 700 bushels of grain an hour. Seeds of cereal grains, legumes, grasses, cotton, and vegetables can be treated. Attachments enable the simultaneous application of liquid fungicides or insecticides and wettable powders or liquid fungicides and liquid insecticides. The treater has a small electric motor.

The mist-type treater is designed to apply low dosages of liquid fungicides. It has an adjustable hopper that regulates the flow of seeds into the machine; a positive metering device; a seed-dispersing cone; and a rapidly spinning disk, which breaks up the liquid fungicide into droplets. The dispersion cone causes the seeds to fall in a layer through the droplets.

A treater with three rotating disks in series was designed to provide more complete and uniform coverage with concentrated liquid fungicides. It is well suited to the application of wettable powders. The fungicide needed to treat a mass of seed is divided into three parts, each of which is broken up into a fog by a separate disk. The triple treater can also be modified to apply one, two, or three different formulations at one time.

A continuous-spray type of treater has come into extensive use for treating seeds of sugarbeets. Coverage obtained in an experimental model was nearly 100 percent. This method does not have the objectionable features of dust machines that once were used to treat sugarbeet seeds.

The continuous spray-type treater has an adjustable seed metering device, which is equipped with a switch that is activated when the hopper is empty; a tank containing the treating mixture, also equipped with a signal device to indicate when the mechanical agitator is in operation; pressure gages that indicate the pressure in pounds per square inch at the tank end and nozzle end of the pressure system; one flat fan nozzle; an indicator system that is activated when the flow of the treating mixture has fallen below a desired

rate; a rotating cylinder about 6 feet long, big enough to allow good distribution of fungicide, and open at both ends; and a corrugated liner inside the cylinder. The fungicide mixture is placed under pressure in the reservoir tank by compressed air. The treating mix flows through the lines to the nozzle and is sprayed on the seeds.

The fungicide mixture is sprayed on decorticated seeds of sugarbeet at the rate of 2 quarts per hundredweight of seeds. This applies 4 percent moisture to the seeds.

The treater drum or cylinder is powered by an electric motor of three-fourths horsepower. Its capacity is 2,500 to 3,500 pounds of treated decorticated sugarbeet seeds an hour. The treated seeds are elevated in airlift elevators to storage tanks, from which the seeds are bagged.

Coloring agents or dyes are added to the treating mix to denote specific treatments—green for seeds treated with wireworm repellant-fungicide; red for seeds treated with wireworm repellant; and yellow for fungicide-treated seeds. The colors also indicate the uniformity of coverage.

The high price and capacity of the machine may limit its general use to processors who handle large amounts.

The coverage obtained with most commercial seed-treating machines is incomplete. The coverage provided by the slurry-type machines, for example, is 75 to 90 percent. Drum and triple treat mist-type machines give about 80–95 percent coverage. The spray-type treater provides coverage of 96 to 100 percent.

LAURENCE H. PURDY *is a plant pathologist in the Cereal Crops Research Division, Regional Smut Research Laboratory, Pullman, Wash.*

JESSE E. HARMOND *is Head, Small Seed Harvesting and Processing Section, Agricultural Engineering Research Division, Corvallis, Oreg.*

G. BURNS WELCH *is an agricultural engineer, Mississippi State University, State College, Miss.*

Packages That Protect Seeds

LOUIS N. BASS, TE MAY CHING, AND
FLOYD L. WINTER

PACKAGES for seeds used to be mere containers. Modern packaging uses dozens of methods and materials to keep seeds at their original quality from the time they are processed to the time they are planted.

How seeds are packaged affects their physical characteristics of size; weight; color; moisture content; purity (freedom from weed seeds, inert matter, and other crop seeds); and freedom from disease organisms, insects, rodents, and mechanical damage. Physiological aspects like viability, vigor, and dormancy are affected but not the genetic qualities, except under unusual conditions.

The best way to maintain good viability and vigor of many kinds of seeds is to store them in a dry, cold (near or below freezing) place.

Many kinds will retain good viability and vigor for several years even at quite high temperatures if they are kept very dry. But when dry seeds in porous containers (burlap, cotton, paper) are removed from refrigerated and dehumidified storage, they absorb moisture rapidly from the atmosphere and may absorb so much moisture that viability is impaired in a few days or weeks. If very dry seeds are stored in moistureproof containers, however, absorption of moisture when they leave storage is not a problem.

Very dry seeds—of 3 to 8 percent moisture—that are kept in moistureproof containers retain good viability and vigor in various conditions of temperature and humidity. Moistureproof packaging therefore seems to be the most economical way to maintain the quality of processed seeds during storage and marketing.

Packages designed to protect most physical qualities of seeds are made of materials that have sufficient tensile strength, bursting strength, and tearing resistance to withstand the normal handling procedures. Such materials, however, may not protect seeds against either insects and rodents or changes in moisture unless special protective qualities are built into them.

Packages for processed seeds are made of burlap, cotton cloth, paper, films, metal, glass, fiberboard, and various combinations of materials. Some offer moisture protection. Others do not. Each material has characteristics that make it suitable for a particular type of package, however.

BURLAP is a low-cost fabric woven of good-quality jute yarn. Usually it is 40 inches wide and weighs 7 to 12 ounces a yard. Both cloth and bags are made in a variety of fabric constructions to conform to the buyers' specifications.

Burlap is strong in tensile strength and tear resistance. Burlap bags can be stacked high in storage and withstand rough handling in distribution. Burlap cloth usually holds its original qualities for several years under normal usage. Long exposure to water or dampness and to strong sunlight weakens burlap. The bags may be reused many times and still adequately protect most of the physical qualities of seed lots.

Burlap cloth is used in laminations with various other flexible materials, such as asphalt, films, and paper. Laminated burlap bags can be made that are resistant to moisture transmission, insects, and rodents. Some types of laminated bags retain the gases for fumigation and seed treatment. Many burlap and burlap-laminated bags are used for strength instead of their barrier properties.

COTTON BAGS for seeds are made from sheeting, printcloth, drill, osnaburg, and a special seamless material.

Cotton fabrics are produced in different widths and weights, each designed for a special purpose. Osnaburg, which is stout and coarse, and seamless fabrics have the greatest tensile strength and tear resistance of the cotton materials and are used most. Seamless cotton bags often are reused many times, but the other cotton bags normally are used only once.

Cotton fabrics can be coated and laminated. Selected laminating materials are bonded together by asphalt or vegetable or compounded latex adhesives; the cotton cloth provides the needed strength and protective properties.

Cotton bags protect physical quality, but have no effect upon moisture content, insects, or rodents, unless special barrier properties are built in. The two most widely used laminated moistureproof bags consist of one or two sheets of paper attached to a fabric with asphalt or a compounded latex adhesive. Other moistureproof constructions utilize such barrier materials as vegetable parchment, Pliofilm, polyethylene, and rubber coatings. Moistureproof liners sometimes are used inside cotton bags.

PAPER PRODUCTS are used extensively for packaging seed.

Most small packets are made of bleached sulfite or bleached kraft paper, which is coated with white clay to facilitate printing. A typical paper stock for small packets has a basic weight of 70 pounds per 500 sheets (25 x 38 inches). The packets are designed to contain a measured amount of seed without loss, but not to protect viability under unfavorable conditions.

Many paper seed bags have multiple plies or layers. These multiwall bags can be constructed of various thicknesses of smooth or crinkled paper. The kraft paper commonly used in them has a basic weight of 40 to 50 pounds per 500 sheets (24 x 36 inches).

Multiwall bags of smooth paper are produced in a variety of constructions, each designed for a specific purpose. Regular multiwall bags consist of two or more plies of kraft paper. The outside ply is heavy to take wear. Special plies are hidden among the layers of the multiwall. When moisture protection is required, a special barrier material, such as asphalt, polyethylene, or aluminum foil, is included. Barrier materials can be used for any layer, but usually they are between the two outer layers of paper.

A new trend for materials that readily absorb moisture, such as seeds, is to place a thin film laminate on the inside surface of the inner ply. Sometimes a film laminate is applied to the outside surface of the outer ply.

Ordinary multiwall bags have poor bursting strength. When they are piled high, the bottom bags burst. The top bags in high piles often slip. Ordinary multiwall bags tend to dry out in dry climates and become brittle along folds and on the corners at wear points.

ELASTIC MULTIWALL paper bags have several walls of crinkled paper. The number of plies depends on the weight of the product to be packaged. Often the two outer plies are laminated together with asphalt to provide a proper moisture-vapor barrier. The moistureproof outer layer also protects the inner layers of paper from damage by rain.

Elastic materials cannot be evaluated by the usual physical test data for tensile and tear strength because the entire principle of the elastic multiwall bag depends upon the stretchability of the paper. The weight of paper generally used (untreated per ply) is 45 pounds per 500 sheets (24 x 36 inches) in the flat or uncrinkled form. A 15-percent stretch gives a finished weight of about 52 pounds per 500 sheets.

The asphalt-laminated outer duplex ply consists of two sheets of 45-pound kraft held together with 40 pounds of asphalt laminate. Adding a 15-percent stretch to the outer ply makes a finished weight of about 150 pounds per 500 sheets.

This outer ply provides the moisture

barrier to prevent wetting or moisture absorption of the seed within the bag. At 80° F. and relative humidity of 75 percent, this ply has a moisture-vapor transmission rate of 0.17 gram per 100 square inches per 24 hours. This layer resists passage of water indefinitely.

The duplex-ply paper bag is considered to be airtight, but there may be some interchange of gases through the top closure sewing holes.

The thickness, toughness, and stretch of the outer ply provides the elastic multiwall paper bag with excellent puncture resistance. The resilience of the elastic multiwall material absorbs the shock of impacts and keeps the bag from splitting.

Some seed bags are made of laminates of paper/polyethylene/aluminum foil. These combinations afford better protection against moisture than foil or polyethylene used alone with paper. Paper can be treated to repel insects and rodents.

Multiwall paper and laminated cotton and burlap bags are designed to meet specific requirements of a variety of conditions of weather, shipping, handling, and storage. Manufacturers therefore seldom supply the same type of bag for a particular seed throughout the country or even to two seedsmen in the same locality.

Seed companies do not use the same type of bag for all kinds of seed. They package seed, such as corn, in two or three types of bags—for example, osnaburg, elastic multiwall paper with an asphalt barrier ply, and 10-mil (0.01 inch) polyethylene.

Films of cellophane, Pliofilm, polyester, polyvinyl, aluminum foil, and polyethylene are used alone or in various combinations.

Cellophane, made of regenerated cellulose, is produced in more than 100 varieties. Each is designed for specific purposes.

Moistureproof types, which have low moisture-vapor transmission rates, are used for small packages. Cellophane

alone may become brittle with age or in dry localities and break easily, but several firms produce combinations of cellophane and polyethylene that do not become brittle, like cellophane alone, and offer quite good moisture protection.

Polyethylene - cellophane laminates heat-seal easily and perform well on automatic packaging machines.

Pliofilm is a thermoplastic rubber hydrochloride plastic film. It resists ripping, tearing, and splitting. It seals well at low temperatures, has good moisture-barrier properties, and can be laminated to itself, paper, foils, and other films. Pliofilm can be used on most packaging machines designed for flexible-film packaging. It may deteriorate in strong light.

Polyester films are heat - sealable, transparent, flexible plastic materials with low moisture-vapor, carbon dioxide, and oxygen transmission rates. They have great tensile strength. They will not dry out or become brittle with age because they contain no plasticizer. Polyester film can be laminated to itself and practically any other material. Its flexible laminates can be used with most flexible packaging equipment. A new construction that utilizes a base of light cotton fabric and metalized polyester film offers easier fabrication, stronger seals, and resistance to flex damage, rough handling, and pinholes.

Polyvinyl films are heat sealable, deteriorate slowly in sunlight, and have outstanding tensile strength and tear resistance. They provide only moderate moisture protection unless they are laminated to a good moisture-barrier material. They heat-seal over a wide range of temperatures, are ideal for automatic packaging machinery, and laminate well to paper, foil, or other films.

Annealed aluminum foil has a tensile strength of 8.5 pounds per inch of width per mil thickness. Tensile strength and resistance to tearing and bursting are greater for strain-hardened foil than for annealed foil of the same thickness. Aluminum foil increases in strength as the gage (thickness) is increased and temperature drops.

Aluminum foil has a low moisture-vapor transmission rate, even for thicknesses less than 0.0015 inch, which have tiny perforations called pinholes. These seem to be inevitable when metal is rolled to very thin gages. Microscopic measurements of all the pinholes in 100 square inches of 0.0004-inch foil gave an estimated area of 0.00004 square inch. A single hole of this area would transmit about 0.19 gram of water vapor per 24 hours at 100° and 100 percent relative humidity. The number and size of pinholes decrease with increasing foil thickness.

Moisture-vapor transmission also declines with increasing foil thickness. A 0.00035-inch foil will transmit approximately 0.29 gram of water vapor per 100 square inches of foil per 24 hours at 100° and 100 percent relative humidity. A 0.0005-inch foil transmits 0.12 gram of water vapor under the same conditions. Thicker foils transmit almost no water vapor at all.

Aluminum foil alone does not make good packages for seeds, but it can be bonded to other materials to produce combinations having almost any desired characteristics. Even though thin gages of aluminum foil have some pinholes, combinations with various supporting materials, such as paper or plastic films, offer effective barriers to moisture vapor and gas transfer. With the proper selection of materials, combinations can be produced that will restrict vapor transfer completely.

LAMINATIONS—such as aluminum foil/glassine paper/aluminum foil/heat-sealing lacquer; aluminum foil/tissue paper/polyethylene; and the paper/polyethylene/aluminum foil-polyethylene—have been used satisfactorily.

Foil is used also as a coating and as an overwrap material for cardboard.

POLYETHYLENE, the most extensively used thermoplastic film, is made from aliphatic hydrocarbon resins. Polyethylene resins are polymers of ethylene gas.

Commercially available polyethylene resins fall into three groups on the basis of their density, which is due to differences in molecular structure. Molecular structure determines the physical structure of the resins. Resin properties and extrusion variables determine film properties, which in turn determine the utility of the film.

Such physical properties as tensile strength, tearing strength, bursting strength, moisture-vapor transmission rate, carbon dioxide and oxygen transmission rates, sealability, and elongation and folding endurance determine the usefulness of a film.

Conventional low-density films have been considered better for seed packages than medium- and high-density films because of differences in bursting and tearing strength and stretch, but a special new medium-density film shows considerable promise.

The medium- and high-density films tend to show progressively less permeability to moisture vapor and gases than conventional low-density films. A 1-mil low-density film tested at 100° and 100 percent relative humidity will permit passage of 1.4 grams of moisture vapor through 100 square inches of film in 24 hours, a medium-density film will transmit 0.7 gram, and a high-density film 0.3 gram under the same conditions. A 10-mil low-density film at 100° and 100 percent relative humidity will transmit 0.13 gram of moisture vapor per 100 square inches per 24 hours, approximately one-tenth the amount transmitted by the 1-mil film.

A polyethylene film of medium density (specific gravity 0.938) has been developed that surpasses the performance of conventional polyethylene. A 7-mil film of this special material has a moisture-vapor transmission rate of 0.10 gram per 24 hours per 100 square inches which is less than that of 10-mil conventional polyethylene. This special medium-density film has better tensile properties and greater elongation than conventional polyethylene. Because of its high percentage of stretch, this medium-density film has good resistance to puncture.

Clear conventional polyethylene and the special translucent white medium-density polyethylene films are subject to slow deterioration on direct exposure to strong sunlight and ultraviolet radiation. Deterioration can be retarded by incorporating carbon black or other pigments that absorb the ultraviolet rays. The special medium-density film has high resistance to stress cracking.

Rats and mice sometimes present a problem with conventional polyethylene, but we have had no reports of rodent attack on bags made of the special medium-density material. Perhaps this material is an answer to rodent problems.

With a tight closure, such as is produced with a heat-seal, both 10-mil conventional polyethylene and 7-mil medium-density polyethylene bags are almost completely insectproof. Some insects may penetrate thinner polyethylene films.

Polyethylene films can be laminated to themselves, other films, foil, paper, textile fabrics, and fiberboard. Moisture barrier and other physical properties may be improved by laminations. The various properties of each film included in a laminate are more or less additive. Some laminated films are completely impervious to various gases and practically impervious to moisture vapor.

Some laminated materials handle well on automatic packaging machinery and others handle best by hand, depending on the nature of the materials used in the laminations.

METAL CONTAINERS, properly sealed, provide an absolute barrier to moisture and gas and shield the product from light. They provide complete protection against rodents, insects, changing humidity, floods, and harmful fumes, and protect the factors of physical quality, including moisture content. Metal cans can be filled and sealed automatically and quickly.

Glass containers are not used very much for packaging seeds. They provide essentially the same protection as metal, but glass breaks easily.

Glass containers are used in research and occasionally as display receptacles in stores where bulk sales are made. Some persons use glass jars for keeping seed from one season to the next.

Cardboard in the form of boxes and cans is used extensively. Cardboard cans have metal lids and bottoms. Conventional boxboard—cardboard— has no moisture-barrier qualities, but they are achieved by laminating polyethylene, aluminum foil, or some other barrier material to the boxboard or by overwrapping the carton with waxpaper, aluminum foil, or polyethylene.

Cardboard containers provide good protection to most physical qualities of seeds, but they protect the moisture content only when the special barrier properties are added as laminates or overwraps.

Cardboard containers are well adapted for automatic filling and sealing.

Tests of all kinds of packaging materials for moisture-vapor transmission are conducted in a situation of relative humidity so high that it is seldom encountered in the marketing and storage of seeds. The rate of moisture-vapor penetration of most materials consequently is less under normal use than that indicated by tests.

LONGEVITY of seeds—the maintenance of their viability—is associated closely with the moisture in them. In open or porous containers, the moisture content is controlled by the relative humidity of the surrounding atmosphere and the temperature of the storage area.

Different kinds of seeds absorb different amounts of water under identical conditions. Each kind has its own equilibrium content of moisture for a given temperature and relative humidity. It drops or rises as atmospheric relative humidity goes down or up.

Seeds absorb or give off moisture according to the degree of saturation of the surrounding atmosphere—not the actual amount of water vapor present in a unit volume of air.

Seeds subjected to fluctuating levels of moisture tend to deteriorate faster than seeds held at a constant level of moisture. A constant moisture content can be maintained by controlling the temperature and relative humidity of the storage area or placing the seeds in a moisture-barrier package, which may be completely or partly impervious to moisture vapor.

Hermetically sealed metal and glass containers are completely impervious to moisture vapor and gases. Containers made of flexible packaging materials resist transmission of moisture vapor and gases only to the extent that the special barrier properties are built into them.

In completely impervious packages, in which the relative humidity of the atmosphere is determined primarily by the moisture content of the seed, any rise or drop in its moisture is limited to the small effect of temperature.

The relative humidity in packages made of materials with limited permeability is determined by the seed moisture, temperature and relative humidity of the storage chamber, permeability of the packaging material, and size of the package.

Seeds in packages that are not completely impervious to moisture vapor may gain or lose moisture with time. The direction, rate, and amount of change of the moisture are controlled by the temperature and relative humidity of the storage area, moisture-vapor transmission rate of the packaging material, equilibrium moisture content of the seeds for the surrounding temperature and humidity, and the ratio of surface area of seeds to the surface area of the package.

Because the small packages contain fewer seeds than large packages per unit area of package surface, each seed in a small package gives up or absorbs a larger part of the moisture vapor transmitted through the package surface. Seeds in small packages of a given material therefore gain or lose moisture faster than seeds in large packages of the same material held under the same conditions of temperature and relative humidity. Small packages thus require better moisture-barrier materials than large packages in order to provide the same amount of moisture protection to the seeds inside.

The substitution of carbon dioxide, nitrogen, or a partial vacuum for the normal atmosphere in sealed gastight containers may or may not increase longevity of seed. Seeds held under unfavorable conditions may deteriorate faster than normal. Seeds under good storage conditions may not be affected at all. In the instances where carbon dioxide, nitrogen, and vacuum have prolonged the viability, the beneficial effects usually were not pronounced.

Many kinds of seeds do not require special moisture protection during the first winter following production when they are held in the area where they were produced or under similar climatic conditions. Seeds carried over to the second planting season following production often require drying and packaging in moisture-barrier containers to prevent loss of viability.

Each kind of seed has its own safe moisture content for sealed storage in the Temperate Zone. Tomato, pepper, cabbage, and cauliflower seed should not contain more than 5 percent of moisture for safe storage in hermetically sealed metal cans held at moderate temperatures. Other maximum seed moisture levels for safe storage in such cans are: Celery and lettuce, 5.5 percent; cucumbers, watermelons, cantaloups, onions, and eggplants, 6 percent; parsley, 6.5 percent; carrots, peas, 7 percent; beets, 7.5 percent; and spinach, sweet corn, beans, lawn grasses, 8 percent.

PACKAGES are filled in many ways. The equipment may be a simple spoon or seed scoop; the gravity flow from a manually controlled bin; or a high-speed, completely automatic small packet, metal can, or plastic bag filler. Most filling equipment has a measuring device or is controlled manually or automatically on a signal from a weighing device.

Practically all seeds, except those in small packets, are sold on a weight or volume basis. Even those seeds that appear to be sold on a volume basis are associated with weight—for example, a bushel of corn is 56 pounds; a bushel of wrinkled peas is 56 pounds; a bushel of smooth peas is 60 pounds.

To meet these requirements, it is necessary to put into the individual packages a selected amount of seed by weight or by volume, the latter being related to a selected weight. Weighing devices range from an ordinary beam scale to an elaborate scale that activates a pneumatic or an electrical device to shut off the flow of seed when a weight or volume is reached.

Rigid containers always have the same volume, but the seed placed in them may vary in weight for the same volume. Oats, for example, may weigh 34 pounds to a bushel one year and 28 pounds the next. A similar variation may occur in different areas the same year. In order to get the proper weight of seed into a rigid container, it may have to be vibrated while it is being filled, particularly if the seeds are light and fluffy or do not flow readily. The vibrator may be attached to the platform that supports the container while it is being filled or the side of the container may be placed in contact with a vibrator.

Some seeds are sold on the basis of number, either actual or adjusted for percentage of pure live seed (the percentage of pure seed times the germination percentage). It may well be that in time most seed will be sold on a pure, live-seed basis. Some companies package hybrid corn seed in acre units. Each package contains the correct amount of seed for planting a specified number of acres.

Except in small operations, seeds to be packaged are delivered to hopper bins above the filling machines. Seeds may come to the hopper from bulk storage bins by gravity flow through pipes, by airlift, belt conveyors, storage boxes or in bags handled by bag elevators, forklifts, or on a man's shoulder.

All handling of the seeds must be done with care, as there may be some effect on the physical quality through impact or undue pressure.

Heavy seeds, especially those of beans, peas, corn, and soybeans, can be fractured if they strike or are struck by a hard object or firm surface. The breaks may not be readily visible in the dry seeds. The severity of injury is related to the moisture content and the force of impact. Seeds that contain too much or too little moisture are damaged easily. Seeds may be damaged when they are forced through a restricted opening.

Injuries may also be caused by rough handling of packages and planting with equipment that squeezes the seeds as they are fed into the planting spout. The damage may kill the embryo or cause a weak or abnormal seedling to be produced—for example, beans without complete cotyledons and baldhead bean seedlings, which lack a terminal growing point. Mechanical damage also shortens the storage life of seeds, even when they are held under the most favorable conditions of storage.

The types and sizes of packages used for wholesale distribution often are quite different from the ones used for retail sales. Processors usually package seeds in burlap, osnaburg, or seamless and multiwall paper bags that hold 50 or 100 pounds or one-half to 3 bushels.

A number of companies use moisture-barrier packages (such as elastic multiwall paper bags with an asphalt or a polyethylene or aluminum foil barrier ply in the multiwall), burlap or cotton bags with polyethylene liners and burlap/asphalt/paper bags for seed of cereal grains, soybeans, hybrid sorghums, hybrid corn, cotton, peas, beans, sweet corn, coniferous and broad-leaved trees, and various other kinds. Hybrid corn seed is also packaged in 7- or 10-mil polyethylene bags.

A valve-type polyethylene bag, developed in 1959, prevents loss of material while filling and is sealed more easily than the conventional bag. Fumigants and inert gases can be easily introduced into the filled bags. Some alfalfa seed is packaged in large cardboard cartons. Flower seeds are sometimes packaged in cans.

Large, nonrigid containers (burlap, cotton, lined bags, multiwall and 7- and 10-mil polyethylene bags) are usually positioned manually. They are held in place by hooks or clamps or by hand during filling.

Hand tying of the open ends of cotton and fiber bags has been largely replaced by sewing, done mostly with sewing machines adapted for this purpose. Multiwall paper and laminated bags are closed by sewing or sewing and taping, and polyethylene bags are closed by heat sealing.

Heat sealing of polyethylene and other thermoplastic materials is accomplished by applying heat (200°–400°) to the film while the point of closure is under pressure. Each kind and thickness of material has specific requirements as to temperature, time, and pressure for proper sealing.

Heat sealers include small hand irons or rollers, hand- or foot-operated jaws or clamps, and elaborate, automatic machines for forming, filling, and sealing bags and pouches. Some sealers use thermostatically controlled bars, bands, or rollers. Others use a brief, high-intensity thermal impulse. Most sealers are readily adjustable for use with many kinds of materials.

A wide variety of materials and package sizes are utilized in preparing seed for retail sales. Most field seeds are sold at retail in the original wholesale packages, but seeds of vegetables, flowers, and lawn grasses are packaged for various types of retail customers. Multiwall paper, cloth, and plastic bags; cardboard boxes and drums; and metal cans of 1 to 10 pounds' capacity

are used for grass and vegetable seeds for truck farmers.

Small paper, foil, and plastic packets and cardboard boxes that contain a few seeds, a fraction of an ounce, or several ounces are used for mail-order and store sales of vegetable and flower seeds. Tobacco seeds usually are packaged in paper packets that hold one-half ounce and 1 ounce.

The medium and small flexible and semirigid containers used for retail packages may be preformed or formed into bags or packets from sheets or rolls. Preformed containers can be opened with a jet of air and automatically or manually positioned for filling. The high-speed automatic fillers pick up and position the individual packets in ferris wheel or merry-go-round fashion. A specified amount of seed is injected into each opened packet at the rate of one per second. When bags or packets are formed from sheets or rolls, they are formed, filled, and sealed in one continuous operation on a single- or a many-unit machine.

Metal cans, glass jars, and fiber drums come from the manufacturer ready for filling. Usually they are delivered to the filler by conveyors which automatically position each unit.

Most fabric and some paper containers are sealed by sewing or sewing and taping. Most paper and cardboard containers are sealed with cold or hot glue. If the number of packages processed at a time is fairly large, sealing is done automatically with hot glue. The various types of plastic packages are heat sealed.

Rigid containers, such as fiber drums, may have slip-on caps or lids that clamp into position and are applied manually. Metal and glass containers usually have the lid end sealed with special closing machines.

Can sealers are manually operated, semiautomatic, and fully automatic.

Placing seed in rolls of tape may be considered a form of packaging. The American Seed Tape Co. in the 1920's developed machines for forming the tape, placing the seed, and making the roll. This form of packaging did not become an accepted sales instrument at that time, but was revived later.

Seed packages must be labeled to show the species, variety, percentage of live seed, purity, content of noxious weeds, and seed treatment, if any. The information may be printed on a tag attached to the bag. It may be printed on a label that is glued to the container. It may be printed or stamped directly on the container. Seedsmen usually print their own tags and labels.

Stenciling on bags may be done manually or automatically by rotary printer as the container passes a point on an assembly line. Embossing normally is done by the closing machine.

Special labeling machines can apply glue to the can or label and wrap the label around the can as it rolls through the machine. A special printer may imprint information on the can before the label is applied so that it can be identified even if the label is removed.

The final packaging operation is the assembling of the packages. Large containers may be brought together by belt or roller conveyor or placed by hand on pallets handled by forklift, or by use of handtrucks. Smaller units frequently are placed in larger cartons by hand or automatically with equipment built to assemble a selected number of units and place them in cartons.

The seeds are then ready for transportation and distribution to their eventual destination—in the good earth, where their germination will demonstrate the protective value of modern packaging.

LOUIS N. BASS *is a plant physiologist in the Agricultural Research Service, National Seed Storage Laboratory, Fort Collins, Colo. Formerly he was assistant professor of botany and plant pathology in Iowa State University.*

TE MAY CHING *is an assistant agronomist, Farm Crops Department, Oregon Agricultural Experiment Station, Corvallis.*

FLOYD L. WINTER *is vice president and director of breeding and research, Asgrow Seed Co., New Haven, Conn.*

Transporting, Handling, and Storing Seeds

LEO E. HOLMAN AND JAMES R. SNITZLER

FARMERS plant alfalfa seed from California, ryegrass seed from Oregon, whiteclover seed from Idaho, redtop seed from Illinois or Missouri, sudangrass seed from Texas, tall fescue seed from Kentucky, and orchardgrass seed from Virginia.

The seed is transported from the place of production to the place of planting by railroads, trucks, and ships. The primary users of these facilities are middlemen, who assemble, process (the seed industry calls it conditioning), store, and ship the seed to large-scale growers or to other middlemen, who sell it to those who plant it.

More than 3 million tons of seeds were transported from producer to user in 1959. That tonnage would fill about 200 thousand tractor-trailers or 100 thousand rail cars.

That fact brings out an interesting point.

THE TONNAGE of seeds is substantial, but it is small compared to the total tonnage of agricultural products that the carriers haul. It was only 2.6 percent of the tonnage of agricultural products hauled by the railroads and about 1 percent of the combined tonnage of agricultural products hauled by the three major types of carriers.

The small percentage that seed bears to total agricultural tonnage belies its importance to the carriers and to the Nation's economy. Our entire agricultural production depends on the delivery of seed to the right place, at the right time, and in the right condition. The tonnage of seeds thus is a generator for the total tonnage of our agricultural products.

Domestic-grown seed sold off farms was 94 percent of the total seed hauled in this country in 1959. The rest was imported.

Wheat, corn, rye, oats, rice, sorghums, barley, and buckwheat made up 41 percent of the total tonnage.

Vegetable seeds and potatoes were next in importance—29 percent. Field seeds (principally grasses and legumes) and oilseeds (soybeans, peanuts, and flax) each accounted for about 14 percent. A miscellaneous group consisting of seeds of cotton, tobacco, flowers (imported), trees, and shrubs made up the remaining 2 percent.

ALL MODES of transport are used in hauling seeds. The railroads, the predominant carriers, hauled 1.8 million tons, or 60 percent of the total. These rail and truck percentages represent primarily the long-haul movement of seeds—that is, from the country assembly points through the various wholesale trade channels to the retail stores. The short-haul movement, from the farm to the country assembly point and from the retail outlet to the farm, is nearly all by truck.

The long-haul movement of seeds also involved the use of boats and airplanes, but the combined tonnage hauled by them probably did not exceed 3 percent in 1959.

Most of the tonnage carried in barges and lake and coastwise freighters consisted of grass and legume seeds grown in Oregon and shipped through the port of Portland to destinations on the gulf and Atlantic coasts.

Seed shipped by air is primarily experimental and high-value seed for which the buyer is willing to pay the higher cost of this premium service.

Parcel post is used extensively for small shipments of vegetable and flower seeds, but it utilizes one or more of the types of carriers previously mentioned—mainly rail and truck.

Privately owned and for-hire trucks are used to transport seeds.

Private trucks do most of the short-haul shipments. They are owned or leased by producers and wholesale buyers, who haul the seeds from the farm to the country assembly point for reshipment; farmers, who purchase the seed from the local retail seed dealers and haul it to their farms; and retail dealers, who provide delivery service to the farm.

The truck share of the long-haul movement (from the country assembly point to the retail outlet) is hauled largely by for-hire motor carriers. These are truck operators whose primary business is to haul commodities or other types of merchandise for the general public for compensation.

Two types of for-hire motor carriers engage in hauling seeds—exempt and regulated. This distinction is based upon the Motor Carrier Act of 1935, which provided generally for the Federal regulation of motor carriers engaged in interstate transportation.

The act contained exemptions for vehicles hauling nonmanufactured agricultural commodities, such as fresh fruit and vegetables, grain, poultry and eggs, ordinary livestock, and seeds.

The term "exempt carrier" is applied to motor carriers that haul exempt commodities only. They are subject to rules and regulations of the Interstate Commerce Commission as to safety and hours of service of drivers, but they are not subject to regulation by the Commission over entry into the trucking business, the rates charged, and routes served.

Regulated carriers hold authority from the ICC for the transportation of other than exempt commodities. They may also haul exempt commodities and, when doing so, are not subject to economic regulation by the ICC as to those commodities, as long as no nonexempt commodities are moved in the same truck at the same time.

Exempt agricultural commodities, such as seeds, serve to balance out the return-haul movement for many regulated motor carriers, particularly the

340

large regulated motor carriers in the Far West, since their inbound tonnage of manufactured goods for California and the Pacific Northwest exceeds the outbound tonnage of this type of merchandise. Not all of the truck portion of the seed tonnage moving from the Far West is hauled by the regulated motor carriers, however. Exempt motor carriers also haul a part.

Both exempt and regulated motor carriers haul seed grain from the production branches or country warehouses of seed wholesalers in the Midwest to their retail dealers. Exempt truckers are also used extensively in hauling seed potatoes from Boston to growers and dealers in the Middle Atlantic and Southeastern States. This haul is particularly attractive to the exempt trucker, since ordinarily he has delivered a load of fresh fruit, vegetables, or citrus fruit to New England and is looking for a return haul to the Southeast.

AN ADVANTAGE of using rail carriers to ship seed is the transit arrangement. Seed may be shipped from California to a wholesaler in the Midwest, where it may undergo further processing and then be forwarded to the final destination at the rate that applied to a direct movement of seed from its origin to final destination.

An example, based on the rail rates in effect in February 1960, illustrates the cost advantage of this transit privilege to a Midwest wholesaler. The through rate for a shipment moving directly from California to final destination in Illinois is 1.35 dollars per hundredweight. Without the transit privilege, the wholesaler would pay the local rate of 1.29 dollars from the California production area to a transit point in Missouri. After the seed has been processed and prepared for reshipment, he would again pay a local rate—this time 99 cents from the transit point to Illinois. The combination of local rates would result in a total transportation cost of 2.98 dollars per hundredweight.

Under the transit arrangement, the wholesaler would pay only 1.405 dollars per 100 pounds. This includes the local rate of 1.29 dollars from the California production area to the Missouri transit point, a separate transit charge of 5.5 cents per 100 pounds, and a balance on the outbound shipment of 6 cents per 100 pounds (the difference between the local rate of 1.29 dollars and the through rate of 1.35 dollars).

The saving on the transit privilege is 87.5 cents per 100 pounds, or 700 dollars on a carload shipment of 80 thousand pounds.

The saving is a major reason why many shippers of seeds prefer rail transportation. Some shippers, however, have found that sometimes it is cheaper to use trucks for either the inbound or outbound movement, although by so doing they give up the transit privilege and thus must pay the local rail rate in combination with the truck rate. The railroads have lowered their rates in some instances to meet this truck competition.

Convenience of loading and unloading is another advantage of using rail transportation for shipping seeds. The shipper or receiver has 48 hours free of charge for loading or unloading the car after it has been placed at his disposal. Additional time beyond the 48 hours is subject to the payment of a published demurrage charge.

Trucking companies do not consider this type of service economically feasible, because the driver and perhaps an alternate driver will accompany the equipment and must be paid for waiting time. The truckers therefore are anxious to get their equipment loaded and unloaded as quickly as possible and back on the road.

Rail carriers can handle large shipments on long hauls at low rates. For example, some seeds, such as beans and peas, are shipped from the Far West with minimum carload quantities as high as 80 thousand pounds. The railroads introduced these high minimum carload weights to encourage the shippers to load the cars more heavily. For example, the rail rate on dry beans shipped from California to Texas is 1 dollar per 100 pounds for carloads with a minimum weight of 80 thousand pounds. The rate is 2.24 dollars a hundredweight for carload shipments with a minimum of 40 thousand pounds.

TRUCKS usually can make deliveries from the warehouse of a seed wholesaler to his customers in less time than it would take to move them by rail.

Speed is important late in the planting season, when retail dealers may run out of certain varieties of seeds and need refill orders immediately or when emergency conditions, such as floods and droughts, may have ruined a farmer's first planting and he needs seed for replanting.

Speed also is important in the servicing of the supermarket trade by seed wholesalers. Because the large chains operate on the basis of a fast turnover and a minimum of inventory, they need to replenish their stocks of seeds several times during the season. They therefore specify the date and hour of delivery, a date that makes mandatory the fastest transportation.

A large share of the seed-marketing business does not require fast delivery service, of course. Because most of the seed of grass, legumes, grains, vegetables, and flowers are harvested in the late summer and fall, several months elapse before it is needed for planting. During this interval, the seed is in storage in the wholesaler's warehouse. In order to reduce his storage risk and to insure a more orderly method of distribution, he begins shipments to independent retail seed dealers as early as December. He uses rail and truck transportation.

To induce the retailer to carry an inventory of seeds during the winter, the wholesaler may postpone payment of the invoice until April or May, grant quantity discounts, and allow the retailer to deduct a warehousing allowance from the invoice.

Motortrucks also provide pickup and delivery service. This service is particularly important for customers who are not on a railroad. Among them are farmer agents, who, as sales agents for the wholesalers, sell seed to other farmers in their locality.

Whether he uses railroad or truck transportation, the shipper ordinarily can partly load the car or truck at one place and complete the loading somewhere else. The car or truck may also be stopped for unloading at several places. This service is important, especially for rail shipments, because many retail dealers lack storage space for handling a full carload of seed.

The motor carriers generally make a separate charge ranging from 5 to 10 dollars a stop, and the railroads 15 to 20 dollars, depending on the area.

Stopping in transit to load or unload some of the seed allows the buyers to obtain the benefit of lower carload rates that are often available on heavier shipments.

BOTH SHIPPERS and carriers are responsible for taking protective measures to insure that seed arrives at its destination in satisfactory condition. The shipper's responsibility is to see that the seed is properly loaded and secure from the ordinary transportation hazards. The carrier's responsibility is to deliver the seed to the destination in the same condition that it was received at the shipping point.

A major type of loss and damage to seed shipments is from torn sacks or bags. It is associated largely with rail shipments. It causes loss of the seed containers and the seed itself. A common cause is protruding nails and bolts and loose or splintered boards. Any shifting of the load when one car bumps into another in switching operations or when a long freight train starts or stops can cause a bag of seed to be ripped open if it is lying against a rough or sharp object.

Water may cause shipping containers to split apart. It may damage the seed itself, for excess moisture and warm temperature can cause enough heat to generate in the seed to destroy its ability to germinate or to give it an odor strong enough to make it unsalable. Leaky roofs, loose-fitting doors, and worn tarpaulins may lead to such damage, which occurs more frequently in truck shipments than in rail.

Industrial chemicals and oil residues that were not removed from the rail car or truck before loading may cause the bags to disintegrate. The container may soak up some of the residues or take up an odor from them.

Freezing hurts some seeds, such as potatoes. To avoid that, portable heaters are placed in the truck or car for shipments in winter, but overheating is not good.

Grain that is moved in bulk into the wholesaler's plant for further processing may suffer damage and loss in transit because of loose doors, loose or broken floorboards, or cracks in the floor.

Protective measures include inspection of the carrier's equipment by the shipper to determine whether it is in fit condition for hauling seeds. Since the general rule is to keep seeds dry and cool, even a brief inspection of the inside and outside of a rail car or truck should reveal whether it is possible to maintain these conditions.

Such inspection should also reveal the presence of loose or broken wallboards or floorboards, protruding nails or bolts, broken pieces of wire strapping, chemical or oil residues or other material left in the car which might damage the seed or its containers.

If it appears that the equipment cannot be put in satisfactory condition, the shipper should ask the carrier to replace it with equipment that is fit for hauling seeds, since the responsibility for accepting or rejecting equipment for loading rests with the shipper.

Once the carrier has provided adequate equipment, the responsibility for preparing it for loading rests with the shipper only when shipping in rail carlots, because only then is the responsibility for loading his. For shipments by truck, the truck operators generally do their own loading and must see to it that their equipment is in proper condition. Not, however, that these protective measures are solely for the benefit of shippers: Truck operators also can benefit thereby through reductions in loss and damage claims.

An additional step in preparation for loading is to sweep out the car carefully. The floor, sidewalls, and ends of the car should then be lined with heavy kraft paper.

Special precautions need to be taken for bags or cartons stacked near the doorway of a rail car. That can be done by using strips made of heavy paper, reinforced at regular intervals with steel strapping and nailed to the doorposts through prepunched holes in the strappings. For bulk shipments, one-piece doors of wood or heavy-duty, water-repellent paperboard, reinforced with steel strapping, are placed inside the regular car doors.

Another protective measure for loads of bags of various weights is to place the heaviest bags on the bottom to prevent the bags splitting open from the overhead weight. The bags should be stacked tightly together in an interlocking pattern to lessen chances that the load may shift in transit.

Sometimes a properly loaded shipment may be damaged by the receiver when it is being unloaded. To prevent this loss, one shipper prints this note of caution on the loading chart and tally sheet, which is tacked to the wall inside the loaded car: "Do not drag bags over the car floor. Be careful in removing bottom and outside layer of bags. Care has been taken to remove all nails and bolts before loading, but some may work out in transit. A little care on your part will offset considerable damage to the goods."

SEEDS SHOULD be handled more like eggs than like stones.

Much of the modern equipment for handling materials can be used safely for handling most kinds of seeds.

Bucket elevators or legs of the centrifugal-discharge type are used extensively to move seeds vertically in bulk. Buckets, mounted at spaced intervals on belts or chains, are loaded by scooping up seeds from the boot at the bottom. The seeds are discharged by centrifugal action as the belt passes over the head wheel. The speed of the belt must be held within close limits so the seeds will discharge properly—fast enough that the seeds will not follow the buckets downward and slow enough that the seeds will not be damaged by striking against the discharge chute. Capacities usually range up to 175 tons an hour. The horsepower required can be estimated as follows: Hp.=2 × tons per hour × the lift in feet, with the product divided by 1,000.

This type of elevator is not self-cleaning. Considerable time is required to clean it thoroughly when handling different lots of seed whose identity must be preserved. Good commercial vacuum cleaners are available, however, that make it easier to do a good cleaning job.

A self-cleaning vertical elevator for handling seed in bulk is available. It has two chains. A series of pivoted buckets is attached to the chains. The elevator has no lower boot and no discharge head at the upper end and is not enclosed in a housing. The seed is fed into the buckets by a feeder—a small hopper bin—between the two sets of sprocket wheels along the lower horizontal run. There is little or no spilling of the seeds, as the lip of one cup overlaps that of the adjoining cup. The seed is elevated and discharged into a distributor on the upper horizontal run. Little or no cleaning of the elevator is required between different lots of seeds. The danger of damaging the seeds is small.

Pneumatic conveyors, which carry materials within a pipe in a high-velocity stream of air, also are used for handling seeds in bulk. They are self-cleaning, simple, and inexpensive to maintain. The fan is the only major moving part. Seed can be conveyed up or down, around corners—anywhere the conveyor pipe can be laid. These conveyors eliminate much of the dust associated with seed handling. They have high power requirements. Seeds may be damaged unless the system is properly designed and operated correctly; therefore the indirect system of conveying should be used so the seeds will not pass through the fan.

Most seeds can be conveyed satisfactorily with air velocities up to 5 thousand feet per minute with little damage. From 35 to 50 cubic feet of air per pound of seed are needed to operate a low-pressure system. A rule of thumb is that seeds weighing 40 to 60 pounds a cubic foot can be conveyed at a rate of 4 tons an hour through a pipe 10 inches in diameter at an air velocity of 5 thousand f.p.m. Well-designed systems should convey one thousand pounds per hour per horsepower.

N. R. Brandenburg, of the Department of Agriculture, studied the possible application of fluidized conveying to handling seeds. It differs from conventional pneumatic conveying in that seeds move and act like a liquid as they move through a pipe. Velocity and power requirements are usually much less and the size of conveying pipe is much smaller for fluidized conveying. Air pressures are much higher. This method was in the development stage in 1961. It seems to have promise, particularly for seeds that are easily damaged.

BELT conveyors are used for moving seeds in bag or in bulk in a horizontal or inclined direction. Flat-belt conveyors are used for bagged or packaged seeds, and troughed-belt conveyors for bulk seed. They work smoothly and noiselessly. They can be run in either direction. They are well adapted to portable operation. They operate more efficiently at high speeds than any other continuous conveyor and there is little damage to the seeds. They are especially suitable for handling bags or packages.

Belt conveyors are limited to a maximum incline of about 17° for handling seeds in bulk. The recommended maximum speed is about 300 feet per minute for a belt 10 inches wide for conveying small seeds in bulk and up to 400 f.p.m. for such seeds as wheat, corn, and soybeans. About 10 f.p.m. can be added for each additional inch of belt width. Flat conveyors carrying bagged or packaged seeds generally operate best at about 100 f.p.m.

A RULE OF THUMB that can be used for estimating the horsepower required for any belt conveyor is to take 2 percent of the number of tons of seed carried per hour for each 100 feet of horizontal belt. For example: 100 tons per hour to be carried 150 feet=0.02×100×1.5=3 horsepower. For inclined conveyors, an additional 1 percent should be added for each additional 10 feet of rise in incline.

Portable belt conveyors, with platform elevators, are used in warehouses for piling bagged seeds, removing bags from the piles, and moving bagged seed into and out of the warehouse. They can move few or many bags at a time.

The industrial fork truck is used with pallets to handle bagged or packaged seed in warehouses that have suitable floors and column arrangements. This method is adapted to picking up and stacking unit loads—groups of bags or packages—rather than single bags and transporting the loads 500 feet or more.

Fork trucks with a capacity of 3 thousand to 4 thousand pounds are suitable for handling bagged seeds in many warehouses. They usually have a turning radius of 72 to 78 inches. They can be powered by electric, gasoline, or bottled-gas motors. They can travel 7 to 11 miles an hour.

Smooth, level floors and runways speed the movement of fork trucks. A 1-percent grade requires an additional 20 pounds of tractive effort per ton handled. Hard asphalt, good, smooth concrete, and planking make acceptable floors. Rough, uneven, and soft floors require additional power for moving the trucks. The spacing of columns and posts also affects their movement. Columns usually are 16 to 20 feet on centers in conventional wood-framed warehouses. The spacing in more modern warehouses may be greater. Aisles at least 10 feet wide are needed for easy manipulation of the trucks in handling loads into and out of the stacks. Main aisles should be about 20 feet wide.

Pallets form a natural base for transporting unit loads by fork truck. The 4- x 4-foot double-faced wood pallet is used widely because of its relatively low cost, fairly light weight, and durability. Metal skids of various types and sizes are also available, but generally at a higher cost. If the pallets accompany the rail and truck shipments, the charges for the return shipment of empty pallets often are sizable.

A pusher-bar installed on the front end of a fork truck can be used to push the load off a pallet onto the floor of the rail car or road truck, and the pallet need not be shipped.

Expendable one-trip paper pallets are used in some industries to save the cost of the return freight.

PORTABLE BINS, called tote bins or pallet boxes, were used in connection with fork trucks in some warehouses in 1959 to handle and store bulk seeds. These bins vary in size and design, but are large enough to hold about 50 bushels of small grains. Tote bins can be loaded by the producer, transported to the warehouse by truck, and handled into and in the warehouse by fork trucks. They also are useful for keeping lots of seed segregated during processing and storage. Tote bins are relatively expensive to buy, store, and maintain, particularly in places where they cannot be stored outside.

Screw conveyors are used somewhat for the horizontal movement of seeds that are not easily broken or damaged. These conveyors usually are as cheap as any other type, but power requirements are relatively high, and the

Natural Air Movement Causes Translocation and Condensation of Moisture in Stored Seed

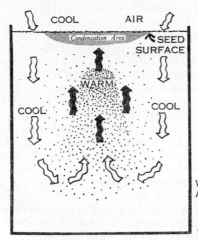

Forced Air Movement (Aeration) Prevents Translocation and Condensation of Moisture in Stored Seed

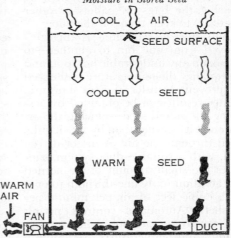

length of single sections is limited. The main disadvantage is the tendency of the conveyor to crack or break the seeds, particularly when the trough does not fit the spiral closely and when the conveyor is operated at excessive speed. Capacities range from 250 bushels (300 cubic feet) an hour with a 6-inch-diameter screw operated at a recommended 180 revolutions per minute to about 6 thousand bushels (7,500 cubic feet), with an 18-inch screw at 120 r.p.m.

SEEDS should be stored dry and kept dry.

The length of time that seeds can be stored without loss of viability depends largely on their storage environment. The main factors are the moisture content of the seeds while in storage and the temperature within the storage.

The simplest and oldest method of storage is to store dry seeds in bags or in bulk near air temperature. Many species can be stored in this way for a year or longer in well-managed conventional storages. Conditioned storage (40° to 50° F.) is necessary for longer periods, for certain regions, and for certain species of seed.

Special conditions may exist in stored seeds that can affect their storability. For example: Most seeds are good insulators. Wheat is 6 to 10 times as good as concrete. Even minor sources of heat at the center of a seed mass may cause a serious rise in its temperature so that hot spots develop. Temperature differentials can cause a movement of water vapor from the warmer to the cooler parts of the mass. Usually this happens in the upper layers of seeds, where warm air rising from within the mass hits the cool upper surface.

D. G. Carter and M. D. Farrar, of the University of Illinois, found moisture concentrations of 16 to 19 percent in the upper layers of soybeans that had an initial uniform moisture content of 12 percent before they were stored in bulk. This occurred after a few weeks in storage and as the outside air temperatures fell. Similar instances have been reported for other kinds of seeds. A surface layer of damp, moldy, and sprouting seeds may form as a result of this moisture translocation and accumulation.

Another common example of moisture translocation is the sweating of warm seeds in bags, particularly at the bottom of a pile stored on concrete floors. Sweating can be prevented by placing the bags on pallets or other material to keep them off the floor.

Bulk-stored seed often is turned—moved from one bin to another—to break up any undesirable hot spots and to equalize the temperature of the seed to prevent translocation of moisture. Better results can be obtained by aerating the stored seed—moving the air through it—rather than by moving the seed through the air. A motor-driven fan, with a suitable duct system, supplies the small amount of air needed for aeration (only one-thirtieth to one-fifth cubic feet of air per minute per bushel). Automatic controls permit the fan to operate only when air humidity and temperatures are within a selected range.

Seeds absorb or give up moisture until they are in equilibrium with the surrounding air. Eben H. Toole, of the Department of Agriculture, found in a series of studies that, at a relative humidity of 65 percent (80°), turnip seeds reached an equilibrium moisture content of 8 percent and kidney beans reached 12 percent. Most seeds will reach equilibrium within this range under similar atmospheric conditions.

Temperature has little effect on the moisture content of seeds at a given relative humidity, but it does have a decided effect on the rate of deterioration.

Dr. Toole offered the following recommendations concerning desirable humidity and temperature conditions for vegetable seeds: For seeds stored at 80°, the relative humidity should be no higher than 45 percent and no higher than 60 percent at 70°. Short-lived seeds, such as onion and shelled peanut, should be stored at a lower humidity under similar temperature conditions. For seeds in cold storage at 40° to 50°, the air relative humidity should be no higher than 70 percent and preferably no higher than 50 percent. The recommendations also apply to most field seeds.

Conditioned storage rooms usually are designed to provide storage temperatures between 40° and 50°. Relative humidity is controlled in some.

Unit systems—the factory-assembled equipment—are available in sizes from one-third ton to 20 tons. Often they are placed directly in the conditioned space. Built-up central systems, field assembled, can be designed in shape, size, and capacity for any application.

The size, in tons, of the cooling system needed can be estimated by dividing by 12 thousand the heat gain of the storage—heat gained from the stored seeds and through the walls, roof, and windows—expressed in British thermal units per hour.

It is seldom practical to operate a conditioned storage without some insulation in the walls and roof.

A rule of thumb for any storage held at 40° to 50° is to insulate with at least 3 to 4 inches of sheet or block insulation having a conductivity equal to that of corkboard. Unusual conditions of climate or use should modify normal recommendations. The manufacturer's recommendations should be followed.

Attempts have been made to use nuclear magnetic resonance to measure the moisture content of grain. If successful, this could provide a wide-range method that would be useful for the rapid measurement of the moisture content of seeds, the continuous monitoring of moisture during seed processing, and the determination of moisture content without destroying the seed.

If the temperature within a storage cannot be controlled, the operator can do little but work with the atmospheric conditions within and around the storage. Then he limits the moisture content of the seed he stores by receiving dry seed or by drying it after receiving. He also takes advantage of any good weather for ventilating warehouses, for circulating air around the stored bags to minimize extremes of high humidity and temperatures, and for aerating bulk stored seed to prevent hot spots and translocation of moisture.

Most field, grass, and vegetable seeds will store for a season with no serious loss in viability if their moisture content is not more than 12 to 12.5 percent.

For example, we found in studies in Illinois that soybeans stored in bulk at 12 to 12.5 percent moisture maintained their viability for some 175 days; those at 8 to 9 percent, for more than 650 days; but those at 15 percent, for less than 50 days.

Sealed storage, or storage under inert gases, presents some attractive advantages for preventing growth of mold and insect activity in stored seeds.

Some dangers are involved, however. Anaerobic—absence of oxygen—respiration of the seed can occur. It soon produces dead seed. Damp seeds may be killed as quickly under anaerobic conditions as in free air. Seeds to be stored in sealed containers or bins therefore should be at least 1 percent drier than seed stored under ordinary atmospheric conditions.

Bagged seeds are stored in both single- and multiple-story warehouses. The main requirements are weather-tight roofs and walls; strong, smooth floors and properly spaced columns that permit the efficient use of fork trucks and other machines; and ceiling and truss heights that permit bags to be stacked 16 feet and higher.

Bulk seeds are stored in bins or tanks separate from or within warehouses. The strength required for these storages varies with their size and the kinds of seeds to be stored. Wheat, soybeans, alfalfa, and clover, each weighing 48 pounds per cubic foot, are some of the heavier seeds that are stored in bulk.

Bin walls and floors must be strong enough to support both the lateral (horizontal) and vertical pressures exerted by the stored seed.

The design of structures for bulk seed or grain is complicated, but the following general conclusions can be offered: The pressure of the seed on bin walls and floors follows the law of semifluids rather than that of fluids.

The lateral pressure of seeds on bin walls is but 0.3 to 0.6 of the vertical pressure and increases little after the seed depth is 2.5 to 3 times the width or diameter of the bin. The ratio of the lateral to the vertical pressure, which can be determined only by experiments, is not constant but varies with different seeds and bins.

Storages for bulk seeds normally should be designed by an engineer familiar with the structural requirements, or well-tested and recommended plans should be used.

Rodents are a problem in seed storages and warehouses. In one multistory bag storage in Maryland, each floor is isolated so no mice or rats can get onto a floor except in bags of incoming seed. The operator does not depend only on seeing the live rodents. He judges their presence by the signs they leave. An open space about a foot wide is left between the stacked bags and the wall, and this strip of floor is painted white. Rodent tracks and excreta show up easily on it. Traps, poison, or gas are used to get rid of the occasional rodents that do get in. The regular fumigations are depended upon for control in some warehouses and storages.

LEO E. HOLMAN *is an agricultural engineer in the Transportation and Facilities Research Division, Agricultural Marketing Service. He began supervising research on handling and storing seed and grain for the Agricultural Marketing Service in 1954. He has written widely on the design and use of aeration systems in maintaining the quality of stored grain. His degrees are from the North Dakota State University.*

JAMES R. SNITZLER *is an associate member of the W. B. Saunders & Co., Transportation Consultants, Washington, D.C. He was formerly an employee of the Department of Agriculture from 1952 through August 1960. Since 1956 he served as Assistant Chief, Transportation Research Branch, Agricultural Marketing Service. He has written many research publications on transportation economics.*

Postharvest Control of
Insects and Fungi

LYMAN S. HENDERSON AND
CLYDE M. CHRISTENSEN

INSECTS and fungi attack seed in storage to the extent that its viability will be reduced or completely destroyed if preventive steps are not taken. It is foolish to make the considerable investment in all that is required to produce good seed and then allow it to become inferior through the damage inflicted by insects and fungi during storage.

Only since about 1940 have we become fully aware of the extensive storage losses that were occurring. In the meantime we have learned much about how to reduce the losses.

It turns out to be a fortunate coincidence that the same conditions required to prevent insect or fungus attack on seeds are ones that are favorable for the preservation of other qualities of seeds.

The important facts can be oversimplified in the statement that dry, clean seeds should be stored under cool, dry, clean conditions. This chapter expands on these ideas, discusses other preventive and control measures, and gives some additional background information.

Insects can be one of the most important single causes of damage to seeds after harvest if infestation is not prevented.

The kinds of insects that attack stored seeds are primarily the same that infest stored grain, cereal products, and a number of other commodities. They are commonly called stored-product insects and mostly are general feeders on plant products.

About a dozen species are responsible for most of the damage. Another 50 kinds frequently infest stored products, including seeds.

The insects found most commonly in stored seeds are rice weevil, *Sitophilus oryza;* granary weevil, *Sitophilus granarius;* lesser grain borer, *Rhyzopertha dominica;* Angoumois grain moth, *Sitotroga cerealella;* cadelle, *Tenebroides mauritanicus;* saw-toothed grain beetle, *Oryzaephilus surinamensis;* flat grain beetle, *Cryptolestes pusillus;* flour beetles, *Tribolium* species; dermestids, *Trogoderma* species; bruchids, several bean and cowpea weevils; Indian-meal moth, *Plodia interpunctella;* and almond moth, *Ephestia cautella.*

These insects cause several kinds of damage to seeds. The most serious is that they chew out the germ, which is rich in food value and is often the first part of the seed attacked by some of the moths and beetles. Then, of course, the seed cannot germinate.

Some insects live inside the seeds and feed primarily on the endosperm. The germ may not be damaged directly, but partial or complete reduction of the endosperm lowers the vitality of the seed, or the seedlings may be weak and unable to survive.

The moth larvae spin large amounts of webbing that entangles the seeds in ropy masses. The webbing may build up into unsightly films over the surface of bags of seed or on top of seed stored in bulk. It is a sign of potential damage to the germ. Some of the seed-infesting insects chew holes through fabric, film, and paper containers.

Most of the insect infestation originates after the seed is placed in storage. The kinds of insects involved are widely distributed, abundant, and feed on a wide variety of grains, cereal products, animal feeds, and other commodities. They occur commonly in warehouses, storage bins, barns, feed sheds, and homes. Seeds may become infested during temporary storage on the farm or during warehouse storage if it is near infested products or put into infested bins or structures.

Many of the insects are strong fliers and can move into storage structures to start infestations if preventive measures are not carried out. Used bags can also be a source of infestation if they are not cleaned thoroughly or fumigated before refilling.

Bagged or packaged seeds carried over from one season to the next provide an infestation hazard. The presence of insects inside the containers may not be detected. Adult beetles or moths lay their eggs near or on packages. The tiny, newly hatched larvae can crawl in through minute openings. The first external evidence of trouble may be when the mature insects cut holes in the package through which to emerge after their development is completed. By this time extensive damage may have been caused and moth larvae will have spun webbing.

The necessary reserve stocks of seeds are another source of difficulty. The longer storage period provides time for the development of more generations of insects and possibly a tremendous increase in numbers. The older seeds may also become more susceptible to attack if storage conditions have not been proper.

Seeds may become infested in the field before harvest in the Southern States, notably by the rice weevil and the Angoumois grain moth. They can complete their development and continue to reproduce after the seed is put into storage. Damage from field infestation can be kept to a minimum by prompt harvesting and proper handling, which may include drying or fumigation, or both.

Field infestation by stored-product insects is not common in the Northern States where much of our seed is produced. An exception is the attack of bruchid beetles on beans, peas, and other legumes. Most of the species continue to reproduce after the seed is harvested and stored. Insecticides should be applied in the field to prevent or reduce this infestation. Proper harvesting and handling procedures will stop further damage.

Temperature and moisture are important factors in relation to infestation. As the temperature and moisture become lower, the rate of insect activity, feeding, development, and reproduction is reduced. Low moisture and temperature also help to keep seed in the dormant condition that is necessary to maintain its quality. We can take advantage of these conditions to preserve seeds and at the same time prevent insect damage.

The amount of dockage in seed also influences its susceptibility to attack. Clean seed is of better quality and is better able to resist infestation.

A further preventive measure is to clean the storage structures and bins thoroughly so they are free of infestation before seed is placed in them.

Protectants applied directly to the seeds are especially useful for preventing infestation in bulk storage. Insect-resistant packages protect seeds after they are placed in containers of various types.

Control or corrective treatments are required when seed becomes infested before protective measures can be applied, or when such measures have been inadequate. These treatments may include fumigation, the application of an insecticidal spray or dust, or the use of controlled heat. We discuss them in more detail later.

FUNGI probably always have caused losses in stored seeds of all kinds when storage conditions were improper. The losses were overlooked for centuries. Now we have found out how common and significant they are. We know how to detect them and recognize the causative organisms. We have learned how to avoid the damage.

About a dozen species of *Aspergillus* and several species of *Penicillium* comprise the storage fungi. They invade seeds almost solely after harvest. They are different from the field fungi, such as *Alternaria*, *Fusarium*, and *Helminthosporium*, that cause seedborne diseases and infest the seeds as they are developing on the plants in the field. The moisture content of harvested seed is so low that these fungi do not continue to grow. They are dormant and do not cause losses of seeds during storage. They cause root rots or blights of the germinating seeds or diseases of the growing plants.

The primary damage caused by storage fungi is their effect on the germination of seed. Invasion of seeds by storage fungi can weaken or kill them. The result is slow or erratic germination when the seeds are planted or a low percentage of germination.

Stored seed may be damaged by heat as a result of the activity of storage fungi. Heating is common in baled cotton or wool, hay, grain, or seeds stored in fairly large bulks. At one time the heating was thought to be due to the natural respiration of the grain or seed itself. Many practical storage men still believe this to be true. They do not know that moist grain or seed is killed in a few hours by temperatures slightly above 100° F., and that after death there is no respiration. There is no evidence that seeds or grain stored at moisture contents below 18 percent will respire rapidly enough to cause any great increase in temperature.

Insect infestation will cause an increase in temperature to as high as 108°. Storage fungi accompanying or following insect infestation, or developing independently, will raise the temperature up to 130°. In the process, they may produce enough moisture to permit thermophilic (heat-loving) bacteria to grow. They may further raise the temperature to about 175°. If conditions are right, compounds produced by the growth of fungi and bacteria may undergo oxidation that will cause heating up to the point of spontaneous combustion.

Mustiness is another result of activity of storage fungi. When fungi have extensively invaded and partly consumed seeds, they have produced masses of spores. The seeds have a musty odor and a moldy appearance. They may be caked together by the fungi. This is the first evidence of fungi to many

who store seeds, and unless it reaches this stage they are unaware of the infestation. It is, however, the final stage of spoilage. The preliminary stages that precede damage can be detected only by special techniques.

"Germ damage" is a term applied to dark brown or black embryos or germs in small grains and corn caused by storage fungi. This type of damage is important in grain or seed that is to be processed into flour, meal, or other food. The damaged germs may end up as dark particles in the final product. Damaged germs usually contain large quantities of fatty acids and often are extremely moldy. They impart undesirable flavors to the food. Damaged germs reduce the market grade and price of food grains. They are an indication of possible poor quality in seed.

Spores of storage fungi occur in small numbers on the outside of seeds at harvesttime. There also may be some slight and superficial infection of the outer parts of the seeds. Even when plants are subjected to continued moist weather at harvest, however, the fungi do not invade seeds sufficiently to cause any reduction in germination. Damaging infection occurs later, after the seeds have been stored, and only if the conditions of storage are such as to permit the inoculum naturally present to grow.

We have accumulated abundant evidence from thousands of tests on many kinds of seeds, including all the common cereal grains, that storage fungi do not infect seeds to more than a very minor degree before harvest.

This is an important point, because in many instances where extensive losses of seed or grain have occurred in storage, those in charge of the storage have maintained that the trouble must have been due to something that happened to the seed before it was stored—not to conditions that prevailed in storage. That is not true.

Seed may receive improper care on the farm or in temporary storage and become heavily invaded by hidden storage fungi. Upon transfer to another storehouse, it may spoil more rapidly than really sound seed. Invasion by storage fungi may occur very shortly after harvest.

We have found wheat coming out of a country elevator, 2 weeks after harvest, to be much more heavily infected than when it went into the elevator. We have found some lots of grain going into supposedly long-term storage to be infected so heavily by storage fungi that they were on the verge of spoilage.

SEED INVADED BY STORAGE fungi is already deteriorated to some extent and is much more subject to spoilage in storage than is sound seed. The latter could endure unfavorable storage conditions for some time without any damage.

Seeds or grain heavily invaded by storage fungi and almost ready to spoil often receive the same grade and command the same price as other lots free of fungi. Ordinary inspection procedures for quality, grade, and price fail to detect this condition. The invasion of seeds by storage fungi sufficient to cause a large decrease in germination ordinarily is not detectable by inspection with the naked eye, or even with a microscope.

The knowledge and techniques required to determine whether a given lot of seed is really sound or whether it has been invaded by storage fungi are now available. The technique can be used by almost anyone. It involves culturing the seeds on agar media developed especially for the purpose.

The major factors that determine whether a given lot of seeds will be invaded by storage fungi sufficiently to cause damage are moisture content, temperature, duration of storage, insect infestation, and condition of the seed when placed in storage.

Damage is relatively uncommon in seeds stored dry and cool. It may be significant when the weather between harvest and planting is warm and humid or if other storage conditions are improper. The amount of damage

that will occur is a function of time in relation to moisture content and temperature. The lower the moisture and temperature, the longer seed can be stored without damage. Furthermore, there is an interrelation between moisture and temperature, so that within limits a drop in one compensates for a rise in the other.

Emphasis on prevention is even more important for storage fungi than for insects. No suitable chemical treatment has been developed to prevent infection by storage fungi or to control the infection once it is established. None of the seed-treating fungicides used to prevent attack of fungi that cause damping-off or root rot in seedlings is of value against the storage fungi. Damage in storage can be avoided only by maintaining the moisture content or the temperature, or both, at a level so low the fungi cannot grow. Both should be kept low for safety, especially in long storage.

One can use the agar culture test to determine how many and what kinds of hidden storage fungi may be present when seed goes into storage. The test should be applied to samples taken at intervals during storage to learn whether fungi are developing and whether the seed is safe for continued storage or is in danger of spoilage.

THE RELATION between insects and fungi in stored grain has been studied at the University of Minnesota.

We have found that invasion by such insects as the weevils is almost always accompanied by fungi, which add to the damage done by the insects. As the insects develop, they increase the moisture content of the grain by adding metabolic water from their life processes. This makes a condition more favorable for growth of fungus. The moisture can migrate to adjacent portions of the bulk of grain and start fungus growth even beyond the focal point of insect infestation. Because fumigation will kill the insects but not the fungi, damage can continue even after fumigation.

MOISTURE CONTENT of seed and drying newly harvested high-moisture seed to a safe storage level are important in preventing damage by insects and fungi. Seed that is harvested dry or dried soon after harvest and is free of insects will remain sound, in good condition, and of high germination for years. Many samples of wheat and corn stored 4 to 6 years at a moisture content of 10 to 12 percent have germinated more than 90 percent and were as sound as when placed in storage.

The upper limit of moisture content that seeds can tolerate varies with the kind of seed, the temperature, and the duration of storage.

The upper limits generally considered safe for long-time storage under average conditions are 13 percent for beans, peas, and cereal grains, including corn; 12.5 percent for soybeans; 10.5 percent for flaxseed; and somewhat lower for most vegetable seeds and peanuts. Seed stocks of most of these crops are stored at lower levels than those indicated. That is why loss in germination caused by storage fungi is relatively uncommon.

Seeds stored at a uniform and low moisture content may not remain so—especially in bulk storage where temperature differentials may cause moisture migration. In the fall and early winter, the top and sides of a storage bin cool off first. Warm, moist air rises through the center of the bin, and moisture condenses out as it reaches the cool seed at the top. When the seed warms up in the spring, the moist grain at the surface may be invaded rapidly and spoiled by fungi.

This transfer of moisture may be so great that some of the seed is damp enough to germinate when it gets warm in the spring. It is not true that seed has an urge to heat and germinate in the spring. Seed will germinate when it becomes wet and warm enough. It does not feel the urge of spring any more than a stack of hay or a bale of cotton, both of which will heat if they are moist enough for the fungi that cause heating.

Moisture migration is of minor importance in small bulks of seed or in bagged seed. The latter may take up moisture from the surrounding air in the warm, humid climate of the South or Southeast. Moisture pickup from the surrounding air is usually limited to the outer few inches in bulk storage. The relative humidity of the interstitial air in bulk storage is related more closely to the moisture content of the seed than to that of the surrounding air. That is why it is important to store seed dry initially. When the seed is dry enough, both the seed and the interstitial air are so dry the fungi will not grow.

The rice and granary weevils do not develop in seeds that contain less than 8 percent moisture and do not grow well when the moisture is less than 11 percent, unless the seed temperature is 85° to 90°.

The bran beetles, such as the sawtoothed grain beetle and flour beetles, can live on food almost devoid of moisture if the temperature is favorable. They do, however, grow and reproduce more rapidly as the moisture content goes up.

Measuring the moisture content of seed is important but not always easy. Electric moisture meters often are used to give a rapid determination. They do not measure moisture directly; they measure the electrical properties of seeds or grain as influenced by moisture content. They have some limitations, because other factors may affect the electrical properties of seeds, the meter must be calibrated properly, and the instrument may get out of adjustment. With some instruments, measurement of the temperature or the amount of seed is a critical factor.

Electric moisture meters may give a reading as much as 1.5 percent above or below the results obtained by the oven-drying method. The error may be even greater in recently dried seeds, where the moisture content is lower in the outer layer of the seeds than in the interior. Here the reading may be 2 to 5 percent lower than by the oven method. These differences are important if the moisture content of the seeds is on the borderline of safe storage.

Sometimes lots of seed with different contents of moisture are blended to produce a mixture believed to have a moisture content safe for storage. It is assumed that if equal portions of 16-percent and 12-percent moisture content seed are blended, the mixture soon will have a moisture content of 14 percent. This is not so. The seeds with the original high moisture content will remain higher than the average, and those with the lower moisture content will remain drier than the average. Much of the seed may retain enough moisture to permit a fungus attack, figures in the record books notwithstanding.

Assuming that accurate moisture readings are obtained, there are still snares to avoid. Care may be taken to obtain an average sample of seed upon which to determine moisture content. It is on the basis of average moisture content that seed is bought, sold, and often stored. There may be, however, portions with enough moisture to permit fungus attack. There may be a difference of as much as 7 percent between different locations in a large storage bulk. Differences of 2 to 4 percent are common. An average figure of moisture content is obviously of no value in evaluating the risk of spoilage when there is such variation.

Even individual seeds from a supposedly uniform lot may differ by as much as 1 to 2 percent in moisture. The usual methods of measurement will not reveal such a condition, but it can be important in storing seeds.

Considering the importance of moisture and the possible errors in its measurement, it is not surprising that most of fungus damage occurs in stored seed with a moisture content higher than it is believed to be by those responsible for the storage.

COOL STORAGE of seed is important because of the relationships between temperature and moisture in their

effect on the development of insects and fungi.

The optimum temperature for most seed-infesting insects is 80° to 85°. Temperatures above 95° are not favorable and below 70° development is retarded. Flour beetles do not reproduce below 65°. The granary and rice weevils do not reproduce below about 60°. Most of the stored-product insects cease feeding and become inactive between 40° and 50°. Some species of mites will reproduce at 40° or even lower, but only if the moisture content of the seed is above 12 percent.

The optimum temperature for most storage fungi is 85° to 95°. As with the insects, development is retarded below 70°, and most of them grow very slowly, if at all, below 50°. A few species, however, will grow slowly below 50°. They may gradually invade seeds during the winter. When the seed warms up in the spring, they will develop rapidly and cause extensive spoilage.

MOST OF THE LARGE, modern storage bins have devices to measure temperature at different locations throughout the storage bulk. These are useful for detecting a rise in temperature caused by insects. Corrective measures can then be taken. Heating by fungi is an indication of the final stages of spoilage. If the temperature increases 20° in a portion of the bin, it is not an indication that trouble is coming, but that trouble is already there. Seed has already been damaged. Prompt action may prevent it from spreading further.

Refrigeration to provide cold storage is impractical or too expensive for protecting most seeds. The cost may be justified for limited quantities of valuable seed stock or if the infestation hazard is unusually high. Even in cold storage, the moisture content must be low, and the relative atmospheric humidity must be kept down to avoid damage to germination.

Upon removal from cold storage, there can be difficulty from condensation. Seed with high moisture removed from cold storage and subjected to high summer temperatures will deteriorate so rapidly that in a few weeks the benefit of cold storage will be lost. Unless the seed is to be planted at once, the moisture content should be determined when it comes out of cold storage. If it is above the safe limit for the temperature to which it will be exposed, it should be dried carefully to a safe level.

SEED CLEANING can be of great benefit in preventing insect infestation and indirectly in avoiding fungus attack.

The young larvae of the bran beetles do not feed readily on sound, unbroken seeds. It is difficult therefore for an infestation to get started in clean seed. They can, however, feed on broken seeds and floury dust that may be present as dockage.

After the infestation gets started, the larger larvae and adults may be able to attack sound seeds, making available additional food for young larvae. In filling bulk bins, the dockage tends to concentrate in layers or columns, which are especially susceptible to insect attack. The typical sequence of increased moisture, rise in temperature, and subsequent growth of fungi is quite likely to center around these concentrations of dockage.

The dense, compact nature of the dust and dockage, plus the moisture and results of fungus activity, create a mass that is hard to fumigate. The gas penetrates it poorly or not at all and tends to channel around the spot. If aeration is being used for cooling or the forced distribution of fumigants, interference with airflow reduces the effectiveness. When dockage is scattered throughout bulk seed, the fine material absorbs a great deal of any fumigant gas that may be applied and reduces the effectiveness of the treatments.

It is apparent that the more thoroughly seed is cleaned the less hazard there will be of insect infestation. A concentration of 0.5 percent of dockage may be critical at a seed moisture content of 9 or 10 percent. A smaller amount is critical at 12 percent moisture or higher.

Thorough seed cleaning will remove most or all of the external forms of insects. It will not remove the insects, such as weevil larvae, that develop inside the seeds.

SEED PROTECTANTS and coatings of pesticides often are used to prevent damage by fungi or insects after planting. As we said, the fungicides are of no value against storage fungi. They have little or no effect on insects.

Dieldrin as applied to seeds for protection against insects after planting is also effective in preventing infestation during storage before planting.

Other insecticides, such as malathion, synergized pyrethrum, lindane, methoxychlor, and DDT, may be applied to seeds as a dust, slurry, or spray treatment to protect it against insect damage during storage.

Tolerances have been established for pyrethrum and malathion under the Food, Drug, and Cosmetic Act to permit their use as protectants on food and feed grains. Surplus or reserve seed stocks treated with these materials therefore can be diverted for use as animal feed or human food if the tolerance level has not been exceeded. Seeds treated with dieldrin, lindane, methoxychlor, or DDT must not be so diverted.

A NUMBER of chemically inert dusts can also be used effectively and economically on seeds to prevent infestation. These treatments are less effective as the moisture content of the seeds increases over 12 percent. The kinds of inert dusts found satisfactory include silica gel, magnesium oxide, diatomaceous earth, rock phosphates, precipitated chalk, and aluminum oxide. The particle size should be 1 micron or less. A common application rate is 1 part of dust per 1,000 parts of seed by weight, or about 1 ounce per bushel.

Any one of several methods of application or kinds of equipment may be suitable for treating the seed. The important consideration is to insure uniform coverage. None of the inert dusts or pesticides we have mentioned has been found to have any adverse effect on germination.

INSECT CONTROL in warehouses may vary somewhat, depending on whether the seed is stored in bulk or in bags and according to the type of storage structure. The basic principles are the same in all cases. Best results are obtained by emphasizing preventive measures.

The importance of temperature, moisture content, relative atmospheric humidity, and clean seed have been discussed. Add to these thorough cleaning of the warehouse or storage structure, inside and out, before bringing in new seed. One should get rid of spilled seed, grain, or animal feed. Any old stocks of these materials that may be infested should be removed or fumigated. A heavy-duty commercial vacuum cleaner should be used. Walls, window sills, beams, ledges, floors, and other places where old seed and dirt can lodge should be swept. All parts of elevators and conveyors should be cleaned. Attention must be given to places under loading platforms and to buildings that are off the ground. One should burn, bury, or haul away all refuse and cleanings, so that infestation does not spread to new seed when it is brought in.

It is well to apply a residual spray of premium-grade malathion or DDT to kill out any infestation remaining in the structure after the cleanup. It should be done 1 or 2 weeks before new seed is stored. DDT should not be used if the seed may be diverted to food or feed channels.

The application of a protectant as seed goes into storage is another highly desirable procedure if the storage period is to be more than just a few weeks. The premium-grade malathion, synergized pyrethrum, or one of the inert dusts may be used.

The periodic application of a residual spray over the surface of stacks of bagged seed is another desirable preventive measure. This will be useful to avoid infestation by beetles or moths.

The seed must be free of infestation when the stacks are formed, and the treatments must be started immediately for best results. With malathion, a second application in 2 weeks and monthly thereafter while temperatures are above 70° is usually adequate. With pyrethrum, a 2-week continuing schedule should be maintained during warm weather. Similar treatments on the surface of bulk-stored seed are useful where there is a hazard of moth infestation.

Space treatments with aerosols or mist sprays appear to give rapid and spectacular results, especially against moths. Their real value is limited as a control measure. They can be useful as a supplemental preventive procedure.

SEED THAT is infested at harvesttime must be fumigated before, during, or immediately after it is placed in storage. Fumigation is the most effective corrective measure to apply when an infestation develops in storage when preventive steps have been lacking or inadequate.

Fumigation can reduce or destroy germination. The effect involves a complex relationship of dosage, time, temperature, and moisture. It is wise not to fumigate seed having a moisture content of more than 12 percent or a temperature of more than 85°. Recommended dosages should be used.

Mixtures containing ethylene dichloride, carbon tetrachloride, or carbon disulfide are safest, but the seed should be aerated after 3 to 5 days. Phosphine is safe on the cereal grain seeds and apparently most of the others, except the legumes. Normal dosages of hydrogen cyanide or methyl bromide within the temperature and moisture limits we named are safe with a fumigation period of not more than 24 hours.

Chloropicrin, acrylonitrile, and some other fumigants can be highly injurious to germination.

INSECT-RESISTANT PACKAGING is useful for protecting seed during storage and until it is ready for planting. Even closely woven fabric bags offer little protection against insect invasion. Multiwall paper bags, laminates, and plastic films are somewhat more resistant but fall short of being insectproof. Paper bags treated with synergized pyrethrum or methoxychlor can be highly effective for one season of storage in protecting against invasion or penetration. The bags must be well constructed and have tight closures. DDT could be used on bags for seed that will not be diverted for use as food or feed. None of the treatments is completely effective on fabric bags.

PREVENTING DAMAGE TO SEED by insects and fungi after harvest can be accomplished by the following procedures:

Harvest promptly.

Clean and dry seed before storage.

Clean up the storage structure and apply residual spray before bringing seed in.

Apply a protectant to seed as it is placed in storage.

Keep the seed and the warehouse cool and dry.

Make frequent culture tests to be sure storage fungi are not invading seed.

Apply residual sprays on a periodic preventive maintenance schedule.

Fumigate if and when necessary.

Use protective packaging.

LYMAN S. HENDERSON *is Chief of the Stored-Product Insects Branch, Agricultural Marketing Service. He has been with the Department of Agriculture since 1938. He has administered research programs in insect control since 1945.*

CLYDE M. CHRISTENSEN *is a professor in the Department of Plant Pathology and Botany at the University of Minnesota. He was on special assignment with the Rockefeller Foundation agricultural program in Mexico during 1959. He conducts research on the deterioration of grains caused by storage fungi.*

Questions and Answers

What proportion of the annual cost of production of the average farmer is spent for seeds?

About 2 percent—the least of any major element in his cost of operations.

What is the estimated age of the oldest known viable seed?

Certain lotus seeds believed to be more than 1 thousand years old have germinated. This is unusual, however, since most agricultural seeds lose their viability in a few years. Weed seeds may remain viable 25, 50, or 100 years.

What part of plants constitutes the greatest portion of the world's human food supply?

Seeds.

From what part of plants are most "vegetable oils" derived for industrial and food uses?

The seeds.

Do the characteristics and uniformity of a seed-propagated variety or stock remain constant?

No. Characteristics and uniformity of varieties and stocks of naturally cross-pollinating crops tend to change to some degree under natural (or artificial) selection pressures. Theoretically at least, varieties of self-pollinated crops should remain constant indefinitely. Accidental mixtures of varieties, however, frequently occur. Mutations of genes also occur infrequently. As a consequence, even varieties of self-pollinated crops may change. Constant and skillful effort is required to keep varieties and stocks in close conformity to the desired standards.

How many seeds does one parent plant produce?
Some annual species may produce an average number as low as a dozen; others, 200 thousand or more. Some trees in a lifetime produce many millions.

What is breeder seed?
Seed produced by the originator of a new variety that is planted for the production of foundation seed or "stock seed."

What is "stock" seed?
To the producers of vegetables and flower seeds, it is the carefully rogued and otherwise "controlled" seed from which seeds are grown for planting crops for ordinary home or commercial use.

Can all species of crop plants be identified by the appearance of their seeds alone?
No; although most of them can be. Two or more species within some genera may produce seeds that appear the same.

Can varieties of crops be identified only by the appearance of the seeds?
Some varieties of peas, beans, corn, and other relatively large-seeded plants produce seeds so distinctly characteristic of the respective varieties as to constitute a dependable identification of the variety, but this is not generally true. Stem, leaf, flower, fruit, performance, and other characteristics usually must be taken into account to identify a variety.

Which is richer in vitamins—a dormant seed or a germinating seed?
The germinating seed—hence the nutritive value of bean sprouts and malted grain.

How does a true seed differ from a one-seeded fruit?
A true seed consists of the embryo, endosperm (when present) and integuments (seedcoat or covering) of the ovule from which it developed. A one-seeded fruit has an additional layer in the covering, which is contributed by the ovary wall. Identification of a one-seeded fruit is certain when it is determined that the ovary of the flower develops a single ovule.

Which plants produce the largest and the smallest seeds?
Seeds of some orchids are so small they cannot be seen with the naked eye and look like dust. The largest seed is probably a coconut that is found only in Malagasy and reaches a length of more than 1 foot and may weigh 40 to 50 pounds. The coconut is a dry, one-seeded drupe. The "meat" is the seed. The fibrous and hard shells are part of the ovary walls. The commercial coconut is therefore a fruit and not a seed.

Is the seed a reproductive structure?
Functionally, the seed is a reproductive structure in that it serves to increase and multiply the plant species. Structurally, the seed is a young, resting plant waiting for favorable conditions to again start growing. Processes of sexual reproduction are completed in the ovules of the flower long before seed maturity.

A hickory nut or a walnut that has been kept dry all winter will not germinate in the spring. Why?
Because at maturity the embryo of the nut enters a period of dormancy or rest as soon as it becomes dry, and the only way to break this deep sleep is to keep the seed moist and cool for a certain period (usually 2 months or more). Then it will sprout and grow.

How necessary are pollinating insects in the production of seeds?
Blossoms of some crops are self-sterile, although they contain both pistil and pollen, and to be fruitful need pollen from another plant of the same variety or species. In other crops, the male and female components are borne on separate blossoms on the same plant or different plants.

Some pollens are windborne. Others are heavy, sticky, or spiny and need to be transported by insects. Flowers of certain plants are peculiarly adapted to insect pollination.

How many seed crops are dependent on bees for yields of seeds?

More than 35 seed crops are dependent on bees for seed production or yield more abundantly when bees are present. Among the more important are alfalfa, asparagus, beans, cabbage, carrot, celery, cauliflower, cucumber, clovers, muskmelon, onion, radish, squash, sunflower, vetches, and watermelon.

How many insects are detrimental to seed production?

In the broad sense that any insect that injures the plant affects seed production, probably a few hundred species are involved. Only a few dozen species directly attack the flowering parts or the seed, however, and only some of them inflict serious damage.

Where can I get seeds of fast-growing hybrid pines?

Seeds of hybrid pines are not available commercially. They are being used in research or for forest planting by those who produce them.

How can I get the seed out of a pine cone?

Most cones open up and shed their seeds as they dry out naturally. A few, like jack pine, will open readily only when heated up to about 140° F. for about a day.

How old must a pine tree be before it bears seeds?

Many pines start to bear seeds when they are 15 to 20 years old, occasionally when only 10. Some, like the sugar pine of the West, seldom bear seeds before they are 40 to 50 years old.

Is it necessary to identify clearly as a "brand" the brand or trademark each time it is used in a price list with the name of the kind and variety of seed?

No. We are of the opinion that it is in compliance with the Federal Seed Act to identify clearly in the masthead of a price list the terms used as a brand or trademark without identifying the brand or trademark as such each time it is used on the same page. For example, "The term 'Blank' is our brand (or trademark) and is not a part of the name of the kind or variety."

If I obtain a laboratory report from my supplier, is it necessary for me to have another test made before labeling seeds for interstate shipment?

The basis for labeling seeds in interstate commerce is left to the interstate shipper to determine. If the seeds are labeled correctly, the basis upon which they were labeled will not be questioned. If, however, the seeds are found to be falsely labeled, the shipper's basis for labeling will be subject to inquiry to determine whether he took proper precautions in labeling the seeds. It would appear that a person who, in good faith, obtains his own representative sample from a properly blended lot of seeds as it is received and has it tested by a qualified seed analyst would normally have taken proper precautions. On the other hand, a person who relies on a laboratory report furnished by his supplier is taking a certain amount of risk, as he cannot know whether the sample reported on properly represents the seeds he has received or that the seed lot is uniformly blended.

If seeds are held in storage until the date of test expires, is a retest of the original file sample considered a reliable basis for determining the percentage of germination and renewing the date of test shown on the labels?

No. Seeds stored in a warehouse do not always retain their viability the same as a small sample stored under different conditions. A new sample of the seeds actually in storage should be obtained for the purpose of retesting and relabeling.

THE

CERTIFICATION

OF SEEDS

ψ ψ ψ ψ ψ ψ ψ ψ ψ ψ ψ ψ ψ ψ ψ ψ ψ ψ ψ ψ ψ ψ ψ ψ ψ ψ ψ ψ ψ ψ ψ ψ ψ ψ ψ ψ ψ ψ ψ ψ

Variety Is a Key Word

MARTIN G. WEISS AND ELBERT L. LITTLE, JR.

To BUY, sell, and grow seeds and plants without confusion, we need a system of naming, distinguishing, and classifying the many thousand different kinds and varieties.

We must know also whether one lot of seeds or plants will give the same results as another or differs enough to require a separate name.

The key word "variety" is used for plant populations in two different ways—for a botanical variety and for a cultivated variety.

THE PLANT KINGDOM comprises about 350 thousand known species, or kinds, of living wild plants, of which more than 250 thousand are seed plants. For comparison and study, these plants are classified by their characteristics into higher and higher ranks, or categories.

The scientific names of plants are in Latin form following the *International Code of Botanical Nomenclature* and are universally adopted around the world. The scientific name of a plant consists of its genus and species names. *Trifolium pratense*, for example, is the scientific name for red clover.

The most important rank, the species, is composed of individual plants or plant populations that are similar in appearance and can reproduce or breed among themselves and produce other individuals that resemble the parents.

A genus—plural, genera—is a group of related species. The genus *Trifolium*, clover, includes also the species *Trifolium repens*, whiteclover, and many others.

A family is composed of related genera. Clovers, alfalfa, beans, peas,

359

black locust, and similar plants belong to the legume family, Leguminosae.

Varieties have been recognized in some species. A variety (botanical variety, from Latin *varietas*, abbreviated "var.") is a rank or minor unit within a species composed of individuals which differ slightly from the others. *Trifolium pratense* var. *foliosum*, Orel clover, has been designated as a botanical variety of red clover.

Subspecies (abbreviated "subsp.") is an optional rank below the species but above the variety, based on minor characters and usually having an exclusive geographic range.

Form (abbreviated "f.") is an optional rank based on more trivial characters than a variety—for example, color of flower or shape of the leaves.

Other groups sometimes are distinguished without scientific names.

A race is a group of individuals or population within a species that have general similarities discontinuous and distinct from other populations, although not sufficient for designation by a scientific name.

A geographic race is restricted in distribution to a particular region.

A physiologic race differs in life processes or functions but not necessarily in form—for example, in resistance to disease or in rooting ability.

An ecotype is a race or ecological variation whose characters adapt it to a distinct habitat, such as soil and climate.

THE CULTIVATED VARIETY is the variety of cultivated plants, seeds, and commerce. Equivalent terms are commercial, agronomic, horticultural, and garden variety and cultivar, the shortened form.

The Federal Seed Act of August 9, 1939, defined kind as "one or more related species or subspecies which singly or collectively is known by one common name; for example, wheat, oat, vetch, sweetclover, cabbage, cauliflower, and so forth."

Under the Act, the term "variety" means "a subdivision of a kind which is characterized by growth, plant, fruit, seed, or other characters by which it can be differentiated from other sorts of the kind; for example, Marquis wheat, Flat Dutch cabbage, Manchu soybeans, Oxheart carrot, and so forth."

International Code of Nomenclature of Cultivated Plants (1958) contains this definition: "The term 'variety (cultivar)' denotes an assemblage of cultivated individuals which are distinguished by any characters (morphological, physiological, cytological, chemical, or others) significant for the purposes of agriculture, forestry, or horticulture, and which, when reproduced (sexually or asexually), retain their distinguishing features."

All individual plants of a variety have one or many characters in common that hold them together under the same name and serve for identification yet separate them from all others. Although the degree of uniformity differs within varieties, different samples of seeds and plants of the same variety generally perform similarly under the same conditions. The distinguishing characters must be maintained or inherited when the plants are reproduced over a period of years. The method of propagation, whether vegetative or by seeds, is immaterial.

Cultivated varieties are further distinguished from botanical varieties by their capitalized names in modern languages before the common name of the kind or species, as in Dollard red clover, or after the scientific name. Information for naming new varieties is given in *Rules and Regulations Under the Federal Seed Act* (sec. 201.34) and in the Code. The variety name shall not be misleading.

One variety often becomes known under several names. If no differences can be demonstrated between two or more so-called varieties, the name assigned by the originator is retained, with rare exceptions.

Rejected variety names that have become recognized through broad general usage are known as synonyms.

Some workers, especially in horticulture, have adopted the word "cultivar," an exact equivalent of variety, as a formal, scientific, and international term different from botanical variety. Variety, however, is firmly established in agriculture and is required under the Federal Seed Act and most State seed laws.

Rules and Regulations Under the Federal Seed Act define the term "lot of seed" as: "A definite quantity of seed identified by a lot number, every portion or bag of which is uniform, within permitted tolerance, for the factors which appear in the labeling." A lot thus contains seed treated alike or processed in the same way but has no connotation relative to identity of the seeds.

Under the Federal Seed Act, the term "type" may mean "a group of varieties so nearly similar that the individual varieties cannot be clearly differentiated except under special conditions." The southern bromegrass varieties, for instance, such as Lincoln and Fischer, constitute a type that is distinct in leafiness and other characters from varieties of the northern type, such as Manchar.

Some seeds, such as lawn seed of grasses, represent mixtures of two or more varieties, often in definite percentages. As defined by *Rules and Regulations Under the Federal Seed Act*, "The term 'mixture' means seeds consisting of more than one kind or variety, each present in excess of 5 percent of the whole."

The word "strain" sometimes has been used to designate an improved selection of a variety. Under the Code, any such selection that shows sufficient differences from the parent variety to render it worthy of a name is to be regarded as a distinct variety. Strain has been applied to unnamed experimental varieties. It is considered broader than a variety. Because of the varied usage, it seems preferable not to associate strain with a certain level of classification. Whenever used, its meaning should be explained.

"Blend" is sometimes applied to mixtures of lots of seed within or between varieties but is not equivalent to a variety. For example, a blend may be composed of two seed lots of the same variety with different germination percentages mixed together. Or, blends may be mixtures of varieties or species prepared for different geographic regions.

The term "stock seed" often is applied loosely to designate seed used in the propagation and maintenance of a variety. Breeder seeds, foundation seeds, and registered seeds are frequently referred to as stock seed. In vegetable crops, the term "stock seed" has a more limited implication and often is used to denote foundation seed.

"Common" is a term applied to seed that cannot be identified as to variety and is often a mechanical or genetic mixture. In reference to alfalfa, the term "Common" has been used to denote local strains resulting from natural selection. Such selections have been identified by State of origin, such as Kansas Common, Oklahoma Common, or Utah Common.

A "brand" is a trademark adopted by a particular company or distributor for its seed or plants. A brand is neither a varietal designation nor part of a variety name. Instead, the brand precedes the variety name and may be applied to material of many different varieties or kinds of crops. Variety names have common usage and cannot be trademarked.

ASEXUALLY REPRODUCED CROPS are propagated without the sexual processes of pollination and fertilization in seed formation.

These vegetatively propagated varieties are grown or multiplied from some part of the plant other than the seed. Familiar examples are vegetative propagation by roots, divisions, tubers, bulbs, cuttings, runners, layers, stem sections, grafts, and buds. Any plant part used to reproduce an individual asexually is called a propagule.

A plant grown from a part of another is in effect a continuation of the same tissues and hereditary characteristics.

Obviously, vegetatively propagated varieties are true to type and can be maintained pure indefinitely unless modified by the infrequent, sudden hereditary changes known as mutations or bud sports.

A clone consists of uniform plants or material derived from a single original individual and propagated entirely by vegetative means, as, for instance, by cuttings, divisions, or grafts. The original plant may have been wild, a chance variation or mutation, or a complex hybrid unlikely to breed true from seed.

The clonal members are all plants or progeny that originated by repeated multiplication from a single parent plant. A clonal variety consists of the vegetative propagules of one plant.

Some plants mature viable seeds by asexual reproduction (apomixis) without the normal process of fertilization. Instead of developing from the fertilized egg, the embryo plant in the seed may originate from mother tissues or from an unfertilized egg. An apomictic variety is a variety or clone that is propagated by seeds formed by asexual reproduction. Examples are found in bluegrass, dallisgrass, and other grasses.

NORMALLY SELF-POLLINATED CROPS, such as garden beans, wheat, and soybeans, may have varieties that are comprised of groups of pure breeding plants that have certain characteristics in common or pure line varieties.

Many crops were established by introduction from foreign countries of highly heterogeneous varieties, each with identifiable characters, such as Kherson oats, Turkey wheat, Manchuria barley, and Manchu soybeans. Such varieties conform more nearly to a race rather than a conventional variety. Single plant selections were subsequently made and the seed increased to produce pure line varieties, such as Richland oats, Kanred wheat, OAC 21 barley, and Mandell soybeans.

The term "line," according to the Code, is a "sexually reproducing population of uniform appearance, propagated by seeds or by spores, its stability maintained by selection to a standard."

A pure line variety consists of the genetically identical progeny of a single, self-fertilized, homozygous, or true breeding, plant. Such an individual transmits through its gametes, or germ cells, identical genes—hence all its offspring are identical to it and each other. The variety thus remains pure, except for mutations.

Conversely, a plant from the union of genetically unlike germ cells is heterozygous, or hybrid, for each gene in which the gametes differ.

In self-pollinated crops, heterozygosis largely results from controlled or infrequent natural cross-pollination between plants with different germ plasm. Self-pollination in subsequent generations rapidly reduces the amount of heterozygosity, or genetic variability; in fact, it is halved in each generation.

Among all gene pairs, heterozygous in the first hybrid or first filial generation, commonly designated F_1, only half are heterozygous in the F_2, one-fourth in F_3, and so on. Very rapidly, therefore, the population derived from one hybrid plant becomes segregated into many true breeding plants, no two of which are identical.

Most improved varieties developed from hybrids in self-pollinated crops virtually are pure lines, because final selection of the progenitor plant of the new variety is delayed until a high degree of homozygosis has been attained. This uniformity has advantages in that, barring mixtures, further outcrosses, or mutations, the germ plasm will not change. As offtypes are usually detectable, the task of maintaining purity of the variety is simplified. Uniformity may be disadvantageous, however. If climate or soil is unfavorable for maximum production or if a disease epidemic occurs, every plant in the variety is equally affected.

Certain genetic variability among plants may provide a buffer against adverse environment or diseases. Some plant breeders have developed varieties from plants selected from populations that have undergone only one or two generations of self-pollination, or they have composited a number of homozygous lines from the cross. The new variety Traveler oats is of this type. Such varieties, in effect, are a composite of many closely related plants but not a pure line. Generally the breeder should limit the range of visible characters so that the variety may be distinguished.

Normally cross-pollinated crops may have still greater range of genetic variability within varieties.

Cross-pollinated crops, frequently called open pollinated, can conveniently be grouped into those in which pollination is subject to control on a large-scale field basis and those in which natural cross-pollination must be relied upon for seed production.

Commercial hybrid varieties are supplanting open-pollinated varieties in crops that are subject to controlled pollination.

In crops such as corn and melons, the bearing of pollen (male) and ovule (female) flowers separately on the same plant permits removal of pollen flowers from seed plants.

In crops such as onions, sorghum, sugarbeets, and castorbeans, pollen of seed plants is eliminated through cytoplasmic or genetic male sterility.

In crops bearing pollen and ovule flowers on separate plants, such as spinach, male plants can be cut out of seed rows.

In crops with high self-sterility, such as cabbage and Pensacola bahiagrass, clones or lines may be interplanted.

Rules and Regulations Under the Federal Seed Act contains this definition of hybrid: "The term 'hybrid' means the first generation seed of a cross produced by controlling the pollination and by combining (1) two, three, or four inbred lines; (2) one inbred or a single cross with an open-pollinated variety; or (3) two varieties or species, except open-pollinated varieties of corn (Zea mays)."

A hybrid as a kind of variety is defined by the Code as "a uniform group which is a first generation hybrid (F_1) reconstituted on each occasion by crossing two or more breeding stocks maintained either by inbreeding or as clones."

When plants of a crop are self-fertile, inbred lines usually are developed through self-pollinating plants of highly heterozygous populations. The first generation of inbreeding from controlled self-pollination is designated S_1, the second S_2, and so on. From a genetic standpoint, the S_1 corresponds to the F_2 generation following controlled hybridization. This process is analogous genetically to the development of pure lines from an induced hybrid in a naturally self-pollinated crop.

Commercial usage of the term "hybrid" is restricted to the first generation following hybridization. Several types of hybrids, however, are possible.

When inbred lines are the parental stocks, the hybrid may involve two, three, four or more inbreds, which may be indicated by such terms as "single-cross," "three-way-cross," or "double-cross hybrids."

Parental stocks of double-cross hybrids are single crosses. If the single crosses have been self-pollinated for one or more generations, however, the resulting cross is an advanced generation hybrid.

When the parental stocks involve an inbred line and an open-pollinated variety, the product is a topcross hybrid.

Variety classification is extremely variable in normally cross-pollinated crops where large-scale controlled pollination is not possible. These crops include many forage grasses and legumes; some vegetables, such as carrots, celery, and cauliflower; and many flowering ornamentals. Varietal designation often is given to populations, such as a race, that have evolved naturally under certain environmental conditions and have acquired somewhat constant characters.

Seeds of many modern varieties are

constituted by interplanting selected clones or seed-propagated lines and allowing them and their progenies to intercross under conditions free from foreign pollen. Varieties so formed are known as synthetic varieties. Seed stocks are increased by permitting random mating within the population in each generation. The first generation of seed resulting from intercrossing is known as Syn 1 and the second as Syn 2.

Syn 1 is called composite by corn breeders because it is in effect a composite of single-cross seeds.

The term "polycross" is at times associated with such varieties; probably the usage stems from the similarity of the random interplanting of clones and the establishment of a polycross nursery. Polycross, however, is a term that describes a type of experimental cross to measure the general combining ability of clones and has no commercial usage.

The term "chance hybrid" has been applied to hybrids recently produced without controlled pollination. Equal seed portions of four inbred lines of pearl millet, for instance, are composited for planting as a mixture. The resulting seed is a mixture predominantly of hybrid but with some inbred seed. Plants from the latter are weaker and largely are eliminated by competition during the seedling stage.

Thus, the variety, which is created and maintained by man, is the essential unit of classification in cultivated plants. Though usage differs greatly from crop to crop, varieties are distinguished by constant, inherent characters. Because of its importance, the variety has been called the basis of modern agriculture and horticulture.

MARTIN G. WEISS *is Associate Director, Crops Research Division, Agricultural Research Service, Beltsville, Md.* ELBERT L. LITTLE, JR., *is dendrologist, Forest Service, Washington, D.C. Both are members of the Department of Agriculture Committee on Plant Nomenclature and members of the International Commission for the Nomenclature of Cultivated Plants.*

Policies on the Release of Seeds

R. D. LEWIS AND K. S. QUISENBERRY

NEW PLANT materials and new combinations of germ plasm are located or created by plant explorers, plant geneticists, and plant breeders, public and private. The creation, location, and release to the public of better plants is a major contribution of research to the advancement of agriculture and related industries.

The seed of a new variety or hybrid is a tangible, living organism, which we see and handle—not just an abstract idea. Seeds tie together, in a common undertaking, the plant geneticist, the plant breeder, the tester or evaluator, the seedgrower, the seed processor, and distributors and merchandisers of seeds with those who sow the seed, those who cultivate and harvest the plants, and those who process, market, and consume the products.

Mere location or creation of new plant materials is neither justification nor assurance of their release for use. Decisions as to the probable comparative values and usefulness must be made by the ones who originate or possess the new materials. Thorough testing and evaluation for all factors of performance and quality are therefore basic to the decisions regarding release.

Decisions to release or not to release must also depend upon the existence of adequate breeder's and foundation stocks and on effective nonexploitive methods of increase, so as to insure genetic identity and purity. Unless there are definite provisions for effective increases and merchandising, a decision to release may merely result in disappointment or nonacceptance of the new creation.

Plant geneticists, breeders, and officials of the State agricultural experiment stations as well as the Department of Agriculture are concerned continually with decisions on release of many different kinds of germ plasm, as, for instance, basic genetic stocks, segregating populations, inbred lines, clonal lines, lines in course of selection or purification, male-sterile lines, hybrid combinations, introduced species or varieties, and new strains.

During and following the Second World War, officials of the State agricultural experiment stations and the Department of Agriculture realized the need for stating guiding principles relating to responsibilities, principles, and policies in the development, evaluation, release, and increase of seeds of new varieties, strains, and hybrids developed by these public agencies. Even within many individual stations or agencies, no consistent policy or procedure guided these activities. Confusion and uncertainty often existed.

Consequently a number of regional groups of directors of the State stations developed preliminary statements of responsibilities and policies relating to steps in development, evaluation, and release of seeds. A joint committee representing the directors of the stations and the Agricultural Research Service consolidated and expanded these previous statements. The Agricultural Research Service and the Experiment Station Committee on Organization and Policy in 1954 approved and distributed "A Statement of Responsibilities and Policies Relating to Seeds."

This has become a guide for the further development of policies and procedures in individual States. It recognizes the obligation of both the State stations and the Department to cooperate in developing procedures for making the results of joint genetic and plant breeding efforts available to the public. It neither obligates nor affects the right of an individual State station to make adaptations in line with the specific situations and needs of that State.

The joint statement of 1954 is designed largely to outline general policies and procedures and point up general functions and opportunities for improving both public and private activities and services in the development and use of improved seeds. While adaptations to specific crops are required, it has not yet been found necessary to deviate from the major principles.

As release of seeds is closely identified with other steps in the creation and use of a new variety, we find it inadvisable to confine the following quotations and comments to release alone. The reader should recognize that the following principles and procedures, as quoted from the 1954 statement, are primarily to guide officials and plant breeders of public agencies and to create an understanding of the procedures among users of seeds.

Demonstrated performance is the basis for decisions on the release of new varieties. The general standard of performance is:

"No new variety should be released unless it is distinctly superior to existing commercial varieties in some one or more characteristics important for the crop, and is at least satisfactory in other major requirements. A major menace, which a new variety can overcome, e.g., a highly destructive disease, may justify some leniency in evaluating criteria. In general, however, a new variety should not be released unless it represents a real advance. Varieties with a very limited range in adaptation should not be distributed, unless performance in that limited range is outstandingly superior, or the variety possesses important use values which are needed and not otherwise available."

The background evaluation or test data must be adequate. "New varieties and hybrids should be tested for yield, survival, disease reaction and other important characteristics in comparison with standard commercial varieties, using experimental technics that assure valid measure of differences and their significance. Thus personal and other bias will be eliminated in conducting these tests.

"Crop varieties are not limited in adaptation by State or other political boundaries. Interstate testing and interchange of materials should be encouraged. Regional testing insures more general use of widely adapted varieties. It also reduces time needed to provide reliable information on varietal adaptations.

"New varieties of crops to be used primarily for industrial purposes should be tested for these uses to insure that they are satisfactory. The trade or industry using the crop also should have opportunity to evaluate the new variety before distribution."

Provisions for a systematic, objective review are essential prior to a decision on release.

"Decisions on the release of new varieties should be made for each State by the appropriate agricultural agency of that State. It is recommended that in each State there be a policy committee or board of review charged with the responsibility of reviewing the proposals for the release in that State of each new variety or hybrid. All available information concerning characteristics, performance, use values, seed stocks, and proposed methods of increase and distribution should be presented to this committee as a basis for its decision.

"The committee should have associated with it individuals qualified in the specialties under which the values of the new variety of a specific crop must be determined. Many States now follow this or a similar procedure.

"When a variety has been tested on an interstate basis, opportunity should be given for each State in the interstate program to consider whether the variety should be released in that State. Whenever possible all interested States should release the variety simultaneously. If for some reason prior interstate testing was neglected or impossible, the State which may shortly release a new variety should offer to all interested States in the region seed of the new variety for testing. Thus the nearby States may obtain information to answer questions from their farmers, should the new variety cross State lines."

Correct naming is essential:

"A new variety should be given a permanent designation before it is released. When this designation is a name, this name should consist preferably of one word, the shorter the better. Under no circumstances should a variety be distributed under more than one name. Likewise, distinctly different genetic strains should not be distributed under the same name.

"The name should be agreed upon by the interested States, but the originating agency has the final responsibility. Once it has been established, a varietal name should not be changed.

"The American Society of Agronomy and the Society of Horticultural Science have adopted guides for the naming of varieties, which are consistent and insure names that will not be confusing."

Decisions regarding release often are modified by the basic supplies of breeder's seed and the assurance of continued availability of such seed for increases of foundation and commercial supplies. "When it becomes evident that a new variety is sufficiently promising to merit consideration for release, breeder's seed should be increased to the volume needed to produce and maintain required pure seed stocks (foundation seed). So long as a variety is retained on the recommended list of the originating station, that station should maintain a reasonable reserve of breeder's seed, which can at any time be used to replenish and restore foundation and commercial seed of the variety to desired genetic purity."

That procedure on maintenance is not followed fully. Sometimes full responsibility is turned over to seed producers following the initial release of breeder's and foundation stock seeds to qualified seedsmen.

The possible provisions for increase and maintenance of foundation seed stocks may affect decisions on release. "In foundation seed production programs, special care must be taken to insure that the relatively small amounts of breeder's seed are not wasted by indiscriminate distribution. Only those who have the know-how, the facilities, and who will sow the breeder's seed for production of foundation seed, to be sold at reasonable rates, should be included as foundation seed growers. Foundation seed [of publicly developed varieties] should be kept under institutional guidance.

"A foundation seed program should be of such scale as to assure annual production of sufficient high quality commercial, registered and certified seed for planting the acreage which the variety should occupy. Provision should be made for a reserve of foundation seed to guard against crop failure.

"Any foundation seed program should recognize certain basic principles: (1) Every qualified seed grower should have an opportunity to obtain such seed or its immediate progeny at a reasonable cost; (2) there should be no monopoly in access to foundation seed; (3) the seed should meet high standards of purity and germination; and (4) the end result of commercial certified seed production based on the foundation seed program should be good seed and enough seed at a reasonable price to plant the acreage justified by the interests of American agriculture."

The preceding guides concerning release of new varieties may seem to apply almost exclusively to new varieties and hybrids created in the plant breeding programs of the State stations and the Department. Actually, they also apply to new species and varieties which may arise directly from foreign and domestic plant explorations— commonly termed "introductions."

The introductions by the Department of Agriculture "are made available to public and private agencies and no individual or agency is given exclusive rights to newly introduced materials."

The statement continues: "Reports on observational and performance tests are required from those receiving the newly introduced materials.

"Individuals or organizations proposing to increase and distribute seed or plant materials of such introductions in *their original* genetic form are asked to make this intention known to the agency from which the material came. In such instances plans for joint release can be considered. This is done to avoid confusion arising from duplication of identifying names or numbers given to the same introduction by public or private interests. The source of such plant materials should be publicly acknowledged.

"Where the genetic makeup of the introduced material is modified by selection, inbreeding, or hybridization, the agency providing the original material should be informed of the specific characters in the new strain, which are derived from the original introduction. The original source of these breeding materials, also, should be indicated publicly."

Basic genetic materials generally are involved in the creation of new varieties or hybrids. Furthermore, new varieties or hybrids are often a byproduct of fundamental studies relating to new principles, new methods, or a wider understanding of hereditary processes. Inevitably, then, there arise questions of release of these basic and developmental stocks, as well as the results of these fundamental studies.

"The Department and the State stations are obligated to conduct fundamental studies of the character and properties of plant materials, the modes of reproduction, the inheritance of characters, and the possibilities of modification and control of heredity through cytogenetics, biogenetics, and other advanced methods of improvement. These agencies and their workers are further obligated to make the results of these fundamental studies promptly and freely available to all plant breeders, institutional or private. Effective crop breeding programs are based on the application of such fundamental knowledge.

"Basic genetic materials from such studies useful in crop improvement should be made available to all plant breeders. The term *basic genetic materials* refers to items possessing one or more desirable characters, but which otherwise may not be commercially useful. It is not intended to include inbred lines nor selections in course of development and not ready for complete release.

"In many instances, the development of superior varieties or hybrids to solve a given production problem can only be accomplished after certain fundamental studies of heredity and methods of improvement are carried out. When basic genetic materials resulting from such studies conducted by the public agencies are made available to private or public plant breeders, every effort should be made to insure that these materials are not monopolized by any interests."

A decision to release is a grave responsibility. To aid in discharging this responsibility effectively, those concerned in the decision must see that release is accompanied by an effective informational and educational program. The 1954 statement says:

"Seed producers, distributors and farmers should be informed as fully as possible of the values and the adaptation of new varieties in comparison with varieties already grown.

"To decide on varieties, the farmer must have valid information which is complete, fair, and unbiased. All factors relating to performance, whether favorable or unfavorable, should be presented. The same standards used in deciding upon release of a new variety apply in presenting the case to seed producers, distributors and farmers.

"Seed production and demand must be developed together in so far as pos-

sible. A seed supply and no demand, or demand and no seed supply, both result in confusion and often in failure to do an adequate job; thus, promotional publicity in advance of the release of a new variety is usually not desirable."

Modifications in policies and procedures concerning release of varieties and other plant materials can be expected with advances in genetics and new methods of plant breeding, and with the rise of cooperative effort among public and private agencies in the development of superior seeds for American agriculture.

One slight extension of the 1954 statement was approved in 1956, clarifying the interchange and release of basic genetic materials originating in the State and Federal alfalfa-breeding programs.

Possibly in cotton there was more apparent conflict between public and private breeders than with any other major crop. From 1955 to 1958 a joint committee of station directors, Agricultural Research Service officials, and representatives of private cotton-breeding firms exchanged ideas and finally developed a mutually satisfactory statement of *Private and Public Responsibilities and Opportunities in Cotton Genetics and Breeding*. The approved statement charts the basis for mutual understanding and complementary action by private and public geneticists, breeders, and evaluators to the benefit of the entire industry.

A joint working group of representatives of the alfalfa seed industry, the State and Federal research agencies, and the seed certification agencies started in 1960 to develop the basis for complementary actions directed toward further and more rapid improvements in the alfalfa seed production and distribution industries.

R. D. LEWIS *is Director, Texas Agricultural Experiment Station, College Station, Tex.*

K. S. QUISENBERRY *formerly was Assistant Administrator, Agricultural Research Service.*

Above, left: Hard red winter wheat *(Triticum aestivum)*. Above, right: Hard red spring wheat *(Triticum aestivum)*. Below, left: Durum wheat *(Triticum durum)*. Below, right: Club wheat *(Triticum compactum)*.

Above, left: Oats *(Avena sativa)*.   Above, right: Buckwheat *(Fagopyrum esculentum)*. Below, left: Barley (6-row) *(Hordeum vulgare)*.   Below, right: Barley (2-row) *(Hordeum distichon)*.

Above, left: Soybeans (*Glycine max*).   Above, right: Grain sorghum (*Sorghum vulgare*).   Below, left: Rye (*Secale cereale*).   Below, right: Rye (tetraploid) (*Secale cereale*).

Above, left: Corn *(Zea mays)*.   Above, right: Rice (long-grain) *(Oryza sativa)*.   Below, left: Rice (short-grain) *(Oryza sativa)*.   Below, right: Rice (medium-grain) *(Oryza sativa)*.

Above, left: Tobacco *(Nicotiana tabacum)*. Above, right: Cotton (chemically delinted) *(Gossypium hirsutum)*. Below, left: Cotton (mechanically delinted) *(Gossypium hirsutum)*. Below, right: Cotton (ginned) *(Gossypium hirsutum)*.

Above, left: Hemp *(Cannabis sativa).* Above, right: Flax *(Linum usitatissimum).* Below, left: Sunflower *(Helianthus annuus).* Below, right: Cowpeas (black-eyed) *(Vigna sinensis).*

Above, left: Castorbeans (*Ricinus communis*). Above, right: Safflower (*Carthamus tinctorius*). Below, left: Sesame (*Sesamum indicum*). Below, right: Showy crotalaria (*Crotalaria spectabilis*).

Above, left: Red clover (*Trifolium pratense*).   Above, right: Alsike clover (*Trifolium hybridum*).   Below, left: Whiteclover (*Trifolium repens*).   Below, right: Sweetclover (*Melilotus* spp.).

Above, left: Korean lespedeza *(Lespedeza stipulacea)*.   Above, right: Sericca lespedeza *(Lespedeza cuneata)*.   Below, left: Alfalfa *(Medicago sativa)*.   Below, right: Birdsfoot trefoil *(Lotus corniculatus)*.

Above, left: Orchardgrass *(Dactylis glomerata)*. Above, right: Tall fescue *(Festuca arundinacea)*. Below, left: Sudangrass *(Sorghum sudanense)*. Below, right: Bromegrass *(Bromus inermis)*.

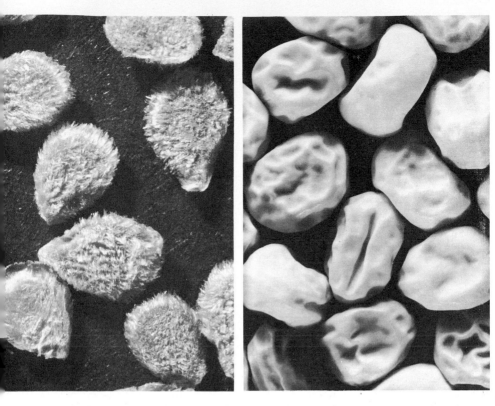

Above, left: Tomato *(Lycopersicon esculentum)*.   Above, right: Pea *(Pisum sativum)*.
Below, left: Beet *(Beta vulgaris)*.   Below, right: Radish *(Raphanus sativus)*.

Above, left: Carrot *(Daucus carota)*.   Above, right: Summer squash *(Cucurbita pepo)*.
Below, left: Parsnip *(Pastinaca sativa)*.   Below, right: Sweet corn *(Zea mays)*.

Above, left: Okra *(Hibiscus esculentus).* Above, right: Watermelon *(Citrullus vul-garis).* Below, left: Butternut squash *(Cucurbita moschata).* Below, right: Pepper *(Capsicum frutescens).*

Above, left: Onion *(Allium cepa).*   Above, right: Kale *(Brassica oleracea* var. *acephala).*
Below, left: Broccoli *(Brassica oleracea* var. *botrytis).*   Below, right: Chinese cabbage
(Brassica pekinensis).

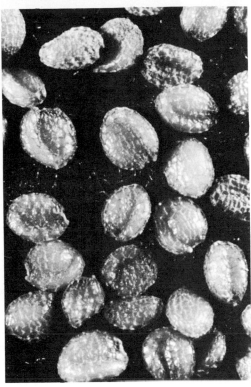

Above, left: Upland cress (*Barbarea verna*).   Above, right: Watercress (*Rorippa nasturtium-aquaticum*).   Below, left: Parsley (*Petroselinum hortense*).   Below, right: Dandelion (*Taraxacum officinale*).

Above, left: New Zealand spinach *(Tetragonia expansa)*.   Above, right: Celery *(Apium graveolens* var. *dulce)*.   Below, left: Asparagus *(Asparagus officinalis)*.   Below, right: Lettuce *(Lactuca sativa)*.

Above, left: Prickly-seed spinach *(Spinacia oleracea)*. Above, right: Tendergreen or "mustard spinach" *(Brassica perviridis)*. Below, left: Globe artichoke *(Cynara scolymus)*. Below, right: Cornsalad or fetticus *(Valerianella locusta* var. *olitoria)*.

Above, left: Garden mustard *(Brassica juncea)*. Above, right: Rhubarb *(Rheum rha-ponticum)*. Below, left: Garden sorrel *(Rumex acetosa)*. Below, right: "Tastee" soybean *(Glycine max)*.

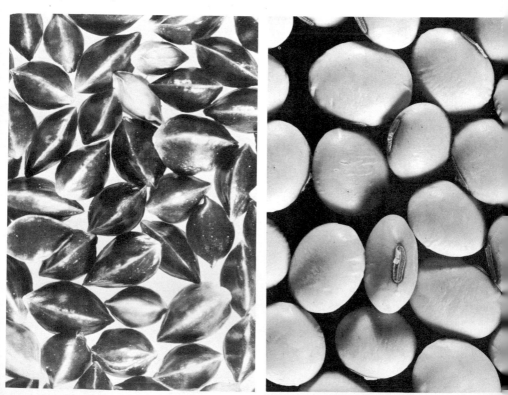

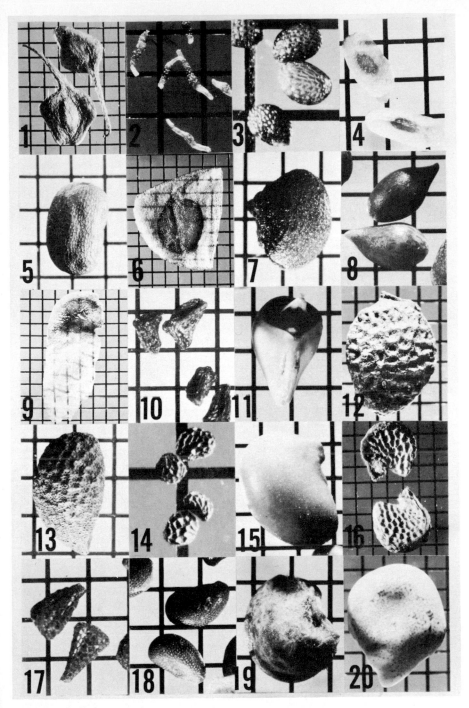

1. Meadow anemone *(Anemone canadensis)*. 2. Pink ladyslipper *(Cypripedium acaule)*. 3. Trailing-arbutus *(Epigaea repens)*. 4. Closed gentian *(Gentiana andrewsii)*. 5. Wild geranium *(Geranium maculatum)*. 6. Tigerlily *(Lilium superbum)*. 7. Large-flowered trillium *(Trillium grandiflorum)*. 8. Blue violet *(Viola papilionacea)*. 9. Yellow jessamine *(Gelsemium sempervirens)*. 10. Purple gerardia *(Gerardia purpurea)*. 11. Puccoon *(Lithospermum canescens)*. 12. Passionflower *(Passiflora incarnata)*. 13. Scorpionweed *(Phacelia bipinnatifida)*. 14. Rosepink *(Sabatia angularis)*. 15. Aarons-rod *(Thermopsis caroliniana)*. 16. Poppy-mallow *(Callirhoe involucrata)*. 17. Indian paintbrush *(Castilleja lindheimeri)*. 18. Purple cactus *(Coryphantha vivipara)*. 19. Bindweed-heliotrope *(Euploca convolvulacea)*. 20. Bluebonnet *(Lupinus texensis)*.

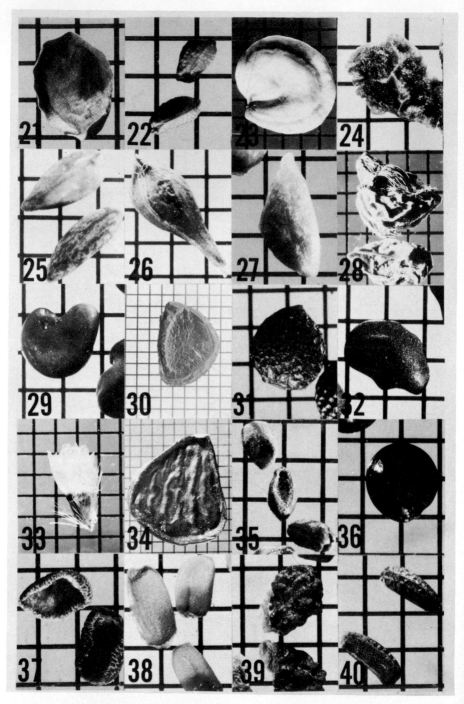

21. Blazing-star *(Mentzelia decapetala)*. 22. Fern-leaf evening-primrose *(Oenothera laciniata)*. 23. Pricklypear *(Opuntia polyacantha)*. 24. Large-flowered beardtongue *(Penstemon grandiflorus)*. 25. Texas-sage *(Salvia coccinea)*. 26. Sulphurflower *(Eriogonum umbellatum)*. 27. Skyrocket *(Gilia aggregata)*. 28. Panicled bluebell *(Mertensia paniculata)*. 29. Stemless locoweed *(Oxytropis lamberti)*. 30. Century-plant *(Agave americana)*. 31. Pricklepoppy *(Argemone mexicana)*. 32. Barrel cactus *(Ferocactus wislizeni)*. 33. Blanketflower *(Gaillardia pulchella)*. 34. Spanish-bayonet *(Yucca baccata)*. 35. Tall clarkia *(Clarkia pulchella)*. 36. Springbeauty *(Claytonia linearis)*. 37. Chinese-houses *(Collinsia bicolor)*. 38. Wallflower *(Erysimum asperum)*. 39. Baby-blue-eyes *(Nemophila insignis)*. 40. Prostrate verbena *(Verbena prostrata)*.

Seedsmen sometimes are asked how they make the seeds they sell. Their reply is "We don't make them. Flowers do." Victor R. Boswell, a Department horticulturist, is shown here in a greenhouse at Beltsville, Md. He is explaining to visitors some aspects of the production of vegetables and seeds: The transfer of pollen by insects so fertilization of flowers can take place; how pollination is controlled so as to breed better plants; some steps in the commercial production of seeds; the growing of plants from cuttings, and so on. This photograph was made by William H. Riess, Jr. He and Dr. Boswell took most of the pictures of seeds that appear in the preceding pages.

A honey bee here collects nectar from an alfalfa flower. Colonies of honey bees are placed at the edge of a field where alfalfa is being grown for seed.

Some insects damage seeds and crops. Above, left, is a lygus bug nymph on an alfalfa stem. Right, above, is normal alfalfa seed. Below, left, are seeds damaged by lygus bugs; right, the emergence hole of the clover seed chalcid on a seed pod of alfalfa.

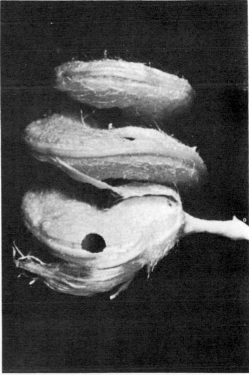

A squash bee *(Peponapis),* above, collects nectar on a female squash flower, whose stigma already is well covered with grains of pollen.   Below are nests of leaf-cutting bees (left) and alkali bees.

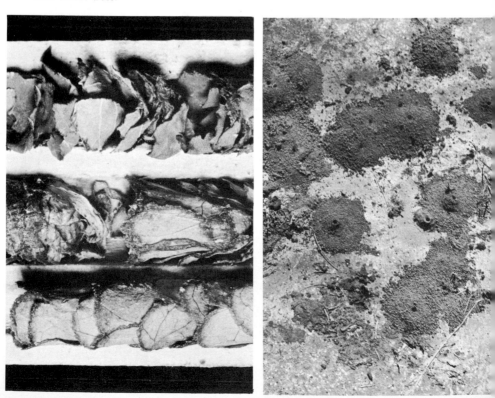

Scientists make many studies of pollen, the male element. Above: Samples of pollen are taken from anthers of peach blossoms treated with the drug colchicine to compare the size of the pollen grains. Below: The anthers in a petunia flower are removed so that their pollen will not reach the stigma, the female organ. The process is called emasculation.

In the commercial production of seeds of flowers, selected female petunia flowers may receive pollen from other petunias chosen as males. Pollen gathered from males in a nearby greenhouse is supplied to workers in a vial. Only a small amount of pollen need adhere to the pencil tip they use. Below: The pollen is applied to the receptive stigma of the female. Its natural pollen was removed earlier, so that the seed it produces will be the result of the two chosen parents (cross-pollination), not that of the female line alone (self-pollination). As new flowers open daily, this operation is carried out thousands of times a day.

Two other interesting details of seed production are illustrated in these two pictures. One is of a field of Crackerjack marigold grown for a seed crop in California. This variety has extremely double flowers, which produce little pollen. Rows of single flowers supply additional pollen, which insects carry to the doubles. This is an example of controlled natural pollination—the resulting seed produces double flowers only because doubleness is dominant in marigolds. The finding of male sterility was an advance in breeding onions. Below are a male-sterile (right) and a normal onion flower.

In fields of Bodger Seeds, Ltd., El Monte, Calif., test lines of F₁ hybrid petunias (left of road) and their inbred parent lines (right of road) are grown. More than a thousand distinct lines grow here. Similar work is carried out with the major species of the 1,500 kinds of seeds of flowers grown commercially. Below: A field of sweet alyssum is grown for seed. The beds are raised to facilitate irrigation.

The picture above is of fields of larkspur grown for seed in the Santa Rosa Valley in California. The seed blocks are long and narrow because machines are used for planting and harvesting. Hand-harvested blocks would be almost square. Divider strips are planted with a later maturing crop whose plants will prevent accidental mixing of larkspur plants when they are cut for threshing. Below: A field in Iowa of hybrid corn being grown for seed. Plants in the rows that have not been detasseled furnish the pollen. Plants in the six-row blocks have been detasseled.

David H. Wallace, an employee of a hybrid seed corn firm near Des Moines, Iowa, is shown here detasseling corn. The lower picture shows how strands of male flowers are placed in the center of the female cluster of date flowers.

At a Plant Materials Center near Spur, Tex., an agronomist checks seed fill in Coronado sideoats grama. Below: A field of orchardgrass grown for foundation seed.

Closely related to the production of seeds is work with plants. Above is a picture of plants of an early variety and a late variety of petunia, each on long and short day. On long day, the four flowered early and simultaneously. On short day, the early one flowered later than it did on long day, and the late one flowered much later. It illustrates the point that plant breeders use photoperiod to synchronize the flowering dates of early and late varieties of plants so they can cross them. Below: A series of celosia plants on various daylengths; they show a graded response to daylength.

Seed crops are harvested in a number of ways. Near Spokane, Wash., where yields of 300 to 600 pounds of seeds per acre are normal, Merion Kentucky bluegrass is combined directly. Below: A farmer uses a tined windrower to swath subterranean clover.

A tractor-drawn combine with windrow pickup and draper feeder lifts and threshes bentgrass seeds from the windrow. Below: Near Winchester, Ky., natural Kentucky bluegrass is sacked off just as it is harvested in the field by McCormick strippers. The green seed is lifted by hand from the hopper and put into large sacks.

To harvest seeds of forest trees, one may have to climb to the sky, as does this forest ranger on Sun Top Mountain in Washington. Below: The ranger later loads sacks of cones of noble fir on pack mules for transport to distant storehouses.

In the hope of reducing greatly t
large losses that attend the handli
of the 200 million dollars' worth
grass and legume seeds produced ea
year in the United States, agricultu
engineers have undertaken to impro
techniques and equipment. This
search is done in a seed laborato
operated by the Department of Ag
culture and the Oregon Agricultu
Experiment Station in Corvallis. So
of the experimental developments
pictured here. A 35-percent reducti
in shatter losses of birdsfoot trefoi
possible when the crop is combin
in windrows on wide sheets of plas
The shattered seeds are gathered
and the plastic is rerolled during co
bining. Like savings are had if
trefoil is cut before shattering sta
cured in loose bales or shocks, a
then combined, as shown in the lo
picture.

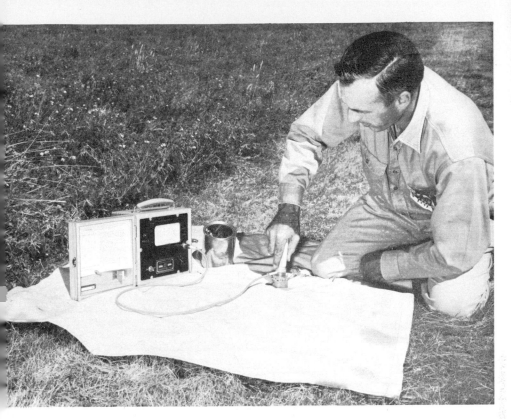

...meter, shown above by Leonard M.
...ein of the Agricultural Research
...rvice, may be useful to farmers to
...termine the best time to harvest
...sses and legumes. A "fluidized"
...nveyor is designed to move seeds
...eumatically at low velocity. It can
...nvey 3 thousand pounds of seeds an
...ur safely through a 1.5-inch pipe.

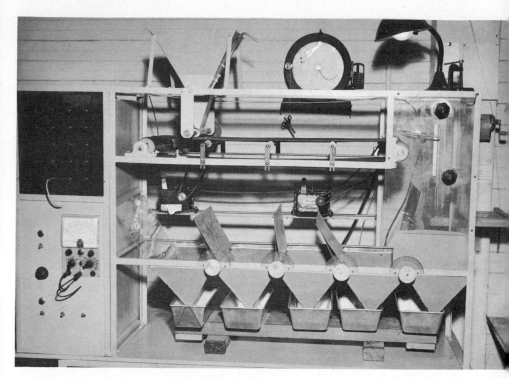

An electrostatic device makes additional separations of seeds possible. It uses an electric charge to hold the seeds temporarily on a moving conveyor belt at the top of the machine. The seeds drop from the belt into appropriate containers when they lose their charge. Below: Another experimental device made by engineers at the Corvallis laboratory removes the tiny seeds of pigweed (which cost the seed industry countless dollars and are hard to separate) from alfalfa seeds. It is a modified-indent cylinder and vacuum system. The pigweed seeds drop into indents and are sucked away through a tube.

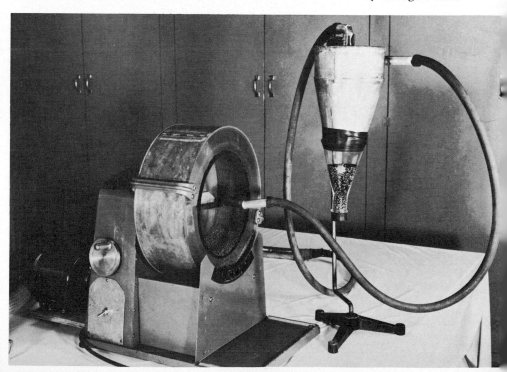

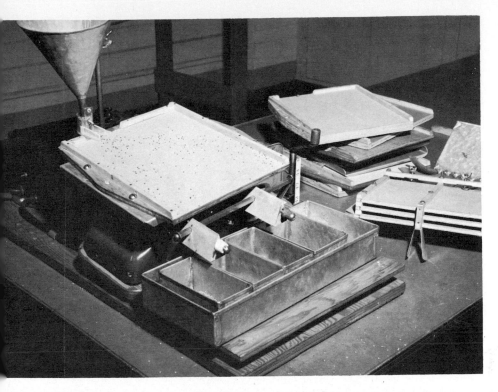

The automatic seed separator pictured above has a vibrating table that may be adjusted in any direction to make separations, previously impossible, on the basis of weight, surface texture, and shapes of seeds. As the table vibrates, different seeds form in paths and drop into various containers. Below: A vibrator-feeder may have several uses in a seed laboratory. It can pass seeds of any size under a microscope for inspection and through an electronic field for counting.

All States have their own laws as to the labeling and sale of seeds among which are seeds of noxious weeds. Many seeds move in interstate commerce, and they are subject to the Federal Seed Act, which is administered by the Agricultural Marketing Service of the Department of Agriculture. On this page and the pages that follow are pictures of some aspects of work under the act to insure good seeds. Above: Orchardgrass seed is unloaded at the cleaning plant of a wholesale seed firm. The seed is in bags just as it came from the threshing machine and is generally referred to as seed "in the dirt." Below: The seed must be cleaned—the pure orchardgrass separated from the weed seeds, chaff, stems, dirt, and pebbles. Usually the first machine the seed is put through is this one that uses screens and wind to separate the pure seed from the inert matter.

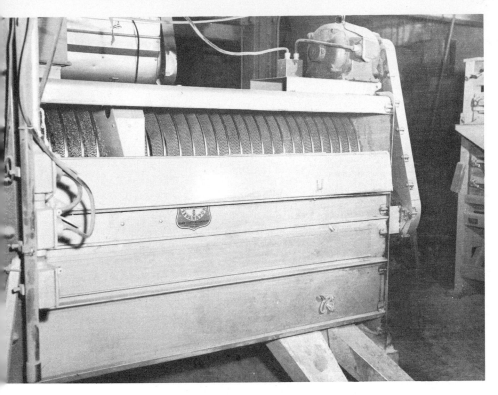

A disk separator. The disks have indentations of different sizes and shapes. As the disks revolve, weed seeds lodge in the indentations and in this way are separated from the pure seed. For example, the seeds of sheep sorrel and dock are separated from orchardgrass. Below: A specific gravity separator.

State Inspector taking a sample with a probe, which reaches the entire length of the sack. A representative sample is obtained and tested in the State seed laboratory to determine its purity, content of seeds of noxious weeds, and germination. Below: In the State seed laboratory the sample of seed is divided mechanically again and again until a working sample is obtained.

The seed analyst is holding a vacuum seed counter that is used in counting seeds for a germination test. The seeds have been placed on a moist blotter. Another moist blotter will be placed over them, and then the blotters with the seeds between them are placed in a germinator, where the temperature is controlled and the humidity is high. Below: A sample of 100 seeds of red clover that have been placed between moist blotters are put in a germinator, from which almost all light is excluded.

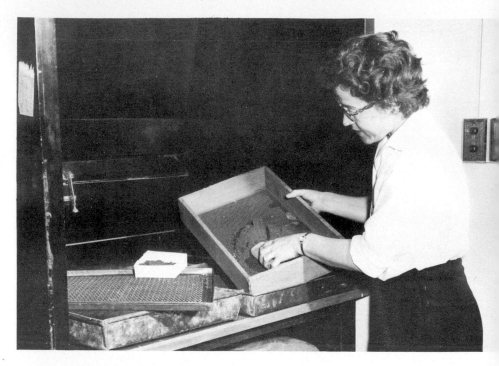

Preparing a soil test that may be used as a check on the germination test by other conventional laboratory methods. The soil test duplicates in part the conditions that seeds will encounter in the field. The same temperatures are used in this test as in the standard germination test. Below: The results of a germination test. The seed with long, vigorous sprouts, in the upper part of the picture, would be expected to produce plants in the field under favorable conditions. The seeds in the lower left are dead. Those in the lower right have shown some life but would not be expected to produce plants in the field and are not included in the percentage of seeds that have germinated.

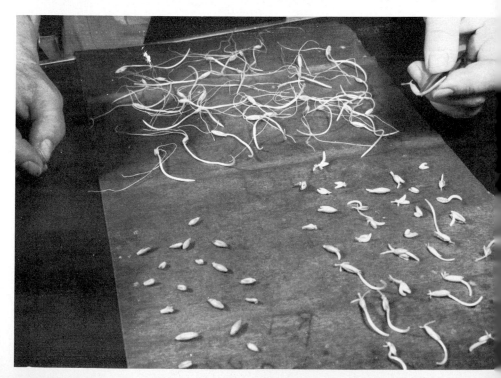

A seed analyst is separating a working sample into its components of pure seed, weed seed, other crop seed, and inert matter. The analyst is expected to identify all seeds, both crop and weed, in the sample. Below: Weighing the different parts into which a seed analyst has divided a seed sample. Later the percentage of each part is calculated.

This Federal Seed Laboratory at Beltsville, Md., makes tests on seeds subject to the Federal Seed Act. Other Federal laboratories are located at Sacramento, Calif., Montgomery, Ala., Kansas City, Mo., Minneapolis, Minn., and New Brunswick, N.J. Below: A representative of the Customs Service prepares a sample to be sent to the Federal Seed Laboratory to determine whether the seed meets standards for imported seed.

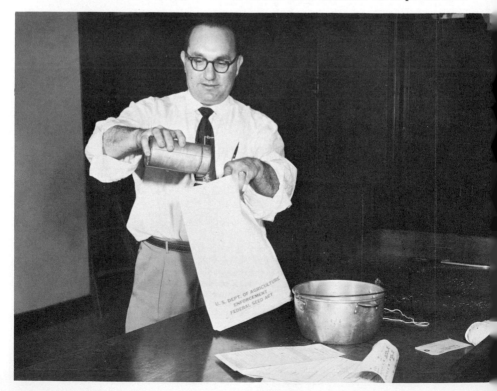

How We Get Stock Seed of Field Crops

CARLTON S. GARRISON

PLANT breeders develop a new, superior variety. What then?

First, stock seed must be increased as rapidly as possible under a plan that will maintain the superior varietal characteristics.

The next step is to distribute the foundation seed in a way that will insure equitable allotments to the experienced growers and seedmen and at the same time avoid exploitation of the new variety.

Thus the production and distribution of adequate supplies of stock seed—which in the case of field-crop varieties is designated as foundation seed—are crucial steps in developing the potential usefulness of a variety.

Foundation seed must be produced before commercial increases of registered and certified seed are possible. It is the stage in which the first large increase of seed is made and the one in which meticulous care must be taken to protect purity as to variety.

New varieties of field crops in the United States are released jointly by the Federal and State agricultural experiment stations or by seed firms that have a plant-breeding program.

A variety originating in a foreign country occasionally is found to be adapted to some section of the United States. It is introduced as though it had originated in this country. An experiment station or seed firm sponsors it and is responsible for the adequacy of foundation seed.

The procedures the public agencies and private firms follow in releasing seed of superior varieties are different,

but both aim to provide adequate quantities of foundation seed while maintaining varietal purity.

Varieties, hybrids, and inbred lines of field crops developed by public research agencies are released through foundation seed programs, which are of three types: Projects operating within a State agricultural experiment station or Government agency; private organizations, directed by persons from public agencies; and private organizations controlled by growers.

THE STATE FOUNDATION seed programs that are part of the work of an agricultural experiment station sometimes are assigned to a specific department. In Alabama, California, Minnesota, and Wisconsin, for example, the department of agronomy supervises them.

In other States, such as Idaho, Pennsylvania, and Wyoming, the foundation seed project operates under the direction of the director of the experiment station.

The programs are under the supervision of a foundation seed stocks committee, which usually comprises the director of the experiment station, the chairmen of the departments of agronomy and horticulture, the manager of the seed-certifying agency, and a representative of the Extension Service. Often the superintendents of the branch experiment stations and sometimes a representative of the seedgrowers and seed trade are members. A member of the staff of the experiment station or Extension Service usually is assigned to manage the production and distribution of foundation seed.

Funds to cover the production, processing, storage, and distribution of the foundation seed and related expenses are made available from State appropriations or from sales of the seed. The source of funds varies from State to State—from 100 percent appropriated funds to 100 percent funds acquired from seed dealers. Many States use both types of funds. They pay the salaries of the management from appropriated funds, and the costs for producing, processing, storing, and distributing the seed are paid from the seed sales fund.

IN A FEW STATES, the foundation seed organizations are private corporations, whose directors are mainly members of the staffs of the experiment stations and Extension Service. The experiment station thus controls the work.

Oklahoma Foundation Seed Stock, for example, is a private corporation, all of whose board members are on the staff of Oklahoma State University. The board of the Foundation Seed Stock Division at South Dakota State College has six members from the college and five who are nominated by the South Dakota Crop Improvement Association—the State seed-certifying agency—to represent major crop-producing areas of the State. The managers of both the Oklahoma and the South Dakota organizations are staff members of the experiment station or the Extension Service. All operating costs are paid from income from sales of seed.

The third type of organization that produces foundation seed for public research agencies is strictly private. It may be a nonprofit corporation or a growers' cooperative. Georgia, Indiana, Iowa, and New York have organizations of this kind.

The board of directors is elected by the members of the corporation or cooperative. A representative of the experiment station sometimes is a member of the board. Sometimes the boards have established a seed stock advisory committee comprising representatives of the experiment station, Extension Service, and the seed-certifying agency.

Since these private organizations handle the increase and distribution of stock seed of new varieties bred by public research agencies, a memorandum of understanding or some contractual arrangement is developed between the foundation seed organization and the State experiment sta-

tion. Its main purpose is to define responsibilities and working arrangements. This is important, because the foundation seed organization is given exclusive rights to new varieties developed by public agencies. The interest of the public is protected by the memorandum of understanding and representation of the experiment station on the organization's board of directors or through an advisory seed stocks committee.

Private funds are used to finance the operations of this type of foundation seed organization, but occasionally the State makes an initial grant of funds. Office and warehouse facilities are provided by the experiment station in some States.

The foundation seed of the small grains, inbred lines and single crosses of corn, sorghum, oil, and fiber crops, and some of the forage crops is produced mostly in the State or region where it will be used.

On the other hand, foundation seed of many varieties of forage crops is produced away from its place of origin—that is, in areas where the seed can be multiplied more efficiently. The distance between the State where the variety originated and where the foundation seed is grown sometimes is more than 2 thousand miles.

BEFORE SEED can be tagged and sealed as foundation seed, requirements specified by the State seed-certifying agency must be met. The minimum seed certification standards specify the requirements for eligibility of planting stock, land requirements, isolation, field inspection, and seed standards.

Eligible planting stock—breeder seed —must be used in the production of foundation seed. Usually it is supplied by the plant breeder. Special programs are maintained in many States to assure the purity of the stock from which the foundation seed is grown. For small grains, for example, a head-to-row planting is made of selected heads. After careful roguing by the breeder and representatives of the foundation seed organization, the true-to-variety rows are harvested as breeder seed for the production of foundation seed.

Similar systems are used for most of the crops. For forage crops, however, their heterogeneity requires that the originating breeder maintain a recurring supply of breeder seed since the number of generations of increase permissible from breeder seed usually is limited. Most forage varieties are limited to one generation each of foundation, registered, and certified seed, but the registered seed class is being eliminated whenever the required volume of certified seed can be produced without it.

The certification standards normally specify that foundation seed be grown on land that has not been seeded to the crop for a specific number of years. To be eligible to produce foundation seed of small grains, soybeans, millet, and sorghum, the land must not have produced the respective crop the previous year.

The interval is lengthened for crops in which hard seeds or seed dormancy are factors in germination. For alfalfa, the period during which the land must not have grown the same seed crop is 4 years; grasses, 5 years; red clover, 6 years; and sweetclover, 10 years.

Adequate isolation distances are required to avoid contamination in foundation seed fields. The minimum distance for the cross-pollinated species (except corn) is 80 rods. Cornfields must be at least 40 rods apart or less if there are border rows or natural barriers.

An isolation strip about 10 feet wide, or the width of one drill, is required between foundation seed fields of self-pollinated crops and contaminating plant materials.

Fields of foundation seed must be inspected each year. For some crops the requirements are specific as to the number and timing of inspections. At least four inspections are required for corn during the pollinating period. One inspection is required for the grasses, but it must be made after heading and before harvest.

Fields producing foundation seed must be free of other varieties or offtype plants. Offtypes can cause the seed to be declared ineligible as foundation seed. The seed fields therefore must be rogued several times during the season.

The certification procedures include maximum allowances for other crops, weeds, and inert matter, and minimum requirements for purity and germination. Usually the minimum germination plus hard seed is 80 percent. The minimum purity is 97 percent or better, but for many of the grasses it has to be lower because of the chaffy characteristics of some species.

The certification agency checks the harvesters and seed cleaners before they are used for foundation seed.

The seed is tagged and sealed after it is cleaned and found to meet all requirements for certification. A white tag is used to denote foundation seed.

Arrangements for producing foundation seed of field-crop varieties depend somewhat on the type of organization responsible for it.

In places where the foundation seed projects are a part of the experiment station, much of the foundation seed is grown at the branch experiment stations. Thus it is under the control of the foundation seed project at all times.

When the required production is greater than the capacity of the experiment station farms, the seed is produced under contract by registered or certified seedgrowers who have had experience with the crop.

Sometimes the seed is grown by the foundation seed project on rented land.

When the production of foundation seed is the responsibility of an "official" private organization, it is produced on the organization's own farms, under contract, or on the land the organization rents and farms.

Regardless of the type of organization that produces it, the seed is taken to the headquarters of the foundation seed organization for cleaning, bagging, tagging, sealing, and storage. This reduces the possibility of admixtures, which occur sometimes in commercial seed-cleaning plants.

The normal steps in multiplying foundation seed of a new variety are not always fast enough to meet the need. A new variety of grain or an inbred line of corn may be released, and the growers in a locality may urgently need certified seed of it. Stock seed therefore must be increased quickly.

To meet the need, the initial supplies of foundation seed may be built up by overwinter increases—for example, in Arizona, Florida, Texas, and Mexico.

A small amount of breeder seed—a few kernels of an inbred line of corn or a few bushels of a variety of oats, flax, wheat, or barley produced by the originating breeder—is shipped south after harvest. The seed is planted in the fall, and a seed crop is grown during the winter. It is ready for harvest by early May. It is shipped immediately after harvest to the originating State, where it is cleaned, tagged, and distributed as planting stock for the next generation of increase.

Overwinter increases frequently are made for new varieties of wheat, barley, oats, and flax and for inbred lines and single crosses of corn.

Just how effective is this plan? Let's assume that the Minnesota Agricultural Experiment Station decides to release a new rust-resistant variety of spring wheat after the harvest season in 1962. The plant breeder has only 10 bushels of seed, and there will be need for several hundred bushels of foundation seed next spring.

The Minnesota Foundation Seed Project arranges for an increase in Yuma County, Ariz., through the Arizona Agricultural Experiment Station and Arizona Crop Improvement Association. In early fall the 10 bushels of breeder seed are shipped to Yuma County, where 20 acres are planted at the rate of 30 pounds an acre. The following spring, about May 1, the seed crop is harvested.

The seed is shipped to the Foundation Seed Project in Minnesota, where it is cleaned. After cleaning, there are 900 bushels of eligible foundation seed—an increase of 90 bushels for every bushel planted. This foundation seed is bagged, tagged, sealed, and distributed to local seedgrowers for immediate planting. They are asked to plant at the rate of 1 bushel to the acre for a maximum seed increase. By late summer, 1 year after the release of the breeder seed, a seed crop of 36 thousand bushels is harvested from the 900 acres—a good start toward making this improved wheat available to all Minnesota farmers who want it.

The special overwinter increases are costly. The minimum charge for small grains is usually 150 to 350 dollars an acre, depending on the size of the seed field. Delays frequently are encountered at harvesttime—a critical matter because the interval between harvest in the South and planting in the North is only a few days. Late plantings in the originating area would reduce seed yields, and thus part of the advantage gained by overwinter increases would be lost. Transportation adds considerably to the cost of the seed since it is returned "in-the-dirt."

PROCEDURES for allocating foundation seed vary from State to State. The objective, however it is done, is to obtain efficient and equitable distribution and a rapid increase of registered and certified seed.

The distribution of foundation seed in many States is handled by the board of directors of the foundation seed organization. Some States have allocation committees of the representatives from the experiment station, the seed-certifying agency, and the seed trade.

The actual method used in allocating the seed depends somewhat on the supply. If there is an adequate supply, it is possible to make a general release. Pro rata allotments must be made if the demand is greater than the supply.

Growers and seedsmen in some States make an application for foundation seed directly to the foundation seed organization, which often requires advance orders and a partial prepayment. When the deadline for receiving requests is past and the foundation seed supply is definitely known, the allocation committee meets and considers each request.

The applicant often is required to furnish information on the location of the field; provisions for isolation; his experience in growing, harvesting, and handling registered or certified seed; and his facilities for cleaning and storing seed. Such a statement usually bears the approval of his county agent. The committee gives priority to the most experienced and capable growers in the localities where the crop is of primary importance.

Some States have county crop improvement associations that submit applications for a county allocation of seed. In reviewing such requests, the State allocations committee considers the importance of the crop in the area, the success of the growers in producing certified seed, the troublesome weeds in the county, and the volume of foundation seed used in previous years.

After the county crop improvement association has received its allotment, it follows a procedure similar to that used by the State organization in considering requests from the individual growers and in making allocations.

Some counties have a seed committee, which selects and nominates growers, who submit their requests for foundation seed to the State allocations committee. The number of growers nominated in a county is based on the county acreage of the crop that is to be grown for seed.

When foundation seed is in plentiful supply, the job of allocating it to growers and seedsmen is simple. Often it is first-come, first-served. Only when the demand exceeds the supply do problems arise: All applicants must be treated fairly and the consumer's interest must be protected by making sure the available foundation seed is allocated to experienced growers in localities where maximum increases per unit of seed planted can be obtained.

Procedures for allocating seed in short supply are specific in some States. The allocations committee in one State, for example, decides the amount of seed that will plant an economical acreage. Ten acres are often considered such a unit. Then the committee allots enough seed to each approved grower to plant a specific acreage. Twelve bushels of wheat are considered enough to plant 10 acres, 25 bushels of oats for 10 to 12 acres, and 30 pounds of sorghum for each field of 10 to 12 acres. Smaller allocations often end up in neglected patches, where the seed may be lost.

Another system is to withhold the initial release of foundation seed until the supply is adequate to provide 80 percent of the requirements. Then each grower receives approximately the amount he requested and can handle.

Foundation seed of new varieties is allotted to neighboring States interested in them by the originator. This is in accordance with the generally accepted policy on varietal release developed by the State experiment stations and the Department.

A CARRYOVER of foundation seed from one planting season to the next is a good protection against crop failures and a possible seed shortage. It provides for a continuing supply of foundation seed. The desirable amount of carryover varies with different crops.

The foundation seed organization generally tries to carry over 1 to 3 years' seed supply of inbred lines of corn and one-half to a year's supply of single crosses. For small grains, soybeans, flax, and similar crops, the planned carryover varies from none to about 25 percent of 1 year's needs. In the drier areas, where the planting quality of small-grains seed remains high for long periods of time, carryover reserves equal to a 3-year supply often are maintained. A 1- to 3-year supply of foundation grass and legume seed frequently is held in reserve.

Modern storage facilities, which have controlled temperature and humidity, improved storage containers, and better insecticides, keep breeder and foundation seed viable several years.

Private seed firms have a slightly different procedure. They maintain ownership of their stock seed—seed that is equivalent to foundation and registered seed of varieties released by the State and Federal experiment stations.

For example, stock seed of their small grains and soybeans varieties is sold to growers only for the production of the commercial seed crop. Some firms have their stock seed inspected, tagged, and sealed as registered seed by the seed-certifying agency. It is then eligible as planting stock for growing certified seed.

In the case of corn hybrids, all the inbreds and single and double crosses are produced by the originating firms.

All the stock seed of grass and legume varieties as well as the first generation of increase from it remain under the control of the originating or sponsoring seed firm.

Seed firms producing stock seed grow it on their own farms or on rented land or under contract with a qualified grower. When additional acreage is needed to produce the required planting stock seed, many firms prefer to rent land rather than have the seed grown under contract. Then they can do all the farming, roguing, weeding, and harvesting without having to depend on a grower who may have less interest in the seed crop.

SEED STOCKS of promising new selections often are increased by the private plant breeders simultaneously with the testing program so that enough seed will be available for distribution as soon as the value of the variety has been proved in performance tests. Thus a breeder must increase a large number of selections, all of which are discarded except the one finally chosen for release to the farmer.

An example is Coker's Pedigreed Seed Co. in South Carolina. In their oats-breeding work, 20 thousand head selections were increased in 6-foot rows during the first year. In the second year, the plant breeder increased 600 selected lots in small plots. The seed from 50 of the best plots was increased in half-acre blocks during the third year. Three or four of the most promising lots were selected and were increased in 20-acre blocks the following season. The best strain was selected and multiplied in large increase fields during the fifth year. This seed was then sold to certified seedgrowers or farmers for further increase during the sixth growing season. Seed of the several strains not selected for release was discarded.

Using the same practice as the public agencies, private seed companies frequently build up the supply of stock seed by an overwinter increase in the South so that a variety will be ready for distribution a year earlier than otherwise would be possible. Occasionally a reverse plan is used. A winter small grain adapted in the South may be grown as a summer crop in Idaho. Again a full year is gained in building up the stock seed of a new variety.

The private firm plans to carry over in reserve from one planting season to the next 25 percent to 100 percent of a year's supply of stock seed. Often private firms spread the risk of unfavorable weather by multiplying the stock seed in different areas. The carryover inventory need not be so great then because there is not the danger that a crop failure will occur in all the sections in the same season.

THE PRODUCTION of foundation seed of forage crops is a hazardous enterprise in many areas, especially in the Central, Eastern, and Southern States, because of unfavorable weather, low yields, and inadequate isolation. Sometimes the crops must be used for forage instead of seed.

Foundation seed of many improved grass and legume varieties therefore is grown in the West, where conditions are better.

To make the most of the favorable situation, a close liaison was needed between the seed-producing and the seed-using States. It was provided by the formation of the National Foundation Seed Project in 1949 by the Department of Agriculture to assist the States in the rapid buildup and maintenance of foundation seed supplies of improved varieties of grasses and legumes. It brings together the knowledge and experience of workers in the State agricultural experiment stations and the Department, commercial seedsmen, and workers in the State foundation seed organizations and seed-certifying agencies.

Two agencies in the Department of Agriculture are concerned with the project. The Agricultural Research Service is responsible for the operation and coordination of the program with the States under several memoranda of understanding. The Commodity Stabilization Service arranges for funds to finance the production and purchase of foundation seed through the Commodity Credit Corporation. Frequently breeder seed, the small quantity of seed provided by the plant breeder, is purchased and held in reserve to insure a continuing supply of foundation seed.

The Foundation Seed Project is guided by a 16-man advisory committee—the Planning Conference—whose members represent the State agricultural experiment stations, International Crop Improvement Association, American Seed Trade Association, and the Agricultural Research Service and the Commodity Stabilization Service. The Planning Conference develops the policies and procedures for operating the project.

Only superior forage crop varieties are included in the Project.

Before a variety can be accepted, it must be recommended to the project by at least one of the Regional Forage Crops Technical Committees in the Northeastern, Southern, North Central, and Western Experiment Station Regions.

The recommendation must include a description of the variety, a listing of its superior characteristics, the performance data that serve as a basis for the recommendation, seed-production capabilities, area of adaptation for forage and seed production, the number of generations of increase in the different areas, present and future supplies of breeder seed, the estimated need for certified seed, and other facts that aid the Planning Conference in determining whether the variety should be accepted.

When a variety is taken into the Foundation Seed Project, any special requirements or limitations placed on the variety by the originating experiment station or the Regional Forage Crops Technical Committee, such as number of generations of increase or area for foundation seed production, are included in the acceptance.

After a variety is accepted, the operational policies and procedures developed by the Planning Conference apply to the increase and distribution of foundation seed.

ARRANGEMENTS for producing and distributing foundation seed in each cooperating State are the responsibility of the State representative, who is appointed by the respective State agricultural experiment station director and is responsible for all in-State activities and for contacts and arrangements with the Project.

Breeder seed is made available to the Foundation Seed Project by the plant breeder at the experiment station where the variety originated. Upon recommendation of the Planning Conference, the Project personnel allocate the available breeder seed for planting in States best suited for the production of foundation seed. Allocations are based on the previous history of seed production potentialities of a given area, consideration of the wishes of the originating station and of the plant breeder, and any other factor that will assure maximum returns from each pound of breeder seed planted.

The State allotment of breeder seed

goes to the State representative. Aided by the experiment station group that normally makes allocations of stock seed, he allocates breeder seed to growers and seedsmen who have the interest and ability to produce foundation seed. He arranges for production contracts between growers and the Commodity Credit Corporation covering the production and purchase of the foundation seed at a guaranteed price.

All growers who receive breeder seed must agree to make all foundation seed produced available to the State representative and, through him, to the Project and the Planning Conference. All of it is assembled and stored in approved warehouses.

Upon the recommendation of the Planning Conference, the Project workers allocate the foundation seed to the States for the production of registered or certified seed.

It again goes to the State representative who, working through the State allocations procedure, allots it to growers and seedsmen as he did the breeder seed. Each grower who obtains foundation seed agrees to plant it for the production of registered or certified seed. Contracts of the Commodity Credit Corporation ordinarily are not used to cover the production of registered seed, but at the discretion of the Planning Conference it is possible to purchase seed of this class in the initial stages of increase of a new variety.

Registered seed normally is distributed by growers or seedsmen as planting stock for the production of certified seed. Certified seed is moved through the normal seed trade channels to the consuming area. This is necessary since much of it is produced 1,500 miles or more from the area where it is planted.

The contract for the production of foundation seed includes sections covering acreage and price; eligibility requirements for foundation seed producers; the production requirements; quality, sale, and delivery of the seed;

cleaning, handling, packaging, tagging, and marking of each container; sampling and testing; schedule for purchasing substandard seed; invoicing for payment for seed; damages for delays or failure to deliver the seed; assignments; and renewals.

Although these specifications make a long contract, all pertinent details are covered, and misunderstanding is avoided as to the production requirements, prices, delivery of the seed, and arrangements for renewals.

Several features of the contract are especially useful. They deal primarily with the purchase prices for foundation seed, incentive premiums for producing high-quality seed, and a plan to avoid the accumulation of excessive reserves of high-priced seed.

The contract price is set at a level to interest the specialized grower to produce foundation seed. This is identified as the standard price. For example, the standard price of alfalfa was 60 cents a pound in 1961; red clover, 55 cents; and 25 cents to 35 cents for inbred lines of Gahi-1 pearl millet.

A fair average seed yield is established for the acreage to be placed under contract. This average yield multiplied by the acreage determines the basic allotment—that is, the amount of foundation seed that will be purchased at the standard price. Seed in excess of the basic allotment is purchased at a price estimated to approximate that of certified seed. This is usually 15 cents to 20 cents a pound lower than the standard price for foundation seed. Thus, excess seed cannot cause high financial loss to the Project in years of unusual yields.

A few years ago it was recommended that a special premium be paid for the production of foundation alfalfa seed free of seeds of other crop plants and weeds. The premium that covers the added costs involved in production of top-quality seed was originally 15 cents per pound. It was found to be excessive and has been reduced to 5 cents.

The contract requires that all foundation seed be produced in accordance with the certification regulations and standards approved by the State agricultural experiment station and seed-certifying agency, except that these standards shall not be lower than those prescribed by the International Crop Improvement Association.

The renewal section states that the Commodity Credit Corporation reserves the right to renew the contract from year to year by giving written notice to the producers on or before December 1 of each year. Commodity Credit Corporation also reserves the right in any renewal to adjust the prices to be paid.

All foundation seed is packaged 30 or 50 pounds to a bag, depending on the crop. Since a grower would use at least one bag in establishing a seed field, these small units avoid the necessity for breaking seals, rebagging, and retagging under the supervision of the certifying agency. The loss is less if the bags are damaged in transit.

CARRYOVER RESERVES are essential for maintaining a continuous supply of foundation seed. It is estimated there should be at least a year's supply on hand at all times as a protection against a short crop and as a source for filling requests received before the next seed crop is available.

The reserve has proved valuable in filling requests for foundation seed from areas where fall seeding is practiced. For example, many seedgrowers in Arizona and California prefer to make their seedings of alfalfa and red clover in October to December. The seedlings then can make adequate growth during the winter and early spring and produce a full seed crop the first year. Foundation seed to fill these early requests must be carried over from the previous year's crop.

ANY QUALIFIED grower or seedsman planning to produce registered or certified seed may purchase foundation seed. All requests for foundation seed must be placed through the State foundation seed representative, who approves each sale in his State. Thus, liaison is maintained between the sale and distribution of foundation seed and inclusion of the planted acreage in the certification program.

The sale price for foundation seed is usually 10 to 15 cents a pound higher than the contract-grower price. This markup covers storage, handling, and blending charges; losses resulting from deteriorated seed; and the sale of surplus foundation seed at prices lower than cost.

Payment for foundation seed must be made before delivery, except when the order is placed by a branch of a State government (such as the State university or the agricultural experiment station). That seed can be shipped on receipt of order, and the invoice can be submitted after delivery.

THE EFFECTIVENESS of the cooperative Foundation Seed Project is illustrated in the rapid increase of certified seed of Vernal alfalfa, Gahi-1 pearl millet, and Kenland red clover.

Vernal alfalfa was released jointly by the Wisconsin and Utah Agricultural Experiment Stations and the Department of Agriculture in February 1953. Sixty pounds of breeder seed were available and were used to plant a 31-acre field in April in Washington to produce foundation seed. A 13-acre foundation seed field had been established in 1952 in Utah. In the fall of 1953, 9,599 pounds of foundation seed were harvested. Approximately half of the foundation seed was distributed in Arizona and California and the remainder in the Northern States for the production of certified seed. (The registered class is not used in the increase of Vernal.) When the crop was harvested in 1954, there were 2.1 million pounds of certified Vernal seed. This large volume of seed was available 18 months after the variety was released.

The production of certified Vernal rose to more than 10 million pounds annually. In comparison, 1,101,235 pounds of certified Ranger alfalfa and 14,568 pounds of certified Atlantic alfalfa were produced, 6 and 8 years following release, respectively, preceding the functioning of the Foundation Seed Project.

Gahi-1 pearl millet was developed by the Georgia Agricultural Experiment Station and the Department of Agriculture at Tifton, Ga. Gahi-1 is a chance hybrid consisting of four inbred lines. Consequently, seed of each of the inbred lines must be produced separately. Thus, foundation seed of Gahi-1 is a mechanical blend of equal amounts of pure live seed from each of the lines.

Gahi-1 was accepted by the Planning Conference in 1958. A little more than 11 thousand pounds of foundation seed were produced that year in Arizona. The foundation seed was distributed to growers and seedsmen in Arizona, Georgia, New Mexico, and Texas in the spring of 1959 for the production of certified seed. Seven months later, the growers harvested more than 3 million pounds of certified seed, which were distributed by the seed trade to farmers in the Southern States for the production of forage—2 years after the variety was released.

Kenland red clover, developed at the Kentucky Experiment Station, was released in 1947. It was one of the first varieties included in the Foundation Seed Project. Breeder seed was planted in California, Idaho, Montana, Oregon, Utah, and Washington in 1949 and 1950. The foundation seed was used to produce registered and certified seed. By the spring of 1952, farmers in the Central and Eastern States had about 4 million pounds of certified Kenland to plant.

In comparison, Cumberland red clover—Kenland's predecessor—was released in 1938. The largest production in any one year was 900 thousand pounds, and that came 7 years after its release. At that time there was no coordinated program to manage the production and distribution of foun-dation seed. Cumberland therefore never made the contribution to our agriculture that it should have.

The potential value of numerous forage-crop varieties has been lost because of various breakdowns during the seed multiplication process. This is why a coordinated program to assure an adequate and continuing supply of foundation seed is so useful.

Another feature of a coordinated program such as the Foundation Seed Project is the opportunity to check the varietal purity of each lot of foundation seed. This is particularly important when foundation seed is produced in seed-growing areas hundreds or thousands of miles from its origin.

VARIETAL IMPURITIES and shifts in characteristics can result when pollen moves unusual distances from a contaminating field, when viable seeds remain in the soil from a crop grown on the land many years prior to planting the foundation seed field, or when the environment influences plant growth. When all foundation seed of a variety are within one program, samples of each seed lot can be planted in uniform tests to determine its trueness to variety.

A seed lot occasionally is found with offtype plants. It is eliminated immediately from the foundation seed supplies.

All breeder and foundation seed lots of each of the four inbred lines of Gahi-1 pearl millet were tested recently for trueness to variety. Two lots were found to contain contaminants. Both were sold for feed. A new, pure supply of seeds was produced.

These and other intricate steps are taken to protect the superior characteristics of varieties and to assure seedsmen and seedgrowers of foundation seed that is true to variety.

CARLTON S. GARRISON *is Research Leader, Seed Production Investigations, Forage and Range Research Branch, Crops Research Division, Agricultural Research Service. He is in charge of the Foundation Seed Project of the Department.*

Making Better Forest
Trees Available

H. A. FOWELLS

FOREST geneticists create or find trees that are new or better in resistance to diseases or insects, quality of wood, branch form, and growth.

Selection is one way of obtaining superior trees. In the forests there are trees that are better than average and can transmit some of this superiority to their progeny through their seeds.

Crossing two trees with the aim of combining in the progeny desirable traits of the parents is another method. Usually the progeny are intermediate between the two parents with respect to their characteristics. Sometimes they inherit the trait of one and not the other. Occasionally the offspring exhibits the phenomenon called hybrid vigor and surpasses its parents.

Hand—or controlled—pollination is the usual method of creating hybrid forest trees. Pollen from one parent tree is placed on the flower of another parent tree. The forest geneticist covers the female flower (or conelet, in the conifers) of the seed-bearing parent with a bag of cloth or plastic material before the flower is ready to receive the pollen. Then, at the right time, he squirts some pollen into the bag with a syringe so that the flower is thoroughly dusted with it. He leaves the bag over the flower at least until the danger of contamination by other pollen has passed.

In the pines, which take 2 or 3 years to mature cones, fertilization takes place about a year after pollination, and he may have to protect the developing cone and its hybrid seed from insects, fungi, and squirrels.

Producing seeds in this way is a tedious job, but in Korea the hybrid between pitch pine and loblolly pine is being produced on a large scale by hand pollination. The Koreans put on about 23,500 pollination bags in 1956 and estimated that 2-year-old trees from the hybrid seeds would cost about 1.50 dollars per thousand more than 2-year-old trees from ordinary seeds.

The production of hybrid poplar seed is a special case of controlled pollination. One poplar has flowers that are all or mostly male. Another has predominately female flowers. Therefore one can bring into the greenhouse branches of the male parent and the female parent. The flowers mature if the ends of the branches are placed in water. Intermingling of the branches promotes pollination, or the pollen may be collected and placed on the female flowers. The seeds mature in 4 to 6 weeks.

MASS—or semicontrolled—pollination is a proposed method for distributing pollen to the flower with less work than is required in pollination by hand.

By this method, pollen of one parent tree or trees is blown onto the crown or flower-bearing branch of the tree selected to bear the seed, when the flowers are receptive.

Obviously much pollen, which is expensive, would be wasted. Pine pollen cost as much as 95 dollars a pound in 1959. But J. W. Duffield and R. Z. Callaham, two forest geneticists who worked at the Western Institute of Forest Genetics in California, demonstrated that pollen can be diluted with old pollen or incompatible pollen without seriously reducing the amount of good seeds produced. They discovered that a mixture containing 50 percent of old, nonviable pollen reduced the yield of seed only slightly.

Because pollination by other trees is possible, the seed parent tree must be isolated from contaminating sources of pollen. The seed parent must be self-incompatible or produce female flowers at an earlier age than it produces male flowers. J. W. Wright, of Michigan State University, found that white pine (*Pinus strobus*) and Norway spruce (*Picea abies*) produced many female flowers for at least 10 years before they began to produce male flowers.

SEED ORCHARDS are comparable to fruit orchards, except that the product is tree seed instead of edible fruit.

In seed orchards, the superior parent trees are planted at regular intervals to insure that cross-pollination takes place. If the trees are of the same species, cross-pollination takes place readily. The production of F_1 interspecific hybrids, or first generation hybrids between two different species, in seed orchards is complicated by the fact that in only a few species do the male and female flowers of the two species mature at the same time.

The difference in time of flowering may be so great that, as Dr. Wright estimated, at least 90 percent of the reported crosses in pine, spruce, poplar, and maple would have to be made by hand pollination with pollen collected and stored until the time of pollination.

However, F_2 hybrids, the second generation hybrids, can be produced in seed orchards if the F_1 hybrids are fertile. The F_2 hybrids will be less uniform than the F_1, but uniformity is not always necessary in forestry.

Not all of the planted trees grow to maturity. The rest are harvested in intermediate cuts and are useful in keeping the stand closed, thereby utilizing the capacity of the site and making for trees of better form.

NEW KINDS of forest trees also can be multiplied or increased by vegetative propagation, but for most species doing that is less feasible than by seed. Because forest trees do not breed true, however, vegetative propagation is a means of preserving a particular genotype. This is particularly important for trees that have value as ornamentals because of form or color of foliage.

Two main methods of vegetative propagation are the rooting of cuttings and the grafting of scion wood of the selected tree upon a root stock.

Cuttings of many species of forest trees will root, but a number can be rooted only with such difficulty that this process is not used widely for extensive planting of new trees.

The exceptions are willow and poplar. Some poplar hybrids and selected cottonwoods have grown extremely fast on sites that suit them. With more intensive forestry practice in this country, the planting of poplars and cottonwoods, particularly on overflow and bottom land, will become more common.

One procedure for planting poplars and cottonwoods is to root the cuttings in nurseries and then to plant the rooted cutting. Another is to plant the cuttings directly in the field or forest. Poplar cuttings are made from dormant year-old wood and generally are 12 to 18 inches long and ½ to 1 inch in diameter.

Cuttings from selected Monterey pine trees (*Pinus radiata*) were produced in Australia on a large scale for forest planting. The cuttings were rooted in a nursery in metal tubes, which could be collapsed and removed when the new trees were planted out. Cuttings of 1-, 2-, 3-, and 4-year-old wood of Monterey pine, which is widely planted in Australia and New Zealand, were rooted.

Growth substances, like indoleacetic acid, indolebutyric acid, and naphthaleneacetic acid, have been effective in increasing the number of roots formed on cuttings. To apply the growth substances, the forester dips the base of the cutting in a solution of the substance or in a mixture of the substance and talc. The concentration of the substance in solution varies from a few to several hundred parts per million. The dry powder mixture often contains about 1 percent of the growth substance. Growth substances generally are most useful in increasing the degree of rooting. They seldom are effective in promoting the rooting of cuttings that do not root without the addition of the growth substance.

Air layers are a variation of the common type of rooted cuttings. In preparing an air layer, the forester girdles a branch through the bark and cambium and surrounds the girdle and 4 to 6 inches of stem above the girdle with moist sphagnum moss enclosed in a plastic bag.

At Lake City, Fla., Francois Mergen obtained 85 percent success in rooting branches of slash pine (*Pinus elliottii*). He treated the girdle with indolebutyric acid. Roots appeared within 6 weeks on branches on which air layers were installed in August.

Needle fascicles are potentially a great source of plant material for vegetative propagation. The fascicle can develop a shoot; the bud arises inside the needle bundle in pines. In species having only a single needle, as the firs and spruces, a bud may arise from the axil of the needle. When they are detached from a branch and placed in a rooting medium, needle fascicles will root and occasionally develop shoots. Procedures for consistently obtaining root and shoot development have not been worked out. B. Zak, of the Southeastern Forest Experiment Station, has caused roots and shoots to be formed on needle bundles of slash pine and roots alone on bundles of shortleaf pine (*Pinus echinata*).

GRAFTING of forest trees does not differ from procedures in use for horticultural plants. The veneer graft and the cleft crown graft are the types used most commonly when the scion is detached.

For approach grafting, the bottle graft was used successfully in a plantation of slash pine selected for high yield of gum in Florida. In this method, the end of the scion is kept in a bottle of water until the tissue of the scion and stock unite. Dormant scions commonly are grafted upon active rootstocks. In forestry practice, this requires that cuttings are taken during the winter and kept under refrigeration until the stock trees are active.

Fall grafting is successful, however, as demonstrated with spruce by Hans Nienstaedt, of the Northern Institute of Forest Genetics, Rhinelander, Wis. Succulent tissue grafting makes possible a much longer period in which grafts can be made. Furthermore, the union between the stock and scion appears to be stronger than occurs when the scion is of year-old tissue.

Plastic or paper bags are used to protect grafts made in the forest. A combination of a plastic bag and a paper bag has given the best protection in several trials.

DISTRIBUTION of new trees produced by the Forest Service may be made directly to planters of forest trees or through State forestry agencies.

The McSweeney-McNary Act authorized the Forest Service to enter into cooperative agreements to further research in subjects of mutual interest.

The Forest Service may send newly developed trees for foundation stock to individuals, associations, private nurseries, industries, or public agencies that agree to cooperate in research on the tree.

Several thousand persons, for example, obtained cuttings of hybrid poplars grown by the Northeastern Forest Experiment Station in Pennsylvania. Each recipient agreed to furnish the station information about the survival and growth of the poplars he received. The station thereby furthered its research on the hybrid poplars, and the people received new trees, which could furnish cuttings for greatly expanding production of desirable hybrids.

Similarly, a mining company agreed to plant certain pine hybrids on its holdings to help determine whether the hybrids would thrive in the locality where the company operated.

Exchange of seed or seedlings with public agencies is authorized by the Granger-Thye Act. The Forest Service can furnish public agencies, such as forest schools, State forestry departments, and experiment stations, seeds or seedlings of newly developed trees if the Forest Service receives in return property (seed or seedlings, for example) of equal value.

State nurseries, operating under the provisions of the Clarke-McNary Act, undoubtedly will supply most of the new trees for planting on State and private lands in the future. Under the provisions of this act, the Forest Service may provide seed or trees to the nurseries. The ordinary value of the material is credited to the Federal Government's share in operating the nursery. A Clarke-McNary nursery may then sell the trees it grows to forest planters in line with its policy of providing trees at reasonable cost.

The following situation illustrates how this would work out. At the Lake City Research Center in Florida, forest geneticists selected and bred trees that yield twice the average amount of gum for naval stores. They demonstrated that the tendency was an inherited characteristic. Cuttings of these trees may be made available to State nurseries, as in Florida and Georgia, whose foresters would use the cuttings in developing seed orchards. Seed would be produced in about 10 years. This seed would then be sown in the nursery to grow superior gum-yielding pines for tree farmers and forest industries.

The Forest Service produces superior trees in its nurseries for planting in the national forests. In California, hybrid seed of Jeffrey pine (*Pinus jeffreyii*) and Coulter pine (*P. coulterii*) and of knobcone pine (*P. attenuata*) and Monterey pine (*P. radiata*) have been produced in quantity by controlled pollination. Seed will be sown in the Forest Service nursery near Placerville to produce hybrid trees for planting in the national forests.

H. A. FOWELLS *has been a member of the Division of Forest Management Research, Forest Service, Washington, D.C., with assignment to the fields of genetics and physiology, since 1954. He entered the Forest Service in 1934.*

Introducing New Horticultural Varieties

VICTOR R. BOSWELL

A EUROPEAN visitor to the Plant Industry Station of the Department of Agriculture at Beltsville, Md., once asked us, "When your plant breeders develop a new horticultural variety, do you have any difficulty in getting farmers and gardeners to grow it?"

We replied that the Department has no trouble in obtaining prompt and widespread use of a truly improved sort, but that we do have difficulty of an opposite kind.

It is generally difficult to persuade prospective growers and users of a promising new variety to be patient until we feel sure that the variety merits introduction to the public and to wait until enough seed or other propagating material can be produced.

And thereby hangs this tale, which describes how breeders in this country introduce new horticultural varieties. It is devoted mainly to seed-propagated varieties.

The breeding and evaluation of a superior variety is one problem. Introducing that variety to the public on a large scale for prompt and widespread commercial or amateur planting is another kind of problem.

Solutions of the two problems are interdependent. In practice, the solution of the second overlaps the first; evaluation is still continuing while seedsmen or other propagators are developing the first commercial supplies for planting.

An element of risk exists in the acceptance of any new variety. Why, then, are planters so eager to grow new varieties that are developed by breeders in public and private agencies?

American farmers and gardeners are justifiably optimistic. They have observed the progress in varietal improvement over many years and are confident that it will continue. Furthermore, for economic and esthetic reasons, they need improvements in quality and yield of plant products.

Growers know that many promising varieties fail to live up to their promise. Nevertheless, depending chiefly on the originators' record of successes and failures, American growers often switch to new, improved varieties with amazing speed. Such a switch can be made rapidly and on a large scale only when the originator and the commercial seedsmen or other propagators work together with perfect coordination of evaluations, the making of decisions, the increasing of supplies of seeds, and the timing of appropriate announcements.

Vegetable seedsmen and nurserymen in America are to be commended for the remarkable manner in which they have voluntarily collaborated with each other and with public agencies in developing and operating our current practices for introducing the horticultural varieties that are produced by public agencies.

Systems introducing horticultural varieties differ somewhat among the States. State and Federal agencies and public and private agencies also may follow somewhat different procedures. All, however, are attempting to attain much the same ends by means most advantageous under their respective circumstances.

Before the present system of introducing vegetable varieties by the Department of Agriculture was established in 1944, we had failed to appreciate the necessity of perfect coordination between the Department and the vegetable seed industry in all the details of evaluation, development of commercial supplies, formal introduction, and announcements of a new variety. Wide publicity before ample commercial supplies were available created a demand that the seedsmen could not meet. By the time supplies were ample, the publicity was forgotten, and there were few orders for the new variety. This kind of error can retard the acceptance of a new variety, however good it may be.

If the seedsman is to be able to meet a demand created for a new variety, he must first be familiar with that variety and all the facts concerning the preparation for its introduction.

THE PRESENT SYSTEM of introducing new varieties of seed-propagated vegetables bred by the Department and jointly by the Department and State agricultural experiment stations is simple in principle.

It was developed by the Department and the Garden Seed Research Committee of the American Seed Trade Association. It is designed to accomplish three major objectives: Insure adequate evaluation of a new variety before a decision is reached to increase seed supplies for introduction to the public; insure rapid, equable, and technically sound procedures for developing large supplies of commercial seed to meet initial public demands; provide for simultaneous and adequate publicity and catalog listing and other advertising by the respective agencies as soon as there is enough seed for general sale.

As soon as the plant breeder selects a line that appears significantly superior, he must provide enough seeds of it to permit its evaluation by cooperating agencies under a wide range of conditions. Workers at experiment stations, seedsmen, farmers, shippers, food processors, and consumers all usually take part ultimately in these evaluations.

If it is feasible, the breeder produces seed of high quality for the required commercial tests. Usually, however, we find it better to make a contract with one or two seedsmen to produce the necessary seed under carefully controlled conditions. This seed, called the initial increase, is the property of the Government, and it is all delivered to us in accord with the terms of the contract.

Next, we supply without charge a small amount of the initial increase to each of numerous cooperators for observation and evaluation of the variety. The cooperators agree to refrain from increasing the seed or selling it or giving it away without specific permission. The variety is still the property of the Government and has not been released.

If the prospective new variety passes its examinations, we then release breeder seed to bona fide seed producers, "for increase only." This is a decisive step toward introduction but not the final one.

Before we release seed "for increase only," we offer a share of the breeder seed to all bona fide, primary seed producers and State foundation seed organizations in the country that are known to us. We then supply seed to each one who asks for it and who agrees to certain well-established mutual arrangements.

Receivers agree to increase the seed for commercial use but to refrain from advertising it, listing it in a catalog, or selling it to the public until the public introduction date, which is announced by the Department. This date is determined by consultation between the Department and the seedsmen.

The seedsman also agrees to report to the Department each autumn how much seed of the new item he has produced and how much he plans to plant for further increase the next year. The Department agrees to report the total amount reported by the several seedsmen to all seedsmen who are increasing the variety so that all can see how the total supply is developing.

As soon as it appears that the industry has enough seed on hand to meet the initial public demand for the new variety, the Department (independently or jointly with States) names it, announces its availability to the public, and publishes appropriate information about it. At the same time, the seedsmen list the variety in their cata-

logs and otherwise advertise it and offer it for sale.

Some nice judgments are involved in these procedures. Seed of some vegetables can be increased very fast, the quantity required to plant an acre is very small, and a certain new variety may appear promising for only limited areas or uses. It is feasible in such instances to announce a future date for introduction to the public at the time breeder seed is supplied to seedsmen for growing foundation stock and for commercial increase. Occasionally the date of sale is unrestricted.

The required initial commercial supplies of such seeds as tomato and lettuce can be produced quickly; usually only a year is needed after deciding that a variety merits introduction to the public. Obtaining enough seeds of beans and of peas takes 3 or 4 years and sometimes longer.

This system usually works without any serious hitch.

One should remember, however, that during the period when initial commercial seed supplies are being increased and before introduction to the public, extensive and rigorous evaluations are continuing in commercial-scale tests.

These tests sometimes reveal weaknesses that escaped earlier detection. They may disclose no serious weakness in the new sort but only a lack of any overall superiority. In a few instances the Department has decided during the stage of commercial increase to "kill" a potential variety because it lacked the superiority that would justify introduction.

THE COMMERCIAL VEGETABLE seedsmen of the United States deserve the greatest share of the credit for this system of increase, evaluation, and introduction. It could not have become possible without their thorough understanding and approval of the Department's points of view; without their knowledge and judgment regarding technical and operating problems; and without their wise devotion to the common good. The system has been invaluable to the vegetable, seed, and vegetable-processing industries, and to the general public.

This system, as followed by the Department of Agriculture and vegetable seed producers, is now largely taken for granted in the United States, but it is not clear to others why competing American seedsmen voluntarily and apparently at their own risk produce hundreds of thousands of pounds of a new variety of bean, for example, that has not yet been introduced to the public by the breeder. Neither is it clear why we, in public agencies, do not hesitate to furnish our breeding lines and potential varieties, years in advance of introduction, to private seedsmen for study and evaluation. This unforced, voluntary collaboration between industry and public agencies and within the industry is built solidly on mutual confidence and enlightened self-interest.

Any unauthorized use or sale of any of our material is so exceptional that we do not consider it a hazard. Apparently, a system like this is now used nowhere but in America. We salute our collaborators in private industry!

The system I have described for vegetable seeds has not been used with flower seeds by the Department of Agriculture because the Department is not developing seed-propagated types of flowers. We see no reason, however, why the procedure should be any less successful with flower seeds than with vegetable seeds.

ONCE THE DEPARTMENT of Agriculture has distributed breeder seed of a vegetable variety to a seed producer, we do not resupply him with seed. From the initial distribution onward, each firm that produces a particular variety maintains its own foundation seed (usually called "stock seed" in the vegetable seed industry).

If a seedsman loses his stock seed or lets it deviate from type or become mixed to an objectionable degree, he is in trouble. He must buy good stock seed from a competitor (that may be difficult) or make a new start with his stock or with commercial seed, and select a new stock having acceptable conformity to the original.

Most American vegetable seedsmen do a good job of maintaining stock seeds of varieties. To those who are doing a good job, it therefore seems unfair for the Department to bail out the careless vegetable seedsman by resupplying him with stock seed. Each vegetable seedsman has a responsibility to maintain what public research has supplied to him or to regain its equivalent at his own expense. Vegetable breeders in the Department thus are relieved of the responsibility of maintaining stock seed at public cost.

THE RELEASE, or introduction, of inbreds by public agencies for the production of hybrid vegetable seed involves some considerations not encountered in the introduction of conventional varieties.

Inbreds generally are introduced for their value as parents, either in producing hybrids or in genetic and breeding work. They are rarely planted for the production of commercial vegetables or in home gardens. They therefore do not normally enter retail trade channels as such.

Recently, however, after we had introduced a certain inbred for the usual purposes, different seed firms judged it to be an attractive variety in its own right. Each wanted to name it, describe it in its catalog, and promote it as a conventional variety. Who should name it? Who should "introduce" it as a conventional variety? As this is written, these questions have not been completely resolved.

Comparatively few producers of vegetable seeds are involved with commercial production of hybrids, except those of sweet corn and onions. The distribution of breeder seed therefore is easy. Because of the way inbreds are used incidental to the development of commercial hybrids, only very small lots of inbred seed need to be furnished each seedsman to meet his initial requirements. This, too, simplifies the distribution.

Inbreds are "introduced" to seedsmen and breeders with far less publicity than conventional varieties are introduced to the public and with no problem of coordinating commercial supplies and publicity.

If a seedsman or other breeder introduces a hybrid (or a conventional variety) of which a public-produced inbred is a parent, his acknowledging the use of the public inbred and crediting its originator appears definitely to be in the public interest.

Combinations of inbreds that produce superior hybrids are "introduced" after extensive commercial evaluations of the hybrids themselves and with much the same fanfare that a conventional variety is introduced. In a way, however, "introduction of a hybrid" might be considered as a misstatement.

When a public agency "introduces a hybrid," it actually introduces no hybrid seed. It publishes information on how to produce the hybrid and on the properties and performance of the hybrid and its inbred parents. It releases—introduces—seed of the inbreds to the few producers of hybrid seed. Sometimes the inbreds already have been released for another purpose or purposes when an especially attractive hybrid involving them is first announced.

When a private firm introduces a hybrid that it has developed from its own privately developed inbreds, the firm does not ordinarily reveal the identity of the inbreds. Neither does a private firm share with others the seed of the inbreds it has developed.

If a publicly developed inbred parent or both parents should be involved in a privately developed and introduced hybrid, the agency originating the inbreds believes that it is entitled to know that and to know the identity of the inbred. This information constitutes evidence of the value and use of a research product of a public research agency.

The privately developed inbred parents of any privately introduced hybrid are looked upon as strictly private property. Even the identity of such parents of privately developed hybrids is the confidential knowledge of the owner. Thus the private breeder has a way to maintain sole control of his varietal introduction when it is a so-called "closed-formula" hybrid.

STATE BREEDING agencies often are in a somewhat less favorable position than the Department of Agriculture for conducting widespread and extensive evaluations of their potential new horticultural varieties and for stimulating the rapid buildup of large initial commercial stocks.

State agencies are less free to engage in operations of national and interregional scope than are Federal agencies. With more restricted objectives and areas of operation, it is often less easy to attract the widest commercial interest in the exhaustive testing and expansion of use of new horticultural sorts.

There is, of course, no reason why a State-produced new variety cannot attain as widespread and great use as one produced, tested, and introduced by the Department or in cooperation with the Department. In fact, some State introductions, such as Rutgers tomato, have attained top rank.

State agencies therefore generally handle their own vegetable introductions a little differently.

Some States have foundation seed organizations that receive their breeder seed and produce original foundation stock (stock seed) for sale to vegetable seedsmen. A few such organizations also continue to produce and maintain foundation seed of a limited number of items for sale to growers of certified seed.

Little certified true seed of vegetables is produced in this country. Keen competition in the vegetable seed industry, the pressing demands of critical customers, and the limited number of producers of seeds of any one vegetable have combined to keep the general level of excellence of commercial stocks high enough that certified seed has not gained any great use.

Foundation seed organizations were established within individual States largely to do with certain "farm seeds" what the vegetable seedsmen are doing with vegetable seeds. The volume of farm seed required and numbers of seedgrowers to produce and distribute it are enormously greater than for vegetable seeds. The problems of management and quality control consequently are far greater.

For the production of a few vegetable seeds officially certified by State agencies, seedgrowers are required to return periodically to an official source of foundation seed. There is virtually no other continuing function for a foundation seed organization to perform with seeds that are generally produced on a large scale by well-established vegetable seedsmen.

Foundation seed organizations, however, do perform a vital continuing function in maintaining disease-free stocks of potatoes on a large scale for the production of certified seed potatoes. Potatoes and sweetpotatoes for planting purposes are not produced by vegetable seedsmen.

Sometimes a State agency will organize a small association for producing stock seed of one or a few items to meet difficult and exacting standards, and for producing limited quantities of vegetable seed for commercial planting. This is unusual, but it is sometimes necessary with a special item of critical importance to a limited area and number of growers.

Disease-resistant celery for a single area is an example. The volume of seed business with such items may be too small for any one of them and the production problems too great to justify production by vegetable seedsmen generally. A foundation seed association could perform this function when necessary.

Occasionally a State agency and one private seed firm will enter into a cooperative plant-breeding arrangement that grants the firm an exclusive right to propagate and sell seeds of a new jointly produced variety for a limited time before the seeds are available to other seedsmen. Such arrangements are uncommon and are unlikely to become popular.

The prevailing policy among public agricultural research agencies is to grant no exclusive rights to any product of research that is developed wholly or partly with public funds.

The procedures for increase and introduction of vegetable seeds in most States are basically similar to those I have described for the Department of Agriculture.

There may be some differences: Commercial evaluation tests are less widespread and there is less general prerelease knowledge of and interest in the prospective variety. Breeder seed is not always offered initially to all who are bona fide producers of the kind of seed involved. Seedsmen sometimes pay for breeder seed. States generally will resupply foundation seed, especially of varieties of limited use. Often there is less formality concerning public release dates.

It may never be feasible or necessary for most State agencies to engage in commercial evaluations quite as widely as the Department is obligated to do. It seems, however, that more widespread commercial evaluations of State and Federal productions before release would be helpful to all agencies and growers concerned.

Private seed producers feel strongly that they all should have the opportunity to accept or decline a share of original breeder seed from any public agency when it is available to a competitor.

IN INTRODUCING a new variety, the private breeders-seedsmen face many of the problems that public agencies do, but the seedsmen solve the problems differently. Business rivalries and competition lead private firms to develop and evaluate their introductions as quietly as possible.

It is difficult for the private breeders to obtain the widespread commercial evaluations that they need without revealing their progress to competitors. By working through their own laboratories and field stations and their trusted associates and the customers, though, seedsmen can evaluate their productions and make their independent decisions as to whether to introduce specific varieties.

As the seedsman increases the seed of a new variety preparatory to introduction, he supplies substantial quantities to selected customers for final trial. If all goes well, the seedsman names the variety and introduces it by means of catalog listing and description, advertising, and personal salesmanship.

Private firms have no problems of joint decisions or coordination of plans and actions with other agencies. At the same time, it is a hard problem to coordinate testing and evaluation, seed production, publicity, and sales among different departments in a large firm with farflung operations.

The seedsman often takes greater financial risks on his own introductions than on public introductions. He may not have opportunity for adequate evaluation. He does not have, at introduction, the extension and publicity services that are available to public agencies for announcing a new sort.

Even so, the private breeders-seedsmen have done very well in this country. They have produced and introduced the greater proportion of the varieties of vegetables grown today and have made their work profitable. In this country, the private breeders have no control over seeds of the "open-pollinated" varieties they introduce, once the seed is sold to the public. Their superior introductions, however, gain prestige and attract increased volumes of business for their respective firms. That is how private vegetable breeding can be profitable in this country.

There is no doubt in our minds that unrestricted sale of seed of new vegetable varieties in this country has been a boon to vegetable growers, food processors, and consumers. It appears, also, that under the policies and practices of the American seed trade, the aggressive breeder-seedsman is no less prosperous than his fellow seedsman abroad who has the protection of "breeder's rights."

THE "INTRODUCTION" of a new variety of seed-propagated vegetable is but a landmark in its early history. It marks the end of its developmental phase but only the beginning of an arduous maintenance history.

Seedsmen face difficult problems in maintaining foundation or stock seed of a vegetable variety, true to its original characteristics, performance, and uniformity.

The seedsman must guard against seedborne diseases, mixture with seeds of other varieties, and cross-pollination with other varieties. These are largely mechanical problems. They generally are not too difficult to handle, but they require vigilance and scrupulous care.

It is harder to control a variety's inherent tendency to vary and to change as a result of natural selection or of the seedsman's selection. Minimizing the effects of variability is difficult enough in relatively stable lines of self-pollinated species, but it is especially difficult in the less stable, cross-pollinated kinds.

No variety is absolutely uniform and fixed. Although the plants from seeds of a variety may appear as alike as peas in a pod at the time of introduction, they are not all exactly alike genetically. As numbers of plants increase in succeeding generations, after repeated shuffling of countless genes, characteristics emerge that did not have the mathematical opportunity to appear earlier.

These offtype plants must be removed—rogued—from a stock before they bloom, lest they cross with the others and cause an increase in frequency of occurrence of offtypes in successive generations. Seeds of offtype plants must not be allowed to develop and become mixed among the seeds of typical plants. The undesired variants often are more prolific producers of seeds than plants of the desired type and so in time tend to predominate unless they are kept out.

Offtype plants can also arise by mutation and perpetuate their characteristics by seeds.

Notable deviations from good type can appear suddenly in a supposedly well-fixed stock of an inherently variable species at any time that it is grown in a markedly different environment. The cabbage family clearly exhibits this tendency.

A stock of cabbage may appear uniform and true to variety when the plants are grown in an environment like the one in which it was selected.

Other plants grown from the same package of seed, but under a different pattern of temperature, are likely to be rather highly variable. Some of them may be extremely offtype. The variety has not broken down. It has not reverted. It was like that from the start. It simply has been grown in the "wrong" environment.

We need to remember that the detailed features of a plant are the result of neither its hereditary makeup alone nor of its environment alone. They are the result of the interplay between its hereditary entities (its genes) and its environment. And we need to remember that no seed-propagated variety or stock is absolutely uniform in its hereditary makeup. Some are less variable than others, but they all vary.

The plant breeder or seed producer selects and reselects successive generations of a stock to make it or keep it as uniform and true to the ideal as he can. He faces a basic problem, however, for which we have no complete practical solution.

The selector can discard or retain genes in a stock only as they happen to react with the environment in which

he is doing the selecting and in such a way as to produce some observable effect. All he can do is select plants carrying collections of genes that happen to produce uniformly desirable plants in that particular environment.

In some of those plants that look alike, there are genes that will react with another environment in a manner unlike that shown by other plants in the stock, or to a different degree. There is no way in any environment to determine how any of the plants or the entire stock will behave in another environment. That is why breeders must test and evaluate potential varieties in several environments.

Not all crop varieties are so varied in their hereditary makeup as cabbage or so variable within varieties in their reactions to environment. It is highly important, however, to remember that these variabilities of hereditary makeup and of response to environment are universal. They must never be ignored in the maintenance of stocks.

Lots of stock seed of a variety often are maintained in one or more environments notably different from the one where the original stock was selected for conformity to type. Each different environment tends to increase variability of appearance or behavior among plants within the stock. Certain gene differences among plants that were not expressed in the original location are variously expressed in the new locations.

The seedsman does his best to remove from a stock in a new location any plants that appear different from the original standard. In a few generations, he may select the stock so that in that new location it looks uniformly like the original in the original place.

It may seem that by all that careful work the seedsman has done a commendable job. But, alas, customers in the region where the stock originated may complain that plants from the reselected stock are not quite like the original stock. The seedsman looks into the complaint. He may note that the plants are different from the original stock and different from those of the same stock growing in his seed field far away. The interplay of genes and environment is the reason.

Many seedsmen are well aware of the hazard involved in stock selection in an environment widely different from that where the commercial seed is to be used.

Suppose a seedsman decides that he must maintain his stock seed in an environment quite different from the one where his stock was originated and selected. Then suppose he decides to refrain completely from any roguing or selection in an effort to avoid interfering with the composition of the original stock. Unfortunately, sooner or later, he finds that the stock has drifted off to some degree, although he has not tinkered with it in the least. What happens?

Again, the interplay of genes and environment tends to upset the seed-cart. Natural selection and selection by man bring about a shift in the collection of variable living things that make up a stock. In the different environment, some of the variants that appear produce more seeds or fewer seeds than other plants in the stock. In time, the stock contains a large proportion of plants having hereditary makeups that are somewhat different from those of most of the plants of the original stock.

Inbreds, which have been very closely bred and selected for a low degree of variation in hereditary makeup, also tend to drift, especially when they are maintained in an environment quite different from their original one. Inbreds, too, respond to the forces of selection—natural or artificial—that inevitably bear upon differences in properties induced by the interaction of genes and environment.

Inbreds generally tend to drift less rapidly than open-pollinated stocks, because they are less variable in makeup at the start. But they are variable and fluid to some degree.

We think we want commercial varieties that are absolutely uniform and genetically stable and that behave the same in one place as in any other where they will grow. There is no such thing and probably never will be. We can only settle for the best compromise that is feasible. What we are willing to accept—what we can afford to hold out for—depends on a welter of economic considerations and what is biologically possible. Satisfactory compromises are attainable.

Biological research and experience in plant breeding and seed production are making those compromises more favorable. Many of our present varieties behave with satisfactory constancy under a relatively wide range of growing conditions. Breeders now make special efforts to insure that a variety has such a genetic makeup that it can perform rather consistently in different places and seasons. There is a limit, though.

Seedsmen more and more maintain seed stock operations in regions where the commercial seeds from those stocks are to be used. They help thereby to retain the genes in a stock that are essential for the expression of the desired properties and performance in those regions. Through the continuing evaluation of the performance of their commercial stocks, seedsmen get information to help in making sound judgments in the difficult task of control of seed stock.

MOST OF THE breeding of potatoes and sweetpotatoes in the United States is done cooperatively by the Department of Agriculture and the State agricultural experiment stations.

Original potato seedlings of controlled parentage are first propagated on isolated "seed" farms, on which no field-grown tubers from other fields are planted. Only original greenhouse-grown seedlings and local propagations of those seedlings are grown on the isolation farms. The farms are kept scrupulously isolated and free of virus diseases, so that stock of any seedling later found worthy of introduction can be distributed to foundation stock growers in a virus-free condition. Virus infection at this stage might make a potential new variety worthless.

Seedlings and stocks of sweetpotatoes propagated from them have not been produced under the rigid control that is practiced with potatoes. With increasing troubles from virus diseases in the sweetpotato, however, there is need for similar control.

In supplying propagating material of potatoes and sweetpotatoes to cooperators for evaluation of new seedlings, the breeder usually sends a few tubers (or roots of sweetpotato) to each from his own initial increase plots.

The cooperator easily produces enough stock for further tests while he grows these new items for his first observations. In the South, however, where it is not feasible to produce good seed potatoes, investigators must get their planting stock from favorable lo cations in the mountains or in the North.

Sometimes the breeder furnishes enough stock for immediate sizable tests (as for southern locations), but he tries to avoid it because of the great bulk and the costs of shipping seed potatoes.

Cooperative evaluations of potatoes and sweetpotatoes are conducted in essentially the same way as seed-propagated plants are.

When cooperating public agencies decide to introduce a variety of potato, one of the agencies furnishes virus-free stock to the foundation seed organizations of the States participating in the introduction of the variety.

These organizations increase the stock under rigid disease control and sell foundation "seed" to the producers of certified seed potatoes. These growers, in turn, produce seed potatoes under official supervision, which is then sold to the commercial growers of potatoes for food. Most of the commercial potatoes in this country are grown from certified seed.

The public agencies introducing a new variety of potato make a joint announcement naming, describing, and "introducing" the variety as soon as modest supplies of stock are available from a few producers of foundation seed. This announcement is directed mainly to seedgrowers and public agencies rather than to the general public and tells where foundation stock is available. Further publicity is released later as seed supplies become more widely available.

Growers of foundation seed and certified seed potatoes are the counterpart of the producer of vegetable seeds. There are hundreds of such growers in the Northern and Western States.

Fewer than a half dozen of them are breeders, whose objectives and methods differ greatly. Some freely exchange their potential varieties, under agreement, very much as public agencies do, and introduce varieties in about the same way. Others operate more nearly as the private breeder-seedsman does.

When the Department of Agriculture introduces a variety of sweetpotato, it usually acts jointly with one or more States. Introduction consists of a joint announcement naming the variety, describing it, and stating where propagating stock is available. In the absence of a well-established seed sweetpotato "industry," initial stock is furnished to a few selected growers who can meet initial demands.

Some State agencies produce and introduce new varieties of sweetpotato independently in a similar fashion, after evaluating them for their own conditions. In a few States, foundation seed organizations or similar groups grow the foundation stock of sweetpotatoes for producers of seed sweetpotatoes.

PUBLIC AGENCIES often introduce new varieties of tree fruits and nuts, grapes, berries, and vegetatively propagated ornamentals through limited numbers of nurserymen or special propagating agencies, from whom other nurserymen purchase their initial foundation stocks. Practices vary so much among agencies and among crops both within and among agencies, however, that it is hardly feasible to speak of any general pattern.

Breeders in public agencies generally propagate promising new fruits and ornamentals themselves for further test and evaluation, but there are exceptions. Most of these breeders also directly supply stock to whatever agencies undertake the propagation of foundation stock.

The Department of Agriculture and some State agencies make no charge for breeder stock supplied to propagators of foundation stock. Other State agencies sell breeder stock.

Rarely does a State agency place breeder stock in the hands of but a single private propagator. The Department of Agriculture never does. Stock of State origin often is furnished to all within a State (usually a small number) who request stock and who qualify as dependable, competent, bona fide propagators of the plant. In a few States, the breeders furnish stock exclusively to State-operated foundation stock enterprises, which sell their product to commercial propagators.

Federal and State agencies commonly establish a formal public introduction date, after which stock of a new sort may be sold to the public. The date is set after consultation with propagators to coincide with the availability of a fair supply of commercial stock.

A few States have organizations of growers and nurserymen or other crop specialists who arrange for effective and fair propagation and distribution of foundation stocks of new varieties. As examples:

The New Jersey Peach Council, Inc., cooperates with the State experiment station on evaluation, is consulted about introduction, and propagates and sells the initial supplies of certified stock.

The New York State Fruit Testing Cooperative Association helps evaluate new varieties bred by State agencies, propagates those specified for propagation, and sells foundation stock of introduced varieties to nurseries and the public.

Oklahoma Foundation Seed Stocks, Inc., receives breeder stock, produces foundation stock of peaches and other fruits for sale to nurseries, and handles foundation seed.

Many serious virus diseases are transmitted by vegetative propagation. Some viruses have been eliminated from some kinds of plants by heat treatment or other means, but generally an infected stock remains so.

Infection of an original stock may render it worthless. Careful controls over the production of original plants and foundation stock of vegetatively propagated varieties are necessary.

As an example of this control, the Foundation Plant Materials Service of the University of California tests both old and new varieties of several fruits, including stone fruits, pears, and grapes, for virus infection. It may take up to 6 years to be sure a stock is free of virus. If the service certifies a stock of a variety to be free of virus, the stock is placed under the supervision of the State department of agriculture, which authorizes nurseries to propagate it. The nurseries then sell propagating material or trees to growers within the State and later to growers elsewhere. The foundation trees are continually tested to assure that they remain free of virus.

After preliminary evaluation of potential varieties of strawberries bred by the Department of Agriculture and cooperating States, virus-free plants are furnished to selected nurseries. These firms are certified by their respective State control agencies as qualified to propagate stocks under conditions that will keep them virus free.

After 1 to 5 years of evaluation and propagation in these nurseries, a variety may be introduced. The nurseries then supply virus-free stock of it to specified "first-year virus-free stock growers" in various States. These stock growers are certified by their respective State inspection services as qualified to produce foundation stock; they produce commercial plants for sale to strawberry growers.

In breeding blueberries, the Department of Agriculture produces tens of thousands of seeds of controlled parentage each year. The task of growing, propagating, and evaluating seedlings from those seeds is formidable for one agency. The Department therefore enters into cooperative agreements with State experiment stations and with able and interested commercial growers who help do this job.

The Department selects a few of the best seedlings each year for further evaluation. The cooperating growers may propagate and sell a few plants for evaluation studies to cooperating experiment stations and others. By the time any superior seedling is ready for naming and introduction, the original grower of it and a few cooperating fellow-growers will have developed small supplies of propagating material that can be sold to nurserymen and others.

Each kind of fruit crop has its own peculiar problems of propagation, evaluation, and introduction. There are many modifications of the several basic plans described for various fruits to suit specific crops and also sets of circumstances.

THE DEPARTMENT of Agriculture breeds and introduces many varieties of asexually propagated ornamentals, such as lilies, chrysanthemums, and azaleas. When evaluation indicates that a variety merits introduction, it is named and described. An appropriate announcement is sent to commercial propagators.

Upon introduction, a small amount of breeder stock of a variety is furnished to each of a number of nurserymen from a selected list designated by the American Association of Nurserymen, Inc. These selected firms propagate the breeder stock and sell foundation stock to other nurserymen, in accord with an agreement between the Department and the association, which represents the nursery industry in these matters.

Horticultural varieties of fruits and ornamentals that must be propagated vegetatively can be patented in this country. Many of those introduced by private breeders are patented, but public agencies generally do not patent their introductions.

As with seed-propagated varieties, private breeders of vegetatively propagated varieties generally conduct their work in as inconspicuous a manner as possible and retain strict control of their materials. They introduce their new vegetatively propagated varieties in essentially the same way as seed-propagated varieties, except that the former may be patented before it is introduced publicly and offered for sale.

IT IS EASY to state the objective and principles of orderly, effective, and equable introduction of a new variety by a public agency, but it is quite another matter to get the job done.

Together with the numerous segments of the industries involved, we all are continuing to develop procedures and facilities for introducing a very wide range of crop species in progressively better and more mutually satisfying ways.

Scientific and technical competence in crop improvement has been progressing in the vegetable seed industry at the same time as in public research agencies. Some of us believe that henceforth private enterprise can and will conduct a still larger share of the "applied research and development" in producing new, improved varieties of vegetables. This is desirable because it will permit public agencies to give more attention to important basic problems in genetics, pathology, and physiology that must be solved to afford a basis for further progress.

VICTOR R. BOSWELL *is Chief, Vegetables and Ornamentals Research Branch, Crops Research Division, Agricultural Research Service, Beltsville, Md.*

Seed Certification

in the United States

FRANK G. PARSONS, CARLTON S. GARRISON, AND KELLER E. BEESON

SEED certification is the system used to keep pedigree records for crop varieties and to make available sources of genetically pure seed and propagating materials for general distribution.

Seed certification does this by means of inspections of fields and seeds and regulations for checking on the production, harvesting, and cleaning of each lot of seed. Seedsmen and farmers thus have assurance of getting genetically pure seeds when they distribute or use certified seeds.

Without such a system, seeds of varieties tend to become contaminated and mixed and to lose identity.

Workers in agricultural experiment stations started before 1900 to select and release better varieties of crops. The seeds of a new variety were given in small amounts to growers, who agreed to multiply and distribute the seeds to their neighbors. At that time there were several good reasons for the practice.

Agronomists and plant breeders had relatively little land at their disposal and therefore could produce a limited amount of seeds. The staff at most experiment stations was so small that few breeders had enough help and time to make substantial increases of seed before it was released. Many believed that once a small increase was made it was the farmer's duty to multiply and distribute the seed to the farmers. The research workers looked to the farmer-cooperators for reports on yield and a rough evaluation of the variety under farm conditions. This was one of the accepted methods of giving information on the adaptation and performance of new varieties.

The plan gave the experiment stations a method of introducing improved varieties and strains to farmers of their respective States, but it was not efficient. Many times the seed was wasted or became so contaminated that its true value was lost, although the new varieties produced at public expense represented many years of effort and were valuable.

Seedsmen and farmers were also distributing so-called new varieties with little regard for their adaptation and value. It was a common practice to rename varieties and so to cause them to lose their original identity. The question was raised as to what could be done to maintain the identity of a variety after it had left the plant breeder.

Members of the Congress distributed seeds of new varieties during the early 1900's. Many farmers got some seeds for increase, but usually the distribution benefited only the farmers who got the seeds.

Because of the difficulties experienced in increasing and distributing seeds of new varieties, agronomists at several of the State agricultural experiment stations began to help growers by inspecting their seed-increase fields before harvest. Wisconsin in 1913 started field inspection work for members of the Wisconsin Agricultural Experiment Station. Montana did so in 1915, Minnesota and Missouri in 1916, and Ohio in 1919.

Seed certification grew from these efforts.

SEED CERTIFICATION is a responsibility of the States. Authority to carry on this service is given by legislation to an agency or organization whose responsibility for the work is defined in the law.

The certifying agencies work closely with the State agricultural experiment stations, the Extension Service, the State departments of agriculture, seed analysts, and control officials. Policies and regulations pertaining to certification usually are initiated by joint action of the experiment station and the certifying agency.

The U.S. Department of Agriculture has no direct responsibility for seed certification, but employees of the Agricultural Marketing Service, the Agricultural Research Service, and the Extension Service assist the State certifying agencies and the International Crop Improvement Association in developing procedures for producing and marketing certified seeds.

There are three types of certification agencies. Some are operated by the agricultural experiment station or the Extension Service. Some are operated by State departments of agriculture. Most of them are crop improvement associations.

A State crop improvement association usually has a board of directors, most of whom are seed producers elected by the grower members; a representative of the experiment station; and an advisory committee of representatives of the experiment station. The agricultural division of the State college or experiment station usually provides office facilities and part of the expenses of maintaining the secretary-manager of the association. He usually is a staff member of the college or experiment station.

Most certification agencies do not receive appropriated State funds but obtain operating income by charging fees for their services. The fee schedule includes farm, field, and acreage fees and sometimes a tag and sealing fee. The acreage fee provides the greatest source of income. It varies with the crop, the extent of the certification program in the State, and the amount of funds required to provide the certification services. For example, in 1960 the acreage fees set by the certification agencies ranged from 15 cents to about 1 dollar an acre for small grains and similar crops, but were 5 dollars or more an acre for crops requiring numerous inspections, such as hybrid corn.

About 2.5 billion pounds of farm seeds and a like amount of seed potatoes were certified annually in the United States in the years 1955–1960. Certification has usually been confined to seeds of farm crops, although a small amount of vegetable seeds is certified in some States.

Forty-five States had certification programs by 1959 that embraced a few hundred acres to more than 200 thousand acres. In total, more than 1,500 hybrids and varieties were certified in 1959.

PARTICIPATION in the certification of seed and other propagating materials usually is open to all growers. The production and processing of certified seeds is a specialized business, however, that one should enter only as a carefully studied, long-time venture.

Most of the varieties that are accepted for certification have been developed and released by State agricultural experiment stations, but there is a growing interest among some private breeders in having their own varieties certified. This varies with seed firms, for it usually relates to the kinds of seed crops they sell.

Some varieties developed by private breeders have been certified, but private plant breeding of field crops (except cotton, hybrid corn, and tobacco) has not been practiced extensively in the United States. Private breeders were beginning to work with other field crops, however, by the late 1950's. Nothing in the certification procedure prevents the acceptance of privately developed varieties if their owners want certification and comply with the requirements as to eligibility.

In most States, a committee of representatives of agricultural experiment stations decides whether a variety is acceptable for certification. The approval of the experiment station or committee becomes final when the new variety is accepted by the State certification agency.

The requirements for accepting varieties into certification vary.

One reason for this is that consideration must be given to the nature of the breeding or selection involved in the development of the variety. The reproductive habits of different crop plants determine the precautions that must be taken to maintain uniform performance in successive increases of seeds. The method of plant breeding often determines the amount of testing necessary to determine the value of a variety.

It is important, furthermore, to decide whether the variety is to be produced for use within the State or elsewhere. Seeds of cereal, oil, and fiber crops can be grown in the areas where they were developed and are used most, but seeds of some crops, particularly forages, must be produced in areas at considerable distance from where the varieties were bred and where they will be used. That point having been decided, specific requirements are developed to protect the original characteristics of the varieties.

Certification procedures were developed in 1938–1945 for growing seeds of forage crops outside their regions of origin or where they are best adapted for forage. These procedures, which designate the stock seeds to be planted, the limitations on the number of generations of increase, and the number of crops of seeds that can be harvested from a stand, assure the consumer that he can rely on certified seeds of the improved varieties regardless of where they were produced.

The large production in the West of certified seeds of improved varieties of alfalfa and red clover, adapted to the Central, Eastern, and Southern States, was made possible by these special regulations.

FOUR CLASSES of certified seed are recognized in the certification programs throughout the United States. These are listed and defined by the International Crop Improvement Association thus:

"Breeder seed shall be seed or vegetative propagating material directly controlled by the originating, or in certain cases the sponsoring plant breeder or institution, and which provides the source for the initial and recurring increase of foundation seed."

"Foundation seed, including elite in Canada, shall be seed stocks that are so handled as to most nearly maintain specific genetic identity and purity and that may be designated or distributed by an agricultural experiment station. Production must be carefully supervised or approved by representatives of an agricultural experiment station. Foundation seed shall be the source of all other certified seed classes, either directly or through registered seed."

"Registered seed shall be the progeny of foundation or registered seed that is so handled as to maintain satisfactory genetic identity and purity and that has been approved and certified by the certifying agency. This class of seed should be of a quality suitable for the production of certified seed."

"Certified seed shall be the progeny of foundation, registered or certified seed that is so handled as to maintain satisfactory genetic identity and purity and that has been approved and certified by the certifying agency."

Breeder seed generally remains exclusively in the hands of the originating plant breeder or institution and is limited in amount.

Foundation seed usually is under the control of the State agricultural experiment station. Sometimes this control is vested in an organization that produces foundation seed. The agricultural experiment station has some degree of control over the organization. Various State and national programs are responsible for the production and maintenance of foundation seed.

Registered seed, usually one generation advanced from the foundation seed, is used as planting stock for the production of the certified seed.

Registered and certified seed are distributed through regular seed trade channels.

All classes of certified seed must meet

standards as to eligibility of planting seed, procedures for increasing certain hybrids and varieties, land requirements, and field and seed inspection.

THE CERTIFICATION process begins for the grower when he files an application with the certifying agency. The application includes information on the identity of the seeds and the cropping history of the field. The land to be eligible must not have grown the same crop for a definite preceding period, unless the seed crop was of the same variety and of the proper certified class. The tendency of the seeds to live over in the soil has a bearing. For example, land on which certified seeds of small grain are to be grown need only be out of the crop for the previous year, but a crop likely to leave hard seeds or surviving plants (such as whiteclover) in the soil may have to be out of the crop for as much as 4 years. The International Crop Improvement Association specifics that registered seed for the production of certified seed shall be planted only on land on which no whiteclover plants of any type have grown for at least the preceding 4 years, during two of which the land must be cultivated. The standards also specify the arrangement of pollen and female parents in a field producing hybrid seeds and the omission of the registered class for certain of the alfalfa varieties.

When the proper seeds have been planted and the land is free of plants or seeds that would dilute varietal purity, field inspection becomes the next important feature of certification. On it hinges the varietal purity of succeeding generations, for any observable mixtures of other crops and other varieties and the presence of seedborne diseases are determined then.

Isolation is another factor that is checked during field inspection. Minimum isolation distances have been established for insect- and wind-pollinated species. Corn, rye, sorghum, millet, and many forage grasses are wind-pollinated crops. Alfalfa, the clovers, cotton, okra, onions, and watermelons are among the plants that depend on pollinating insects.

The effectiveness of isolation in preventing contamination in certified-seed fields is influenced by temperature, humidity, the natural barriers, border rows, differing maturity dates, the size of the fields, the amount of bloom, and the attractiveness of flowers to insect pollinators. The pollen of open-pollinated crops can be transported considerable distances by wind and insects.

At the University of Nebraska, M. D. Jones and L. C. Newell studied pollen dispersal of corn, rye, and five forage grasses. Assigning 100 percent to represent the pollen in the center of the field, they found 31 percent of the pollen remained in the air at 5 rods, 10 percent at 15 rods, 4.4 percent at 25 rods, 1.2 percent at 40 rods from the border of the field, and 0.8 percent at 60 rods.

D. J. Griffiths, at the Welsh Plant Breeding Station, found the amount of outcrossing in a seed field is lessened by the protective effect of pollen released by the variety itself. He observed that contamination in seeds from the first and sixth rows of several perennial ryegrass plantings, spaced at varying distances from a contaminating field, was 41.63 percent and 17.86 percent at 1.5 rods isolation, 5.60 percent and 1.65 percent at 6 rods, and 0.81 and 0.59 percent at 24 rods.

The isolation requirements for all crops must be enough to keep outcrossing at a minimum but sufficiently realistic to permit the efficient production of certified seed. The minimum isolation distances for most of the open-pollinated crops are 80 rods for foundation seed, 20 rods for registered seed, and 10 rods for certified seed. Occasionally these requirements as to isolation are increased for certain crops in which a very small amount of contamination would adversely affect varietal performance or acceptability. Natural barriers or border rows are used for some crops as a partial replacement for isolation distances. In the production of certified hybrid corn seed, the minimum distance can be modified by planting border rows of pollen parents. The number of border rows is determined by the size of the field and the actual distance between it and the source of contaminating pollen.

The smaller the seed field, the greater is the possibility for outcrossing. The isolation requirement for many open-pollinated crops thus is greater for small fields. Typical examples are the requirements for the production of seeds of alfalfa, birdsfoot trefoil, red clover and whiteclover. For fields smaller than 5 acres, the minimum isolation distances for the registered and certified seed classes are 40 and 20 rods. For fields of 5 acres or more, the minimum distances are 20 and 10 rods, respectively.

Isolation requirements are included in the certification standards for the self-pollinated crops, such as soybeans, wheat, barley, oats, lespedeza, and garden and field beans. The required distances between varieties of the same species are usually about 10 feet, or one drill or seeder width. The primary reason for this isolation is to avoid mixtures during harvest. Observations on the amount of crossing between varieties of wheat, however, may make greater isolation distances necessary for wheat. A crossing of more than 15 percent has been noted between some wheat varieties in adjacent plantings.

The field inspection sees to it that every part of the inspected field meets the requirements. Self-pollinated annual crops generally are inspected once, at about maturity. Forage crops, such as alfalfa, red clover, and the grasses are inspected once, during the full bloom stage. The inspection of hybrid corn requires several inspections to determine that pollination is controlled as required for the variety. The field inspector's report as to the presence of other crops and varieties, diseases and weeds, isolation distances, and pollination control is compared with the standards to determine if the crop

of seeds meets the field requirements for certification.

A further safeguard is a limitation on the number of generations the seeds may be increased for specific varieties or crops. Known as the limited generation program, it restricts the number of multiplications that can be made from breeder or foundation seed. Growers of registered or certified seed thus must obtain planting stock of a higher class at specified intervals to retain eligibility for certification. This limitation on the number of generations of increase minimizes the effect of possible genetic shifts or contamination on varietal purity and performance.

For many forage crops, the number of multiplications is limited to three generations of increase from breeder seed—one each for foundation, registered, and certified seed production.

In some varieties, such as Vernal and Lahontan alfalfas, Dollard and Lakeland red clover, Potomac and Pennlate orchardgrass, and Saratoga bromegrass, the registered class has been omitted. The required volume of certified seed can be produced without the registered generation. Through its elimination, there is one less chance of introducing or multiplying any contaminant that may adversely affect varietal purity.

The age of stand and number of certified seed crops that can be harvested also are limited for some crops.

For certain small grains and cotton, some States limit the number of multiplications to three generations of increase from foundation seed. It may be one generation of the registered class and two of the certified class or two generations of registered seed and one of certified seed. Whichever sequence is followed, the final multiplication is not eligible as planting stock for the production of certified seed.

SEED INSPECTIONS are made to determine whether the certified seed is of reasonably good planting quality. It is made on a representative sample of the cleaned seeds submitted to the certifying agency. From these samples, analysts determine the percentage of mechanical purity and of weeds, other crops, and inert matter and germination. Each certifying agency has standards that define the requirements for certified seed as determined by seed inspection. Generally it is impossible to determine varietal identification by characteristics of the seeds.

The standards of the International Crop Improvement Association, which are a guide for State certifying agencies, require that most crops show a germination of at least 80 percent. Maximum tolerances for weed seeds, seeds of other crops, and inert matter are somewhat different for each crop. The level of such impurities is held to a practical limit consistent with what is considered acceptable planting seeds.

Certified seed is packaged in various kinds of containers, but on each one an appropriate sealing device is used. Field seeds often are packaged in cloth bags. The twine with which they are sewn or tied is sealed with a metal seal that cannot be removed and used again. The seal is the property of the certification agency, and its use by any other agency is illegal. The seal protects the bag from being opened and prevents the official certification tag from being removed.

All States use a blue tag for certified seed, generally a purple tag for registered seed, and a white tag for foundation seed. The tag usually carries a statement that the seed is certified. It tells which State has performed the certification, gives the crop and variety name, and includes a number, which identifies the grower and the lot of seed or may be a serial number by which the certification records can be traced.

The certification tags usually do not include information regarding the inspection and testing of the seeds. This information is carried on another tag, usually supplied by the grower, handler, or vendor. The separate tag makes it possible for the distributor to relabel the certified seed to comply with State and Federal laws without disturbing the certification tag, and emphasizes that responsibility for correct labeling rests with the handler.

Methods for labeling and sealing containers of materials other than cloth vary with the type of package. Paper containers may bear a certification label that is glued or cemented to the container across the opening in such a way that it must be torn when the package is opened. The certifying agency determines the effectiveness of sealing devices for special containers. Sometimes a certifying agency authorizes the imprinting of the certification label on the container.

TWO OR MORE agencies may perform the services required to certify a lot of seed. This is referred to as interagency certification. Special procedures have been developed to cover it. For example, certified seed might be produced, processed, tagged, and sealed by the certifying agency in State A. The seed moves through trade channels to State B, where the seed law might require recleaning of the seed. The certification agency in State B supervises the breaking of the original seals, removal of the tags, and the reprocessing. When the seed meets the requirements, it retags and reseals the seed without the prior approval of State A.

Sometimes an agency in State C may make the field inspection and supervise the harvesting of the seeds. That agency seals the seed in containers with official evidence of its eligibility. The seed is then shipped into the jurisdiction of a fourth agency, D, for cleaning, sampling, testing, and, after all requirements are met, the final tagging and sealing of the seeds. The label attached to such seeds indicates the States participating in the certification procedure. Seeds may also be completely certified in one State and may be further processed under interagency certification in another State, or they may be blended with other lots of seed in another State.

THE INTERNATIONAL Crop Improvement Association has had a significant influence on certification policy in the United States and Canada. The idea of obtaining greater uniformity in certified seed produced under the supervision of the different seed-certifying agencies was first discussed at a meeting in St. Paul, Minn., on July 11, 1919. Six men from Ontario, Michigan, Minnesota, North Dakota, South Dakota, and Wisconsin gathered to discuss the possibilities of forming an organization to strengthen the efforts of individual seed-certification agencies.

This conference led to the organization of the International Crop Improvement Association (ICIA) in Chicago, Ill., on December 2, 1919.

The first comprehensive set of minimum standards for the certification of seeds was prepared by the ICIA in the early 1940's and published in 1945. These have become the reference for certifying agencies in the United States and Canada. Other organizations throughout the world have used them as guides in setting up certification schemes. The standards have been revised from time to time. Copies of the booklet are available from State seed-certifying agencies.

The ICIA also developed procedures for interagency certification and helped to establish the National Foundation Seed Program.

Nearly all the certification agencies in Canada and the United States were affiliated with ICIA in 1961. It has brought plant breeders, seed specialists, analysts, control officials, research workers, certification personnel, and the seed industry together to develop better methods for making seeds of improved varieties available to the consumer.

That certification of seeds in the United States is important is attested by the fact that 45 States operated certification programs in 1961 and more than 5 billion pounds of seed and propagating materials of good varieties were certified.

The basic function of a seed certification program is to serve agriculture. A measure of the service is the thoroughness with which improved varieties have been distributed to American farmers. Not all farmers plant certified seed regularly, but at least a few farmers in nearly every community plant certified seed of improved varieties often enough to have a beneficial effect on the entire community.

It is mainly through the certification programs that varieties released by experiment stations have been increased and distributed.

The certification tag or label tells the planter that the seed so labeled is the variety it is said to be; that the germ plasm and performance were known to the plant breeder who developed the variety; that it has been tested under various environments and management systems; and that its potential is known.

It tells him that it is a good variety—not necessarily the best under all conditions but a satisfactory one where its use is recommended.

It also tells him that a sample of the seed has been tested in the laboratory and found to meet certain minimum requirements as to germination and that it met certain requirements as to limitation of weed seeds, other crop seeds, and inert matter.

The certification label can be thought of as the stamp of acceptability from an impartial agency. The label does not mean that the seed is perfect—the physical quality of the seed may vary. But it is a safety feature for sellers and buyers of seeds. For example, tests of trueness to type with Ranger alfalfa showed that farmers who buy noncertified Ranger seed have less than a 50-percent chance of getting actual Ranger performance in the crop.

The certification agencies do not buy or sell certified seed or market it directly. They develop programs to promote the use of certified seed of adapted varieties.

Certified seed is distributed through

the established seed-marketing channels—seed firms, brokers, retailers, and
others who normally engage in the
merchandising of seeds. In some crops,
such as small grains, soybeans, and
hybrid corn, certified seed is often sold
by the growers to other farmers.

Production of certified seed is increasing throughout the world.

Each year more certified seed gets
into national and international trade
channels—hence a need for minimum
certification standards having world-
wide acceptance.

Under the sponsorship of the Food
and Agriculture Organization of the
United Nations, "Minimum Certification Standards for Maize in European
and Mediterranean Countries" and
"Minimum Certification Standards
for Cereals in the Near East" have
been developed and adopted by the
countries in the respective regions.

More recently, the Organization for
European Economic Cooperation developed a "Scheme for the Certification of Herbage Seeds Moving in
International Trade," which has been
accepted by all member countries in
Europe.

Such an international certification
scheme is of interest to seedgrowers
and seedsmen in the United States as
seeds of varieties from several European countries are being produced in
the Western States for export to the
respective originating countries.

FRANK G. PARSONS *is a specialist in
the Department of Agronomy, University of
California, at Davis, and secretary-treasurer of the California Crop Improvement
Association.*

CARLTON S. GARRISON *is Leader,
Seed Production Investigations, Forage and
Range Research Branch, Agricultural Re-
search Service. He was secretary-treasurer
of the International Crop Improvement
Association for 12 years.*

KELLER E. BEESON *is an extension
agronomist in the Department of Agronomy
of Purdue University and secretary-treasurer of the Indiana Crop Improvement
Association.*

556888°—61——27

Growing Seeds of Forages
Outside Their Regions of Use

CARLTON S. GARRISON AND
RAYMOND J. BULA

REGARDLESS of how superior a new
variety of grass or legume may be, it
is of no value until seed of it is available
and planted.

Limited supplies of seeds of new
varieties retarded their use for many
years on American farms. Because of
difficulties associated with increasing
the seed, some superior varieties of
forage fell by the way because adequate
supplies of seeds were never made
available. As recently as 1948, less than
2 percent of all the grass and legume
seeds planted in this country were of
improved varieties.

The largest acreages of alfalfa, red
clover, timothy, orchardgrass, bromegrass, alsike clover, hairy vetch, crimson clover, and other crops are in the
Central, Eastern, and Southern States,
but they are used primarily for forage
or soil improvement. Their yields of
seeds there often are low and of poor
quality, and seed production tends to
be an incidental farm enterprise. In
sections where a crop is grown extensively for forage, moreover, it is
not easy to locate fields eligible to
produce certified seed because of the
problem of isolation from contaminating sources and volunteer plants.

The production of seeds of the improved varieties therefore has shifted
more and more to the specialized seed-
producing areas in the Western States,
where a dry, sunny climate and controlled irrigation make conditions ideal
for growing and harvesting the seeds
and yields are dependable.

To utilize these new seed-growing

regions, plant breeders, seed-production specialists, and State seed-certifying agencies had to develop procedures for growing seeds of forage varieties outside the area where they were bred and where they are used—what is referred to as the variety's region of adaptation.

These procedures have made it possible to increase rapidly the seeds of forage varieties in the West and to maintain at the same time their superior characteristics. For instance, the special procedures have been included in the certification standards for several crops—alfalfa, birdsfoot trefoil, clovers, and some grasses.

PROCEDURES developed for the production of certified alfalfa seed are typical of the limitations for growing certified seed of an improved variety outside its region of adaptation.

Three requirements must be met.

Seed fields must be planted with foundation or registered seed that is produced in the variety's region of adaptation. Seed from these fields is labeled "certified" regardless of whether foundation or registered seed was planted.

Only one generation of seed increase is permitted outside a variety's region of adaptation.

Certified seed production is limited to stands not more than 6 years old. In practice, the seed is harvested from stands usually not more than 3 or 4 years old.

The same limitations set up for alfalfa apply to varieties of birdsfoot trefoil when seed is grown outside their regions of origin.

The certification requirements for red clover differ slightly from those for alfalfa and birdsfoot trefoil. Changes in varietal characteristics are more pronounced in red clover than in alfalfa. Specific requirements in the certification standards consequently must minimize any changes that may result from the effect of daylength, temperature, management practices, age of stand, and diseases during the process of seed multiplication.

Kenland red clover, for example, has resistance to southern anthracnose (*Colletotrichum trifolii*), a disease of major importance in Kentucky, Indiana, Illinois, Ohio, Virginia, Tennessee, Maryland, and Delaware. It has not been found in the West. When Kenland red clover is grown there, the nonresistant types usually are heavy seeders. Thus there is a shift toward plants that are poorly adapted to eastern and central conditions. The requirement that only two generations of increase be grown from breeder seed insures that Kenland does not lose its resistance to southern anthracnose.

Three requirements pertain to growing seed of red clover varieties outside their regions: Only two generations of increase are permitted from breeder seed—one each of foundation and certified seed. Only two seed crops can be harvested from a planting—in the same or consecutive years. Foundation seed cannot be produced on seeding-year stands for varieties, such as Dollard and Lakeland, that are adapted to the Northern States.

UP-TO-DATE methods and technology have made it possible to increase rapidly the supplies of seeds of an improved variety. Planters can have more of the seeds sooner.

The success of these procedures is illustrated by the production of seeds of six varieties of alfalfa within and outside the regions of adaptation. Four—DuPuits, Narragansett, Ranger, and Vernal—are recommended in the North Central and the Northeastern States. Atlantic and Buffalo are used widely in the Central, Eastern, and Southern States.

The total production of certified seed of the six varieties has amounted to more than 470 million pounds, 85 percent of it outside the regions of adaptation. California alone produced more than 375 million pounds.

More than 65 percent of our alfalfa acreage was planted with the six varieties in 1958; the acreage would have been smaller had not large amounts of seed been grown outside the region of adaptation. Farmers thus got dividends from varieties that have greater persistence, give better yields, and are more resistant to bacterial wilt.

In the same way, supplies of seeds of Dollard, Kenland, and Pennscott red clovers have been built up rapidly by producing certified seed in the specialized areas in the West. The practice started in the late 1930's for such varieties as Cumberland and Midland, but the greatest progress occurred after 1950. The National Foundation Seed Program helped greatly in the essential work of coordinating the production and distribution of the foundation seed.

More than 33 million pounds of certified seeds of Dollard, Kenland, and Pennscott red clover have been grown—98 percent of it in the West, mostly in Washington, Idaho, and Oregon. Farmers in the Central and Eastern States, where these varieties are adapted, depend on supplies of western-grown seeds.

Certified seed of Pennlawn red fescue, Penncross and Pennlu bentgrasses, Pennlate and Potomac orchardgrass, Saratoga bromegrass, Essex timothy, Romack field pea, Dixie crimson clover, Pilgrim Ladino clover, Auburn vetch, Merion Kentucky bluegrass, and Chesapeake red clover also is produced in the West.

Without the specialized seed production in the West, commercial supplies of seeds of many grass and legume varieties would not exist. The physiological and genetic characteristics of many forages complicate their culture for seed production in those areas, however.

This is not strange when we consider the genetic variability in the cross-pollinated forage varieties and the fact that certain plant types (genotypes) may set more or fewer seeds than expected when subjected to different environments. During the multiplication of seeds, climatic conditions and farm-management practices in the western seed-growing sections can cause changes in a grass or legume variety developed in the Eastern States.

Through each generation of seed increase, Nature closely screens the plant population in a variety. Some plant types may succumb to various elements of environment, like climate, or improper watering, or mowing at the wrong time. Others may produce few seeds to perpetuate themselves in the next generation. Such effects may show up strongly in varieties when seeds are grown in different places, for some regions may favor specific segments of the plant population. The results can be so pronounced as to affect the performance of the variety itself.

How, then, can one predict the reaction of a variety to varying environmental and management pressures?

The answer is simple. We cannot make such predictions, because we do not understand fully the flowering response of forage species. The growth and flowering habits of plants become highly important, however, when they are grown for seeds, particularly outside the regions of adaptation.

DIFFERENCES in daylengths from north to south affect the flowering of many forage species. Ladino clover produces an unlimited number of flowers in the Northern States but flowers sparsely south of the line running through Savannah, Ga., and Shreveport, La. That is roughly 32° latitude, where the longest day is a little more than 14 hours. Ladino clover needs more than 14 hours of daylight to flower heavily.

The flowering habit of certified seed of Ladino clover produced in four Western States was studied at the University of Illinois by J. A. Jackobs and C. N. Hittle. The seeds produced in California had fewer blooms than the seeds produced in Idaho, Oregon, and Washington.

Variations in flowering response to overwinter temperatures and daylengths among the parental clones of Pilgrim Ladino clover have been reported by scientists at the California and Washington Agricultural Experiment Stations. When the 21 clones used in their study were established vegetatively—not by seed—at Davis, Calif. (38° latitude), and Prosser, Wash. (46° latitude), flowering was more uniform and persisted longer at Prosser, where the days are longer during the growing season.

The degree and likelihood of a genetic shift in Pilgrim Ladino clover therefore would be much greater in seeds produced in California than seeds produced in Washington.

The season, of course, determines the number of hours of daylight the plants get in the field. As days get longer from December 21 to June 21 and shorter after June 21, the effect on the flowering habit of red clover is marked.

These seasonal effects on Kenland and Pennscott were studied by men in the Department of Agriculture and the Indiana Agricultural Experiment Station. Nearly all plants established as spaced plants in rows in mid-May had flowering stems and produced seed by late October. Later seedings, up to mid-July, gave a smaller percentage of flowering plants. Fewer than 1 percent of the plants from the mid-July seedings produced flower stems, and none produced mature seeds.

This flowering pattern coincides with the change in daylength from mid-May to mid-July. The May seedings are well established by the time they are exposed to the longest days after mid-June. The percentage of flowering plants is high. On the other hand, the mid-July seedings are exposed to the shortening days of July and August. These daylengths are not effective in stimulating red clover to produce flowering stems.

Special studies in controlled-environment rooms have demonstrated that varieties of medium red clover will not flower very much if daylengths are shorter than 16 hours.

These facts help us understand how a change could occur in a variety of red clover if its seed is produced in a region where days are too short to induce all the plant types in the variety to flower.

TEMPERATURE also must be considered in seed setting. Some forage species require an exposure to low temperatures before they will flower.

Varieties of red clover, which contain germ plasm from mammoth or single-cut types, require exposure to low temperatures before they will produce normal bloom. Among them are Dollard, Lakeland, LaSalle, and the Finnish Tammisto. Genetic shifts occur in such varieties when seeds are harvested before the plants have been exposed to overwintering temperatures.

H. A. Steppler and L. C. Raymond, of Macdonald College in Canada, reported a marked change in the relative proportions of plant types in LaSalle red clover when seeds were harvested in the fall following a spring seeding. A similar change was reported for the Tammisto red clover when seeds were harvested from a seeding-year stand. The percentage of rosette-type plants was 33 percent in the original Tammisto seeds, but only 13 percent in the seeds harvested from the seeding-year stand. Seeds from the 2-year-old stand were similar to true Tammisto seeds.

Thus, to minimize changes that may occur in varieties containing single-cut plant types, it is necessary to avoid production of seeds from seeding-year stands and to limit the increases in southern latitudes to one generation.

Most of the cool-season forage grasses require much the same environmental conditions for floral development as the single-cut red clover varieties do. Selected plants from these species, however, will flower to some extent without exposure to low temperatures. Thus a variety of grass may consist of a mixture of plant types. Some plants would require exposure to definite low temperatures. In others, low temperature would increase greatly the amount of flowering. The rest of the plants would not be affected.

An example of this varied response was observed in a variety of orchardgrass made by combining four parental plants (clones) adapted to the Eastern States. Tests were established with vegetative propagations at Prosser, Wash. (46° latitude); Logan, Utah (41° latitude); and Shafter and Tehachapi, Calif. (35° latitude).

The four clones were similar in flowering habit in Washington and Utah. There was a difference of 6 to 7 days in flowering between the earliest and latest clones. The flowering habit at Tehachapi, Calif., was like that in the northern locations, except that the late clones flowered 15 days after the early ones. The difference at Shafter was 23 days. At all four locations, the same clones were consistently the earliest flowering and the latest flowering.

Similar flowering responses were noted in another four-clone variety of orchardgrass grown at each of the four places. The greatest differential in flowering response was found at Shafter, where the early- and the late-flowering clones were 39 days apart.

Shafter and Tehachapi are at approximately the same latitude but differ greatly in seasonal temperatures. The plantings at Shafter were in the southern part of the San Joaquin Valley at an elevation of 352 feet; the plants were limited in their exposure to freezing temperatures. The plantings at Tehachapi were on a mountain plateau at an elevation of 4 thousand feet. Freezing temperatures occur there anytime after early September.

The floral response of the clones in these two synthetic varieties of orchardgrass illustrates the effect of temperature and daylength in regulating flowering in many grasses. It is important therefore that precautions be taken to grow the seeds of orchardgrass and other grasses that have similar responses in conditions that will minimize differences in flowering among the various plant types (genotypes) in a variety.

Alfalfa is equally responsive to variations in the environment, even though its floral response differs from that of the grasses or red clover.

Dale Smith and L. F. Graber, of the Wisconsin Agricultural Experiment Station, were the first to direct attention to the differences in height of Ranger plants, grown from seeds produced in Arizona and Montana, during the fall of the seeding year. Under the shortening autumn days in Wisconsin, the average height of fall regrowth was unmistakably taller in the plants from Arizona-grown Ranger seeds than from the Montana seeds. Differences in plant height from seeds increased for a second generation in the southern latitudes were even more pronounced.

In another study, foundation and certified seed lots of Vernal alfalfa produced in nine States and two Canadian Provinces were compared at Lafayette, Ind. Many of the foundation seed lots produced a larger number of taller plants than the check samples (breeder seed) provided by the originator of the variety. However, most of the certified seed lots increased in the Northern States and all those from the Southwest produced taller plants than the foundation seed from which they were grown.

A shift toward taller plants appears to be more pronounced in Vernal than in Ranger—perhaps a reflection of the greater diversity in germ plasm used in breeding the Vernal variety.

The changes or shifts in varietal characteristics could destroy the superiority of the variety if they were allowed to continue from generation to generation. The seed-production practices for many of the forage varieties therefore must be regulated to keep the changes to the minimum. When the approved procedures are followed, seeds produced outside a variety's region of adaptation give forage yields equal to that grown within the region.

In forage tests comparing the four classes of certified seed, breeder, foundation, registered, and certified seed, of Atlantic, Buffalo, Ranger, and Vernal varieties of alfalfa, no significant differences in yields of hay were found among the various classes of certified seed or among seed lots from different parts of the country.

A collection of 25 lots of breeder, foundation, and certified seed of Vernal was included in a test of hay yield at Lafayette. There were no significant differences in yields, even though some of the foundation and certified lots were known to have a higher percentage of tall plants than the breeder seed.

A series of tests with Atlantic, Buffalo, and Ranger alfalfa at 12 State agricultural experiment stations showed no significant differences in hay yields among the breeder, foundation, registered, and certified seed classes. Likewise, there was no difference in yields between certified seed produced within and outside the varieties' regions of adaptation.

A plan for the increase of seeds of varieties outside their regions of adaptation must provide for a limitation on generations of increase; the exclusion of management and cultural practices that will have abnormal effects on growth, flowering, and seed-setting habits; the control of volunteer plants; and adequate isolation from other fields of the same crop.

The seed-certification standards include the essential requirements to safeguard against serious genetic shifts in forage crop varieties. Thus the production of seeds in different regions has had no major effect on the performance of forage crop varieties—a heartening proof of the soundness of the seed-certification system.

The successful production in the Western States of legume seeds for use elsewhere has been followed with interest in other countries. The Organization for European Economic Cooperation developed a similar system for increasing seed supplies for its member countries.

Northern European countries encounter the same problems in growing legume seeds as we do in the Central and Eastern States. Weather is fre-

quently unfavorable for good pollination, development of seeds, and harvesting.

Under OEEC sponsorship, alfalfa varieties from Austria, Germany, Sweden, and the United Kingdom were multiplied in France, Greece, Italy, Portugal, and Turkey. Varieties of red clover from Belgium, Germany, the Netherlands, and Norway were increased in France, Greece, Italy, Portugal, and Turkey. Sweet lupines from Denmark, Germany, and Sweden were grown in Greece and Portugal. Vetches from Denmark, Germany, and Sweden were reproduced in Greece, Italy, Portugal, and Turkey.

Seeds of each variety produced in the different countries were planted in "growing-on-tests" by the Danish Seed Testing Station at Copenhagen to determine whether genetic changes had taken place in the varieties during the seed-multiplication process.

The control plantings showed no visible differences between the alfalfa seed lots increased in the southern European countries and the basic— foundation—seed from which they were grown.

Some of the red clover seeds were earlier in flowering and less vigorous than the parent seeds.

Plants of the lupine varieties grown from seed produced in the southern countries did not deviate from the control sample. The same was true for the vetches, except for an occasional seed lot that produced plants that were shorter, earlier flowering, and lighter green than those grown from the basic seed.

CARLTON S. GARRISON is Leader, Seed Production Investigations, Forage and Range Research Branch, Crops Research Division, Beltsville, Md.

RAYMOND J. BULA is a research agronomist in the Forage and Range Research Branch, Crops Research Division, of the Agricultural Research Service. He is stationed in Lafayette, Ind., where he conducts cooperative research work with Purdue University.

THE

TESTING

OF SEEDS

ψ ψ ψ ψ ψ ψ ψ ψ ψ ψ ψ ψ ψ ψ ψ ψ ψ ψ ψ ψ ψ ψ ψ ψ ψ ψ ψ ψ ψ ψ ψ ψ ψ ψ ψ ψ ψ ψ ψ ψ

The Science of

Seed Testing

OREN L. JUSTICE

ADULTERATION of seed used to be fairly common. Crop seeds were mixed with other kinds of less expensive seed or inert material so like the desirable seed that they were hard to detect.

Some European seedsmen screened and stained sand to the size and color of clover seeds, with which they mixed it. Expensive seeds, such as cauliflower, were adulterated with less expensive kinds that could not be distinguished by seed characteristics. Factories existed in England in which the adulterants were devitalized to avoid detection. To stop them, Parliament adopted the Adulterated Seeds Act in 1869.

We have many records of seed adulteration in the United States during 1890–1915. Common examples include sweetclover and black medic in alfalfa and red clover; Canada bluegrass in Kentucky bluegrass; and perennial ryegrass in meadow fescue or vice versa, depending on the difference in prices.

Screenings containing relatively high percentages of weed seeds were frequently used as adulterants.

Seeds of dodder, a parasitic pest, were such a common impurity in forage seeds that western European countries, Canada, and Argentina legislated against the practice. An examination of 873 samples of red clover and alfalfa seed by the Federal seed laboratory in 1906 showed that 30.6 percent of the samples contained dodder.

Analyses of 61 samples of low-quality red clover seeds imported into the United States in 1905 and 1906 revealed averages of 30 kinds of weed seeds per sample, 3,088 weed seeds per

407

ounce, 74 percent of pure seed, and dodder in 75 percent of the samples.

The sale of low-germinating seeds or dead seeds in Europe and America added to the uncertainties of crop production. The average germination of 12,454 packets of vegetable seeds collected from commission boxes and tested by the Federal seed laboratory in Washington from 1907 to 1910 was 60.5 percent. Mail-order seed was somewhat better; 6,117 samples purchased in 1911 gave an average germination of 77.5 percent.

These and other unscrupulous practices stimulated the study of seeds in many countries and States and led to the establishment of laboratories where seeds could be tested.

THE FIRST STATION for testing seed was established at Tharand in Saxony, Germany, in 1869, under the direction of Friedrich Nobbe.

E. Møller-Holst was planning a private seed-testing station in Copenhagen, Denmark, at the same time. It opened in 1871 and later was supported by public funds. By 1904, there were more than 130 seed-testing stations outside the United States.

Some farsighted men in the United States saw the need and began studies and examinations of seeds before the adoption of seed laws or establishment of seed laboratories.

The first laboratory for the examination of seed in this country was established at the Connecticut Agricultural Experiment Station in 1876 by E. H. Jenkins, who had studied in Germany and spent some time with Dr. Nobbe.

Seed testing was well established by 1900 in the U.S. Department of Agriculture, Connecticut, Maine, Massachusetts, Michigan, New York, and Vermont. Within the next 10 years, at least 10 other States were testing seeds. The Federal laboratory gave impetus to this movement by the establishment of several cooperative Federal-State laboratories in the South, Middle West, and Far West.

Forty-four States were operating seed-testing laboratories in 1930. Two more opened laboratories by 1941. Three States have found it more economical to have their samples tested by other laboratories on a fee basis than to maintain their own facilities.

Now there are well-equipped laboratories with trained personnel to test seed for purity, germination, seeds of noxious weeds, and moisture content. Several laboratories are prepared to make variety tests for control purposes. A few conduct tests for designated disease organisms.

FACTORS of seed quality include: Percentages of pure seeds, other crop seeds, weed seeds, and inert matter; percentages of germination and hard seeds when present; the rate of occurrence of designated seeds of noxious weeds; varietal purity; freedom from disease and disease organisms; moisture content; origin of production; and test weight (the bushel weight, hectoliter weight, 1,000-seed weight).

The chief aim in testing seeds is to assess the value of each sample or lot of seeds tested in accordance with the quality factors. Successful testing for them requires adequate facilities, a trained staff, uniform methods or procedures, and a research program that looks to the improvement of methods and procedures.

In developing standard testing procedures, primary consideration is given to providing methods by which accurate and reliable information may be obtained. This is essential if the test results are to be of value to the planter.

The second consideration is to provide methods by which uniform results may be obtained.

Because seed is a commodity of commerce, the testing procedures have to be standardized to the extent that results obtained on a sample in one laboratory can be repeated within accepted tolerances by another laboratory. Whether the original test is made by a private, commercial, State, or Federal analyst, the seed lot may be tested again in a distant State or in a foreign country. Financial transactions in seed, movement of seed in domestic and international commerce, and administration of seed laws would be greatly handicapped without confidence in the test results.

Finally, the methods must be practical. The degree of accuracy and uniformity of the results and the number of samples that can be tested are limited by the equipment and amount of work required in making the test, the number of days before the results are available, the kind of seed, and how well the seeds have been cleaned.

THE METHODS of testing seeds have been published under different titles and by various institutions and organizations and are referred to as rules.

The first rules in North America were prepared and published in 1897 in a circular entitled, "Rules and Apparatus for Seed Testing," by the Department of Agriculture as unofficial guides for seed analysts.

They specified the minimum size of samples for purity analysis and provided general instructions for making tests of germination. Equipment used for testing at that time was described and illustrated.

The publication was revised and expanded in 1904 to include methods of sampling seed lots, give more specific methods of testing for purity and germination, define the components of the purity analysis, and to specify the conditions for testing 63 kinds of agricultural and vegetable seeds for germination.

A group of persons from 16 States, the Department of Agriculture, and the Canada Department of Agriculture met in Washington, D.C., in 1908 to consider uniform methods of testing seeds and a model seed law. They formed an organization, which they named Association of Official Seed Analysts of North America. (It was shortened in 1939 to Association of Official Seed Analysts.)

One of the main functions of the association has been the preparation and adoption of official rules. Publication of the rules adopted by the association dates from 1917. Revisions since have been published by the New York Agricultural Experiment Station, the Department of Agriculture, and the association.

The Federal Seed Act of 1939 instructed the Secretary of Agriculture to develop and publish procedures for testing seeds to be used in the administration of the act. Consequently, appropriate procedures were published in 1940 as a part of the *Rules and Regulations Under the Federal Seed Act*. Revisions were made in 1946, 1950, 1956, and 1960.

The commercial seed analysts, through their organization, the Society of Commercial Seed Technologists, also assist in the formulation of the rules. To avoid conflict between the two sets of rules, Federal employees take part in the development of the rules of the Association of Official Seed Analysts. The amendments adopted by the Association of Official Seed Analysts are then incorporated as far as possible into the regulations under the Federal Seed Act.

To take advantage of developments in seed testing, the rules have been revised at least every 5 years since 1940. Amendments and minor revisions can be made each year if necessary. The association maintains a standing committee to review research data and other information that may lead to improvement in the rules.

Members of the committee are persons from the State seed laboratories, the Department of Agriculture, the Canada Department of Agriculture, and the Society of Commercial Seed Technologists.

The International Rules for Seed Testing provide uniform methods of evaluating the quality of seeds moving in foreign commerce. These rules, first published in 1931 in English, French, and German, have been revised five times. Before 1950, there were some important differences between the North

American rules and the international rules, but the major differences were compromised in 1953.

Many countries now use the international rules when testing for both domestic and foreign purposes. When requested, seed-testing stations belonging to the International Seed Testing Association sample seeds intended for foreign commerce and test the samples by the international rules for the issuance of certificates of quality.

MOST OF THE research on methods of testing seeds in this country has been done in the Federal seed laboratory and a few State laboratories, where testing is part of the agricultural experiment station or the agricultural college.

A research project on sampling and testing seeds was inaugurated by the Federal seed laboratory in 1948 under the Research and Marketing Act of 1946. Varying amounts of research on methods have been conducted since then in the Department. Much of the research conducted by the State agricultural experiment stations since 1956 has been coordinated on a regional basis.

The problems in seed technology are so numerous that a strong research program is needed. The nature of the problems calls for the services of specialists in the various disciplines of plant science as well as chemists, physicists, and engineers.

A well-balanced research program should seek to improve methods of testing, investigate the possibility of adapting new information or principles, and conduct research on which new methods of testing or evaluating quality can be based.

Research on seed purity has dealt primarily with three types of problems.

The first type relates to specifying differences between crop and weed seeds and inert matter, which in seed testing is any material other than seeds.

An illustration is wild garlic (*Allium vineale*) and wild onion (*A. canadense*), which are common in lawns, pastures, and hayfields. The aerial bulblets of wild garlic and wild onion, which function as seeds, often are found in agricultural seeds. It was known that the larger, undamaged bulblets could produce plants, but there was suspicion that the small, dry bulblets were dead. It was demonstrated that the small, desiccated bulblets and large bulblets, damaged at the basal end, are not viable. Acceptable methods of making separations have been developed.

The second type of research is illustrated by mechanical methods of separating inert matter from pure seed. In the grasses, a seedlike structure, consisting of either glumes and flower parts or glumes and a mature seed, is called a floret. The separation of filled and empty florets by conventional methods is difficult. Research on seed blowers and standard blowing techniques reduced considerably the time and tedium required to test some chaffy grasses. When testing seed by the standard blowing procedure, the blower is calibrated by using a prepared standard sample of the kind of seed being tested, in which the heavy and light seeds are stained opposing colors. The blower setting to be used is determined by blowing the standard sample until the best separation is obtained. This method has been adopted by the Association of Official Seed Analysts for testing seed of Kentucky bluegrass.

The third type of research in testing for purity is seed identification. Considerable attention has been given to illustrations, keys, and descriptions of seeds to aid in identification. Because of the minuteness of seed characteristics used for identification purposes, keys and descriptions by themselves are usually not sufficient. Photographs of seeds usually fall short of desired results.

Good, accurate drawings of seeds that can be duplicated by photography usually are better than direct photographs of the seeds. The plates prepared by Department of Agriculture workers, F. H. Hillman, Helen H.

Henry, Albina F. Musil, and Regina O. Hughes, are well known.

A combination of keys, descriptions, and plates, supported by a good seed herbarium, provide excellent facilities for identifying seeds.

As commerce in seeds has expanded over the years, the number of kinds that the analyst must identify has increased greatly. This is particularly true in a country having such a vast range of growing conditions as the United States. The importation of seeds from many parts of the world has magnified the problems in identification of seeds.

Research on germination has been concerned largely with dormancy. A seed that does not germinate in a properly conducted test may be alive or dead. If it is alive, it is dormant.

Because many kinds of crop seeds are dormant when tested, considerable research has been concerned with finding practical methods of evaluating samples with dormant seeds. Cereal and grass seeds have been the subject of many of these investigations. Samples suspected of dormancy are frequently tested by the method for nondormant seeds and the method for dormant seeds. Duplicate testing in this way is expensive; testing by only one method may give incomplete germination.

Unless there is a fair degree of correlation between germination tests in the laboratory and field stands, the germination test would have little value.

In the early days of seed testing, practically any seed that produced a radicle—first root—was regarded as having germinated.

Tests conducted in the Federal seed laboratory by W. L. Goss as early as 1915 showed that weak and defective sprouts did not develop into plants. Laboratory results from 292 samples of crimson clover seeds were 10 percent higher than results in the greenhouse. It is likely that differences between laboratory and field tests would have been greater.

Considerable research in the United States and Canada since that time has gone into evaluation of seedlings. More research has been conducted on the garden bean than on any other single crop. The research has been fruitful in that it has resulted in classifying as abnormal the seedlings that are weak and defective. It also has led to the establishment of specific guides for the separation of normal and abnormal seedlings. Problems remain, however.

The time seeds need to germinate is an important consideration. The germination of radish seed usually is complete by the end of the fifth day of test. Some grasses require up to 42 days for completion of the test. Reduction of the test period would be desirable. Determination of viability by chemical tests, acceleration of germination at increased temperatures, stimulation with chemicals, and excision of embryos have been investigated as means of making quick tests. No completely reliable method of determining viability by quick tests has yet been developed.

The planting value of hard seeds in a few leguminous crops has been studied. Seed analysts do not have to concern themselves with the value of hard seed, but they must determine the number of hard seeds that may remain at the conclusion of the germination test.

Varying numbers of seeds of some grasses are so dormant when tested that they fail to germinate by established procedures. Dormant seeds are alive, but little information is available about their planting value. To evaluate seed lots containing dormant seeds properly, analysts and control officials alike need to know more about the planting value of firm, ungerminated seed in different crops.

RESEARCH on factors of quality of seeds other than purity and germination has been limited.

Some research on the vigor of corn has led to a method of detecting weak lots which may result in crop failures under adverse weather and soil conditions. Attempts at developing a vigor test for garden peas have been less successful.

Additional information is needed on methods of determining variety by examination of seeds and seedlings. Growing tests are expensive to make, and the value of the results often drops in proportion to the time required to complete the tests.

Improvements of methods of determining the kind and incidence of disease organisms on seeds and ways to detect seed treatments are needed.

We now have greater understanding with respect to the use and application of tolerances to test results. It is not likely that two samples drawn from the same seed lot or from a larger master sample will be exactly the same. Replicate test results consequently can be expected to vary. The variations can be calculated and are called tolerances. Early tolerances were little more than estimates, but statisticians have been working on them over the years to put them on sound statistical bases.

Differences in test results on the same lot of seed often can be traced to lack of uniformity among the different bags. Seedsmen have been informed of their responsibility in this connection, and research agencies are seeking methods by which seed lots can be reliably mixed to uniformity.

Statisticians have developed minimum latitudes of variation between bags for the different quality factors, making possible homogeneity tests by which bag-to-bag variation can be determined. The principal weakness in this procedure is the large amount of time required to make tests on individual-bag samples.

THE EDUCATION and training of seed analysts depend on several factors, including the number and kinds of crop seeds the analyst is expected to test, the area from which the seeds come, the kinds of tests they are expected to make, and the supervision they have.

Analysts in large laboratories often work under supervision and are expected to perform only one phase of testing, such as tests of purity or germi-nation. Analysts in some small, private laboratories must be prepared to make various tests on any submitted sample, without supervision. Various intermediate arrangements exist.

Analysts who must assume the responsibility for the tests should have earned at least a college degree in one of the plant sciences, preferably botany. After his college training, the prospective analyst should work under the guidance of an experienced technician. Analysts having less responsibility and working under direct supervision may not need the college background; without it, however, the chances are greatly reduced that the analyst will be able to cope with new and difficult situations.

Many a seed analyst has received his basic training by working as an apprentice under an experienced technician, completing all or part of a college education, followed by supervised laboratory experience, and studying seed testing while working toward a degree.

In large laboratories, where specialization is possible, the purity analyst should have a working knowledge of plant taxonomy and some familiarity with the plant diseases that may be detected on dry seeds. The purity analyst must know a large variety of crop and weed seeds, including the variation in characteristics of the commonly tested crop seeds and associated weed seeds. Through experience, the analyst learns the differences between seeds and inert matter in species that produce empty seeds.

The germination analyst should have training in plant physiology and a familiarity with symptoms of plant diseases. Alertness and an awareness that low germination may be the result of improper testing are prime considerations. He must recognize dormant seeds in the test, as distinguished from dead seeds, and use methods that will promote germination. Testing for variety, health of seed, seedling vigor, and moisture content requires the services of persons who have had special training in the area of work to be undertaken.

C. H. Lawshe and L. E. Albright, of Purdue University, developed tests for the selection of purity analysts by measuring adaptability, manual dexterity, and visual acuity. The tests are described in a 14-page brochure published by the Purdue University Agricultural Experiment Station, Lafayette, Ind., under the title, "A Manual for the Selection of Competent Seed Analysts."

Training programs have been instituted at Iowa State University, Mississippi State University, Oregon State College, and Purdue University. Before 1940, many supervisors in Federal, State, and commercial laboratories received their training at the Federal seed laboratory in Washington, on an apprenticeship basis. From 1940 to 1950, Federal analysts conducted regional, 1-week short courses at State and Federal laboratories. This in-service instruction was open to all analysts working in State, commercial, and private laboratories. Demands became so great that in 1951 a Federal employee was assigned full time to instruction work. Short courses have been held throughout the country.

LABORATORIES for testing seeds may be Federal, State, commercial, or private.

There are Federal laboratories at Beltsville, Md., New Brunswick, N.J., Montgomery, Ala., Kansas City, Mo., and Minneapolis, Minn. There is a Federal-State laboratory in Sacramento, Calif. These laboratories are maintained to administer the import and interstate provisions of the Federal Seed Act. They also conduct a limited amount of testing for the import and export trade and for Government agencies.

All States but three operate one or more seed-testing laboratories, which exist primarily to implement the administration of State seed laws and to test samples for farmers and seedsmen. Commercial seed laboratories test samples received from any person who desires the service on a fee basis. Some commercial laboratories have standing contracts with seed firms. There are about 30 such laboratories in the country.

Many seed firms maintain their own private laboratories to perform testing services incidental to their operations. Most employ one analyst, but a few are large enough to permit specialization of work.

THREE organizations have helped to further testing in the United States.

They are the Association of Official Seed Analysts, whose members work in Government laboratories in the United States and Canada; the International Seed Testing Association, whose secretariat is in Europe and whose members are national governments; and the Society of Commercial Seed Technologists, whose members are Americans and Canadians.

The main objectives of the three organizations are basically the same: The development and adoption of standard methods of testing seeds, promotion of research leading to the improvement of seed testing, and exchange of information through meetings and publications.

Since 1950 the Association of Official Seed Analysts and the International Seed Testing Association have worked closely together. The differences that previously existed between the American-Canadian *Rules* and the International *Rules* have been largely eliminated. A realization of the need for uniform testing procedures on an international basis and a willingness to compromise differences have made this possible.

OREN L. JUSTICE *is a seed botanist and Head of the Testing Section, Seed Branch, Grain Division, Agricultural Marketing Service, U.S. Department of Agriculture. He holds advanced degrees from Ohio University and Cornell. Dr. Justice is author of numerous articles on seed dormancy and seed testing.*

In Testing, the Sample
Is All-Important

A. S. CARTER

WE MEASURE the quality of seed by testing a representative sample of a lot. Often it is small compared to the lot itself. The test sample used to determine the content of pure seed of the 20 thousand pounds in a carload of Kentucky bluegrass weighs only 1 gram—454 grams weigh a pound.

Yet a test of this small sample is dependable if the carload of seed was uniformly blended and if the sample is properly drawn and handled.

Seed is sampled, examined, and tested repeatedly during normal production, processing, and distribution.

A test of a sample obtained by a country buyer determines the price paid to the grower. Samples drawn before and during processing determine the processing needed to make the seed marketable. One or more additional samples are tested to obtain labeling information before seed is offered for sale under a label. If the seed is certified, seed-certification inspectors also sample and test the seed at least once. Finally, State and Federal control officials very likely sample and test the seed after it is offered for sale to determine whether the seed and its labeling meet applicable laws.

Time spent testing carelessly drawn samples may be time wasted; the test is no more accurate than the sample. Much of the variations in tests made by different seed laboratories and analysts can be attributed to samples that are not representative of the lot.

The Rules for Testing Seeds developed by the Association of Official Seed Analysts and the rules followed in the administration of the Federal Seed Act include rules for sampling. The rules are followed by official seed certification and commercial laboratories in North America and are similar to the rules of the International Seed Testing Association commonly used when sampling and testing seed that is to be shipped in international commerce.

OFFICIAL sampling rules provide for using a trier, or probe, long enough to reach all areas in a seed bag. The trier must be designed to remove an equal volume of seed from each area through which it travels. A trier with no partitions in the seed chamber must be inserted into the bags horizontally. It is hard to get samples of seeds that are not freeflowing, such as certain chaffy grasses, with a trier, but one can thrust the hand into the seed and remove representative portions.

The trier that meets official requirements is a hollow tube that is pointed at one end and open at the other and has a continuous slot on one side. It is inserted into the bag horizontally with the slot down. The slot is turned up to fill, the trier is removed, and the seed is allowed to run into the sample container. The proper use of this trier will give one a representative sample.

Double-tube triers often are used, but it is doubtful whether they are superior to the single tube in sampling bagged seed. Many double-tube triers are hard to use. In those that have cross ribs, seeds may be pushed along with the trier so that too many seeds from places near the point of insertion are included in the sample.

For small seeds in bags, such as alfalfa and timothy, the trier need not be more than three-eighths inch in diameter. For larger seeds, such as cereals and soybeans, the diameter should be $7/8$ inch to 1 inch.

Seed stored in bins can be sampled best by using a standard grain probe with partitions.

Bulk seed also can be sampled as it is being transferred to the bin after cleaning or bulking. That is done by removing representative portions from the moving stream of seeds falling into the bin. At intervals, a pan is moved across the entire stream with one motion. It is necessary to do it that way because seeds may segregate in the stream.

Certain instruments and methods are not recommended because they do not provide an accurate sample. A 6- or 9-inch tapered trier, frequently referred to as a thief, often is used because it is easy to use. The thief trier is inserted upward through the fabric of the bag, and seed is allowed to run into the hand or a sample container. It removes seeds only from a place immediately inside the bag and above the point of insertion. It cannot draw a representative sample.

A standard tube (or stick) trier, even one with a sleeve, inserted vertically in a bag gives a sample with a disproportionately large number of seeds from the top of the bag near the place of insertion, because the pull of gravity is greater than the slight sideward pressure exerted by seeds deep in the bag. A trier should not be inserted in a bag vertically unless the trier has partitions to lessen the downward movement of seed.

SAMPLING would be easy if seed could be blended so that it is completely uniform. Then one could take a test sample from one place in one bag or bulk lot. Complete uniformity seldom is achieved, however, and the sampler must always bear in mind that the lot may not be absolutely uniform. Many bags and many parts of bulk lots therefore must be probed to be sure that the composite sample of the lot is representative.

The Rules for Testing Seeds require the sampling of each bag in a lot consisting of five bags or fewer and (for larger lots) the sampling of five bags plus 10 percent of the bags in the lot. Regardless of size of the lot, it is not necessary to sample more than 30 bags, because the increase in precision

achieved by sampling more than 30 bags is not enough to justify the extra work.

The sampler actually attempts to get a representative sample of a lot of seed. A lot of seed has been defined in the Federal Seed Act regulations and in many State laws as a definite amount of seed, identified by a lot number, every portion or bag of which is uniform, within permitted tolerances, for the factors that appear on the label.

The lot may be large or small. Usually the actual size is not limited, except that it must be reasonably uniform. The establishment of maximums for lot size has been considered but never officially adopted because one distributor may blend a carload of seed to greater uniformity than another could achieve with a much smaller amount.

Wholesalers often blend a lot of seed, and fractions of the lot are shipped to retailers. That is a good test of blending efficiency, because a test of the fraction, or a part of it, has to agree, within specified tolerances, with the label. Otherwise it will be classed as mislabeled.

OTHER THINGS being equal, a large sample is more representative of a seed lot than a small sample. A sample must be large enough to permit a test and retest.

The following amounts usually are sufficient: Two ounces of the fine grasses, whiteclover, and all seeds of similar size; 5 ounces of red clover, lespedeza, bromegrass, flax, and seeds of similar size; 1 pound of sudangrass, sorghums, proso, and seeds of similar size; 2.5 pounds of cereal, vetch, and the larger seeds; 800 seeds of vegetable seeds, which require a germination test only.

Additional seeds must be available if varietal trials are to be conducted in the field or greenhouse.

If these sampling procedures are followed, the bulk sample submitted to the laboratory will be larger than the amount needed for testing. The method used to obtain the working sample from the bulk sample submitted will determine how well the test results describe the seed under consideration.

The International Seed Testing Association studied several methods of subdividing samples and found the use of a good mechanical divider is better than the halving method.

In the halving method, the sample is placed on a clean piece of paper or oilcloth, mixed with a spatula and rolled on the paper or cloth, and marked into quarters with a spatula. Opposite quarters are discarded. This process is followed until the final sample is about the size required for analysis. This method theoretically should yield representative subdivisions, but in practice it does not. It is not recommended for field or laboratory use.

Mechanical dividers produce repeated working samples that are about as uniform as one can expect from true random samples.

Several kinds of mechanical dividers are available. The Boerner type is used widely. It is available for small and large seeds. Any riffle-type mechanical divider is superior to hand methods for reducing the bulk sample to the working sample.

Some State seed laws require that the inspector divide the sample as soon as it is drawn and leave a portion with the retailer. This provision is satisfactory if a good mechanical divider is used to divide the sample, but the shortcomings of hand division make the use of this method in the field or in the laboratory questionable.

The warehouse is a poor place to subdivide a sample. Warehouses are apt to be cold or hot or drafty—not good places in which to subdivide seed samples. It is much better, when the rules allow it, to take the entire sample to the laboratory where mechanical dividers are available.

THE PERSON who does the sampling needs to be trained in the methods of obtaining a true sample. He should have proper equipment.

In drawing a composite sample to determine the quality of a lot, the labeling on each bag sampled must be examined to be sure that all bags belong to the same lot. Each trierful should be examined to detect noticeable variation before combining. If variations from bag to bag are noted, individual bag samples should be drawn to determine the extent of the lack of uniformity in the lot. When the sample is drawn, the sampler must identify the containers into which it is placed before he draws another sample. He must be careful that the sample is not contaminated with dirt or other material.

The identity of each sample must be maintained throughout the sampling and distribution process. Most official samplers put an inspection slip inside the container with the seed and also identify it by writing a description on the outside of the package. Records accompanying the sample must be complete so there will be no difficulty in associating the final report with the "definite quantity of seed" that has been sampled.

Some farmers prefer to sell seed at wholesale and let the seedsmen worry about testing and labeling it. Others prefer to process and market the seed they produce.

Because most State laws require farmers to label seed offered for retail sale, farmers often are required to draw samples of seed lots and submit them to commercial or State laboratories for testing. Other farmers get their homegrown seed tested to determine its planting value.

Farmers usually do not have triers and mechanical dividers and other equipment. They can draw a fairly representative sample, however, by taking handfuls of seed from different places in different bags in the lot, or in different parts of the bulk lot, mixing this seed together, and taking handfuls of the composite. This sample will not be so accurate as one drawn with an approved trier by a professional inspector, but it will be acceptable.

Farmers may fail to submit satisfactory samples because they sample only one bag or too few bags or too few places in each bag; their samples may be too small for a complete test; samples of bins of seed often are taken from the place most easily reached, instead of from different places and depths in the bin.

Farmers often do not identify samples properly as to lot number or other designation when they send them to the laboratory.

So the sample is all-important. It should be drawn by a trained person using good equipment and procedures. It should be subsequently subdivided with the best mechanical divider available and with utmost care. Commercial samplers and official inspectors should always be warned that the sampler of seed has someone's reputation and well-being in his two hands.

A. S. CARTER, *Director of Seed Control and State Chemist Services, Biochemistry Department, Purdue University, is concerned with the administration of the Indiana seed, feed, and fertilizer laws. He has conducted research in seed technology, including the sampling of seeds.*

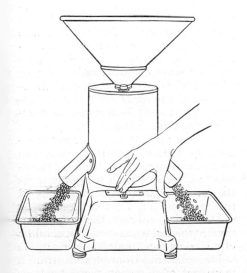

A seed mixer and divider, which is used to reduce a laboratory bulk sample to a working-sample size.

556888°—61——28

Testing Seeds for Purity and Origin

ALBINA F. MUSIL

THE SCIENTIST who is called on to analyze seeds may have to determine the purity of a sample of seeds, examine it for seeds of noxious weeds, find out its origin, and ascertain the varietal purity of the seed stock.

The person who submits the seeds to the laboratory for test usually specifies the services he desires.

The purity test determines what proportion of the sample is pure crop seed and what proportion is seeds of weeds, seeds of other crops, and inert matter.

Assuming that the sample he receives is of adequate size and is representative of the seed lot, the seed analyst or technician reduces the bulk sample he receives to a smaller sample on which the test is to be made, usually referred to as the working sample.

Most kinds of seeds are mixed and divided by means of a mechanical divider, a device that mixes and divides the sample into two parts. The dividing process is repeated until the desired size of sample is obtained. Samples of seeds that are not free flowing, such as cotton and certain chaffy grasses, must be divided by hand. The seed is poured into a pile on the table, mixed thoroughly, and halved repeatedly until the amount is right.

The minimum weights to be used for working samples of agricultural seeds, vegetable seeds, and certain herb seeds are prescribed in the Rules for Testing Seeds, formulated by the Association of Official Seed Analysts, and the rules and regulations under the Federal Seed Act.

The amount varies with the size and nature of the seed to be tested. Seeds as small as redtop (*Agrostis alba*), which averages about 11 thousand seeds per gram, require 0.5 of a gram; Kentucky bluegrass (*Poa pratensis*), averaging about 4,800 seeds per gram, requires 1 gram; hairy vetch (*Vicia villosa*), with approximately 36 seeds per gram, requires 100 grams; field pea (*Pisum sativum*), with only about 4 seeds per gram, requires 500 grams.

To avoid errors due to any hand manipulation, the bulk sample is reduced to the nearest minimum weight specified in the rules. The working sample may exceed the prescribed weight but should never be less.

After the bulk sample has been reduced to the prescribed size, the working sample is weighed and taken to a workboard, where it is examined for trueness to name. The sample is then separated into its four components: Pure seed, other crop seeds, weed seeds, and inert matter.

Because of the small size of the units that make up most seed samples, the separation must usually be made under magnification. A hand lens of 6 × or 7 × magnification is suitable for most samples. The lower magnification of an ordinary reading glass is adequate for large seeds. The technician must be able to identify correctly every particle in the sample.

The component parts are weighed on an analytical balance that can weigh accurately to three or four decimal places. The less sensitive torsion balance may be used for large seeds, such as beans or peas. The percentage of each component is calculated on the total combined weight, and the kind and number of other crop seeds and weed seeds are recorded.

As a check against possible loss of material in the process of making the separation, the combined weights of the components and the original weight of the sample are compared. Another test is made if there is an appreciable difference between the two weights.

The evaluation of damaged or undeveloped seeds may present difficulties. Seeds of crops and weeds may be broken or otherwise injured, or the seed unit may be of such nature that it is difficult to determine visually whether a grain or embryo is present. The technician must determine whether they should be classified as "good" seeds or as inert matter. The standards for evaluating crop and weed seeds of this nature differ in some important respects. To assure uniformity in interpretation among seed technicians, the rules give specific instructions for the classification of questionable units.

A damaged crop seed, such as a broken alfalfa seed, obviously should not be counted as two seeds instead of one. In such cases, the rules provide that pieces of crop seeds larger than one-half the original size are to be classified as pure seed; pieces one-half the original size or less are classified as inert matter.

The broken part that is classified as pure seed may or may not produce a plant. Its planting value will be determined later in the germination test. The determination of potential germinability of agricultural seeds is not considered a function of the purity test.

The rules provide that diseased agricultural seeds shall be classified as pure seed. Those whose contents are replaced by fungus bodies—such as ergot or other sclerotia, smut balls, or nematode galls—however, are classified as inert matter.

Damaged weed seeds require a somewhat different interpretation. Because weed seeds are not tested for germination, as agricultural seeds are, the seed sample is not penalized by classifying as "good" weed seeds the seeds that are too damaged or undeveloped to grow.

The rules specify the conditions under which a weed-seed unit shall be classified as inert matter.

The following examples illustrate a few cases of damaged weed seeds or seedlike structures that would be classified as inert matter: Hulled dock (*Rumex*), more than half of whose embryo is missing; seeds of dodder (*Cuscuta*) that contain no embryo; bulblets of wild onion (*Allium*) that show damage at the basal end or are devoid of husk and pass through a ¹⁄₁₃-inch round-hole sieve; immature florets of quackgrass (*Agropyron repens*), in which the caryopsis (grain) is less than one-third the length of the palea; empty hulls of seeds (achenes), such as the sunflower (*Helianthus*) or the docks (*Rumex*).

The absence of embryo or endosperm may have to be determined by dissection or by examination over a diaphanoscope. A diaphanoscope is a device in which a strong beam of light is directed upward against a pane of clear glass, over which the seeds are examined with a hand lens. A light intensity of about 200 foot-candles is usually strong enough to penetrate the hull or seedcoat of most kinds of seeds.

Special techniques sometimes are used to establish trueness to name of the sample.

We do not attempt to distinguish individual seeds of perennial ryegrass (*Lolium perenne*) and Italian ryegrass (*L. multiflorum*). The possible diagnostic structures, such as awns and pubescence, usually are removed or damaged in harvesting and cleaning to such an extent that the seeds are indistinguishable. The fluorescence test is used exclusively to detect seeds of Italian ryegrass and hybrids in lots of perennial ryegrass or to determine perennial ryegrass in Italian ryegrass.

The fluorescence test involves a germination test. Four hundred seeds are taken from the pure seed fraction of the purity test and germinated on filter paper. The seedlings are examined under ultraviolet light, and the percentage of fluorescence and nonfluorescence is determined.

The results are then subjected to either of two formulas to calculate the proportion of each kind in the sample. The first is: The percentage of perennial ryegrass is 1.0526 times the percentage of nonfluorescence times the percentage of pure ryegrass divided by the percentage of germination.

The second formula is: The percentage of pure ryegrass or hybrids, or both, equals the percentage of pure ryegrass times the percentage of fluorescence minus the sum of 0.0526 times the percentage of nonfluorescence divided by the percentage of germination.

The formulas take into consideration a small percentage of short-lived perennial plants that may normally be present in perennial ryegrass.

We have no way to tell individual seeds of white-blossom sweetclover (*Melilotus alba*) from yellow-blossom sweetclover (*M. officinalis*). Yellow-blossom sweetclover produces a variable proportion of seeds that are spotted—often faintly—with purple. They are referred to as mottled seeds. As far as we know, the varieties of white-blossom sweetclover grown in the United States do not produce mottled seeds. When mottled seeds are observed in a sample labeled "white-

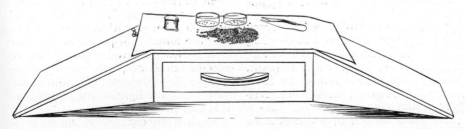

A workboard, which elevates the working area above the level of the tabletop and so minimizes fatigue of the eyes, neck, and shoulders of the technician who makes an analysis of the purity of seed.

blossom sweetclover," it can be assumed that seeds of yellow-blossom sweetclover are present. Most samples from plantings in fields and greenhouses have indicated that about four times as many yellow-blossom plants will be produced as there are mottled seeds. We conclude therefrom that each 1 percent of mottled seed represents 4 percent of yellow-blossom sweetclover.

If a sample is submitted as white-blossom sweetclover, a mottled-seed test is made to determine the possible presence of yellow-blossom sweetclover. A minimum of 400 seeds, taken from the pure seed fraction of the purity test, is examined. The entire 5-gram working sample is examined in some laboratories. A hand lens or a higher magnification may be necessary to detect the fainter markings.

The rules provide the following formula for the determination of percentage of yellow-blossom sweetclover in a sample of white-blossom sweetclover: Weight of mottled seeds (in grams) times 4 times percent of pure sweetclover.

Several new varieties of yellow-blossom sweetclover have been introduced. Some of them show great variation in content of mottled seed. There is strong evidence that the area and year of production strongly influence the percentage of mottled seed. These findings indicate that our formula for determining the extent of an admixture should be considered only an estimate rather than an accurate analysis. A field or greenhouse test should be made when an accurate determination is required.

PELLETED, or coated, seed may contain single seeds or several seeds each. The pellets are designed to make small or irregular seed units easier to plant. The coating material may be inert material or it may contain some fertilizer or fungicide.

The rules do not prescribe specific procedures for purity tests for pelleted seed. Since the coating material is not a part of the true seed or its accessory structures, it is interpreted that the inert coating material should be removed and added to other inert matter that may be present in the sample. The sample accordingly is reduced to the prescribed working-sample size and weighed. The coating is removed by soaking for a few minutes. The seed is then blotted dry and weighed again. The difference between this weight and the original weight is added to the total inert matter in the sample.

TESTING SEEDS of poorly cleaned samples or seeds of chaffy grasses takes work and time.

Several helpful devices are available. A set of graduated sieves is useful for separating samples that consist of particles of various sizes into size groups. The groups must still be examined under magnification, but the grading of the particles saves a great deal of handpicking.

The grain of many kinds of grasses is enclosed in a pair of chaffy or hardened scales (lemma and palea), which usually are opaque. The technician must examine every seed unit in the sample to determine if it contains a grain or if the structure is empty. This may be done by light pressure with forceps or by examination over strong light—a time-consuming procedure, especially for the small-seeded kinds, such as bluegrass.

Two mechanical aids are available for testing chaffy grasses—the vertical airblast seed blower or separator and a diaphanoscope.

Several types of seed blowers have been developed. A simple form consists of a uniform flow of air (up to about 6 pounds) with a valve to regulate the amount of pressure. The airflow is directed upward into a tube of specified diameter, which contains the sample. Two traps near the top of the tube catch the lightweight material as it is blown upward.

By carefully controlling the air pressure, one can make several blowings, which separate the empty and lightweight units from the heavy seeds. The first blowing usually consists entirely of empty florets. The second and third

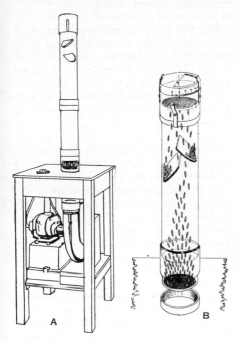

A. One of the simpler types of seed blower used as an aid in separating empty florets from filled florets in making a purity test of grass seeds. B. Detail of tube of blower, showing principle of operation.

blowings may consist in part of the heavier empty florets and the florets that contain small or poorly developed grains. The residue in the tube usually consists of the heavy, filled florets. The separate blowings are then examined under magnification to remove all empty florets from the filled florets. This is done on the workboard by light pressure with forceps or by examination over a diaphanoscope.

The florets of grasses are produced in clusters, called spikelets, which may have many flowers as in ryegrass, or may be single flowered, as in redtop.

Not all of the florets of the many-flowered spikelets may contain grains. The mature spikelets in some species break apart readily, and the empty florets are removed in processing. In other species, the spikelets do not break apart easily, and the seed sample may contain a variable proportion of spikelets that contain both filled and empty florets. These are referred to as multiple units.

The rules enumerate certain species in which the presence of the attached empty florets is negligible and the multiple units need not be separated in the purity test. These include blue-grass (*Poa*), rhodesgrass (*Chloris gayana*), bluestem (*Andropogon*), gramagrass (*Bouteloua*), and oats (*Avena*).

The separation of multiple units for the purity test may be exceedingly tedious in the following species: Creeping red fescue (*Festuca rubra*), chewings fescue (*F. rubra* var. *commutata*), crested wheatgrass (*Agropyron desertorum*), orchardgrass (*Dactylis glomerata*), and intermediate wheatgrass (*Agropyron intermedium*).

A modified procedure has been adopted in the rules for testing them. All multiple units that contain one or more grains are weighed with the pure-seed single florets. Then they are removed and weighed separately. If the weight of the multiple units is less than 5 percent of the total pure seed, the empty florets are removed manually and added to the other inert matter in the sample; if greater than 5 percent, the florets are not separated, but a prescribed portion of their weight is added to the percent of pure seed and the remainder is added to the inert matter. The specific factor that is applied is determined by the percentage of single florets present in the sample, as well as the kind of seed under consideration.

For example: A sample of orchard-grass was composed of 60 percent of fertile single florets, 30 percent of multiple units, and 7.5 percent of inert matter. The factor for 60 percent of single florets in orchardgrass is 81 percent.

Thus, 81 percent of 30 would be added to the pure seed fraction (60+24.3), a total of 84.3 percent of pure seed. The remainder of the multiple units

(30—24.3) or 5.7, would be added to the inert fraction (7.5+5.7), a total of 13.2 percent of inert matter.

The classification of incidental "other crop" seeds in a purity test often poses a problem.

Because of the wide diversity of climate, soils, topography, and prevailing cultural practices, a plant that is a valuable economic crop in one situation may be a weed elsewhere. The disposition of such seeds in a purity test may depend somewhat on the use for which the seed lot is intended. A plant that may be valuable in pastures may be objectionable in a lawn—perennial ryegrass (*Lolium perenne*) and black medic (*Medicago lupulina*), for example. Sweetclover, once considered a weed, now is classified generally as a crop seed.

The rules under the Federal Seed Act list the kinds of agricultural and vegetable seeds that are to be classified as weed seeds when occurring incidentally in imported samples of agricultural and vegetable seeds. In determining whether a certain kind of seed should be classified as a crop or a weed, the technician must be guided by the accepted practice in the State where the seed is to be sold.

THE TERM "weed seeds" includes seeds of all plants generally recognized as weeds.

From an agricultural viewpoint, weeds fall into two categories: Relatively harmless plants, usually annuals, that are easily controlled by ordinary cultural methods and are objectionable only as they occur in quantity; and weeds that are objectionable or detrimental to the land. The latter are noxious weeds. Noxious weeds not only produce seed but also spread by underground roots or stems, which, when well established, are highly destructive and difficult to eradicate or control by ordinary good cultural methods.

Each State seed law contains a list of noxious-weed seeds, a combined total of about 150 species. The Federal Seed Act recognizes these kinds as noxious weeds in interstate commerce. A separate list of noxious-weed seeds is recognized under the Federal Seed Act for imported seed. The lists are subject to change as conditions warrant.

The test for seeds of noxious weeds is made on a larger amount of seed than that prescribed for the purity test. The reason is plain. Seeds of a noxious weed, such as dodder, might be present in a lot of red clover, but fail to appear in the small 5-gram working sample of the purity test.

The rules specify the minimum amount to be examined for the noxious-weed test for the different kinds of agricultural seeds. The quantity varies with the relative size and nature of the seed from 25 grams for the very small-seeded kinds up to 500 grams for large seeds. The laboratory sample is reduced to the prescribed size by means of a mechanical mixer and divider.

The test consists of removing the noxious-weed seeds only. The seeds are counted, and the number of each kind per unit weight (grams) of the sample examined is recorded. Federal seed laws and those of most States require that the number of each kind per pound be stated.

The following conversion table is convenient for converting from the gram basis to pound or ounce.

Size of sample examined (grams)	Factor to be used for number of seeds per pound	Factor to be used for number of seeds per ounce
25	18. 0	1. 14
35	13. 0	0. 81
50	9. 0	0. 57
100	4. 5	0. 29

Thus, if two seeds of dodder were found in a sample of 50 grams, 18 seeds per pound would be reported.

The seed technician making the noxious-weed test is guided by the list published in the laws or regulations of the State where the seed is to be sold.

The test consists of the removal of seeds of the kinds specified for that particular State only. The individual requesting the test usually specifies the

State or States for which the information is desired, or he may request a test for noxious weeds for all States. In the

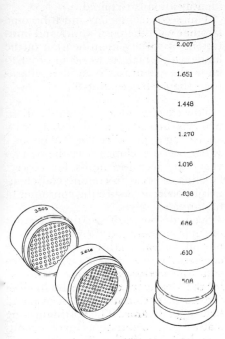

Graduated sieves may serve as an aid in making a purity separation.

latter instance, all seeds designated as noxious would be removed from the sample.

If a noxious-weed test is desired for export purposes, the exporter would request an examination for certain weeds only, such as dodder.

The importance of the origin of agricultural seeds is recognized in State and Federal seed laws that require the origin of specified seeds to be stated on the label attached to the seed.

The Federal Seed Act requires that imported seed of alfalfa and red clover be stained in certain proportions with colors that indicate the origin or general adaptation of the seed in the United States.

The place of origin of seeds of forest trees may affect the form, rate of growth, and even survival after planting. A transfer of altitude of 500 feet

or more is known to be unfavorable to some kinds. We know of no method of determining the origin by an inspection of the seed. Some States have enacted laws regulating the labeling and sale of tree seeds with regard to geographic origin.

Some agricultural crops produced in one locality have characteristics that are a result of temperature, rainfall, and altitude. Some varieties often are grown to the exclusion of other varieties because of their adaptation—such as winter hardiness—to local conditions. Sometimes plants grown from seed produced in one region may be susceptible to a disease that is prevalent in another region, and certain areas may have diseases that would be harmful if introduced into another region. It is important therefore to know the origin of certain crop seeds.

An experienced seed technician often can determine the origin of agricultural seeds by carefully examining extraneous material, such as weed seeds and other crop seeds, that may be present in the sample.

The size of the sample to be examined for origin cannot be specified definitely. The usual practice is to continue the examination until conclusive evidence is found—maybe in a small amount of seed or maybe in the entire sample submitted. If no evidence is found in about a pound of such seed as alfalfa or red clover, however, it would appear that little or no useful purpose would be served by further search.

The correct evaluation of the impurities in a sample requires a wide knowledge of plant distribution and good judgment on the part of the seed technician. An illustration: A lot of alfalfa seed offered for sale in the North as a winter-hardy variety was tested for origin. Examination of the seed disclosed the presence of a few seeds of silversheath knotweed (*Polygonum argyrocoleon*), a plant that is not known to occur in the northern latitudes. Its presence, together with other evidence, established the fact that the alfalfa seed was of southwestern origin and not the winter-hardy variety it was claimed to be.

Varietal identification by seed characters has certain possibilities, the limits of which the skilled technician learns to recognize.

The problem can be considered in three parts.

First are the varieties that can be identified accurately both in the bulk and as individual seeds. This can be illustrated by Kentucky bluegrass (*Poa pratensis*) and Merion Kentucky bluegrass (*P. pratensis* var. Merion). Size and color are not reliable criteria because of the variation that may be evident in Kentucky bluegrass from different areas of production. The outstanding distinguishing features are shape of seed (floret), as it appears in outline in lateral view, and texture and nerves of the lemma.

Another example is Highland bentgrass (*Agrostis tenuis* var. Highland bent). This minute seed is distinguishable from Colonial bentgrass and Astoria bentgrass, both of which are varieties of *Agrostis tenuis*. In this case, the main distinguishing features are shape of seed in dorsal view and the character of the apex of the palea.

Striate lespedeza (*Lespedeza striata*) and Kobe lespedeza (*L. striata* var. Kobe) can be distinguished by size and color.

Second are varieties that are distinguishable in the bulk, although not all of the individual seeds can be recognized with certainty. Such separations are useful as indicators of a mixture of varieties and may produce sufficient evidence to detect a mislabeled sample. Certain varieties of oats, soybeans, sorghums, and others are among them. Such groups have many agronomic varieties when considered on a countrywide basis. Many laboratories work with only a few local varieties, however, and it is often possible to identify the individual seeds accurately.

Third are varieties that appear to have no diagnostic features of the seeds, either in bulk or as individual seeds. Among them are varieties of such plants as alfalfa, red clover, certain varieties of oats, and soybeans. A growing test should be made if varietal identification is required.

The seed technician must become familiar with the possibilities and limitations of variety identification of the kinds with which he works in order to know the extent to which such separations should be attempted.

THE SCIENCE of seed identification, which is such an essential part of purity analysis, is a specialized field of botany. It has been developed over the past 50 years to meet the needs for correct labeling of seeds in commercial channels in order to assure the consumer of high-quality seeds.

Seeds do not vary greatly as a result of environment, and the characteristic morphological features remain fairly constant. It has been possible to illustrate the seeds and prepare seed keys for the identification of species in all of the more important genera of crop and field-weed plants. The distinguishing features between the species of a genus may be fairly similar. The differences often are minute or obscure. A wide-field stereoscopic microscope equipped to give magnifications of about 20 X and 40 X is essential for viewing the finer structures.

Most agricultural plants belong to one of two families—the grass family (Gramineae) and the legume family (Leguminosae). A representative genus of each family has been selected to illustrate the technique of seed identification by means of a seed key and illustrations of the seeds.

IN THE GRASS family, the grain is classified botanically as a fruit, which is called a caryopsis. The embryo lies on the outside of the endosperm in an oval area toward the base of the seed. The root-shoot axis of the embryo, often protected by only a thin membrane, appears as a raised line, or ridge, down the middle of the oval area. The caryopsis is enclosed by two bracts, the lemma and palea. The

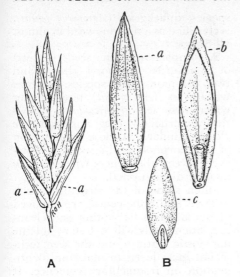

A   B

A. Grass spikelet, which has six florets and a pair of glumes at the base (a). B. Detail of a single floret: (a) Lemma on dorsal side of floret; (b) ventral side of floret showing the palea and rachilla segment; (c) dorsal side of the caryopsis (grain) showing the embryo at the base.

bracts may be thin and chaffy, as in bluegrass, or they may be thick and hardened, as in the millets (*Setaria*).

The so-called seeds that compose a grass-seed sample may consist entirely of the mature florets (caryopses within their lemmas and paleas) or of the hulled caryopses. Some samples may be a mixture of both. The seed technician must become familiar with the morphological features that are characteristic of both forms.

The bluegrass genus (*Poa*) comprises about 20 species that are used for lawn, pasture, hay, and range purposes. About half of this number are in commercial production, and three or four species may appear incidentally in other crop-seed samples.

An abbreviated seed key, classifying five species and one variety of the more widely distributed species of bluegrass, will serve as an example for the identification of grass seeds. (Page 426.)

The illustrations show the seed types that may occur in a single spikelet.

THE LEGUME FAMILY includes such crops as alfalfa (*Medicago sativa*), the true clovers (*Trifolium*), sweetclovers (*Melilotus*), vetches (*Vicia*), soybeans (*Glycine max*), peanuts (*Arachis hypogaea*), and many others.

The seeds vary widely in size, shape, and color, but they have certain structural features that immediately place them in the legume family.

With the exception of the peanut, the seedcoat tends to be hard and brittle and often impervious to water. Such seeds are sometimes damaged by cracking or chipping of the seedcoat in processing.

The embryo fills the entire cavity and consists of two large, thick cotyledons, with the radicle (root) bent back against them.

The *hilum* (seed scar) is evident on the seed surface near the tip of the radicle. It is usually an oval, circular, or oblong area with a longitudinal groove or slit down the middle. The area may be minute, as in some of the clovers, or it may be large and conspicuous, as in vetch and soybean. In some species, the slit in the hilum is obscured by a persisting layer of corky tissue, as in cowpeas (*Vigna sinensis*) and beans. The size, shape, and position of the hilum are important diagnostic features.

A small, dark-colored elevation, the *chalaza*, may be evident on the surface of many legume seeds. Its prominence and its position in relation to the hilum are also important diagnostic features.

A seed key and illustrations of the seeds of the vetches (*Vicia*) illustrate the identification of seeds of one genus of the legume family. Eighteen species of vetch are of interest in our agriculture. Eight of these species are cultivated crops in this country. Ten species may occur incidentally in other vetch samples or with other crops, and these are usually classified as weed seeds.

PLANT GENERA that include valuable agricultural species may also contain one or more species that are recognized as noxious weeds.

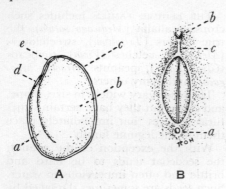

A. *Seed of clover in longitudinal section: (a) The radicle; (b) cotyledons; (c) seedcoat; (d) position of hilum and (e) chalaza. B. Hilar area showing the longitudinal groove of the hilum and (a) the micropyle, (b) chalaza, (c) the raphe.*

The seed technician must assume the responsibility for distinguishing the seeds of the noxious-weed species from those that may be crop species of similar appearance. This can be illustrated by the wheatgrass genus (*Agropyron*).

THIRTEEN SPECIES OF wheatgrasses appear in our agriculture. Ten of the species are valuable forage, hay, or range grasses. Two of the species are classified as weeds that appear occasionally in cultivated fields. One

species, quackgrass (*Agropyron repens*), is classified as a noxious weed in almost all States.

A comparison of the seeds (florets) of quackgrass (*Agropyron repens*) and two common crop species, western wheatgrass (*A. smithii*) and slender wheatgrass (*A. trachycaulum*), shows that superficially they appear to be closely similar. A close examination of the morphological structures, however, reveals differences whereby they may be distinguished.

Often some of the structures, such as awns and pubescence, are removed or damaged in harvesting and cleaning. Such seeds will not show all the diagnostic features and the seed technician must learn to make an identification on fragmentary evidence. It requires study and practice on the part of the technician to develop the skill and proficiency necessary for accurate work.

ALBINA F. MUSIL *was a seed botanist in the Seed Branch of the Grain Division, Agricultural Marketing Service, before her retirement in 1960. After graduation from the University of Nebraska, she joined the Division of Seed Investigations in 1927 and was engaged in seed research and teaching seed analysis in regional schools under the Federal Seed Act.*

POA, BLUEGRASS

A SEED KEY

1a. Intermediate nerves of lemma distinct to the base; lemma pointed, the apex folded.
   2a. Pubescence on midnerve and marginal nerves only, the pubescence long and dense; lemma 5–6½ mm. long. Hairs on keels of palea short on upper half, long and dense on lower half.
       Poa arachnifera, Texas bluegrass (figure 6).
   2b. Pubescence on all nerves; lemma 2½–3 mm. long.
     3a. Pubescence long and dense; hairs on keels of palea long, dense, do not extend to tip of palea.....*P. annua*, annual bluegrass (figure 5).
     3b. Pubescence on nerves shorter, confined to lower half of nerves.
       4a. Lemma evenly brownish straw-color, close-fitting on the grain, the intermediate and marginal nerves distinct to the tip; hairs

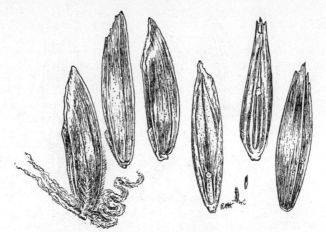

FIGURE 1.   *Poa pratensis.*

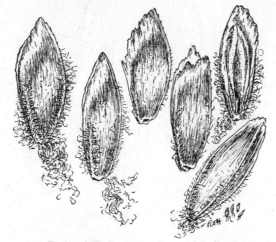

FIGURE 2.   *Poa pratensis*, var. Merion.

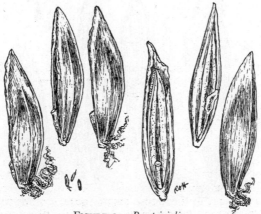

FIGURE 3.   *Poa trivialis.*

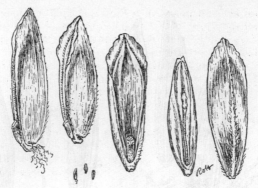

FIGURE 4.   *Poa compressa.*

FIGURE 5.   *Poa annua.*

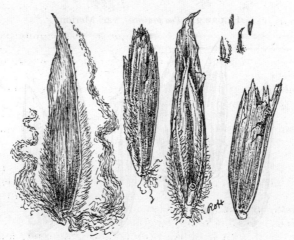

FIGURE 6.   *Poa arachnifera.*

on keels of palea very fine, short, close-spaced, extend to tip of
palea. . . . . *P. trivialis*, rough-stalked bluegrass (figure 3).

4b. Lemma light to dark straw-color, darker brown toward the
base, smooth fitting on the grain; hairs on keels of palea coarse,
short, wide-spaced, do not extend to tip of palea.
P. pratensis, Kentucky bluegrass (figure 1).

1b. Intermediate nerves of lemma lacking or obscure.

5a. Lemma broad, short-pointed, the apex expanded, light straw-color,
loose-fitting on the grain.

6a. Hairs on keels of palea short, fine, close-spaced, or longer about
midway, extend to tip of palea; length 2–2½ mm.
P. compressa, Canada bluegrass (figure 4).

6b. Hairs on keels of palea short, coarse, wide-spaced, do not extend to
tip of palea; length 2½–3 mm.
P. pratensis var. Merion Kentucky bluegrass (figure 2).

5b. Lemma pointed, slender, delicate, loose-fitting on the grain, light straw-
color, often gold-tipped or purplish; rachilla long, slender; hairs on
keels of palea short, or longer about midway, close-spaced, extend to tip
of palea; length 2–2½ mm. . . . . *P. palustris*, fowl bluegrass.

VICIA, VETCH

A SEED KEY

1a. Chalaza on the back, opposite the hilum.

2a. Hilum about 2 mm. long, flush with surface of the seed or nearly so.

3a. Hilum narrowly oblong, ½ to ¾ mm. wide; seed 4–4½ mm. long.
V. pannonica, Hungarian vetch (figure *H*).

3b. Hilum short-oval, about 1¼ mm. wide; seed 5 mm. long.
V. hybrida, no common name (figure *J*).

2b. Hilum about 4 mm. long, oblong.

4a. Hilum narrow (½ to ¾ mm.), slightly depressed at the margins; seed
6–6½ mm. long, may be variously compressed.
V. lutea, yellow vetch (figure *I*).

4b. Hilum wide (1 mm. or more), flush with surface of seed or nearly so;
seed 4½ to 5 mm. long.
V. melanops, no common name (figure *K*).

1b. Chalaza near one end of the hilum.

5a. Hilum linear, obscured by a persisting whitish, frill-like tissue; seeds 3–4
mm. long.

6a. Hilum about two-thirds the length of the circumference; seed lens-
shaped, brownish and faintly mottled.
V. grandiflora, showy vetch (figure *C*).

6b. Hilum 1–3 mm. long; seed slightly flattened but not lens-shaped.

7a. Hilum 2½ to 3 mm. long; seed dull black.
V. bengalensis, purple vetch (figure *B*).
(*V. atropurpurea*)

7b. Hilum about 1 mm. long; seed brownish, faintly mottled.
V. monantha, Bard vetch (not illustrated).

5b. Hilum not obscured by persisting tissue.

8a. Seeds relatively small, length 1½–2 or 3 mm.

9a. Seed with knoblike protuberances, minutely stippled, appears
4-sided in outline. Hilum dark reddish brown, short-oval, length

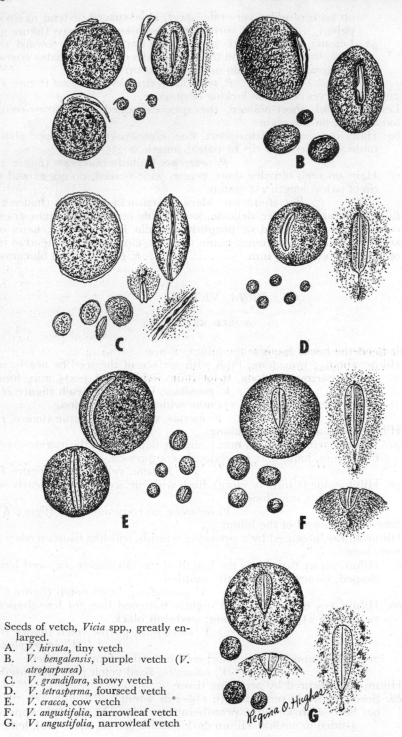

Seeds of vetch, *Vicia* spp., greatly enlarged.

A. *V. hirsuta*, tiny vetch
B. *V. bengalensis*, purple vetch (*V. atropurpurea*)
C. *V. grandiflora*, showy vetch
D. *V. tetrasperma*, fourseed vetch
E. *V. cracca*, cow vetch
F. *V. angustifolia*, narrowleaf vetch
G. *V. angustifolia*, narrowleaf vetch

1 mm., width ½ mm.; seed light grayish brown with a prominent chalaza near end of hilum, length 2 mm.

    V. lathroides, low pea vetch (not illustrated).

9b. Seed smooth, mostly spherical.

 10a. Hilum oblong, length 1¼ mm., width ½ mm. or less; seed reddish brown and finely mottled, length 2–2½ mm.

    V. tetrasperma, fourseed vetch (figure *D*).

 10b. Hilum markedly longer, 2–3 or 3¼ mm.

  11a. Hilum linear-oblong, width ½ mm. or less.

   12a. Seed glossy, yellowish or brownish, copiously mottled with purple; hilum 2–2½ mm. long, commonly with a stalklike appendage loosely persisting.........*V. hirsuta*, tiny vetch (figure *A*).

   12b. Seed dull, black or lighter and mottled; hilum 2½ to 3 mm. long...*V. cracca*, cow vetch (figure *E*).

  11b. Hilum linear-ovate, width at broader end about ¾ mm.

   13a. Hilum about 2 mm. long, slightly raised along the groove down the middle; seed spherical, black and lustrous or dull greenish with dark mottling. *V. angustifolia*, narrowleaf vetch (figures *F* and *G*).

   13b. Hilum about 3½ mm. long, flat, grayish and scurfy; seeds slightly flattened, dark brown with obscure mottling.

    V. americana, American vetch (not illustrated).

8b. Seeds relatively large, length 4–5 or 6 mm., up to 14 mm. in *faba*.

 14a. Chalaza 2½–3 mm. from end of hilum; hilum about 1 mm. long, ½ mm. wide. Seed dull, pale brownish and usually mottled with dark green, the side opposite the chalaza flattened at right angles to the hilum so that seed appears triangular in outline.........*V. ervilia*, bitter vetch (not illustrated).

 14b. Chalaza 1 mm. or less from end of hilum.

  15a. Seed spherical or slightly flattened.

   16a. Hilum flush with seed surface, smooth and flat, color black or reddish, length about 2 mm., width 1 mm., seeds black or obscurely mottled.

    V. villosa, hairy vetch (figure *M*).

    V. villosa var. *glabrescens*, smooth vetch.

   16b. Hilum depressed at the margins.

   17a. Hilum linear-oval, flat, the surface slightly granular and scurfy with a light-colored strip along the groove down the center, length about 2 mm., width ¾ mm. or less; seed dull black or obscurely mottled.

    V. dasycarpa, woollypod vetch (figure *N*).

   17b. Hilum linear-ovate, raised down the middle along the groove, length 2–2½ mm., width ½ mm.; seed color variable, commonly reddish brown and obscurely mottled. A variable species.

    V. sativa, common vetch (figure *L*).

 15b. Seed broadly oblong or oval, thick, flattened, reddish brown, length 13–14 mm., width 8–9 mm., hilum lies along the narrower end, length 5–6 mm., width 1–1½ mm.

    V. faba, horsebean (not illustrated).

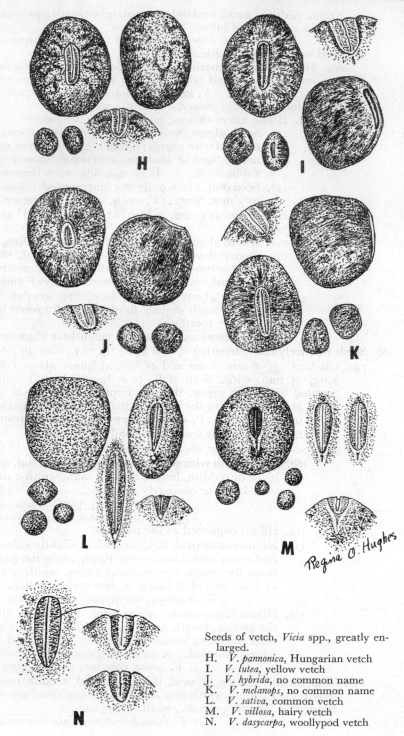

Regina O. Hughes

Seeds of vetch, *Vicia* spp., greatly enlarged.
H.   *V. pannonica*, Hungarian vetch
I.   *V. lutea*, yellow vetch
J.   *V. hybrida*, no common name
K.   *V. melanops*, no common name
L.   *V. sativa*, common vetch
M.   *V. villosa*, hairy vetch
N.   *V. dasycarpa*, woollypod vetch

Tests for Germination In the Laboratory

VERA L. COLBRY, THOMAS F. SWOFFORD, AND ROBERT P. MOORE

WHATSOEVER a man soweth, that shall he also reap applies to the seeds you plant for crops, gardens, lawns, and forests. Sowing seeds that will not grow or are low in viability is a loss of money and time.

To save both, we have the laboratory germination test.

It is designed to indicate as closely as possible the proportion of the seeds that can be expected to sprout and develop into strong plants in the field, garden, and forest.

Experience has taught us that the mere fact a seed will absorb water, swell, and send out a tiny root does not guarantee that it will continue to grow and develop into a plant. It may have only enough vigor to form a root, or it may start to form a shoot and then die. It may even grow into a seedling, but one so weak that it cannot establish itself in the soil and continue to develop into a strong plant. So many hazards are encountered in establishing plants in nurseries, fields, gardens, and lawns that it is only commonsense to plant seeds that will have a good chance of survival.

AGRICULTURAL, vegetable, flower, and herb seeds grown for seeding in the United States are regularly tested for germination by private, commercial, State, and Federal laboratories.

The term "agricultural seeds" denotes the kinds that are planted as field crops or lawns and are not ordinarily considered as vegetables. Herb seeds are those of plants, such as sage and dill, that are grown mostly for food seasonings.

To comply with State laws and interstate and import provisions of the Federal Seed Act, agricultural and vegetable seeds ordinarily are tested before being placed on the market. They also may be tested later by seed law enforcement laboratories. Standardized procedures are necessary to assure that results of the different laboratories are uniform.

Flower and herb seeds usually need not be labeled to meet minimum germination standards. Many kinds of them are tested nevertheless.

The adoption of uniform rules for testing these seeds has been slow, partly because economically they are less necessary than agricultural and vegetable seeds. Testing them has been done mostly in laboratories that serve producers and distributors.

Flower and herb seeds and several new kinds of agricultural and vegetable seeds were added in 1959 to the rules for testing seeds of the Association of Official Seed Analysts. We have standardized germination procedures for 172 kinds of agricultural seeds, 60 kinds of vegetable seeds, 145 kinds of flower seeds, and 18 kinds of herbs.

Uniform germination results cannot be expected unless the analysts follow precise laboratory procedures, among them such operations as subdividing the sample to be used, unbiased selection of the seeds tested, the use of a standard number of seeds for the test (400 is the usual number), adequate spacing of the seeds on the germination medium, and correct regulation of moisture of the substratum, which is the material or medium on which the seeds are placed.

THE EQUIPMENT and substrata must provide and maintain throughout the test period the conditions of moisture, temperatures, aeration, and light to induce the various kinds of seeds to sprout.

An adequate space under controlled

Seedling Classification of Garden Bean (Phaseolus vulgaris)

8-DAY-OLD SEEDLINGS

NORMAL | ABNORMAL, *caused by mechanical damage to the seeds*

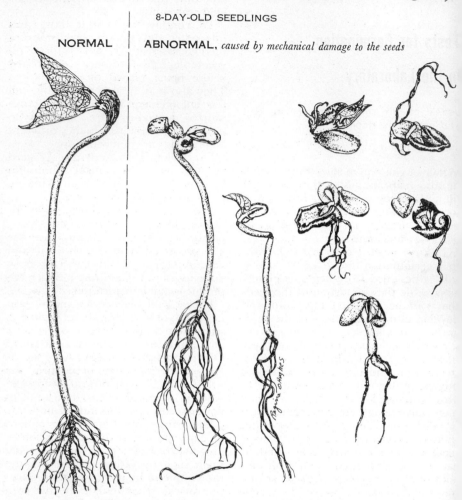

conditions also must be provided for conducting sand or soil tests. The amount depends on the kinds of seeds tested in the laboratory and any problems the samples present in evaluation of seedlings that make it necessary to test them in soil or sand.

The usual type of germinator in the United States is the insulated cabinet or sometimes a room equipped with movable shelves or trays, on which the tests are placed. The temperature is controlled by a regulated balance be-

tween refrigerated water and heating coils, both controlled by thermostats Light comes through glass walls or doors and from electric lights.

Most of the testing is done on nontoxic substrata such as blotters, towels or filter paper, which are used alone or enclosed in glass petri dishes or other containers. This type of test saves germinator space and is easy to do.

Sand or soil must be sterilized before use as germination media to destroy fungi, bacteria, and weed seeds. Expanded mica and granulated peat moss, alone or mixed with sand or soil, are used in some laboratories, especially for tests that require long prechilling or test periods.

ADEQUATE MOISTURE must be supplied to seeds throughout the test period.

Except for a few kinds adapted to growth in water, the moisture in the substrata should never be so much that a visible film of water surrounds the seeds. Excessive moisture can cause restriction of respiration (the intake of oxygen and the giving off of carbon dioxide by the seed) and stop germination of the seed. It also can cause certain types of abnormal development, such as lack of root hairs and transparent or "glassy" seedlings.

The temperature must be controlled accurately. Some kinds of seeds germinate over a fairly wide range of temperature, but others sprout promptly only in certain narrow ranges. Seeds germinate generally at temperatures to which they have been acclimated in the place they were produced. For instance, seeds of crops grown in the Southern States germinate well under warm, alternating temperatures; seeds of crops grown in Northern States germinate well in cool temperatures.

Most nondormant seeds are tested at temperatures of 59° to 86° F. A few southern crops require temperatures as high as 95°. The particular temperature under which seeds are placed depends on the kind. Some are placed at constant temperatures, usually 59° or 68°. Others are subjected to temperature alternations during the course of the test period. That is, they are placed at a low temperature during the night (16 hours) and at a higher temperature during the day (8 hours). The most common alternation is 68° at night and 86° during the day.

Light is supplied for a few hours daily to most of the grasses and to some of the vegetable, flower, and herb seeds, whether they are dormant or not. This is because light has a stimulating effect on the germination of many seeds of these kinds, especially when they are freshly harvested, and seedlings exposed to light during part of their test period are easier to evaluate because they are not too pale.

BREAKING the dormancy is a big problem in inducing seeds to sprout. Seed analysts consider dormant seeds as those that are potentially viable but do not sprout promptly when placed under favorable temperature conditions unless they have been subjected to some special treatment. Seeds that have been domesticated for long periods generally germinate readily. They comprise such crops as beans, corn, wheat, rye, peas, and onions. Range grasses are hard to germinate.

Laboratory methods for overcoming dormancy have been restricted as far as possible to techniques that are practical, rapid, and easily performed, will not require excessive equipment, and will approximate the field performance of the seeds.

Sometimes several treatments are necessary. The analyst draws on his experience as to the requirements of the seeds usually grown or received for test in a certain area and as to the age of the seed. If information is lacking about the previous history of samples, he often has to conduct a double test—one under usual conditions and one under conditions specified for dormant seeds.

Commonly used treatments for overcoming dormancy are prechilling, the use of low-high alternating temperatures during the test period, moistening the substratum with a dilute solution of potassium nitrate, and predrying.

Hard seeds, which do not absorb water during the test period because of impermeable seedcoats, is a type of dormancy that occurs mainly in legumes. No attempt is made in the laboratory to overcome this condition. The hard seeds are reported and shown on the label when the seeds are offered for sale. These seeds will soften

Seedling Classification of Soybean (Glycine max)

8-DAY-OLD SEEDLINGS

NORMAL | ABNORMAL, *caused by mechanical damage to the seeds*

gradually and absorb water. They may have considerable field value.

Most of the kinds commonly tested can be removed from test 7 to 14 days from the time they are planted. Grasses as a group require longer periods—21, 28, or even 35 days. If seeds are dormant, the test period is extended to include the time allowed for pretreatments to overcome dormancy. That usually is 3 to 7 days or, for a few kinds of seeds, 2 or 3 weeks.

EVALUATION of the sprouted seeds is just as important as inducing the seeds to sprout.

The germination analyst reports as normal only the seedlings that will continue to develop into strong plants under favorable field conditions. All badly broken, weak, and obviously malformed seedlings are considered as abnormal and are not included in the germination percentage.

Some samples may have up to 30 percent of abnormal seedlings. Correct seedling evaluation therefore can be a critical part of the germination test. Sprouts must not be counted as normal and discarded until they have grown large enough for the analyst to observe whether their essential seedling parts are present.

Guides for seedling classification are

given in the rules for seed testing and in U.S. Department of Agriculture Handbook No. 30. They include detailed descriptions and photographs of normal and abnormal seedlings of most of the kinds tested commercially.

Because evaluation of seedlings is based on their estimated field performance, testing in sterilized soil or sand is a recommended procedure for seeds that may produce seedlings difficult to evaluate when they are grown on artificial media.

Abnormal seedlings may be due to several causes, the recognition and reporting of which may help the seed-grower, merchant, and processor to avoid future losses.

Perhaps the most serious abnormalities are the ones caused by mechanical damage to the seeds, insect infestation, decay of seedling parts because of certain disease organisms, injury from various chemicals, and frost damage.

Mechanical injury is any sort of breakage to the seed, usually caused by threshing operations, cleaning, or scarification processes (the abrasion of the seedcoats to reduce the percentage of hard seeds in such seeds as clovers).

The injury may be externally visible, or it may be internal and may not be discovered until the seeds have germinated. Some kinds of seeds are more susceptible to injury of this type than others because of the size and location of the tiny embryonic plant within the seed. Beans, peas, soybeans, clovers, alfalfa, and some of the cereals are particularly susceptible to mechanical breakage of embryo parts. Seed analysts have also detected similar damage in seeds such as garden spinach and some severely milled grass and flower seeds.

Insect infestation occurs oftenest in such seeds as vetch, field pea, some of the clovers, alfalfa, and cowpea and sometimes in stored seeds, such as wheat. The analyst has the problem of classifying seedlings that are partly injured by insects or weakened because most of the stored food in the seed has been eaten.

Some seedlings show the result of exposure of the seeds to chemicals—notably the overtreatment of seeds with fungicides.

Injury from treatment or accidental exposure to insecticides and herbicides, such as DDT and 2,4-D, has also been observed. The seedling symptoms of both types of injury are much the same—a thickening of the root and lower stem region often so extensive that the seedlings grow just a little.

Frost can cause serious damage to seedlings, especially in grains grown in cold climates. Some years certain samples of northern-grown oats contain seeds that produce a high percentage of frost-damaged seedlings, which exhibit a weakness in the lower shoot region.

Decay of seedling parts during the test period may indicate the presence of serious diseases, which may attack the plants in the field. This problem in seedling evaluation has not been solved entirely. Research into the development and adoption of laboratory techniques for the detection of serious seedborne diseases may help answer it.

The cause for some types of seedling abnormalities has not been established. For instance, certain samples of lettuce produce weakened seedlings that have dark places on the tiny leaves and a general shortening of the sprouts. Such seedlings die or do not grow strongly. They may reflect a physiological weakness within the seeds.

A seedling is indeed a miraculous organism. As it develops from a tiny, embryonic plant within the resting seed, it reveals the secrets which were hidden beneath its protective seed covering. The seed analyst can then convey these secrets to the ultimate planter of the seeds.

TESTING seed of trees for germination is a specialized procedure whose objectives, problems, and techniques differ from those encountered in the testing of other types of seeds.

Seedling Classification of Oat (Avena sativa)

10-DAY-OLD SEEDLINGS

NORMAL | **ABNORMAL,** *caused by frost damage to the seeds*

Tree seed is unlike many other seeds in that a fresh supply cannot always be expected each year. It is grown under uncontrolled environmental conditions. Because of extremes of climate and attacks by insects and fungi, the interval between crops of tree seeds in commercial quantities varies with kinds and may range from once every year to once in 8 years. The storage of tree seed therefore becomes necessary.

Results of the germination test can indicate the temperature and moisture limits for successful storage of each kind and whether the original levels of quality are being maintained.

Expanding nursery production and the development in recent years of direct seeding of areas to be converted into forests have created an increasing demand for tree seed. Since the collection season is short and the seed is perishable, the production of large amounts of high-quality seed requires that it be processed as quickly as possible. The germination test can indicate the need for changes in methods of collecting cones and fruits, temporary storage, and design of processing machinery to prevent injury to the seed.

Seedlings must have proper spacing in nursery beds if they are to become straight and strong. The nursery manager therefore must know how many seeds to sow so as to grow seedlings within the desired density range. Data from germination tests and related information will enable him to calculate the required sowing rate.

Georgia, South Carolina, New York, and South Dakota have set up standards for certification of tree seeds. Pennsylvania, Massachusetts, and Michigan have adopted laws on labeling seed as to quality. Germination tests reveal whether a seed lot fulfills the minimum requirements for certification.

As for pelleted seed of trees, the germination test can determine whether the sticker material and the repellent chemicals used in pelleting are harmful to the seed. Special germination testing techniques usually are needed for that.

The International Seed Testing Association has set up testing rules for 96 different species of trees. A committee of the Association of Official Seed Analysts started working in 1958 on testing rules for tree and shrub seeds of the United States. The Northwest Forest Tree Seed Committee, Corvallis, Oreg., in 1959 proposed testing rules for seeds of 23 tree species in the Pacific Northwest. The Region 8 Tree Seed Testing Laboratory, Macon, Ga., in 1959 proposed testing rules for seed of 20 tree species in the Eastern and Southern States.

Delay in the adoption of uniform rules is due probably to the difficulty encountered in inducing certain kinds of tree seeds to germinate. As research progresses toward the solution of these problems, the probability of general agreement on testing rules will increase.

Dormancy is the condition that prevents germination even when light, moisture, aeration, and temperature are satisfactory. It may be a hereditary characteristic or it may be induced during extraction or storage. Some kinds of trees always have dormant seeds, others almost never, and still others only occasionally. Dormancy may result from impervious seedcoats, which prevent absorption of water and oxygen, or from the condition of the seed parts inside the seedcoat.

The geographical source of the seed has little apparent relationship to dormancy in most kinds of trees. Some that grow throughout a wide range of climatic conditions are the exceptions, however. For example, eastern white pine and Scotch pine usually produce dormant seeds in the southern part of the range, but in the northern part of the range their seeds may or may not be dormant.

The quality evaluation of dormant tree seeds can be made only after a proper pregermination treatment.

Two germination tests are required for species that have dormant seeds occasionally. Upon the basis of comparative tests made before and after pregermination treatment, the presence of seed dormancy can be determined and a decision be made as to the best test method and field treatment.

When dormancy is due to impervious seedcoats, pregermination treatment of tree seed may be acid or mechanical scarification, or soaking in water or in solvents, such as ether, alcohol, or acetone. If a chemical in the seedcoat prevents germination, as in baldcypress, soaking in a solvent will remove the inhibitor and soften the seedcoat.

Methods used to overcome dormancy due to the internal condition of the seeds are temporary storage under cold, moist conditions; temporary storage in a warm, moist condition, followed by cold, moist conditions; temporary storage in cracked ice; alternating the temperatures during testing; and cold, dry storage.

Seedling Classification of Field Pea *(Pisum sativum arvense)*

8-DAY-OLD SEEDLINGS

NORMAL | ABNORMAL, *caused by weevil damage to the seeds*

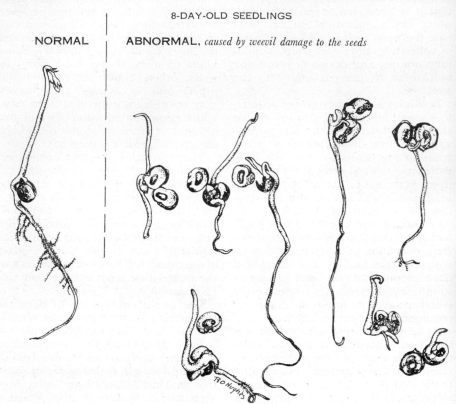

Even the most rapidly germinating tree seeds require a longer testing period than most agricultural seeds. When severe dormancy is encountered, the time required for pregermination treatment and the germination test may be several months. Research has been undertaken to develop faster methods of breaking dormancy. Of course, any method developed for laboratory use must also be practical for use in the field with large masses of seeds.

The excised-embryo method of determining the germinative capacity of tree seeds is useful for many kinds that exhibit dormancy. An approximate measure of germination may be obtained in a week or 10 days instead of months required to complete regular

pregermination treatments and testing. The embryo is removed from all enclosing seed structures and placed upon the germination medium. Seeds with extremely hard coats must be cracked before the embryo can be removed. Seeds with soft to moderately hard coats are soaked in water 1 to 4 days to facilitate removal of the embryo. Scarification with acid before soaking in water helps soften impervious coats.

Germination is indicated when growth starts or the embryo remains white and firm at the end of the test. Nonviable embryos become discolored and soon deteriorate. Since embryos only are used in this test, a correction for empty seed or discarded shriveled embryos in the original seed must be made. This method of germination testing is limited to kinds of tree seed whose embryos can be removed easily.

A NEW TYPE of test of seed quality involving the differential chemical staining of strong, weak, and dead tissues has come into use. Trained analysts can use it and get rapid, informative, and encouraging results. Of the chemicals tried, tetrazolium salts are the most promising and widely used.

Testing with tetrazolium (TZ) is based on the principle that respiration processes within living tissues release hydrogen, which combines with the colorless tetrazolium solution and produces a red pigment. Strong, healthy tissues develop a normal red stain. Aged tissues reveal a pale or mottled stain. Dead tissues remain white. Staining, however, is only one part of a chemical seed test. Factors other than death prevent the germination of many seeds.

Tetrazolium testing was started in 1941 by the late Georg Lakon of Germany, who used it as a substitute for a poisonous selenium salt that was used in studies of seed. Tetrazolium became available in the United States about 4 years later. It is now used in many countries and States. In the United States, it is largely used as a rapid, nonofficial testing supplement to standard methods. A few laboratories make a specialty of chemical seed testing.

The TZ test makes it possible to determine the potential viability and vigor ratings within 15 minutes to 24 hours. It also provides a different approach to testing and new insights into seed evaluation. It can reveal causes for seed troubles that may remain concealed or uncertain in growth tests. These informative insights make the test useful in predicting or diagnosing reasons for failures of germination due to storage, laboratory, or field conditions. The TZ test is especially useful in evaluating dormant seeds at harvest or seeds that require long or uncertain testing periods otherwise.

Another good opportunity to use TZ testing is in the evaluation of seeds that remain firm at the end of growth tests. Producers of seed of corn and sorghum use the test before processing to evaluate the seriousness of injury by early frosts.

TZ testing is not infallible and is not a final answer to all testing problems. It is merely another useful tool. The test can only reveal. The accuracy of results depends on the qualifications of the analysts who interpret it.

One objection to the widespread use of TZ tests in trade channels is that a uniform system of standards is yet to be established and coordinated for most kinds of seed. Furthermore, unless TZ testing is approved as official for given kinds of seeds, the results are not acceptable in labeling for legal requirements. Another objection is the extra time needed to prepare and examine individual seeds.

Another consideration is that TZ tests reveal potential germination percentages based strictly on internal seed condition, but growth tests reveal a combined performance of seed quality and a given growing condition. Germination evaluations from the two approaches to testing are often similar, especially if disease-susceptible seed lots are treated with a fungicide prior to growth testing under favorable conditions. TZ tests may not detect recent applications of toxic levels of fungicides.

When TZ tests are properly evaluated, the limitations usually are not so serious as they appear at first, especially if they are evaluated along with weaknesses of any other single type of test. The limitations should not discourage a person from taking full advantage of the potential usefulness of TZ testing for vigor and viability.

A knowledge of internal embryo parts as they relate to the development of seedling structures is essential for a proper evaluation of TZ tests. Most agricultural seeds are characterized by one cotyledon, or seed leaf, as in

Viability of Embryos

A   B   C   D   E

In one test of quality, a colorless solution produces a red pigment in strong, healthy tissues. In these drawings the shaded parts represent the red staining and show the live cells in embryos. a, corn; b, sorghum; c, wheat—cut surface of upper half of embryo; d, bluegrass—noncut surface; e, soybean—noncut surface.

grasses, or by two cotyledons, as in legumes. A knowledge of embryo structures of the two groups is a guide for understanding many kinds of seeds.

Testing techniques require that certain basic procedures be followed. Seeds should first be softened in water to activate enzyme systems, and to promote clean cutting and uniform absorption of tetrazolium. Seeds with fragile structures, such as snap beans, should be preconditioned first by slow absorption of water from a moist medium to avoid critical fracturing.

Seeds are prepared for absorption of tetrazolium by methods appropriate for the kind involved. Corn and large-seeded grasses are cut longitudinally through the center of germs to expose embryo leaves and root buds. Fine-seeded grasses are punctured or cut crosswise immediately back of the germ, or under it. Seeds of legumes and other crops, which absorb tetrazolium through seedcoats, are stained without previous physical alteration.

A satisfactory testing solution consists of 0.5 gram of 2,3,5-tripheynl tetrazolium chloride in 200 cubic centimeters of water.

Staining should occur in darkness and at temperatures near 70° to 90° F. Approximate staining times at 86° are: Corn and other cut seeds, 2 to 4 hours; cotton, peanuts, and other seeds with exposed noncut embryos, 4 to 6 hours; beans, grasses, and other crops in seedcoats, 6 to 18 hours.

When adequate staining has occurred, the solution should be discarded, and the seeds covered with water and refrigerated at 40° to 50° until analyzed. Seeds should be kept moist until evaluated.

SATISFACTORY interpretation of potential germination can best be acquired by an inexperienced analyst by comparing results from growth tests with observations from TZ tests.

Evaluation for vigor and viability requires observation of individual structures of each embryo and the relating of the condition of the decisive parts to the potential formation of normal or acceptable seedlings. Embryos should be observed individually, preferably under 5 to 10 × magnification, for the presence, extent, and seriousness of trouble areas. Variations in color patterns, texture, bruises, fractures, abnormal structures, infected areas, and insect infestation are all of potential importance. Firm, hard, or dormant seeds react normally to TZ staining and may be either germinative or nongerminative.

It is informative to classify individual germinative seeds within a lot on the basis of 1 to 5 and nongerminative 6 to 8. The physical condition of the embryo is used for these ratings. The percentage of seed in each class establishes different levels of vigor which is useful in predicting relative storage life of seed lots and response to adverse germinating conditions.

Advanced degrees of a localized or general aging, revealed as pale-red, mottled, necrotic, or flaccid tissues, cause more difficulty in interpretation than most other seed conditions. Interpretations of aging symptoms can be mastered with experience, and with this mastery will come a deeper appreciation of the gradual process of aging and the formation and enlargement of necrotic areas that tend to lead first to a nongerminative condition and later to complete death.

The TZ test has given us many insights into the mysteries of seeds. We expect to get more as its techniques are refined to reveal the causes of weaknesses of seeds and failures in germination. The advantages commend its use by agencies that need nonofficial evaluations quickly.

VERA L. COLBRY *is a seed technologist in the Seed Branch, Grain Division, Agricultural Marketing Service, Agricultural Research Center, Beltsville, Md. She holds degrees from Oregon State Agricultural College and George Washington University. She has worked in the field of seed technology since 1931.*

THOMAS F. SWOFFORD *is in charge of the Region 8 Tree Seed Testing Laboratory, Macon, Ga. Other assignments have been administrative positions at various national forests in the South and Pacific Northwest. Mr. Swofford is a graduate in forestry of the University of Washington and Yale.*

ROBERT P. MOORE *is professor of research, crop stands, North Carolina Agricultural Experiment Station, Raleigh. He was formerly a teacher of field crop courses at the Oklahoma State University and the University of Tennessee; a graduate assistant with the Ohio Seed Improvement Association, Columbus; and Director in charge of the North Carolina Seed Improvement Association.*

Ways To Test Seeds For Moisture

LAWRENCE ZELENY

THE MOISTURE in a seed has a strong bearing on the length of time it remains viable. Seeds may sprout or molds may develop at high levels of moisture, and the seeds may lose viability in a few days.

At the ordinary temperatures, if the relative humidity of the air around the seeds is more than 75 percent, the seeds are likely to support the growth of molds to the extent that they should not be stored even for a short time. The moisture content of seeds in equilibrium with this critical relative humidity varies among different kinds. For the various cereal grains, an atmospheric relative humidity of 75 percent corresponds to moisture contents in the range of 13.5 to 15 percent. Seeds high in oil usually have a lower moisture content at this humidity.

Moisture levels below those that cause actual sprouting or mold development may still be high enough to support fairly active physiological activity within the living seeds. Such activity will result in time in premature weakening and loss of viability.

Within certain limits, the lower the moisture content of any kind of seed, the greater the time it will maintain viability. The optimum moisture level for the storage of many kinds appears to be between 6 and 8 percent. Excessively low moisture may cause injury to the embryo. Complete dehydration no doubt would destroy the life of the embryo. Unless artificial drying with heat is employed, however, excessive dryness in seeds is rarely a practical problem.

THE BASIC methods for determining moisture in seeds are those by which a weighed sample is heated in an oven at a specified temperature for a specified time or until they attain constant weight. The loss in weight as a result of heating is taken to be equivalent to the moisture content of the original material. Various types of ovens are used, and various temperatures and times of heating are specified.

Actually, in biological materials it probably is not possible to drive off all moisture by heating without at the same time losing at least traces of other volatile substances or else producing weight changes in some of the constituents of the material as a result of oxidation or decomposition. It is difficult by any known method therefore to determine precisely the true moisture content of any sample of seed.

Because different "basic" methods may yield somewhat different results, for comparative purposes it is desirable to make all tests of a given kind of seed by the same method.

AIR-OVEN METHODS are used commonly for moisture determinations. The air ovens are electrically heated. The air within them is at atmospheric pressure and is circulated by convection or mechanical means. A temperature of 130° C. and a heating time of 1 hour are specified for most kinds of seeds.

The loss of weight that occurs during drying, calculated on a percentage basis, is taken to be the percentage of moisture in the seed before drying.

Large seeds, such as cereal grains, beans, and peas, must be ground before one determines moisture by this method in order to provide rapid enough penetration of heat and ready escape of moisture. Small seeds, such as those of the grasses, do not require grinding.

When this method is applied to large seeds that are too wet to be ground easily without losing moisture in the grinding process, a two-stage procedure is used. A weighed portion of the seeds is partly dried by exposing it to the air in a warm place. The loss of weight in this preliminary drying is determined. The partly dried sample is then ground, and the moisture content of it is determined in the usual manner. The moisture lost in both stages of the procedure must be considered in calculating the moisture content of the original seeds.

Seeds of a high oil content usually should not be ground for oven moisture determinations because they are difficult to grind properly and because oxidation of the oil during drying may result in a gain in weight of the oil. Errors therefore may be made in the determination of moisture. Oxidation of oil is a particularly serious consideration in seeds, such as those of flax that contain oils of high iodine number ("drying" oils).

Certain seeds contain constituents other than moisture that are volatile at 130° C. and hence cannot be subjected to that temperature in the determination of moisture without introducing errors in the determination.

The rules of the International Seed Testing Association specify that for such seeds a drying temperature of 105° C. be used and that the drying time be 16 hours. The following seeds are in this classification: Shallot (*Allium ascalonicum*), onion (*Allium cepa*), leek (*Allium porrum*), garlic (*Allium sativum*), carob (*Ceratonia siliqua*), soybean (*Glycine max*), and radish (*Raphanus sativus*).

The seeds of *Abies* (fir) and *Picea* (spruce) contain constituents of such high volatility that oven methods are not recommended. The toluene distillation method is recommended.

Air-oven methods are specified as the basic methods for determining moisture under the Official Grain Standards of the United States and the United States Standards for rice, beans, peas, and lentils. A 130° C., 1-hour, air-oven method is specified for wheat, barley, oats, rye, grain sorghums, soybeans, rice, peas, and lentils. The method provides for grinding the seed before drying. A 103° C., 72-hour air-oven method is specified for corn and beans and a 103° C., 4-hour, air-oven method is specified for flax seed. These methods for corn, beans, and flax do not require grinding of the seed.

Special types of air ovens have a built-in balance for weighing the dried samples while they are still in the oven. The balances are calibrated directly in terms of percentage of moisture so that no calculation is required when the designated weight of sample is used initially.

A vacuum-oven method is one of the official methods of the Association of Official Agricultural Chemists for determining moisture in the cereal grains. A weighed portion of the finely ground grain is heated at 98° to 100° C. in an oven in which a partial vacuum is maintained at a pressure equivalent to 25 millimeters of mercury or less. Heating is continued until no appreciable further loss of weight occurs (usually about 5 hours). The moisture content is calculated from the loss of weight as in air-oven methods. The results, applied to cereal grains, are approximately the same as those obtained by the 130° C., 1-hour, air-oven method.

Desiccants—drying agents—are used sometimes to remove moisture from materials and thus to provide a method for determining moisture. The moisture in seeds and other materials may be determined by placing a weighed amount of the finely ground material in a closed container with a relatively large amount of an efficient desiccant. The desiccant must have a lower vapor tension than the material that is being dried. The moisture in the material will gradually be vaporized and absorbed by the desiccant. Moisture content is determined by the loss in weight of the original material after it finally attains constant weight.

Reducing and maintaining the atmospheric pressure in the container to a low level will greatly reduce the time required to complete the operation,

but even when this is done the time required is too great for most practical purposes. In one of the official methods of the Association of Official Agricultural Chemists for determining moisture in grain, however, the finely ground material is held under vacuum in the presence of concentrated sulfuric acid until constant weight is attained.

One advantage of the method is that it does not involve the hazard of possible decomposition of organic material by heat. Seed of high moisture content, however, may decompose as a result of the action of molds and bacteria before the moisture is reduced enough to inhibit the growth of the organisms.

THE TOLUENE distillation method is sometimes used. A weighed portion of the finely ground seed is boiled in toluene in an apparatus that condenses the volatilized materials, collects the condensed water in a tube, and returns the condensed toluene to the boiling flask. The boiling is continued as long as any water continues to accumulate in the tube provided for that purpose, and the moisture in the seed is calculated from the volume of water condensed.

This method is one of the official methods of the Association of Official Agricultural Chemists for determining moisture in grain. The method should prove to be reasonably satisfactory for most seeds that can be satisfactorily ground without any appreciable loss or gain in moisture. It has the advantage that no water-insoluble volatile matter can be measured as moisture. Difficulty is sometimes encountered in reading accurately the volume of water distilled, because the separation between the toluene and water may not be sharp.

THE KARL FISCHER method depends on the reaction of iodine with water in the presence of sulfur dioxide and pyridine to form hydriodic acid and sulfuric acid. It is one of the most accurate methods.

The seed must first be finely ground and the moisture extracted with methyl alcohol or other water solvent.

The method has not been widely used under practical conditions, since it involves rather complicated equipment and intricate technique. Its greatest usefulness in respect to determination of seed moisture seems to be in checking the reliability of oven methods and in providing fundamental data for use in devising oven procedures that will give the greatest possible accuracy in the determination of moisture content.

Data of this type have been obtained for a number of different agricultural and vegetable seeds and are published in Marketing Research Report No. 304, "Oven Methods for Precise Measurement of Moisture Content of Seeds," issued in 1959 by the Agricultural Marketing Service.

PRACTICAL METHODS for determining the moisture of seed are needed under many circumstances where the basic methods take too much time. Practical methods standardized against one or more of the basic methods therefore have been devised. The results generally are likely to be less accurate than those obtained by the basic methods, but they may be good enough for most practical purposes.

Other heating methods sometimes are used to shorten the time required by standard oven methods for determining moisture content. In general, these methods require heating of the material to considerably higher temperatures than those employed in the usual oven methods. Heating may be accomplished by ordinary electric heating coils, by radiation from infrared lamps, or by means of a high-frequency, high-voltage field. When these methods are employed, it is customary to determine in advance the time of heating and the temperature or other adjustment of the equipment required for each type of material to be tested in order to obtain results in reasonably good agreement with those obtained by one or more of the basic methods.

These methods should be quite useful in certain types of practical seed-testing work because the time required to complete a test is usually considerably less than 1 hour (in some instances 10 to 15 minutes), a number of tests may often be made at the same time, the cost of equipment usually is low, and the accuracy may be fairly high if the proper conditions for making the test are accurately determined for each kind of seed to be tested.

THE BROWN-DUVEL DISTILLATION method was used for many years in the routine inspection of grain. It is still used when the faster electrical methods cannot be used satisfactorily. A weighed amount of unground grain is heated in oil to a definite temperature. The moisture volatilized is condensed, collected, and measured in a graduated cylinder. The apparatus must be standardized to provide a definite amount of heat in a definite period of time. The method is arbitrary, and the exact procedure to be followed for each kind of grain in order to obtain results equivalent to those obtained by an official basic oven method must be determined.

The Brown-Duvel method should be applicable to most seeds except those that are light and chaffy. Before it can be used, however, it would be necessary to determine the exact procedure for each kind of seed in order to obtain results equivalent to those obtained by an appropriate basic method. The proper procedures have been established for seeds of wheat, corn, oats, rye, grain sorghums, barley, buckwheat, flax, soybeans, emmer, rice, beans, peas, mustard, cotton, and shelled peanuts.

CALCIUM CARBIDE reacts chemically with water to produce acetylene gas. This reaction has been used for determining the moisture content of various materials by measuring the weight lost, or, in a closed system, the pressure produced by the evolution of acetylene.

A special device with which pressure

is measured is available for making moisture determinations on finely ground materials by use of this principle. This device has been used in testing various kinds of seeds. Theoretically, if the same weight of seed and calcium carbide were used in all tests, the relation between moisture content and pressure developed would be the same for all kinds of seeds. In actual practice, however, no such constant relationship appears to exist, and it is necessary therefore to calibrate the equipment against some basic method for each kind of seed tested.

ELECTRIC moisture meters, used in routine work, have an advantage in speed over all other methods for determining moisture.

Most of these instruments are based on measurements of either the conductivity or the dielectric properties of the grain, both of which depend primarily on the moisture content and temperature of the seed, but they also are affected to some extent by many other variable factors. Electrical methods therefore cannot be depended on to give reliable results under all circumstances.

The moisture content of most kinds of seeds probably can be determined fairly accurately under most circumstances by means of electric moisture testers, but they have to be calibrated against an accepted basic moisture-testing method. Separate calibrations must be made for each kind of seed. For some kinds it is also necessary to make separate calibrations for individual classes, varieties, or varietal types.

Because of the errors inherent in the electric methods, each calibration should be based on the testing of a large number of samples, covering a wide range in moisture, obtained from as many different points of origin as possible, and preferably representing the crops of at least several years.

It is obvious therefore that a large amount of work is necessary before a reliable calibration can be made for

use in testing seeds with any electric moisture tester. Much work has been done in calibrating certain electric moisture meters for use with the various cereal grains, but relatively little has yet been accomplished in this field for most other seeds.

Electric moisture meters have a great advantage in speed over other methods. With most of the instruments, a test may be completed in a minute or less. Disadvantages are the relatively high cost of the equipment; the need for painstaking calibration for each kind of seed; and in some instances failure of the method to give results of a sufficiently high degree of accuracy. Factors other than moisture content affect the electrical properties of seed, and a more thorough understanding of these factors will be required before any appreciable increase in accuracy of electric moisture-testing methods can be expected.

LAWRENCE ZELENY *is Chief of the Standardization and Testing Branch, Grain Division, Agricultural Marketing Service.*

For further reading:
Hart, J. R. and Neustadt, M. H.: *Application of the Karl Fischer Method to Grain Moisture Determination.* Cereal Chemistry, volume 34, pages 26–37. 1957.
Hlynka, I. and Robinson, A. D.: Moisture and Its Measurement. Chapter 1, *Storage of Cereal Grains and Their Products.* Published by American Association of Cereal Chemists, St. Paul, Minn. 1954.
Hubbard, J. E., Earle, F. R., and Senti, F. R.: *Moisture Relations in Wheat and Corn.* Cereal Chemistry, volume 34, pages 422-433. 1957.
Methods for Determining Moisture Content as Specified in the Official Grain Standards of the United States and in the United States Standards for Beans, Peas, Lentils, and Rice. Service and Regulatory Announcements, Number 147 (revised). 3 pages. U.S. Department of Agriculture. 1959.
Official Methods of Analysis. 8th Edition. Published by the Association of Official Agricultural Chemists, Washington, D.C. 1955.
Zeleny, Lawrence. *Methods for Grain Moisture Measurement.* Agricultural Engineering, volume 35, pages 252-256. 1954.
Zeleny, Lawrence. *Moisture Measurement in the Grain Industry.* Cereal Science Today, volume 5, pages 130–136. 1960.

How We Try To Measure Trueness to Variety

WALTER A. DAVIDSON AND B. E. CLARK

EVERYBODY knows that some roses are fragrant and some are not; some are red, and others are white, pink, or yellow. It would be inconvenient and confusing if we had no names for them.

Many variations—in color, size, season, shape—exist in each kind of plant. Plant breeders single out the variations to create new varieties.

Thousands of varieties of economic importance have been named and introduced into channels of commerce and are available to farmers and gardeners, but there has been no clear-cut, universally accepted understanding of the amount of variation that would justify a separate variety name.

The American Society of Agronomy in 1917 adopted a code for naming varieties, but not all plant breeders observed it.

The Federal Seed Act of 1939 defined variety as a "subdivision of a kind which is characterized by growth, plant, fruit, seed, or other characters by which it can be differentiated from other sorts of the same kind; for example, Marquis wheat, Flat Dutch cabbage, Manchu soybean, Oxhart carrot, and so forth."

That means that we should be able to tell a new variety from other varieties—but how? No limit was placed on the characters that may be used in distinguishing one variety from another. They may be visible (such as color) or invisible (such as resistance to disease). It is evident, however, that the characters must be discernible by some technique. To be used to the best advantage, the identity of the variety must be made known to seed users through the use of one variety name.

The most vexing problem in connection with the continuous effort to encourage the distribution and use of seeds of superior varieties is the deceptive similarity of characteristics of seeds. The variations we referred to are of many kinds. Some are associated in no way with the difference in the appearance of the seeds.

It is necessary therefore to be careful to keep seed identified. Out of that need came certification of seed and studies of the means by which varieties may be distinguished readily by other than seed characteristics.

AN EXAMPLE of the confused situation that has existed in the naming of varieties of plants is the 2,640 names that were used in 1940 for 600 varieties of wheat, oats, barley, and rye, and the 100-odd names used for one of the first successful varieties of hybrid corn.

The confusion was made worse through the use of one name for more than one variety. Seed buyers over the years have selected well-known varieties and often unknowingly received seed of more readily available varieties. The deception meant that buyers became misinformed as to the true characteristics of the varieties.

Positive steps have been taken to settle the problem. The American Society of Agronomy and the Department of Agriculture in 1922 initiated a system of registration of varieties of wheat, oats, and barley. Registration was limited to varieties distinctly superior to others then available. The registered names and descriptions of the varieties were published in the journal of the society.

Varieties of soybean, flax, alfalfa, sweetclover, and other kinds were added later, but many varieties were introduced into commerce that were not registered. A similar effort was made to standardize the variety names of vegetables through the publication of "type books," but they likewise were limited to a relatively small number of the varieties in channels of commerce. To keep informed of the characteristics and the names of varieties in commerce, one had to read publications of the Department of Agriculture, State agricultural experiment stations, seedsmen, and private plant breeders. The publications had conflicting information.

A SUGGESTED uniform State seed law was adopted in 1917 by the Association of Official Seed Analysts in cooperation with the American Seed Trade Association. The suggested law required that seed be labeled to show the "commonly accepted name." This provision was vague, but most States enacted it into law. Whether the term "commonly accepted name" referred to the variety name or only to the name of the kind was never clear. This situation lasted more than 20 years.

The persistence of this lack of clarity may be attributed generally to three conditions: An inability to identify varieties by seed characters in seed laboratories; lack of facilities, as a part of enforcement of seed laws, to make varietal determinations in the greenhouse or field; and the absence of an adequate standard of variety names and descriptions.

The result was failure to regulate the labeling of seeds as to variety and the use of many names for each variety. Most of the States have corrected this situation. Many now require that agricultural seeds be labeled to show the name of the variety.

Costly field testing is done in several States to determine the variety of seed, which can be determined only during the growing or mature stage on the basis of such characteristics as date of maturity and size, shape, and color of leaf, head, tuber, fruit, and other parts.

Such tests could be avoided if we could find seed or seedling characteristics that could be determined in a relatively short time. Most of this testing is done to determine compliance with the State seed laws, but the results are used under the Federal Seed

Act if the seed proves to be falsely labeled in interstate commerce.

UNDER THE Federal Seed Act, an effort to stabilize variety names and to develop a source of information to which the public may turn for guidance in the labeling of seeds as to variety started in 1939. The agricultural experiment stations have struggled with the same problem and have adopted policy statements for their own guidance.

Several meetings were conducted to develop an understanding with seedsmen, who suddenly found themselves compelled to label vegetable seed as to variety under the Federal Seed Act of 1939. The problems of the seed industry were revealed, and a belief was voiced that the strict enforcement of labeling as to variety would discourage private efforts to develop new and better varieties.

Finally, in 1946, the idea was advanced in the Department of Agriculture of creating variety committees, whose function would be to consider the names and characteristics of varieties to be recognized in the enforcement of the Federal Seed Act. Four committees were formed. Their members had expert knowledge of varieties and represented the Department, State experiment stations, and the American Seed Trade Association.

The four original committees were assigned to soybeans, cabbage, sorghum, and garden beans. Additional committees with wider representation have been added for hybrid corn, hybrid onions, and hybrid sorghum.

The committees inspected plots in which seed of the varieties had been sown. Then they agreed on a list of variety names and descriptions. The lists have been published by the Department and are included in the regulations under the Federal Seed Act as the variety names recognized for the purpose of enforcement. We hope the lists will be extended to include all crops subject to the act.

An amendment to the regulations

under the Federal Seed Act in 1956 set forth certain principles with respect to variety names. They are contained in section 201.34 of the regulations and are published in Service and Regulatory Announcement No. 156. They provide that basically the recognized name of a variety is that assigned by the originator or discoverer of the variety. Variety names that have been in broad, general use before July 28, 1956, are recognized. Hybrid designations are recognized as variety names.

In keeping with the definition of variety that we quoted, the traits and not the parentage determine the variety.

We have known of instances in which a plant breeder has changed characteristics of stock still in his possession after seed of a variety has been made available to the public. The Federal Seed Act provides that when such changes occur, the same variety name cannot be kept for the one that has been changed. When a natural change in plant characteristics has occurred, it must be assumed the seed is no longer the same variety.

Technically, the function of this regulation is to help seedsmen comply with the Federal Seed Act. From a broader point of view, the regulations help carry out the intent of the act.

As stated by the Congress, the act is intended "to regulate interstate and foreign commerce in seed; to require labeling and to prevent misrepresentation of seeds in interstate commerce. . . ." In other words, the intent is to help buyers of seed to select what will best serve their needs.

To do so, the names of varieties must convey knowledge to the buyer of the characteristics of the variety. This can be done only if there is truthful labeling and advertising and if only one name is used for each variety. The regulations under the Federal Seed Act are designed to accomplish this.

It should be noted that the law does not apply directly to the naming of a variety of plants by the plant breeder. It applies only to seed shipped in interstate commerce, and the person who ships the seed or advertises seed for sale is the only person subject to the act. Practically all varieties of seed sooner or later, however, enter channels of commerce and enter interstate commerce. At this point, the labeling of seed as to variety is regulated under the Federal Seed Act. The plant breeder is thus concerned indirectly. It obviously would be unwise for a plant breeder to select a variety name that could not be used in the labeling or advertising of seed in interstate commerce. To do so would cause shippers to violate the law or become unnecessarily confused in their effort to comply with the law. The close cooperation between Federal and State agencies in the enforcement of the seed law is such that similar interpretations as to variety names may be expected in the States.

THE INTERNATIONAL Code of Nomenclature for Cultivated Plants advocates the formation of international registration authorities to assume the responsibility of keeping a record of all varieties.

One of the problems is to be sure, when names are introduced, that the varieties to which they are applied are new and different from the varieties already known. Without this precaution, a variety could be registered several times under as many names. Registration authorities should have the facilities for making the necessary tests.

The goal of tests for trueness to variety is to determine if the seed lot in question has the characteristics of the variety it is represented to be. Varietal characteristics are caused by the genetic complement of the cells. As it is impossible to determine the genetic constitution by examination of the cells, the seed and plant characteristics must be relied upon to determine varietal identity.

Determination of trueness to variety is complicated by the influence of environmental factors. Our methods consequently must be based on diagnostic characteristics, which are not affected by environmental forces; or they must control the environment; or they must compensate for the influences of the environment.

Seed characteristics that are stable despite changes in environment are used in detecting offtypes in some kinds, such as beans.

Growth chambers, in which light, temperature, and humidity can be controlled, are used for testing the trueness to variety of some forage crops. In field trials, where control of environment is not possible, seeds of known variety are planted for comparison. If the seeds under test are of the same variety as those of the authentic stocks, they will be influenced by the existing environment in the same way as the authentic stocks and reliable determinations can be made in spite of environmental influences.

Because of the influence of environment, it is apparent that any method for determining trueness to variety must be carefully tested to determine its validity before it is put into use. Some methods that have been proposed cannot be accepted as being reliable because we do not have enough evidence that the diagnostic characteristics are not affected by environment as well as by heredity.

The tests of trueness to variety that have proved to be reliable fall into three groups.

The first includes tests that can be made on seeds or seedlings in connection with ordinary laboratory purity analyses or germination tests.

The second includes tests conducted by growing seedlings under controlled conditions in a greenhouse or growth chamber.

The third is the field trial.

Relatively few kinds of seed can be tested for trueness to variety in the ordinary seed laboratory, but some determinations are possible. Offtypes in beans, soybeans, and peas can often be detected by the color or shape of the seed. Common Kentucky bluegrass seeds can be distinguished from seeds of the Merion variety by microscopic examination of seed characteristics. Some offtypes in oats, wheat, and barley can be distinguished by the color and shape of the seed.

Some white and yellow oats varieties can be separated through the use of ultraviolet light, which causes radiation of light, called fluorescence. White oats have a light-blue fluorescence. Yellow oats have a dark-bronze fluorescence. The difference can be observed even when the glumes have become so discolored through weathering that it is difficult to determine their color under ordinary light.

Ultraviolet light can be used also to detect certain offtypes in soybeans and peas and to determine the percentage of seeds of annual and perennial ryegrass in mixtures. A few varieties of peas and soybeans produce seedlings whose roots exude a fluorescent material. The fluorescence produced by the roots of these seedlings can be detected under ultraviolet light.

Seedlings of red and white varieties of beets and of red and green varieties of cabbage can be distinguished readily in germination tests. The seedlings of the red varieties of beets and cabbage contain a red pigment that is lacking in the white varieties of beets and green varieties of cabbage.

Attempts have been made to develop chemical tests to determine trueness to variety, but most of them have been unfruitful. Relatively few chemical tests can be applied practically to individual seeds. Also, the chemical composition of seeds usually is influenced by the environment as well as by heredity. Chemical tests therefore tend to be unreliable.

The development of better light conditions for growth chambers has opened a new field for testing. In addition, control over other environmental factors permits conditions that produce the greatest differences in the seedlings or plants of different varieties.

The growing of seedlings under controlled environments in a greenhouse or a growth chamber offers special promise for testing forage crop seeds for trueness. The varieties generally cannot be distinguished on the basis of seed characteristics. Usually, the plants also lack diagnostic characteristics, but the seedlings and plants may be responsive to variations in temperature, daylength, and quality of light.

Seedlings of northern varieties of alfalfa, for instance, have short stems when grown at low temperatures with short photoperiods. Seedlings of southern varieties of alfalfa produce longer stems under the same conditions. The difference provides a way to distinguish between the two. Under similar conditions, Empire birdsfoot trefoil has short stems, and European-type birdsfoot trefoil has long stems. The same type of technique can be applied to other kinds of plants.

Measuring the resistance of seedlings to disease is another means of applying the controlled environment technique. This type of test has been satisfactory for detecting varietal admixture in wheat and oats.

In this test, seedlings are inoculated with a specific race of rust. After inoculation, the seedlings are observed to determine whether they show the resistant or susceptible type of reaction to the race involved. A susceptible-type reaction in a seedling which supposedly is a resistant variety is evidence that there is varietal admixture.

Techniques employing the same principle as the rust-resistance test of wheat and oats can be used to determine wilt resistance in alfalfa seedlings, yellows resistance in cabbage seedlings, mildew resistance in soybean seedlings, and resistance to numerous other diseases in various kinds of seeds.

The commonest test of trueness to variety is the field trial. It can be applied to almost any kind of seed without the development of special techniques. Also, since plants are usually grown to maturity in the field trials, a full range of varietal characteristics is available for observation.

The cost of conducting field trials is one of the disadvantages. During seasons when the weather is unfavorable, there may not be a normal expression of varietal characteristics. In fact, the trials may fail completely.

Probably the most serious shortcoming of the field trial is that it cannot be conducted in advance of the normal planting season. This prevents tests before seeds are put on the market unless it can be done in other places such as the Southern Hemisphere.

Despite their shortcomings, trueness-to-variety trials are an important part of any complete program to control the quality of seeds. They must be carefully conducted in accordance with a few basic principles, however.

WE HAVE indicated that authentic seed stocks for comparison with those under test are an essential part of trueness-to-variety trials. These authentic stocks should be included at close intervals among the stocks being tested. It is also essential to have replications in field trials. Each sample tested should be planted in at least two separate plots.

Another requirement is to have enough plants to detect admixtures with a degree of precision consistent with the purpose of the trial. Large populations are required to detect off-types with a low rate of occurrence. More serious admixtures, on the other hand, can be detected with relatively few plants.

WALTER A. DAVIDSON *is Director of the Grain Division of the Agricultural Marketing Service. He was a Smith-Hughes vocational agriculture teacher before his employment with the North Dakota State Seed Commissioner and later with the Division of Seed Investigations in the Department of Agriculture. He was formerly Chief of the Seed Branch, Agricultural Marketing Service. He is a past president of the International Seed Testing Association.*

B. E. CLARK *since 1952 has been head of the Department of Seed Investigations, New York State Agricultural Experiment Station, Geneva, N.Y.*

Testing Seeds for Seedborne Organisms

ALICE M. ANDERSEN AND CHARLES M. LEACH

THE TESTING of seeds for purity and germination is a recognized practice in many countries. In recent years there has come about a growing realization among scientists, seedsmen, and seedgrowers that testing for purity and germination is not enough and that international methods for testing the most serious seed-transmitted organisms are needed.

C. R. Orton, of the West Virginia Agricultural Experiment Station, in 1931 estimated losses in the United States caused by seedborne diseases to amount to 2.3 percent of the total crop of wheat, 3.1 percent of the barley crop, 3.2 percent of the oats crop, and 6.1 percent of the bean crop. The losses may appear insignificant for the country, but they are significant losses to the growers and to the sections where the losses occur.

A list of seedborne diseases compiled by Mary Noble of Scotland, J. de Tempe of Holland, and Paul Neergaard of Denmark, under the auspices of the International Seed Testing Association and published in 1958 by the Commonwealth Mycological Institute in London, registered approximately 900 plant diseases that may be spread by seedborne organisms.

Four groups of organisms commonly associated with seed cause plant diseases. In order of importance they are the fungi, bacteria, viruses, and nematodes. Some other diseases of seeds result from deficiencies of plant nutrients and from undetermined causes.

Seedborne pathogens affect directly and indirectly the quality of seeds in commerce. Of primary importance is the fact that seedborne plant pathogens introduce diseases such as smuts into newly sown crops thereby causing a reduction in yields and quality. The field germination of seed infected with seedborne pathogens may be reduced because the pathogens attack and kill the seedlings.

Similarly, the accuracy of germination tests in laboratories may be affected by certain seedborne pathogens, which in some instances cause a browning of the seedlings or attack and kill young seedlings during the tests. The viability of seeds in storage may be reduced by molds, which are unimportant in the field but may attack the dormant stored seeds.

Many kinds of crop seeds are treated with fungicides to eradicate seedborne pathogens and to protect them from pathogenic soilborne organisms, but not all seedborne pathogens would be killed even if we treated all seeds.

If buyers of seeds are to be assured of purchasing seeds free from harmful pathogens, some means is needed whereby the amount of infested seed within a seed lot can be ascertained.

Methods for detecting many seedborne pathogens have been devised.

Some pathogens, however, are not easily detected when seedborne, and field inspection of the growing seed crop is probably more practical in those instances than attempts to detect them within seed lots.

A commercial seed lot must be sampled before it can be tested for the presence of pathogens. We have little information on the precise methods for sampling seeds for the presence of pathogens or the size of the samples to be used for pathological testing. The dividers commonly used in North American and European seed-testing laboratories are not entirely suited for the mixing of seeds for pathological testing, principally because they cannot be easily cleaned and disinfected between samples. We believe the Patterson-Kelley "p-K" type of mixer overcomes this objection.

DETECTING seedborne fungi on seeds is accomplished by a number of methods. Examination of dry seeds with the naked eye and at magnifications of 10 to 30 times reveals a number of plant pathogens that occur mixed with the seeds as fungus bodies (for example, sclerotia) or have converted the seed into fungus structures (e.g., ergots). Sclerotia of the fungi *Sclerotinia* and *Typhula* may be mixed with seeds of clovers, crucifers, grasses, and other crop seeds. The fungus *Claviceps purpurea*, the cause of ergot of grasses, often is mixed with seed as ergots.

Also detected by visual examination are certain fungi that form small fungus structures on or in the seedcoat. *Septoria apii*, which causes a blight of celery, forms small structures (pycnidia) embedded in the seedcoat. It can be detected at low magnifications. The fungus *Septoria macropoda*, a pathogen of grasses, forms pycnidia on the glumes of bluegrass seed.

Other fungi may cause such symptoms as sunken, discolored, and dead areas on the seeds. Occasionally the presence of these symptoms may be used to detect pathogenic organisms. Identification of pathogens on the basis of disease symptoms alone is generally not recommended, for errors are easily made.

WHEN SEEDBORNE fungi are present as microscopic spores on the surface of seeds, it is almost impossible to detect them by visual examination at low magnifications. The spores have to be removed from the seed by washing and then examined with a compound microscope. Several procedures have been used.

For the covered smut diseases of cereals, a known weight of seed is added to a measured volume of water to which a little detergent has been added. The seeds are then shaken, and the washings are removed by decanting. The spores in suspension are allowed to settle at their own speed or more rapidly by the use of a centrifuge. The number of spores for a known amount of seed (spore load) is determined microscopically with a hemocytometer counting chamber.

The spores of some pathogens may be associated in such great numbers with individual seeds that merely mounting the seeds in drops of water, tearing the seeds apart, and then examining the exuding spores microscopically is sufficient for detection. This procedure has been used for detecting the honey dew stage of *Claviceps purpurea* (ergot of grasses) and blind seed fungus of ryegrass (*Gloeotinia temulenta*).

In Cereal Chemistry, volume 37, 1960, Robert M. Johnson described five techniques for the determination of covered smut in wheat—light transmittance, sedimentation, catalase activity, light reflection, and light absorption. The first four techniques measure the external smuts. The last employs a smut meter, which measures the internal and external smuts that contaminate the seeds.

THE TECHNIQUE of placing disinfected or untreated seeds on moist blotters and incubating them at specified temperatures has been used in Europe for detecting a number of seedborne pathogens, such as species of *Helminthosporium* and *Fusarium*. After incubating the seeds for a prescribed period, the pathogens are identified on the basis of disease symptoms of the seedlings or microscopic examination of individual seeds for the presence of fruiting structures of fungi.

Disease symptoms should be used with caution for identifying seedborne pathogens because different pathogens can cause similar symptoms of disease. If identification is made on the basis of microscopic examination of fruiting structures, each seed must be examined individually at relatively high magnifications. This is tedious and slow if samples of 400 seeds or more are used.

A modification of the blotter method has been devised, in which a low concentration of 2,4-D is added to the water used for moistening the blotters.

The 2,4-D inhibits germination of the seeds and facilitates microscopic examination of the seeds because they all remain in one plane, unlike the germinating seeds, which lie in many planes.

When the blotter method is used to obtain reproducible results, the incubation temperatures, length of incubation, and type and intensity of lighting must be standardized.

THE AGAR plating method is used widely for detecting fungus pathogens. Surface disinfected or untreated seeds are placed on a variety of agar media. The pathogens grow from the seeds and are identified by their macroscopic colony characteristics. When there is any doubt about their identity, microscopic examinations are made. Malt extract agar and potato dextrose agar are used oftenest.

When the media plating method is employed, standardization of temperatures, length of incubation, pH of the media, and light are important if reproducible results are to be obtained.

Research by Charles M. Leach at the Oregon Agricultural Experiment Station has shown that continuous irradiation with near ultraviolet (UV) 3,200A–4,000A from fluorescent black lamps and light from commercial fluorescent lamps greatly aids sporulation and subsequently the identification of a number of seedborne fungi. Other species of fungi (for example, *Helminthosporium oryzae*) are induced to form spores only if periods of near UV are alternated with dark periods.

Clyde M. Christensen, in Botanical Review, volume 23, 1956, described procedures for detecting molds that cause deterioration of cereal seed in storage. Seeds are pulverized in a medium of sodium chloride and agar. Then the suspension is plated in salt malt agar. Storage molds, particularly species of *Aspergillus* and *Penicillium*, grow well on this medium, but the growth of the saprophytic fungi commonly found on cereal seeds is retarded.

By growing seeds in soil, sand, and ground brick in greenhouse and laboratory, one can detect certain fungus pathogens that sometimes are difficult to detect by other methods. Identification usually is based on disease symptoms. Symptoms of loose smut of oats can be detected within 2 months when seeds are sown in the greenhouse in dry, cool soil. A combination of laboratory and greenhouse methods has been used to detect the fungus *Helminthosporium gramineum*, which causes barley stripe.

The embryo method was developed for determining loose smut of barley and wheat. The seeds are softened with sodium hydroxide to remove the embryos. The embryos are cleared in chloral hydrate or lactophenol and examined microscopically for the presence of fungus hyphae. The hyphae are more clearly seen by staining with cotton blue.

SEEDS infected with bacterial pathogens generally are not distinguishable from healthy seeds. To detect seeds infected with bacteria, two main methods are available.

The first is to grow plants in the laboratory or greenhouse under optimum conditions for the development of the pathogen until disease symptoms are evident. This method has been used in England for the detection of halo blight disease of beans.

A second method is the rapid phage-plaque count technique. It employs bacteriophages (bacteria-destroying agents) capable of lysing, or dissolving, specific bacterial pathogens.

Bacteriophages have been developed for *Pseudomonas pisi*, a bacterial pathogen of peas; *P. atrofaciens* of wheat; *P. coronafaciens* of oats; *Xanthomonas translucens* f. spp. hordei, secalis, and hordei-avenae; *Corynebacterium insidiosum* of alfalfa; and other seedborne bacterial plant pathogens.

SEEDBORNE viruses are rather rare, but a few cause serious diseases.

Virus-infected seeds usually are indistinguishable from the healthy seeds.

The only method for determining whether seeds are infected with a pathogenic virus is to grow them in the laboratory, greenhouse, or field until symptoms are evident. Seed-transmitted lettuce mosaic has received considerable attention.

WHEN nematode-infected seeds are converted into galls, as is the case for the grass and wheat seed nematodes (*Anguina*), the galls are easily detected by examining the dry seeds at low magnifications. When the nematodes are borne externally on the seeds—for example, *Aphelencoides ritzema-bosi* with aster seeds and the stem nematode, *Ditylenchus dipsaci*, with clover seeds—they cannot be detected by examining the dry seeds.

The Baerman funnel method has proved to be successful for detecting nematodes borne loosely on the seedcoat or in debris mixed with the seeds. A known amount of seeds wrapped in cheesecloth or a similar material is placed in a funnel immersed in water. The nematodes migrate from the seeds and the debris and can be collected, identified, and counted by microscopic examination.

ALTHOUGH information on methods for testing seed for seedborne pathogens is available in a number of publications, none covers completely all the methods that are in use.

L. C. Doyer in 1938 wrote one of the first manuals for the determination of seedborne diseases. In a publication of the Kew Mycological Institute in 1958, all the known seedborne pathogens are listed. It supersedes a similar compilation (Bulletin 245, 1931, West Virginia Agricultural Experiment Station) by C. R. Orton.

Many articles on the detection and classification of seedborne organisms have been contributed by Willard F. Crosier of the New York Agricultural Experiment Station and J. W. Groves and A. J. Skolko of the Department of Agriculture, Ottawa, Canada.

A number of methods of detecting seedborne diseases have been described by members of the Association of Official Seed Analysts, compiled by Alice M. Andersen and published in 1958 as a handbook by the Association of Official Seed Analysts. A section is devoted to seedborne diseases in the 1952 Agriculture Handbook No. 30, "Manual for Testing Agricultural and Vegetable Seeds."

Likewise, a section of the 1960 Proceedings of the International Rules for Seed Testing is devoted to the detection of pathogens. The European and Mediterranean Plant Protection Organization published reports on seedborne diseases in 1954 and 1958.

Several organizations in North America are interested in testing seeds for seedborne diseases and other phases of seed pathology. These are the Association of Official Seed Analysts, the International Crop Improvement Association, and the Seed and Plant Material Certification Committee of the Phytopathological Society.

The Plant Disease Committee of the International Seed Testing Association has contributed much to the development of standardized testing procedures, particularly through the distribution of international referee samples containing seedborne organisms.

Routine testing of seeds for pathogens has made greater advances in Europe than in the United States. A number of countries test seeds for plant pathogens. The European testing laboratories are mainly government institutions and usually have mycologists or plant pathologists on their staffs to supervise testing seed for pathogens.

Seed testing in the United States is performed by many private, commercial, State, and Federal laboratories. Most of them have not been prepared to test for seedborne pathogens.

In the United States there was little legislation concerning the testing of seeds for seedborne pathogens and no formal labeling requirements in 1961 for seedborne organisms or diseases of interstate and imported field and vegetable seeds. A few quarantine restrictions pertain to inspection for certain harmful pests upon arrival in the United States. Certificates of health are issued in Europe to facilitate the movement of seeds in international commerce, principally for quarantine purposes. More than 90 different countries have quarantine regulations with respect to seed importation.

THE PRESENT state of testing seeds for seedborne pathogens is somewhat similar to that which existed for purity and germination in 1900 or so. There is a great need for cooperation, coordination, and standardization of national and international sampling and testing procedures.

Until such factors as sampling procedure, size of samples, length of incubation, incubation temperatures, type of lighting, types of substrata, and pH of the media are standardized, the results obtained have little meaning because they are not reproducible from one laboratory to another. Standardization and simplification of these procedures must be based on findings of research. Studies designed to correlate the incidence of pathogens in seed lots with the occurrence of disease in the field after sowing are needed. Only by such studies can scientifically based standards be established.

ALICE M. ANDERSEN *is engaged in research on seeds in the Market Quality Research Division of the U.S. Department of Agriculture at Beltsville, Md. She holds degrees from the University of Nebraska. She is a member of the seed pathology and germination committees of the International Seed Testing Association.*

CHARLES M. LEACH *is an assistant plant pathologist at the Oregon Agricultural Experiment Station. He was graduated from the Queen's University of Belfast and received his doctor's degree at Oregon State College. He is a member of the Seed and Plant Material Certification Committee of the American Phytopathological Society and has worked on various phases of seed pathology and diseases of forage legumes.*

Tolerances in the Testing of Seeds

OREN L. JUSTICE AND EARL E. HOUSEMAN

No TWO samples taken from the same seed bag or same seed lot are likely to be identical. In well-mixed seeds, the particles that make up the lot are randomly distributed, and the variation from sample to sample is limited. Inadequate mixing interferes with random distribution and so lowers the chances of getting a representative sample from the lot.

The size of a lot of seeds may vary from a pound or two of cauliflower or other expensive seed to one or more carloads of alfalfa or wheat. A carload lot of alfalfa seeds contains more than a billion seeds.

Can the germination of this carload lot be determined by testing only 400 seeds or the percentage of pure seeds by testing 3 thousand seeds, or the number of noxious-weed seeds by testing 30 thousand seeds?

By testing all the seeds in the lot, the actual quality can be determined. For obvious reasons, we must content ourselves with testing a relatively small sample to determine within calculated limits the quality of the lot. By "quality of the lot" we mean the average of the entire lot for each quality factor, such as the percentage of pure seed and germination.

Actual percentages of germination, pure seed, or other quality factors cannot be determined. The application of appropriate statistical methods to test results enables us to determine the quality of the lot within a calculated range of limits. In testing seeds, the amount of this range is called the tolerance. It is the expected variation resulting from incomplete mixing of the seed, variations in sampling, and uncontrolled differences in the application of testing procedures.

A TOLERANCE, or expected variation, is expressed in terms of a probability and the amount of the tolerance. We are all familiar with games involving chance and frequently speak of odds. Probability, or probability level, carries the same connotation as odds.

Probabilities are expressed as odds (100 to 1), as percentages (1-percent level), or as decimals (0.01).

The figures in parentheses mean that the result of a subsequent test has a chance of about 1 out of 100 of exceeding the tolerance. In some kinds of work, tolerances that may be exceeded as often as once in 20 trials, the 5-percent level, may be satisfactory. Other types of work require a greater degree of confidence. Tolerances computed at the 1-percent level are greater than those computed at the 5-percent level.

If a representative sample from a well-mixed lot of alfalfa seeds germinates 88 percent in a properly conducted test, the average germination for the entire lot is not necessarily 88 percent. If a second sample is drawn from the lot and properly tested, however, the chances are approximately 20 to 1, according to statistical tolerances calculated by C. W. Leggatt, that the result of the second test will not go below 83.1 percent. The chances are also approximately 40 to 1 that the result of the second test will not fall below 82.4 percent, and approximately 100 to 1 that it will not fall below 80.8 percent. Any sample drawn from this seed lot would be expected to yield results which would fall into this statistical pattern.

The magnitude of tolerances at any given probability level will depend on the percentage of the seed component in the sample for which the tolerance is desired, the variations associated with testing procedures, the characteristics of the seed, and the size of sample tested. It also will depend on whether tolerances are intended to cover the difference between a test and a predetermined standard.

The minimum germination standards that have been established for vegetable seeds are an example of the latter. Because the standard is a fixed figure, only one test can vary.

In the other situation, a seedsman labels his seeds on the basis of a single test. A seed control agency later samples and tests the seeds. In this instance, results of two independent tests are being compared, both of which are subject to variation.

CERTAIN BASIC PRINCIPLES must prevail if the tolerances are to be used properly.

The seed lot from which the sample is drawn should be relatively homogeneous. The sample must be drawn in a random manner from a sufficient number of containers or locations in the lot. Bias must be avoided insofar as possible in conducting tests. Random sampling assumes that each seed or particle in the seed lot has an equal chance of being drawn and that no selection of any type is exercised.

If we assume that a seed lot has been reasonably well mixed, a sample was drawn at random, and a proper test was made, a single test will indicate that in a specified number of cases, say, 95 in 100 or 99 in 100, the true value of the lot is no more than one tolerance range removed from the result of the test. This value may be either higher or lower than the test result. If the seedsman labels his seeds with the result obtained by a proper test, results of later tests should be within tolerance of his statement.

The probability statement allows for an occasional test result to exceed the tolerance range. The number of these exceptions is indicated in the probability statement. When results do exceed the tolerance range, additional tests should be made to determine the cause of the excessive variation.

The purity tolerances were used as early as 1889, only 20 years after the first seed-testing station was established. At this time H. Rodewald, a German, showed that the variation in results of purity and germination tests of red clover agreed well with theoretical expectations.

He recognized several sources of error that led to variation in test results. They included difference in technique, change in the material being tested, accidents, and personal factors. The errors were classified as systematic errors or accidental errors. In testing seeds of orchardgrass for purity, he found the total error to be twice the accidental error, whereas the total error was only 1.4 times as great as the accidental error for red clover.

C. P. Smith, of the University of Maryland, in 1917 proposed arbitrary tolerances for percentages of pure seed.

His formula was based on the premise that the sample was composed of the component under consideration and the sum of all other components. His original formula was simplified to: T (tolerance)$=0.2+20$ percent of the lesser part divided by 100, the lesser part meaning the component under consideration or the sum of all other components, whichever is smaller. It was adopted by the Association of Official Seed Analysts in 1917 and used until 1938.

G. N. Collins, of the Department of Agriculture, published a circular in 1929 under the title, "The Application of Statistical Methods to Seed Testing." He proposed formulas for calculating purity and germination tolerances on the basis of the binomial distribution and for calculating noxious-weed seed tolerances on the basis of the Poisson distribution. Although Dr. Collins' formulas were evidently sounder, they were not adopted by seed analysts' organizations.

The International Seed Testing Association adopted in 1932 for the pure seed component the formula:

$$T=0.6+\left(0.2\ \frac{a\times b}{100}\right),\ \text{where}\ a\ \text{equals}$$

the percentage of the component under

consideration and b equals $100-a$. The tolerances for other crop seeds, weedseeds, and inert matter were calculated by the same formula, except that 0.2 was substituted for 0.6. These formulas were used in the Rules and Regulations under the Federal Seed Act from 1940 and in the Rules for Testing Seeds of the Association of Official Seed Analysts from 1944. Apparently the first term in the formula was intended to cover or compensate for errors incident to testing and the second term to take care of variations associated with random sampling. Tolerances calculated by these formulas have been used for nonchaffy seeds.

Wider tolerances are required for chaffy grass seeds which do not blend so well. These tolerances are obtained by adding to the tolerances calculated by the above formulas an additional tolerance. It is obtained by multiplying the lesser of a and b by the regular tolerance and dividing by 100.

Completely new purity tolerances were accepted by the Association of Official Seed Analysts in 1960. They were based on studies on variations associated with sampling and testing procedures begun in 1953 by S. R. Miles, A. S. Carter, and L. C. Shenberger, of Purdue University. Through cooperative research with 21 seed-testing laboratories, they measured the variations between different seed bags, different probes from the same bag, different test samples from the submitted sample, different analysts, and day-to-day variation of one analyst.

Mr. Miles and his coworkers used the following for calculating tolerances:

$$T=1.414t[(B^2/_n)(N-n)/N+C^2/_n\\+W^2/_n+A^2/_n+I^2/_n]^{1/2}$$

In the formula,

$t=$A factor corresponding to the desired probability level. (The actual factors used were: 5 percent probability level—1.65; 1 percent level—2.33; 0.1 percent level—3.09.)

$B=$Component of variation due to differences among bags.

C=Component of variation due to differences among cores or probes within bags.

W=Variations among working samples taken from the same submitted sample.

A=Component of variation due to the fact that different analysts may test samples differently.

I=A component of variation arising from the fact that the same analyst may test the same sample differently from day to day.

N=Number of bags in lot sampled.

n=Number of units of source of variation shown in same term of the equation.

Appropriate values for the different components of variance are inserted in the formula for the computation of regular tolerances for either nonchaffy seeds or chaffy seeds. The same tolerance is applied to a given percentage, regardless of whether it is pure seed, other crop seeds, weed seeds, or inert matter.

THE NEW tolerances for pure seed of both nonchaffy and chaffy kinds are narrower than the former tolerances. If the pure seed of alfalfa, a nonchaffy kind, is 98 percent, the new tolerance is 0.82 percent, but the old tolerance is 1.00 percent. When the pure seed percentage drops to 95, the old tolerance is 1.55, and the new is 1.21 percent.

The same pattern holds true for tolerances on pure seed of chaffy kinds, but the differences are not very great if the seed is 85 to 100 percent pure. The tolerances for chaffy kinds are slightly greater than for the nonchaffy kinds.

On the other hand, the recent tolerances for other crop seeds, weed seeds, and inert matter are larger than the former tolerances when the component constitutes no more than about 10 percent of the sample and less when the component constitutes more than 10 percent. The tolerance on 1.5 percent of weed seeds in alfalfa would be 0.76 percent by the new formula and 0.49 percent by the old. The new tolerance

on 15 percent of inert matter in Kentucky bluegrass seeds would be 2.14, and the old tolerance would be 2.75.

Mixtures consisting of kinds having unequal seed weights present additional problems. Mr. Miles and his co-workers developed formulas and prepared tables of special tolerances for a number of different particle-weight ratios applicable to mixtures. Most of these tolerances are wider than those for unmixed seed, although under certain circumstances they may be narrower.

GERMINATION TOLERANCES have developed without the benefit of statistical theory or experimentation. The tolerance limits at the various percentage levels have been determined through practice. This has been done by comparing the results of tests on replicate samples from the same seed lot. The tolerances thus determined are somewhat larger than tolerances calculated from statistical theory alone, due to variation incidental to testing.

The tolerances applicable to the various germination percentages are: 96 percent of germination or more, 5 percent; 90 to 95, 6 percent; 80 to 89, 7 percent; 70 to 79, 8 percent; 60 to 69, 9 percent; 59 and less, 10 percent.

The tolerances of 10 percent for all germinations below 60 percent and 5 percent for germinations above 95 percent are unrealistic from the standpoint of statistical considerations.

STATISTICAL tolerances calculated by C. W. Leggatt, of the Canada Department of Agriculture, for two independent 400-seed tests at the 5-percent probability level range from 6.9 at 50 percent germination to 1.8 at 1 percent and 99 percent germination. These tolerances are smaller by about 1.7 to 3.5 for germinations of 40 to 100 percent than tolerances that were in use in 1961.

When the problems in testing are considered, there appears to be some justification for wider tolerances at the lower germinations. Low-germinating samples frequently develop rank growths of molds and bacteria during germination. The organisms interfere with the tests and make evaluation of seedlings less precise than with high-germinating samples.

TESTS FOR SEEDS of noxious weeds, such as dodder and quackgrass, aim to determine the number of dodder or quackgrass seeds per ounce or per pound in the seed lot. The test is quite different from the one that has been described for purity and germination. The number of seeds of noxious weeds usually is low. One therefore has to use a statistical theory known as the Poisson distribution.

The reliability of a test for noxious-weed seeds is related primarily to the number of noxious seeds found in a sample. However, testing procedures based on the rate of occurrence of the noxious-weed seed would not be practical. Uniform sample sizes by weight therefore have been established for the various kinds of agricultural and vegetable seeds. Except for a few large-seeded kinds, the sample size for noxious-weed tests is at least 10 times that for purity analyses.

Noxious-weed seed tolerances are calculated from the formula: $Y = X \mid 1 + 1.96 \sqrt{X}$, in which X is the number of seeds labeled or represented and Y is the maximum number within tolerance of X. Thus, a table with any values of upper and lower limits can be set up. Some examples of tolerances computed by this formula are:

Number labeled or represented (X column)	Maximum number within tolerance (Y column)
0	2
1	4
2	6
3	8
4	9
5	11
6	12
7	13
8	14
9	16
10	17

A farmer or seedsman preparing to market his seed would have it tested for purity, germination, and seeds of noxious weeds. If the seed is alfalfa, the seed laboratory may report that it found 10 dodder seeds in a 50-gram examination. The vendor may label the seed to show 90 dodder seeds per pound. He obtains the figure "90" by multiplying 10 by 9, because 50 grams is approximately one-ninth pound.

Suppose a seed inspector samples this seed at a later date and the control laboratory finds 16 dodder seeds in 50 grams. For a proper comparison, the seedsman's claim of 90 seeds per pound must be reduced to a 50-gram basis, the amount actually tested. Thus, $90 \div 9 = 10$.

We now look in the tolerance table and find that 16 in Y column is within tolerance of 10 in X column. It would not be correct to compare the numbers on a per-ounce or per-pound basis because only one-ninth pound was tested.

SOME seed laws prohibit the sale of seeds containing noxious-weed seeds of certain designated species. It is not feasible to enforce such strict prohibitions. If no prohibited noxious-weed seeds are found in a sample, it cannot be assumed that there are no such noxious-weed seeds in the seed lot. Additional tests may reveal the presence of one or more prohibited noxious-weed seeds. For example, 999 samples drawn from the same lot may reveal no prohibited noxious-weed seed, but one or two such seeds may be found in the thousandth sample.

The seedsman who has his samples tested for labeling purposes faces this problem. That is why tolerances must be applied when seed is labeled to show no noxious seeds. The problem should be recognized by seed control officials when they consider the elimination of tolerances as applied to prohibited noxious-weed seeds.

OTHER TESTS make use of counted numbers of seeds or plants. Some kinds of seeds are so difficult to identify that 400 or 1 thousand seeds are counted out in the purity analysis for the identification of species or variety.

Certain special tests for species identification, such as the mottled-seed test of sweetclover and the ultraviolet test of ryegrass, make use of 400 seeds. Likewise, it is common practice to make varietal identifications on 50 to 1 thousand plants in greenhouse and field trials.

In all these situations, tolerances similar to those calculated by Dr. Leggatt for germination are used directly or in conjunction with other tolerances.

THE VARIETY tolerances have been modified slightly from his formula for convenience of application. If a regular purity analysis is made on Kentucky bluegrass seed and the sample is found to contain seeds of Merion Kentucky bluegrass, 400 bluegrass seeds will be taken at random to determine the proportion of each. The tolerance applicable to each variety of Kentucky bluegrass will be the appropriate tolerance for a 400-seed sample plus one-half the tolerance for the regular purity analysis.

For example, an analyst may find 85 percent of pure bluegrass seeds in a regular purity analysis. If, in a 400-seed examination, he finds that 65 percent of the bluegrass seeds are Merion and 35 percent are common, the tolerances for these percentages, in the Rules for Testing Seeds, are: Merion: $1.10 + 6.5 = 7.60$; common: $1.10 + 6.7 = 7.80$.

OREN L. JUSTICE *is a seed botanist and Head of the Testing Section, Seed Branch, Grain Division, Agricultural Marketing Service. He holds advanced degrees from Ohio University and Cornell. Dr. Justice is the author of a number of articles on seed dormancy and seed testing.*

EARL E. HOUSEMAN, *a mathematical statistician, is Director of the Statistical Standards Division of the Agricultural Marketing Service. He received his statistical training at Iowa State University and has served as a consulting statistician in the Department of Agriculture since 1943.*

What Labels Tell And Do Not Tell

WALTER A. DAVIDSON

DETAILED labeling has been adopted in the United States as the course most helpful to buyers of seeds.

The label on a package of seeds cannot help you if you do not read it.

Time was when the phrase "Buyer, beware!" was more essential than it is now, but it is wise still to be alert to the possibility of deception, even though deception as to the variety and quality of seed is difficult to detect except by testing techniques. The tests are the basis for most of the information on the label. As a buyer, you have little choice but to rely on this information.

The information on labels is not required to be included in advertisements pertaining to seeds. The seed laws prohibit false advertising, but sometimes it is hard to distinguish between statements that are false or misleading and those that are not.

The Supreme Court of the United States at one time excused the puffing sometimes found in advertisements. Some court interpretations have interpreted advertisements from the point of view of an ordinarily prudent person. The net result is that advertisements pertaining to seed may contain exaggerations or, indeed, may not tell the whole truth.

For instance, seeds may be described as being "offcolor" when actually they are screenings containing mostly immature, discolored seeds which may be low in germination and vigor. The advertisement may not mention germination. Such "offcolor" seeds may be described as a bargain in view of the low price, but no reference is made to a large percentage of seeds of weeds. Such inferior seeds may be small, and the advertisement may say there are more seeds per pound, without revealing that the proportion that would produce vigorous seedlings is small.

Mail-order seeds must be labeled, but the buyer ordinarily does not see the information on the label until it is delivered and paid for. It would be well to insist that complete information be supplied before you order such seeds.

Farmers who sell seeds or exchange seeds with their neighbors are exempt from the labeling requirements under the laws in most States. Buying seeds from your neighbor farmer may be advisable from the standpoint of having assurance of the variety, but most farmers do not have cleaning equipment for separating weed seeds. Many farmers do not take the precaution of having such seeds tested for germination. You should insist that a sample of such seeds be tested to determine quality before buying or accepting them in a trade.

To take advantage of detailed labeling, you must be informed as to the kind, variety, and quality of seeds that will best meet your needs. Buyers get more advice from retailers than from any other source. Much good advice is given by retail seedsmen, but I have stood at the counters in drugstores, dime stores, some seedstores, and department stores and have been amazed at the misinformation given by clerks to seed buyers.

It will be easier to understand the label and make decisions when you buy seeds if you are informed and give consideration to the importance of the different quality factors, the average quality of the different kinds, the relationship between quality and money value, and the use to be made of the plants.

THE IMPORTANCE of the different measurements of quality depends on the importance you attach to them. Whether you get your money's worth is determined by the ability of the seeds to produce the plants you want.

Seed labeling includes the percentages of pure seed, germination, other crop seeds, inert matter, and weed seeds; the name of the kind or kind and variety of pure seeds; and the names and number per ounce or pound of noxious-weed seeds.

When the label shows only the name of the kind, the percentage of pure seed is the proportion of the material in the container that is seed of the kind named.

When the variety name is also given, the pure seed represents the proportion that is pure seed of that variety.

The percentage of other crop seeds or other agricultural seeds represents that portion that is not of the kind or the variety considered in the pure seed. Because each kind in the "other crop seed" is not separately shown, it cannot be determined from the label, but when any one kind exceeds 5 percent of the whole contents of the container, it must be separately shown by name and percentage.

Inert matter consists of chaff, dirt, stones, stems, and pieces of seed one-half the original size or less. Broken pieces more than one-half the original size are included in the percentage of pure seed. In seed mixtures, such as seed of lawn grasses, the percentage of inert matter includes all the inert matter; it should not be stated separately for each kind of seed included in the mixture.

The percentage of weed seeds includes seeds of noxious weeds, even though the presence of noxious-weed seeds is shown separately on the label. State law, regulations, or custom determine which plants are weeds as distinguished from crop seeds.

Noxious weeds are plants defined under State law as being particularly injurious. The name and the rate of occurrence of their seeds per ounce or pound of the contents of the containers is shown on the label. In most States, it is illegal to sell seed that contains seeds of certain noxious weeds. The restrictions are meant to protect seed buyers, but you should realize there is no way to be sure there are no noxious-weed seeds in any lot of seed. Up-to-date seed-cleaning equipment can perform marvelous feats in the separation of seeds, but there is always the possibility that a few weed seeds remain.

The germination percentage represents the proportion of the pure seed that will germinate. A label stating "germination 90%" does not mean that 90 percent of the contents of the package or bag will germinate. Neither does the germination percentage pertain to the "other crop seed," for this is normally not tested to determine its germination.

Seed-testing laboratories grow seeds under favorable conditions to measure germination. It would be unusual that such favorable conditions would exist in a field; therefore you should consider the germination percentage in the light of the conditions to which the seed will be subjected before the plant can be produced. A number of conditions affect performance in the field, as compared to the laboratory—the size of the seeds, the natural time taken for germination, the condition of the seedbed, and the vigor of seedlings.

Germination requires the right amount of moisture. A seed absorbs moisture from the particles of soil against which it has come to rest. In a well-prepared seedbed, all of the seeds may come to rest in a position where this is possible. Favorable moisture conditions are usually more likely 2 or 3 inches below the surface. Large seeds can send a sprout this distance to the surface, but many small seeds cannot. If favorable moisture conditions do not exist close to the surface, small seeds that require shallow sowing may not come to rest where moisture is available, and a substantial proportion of the seeds may not produce plants.

Some kinds of seeds may germinate quickly under favorable conditions. Lettuce, for example, may germinate in 3 days. Others may require a longer period. Bluegrass takes about 28 days.

If moisture is not available during the whole time, the seeds may germinate and later become dry and die.

The germination percentage shown on the label usually is a reliable guide, but the conditions I mentioned must be considered when you attempt to interpret the germination in terms of plants in the field.

Furthermore, lots of seed with the same germination percentage may differ in seedling vigor. In other words, 90 percent of the seeds in one lot may germinate and produce vigorous seedlings. Another lot may show an equal percentage of germination, but the seedlings may be weak. Seed analysts have not developed an acceptable means of measuring and expressing this difference in seedling vigor, but low vigor usually is associated with a low percentage of germination.

Hard seeds, found in most legumes, are seeds that will not absorb moisture. Some kinds, such as alfalfa, germinate readily in soil. Others, such as sweet-clover, remain hard in the soil several weeks or several months, depending on temperature and moisture. Hard seeds are objectionable if prompt germination is required. They are not objectionable if germination over a long period of time may increase the chances of a good stand of plants.

Germination is the quality of seeds most certain to change. The germination of seeds that are stored in places of high moisture and high temperature may drop in a few weeks. The same seeds, if the moisture content is reduced to 12 percent or less and they are stored in a moderate temperature, may lose very little germination in several months.

To avoid crop losses due to unsuspected decline in germination, the seed-labeling laws require agricultural seeds to be labeled to show the date on which the germination test was made. The State laws prevent the sale of seed with an old test. Most allow 9 months. The Federal Seed Act prohibits interstate shipment if the test is more than 6 months old. You should avoid buy-

AVERAGE QUALITY—AMOUNT NEEDED FOR A TEST—DAYS FOR GERMINATION

Kind	Pure seed (percent)	Germination (percent)	Weed seed (percent)	Size sample	Days for germination
Alfalfa	99	90	0.50	⅓ cup	7
Bahiagrass	72	70	.50	1 cup	21–28
Barley	99	90	.50	1 qt.	7
Bean	99	90	.00	3 cups	7–10
Beet, field	97	75	.00	1½ qts.	14
Bentgrass	95	90	.50	¼ cup	21–28
Bermudagrass	97	85	1.00	½ cup	21
Bluegrass:					
Kentucky	85	80	1.00	½ cup	21–28
Rough	85	80	1.00	½ cup	21–28
Brome:					
Smooth	92	85	1.00	1 cup	14
Broomcorn	98	85	.50	3 cups	10
Buckwheat	97	85	1.00	3 cups	6
Canarygrass, Reed	96	80	.50	¼ cup	21
Carpetgrass	92	90	.50	½ cup	21
Chickpea	99	90	.00	1 qt.	7
Clovers:					
Alsike	97	90	1.00	¼ cup	7
Alyce	98	90	1.00	⅓ cup	21
Berseem	98	90	.50	⅓ cup	7
Bur (in bur)	90	90	.50	1½ qts.	14
Bur (out of bur)	98	90	.50	⅓ cup	14
Cluster	95	85	1.00	¼ cup	10
Crimson	98	85	.80	⅓ cup	7
Ladino and white	95	90	1.00	¼ cup	7
Persian	95	85	1.00	¼ cup	7
Red	98	90	.50	⅓ cup	7
Sour	98	90	.50	⅓ cup	14
Strawberry	97	90	1.00	⅓ cup	7
Subterranean	99	90	.50	1 cup	14
Sweet	95	90	1.00	¼ cup	7
Corn	99	90	.00	3 cups	7
Cotton	99	85	.00	1¼ qts.	12
Cowpea	98	85	.00	3 cups	8
Crotalaria: Slender leaf	99	80	.50	⅓ cup	10
Dallisgrass	70	70	1.00	1 cup	21
Fescue:					
Meadow	97	90	2.00	1 cup	14
Red, Chewings	97	80	.50	¾ cup	21–28
Tall	97	90	2.00	1 cup	14
Flax	97	85	.50	¾ cup	7
Johnsongrass	98	85	.50	½ cup	35
Kudzu	99	70	.50	1 cup	14
Lespedeza:					
Sericea or Chinese	98	90	1.00	⅔ cup	28
Common and Kobe	96	90	1.00	⅔ cup	14
Korean	97	90	1.00	⅔ cup	14
Lupine	99	90	.00	3 cups	10
Meadow foxtail	90	80	.50	½ cup	14
Medic, Black	98	90	.50	⅓ cup	7
Millet:					
Browntop	96	70	.50	⅔ cup	14
Foxtail, German, Hungarian, or Golden.	98	90	.50	⅔ cup	10
Japanese	97	90	.50	⅔ cup	10
Pearl	98	85	.50	1 cup	7
Proso	98	85	.50	1 cup	7
Oats	98	90	.10	1¼ qts.	10
Oatgrass, Tall	85	80	1.00	1 cup	14
Orchardgrass	85	85	1.50	1 cup	21
Peanuts	99	80	.00	1¼ qts.	10
Peas, Field	99	90	.00	3 cups	8

AVERAGE QUALITY—AMOUNT NEEDED FOR A TEST—DAYS FOR GERMINATION—Continued

Kind	Pure seed (percent)	Germination (percent)	Weed seed (percent)	Size sample	Days for germination
Rape, Dwarf Essex, Winter.....	99	90	.50	½ cup	7–10
Redtop......................	92	90	1.00	½ cup	10
Rescuegrass..................	95	85	1.00	¾ cup	28
Rhodesgrass..................	60	60	1.00	½ cup	14
Rice.........................	99	90	.50	1 qt.	14
Rough pea....................	98	90	.00	3 cups	14
Rye.........................	97	85	.10	3 cups	7
Ryegrass.....................	98	90	.50	⅔ cup	14
Sainfoin.....................	98	70	.50	2 cups	14
Sesbania.....................	99	90	.25	¾ cup	7
Sorghum.....................	98	85	.50	⅔ cup	10
Soybean.....................	98	85	.00	3 cups	8
Sudangrass..................	98	80	.50	1¼ cups	10
Sunflower (Cult).............	99	90	.00	1¾ qts.	7
Timothy.....................	99	90	.50	⅛ cup	10
Trefoil, Big.................	98	80	1.00	¼ cup	10
Trefoil, Birdsfoot.............	96	90	1.00	¼ cup	10
Velvetgrass..................	95	85	.50	½ cup	14
Vetch.......................	97	90	.50	3 cups	10–14
Wheat.......................	99	90	.10	3 cups	7–10
Wheatgrass:					
Crested....................	95	85	.50	⅔ cup	14
Slender....................	95	85	.50	⅔ cup	14
Western...................	80	80	2.00	⅔ cup	28

ing seeds with test dates older than those.

The term "pure live seed" is used often to express the quality of seeds, even though it is not shown on the label. "Pure live seed" is expressed as a percentage—the percentage of the contents of a carton or bag of seeds that is pure seed that will germinate. The percentage is determined by multiplying the percentage of pure seed by the percentage of germination and dividing by 100. For example, if seed is 90 percent pure with 80 percent germination, the pure live seed is 72 percent. This means that 72 percent of the contents of the package or bag consists of pure seed that can produce plants.

Percentage of pure live seed provides a handy way to compare the value and quality of seeds, but it has certain weaknesses.

For example: We may assume that one lot of seed is 99 percent pure and has 90 percent germination. The percentage of pure live seed then is 89.1. Another lot of seed is 90 percent pure but has 99 percent germination; the pure live seed value is again 89.1 per-

cent. In the first instance, however, there is 1 percent of something other than pure seed; in the second instance, there is 10 percent of something other than pure seed. The complete label will show whether the other component consists of other crop seeds, weed seeds, or inert matter. If it should appear in the label that part of the 10 percent in the second instance consists of weed seeds and that some of these are seeds of noxious weeds, the second lot of seed is less desirable and therefore is of lower market value, even though the percentage of pure live seed is the same.

Now we may assume that the lower percentage of pure seed in the second lot in the example is overcome by the higher percentage of germination. This would be a matter of opinion, on which seed buyers may not agree. However, the difference between 90 percent germination, in the first instance, and 99 percent germination, in the second instance, consists of 9 percent dead seed. The buyer would prefer that these be live seeds, but most buyers would prefer to have this amount of dead seed than seeds of other crops or weeds.

Another weakness in the use of pure live seed as a measure of quality lies in the fact that each percentage of germination is given the same value as each percentage of pure seed, yet percentages of pure seed can be determined with a higher degree of accuracy than can percentages of germination. Because germination tests are made on relatively small numbers of seeds, the probability of error is greater. This may be better illustrated by the fact that tests showing 95 percent germination are expected to vary approximately 6 percent, but tests showing 95 percent of pure seed are expected to vary only 1.5 percent.

Here, again, personal judgment and the kind of seed and the reason for sowing may affect the buyer's decision. Perhaps high germination may be of greater importance than high percentage of pure seed.

That, for instance, may be true for corn, for which the accurate spacing of plants is of great importance. Obviously, lower germination will mean a larger number of blank spaces between plants because of the seeds that do not germinate.

The percentage of pure live seed does help you determine the amount of seed you need. The rate of sowing is usually expressed in terms of bushels per acre or pounds per unit area. Greater importance is being attached to the spacing of plants for maximum yield. For instance, the distance between plants for maximum seed production is usually greater than the distance between plants for maximum forage production. Also, spacing of plants for maximum yield is affected by the soil, fertility, and moisture.

A pound of seed that is 50 percent of pure live seed will provide fewer plants than a pound that consists of 90 percent of pure live seed. Recommendations as to the rate of sowing are valuable guides and may be adequate for kinds of seeds that are average in purity and germination. If you want to take advantage of the increased knowledge about maximum yields, however, you must consider the spacing of plants.

You must also decide the rate of sowing and the amount needed on the basis of the quality of seed to be used. There is a good chance that you will need less seed than you assume at first. For this purpose, it would be better if recommended rates of sowing were expressed in ounces, pounds, or bushels of pure live seed per unit of area. It would then be easier to determine how much is needed.

For example, a 100-pound bag of alfalfa, with 98 percent of pure seed and 90 percent germination, contains 88.2 pounds of pure live seed. Another 100-pound bag, with 95 percent of pure seed and 80 percent germination, contains 76 pounds of pure live seed.

If you would sow 8 pounds to the acre, there is enough for about 11 acres in the first bag and 9.5 acres in the second bag. To get enough for 11 acres, 116 pounds of the quality in the second bag would be needed.

Most seed drills can be adjusted to the quantity to be sown. Fewer can be adjusted to the number of seeds per unit area or length of row. If you know how far apart plants should be in the row, you can try to get that spacing by setting the drill to drop the right number of seeds per foot, yard, or rod. You need to allow for casualties from pests, dry soil, or too wet soil, and dead seed. With 80 percent germination, you know that at best only 80 of every 100 seeds will grow. Every fifth seed will not grow. You will have to sow additional seeds to compensate. High-germination seed will have fewer skips or blank spaces, of course.

If you have the time and know the average number of seeds per ounce or pound, which is available from seed analysts, you can determine the amount of pure live seed you need. That would be an interesting project for a long winter evening.

Treating seed to prevent insect damage and to combat disease organisms on the seed and in the soil adds to the assurance of survival of the seedlings. Labeling to show that seed is treated is now required under Federal laws and many State laws. Some of the substances used are poisonous.

KINDS OF SEEDS differ in their average quality.

Perhaps the most difficult seeds to buy on the basis of detailed labeling are seeds for lawns. This is unfortunate, because the average buyer of lawn seeds is only an incidental user of seeds, and therefore does not become acquainted with the kinds, varieties, and the qualities of the several kinds. Lawn seeds generally are small-seeded grass seeds that are difficult to process and clean to a high purity.

The seed of Kentucky bluegrass, for example, is small and has hairy appendages which are hard to remove. It is in the group that we call chaffy grasses. Kentucky bluegrass seed that was 85 percent pure used to be considered to be of good quality, insofar as its purity was concerned. For seed, Kentucky bluegrass of certain improved varieties now is grown in cultivated rows, sometimes under irrigation, so that the seeds are larger, drier, and easier to clean to high purity.

Some grasses, such as fescue, sudangrass, and ryegrass can be cleaned to high purity. Some kinds are notorious for the weeds they often contain—such as quackgrass in smooth brome and the wheatgrasses, wild onion in orchardgrass, and johnsongrass in sudangrass.

Many of the native grasses common to the Plains States are even harder to clean than Kentucky bluegrass, but special cleaning machinery has made it possible to sow them with ordinary farm drills or special grass seeders. In the past, many of these chaffy range grasses were sown in their original chaffy condition, even with such crude equipment as manure spreaders. In some of these kinds, 10 percent pure seed would be considered acceptable.

Seeds of legumes, such as the clovers and alfalfa, are smooth, heavy, and free flowing, as contrasted with the chaffy grass seeds. Legume seeds range in size from the small-seeded whiteclover to the large horsebean. Removing light, chaffy material from them is relatively easy. The most serious difficulty arises with weed seeds that are of similar size and shape, such as dodder in the small-seeded legumes like alfalfa, red clover, and lespedeza. Legume seed should not contain more than one-tenth of 1 percent of weed seeds, and the pure seed should be at least 98 percent.

Germination percentages of legumes are sometimes confusing, because the hard seedcoat on some kinds excludes water. It is not unusual that legume seeds are labeled to show 10 to 20 percent of hard seeds. Some, like alfalfa, will germinate within several weeks in the soil, but the hard seeds of other kinds, such as sweetclover and crotalaria, may remain in the soil for months and years. It is possible to overcome this problem of hard seed by putting the seeds through a scarifying machine, which scratches the seedcoat to permit water to enter.

Seeds of cereals, which include the grain crops, generally are large and free flowing. Purity as high as 99.5 percent is not unusual. Seeds of other crops and sometimes weed seeds cannot be removed, however, or can be removed only with a large loss of seed and at great cost. Germination of the cereals should be 90 percent or more, unless the seeds have been frosted, have been overtreated to control insects or diseases, or have been stored for a long period or with excessive moisture.

THE RELATIONSHIP of quality and price of seeds is not well defined.

We might assume that for each percentage point of difference in pure live seeds there should be a similar difference in money value. In fact, you would not want in any circumstance to buy seeds that are below a certain quality. At that point, in the range of quality for your purposes, the seeds cease to have any value. We should assume then that the reduction in money value should be proportionately more than the reduction in quality, as expressed in the terms of pure live seeds. In actual practice, lower quality seed often is sold at prices higher than it should be, if a comparison of pure live seeds is made.

An example: Lot A may sell for 10 dollars per 100-pound bag, and lot B may sell for 9 dollars per bag. Upon checking the label, we may find lot A has 99 percent pure seed and 90 percent germination, and lot B has 98 percent pure seed and 80 percent germination. From the respective 89.1 and 78.4 percentages of pure live seed in each 100-pound bag, we learn that you would pay at the rate of 11.22 dollars per 100 pounds of pure live seed for lot A and 11.48 dollars for lot B. Measured as to their ability to produce plants, lot A is cheaper and better.

Seed is never 100 percent pure with 100 percent germination. The price of seeds is therefore set for a quality somewhere under this ideal. A difference of 1 percent in the measurement of pure seeds and germination is really more than 1 percent. If maximum germination is 90 percent, for instance, then 80 percent germination is not one-tenth, or 10 percent, lower in quality—it is one-ninth, or about 11 percent, lower in quality. The price should be more than 10 percent less.

As I said, the percentage of pure live seeds is dependable for the purpose of determining the amount of seed needed. It is not an adequate measure of quality. It is better therefore to consider the relationship between quality and money value in terms of the more definite quality factors which are percentage of germination, percentage of pure seeds, percentage of weed seeds, and rate of occurrence of noxious-weed seeds.

The specifications used by the Federal Government for buying seed allow a tolerance or margin for unavoidable variations. Beyond that, for each percentage point of germination below the requirements, a deduction of 2 percent in the purchase price is made. For each 0.5 percent of pure seed below specifications, a 2-percent deduction is made. For each 0.2 percent of weed seeds in excess of the amount allowed, a deduction of 1 percent of the purchase price is made.

It would be difficult to arrive at a mathematical deduction in purchase price that may seem reasonable for seed with noxious-weed seeds compared with seed containing none. The Federal specifications provide for rejection of any seed containing certain noxious-weed seeds at a rate of more than 45 per pound.

THE USE to be made of the crop determines the kind, variety, and quality of seeds that will best serve your needs.

One may advise buyers always to select seed of the highest quality and of the most desirable variety. That is not always possible. A choice may be forced upon the buyer as to the kind, variety, freedom from weeds, and germination. The alternative on occasion may be that of choosing between high germination of the second-choice variety and the first-choice variety that contains seeds of noxious weeds. These selections may be decided on the basis of facts available to the buyer, but in many instances it becomes a question of personal choice and opinion.

The amount of seed bought may may make it worthwhile to send a sample to a seed-testing laboratory to check the quality. One should remember that variations in results of tests must be expected, but the range of reasonable variation is pretty well established. Seed analysts can give advice.

WALTER A. DAVIDSON *is Director of the Grain Division of the Agricultural Marketing Service. He is a graduate in agriculture of the North Dakota State College. He was formerly Chief of the Seed Branch, Agricultural Marketing Service, and past president of the International Seed Testing Association.*

Seed Marketing

Services

WALTER R. CRISPIN

THE SEED VERIFICATION SERVICE is concerned primarily with the origin of seed of alfalfa and red clover—that is, the locality where it is produced.

A voluntary service, it is conducted by the Seed Branch of the Grain Division, Agricultural Marketing Service. It covers shipments of seeds within and between States.

The Department of Agriculture in 1925 decided to investigate the need to set up a system of records that would enable seed dealers and farmers to buy seed of alfalfa and red clover with positive assurance of origin. A study covering records of more than 60 seedsmen indicated that the records and some supplemental information would enable a supervising agency to trace the origin of all lots handled by seedsmen.

After conferences with representatives of the Department of Agriculture, State seed-certifying agencies, State agricultural colleges and experiment stations, the International Crop Improvement Association, National and State Farm Bureaus, and the seed trade, the Seed Verification Service was established in 1927.

The purpose of seed certification is to make available to the public seed of superior varieties of known genetic identity. Much alfalfa seed that for one reason or another is not eligible for certification or is not certified because of the cost is being produced. The demand for it is good when it is truthfully labeled as to origin. The Seed Verification Service facilitates the marketing of this seed, under its true origin, but it does not supplant the State certifying agencies.

Misrepresentation of origin of alfalfa seed before the Seed Verification Service came into being resulted in unfair competition among dealers and in heavy losses to farmers who unknowingly purchased seed that winterkilled because it was not adapted to the localities where it was planted. The names of States, which for years had been producing large quantities of nonhardy alfalfa seed, rarely appeared on tags or invoices.

After inauguration of the Service, the price difference between nonhardy alfalfa seed grown in the Southwestern States and winter-hardy strains produced in the North Central and Northern States increased for a time as a price adjustment to a supply-and-demand basis became effective.

Sowing adapted origins of seed of alfalfa and red clover is important, as indicated by provisions of the Federal Seed Act as to seeds in interstate and foreign commerce. Interstate shipments of alfalfa, red clover, whiteclover, and field corn (except hybrid seed corn) must be labeled to show the origin. If it is not known, a statement that the origin is unknown must be used. Imported seeds of alfalfa and red clover, before being admitted into the commerce of the United States, must be stained to identify the country or countries that produced them.

The climate in which alfalfa seed is grown for any length of time affects its winter hardiness. The rapidly growing, less hardy plants are eliminated by natural selection in a cold climate, as they winterkill. The slow-growing, winter-hardy plants are gradually crowded out in warmer climates by less hardy, rapidly growing plants. Standards of the International Crop Improvement Association specify that when a variety of alfalfa seed is grown outside of its designated region of adaptation, certification shall be limited to one generation from foundation and registered seed. The seed thus produced shall be the certified class.

APPLICATIONS by dealers for enrollment in the Seed Verification Service are made each year. The Service is conducted by offices of the Seed Branch in Washington, D.C., Kansas City, Mo., Minneapolis, Minn., and Sacramento, Calif. Members of the Service are known as verified-origin seed dealers. Before enrollment, the dealer must have his methods of handling seed stocks and records examined and approved by a Federal inspector.

In making application for membership, the dealer agrees to comply with the instructions and procedure for origin verification of seeds; keep prescribed records; confine his purchases of alfalfa seed insofar as possible to lots of seed eligible for verification, with the exception of seeds produced in foreign countries other than Canada; endeavor to obtain acceptable assurances of origin for all such lots; and submit inspection certificate applications for all eligible lots of alfalfa seed, other than State-certified seed. Such seed must also be reported for verification of origin if the dealer desires to sell it as verified-origin seed.

APPLICATIONS for inspection certificates and proof of origin for each lot listed thereon are submitted to the appropriate office for origin verification. Information on the application includes the kind of seed, name and address of the grower or shipper, shipping point, date of shipment or delivery, shipper's lot number, the verified-origin seed dealer's receiving lot number, the quantity in pounds, place where the seed was grown, and the kind of declaration supporting the origin of each lot.

Growers' declarations of origin are furnished on lots of seed purchased from growers, shippers' declarations of origin on lots purchased from country shippers, and verified-origin seed invoices on lots purchased from other verified-origin seed dealers.

Information on verified-origin seed tags and on State-certified seed tags may be accepted as proof of origin, if tags are properly attached to the bags and there is no evidence that the contents of the bags have been tampered with.

When the origin of a lot of seed reported for verification of origin is questioned, it may be deleted from the application, or a sample may be obtained and examined for incidental seeds indicative of origin. The result of the examination is given consideration in determining action to be taken. When approved and signed by a Federal seed inspector, the application becomes an inspection certificate, and the seed listed thereon is known as verified-origin seed.

The fee for verification of origin was 7 cents per hundred pounds in 1960. Fees are charged to cover the cost of the service.

Dealer's report forms as to verified-origin seed are provided by the Service for the use of verified-origin seed dealers in reporting new lots of verified-origin seed which are obtained when a lot is cleaned or blended with other lots and thereby loses its former identity. These reports give a partial transcript of the blending and cleaning records for all bulk lots.

A CONTINUITY of records and lot identification, which enables a Federal inspector to trace any lot of verified-origin seed from the consumer back to the grower, is a fundamental principle of the Seed Verification Service.

The normal movement of alfalfa and red clover seed is from the grower to the country shipper to the dealer. A country shipper is one who confines his purchases of seeds to those produced in his own locality for shipment to seed dealers or to other country shippers. The record requirements of the Service apply primarily to country shippers and dealers in verified-origin seed.

Prescribed records for verified-origin seed dealers, in addition to acceptable assurances of origin, are receiving record, blending and cleaning record, stock record, labeling record, shipping record, sample record, and a storage record.

Country shippers issuing declarations of origin are required to maintain receiving records, original growers' and shippers' declarations of origin obtained, blending and cleaning records for any lots that are processed, shipping records, sample of each lot shipped; and a copy of each shipper's declaration issued.

A lot number is assigned to each lot as it is received. The bags are tagged or marked with this lot number, which is also shown on all records pertaining to the lot. More detailed records are required for country shippers who handle a large amount of seed than for those who handle only a few lots each season.

Origin designations and districts are specified in the regulations. The origin of a verified-origin lot may be a State or two or three States if the northern boundary of the most southern State is in the same latitude or north of the southern boundary of the most northern State. These are some of the exceptions.

For red clover seeds, the country is divided into divisions or districts designated as Western Division, Rocky Mountain Division, and Eastern Division. Red clover seeds grown in one division are not eligible to carry verified-origin seed tags if blended with seeds produced in the other divisions.

California is divided into three districts, designated as northern California, central California, and southern California. Alfalfa seeds grown in California may be blended with that produced in other States only on the basis of California districts.

Designated parts of States are set up as special districts—for example, northwestern Texas.

The origin of seeds produced in Canada and imported from Canada may be shown as Canada, or the Provinces of Canada may be shown.

Not more than three States or three Provinces of Canada may be given as the origin, and the percentage of seed produced in each State or Province must be given in the order of its predominance. The blending of seeds of domestic alfalfa or red clover with such seeds from Canada is prohibited.

VERIFIED-ORIGIN tags and invoices are the commercial documents issued by verified-origin dealers to buyers. They show the origin of seeds of alfalfa and red clover. The documents may be issued only if the information thereon is in harmony with the information on inspection certificates covering the lots and verified-origin seed dealers' reports for bulk or blended lots.

The verified-origin invoice is used primarily in transactions between verified-origin dealers to eliminate the need to attach verified-origin tags.

The verified-origin tag, which shows the kind of seed, where it was grown, and lot number, is the document that reaches the consumer. All verified-origin seeds equal to or better than the standard of quality specified in the regulations must bear verified-origin tags—except seeds shipped to another verified-origin dealer or other dealers who file written requests that such tags not be attached.

Tags must be sewed on all bags by machine or attached by a seal in such a way that the bags cannot be opened without releasing the tags. The lot number must be stenciled on all bags of seeds verified as to origin, regardless of whether tags are attached.

A COMPREHENSIVE system of supervision, devised before the Service was started, provides for inspection in surplus-producing districts, at offices and warehouses of verified-origin dealers, and in consuming sections. It was recognized that records alone would accomplish little unless provision was made to supervise them.

Records of country shippers are inspected to verify information as to origin and weight as shown on shippers' declarations issued to verified-origin dealers. A record is obtained of shipments from production areas in the Southwest to country shippers in the Northern States in order to determine how such seed is represented as to origin when sold.

Records of verified-origin dealers normally are audited in midseason (January) and near the end of the fiscal year (June). Prescribed records, properly maintained, enable a Federal inspector to check the receipt, origin, and disposition of all alfalfa or red clover seed handled.

Retailers in consuming areas are visited to ascertain whether all lots of seed of alfalfa and red clover bearing verified-origin tags have been verified and whether the origin stated is correct. Invoice information is obtained to be checked against stock cards maintained by the dealers to determine whether all shipments are being charged against the proper lots. Samples of the same lot obtained from different shipments, and file samples maintained by verified-origin dealers are compared to ascertain whether there appears to be any substitution.

Samples of lots bearing verified-origin tags are examined for incidental seeds indicative of origin and to determine whether such lots meet the quality requirements of the Service for the attachment of verified-origin tags, which are as follows: The seed shall contain not more than 2 percent of impurities other than crop seeds; not more than 1 percent of weed seeds; and not more than 3 percent of any one kind or a total of more than 5 percent of crop seeds other than alfalfa and red clover.

The total germination and hard seed shall not be less than 80 percent. The seed shall also be of the size, plumpness, color, and the other physical characteristics that ordinarily distinguish seed of good quality.

Each lot of cleaned seed shall be uniform throughout, so that a sample taken from any part of the lot will represent, within tolerances, the quality and condition of the entire lot.

Many country shippers also are reached by mail and are asked to submit growers' and shippers' declarations, which they hold as assurance of origin. Inquiries are sent to growers to verify information given in growers' declarations.

Interest in verified-origin seed has centered largely in alfalfa, probably because origin is more important for alfalfa seed than for seed of red clover and because the producer and the planter of the seed often are in the same locality, whereas alfalfa seed may come some distance.

The amounts verified in 1927–1939 averaged about 39 million pounds of alfalfa seed and 13.5 million pounds of red clover seed.

For the fiscal years 1954–1958, origin verification of alfalfa seed averaged about 70 million pounds (exclusive of reverification) and 68 thousand pounds of red clover seed. The largest amount of alfalfa seed verified for any 12-month period was 91,305,000 pounds, exclusive of reverification, for the fiscal year beginning July 1, 1954. Reverification refers to seed that is sold by one verified-origin seed dealer to another. Each dealer reports the seed for verification of origin.

The number of verified-origin seed dealers has ranged from 46 in 1929 to 124 for the 1955–1956 season; 95 dealers in 19 States were enrolled for the 1959–1960 season.

An inspection service as to quality of seeds was inaugurated by the Seed Branch in November 1951 to determine and certify the quality of agricultural and vegetable seeds based on purity, germination, and content of seed of noxious weeds. The Service was started at the request of seedsmen who engage in foreign commerce. Seedsmen sometimes need a Federal certificate to obtain a price adjustment when imported seeds meet import requirements but fail to conform to contract specifications. Contracts covering the sale of seeds for exportation sometimes specify that a Federal certificate be furnished as proof of quality.

The service is available only for agricultural and vegetable seeds as defined under the Federal Seed Act or seeds purchased by Government agencies. The volume of service is controlled by the facilities available. Service testing is limited to seed owned by or sold or shipped to any department or agency of the U.S. Government or which is in or destined for foreign commerce.

Tests are made in accordance with the methods of seed testing prescribed under the Federal Seed Act or, when requested by the applicant, in accordance with the International Rules for Seed Testing. Samples are tested and certificated for one or more of the factors of quality, as requested by the applicant for the inspection.

Two types of inspection are made. Sample inspection certificates apply only to the sample tested. Lot inspection certificates apply to the lot of seed sampled and tested. Sample inspection service only is available on seeds in or destined for foreign commerce. Lot inspection service is available on seeds tested for other Government agencies and departments, provided the lot of seeds was officially sampled by the Grain Division.

A schedule of fees for different kinds of seeds, based on the cost of the service, has been established. Fees for sampling seeds are based on the time consumed, at an hourly rate plus the cost of travel and other expenses, if any.

Service testing is not available for seeds in interstate or intrastate commerce. State, commercial, and private laboratories perform such service. Most State laboratories test a limited number of samples of seed for farmers and seedsmen free of charge or for a nominal fee after a specified number of free tests have been made. Many of the larger seed firms operate their own seed laboratories. Commercial seed laboratories test seeds on a fee basis.

WALTER R. CRISPIN *is in charge of the district office of the Seed Branch, Grain Division, Agricultural Marketing Service, Kansas City, Mo. He is a graduate of the University of Missouri.*

The Seeds in Your Drill Box

E. R. CLARK AND C. R. PORTER

A FARMER in Kentucky bought 200 pounds of seed of Korean lespedeza at a farm auction. The seed bore no label, and he knew nothing about its ability to germinate, its purity, content of weed seeds, and crop mixture. He paid 8.7 cents a pound for it when the market price for certified seed was more than twice as much. He thought he had a bargain.

Before he planted it, he had it tested. The report of tests in a laboratory at the Kentucky Agricultural Experiment Station showed: Pure seed, 76.85 percent; germination, 26 percent; inert matter, 9.46 percent; weed seeds, 10.96 percent; and other crop seeds, 2.73.

The weed seeds consisted of 39 buckhorn and 543 dodder per ounce, both of which are classified as noxious weeds in Kentucky. The other weeds were common, bracted, and Virginia plantain, beggarstick, paspalum, witchgrass, crabgrass, buttonweed, frostflower, bristlegrass, spiny sida, and heal-all.

By multiplying the percentage of pure seed by the percentage of germination and the number of pounds of seed the farmer bought, we know that he got only 40 pounds of pure live seed. Instead of paying 8.7 cents, the farmer paid 43 cents a pound for the seed that would germinate and grow.

When he got the report on what he thought had been bargain seed, he decided not to sow it but buy good seed instead. He bought 200 pounds of certified Rowan Korean lespedeza at 18 cents a pound. The labels on the bag showed the percentage of pure seed to be 99.95; germination, 94 percent; inert matter, 0.03 percent; weed seeds, 0.02 percent (no noxious weeds); and no other crop seeds.

By using these figures to convert the purchase of 200 pounds of certified Rowan to a basis of pure live seed, we find the farmer paid 19.4 cents a pound: The good seed of an adapted variety cost him only 45 percent as much as his bargain seed.

But that is not the whole story.

Suppose the farmer had not sent the seed to the State seed laboratory but had planted it immediately. What would have been the loss in yield and quality of hay or pasture? What would have been the cost and trouble of cleaning up the weeds if he had sown his bargain seed?

Many farmers penalize themselves by planting poor-quality, weed-infested seeds—a fact that is borne out by the results from surveys of seed in drill boxes—the seeds that are about to be planted.

FOR DRILL-BOX surveys, samples are taken on farms selected at random in the sections to be surveyed. The seed is sampled in the fields where the planters are working whenever it is feasible to do so. If wet weather hinders the planting, samples may be drawn from bags or bins after the seed has been prepared for planting. Seed inspectors, county agents, and students of agriculture conduct the surveys.

They get information as to the history and handling of the seed, the name of the variety, and the source. If the survey covers certified and noncertified, cleaned and uncleaned, or treated and untreated seeds, the farmer is asked about those details.

Drill-box surveys have been made in more than 20 States and Canadian Provinces since 1951. They indicate by and large that the quality of seed in the drill box has not kept up with the great strides that have been made in developing better seed-cleaning machinery and our knowledge of the processing of seed. Seeds of weeds and other crops and varieties, some readily separable by modern machinery, too often are found in the farmers' drill boxes. Failure to prepare this seed properly before planting is a common cause of crop losses.

DRILL-BOX SURVEYS were made in Canada in 1913, when 263 samples of small grains were collected from farmers' drill boxes in Alberta. A survey conducted later by the late W. H. Wright, Chief of the Seed Testing Section of the Canada Department of Agriculture, disclosed that more than 40 percent of the seed sown was inferior to the minimum quality required for grade under the Seed Act.

In Minnesota in 1923, 653 samples were taken from farmers' grain drill boxes. The amounts of foreign material, including other crop seeds, weed seeds, and inert matter, averaged 3.45 to 5.77.

The Agricultural Extension Service in North Dakota made a survey of hard red spring wheat and durum planted in 1940; 34 percent of the spring wheat and 75 percent of the durum lots were considered to be unsatisfactory because of weed seeds and admixtures.

Early and recent surveys have shown that much of the seed grain is homegrown. Wheat, oats, and barley fields usually are planted with seed produced on the same farm or obtained from neighbors. Seeds of legumes and grasses generally come from commercial channels.

A survey in New York indicated that 75.8 percent of the wheat seed had been grown on the same farm and 15.8 percent had been purchased from neighbors.

Surveys in Nebraska showed 77.8 percent of the wheat and 70.8 percent of the oats were homegrown. Only 3.7 percent of both kinds had been purchased from dealers.

Wheat farmers in Virginia bought 9.9 percent of the seed from dealers, but 81.8 percent had been grown on the farm where it was being planted. A different trend was found in Indiana in a survey in 1957. Only 64.5 percent of the oats had been grown by the planter, 10.9 percent had been purchased from other farmers, and 14.3 percent was bought from dealers. The demand for the new variety, Clintland, which had been released by the Purdue Agricultural Experiment Station only a few years previously, may have brought this change of practice. Seed of Clintland was available only from certified seed growers and dealers. The variety-conscious farmers discarded their own seed and purchased Clintland.

That improved varieties are in demand throughout the country is indicated by the surveys in every region.

Workers at Clemson Agricultural College in South Carolina found that 82.5 percent of the farmers used recommended varieties of wheat, 66.6 percent grew recommended varieties of barley, 74.5 percent grew approved varieties of rye, and 78.6 percent grew standard varieties of oats. In South Carolina, as in Indiana, the percentage of farmers who obtained seed grain from dealers—13.8 percent—was higher than indicated by surveys in other States.

Eighty percent of farms covered by the surveys in Nebraska were planted with known varieties of wheat and oats. Eighty-three percent of the farms surveyed in New York grew either Garry or Rodney oats.

TESTING SEED for purity and germination has been recommended by agricultural leaders for a long time, but many farmers still plant seed grain without testing it.

In North Dakota, 54 percent of the seed grain was not tested for germination.

In Indiana, 37 percent was not tested.

In Nebraska, 44 percent of the farmers had not tested their seed grain.

In South Carolina and Virginia, the percentages planted without testing were 85 percent and 83 percent, respectively.

In Michigan, 14 percent of the samples taken from drill boxes tested less than 80 percent in germination.

On the other hand, 81 samples of seed corn taken in a survey at planting time in Nebraska were planted in check plots and compared for stand, yield, and earliness of maturity. Sixty-two samples, which produced yields of 100 bushels or more to the acre, germinated 96 percent or more in standard laboratory tests.

TREATING seed with chemicals to control seedborne and soilborne organisms is recommended. Inexpensive materials and convenient methods have been developed and are used.

Nevertheless, the results of surveys in eight States create doubts as to whether all farmers understand the losses from cereal diseases. The percentages of untreated seed lots were 32 percent to 83 percent. The States are Oklahoma, Nebraska, Illinois, Wisconsin, Indiana, New York, Virginia, and South Carolina.

THE USE of certified seed, as determined by the surveys, was limited, but it seems to be increasing.

Among 698 samples of oats collected in Nebraska in 5 years, only 4.7 percent represented certified seed. Five and four-tenths percent of all samples of oats, wheat, barley, and rye in the studies in Nebraska was certified.

In North Dakota, 5.2 percent of 192 samples of flax in 1953 was certified seed, and 4 percent of the wheat seed in 1954 was certified. In 1956, 861 samples of wheat contained 13.8 percent known to be certified seed. The increase apparently was due to the demand for the new Selkirk variety and for certain new varieties of durum.

In a survey in Arkansas, only 3.6 percent of the total bushels of oats seed, represented by 647 samples, was known to be certified; 22.4 percent of the wheat, covered by 392 samples, was certified.

The demand for seed of a new variety accelerates the use of registered and certified seed. Its genuineness and freedom from varietal mixtures is assured thereby. That may explain the higher percentages of certified seed among the samples gathered in the surveys.

After Clintland oats had been released in Indiana, a survey showed that 20 percent of the 312 samples of oats were certified Clintland. In Illinois, 604 samples of wheat in 29 counties included 12 percent certified; 39 percent of the samples of oats were certified.

Absence of weed seeds is a distinguishing quality in good seed, but the results of the surveys have been disappointing. Too many samples contain an excessive amount of weed seeds, usually because of lack of adequate cleaning. The more recent surveys show little improvement over earlier surveys in this regard. Many samples contained seeds of noxious and common weeds.

A survey of oats seed in Michigan disclosed that 115 of 372 samples contained seeds of noxious weeds; 106 contained quackgrass seeds. In Iowa, 23 of 117 samples carried seeds of quackgrass; 6 samples contained 3 kinds of noxious weeds. Samples of wheat and oats in Nebraska had an average of 135 weed seeds in a pound. Samples of oats and wheat in Oklahoma averaged 128 weed seeds in a pound.

Careful cleaning of seed grain should reduce the number of weed seeds to a maximum of 50 to a pound, but this degree of efficiency is not attained by the practices generally followed. Of 377 samples of seed wheat collected in North Dakota, 175 samples, or 45 percent, contained more than 100 weed seeds to a pound.

THREE systems of cleaning seed grain are in common use: Farm cleaning, with a small fanning mill; custom cleaning, with large, general-purpose cleaning machinery at country elevators; and custom cleaning at approved processing plants.

The practice of cleaning seed on the farm is declining. In North Dakota in 1954, 21 percent of the samples had been cleaned on the farm; in 1956, 15 percent. The farm-cleaned samples averaged 200 weed seeds to a pound in 1954 and 156 weed seeds in 1956.

The ordinary fanning mill, commonly found in farm granaries, cannot do a good job of cleaning. A few farms have large, power-driven cleaners, whose screens and airblasts may be adjusted for most kinds of separations needed for seed of small grain. If such cleaners are not available on the farm, custom cleaning may be advisable.

Country elevators generally are equipped with scalping machines of high capacity. They are made for removing dockage from commercial grain, but do not make the precise separations required for cleaning seed. The elevator legs, storage bins, and parts of the conveyors are not designed to permit convenient and thorough cleanup after each custom job. Furthermore, there is a tendency for operators to exceed the best capacity of the machines for effective work during the seasonal rush at seeding time. The country elevators generally are less satisfactory than the farm fanning mills for cleaning seed. In the North Dakota surveys, seed grain cleaned at country elevators averaged 175 weed seeds to a pound in 1954 and 187 in 1956.

Approved processing plants are equipped and operated in many States in accordance with the recommendation of seed-certification agencies and are approved by the agencies for custom cleaning of seed grain, including certified seed. Besides general-purpose scalping machinery, these plants have special types of cleaners for specific problems in seed separation—gravity mills, disk cleaners, magnetic separators, dodder removers, and many devices for specific separations. The conveyors, storage bins, and all parts in direct contact with the seed are built so they can be cleaned conveniently.

Systems of inspection, registering, and approving custom-cleaning plants for processing certified seed have been used successfully in several States, but the number of approved processing plants available for custom work is inadequate. The movement toward this solution of the cleaning problem is growing and deserves thorough study.

DRILL surveys lead us to the conclusion that the quality of seed grain that is generally planted is far from ideal.

We have no doubt that this phase of crop production could be strengthened by a simple, five-point program:

The use of certified or registered seed to establish new varieties, or to replace mixed stock. The best guarantee of trueness to variety is the certified tag.

The use of homegrown seed for planting commercial acreage, with precautions to avoid admixtures during harvesting, threshing, storing, and all other steps in production.

The custom cleaning of all grain to be used for seed. Approved processing plants should be used in preference to farm cleaning or country elevator work unless the farms or elevators are equipped with specialized seed-cleaning machinery and conveyors.

Testing for germination of all seed intended for planting. Representative samples should be sent to the State seed laboratory or a commercial laboratory. Sending samples early, before the seasonal rush develops, is the best way to obtain prompt service.

Treating all seed grain with fungicides to control the seedborne diseases. Manufacturers' directions should be followed exactly, especially as to the amounts of chemicals used.

E. R. CLARK *became Head of the Seed Laboratory in the North Central States Region in 1940 at Lafayette, Ind., and later at Minneapolis, Minn. From 1920 to 1940 he was pure seed specialist at the University of Minnesota Northwest School and Station.*

C. R. PORTER *became secretary-manager of the Nebraska Hybrid Seed Growers Association, Lincoln, Nebr., in 1958. He was formerly associated with Kansas State University and the University of Nebraska in crop improvement work.*

Sometimes There Are Frauds in Seeds

E. R. CLARK

SOMETIMES frauds occur in seed transactions.

Unusual conditions of supply and demand may tempt an unscrupulous dealer. A short supply of hardy northern-grown seed and a surplus of cheap, nonhardy seed may create an abnormal price spread. The popularity of hybrid corn may suggest to a dishonest advertiser that the term "hybrid" might attract the unwary if he applies it to something else. The need for oil-bearing crops during the war years stimulated interest in "new" varieties alleged to be superior in oil content. At all times a racketeer may exploit the public interest in a new crop.

Sometimes no seed is delivered. The racketeer disappears with the downpayment or the total purchase price. If he can be located, he may be bankrupt, or the so-called contract proves to be only an option.

The loss to farmers and gardeners through frauds in seeds has been enormous. Besides the exorbitant purchase price, the farmer loses from lower yields and sometimes failure of a crop. The loss may extend over several years if it is seed of a perennial.

Seed-control officials have done much to curb these rackets. State seed laws and the Federal Seed Act prohibit false advertising and mislabeling of seed and generally are effective. Other laws, such as the postal fraud law, may apply. The vigilance of the extension agents, postal inspectors, farmers, and legitimate seed dealers has been helpful. Unfortunately, though, the victims of fraud often fail to report their losses promptly through fear of ridicule or loss of prestige.

Promotion schemes sometimes are organized by unscrupulous operators to exploit the demand for superior varieties of grain. The varieties offered may be recent releases from State and Federal or Canadian agricultural experiment stations, but oftener they are old varieties with mediocre records of performance and poorly adapted to the localities where they are sold. Sometimes discarded varieties are offered under new names.

Exploitation of demand for new varieties may be carried on by mail, but such operations more frequently are conducted by sending solicitors or peddlers to visit farmers at home or in the field. The peddlers offer to take orders for "elite" and "foundation" seed. They carry attractive samples of threshed and unthreshed grain and salesmen's kits, which include reports from agricultural experiment stations. They also carefully avoid leaving any printed advertisements, which may come sooner or later into the hands of the seed inspector.

The buy-back contract is a feature of the schemes. The salesman represents that his firm will purchase from the farmer all grain produced from seed furnished by that firm (except a limited amount that the farmer may retain for his own planting) at "50 cents a bushel above the Chicago market price at the date of delivery."

Actually, the contract reads: "The Company agrees to pay the Grower for all grain purchased" at the premium price. This so-called contract to purchase is only an option, which provides that the company may purchase the farmer's crop if it desires. It does not obligate the company.

The peddler's approach to the farmer usually includes the announcement that a limited number of growers, usually two in each township, have been selected to increase this seed and that they have been chosen because of their excellent records as owners and managers of fertile, well-tilled farms. There is, of course, no such limit. Later it may transpire that a dozen neighbors have signed orders for "foundation" seed.

Invariably the scheme calls for a substantial cash payment, at least one-third of the purchase price, with the order. A small discount is allowed if the total amount is paid at the time of the order. The specified time for delivery may be many months distant.

Shortly before planting time, the peddler goes into the open market to buy the seed required to fill his orders. Any standard variety is acceptable. By this time, the "new variety" promised to his customer is no longer available, if it ever existed. Deliveries are made by local railway freight or truck, and the farmer is compelled to pay any balance of the purchase price, plus less-than-carload freight charges and c.o.d. fee.

No attempt is made to buy the farmer's crop. The peddler disappears. Even if he can be located, his financial rating leaves no hope for readjustment.

Peddlers move from place to place, shifting from Minnesota to Oklahoma, from Ohio to North Dakota. They avoid established seed dealers, county agents, and members of crop improvement associations. They speak grandiosely of "our warehouses in all the large cities," "our New York office," and "15 or 20 carloads sold to this firm." Actually, they have neither warehouse nor office—only an order book in their coat pockets.

By the exchange of information among State and Federal seed-control officials, known racketeers may be recognized and identified soon after they begin their operations in a new location.

The Department of Agriculture, in cooperation with State officials, maintains a list of peddlers whose activities have been investigated in any part of the United States. Any suspicious circumstances that may indicate violation of seed laws should be reported promptly to the State seed commissioner or another official.

GOOD RULES for avoiding losses from seed-peddling rackets, to be observed by prospective purchasers, are:

Purchase seed only from established dealers.

Never make cash payments to a stranger for seed for future delivery.

Consult your county agricultural agent in regard to the merits of crop varieties.

Beware of the "salesman" who says: "You have been selected as one of a limited number of farmers in your county to receive this foundation seed."

Be cautious when a seed salesman promises to buy the crop produced from his seed at a premium. Although seedsmen obtain certain kinds of seed from contract growers, no reliable dealer could afford to purchase the crops from all his customers. The so-called contract may bind the farmer but not the dealer.

IT IS ALWAYS difficult and often impossible to prevent seed rackets by enforcing seed laws. The Federal Seed Act and most State seed laws govern the labeling and advertising of seed, but they do not pertain to false promises to buy the crop.

Seed-control officials have found it necessary therefore to work with other enforcement officials in the application of criminal statutes that pertain to fraud. Investigation of advertising and labeling by State and Federal seed inspectors is a deterrent, because rackets do not thrive when brought to light.

RECENT legislation in several States makes it unlawful for a seed salesman to enter into a contract with a purchaser of seed whereby the seedsman agrees to repurchase the seed crop produced at a premium price, unless a bond of 10 thousand dollars has been posted with the State to insure performance of such contract. Seedsmen who file financial statements that show an acceptable degree of accountability are exempt. Since the enactment of this legislation, peddlers have avoided those States, for few of the racketeers are adequately financed.

POSTAL FRAUD LAWS provide severe penalties for using the mails to promote an enterprise that is fraudulent.

Since most businesses use the mails, violation of postal fraud laws sometimes occur. Seed racketeers mail postcard notices of arrival, circular letter announcements, and occasional correspondence, but the direct solicitations usually are made only by personal visits.

The use of interstate telephone and telegraph wires in furthering a fraudulent scheme likewise is unlawful. This feature of Federal laws has been overlooked by racketeers, who were familiar with the risks of using the U.S. mails. The use of the wires may be only incidental and still may constitute a felony. The mail fraud statute is applicable, however, only when the mails or wires were used in furthering a scheme devised and intended to be devised to defraud, and when such mails or wires were used before the consummation of the transaction with the victim.

FEDERAL courts on several occasions have found seed racketeers guilty of fraud because of failure to deliver seed. An Iowa promoter received thousands of dollars from Minnesota farmers by promising to furnish certified oats seed of the Sauk variety for foundation fields and to purchase the crops produced. He used the long-distance telephone lines from his home office in Iowa to "customers" in Minnesota. Since no seed was transported or delivered, no seed laws were applicable, but the telephone calls brought the transaction under Federal jurisdiction and the Federal Bureau of Investigation investigated. The promoter was sentenced to 2 years in a Federal penitentiary and was fined 500 dollars.

Three fraudulent enterprises undertaken in the spring wheat area of the Dakotas in 1954–1955 were checked by application of the postal fraud law.

One peddler collected downpayments and absconded. In another case, the "firm" accepted hundreds of orders and checks but failed to secure a supply of seed in time for spring deliveries. The third instance involved two partners, who devised a scheme to substitute an inferior variety of wheat for one recently released by relabeling the seed with false tags.

An outline of this scheme and the procedure used for investigating and prosecuting the partners illustrates an effective method of protecting the public.

SELKIRK wheat, developed by the Canada Department of Agriculture, combined high-yielding ability and milling quality with resistance to Race 15B stem rust, which was a scourge of the spring wheat region. It was released in Canada in 1952, but the seed supply was limited, and the Canada Department of Agriculture declared an embargo, effective August 16, 1954, in order to conserve the seed for the use of Canadian farmers. Prices for Selkirk rose to high levels in the United States, since only an insignificant amount was available.

One firm continued to take orders in the fall of 1954 through peddlers in North Dakota and South Dakota. In March and April 1955, it delivered 16,510 bushels in 11 railroad cars and 3 trucks. The bags bore blue analysis tags and labels to show the variety to be Selkirk, grown on a ranch near Yakima, Wash.

A check of the Washington ranch revealed that no Selkirk wheat had been grown there, and none had been shipped from that point. On the other hand, it was noted that the firm, using the name of Canadian Importers, had purchased 16,560 bushels of seed wheat in Canada and entered it through the U.S. customs ports in March and April 1955. The wheat had carried the official certification tags and seals of the Canada Government, and the variety was Redman, not Selkirk. It appeared, however, that the similarity of dates and amounts might not be due to chance. Redman resembles Selkirk; in fact, the seeds are indistinguishable by visual inspection. Redman is not resistant to Race 15B wheat stem rust and is a much older variety than Selkirk. Seed of the Redman variety was readily available at about 2 dollars a bushel. Selkirk could be sold at 7 to 10 dollars a bushel.

Samples of the so-called Selkirk were drawn by State seed inspectors in North Dakota and South Dakota. They were compared with samples of the imports of Redman that were in the files of the U.S. Department of Agriculture. Plantings were made in a greenhouse for comparison with known samples of Selkirk and Redman. The seedlings were inoculated with spores of Race 15B rust.

The seedlings grown from the customs samples of the imported wheat were found to be susceptible to this rust. This indicated that the imported wheat undoubtedly was Redman. The seedlings of the so-called Selkirk also were susceptible, like the known sample of Redman and the customs samples of the imported seed. The known sample of Selkirk was resistant.

Further investigation was made of the movement of the imported seed. Railroad freight records revealed that as each car of imported seed arrived at the Minneapolis railroad yards from Winnipeg, it was unloaded onto a motortruck and hauled to the yards of a different railroad company, where it was loaded and billed from Minneapolis to North Dakota or to South Dakota.

A railroad employee working in one of the yards had observed a trucker removing Canadian certification tags and attaching new tags and seals. A Minneapolis printer testified that he had printed 11 thousand analysis tags bearing the name of "Selkirk" and the spurious Washington origin. A truck rental agency identified the seed firm's employee as the party who had rented one of his trucks on the dates when the railroad cars were loaded.

The firm was charged with devising a scheme to defraud and with unlawful use of the United States mail. Among the documents introduced as evidence were letters mailed by the defendants to customers in North Dakota and South Dakota stating that the firm had an adequate supply of Selkirk wheat seed and would make all deliveries as promised. Cards had been mailed to the buyers to notify them when the seed would arrive at the railway freight station.

The Government was able to prove that the firm was financially insolvent throughout its operations and that the defendants were fully aware that they could not furnish seed of the Selkirk variety. Mislabeling the seed as to variety was a misdemeanor under the Federal Seed Act, but using the mails to defraud was a felony under the Postal Fraud Act. The two partners were found guilty of postal fraud and were sentenced to terms of 2 and 3 years in Federal prison.

COMPLIANCE with seed laws requires careful technical work.

Violations may be due to faulty organization, careless procedure, inexperience, or incompetence. Sometimes errors occur through circumstances not under control of the seedsman. All of these may cause loss to the planter.

Seed frauds, on the other hand, are caused by dishonesty, and they are avoidable. Not many outright frauds occur, but proper laws and vigilance will reduce that small number.

The basic difference between these types of violations is important and should be kept in view at all times, lest the legitimate seedsman be condemned unjustly or the activities of the racketeer be condoned.

E. R. CLARK *is a seed marketing specialist in the Seed Branch, Grain Division, Agricultural Marketing Service. He is in charge of the Federal Seed Laboratory at Minneapolis, Minn. He has degrees from the University of Wisconsin and the University of Minnesota.*

Our Laws That Pertain to Seeds

S. F. ROLLIN AND FREDERICK A. JOHNSTON

THE BASIC purpose of the seed laws in the United States is to insure that seed is labeled truthfully.

It is possible for seed dealers legally to sell low-quality but correctly labeled seeds. The purchaser therefore should read and understand the information on the label, which must be attached to the container, to determine whether he wants to buy it.

The laws are not devised solely for the protection of farmers, gardeners, and homeowners. They are designed also for the protection of seedsmen.

Seeds move from one dealer to another in the marketing process, particularly from areas of production to areas of use. Every handler of seeds needs the protection afforded by law.

Homeowners who buy packets of vegetable seeds seldom find any representation as to the percentage of germination. When vegetable seeds are above a certain specified standard in germination, most States do not require that the packet show the actual percentage of germination. Only vegetable seeds that are below the specified standard established for germination must be labeled to show the percentage of germination, the date of the germination test, and the words, "Below Standard."

Connecticut in 1821 passed a law prohibiting the sale of grass seed containing Canada thistle and other weeds. Michigan in 1871 prohibited the sale of seeds containing Canada thistle and milkweed. Illinois, California, Missouri, and Nebraska between 1867 and 1895 legislated against seed containing

Canada thistle. The two earliest vegetable seed laws were adopted by Florida in 1889 and by California in 1891. By 1941, all 48 States had seed laws.

The Congress in 1904 appropriated money to the Department of Agriculture to obtain in the open market samples of seeds of grass, clover, or alfalfa to be tested, and directed the Secretary that if any such seeds were found to be adulterated or misbranded or if any seeds of Canada bluegrass were sold under any other name than Canada bluegrass, the results of the tests should be published, together with the names of the persons by whom the seeds were offered for sale.

Between 1904 and 1919, the Department examined approximately 15 thousand samples of commercial seeds of alfalfa, Kentucky bluegrass, orchardgrass, red clover, meadow fescue, smooth brome, hairy vetch, and redtop and found an average of about 20 percent of the samples adulterated with, or consisting of, other less desirable kinds of seeds, or containing the seeds of dodder, a noxious weed.

As a result of the testing of commercial seed samples in domestic commerce and samples submitted to the Department of Agriculture by the U.S. Customs Service between 1904 and 1912, the Congress passed the Seed Importation Act of 1912. This act restricted the importation of seeds of the principal forage plants on the basis of content of weed seeds and low purity. The act was amended in 1916 by adding a requirement as to live seed.

The Seed Importation Act was amended in 1926 to require that all imported seeds of alfalfa and red clover be colored to indicate the degree of adaptability. It is estimated that the requirement saved American farmers more than 5 million dollars between 1926 and 1938.

The act was further amended in 1926 to prohibit the shipment in interstate commerce of any falsely and fraudulently labeled seeds. Because of the seizure provisions in this amendment, the act was effective in helping States cope with interstate shipments of misbranded seeds.

The criminal provision of the act, as applied to interstate shipments, however, proved ineffective because of the lack of specific labeling requirements and the necessity for proving that the false labeling or false advertising was done knowingly.

A new Federal Seed Act was enacted in 1939. It required detailed labeling of seeds in interstate commerce, did not require proof of intent, and extended the scope of the act as it pertained to imported seeds.

THE RECOMMENDED uniform State seed law has contributed to the uniformity that exists in seed laws among the States and the Federal Seed Act. It is changed periodically by a joint committee representing various interested organizations. This enables seed officials who desire to revise their State seed laws to have an up-to-date guide in recommending the form and wording of revisions that they feel are desirable to promote uniformity.

THE FEDERAL and State laws contain somewhat similar requirements. If seed is labeled to comply with the Federal Seed Act and is shipped in interstate commerce, it will normally comply with the labeling requirements of the State into which it is shipped.

The laws generally require that the label attached to the container of agricultural seeds show the percentage of pure seed, percentage of weed seeds, percentage of other crop seeds, percentage of inert matter, percentage of germination, percentage of hard seeds, if any, the date of the germination test, and the name and address of the shipper, or seller, or person who labeled the seeds.

The label also is required to show the names and rates of occurrence of seeds of noxious weeds recognized by the laws and regulations of the State in which the seed is being sold or into which the seed is shipped.

Most States prohibit the sale of seeds containing seeds of certain noxious weeds or limit the number permitted in seed sold, even if the seed is correctly labeled to indicate their presence.

Mixtures of agricultural seeds must be labeled to show the percentage of each kind of seed present in the mixture to the extent of 5 percent or more.

Some States require agricultural seeds to be labeled as to kind and variety, but most State laws require labeling only as to the kind of seed.

A TRADEMARK—brand—is a term by which goods may be distinguished as coming from a certain source. It is intended to identify the manufacturer or distributor—not the product itself. A trademark is private property and may be used only by the owner or with the owner's permission. When a trademark is made a name of a variety, it is no longer protected as a trademark. Saying that it is still a trademark does not make it one. If the owner of a trademark uses it as a variety name or part of a variety name, he, in effect, loses the protection given trademarks and automatically permits other persons to use it as the name of the variety. If a "trademark" is used to identify genetic makeup instead of source, it is a variety name and not a trademark.

A variety name cannot be a valid trademark. Under the Federal Seed Act, the originator of a new variety has a right to name that variety. If the variety can be reproduced from seed, it may be produced and sold by anyone. Under the Federal Seed Act, the name that is given the variety by its originator must be used. This is true even though the name is a privately owned trademark.

THE PATENT LAWS relating to plants provide for the granting of a patent to anyone who has invented or discovered and asexually reproduced any distinct and new variety of plant, other than a tuber-propagated plant.

Asexually propagated plants are those that are reproduced by means

other than from seeds, such as by rooting of cuttings by layering, budding, and grafting.

The applicant for a patent on a particular plant variety must have done something to create or produce it, and it must be distinct and new. A plant found by a person is not considered patentable.

LAWS REGULATE FARMERS and producers of seed as well as seed dealers and merchants.

Certain features in most of the State laws and in the Federal Seed Act deal specifically with the responsibilities of farmer-producers of seed.

One is that a dealer who buys from a farmer seed indistinguishable as to variety will be held responsible for any misrepresentation as to variety unless the dealer obtains from the farmer a grower's declaration as to variety. If the farmer signs such a declaration, he assumes the responsibility for the representation—whether he sells the seed to a dealer in another State or whether it is sold to a local dealer and the seed is expected to move in interstate commerce. The signing of a grower's declaration without a sound basis for doing so may mean that seed is falsely labeled. Farmers should recognize their responsibility when they sign such declarations.

Provisions in most State laws and in the Federal Seed Act exempt a farmer from having to comply with the labeling requirements for seeds that he sells on his own premises and does not advertise for sale. Some State laws further provide that such seed may not contain prohibited seeds of noxious weeds. To this extent, a farmer may sell seed to his neighbor. More and more people think that such sales should be controlled more strictly, because home-grown seeds and seeds sold by farmer to farmer in the same locality without labeling generally are the poorest seeds sown by farmers.

Most laws exempt from the labeling requirements seeds intended for processing. Seeds moved from the farm to a seed-processing plant need not be labeled to show the detailed information required for processed seed. In interstate commerce, such seed must be labeled as "seed for processing." The seed must actually be intended for processing and should not be labeled in this manner to escape the responsibility established for labeling processed seeds under the seed laws.

Another section of the laws deals with the use of a disclaimer or non-warranty clause on a label. These disclaimers are forbidden under some State seed laws. Under others, they are recognized if they do not disclaim responsibility for the information required to be on the label under the labeling laws. In other words, the seller can disclaim responsibility for the crop that is produced, but not for the percentage of germination or the variety or the purity percentages as labeled.

Farmers or purchasers cannot collect damages through the State seed laws or through the Federal Seed Act. Such damages must, as a last resort, be collected through a separate civil action filed by the buyer against the seller of seeds. The laws provide only for legal action against the seed (seizure) or against the person violating the seed laws (prosecution).

Labeling of treated seed to indicate that it is treated is one other significant feature. Farmer-producers of seeds should recognize that unused treated seed should not be mixed with and sold as part of the seeds produced the following season. Particularly, it should not be sold with a grain crop delivered to an elevator. Such treated seed has caused difficulty in the grain industry. Carloads of grain have been seized and condemned by the Food and Drug Administration because of the presence of treated seeds in the grain. The farmer-grower should take the necessary precautions in handling seed treated with highly toxic materials and should not use leftover seed treated with these materials for feed for any animals on the farm.

QUALITY REQUIREMENTS with respect to imported seeds, as established under the Federal Seed Act, provide that most seeds must consist of at least 75 percent pure live seed. The percentage of pure live seeds is calculated by multiplying the percentage of pure seeds by the percentage of germination and dividing by 100. The minimum of 75 percent of pure live seeds is reduced for certain specified kinds of seeds that are difficult to produce above a 75-percent, pure live seed percentage.

Seeds that are imported into the United States must not contain more than 2 percent of weed seeds. Seeds containing noxious-weed seeds in excess of one in 10 grams of seed the size of timothy, one in 25 grams of seed the size of sorghum, or one in 100 grams of seed the size of wheat, is not permitted entry into the commerce of the United States.

The specific noxious-weed seeds as set forth in the Federal Seed Act are whitetop (*Lepidium draba*, *Lepidium repens*, *Hymenophysa pubescens*); Canada thistle (*Cirsium arvense*); dodder (*Cuscuta* spp.); quackgrass (*Agropyron repens*); johnsongrass (*Sorghum halepense*); bindweed (*Convolvulus arvensis*); Russian-knapweed (*Centaurea picris*); perennial sowthistle (*Sonchus arvensis*); and leafy spurge (*Euphorbia esula*).

Imported seeds of alfalfa and red clover must be stained to indicate their adaptability for growing in this country. Alfalfa and red clover seeds grown in the Dominion of Canada must be stained so that 1 percent of the seed is colored violet. The seed from South America must be stained so that 10 percent of the seed is orange-red in color. Seed from different origins or nonestablished origins must be stained so that 10 percent of it is colored red.

The Customs Service in the Department of the Treasury cooperates with the Department of Agriculture in enforcement of the requirements relating to imported seed. The customs inspectors at the various ports of entry obtain samples of the seed as it arrives at the ports. The samples are submitted to seed laboratories of the Department of Agriculture, where they are tested to determine whether they meet the requirements for importation. As soon as it is determined that the requirements for importation are met, the seeds are released into commerce. Complete germination tests are not made if the standard is met before the test is completed. The importer and the consignee are both informed of release of the seeds.

If the seeds do not meet the quality requirements for importation, they may be reprocessed under supervision to bring them into line with the requirements; they may be destroyed under supervision of a representative of the Department of Agriculture; or they may be exported under the supervision of the Customs Service. In some instances, seeds of alfalfa and red clover that have not been stained properly must be stained under supervision before they are admitted into the commerce of the United States.

When the Secretary of Agriculture finds that a substantial proportion of the importations of any kind of seed is used for other than seeding purposes, he may exempt such kinds from the provisions of the Federal Seed Act. Seed imported for other than seeding purposes under this exemption must be accompanied by a declaration setting forth the use for which the seeds are intended.

Seeds that may be declared as for other than seeding purposes include those of sorghum, barley, field corn, flax, oat, rye, soybean, wheat, and many others.

Seeds exported from the United States can be returned to the United States under certain circumstances even though they may not meet the quality requirements set forth in the Federal Seed Act.

Specified maximum quantities of seeds for experimental or breeding purposes may be imported into the United States regardless of the quality requirements if the seeds are not sold. Small quantities are not ordinarily sampled by customs inspectors; they therefore may be admitted without being tested.

No quality requirements have been established under the Federal Seed Act with respect to seed exported from the United States. Many countries have special requirements for entry of forage seeds, such as germination specifications, staining, or freedom from weed seeds, particularly dodder.

There are no quality requirements for domestic agricultural seeds under the Federal Seed Act except insofar as the noxious-weed requirements of the various States are recognized for seeds shipped in interstate commerce into those States.

Many States have strict requirements with respect to the number of seeds of noxious weeds of certain species or the total number of noxious seeds that will be permitted sale in those States. Some States prohibit seeds of noxious weeds of certain perennial species when present in any amount. Most State seed laws also have a limitation with respect to the percentage of weed seeds that may be contained in agricultural seeds sold within the State. This limitation varies from 0.5 percent to 5 percent, but usually it is about 2 percent.

Many of the State seed laws, particularly in the South, prohibit the sale of seed below a certain germination percentage, usually 60 or 70 percent. Exceptions are made for certain kinds of seeds that cannot normally be produced with a germination that high. Vegetable seeds are sold generally without labeling to show the percentage of germination, particularly on small packets, if the seed is above a certain established germination standard. Many States require large containers of vegetable seeds to be labeled with more detailed information than is required for small packets.

PLANT QUARANTINE REGULATIONS affect the importation, exportation, and interstate movement of seeds.

The regulations are enforced to prevent the introduction and dissemination of injurious foreign insect and disease pests that are new here or are not widely distributed within this country.

Imported seeds may be divided into three general categories depending on their entry status and conditions of importations: Prohibited seeds, restricted seeds subject to inspection and fumigation at special inspection stations, and restricted seeds subject to inspection at any port of entry where plant quarantine inspection services are available.

Seeds in the prohibited category include bamboo, rice, wheat, cotton, corn, barberry, mahonia, mahoberberis, currant, gooseberry, mango, avocado, and others, from all or many foreign countries.

For example, unhusked rice seed from all foreign countries and localities, except Mexico, is prohibited to safeguard against the introduction of a number of injurious rice pests, including downy mildew (*Sclerospora macrocarpa*), leaf smut (*Entyloma oryzae*), blight (*Oospora oryzetorum*), and glume blotch (*Melanomma glumarum*).

Wheat seeds are prohibited from all countries where the flag smut disease (*Urocystis tritici*) is known to occur. These include a number of European, Near East, and Asiatic countries, but only Chile in this hemisphere.

Seeds of corn and closely related plants may not be imported from a number of countries in southeastern Asia because of several downy mildews and other corn diseases occurring in those areas.

Most types of seeds of trees and shrubs fall in the second category and may enter under a plant quarantine import permit subject to inspection and treatment upon arrival in the United States. Treatments are given at specified ports of entry that have approved facilities for the particular treatment required. The most commonly used treatment is fumigation with methyl bromide gas at dosages that will give maximum protection

against pests without serious injury to viability.

The third category includes seeds of nearly all of the common field, vegetable, and flower crops that are essentially herbaceous in character of growth. Entry is allowed without a formal import permit but is subject to inspection upon arrival to determine freedom from harmful pests.

A few types of seeds in this group are subject to mandatory fumigation because of specific foreign insect pests that occur quite generally in such seed. Seeds of sweetpea (*Lathyrus*) and vetch (*Vicia*), for example, are subject to infestation by a number of seed beetles in the family Bruchidae. Several of them do not occur in this country and are known to be serious pests. Treatment therefore is required as a condition of entry. Although mandatory treatment is not required for most seeds in this category, any shipment found to represent a risk of introducing injurious pests is subject to treatment before release. If a suitable treatment is not available, other safeguards, as refusal of entry, may be required.

We have no plant quarantine requirements governing the exportation of seeds. Exportation of tobacco seed, however, is regulated by the Federal Tobacco Seed and Plant Exportation Act. Many foreign countries have laws regulating or prohibiting the entry of seeds. The requirements vary with the country of destination and may relate to entry of all seeds or of specified kinds only. For example, the United Kingdom regulates entry of seeds of lettuce, tomato, and peas. Egypt regulates the importation of all seeds for sowing. Most cotton-growing countries restrict the entry of seed of cotton.

Laws of many States regulate interstate movement thereinto of all seeds or of all except field, vegetable, and flower seeds. Some States have special quarantines relating to specified kinds of seeds, and interstate movement of some kinds is regulated also by one or more of six different Federal Domestic plant quarantines.

Tree and shrub seeds are not admissible to the United States mails unless accompanied by a certificate showing the seeds to be free of insects and plant diseases.

FEDERAL-STATE COOPERATION in the enforcement of seed laws is possible because each of the 50 States has a State seed law. In the enforcement of the State law, seed inspectors visit seed dealers displaying seed for sale and obtain samples. The samples are submitted to the State seed laboratory for testing to determine whether the seeds are correctly labeled to comply with the State law. If there is no evidence that the seeds moved in interstate commerce, the jurisdiction lies entirely within the State law, and appropriate action may be taken under the law. This action usually consists of stopping the sale of the seeds until they are correctly labeled or disposed of in compliance with the law.

Prosecution under State seed laws is also possible but is recommended infrequently. If, however, the seeds moved in interstate commerce and were found to have been falsely labeled by a person in another State, the State law would not have jurisdiction over that person. This is the basic reason for the enactment of the Federal Seed Act.

There is agreement between the Department of Agriculture and the State agencies that when the State officials find in their inspection of seeds within the State evidence of violation of the Federal Seed Act, the information and the sample pertaining to the apparent violation will be forwarded to the appropriate area office of the Department of Agriculture for investigation. A duplicate force of inspectors to enforce the Federal Seed Act is therefore not necessary. After obtaining all the facts in a case that appears to warrant action under the Federal Seed Act, the area office reports the information to the Washington office.

The Washington office may proceed with various types of action under the Federal Seed Act. A warning letter or notice may be issued to the interstate shipper informing him of the apparent violation so that he can take steps to prevent such violations in the future.

A cease-and-desist proceeding may also be instituted. A cease-and-desist proceeding is similar to a court proceeding and may result in the issuance to the interstate shipper by the Secretary of Agriculture of an order to cease and desist from further violations of the Federal Seed Act. The Department must also afford the interstate shipper an opportunity to explain how the apparent violation occurred before a final decision is reached to recommend legal action against the firm. Further action may be held in abeyance for reconsideration at a later date, or the interstate shipper may be prosecuted in Federal court. A forfeiture of not less than 25 dollars nor more than 500 dollars on each count is provided under the civil section of the act in case of a finding for the Government. The interstate shipper may also be prosecuted under the criminal section of the act. A fine of not less than 25 dollars or not more than 1 thousand dollars on the first offense and 2 thousand dollars on each subsequent offense may be assessed in case of guilt.

In addition to these actions under the Federal Seed Act that can be taken against the person responsible, a seizure action can be taken against the seed. The seed that is falsely labeled or prohibited from sale in a particular State is seized by the U.S. marshal and its disposition is determined by the U.S. district court. The court may return the seed to the shipper to be reprocessed and relabeled, the court may permit its sale or shipment into a jurisdiction in which its sale would not be prohibited, or the seed may be destroyed. When no claimant appears, some courts have given seed having a low germination to charitable institutions rather than to destroy it.

SOME OUTSTANDING CASES have occurred between 1939 and 1959. There have been 237 court cases involving prosecution of interstate shippers under the Federal Seed Act. These have involved 170 different persons or firms and 520 separate shipments of seeds.

One of the most important group of cases involved the falsification on the part of a large number of seed dealers of the origin (place where grown) of alfalfa seed. The origin of alfalfa seed is important to farmers, because it indicates the region in which the seed may be hardy or nonhardy. In 1950, when the price of southern-origin alfalfa seed was unusually low compared to the price of northern-origin alfalfa seed, many persons apparently decided that a substitution of southern-origin alfalfa seed for northern-origin alfalfa seed would be profitable and could not be detected. They overlooked the fact that certain weed and crop seeds occur in alfalfa in the southwestern part of of the United States, but not in alfalfa seed produced in the Northern States. By detecting these particular kinds of weed and crop seeds, officials could establish that all the seeds, or part of the seeds in each shipment, originated in the Southwest and not in the Northern States, as claimed. Investigations revealed that approximately 1 million pounds of low-priced southern-origin alfalfa seeds had been misrepresented as higher priced seeds of northern origin. If this fraud had been successful, northern farmers, in addition to paying up to double the market value of the seed, would have faced the loss of most of their alfalfa crops.

In all, 12 criminal cases were filed against 8 firms and 7 individuals for violating the Federal Seed Act in connection with this false labeling as to origin of alfalfa seed. Nine individuals were prosecuted for conspiracy to violate the act and two for violation of the mail fraud statute. The fines totaled more than 25 thousand dollars. Two individuals were placed on probation for 1 year, one for 2 years, and one for 6 months. One defendant was sentenced to imprisonment for 1 year and a day for violation of the mail fraud statute. Nearly 500 thousand

pounds of the mislabeled seeds were seized under Federal court orders and relabeled to show the correct origin.

Another case involved the use of the old Midwest variety of soybean seed that had been discarded as not being of value for planting purposes. A new variety name was assigned to this seed, and it was advertised and distributed as a new, highly productive variety. Growing tests identified the variety as Midwest. The firm was prosecuted under the Federal Seed Act and forced to cease its false advertising.

Another case involved the first court action under the Federal Seed Act of 1939, in which a firm sold for seeding purposes malting barley that was devoid of germination. It had the appearance of good-quality seed, but looks were deceiving.

Another series of cases involved a firm that sold packets of vegetable seeds in display boxes to small general stores. The firm never discarded any of its old, low-germinating seed, but continued to offer for sale the same seed in the same packets year after year. Tests made on the seeds each year at various locations indicated that much of it was worthless for planting purposes. Prosecution of the firm under the Federal Seed Act continued periodically until the death of the owner of the firm. In nine Federal court cases, the firm paid a total of 11 thousand dollars in fines.

Since the enactment of the Federal Seed Act of 1939, attempts have been made to mislead the public with respect to the characteristics of certain kinds and varieties of seed. "Michels grass" was claimed to be a cross between Mosida wheat and Giant wild ryegrass. Chromosome counts and growing tests made by specialists in the Department of Agriculture indicated the seed was rye and that claims made for this so-called cross could not be supported.

The supply of Dwarf Essex rape seed from Europe and Japan was cut off in 1940 because of war. Much annual rape seed was sold as Dwarf Essex rape seed. The high prices of the scarce

Dwarf Essex encouraged some people to import the annual rape seed and mislabel it. One prosecution under the Federal Seed Act resulted and stopped the practice.

Another recurring type of false representation has been the claim that a new variety of wheat produced from a handful of wheat found in King Tut's tomb will produce larger yields of wheat than varieties now in existence.

This wheat has been advertised as "Miracle," "Wonder," "Egyptian," "Seven-Headed," "Thousand Fold," and "King Tut." Investigation invariably establishes that this so-called new variety is one of the varieties of Poulard wheat, sometimes called Polish wheat, which is not suitable for flour for baking purposes in this country. Its value as a feed is inferior, and the claims as to its production are exaggerated.

DECISIONS on Federal Seed Act cases contested in courts have served as guides to enforcement officials and seedsmen.

In one case, the presiding judge in his charge to the jury stated: "Advertising in the mistaken belief that malt barley in the defendant's possession was spring barley would constitute no defense to the charge of falsely advertising spring barley; that the mere fact that some agent or employee of the defendant company unintentionally labeled the product would constitute no defense; that whether the defendant knew the seed being advertised or offered for sale was not truthfully labeled or was misrepresented was immaterial and would be no protection; and that an honest mistake would constitute no defense."

The net result of these statements was that it was not necessary under the new Federal Seed Act to prove intent until 1956. An amendment adopted in 1956 provided for criminal action or for civil action under the act. To proceed with criminal action, it is necessary to establish certain specified elements of intent—namely, gross carelessness, failure to inform oneself of the pertinent facts, or knowledge. Civil action is possible without establishing any element of intent.

In another case, the judge in his charge to the jury on one count directed the jury to return a verdict of not guilty as the evidence showed that the inspector who sampled the seed did not obtain a sample of the minimum size prescribed in the rules and regulations for sampling. In another count, involving labeling of oats seed as to variety, the judge stated that a seedsman who had a sample of the seed tested by two different laboratories had taken the proper precautions to insure the identity of the variety of the seed and was therefore not violating the Federal Seed Act because of the exemption provided in the labeling as to variety of indistinguishable seed.

In an appeal to the United States circuit court of appeals on a cease-and-desist order issued by the Secretary of Agriculture, the court stated that the State and Federal officials followed the rules and regulations substantially in obtaining samples and in making the analyses, but no evidence was presented to show that the petitioner did the same; that samples are receivable in evidence to show the quality or condition of the entire mass of seed from which they are taken; that the difference in time of taking samples is not material, although usually there is some change in germination over a long period; that the burden of knowing what is for sale and telling the truth about it is placed on the distributor under the act because he is presumed to have the better facilities for ascertaining the facts; that the records of the laboratories of the Federal and State Governments are on an equal footing as evidence because of the cooperative agreement in effect; that reports which are of a public nature and taken under competent authority to ascertain a matter of public interest are admissible in evidence; and that the Administrator was free to issue a cease-and-desist order applicable to all shipments made by the petitioner in interstate commerce.

In two cases, which were consolidated for purposes of trial, the defendant waived trial by jury, admitted that the shipments were made as alleged, and admitted that the results of the official tests were correct. The trial in this instance revolved solely around the element of intent. The judge ruled that criminal penalties should not be imposed in cases where a statement may be indicated as false when, after investigation made with reasonable care, the statement was used innocently and without any knowledge on the part of the accused that it was not true at the time made. He also ruled that penalties should not be inflicted where every reasonable precaution has been taken to justify a belief in the mind of the shipper that a true statement has been made and without any proof that the defendant was attempting to avoid or circumvent the penalties involved. The judge found the defendant not guilty.

In the first contested civil action that was decided in favor of the Government in February 1960, the court's opinion included the following statements:

"In House Report No. 2473, subsection (b) of the amendment was described as providing a civil penalty payable to the United States for any violation of the Federal Seed Act or the rules and regulations made and promulgated thereunder, with or without intent.

"The defendant alleged that its good faith in shipping the seed in interstate commerce and in labeling them in accordance with tests conducted by a competent expert and technologist constituted a complete defense in that it showed an absence of any intention on its part or the part of its employees to falsely label or mislead by false labeling. It contended that such good faith on its part also furnished a complete defense to any technical violation that may have resulted or been pro-

duced by other analyses differing with those of the defendant.

"Relative to such prosecutions as there involved, and as is involved in the cases at bar, the Supreme Court said:

"'The prosecution . . . is based on a now familiar type of legislation whereby penalties serve as effective means of regulation. Such legislation dispenses with the conventional requirement for criminal conduct—awareness of some wrongdoing. In the interest of the larger good it puts the burden of acting at hazard upon a person otherwise innocent but standing in responsible relation to a public danger.

"'The teaching of this rule is that such articles may be misbranded without any consciousness of fraud at all. Hardship there doubtless may be under a statute which thus penalizes the transaction though consciousness of wrongdoing may be totally wanting.'"

SEED CONTROL ORGANIZATIONS in the United States consist of State seed officials, who belong to regional organizations and an international organization. The regional organizations consist of one in the Northeastern States, one in the Southern States, one in the North Central States, and one in the Western States.

The regional groups meet annually to discuss problems and procedures to be followed in the enforcement of the laws and recommend procedures to be followed to establish greater uniformity in the administration of the laws in the various States.

Each of these associations is designated by the region in which it operates—for example, the Association of Seed Control Officials of the Northeastern States.

The international organization, which includes representatives from all States and Canada, is called the Association of American Seed Control Officials. This organization meets biennially. The international organization attempts to accomplish the same objectives as the regional organizations, except to operate on an international basis.

PROGRESS AND BENEFITS in enforcement of the seed laws are difficult to measure. In 1940, on the basis of State reports, it was estimated that 25 percent of the seeds in commercial channels was falsely labeled.

The extent of compliance with the State seed laws and the Federal Seed Act between 1946 and 1960 is shown by surveys that indicate that the proportion of inspected seeds in violation of the State seed laws during this period averaged 13 percent. The proportion of inspected seed in interstate commerce in violation of the Federal Seed Act averaged 8 percent.

The findings indicate a considerable improvement from the surveys made between 1904 and 1919 and in 1940, even though the laws have been made stricter. The improvement undoubtedly came about because of greater knowledge among consumers, the increased efficiency of harvesting and cleaning machinery, the awareness of seedsmen that it pays to sell a high-quality product, and the increased activity on the part of officials.

The extent to which these factors influence the quality of any particular kind or lot of seed purchased by consumers varies considerably. For that reason, some seeds of low quality are still sold and purchased, and some seeds are still falsely represented and advertised.

LET NO ONE say, though, that misrepresentation is an ill only of these later days. We know it has existed a long time.

The first law we know of to control the quality of seeds was adopted in the Republic of Berne, Switzerland, on April 2, 1815.

It reads: "Clover seed be sold pure and without any addition of other seeds. The sale of sweet clover seed (*Melilotus alba*), as far as such seed is sold pure and unadulterated, is permitted. On the other hand, the sale of any ordinary or Dutch clover seed, adulterated with sweet clover seed or any impurity, is prohibited and liable to the fine mentioned below.

"In those counties, where a considerable sale of clover seeds takes place, 2 to 4 honourable men, who are experts in clover seeds, shall be appointed as inspectors and their names shall be made known to the vendors of seeds. These inspectors are held to examine clover seed offered for sale on public markets and in stores. If they find clover seeds adulterated with sweet clover or other species, they are held to confiscate such seed and to deposit it with the County Councilor.

"The County Councilor shall consult two more experts, and upon examination, if the seed is really adulterated, cause it to be thrown into the water. The vendor shall be punished the first time by a fine of Frs. 10- . . . in cases of repetition with a fine of Frs. 50. . . .

"The names of the punished shall be announced . . . and be made public through the weekly newspaper. If the inspectors find the seed true to kind, but impure, then they shall be held to have such lots cleaned on the expense of the vendor who, in addition, has to pay a fine of Fr. 1- . . . ."

This law sounds much like a stop-sale, seizure, and court action in the seed laws enforced today in the United States. It even required publicity regarding the court actions. This is also required under the Federal Seed Act.

S. F. ROLLIN *is Chief of the Seed Branch, Grain Division, Agricultural Marketing Service. He has been employed in the Department since 1936 and in various phases of seed law enforcement work under the Federal Seed Act since 1940. He is a graduate of North Dakota State Teachers College.*

FREDERICK A. JOHNSTON *is a member of the Technical Services staff, Plant Quarantine Division, Agricultural Research Service. He is a graduate of the University of Maryland and has been with the Department since 1939.*

THE

MARKETING

OF SEEDS

ᵚᵚ ᵚᵚ

How We Get Seeds of Vegetables and Flowers

WILLIAM B. CARTER AND EDWIN P. BUGBEE, JR.

VEGETABLE and flower seeds are produced by a few companies, mostly in special areas, but they follow many paths from the producer to the planter.

Most of our vegetable seeds are grown in the Western States by firms that produce a full line or by specialists who concentrate on a few species.

Some seed companies own land on which they produce a part of their needs. Such farms offer the advantage of complete control, but they do not provide the economic safety of a more diversified farming operation.

The usual practice is therefore to contract production with independent farmers. Most seed contracts are of the bailor-bailee type, wherein the seedsman is the legal owner of the crop, and all of it is delivered to him.

Contract growing permits the selection of particular areas and even farms that are best adapted to the species. It also facilitates contraction and expansion of acreage as demand fluctuates. It is popular with farmers because it provides a sure market at a definite price, and payment is often made early enough in the fall to help defray harvesting costs for other crops. Furthermore, many seed crops, especially legumes, fit nicely in rotations.

Contract crops are supervised by the seedsman's fieldmen. They advise the farmer on fertilization, irrigation, control of pests, harvesting, and other cultural matters, in order to bring in the best yield of high-quality seeds.

In their peak season, fieldmen may be up at 3 a.m. to direct dusting for insect control. Then they are out checking fields until sundown, about 9 p.m. They also have the responsibility of writing the acreage contracts and maintaining good relations between the farmers and the company.

The fall months are the busy ones for the producers. Cleaning operations begin when the farmers bring in the harvested crops. Activity in the processing plant soon works up to a fever pitch and continues, perhaps with two or more shifts a day, until all the crops are cleaned.

Many tools and techniques are available for removing dirt, weed seeds, and any other impurities. They include airblasts, gravity separators, flat and cylindrical screens, indented disks, velvet rollers, the fractionating spiral slides, magnetic separators, washers, handpicking belts, and electronic machines that sort seed by color.

Seeds of most species are harvested between September and December and are needed in trade channels almost immediately. Fall planters in the Deep South and wholesalers who must package for distribution to dealers require seeds as early as they can be made ready.

Because of this seasonal pressure, seedsmen must have enough plant and equipment to process almost their entire year's product in just a few months—one reason for the relatively low ratio of sales to capital investment that characterizes the seed business.

The commercial grower may receive his supplies of seeds through one of several channels. Some full-line producers solicit business directly from growers and own retail stores in places of concentrated vegetable growing. The stores carry inventory and are a base for sales operations.

The harvested seeds are assembled at central points for packaging and reshipping in combination loads to the retail stores or branch warehouses. This system keeps the seedsman in close touch with the consumer, but it requires heavy investment and commitment to overhead expense.

Other full-line seedgrowers also do central packaging and sell mainly under their own brand, but only through franchised distributors and dealers. They thus take advantage of the greater potential saturation of the market that can be made by firms with a broad range of agricultural products to sell.

The seedsman's salesmen are technical advisers. They make periodic trips with the distributor's men and bring them and their customers up to date on developments. Available capital thus can be spread farther and the rate of turnover can be increased.

A third system is used by certain full-line and specialty seedgrowers who sell bulk, unbranded seeds to wholesale and retail firms that package and sell regionally under their own brand. Here, the seedsman's identity does not become known to the consumer, and his reputation resides within the trade. A great deal of the seed has moved through such outlets in the past 50 years, but the modern trend favors the nationally advertised brand. Its advantages include consistency and uniformity of quality and the use of new merchandising techniques. The middle of the 20th century may be the transition period between the dominance of private, regional brands and the general use of the seedgrower's nationally known brand.

Dealers and distributors normally place advance bookings at definite prices with their suppliers. The orders are subject to pro rata delivery in case of short crops but otherwise are firm. Commercial growers (except very large ones) usually buy their seeds just before planting time.

The growers base their estimates of the year's sales partly on orders they receive before planting time, but they must guess what their subsequent sales will be. For beets, carrots, turnips, and other biennials, the guesses must be made 2 years in advance.

The use of seeds fluctuates with weather, the demands for vegetables, and other things. Therefore, and because of the uncertainty as to yields of the seed crops, the amounts harvested by seedgrowers often fail to match their needs. Surpluses and shortages are common in the business.

The situation becomes acute among companies that sell seeds to canners and freezers. Food processors use a lot of seeds and must have particular varieties. Their growing and selling operations are highly competitive. If a canner needs Tendergreen beans to satisfy his growers and his customers and that variety is scarce, he cannot substitute Landreth Stringless, as a home gardener could.

Processors usually place preplanting orders to protect their supplies of certain varieties. But because markets for canned and frozen foods may become glutted, a reduction of the planned production may become necessary. Then the seedsman usually offers to help by agreeing to defer delivery of the contracted seeds for a year.

Another—and better—approach than acreage reduction is special industry-wide promotion by the food processors to move the surplus off the shelves.

Canners buy their seeds mostly from seedgrowers or large distributors that specialize in vegetable seeds. Delivery normally is made in the spring, shortly before planting time for the crop. The canners charge their growers approximately at cost for the seed as they issue it.

Careful credit management is important for seedsmen serving commercial growers and the processors. The hazards of farming and fluctuations of markets sometimes act to drain off reserves of ready cash in the hands of users of seeds. Credit losses in the business probably are similar to those in other agricultural supply lines, but well above the average of all industries.

Commercial growers, food processors, and their suppliers of seeds have close relationships. They frequently meet with plant scientists of the Department of Agriculture and State agricultural experiment stations to discuss problems of the food industry.

FLOWER SEEDS bought by commercial users are distributed and handled in much the same way as vegetable seeds. Some firms specialize in serving the needs of growers of bedding plants and cut flowers and florists. Other firms maintain separate distributing divisions, whose staffs know the technical requirements of these customers.

Because the income of the commercial user depends to a great extent on the quality of the seeds he plants, the seedsman and the commercial user of flower seeds work together in developing new varieties and improving supplies of seeds to meet the needs of these markets.

Seeds of such flowers as stocks, snapdragons, and sweetpeas are popular with greenhouse growers of cut flowers. Petunias, marigolds, sweet alyssum, and zinnias are important to growers of bedding plants for sales to home gardeners for transplanting.

When a commercial user gets a supply of seeds that perform well, he wants the exact item again—until he finds something better. Strict control is needed in all stages of production to assure that seeds for his next purchase will be identical. The place they are grown, the parent stock, and the method of harvesting and cleaning are factors of moment.

The commercial user of flower seeds usually places contract orders for large quantities with distributors to make sure that a crop will be grown for him. Even so, a poor crop may cut down the amount available and force him to look for a substitute.

So also the grower of bedding plants or cut flowers, who insists on seeds from lots that have done well in the past. He may look to one distributor for some flower classes and to other seedsmen for his other requirements. He is reluctant to change his supply of seeds unless he is assured the seed will give similar performance. A slight change in the number of days until maturity, color, or height, can affect his income.

As new strains and varieties are developed, the seedsman wants them tested and tried by the commercial user. If the tests prove that the new item is better, the distributing seedsman can look for an order. The entire purchaser-supplier relationship is built on cooperation and confidence.

Many pounds of flower seeds are purchased each year by parks, institutions, and estates. These markets are handled much the same as are the commercial growers' market. Several distributing firms prepare catalogs and literature for this trade. Either by salesmen or through direct-mail contact, the seedsman keeps his customers informed of technical advances, techniques, and recommendations. Purchases are usually made on a spot-order basis, but large quantities may be quoted and sold on a bid basis.

Drug companies are large users of certain seeds in their manufacturing or experimental operations. Their requirements are so specialized that each purchase is the product of direct negotiations between the drug company and an experienced grower located in the most advantageous area of production.

The home-garden market for flower and vegetable seeds has been expanding because of the move to the suburbs, the trend to outdoor living, and the increase in population. Distribution of seeds to home gardeners takes many forms.

Distributor seedsmen have their own growing facilities or arrange for their supplies with specialists, with whom they place contracts early in the year before crops are planted so that the seedsman can plan his acreage to meet the demand. Early contracts help to keep supplies level.

Because the reputation of a brand depends on the customer's satisfaction, the quality of seeds is a prime concern. Many steps are taken to assure quality.

One form of quality control is in trial grounds. On regular garden plots the seedsman can rate the performance of his seed at all stages of development. The trials indicate which lots are not performing satisfactorily and which

lines need improvement. Details like uniformity of the plants, blooming dates, number of flowers, and the size of vegetable are watched.

Here also other items and improved varieties are tested for possible addition to the line. Visits to other trial gardens, operated by All America Selections, other seedsmen, and universities are helpful in keeping abreast of developments.

FALL IS a busy time for the distributor. Seeds arrive in bag lots from the growing field and the cleaning plant. They now must be tested, packed, and distributed in a few months. In fact, some shipments, such as those to the South, must be made without delay. Every available person is needed at this peak time, and night shifts are not unusual.

Inspections and tests are made immediately to make sure that every bag of every harvest lot meets the standards of quality. To speed up the process, some tests are started with advance samples rushed from the fields. Seed not properly cleaned is returned for recleaning and processing. Samples are taken from each bag for testing by the seed laboratory. The laboratory is a department in the seedsman's establishment or an organization that does this work for him. Packaging begins if the seeds pass the tests.

Seeds are packaged for the home-garden market in several forms. The old way is to ship bulk seeds in large bags directly to the dealer. The dealer in turn measures out the desired amount to each customer—1 ounce of beet, 1 pound of beans, and so on.

An improved method of distributing quantities larger than a packet to the consumer is the packaged bulk seed unit. Individual paper or cloth bags, and cartons of an ounce, one-fourth pound, or 1 pound may be offered. The unit packages eliminate much handwork and identify the brand name.

Hermetically sealed cans are another development. Cans have several advantages over bags and cartons. Cans protect seeds from moisture, rodents, insects, and crushing. If properly done, canning increases the length of time germination can be maintained before it drops below standard.

Large bags and packaged bulk units are filled by weight. The packaging equipment is semiautomatic in most packaging plants. Most distributors find that it is not economical to mechanize highly for this short period.

The retail seed packets are also filled on semiautomatic machines. Here again, the cost of high-speed automatic machinery in relation to the time it will be used is a determining factor. Because some varieties sell in relatively small amounts, it is impractical to set up an elaborate machine for a short run. The variations of size and shape of seeds also make full automation quite difficult.

The number of seeds per packet is determined by the number needed to plant a row. Packets of flower seeds are filled with a generous supply for the average home planting. Filling of packets is by volume. The number of seeds or the weight of the seeds going into the packet is converted into volume for filling by the machine. Packets are checked often for amount by weighing several packets against a check weight of packets that are known to have been filled exactly.

Retail packets carry a description of the item, planting instructions, and other information to help insure best results.

One type, the picture packets, are distributed for display in dealer stores, but mail-order packets—the other type—usually are printed merely with copy, since the customer has made his purchase on the basis of the picture and description in a catalog. Picture packets are produced by a few printers who maintain large libraries of available color pictures for use by all seedsmen of standard items. They also have special color plates for the exclusive use of individual seedsmen.

Seedsmen selling both types of pack-ets use the same quality and amount of seeds in both.

Some packets show zone maps that indicate the time for planting. Others picture the small plants to help the home gardener in weeding out other plants that sprout at the same time.

Pictures on the packets now may be reproductions of color photographs. They may show the use of the flower and vegetable—corn on the cob ready to eat, flowers in a bouquet, and such. Cellophane jackets are used on some packets to protect the seeds and make the packet look even better.

Some seeds are packaged in forms to make gardening easier. There are several preseeded products, such as seed tapes and garden mats, in which the carrier can be planted along with the seed. Chemicals, fertilizers, and other materials sometimes are included with these carriers.

Preseeded flats for indoor starting of seeds have been put on the market as a convenience to gardeners.

BULK SEEDS and packaged bulk seed units are usually sold to dealers on contract. Contract forms are sent out or delivered by the seedsman from May through July for ordering seeds to be shipped early the following year.

The contracts enable the seedsman to plan his production to best serve the needs of his customers and guarantees to the dealer the lowest price for the year. If the price of the seeds goes down before delivery, he receives the lower price. If the price of the seeds goes up, he is protected against the increase. Fill-in orders are ordered for spot delivery, with prices quoted as of the day he orders.

The color-picture packets usually are sold on a sale-or-return basis. The dealer's contract states that title to the packets passes to the dealer at the time of shipment, but at the end of the season he may return all unsold packets to the distributor for credit. The dealer therefore will receive a completely new assortment the following season.

Color packets and bulk seed are sold

under a warranty clause, like: "Seller warrants to the extent of the purchase price that seeds sold are as described on the container, within recognized tolerances. Seller gives no other or further warranty, expressed or implied."

Shipping dates vary throughout the country. Seeds are needed in the South long before the snow is off the ground in the North. Most shipments are made about 2 months in advance of the retail buying season. The dealer thus can put up his display and make last-minute inventories. When the buying season arrives, he has little time for anything except serving the needs of his customers.

The assortment of packets in the dealer's display depends on several factors. The number of packets depends on his potential sales. A small dealer may receive 500 packets made up of 50 to 75 varieties in his initial shipment. A large dealer could receive as many as 2 thousand packets composed of 150 to 300 different varieties.

Certain items are more popular in some areas than others. The composition of the assortment depends on geography, nationality groups, climatic conditions, and preferences in the section.

With his assortment of seed packets, the dealer receives a display rack free, with the expectation it will be used several years. The display racks have become much more than utility holders of packets. In line with modern merchandising techniques, they are frequently substantial and attractive fixtures that are a focal point for the garden supply section of the store. Banners, posters, and leaflets also are supplied free by the distributor.

Methods of selling and servicing the dealers vary with areas and the distributor. Some firms have salesmen who solicit orders before the season and deliver the rack and packets at the proper time for display. Throughout the selling season, visits are made to make sure the display rack is kept well supplied at all times. Other seedsmen use wholesalers and jobbers or arrange

with rack jobbers to service the dealers and maintain adequate packets on display. Still other seedsmen send seeds and displays to the dealer by mail and service his reorders by mail.

Purchasing seeds from the mail-order catalog is a tradition with countless gardeners. The catalog arrives soon after January 1, but work on it started months before: Pictures were taken in previous summers; decisions were made as to the best varieties to be offered; copy describing each item was written.

Some catalogs are mailed regionally. Others are distributed nationally to several million persons. Since mail-order catalogs draw orders from large areas, they can offer many special seed varieties not profitably handled by the local dealer.

A catalog may list as many as 2 thousand different varieties and give the home gardener a choice of packages of different sizes.

Even seed of unusual or exotic types can be profitably listed. Demand in any one area is small, but overall sales can make it worth while for the mail-order seedsman. In fact, several mail-order catalogs specialize in seeds of unusual plants.

WHATEVER the seedsmen's problems and considerations in preparing the catalogs, the gardener's problem—if that's what it is—is quite different. His is the pleasurable task of selection from the treasures offered him, the exquisite agony of deciding between Moonglow and Silver Star and between Buttersweet and Bountiful. Maybe he ends by ordering them all, but no matter—the price is low; the return is high. For the gardener, few of life's joys surpass the pleasures of perusing seed catalogs the long winter evenings when spring seems far behind.

Seeds of unusual types sometimes carry a problem. If they entail unusual problems of growing, the crop may be harvested by hand from plants growing wild, although today specialists produce most of the items in small demand.

Mail orders must be filled quickly. Most of the orders are received in a period of 3 months or so. Adequate facilities and workers to handle peak-load requirements are the perennial problems of the mail-order distributor. Most firms attempt to utilize their help and facilities to a greater extent by handling commodities that are in demand in other seasons.

Seeds are distributed to home gardeners also in several other channels, such as through schools and organizations, usually in conjunction with an educational or civic program.

THE HOME GARDENER can look to many sources for help in attaining success in his garden. The Garden Seed Sales Promotion Committee of the American Seed Trade Association offers through newspapers, radio, and magazines practical articles that give latest gardening techniques and tell what is new in seeds. All America Selections test new flowers and vegetables in trial gardens throughout the United States. Those selected by a panel of experts as outstanding are awarded All America Medals.

The writings of garden editors in magazines, newspapers, and books and bulletins of the Department of Agriculture, State colleges, and county agents are good sources of information on recommended practices.

WILLIAM B. CARTER *is a vice president of Corneli Seed Co., St. Louis, Mo., and is the manager of that company's garden seed department. He joined the company in 1948, following his graduation from Washington University in St. Louis. He has been a member of several committees of the American Seed Trade Association.*

EDWIN P. BUGBEE, JR., *is a vice president and sales manager of the W. Atlee Burpee Co. He is a graduate of the Wharton School of Business and Finance, University of Pennsylvania. He has served as president of the Pennsylvania Seedsmen's Association and chairman of the Wholesale Packet Seed Division and the Asta Division of the American Seed Trade Association.*

Handling Seeds of the Field Crops

D. K. CHRISTENSEN, EARL SIEVEKING, AND J. W. NEELY

THIS YEAR an American farmer will buy 10 pounds of seeds to thicken a mountain meadow. Another may buy 100 thousand pounds to plant 10 thousand corporate acres. Because American seedsmen have built an efficient distribution system, both buyers will be able to get the best seeds for their purposes.

Behind their purchases lie the marketing, processing, and financial resources of hundreds of firms—handlers of seeds that are backed by the special skills of tens of thousands of farms devoted wholly or partly to the planned production of good seeds.

The marketing channels and practices that provide the hundreds of kinds and varieties of field-crop seeds may be simple or complex. There may be one contributive function or several.

The simplest marketing cycle is completed when one farmer sells his seeds to his neighbor. Millions of pounds move in that way.

Most distribution, however, calls for a more sophisticated chain of events. Distance between the production area and the planter, reliance on special cleaning techniques, research in plant breeding, storage, financing, and problems of handling broaden the base and add to the list of participants.

Seeds of field crops follow no normal route from producer to user. Most movement, however, involves a grower, a wholesaler, and a retailer. The activities of each vary widely, depending on the item handled. The size and location of any of the three segments modify the pattern of their operation.

From a marketing standpoint, seeds of field crops can be grouped as hybrid corn (and hybrid sorghum); self-pollinated crops, such as soybeans and small grains; cotton; small-seeded forage legumes and grasses and cover crops; and tobacco.

Marketing channels and practices for hybrid seed corn require attention because of the tremendous importance of the crop. It is a 150-million-dollar business and holds a unique and basic position in the seed industry. An estimated 14 million bushels of hybrid seeds were used in 1959 to plant nearly 81 million acres and produce a crop of 4 billion bushels of grain.

An overwhelming percentage of the volume is handled by fewer than a dozen large companies. Their hybrids are called "closed pedigree" because the identification of the inbred lines used in formulating them is not disclosed. The companies have their own breeding and research departments and their own sales outlets. The distribution process is highly integrated.

The hybrids are developed from breeding materials provided by public agencies, combined with developments of the wholesaler's own research. Such companies contract for production with expert growers. The grower agrees to deliver his entire crop to the contracting wholesaler. Field inspections, roguing, detasseling, husking, shelling, drying, recleaning, grading, and testing usually are done by the wholesaler.

The large wholesaler then moves his finished hybrid seed corn to the consumer through farmer-dealers or country dealers.

The farmer-dealer usually covers a relatively small area. His coverage is intensive and effective. Because his stocks are usually supplied by the wholesaler on a guaranteed-sale basis, he has little financial risk.

There are thousands of such farmer-dealers. Individually, they form no huge single enterprises, but collectively they sell a high percentage of the hybrid seed corn.

A wholesaler who deals directly with a farmer-dealer bypasses the country dealer, who maintains a place of business and sells other items to the farmer. When such a dealer loses his seed-corn contact with the farmer, he may lose other business. The country dealer therefore is becoming more active on direct farm calls with his own employees or his own version of the farmer-agent.

Besides the privately owned hybrids, a sizable business is done on hybrid seed corn by firms who offer only publicly developed varieties. Public institutions release the basic inbreds, developed by their research, through recognized foundation seed organizations or directly to individual farmers and to small seed firms. The smaller seed firms may then contract with farmers for the production of the hybrid seed. Distribution is handled in much the same manner as privately developed hybrids. Some of the independent farmer-growers perform the wholesale and retail functions themselves.

Much of the seed produced under this plan is certified. Because of the general availability of such hybrids and the obvious need to compete with others producing an almost identical product, price is more of a factor in merchandising than it is for private varieties.

All in all, the marketing of hybrid seed corn is one of the most orderly endeavors in the seed industry.

New hybrids of sorghums, dramatically superior to open-pollinated varieties and types, are handled in much the same way as hybrid seed corn. Large companies that have their own breeding, research, and sales programs and smaller firms that rely mainly on publicly released varieties compete for the farmer's business. Seeds of hybrid sorghums move in volume at retail through the direct-seller or farmer-agents.

The contract grower of both hybrid corn and hybrid sorghum usually is paid some specified premium over grain prices for his special knowledge and effort. The independent grower has no such price or outlet limitations, but he undertakes the considerable responsibility of processing, financing, and marketing.

SMALL GRAINS, such as wheat, oats, and barley, involve the simplest form of marketing activity.

Generally the farmer saves a part of his own production to use as seeds for the succeeding crop. The farmer may have the grain he saves cleaned and treated by a retailer, who has the equipment for it. A few send samples of the seeds to a laboratory for tests of purity and germination. Far too often farmers plant grains for seed that have not been cleaned, treated, or tested. They learn only by results on their farms how well the seeds grow and what kinds of weed seeds they may be planting.

A desire for seeds of better quality or for a newer variety may lead the grain farmer to look beyond his own bin for a source of supply. His neighbor, who has a newer or different variety, or a nearby producer of certified seed will be the most likely candidate for his business. This producer-to-farmer type of transaction is typical of the uninvolved marketing system employed for the movement of most self-pollinated seed grains.

New varieties usually are provided by the public institutions. Private research can hardly afford large sums for breeding and development without some control over production and distribution. Only a small percentage of the publicly developed varieties are handled by the regular wholesale seed trade.

Some large farm operators, notably growers of barley and rice in California, have undertaken the processing and distribution of seeds on a large scale. They grow and sell certified seed. The trading route is grower-producer to grower-consumer. It represents an effort of some depth and may well alter the hit-or-miss marketing practices for grain seeds of the past.

The age of nonprofessional discovery is still with us. It also affects marketing procedures. The principal variety of spring malting barley used in the upper Midwest in the past several years was selected originally by a North Dakota farmer. One of the leading hard red winter wheats used in the Southern Great Plains also was developed by one self-taught farmer-breeder. Both of these prominent varieties were accepted for certification after being tested and recommended by State agricultural experiment stations and are marketed the same way as other self-pollinated seed grains.

Such oil-seed crops as soybeans and flax generally are handled and marketed in the same way as the small grains. Growers have the alternative of selling them for oil or for seed. The need to retain a seed crop until spring—with attendant expenses and market risks—has limited somewhat production exclusively for seeds.

MARKETING PRACTICES for seeds of cotton have been affected by the predominance of varieties developed by private breeders and by the practice of farmers who regularly replace their seed stocks.

Cotton is open pollinated. To avoid the danger of mixtures, farmers do not attempt to maintain their own seed supply to the extent that they do with many grains. Their search for new supplies therefore makes them constant customers of those breeders who do the best job. That and the one-variety plan have developed marketing practices for cotton seeds somewhat different from those for other crops.

The development of marketing channels for cotton seeds has led to the growth of those in private enterprise who maintain effective improvement and maintenance programs. In the South and Southeast, plantings of privately bred varieties range from about 50 percent in Alabama to more than 90 percent in Virginia, North Carolina, South Carolina, Florida, Louisiana, Mississippi, Arkansas, Missouri, and Texas. The situation is reversed in the Southwest; 85 percent to 95 percent of the acreage in California, Arizona, and New Mexico is planted to varieties developed by public agencies.

Registered seed of privately developed varieties usually is grown and distributed by the breeder. Sometimes he may have it grown under firm contract for him. The breeder supervises or handles the production to maintain genetic identity and high purity. The seed is classed as registered if it meets the requirements of the official State seed-certifying agency. The registered seed is then usually sold by the breeder to a wholesaler, who sells it through normal commercial channels.

Registered seed of varieties resulting from public breeding programs usually is sold by the private grower or by a cooperative association of growers, to wholesalers, farmer cooperatives, or to individual farmers. The ginner often does some of the seed distribution. Certified cotton seed is sold sometimes by the grower to the ginner, who may in turn sell to a wholesaler or even direct to the user. Ginners as well as wholesalers on occasion may have firm contracts with growers for certified seed.

Noncertified cotton seed is usually sold direct to the farmer by the ginner or the grower.

Some cotton seed is sold through brokers—an estimated 5 to 10 percent of the total volume of registered and certified seed. Smaller amounts of noncertified seed also are sold through brokers.

The importance of choosing the best varieties for an area has been recognized as a good practice since the time that varietal evaluation was developed and accepted.

One of the first services of the agricultural research agencies in sections where cotton became an important crop was the evaluation of varieties and the recommendation of suitable ones to farmers. A large number of varieties persisted nevertheless, and a large part of the acreage was planted to unadapted, poor-performing varieties or to mixed and deteriorated seed stocks.

This situation was improved markedly by the production of cotton by one-variety communities. An association of cottongrowers voluntarily standardized their production by growing the single variety that was adapted to the growing conditions of the locality and that produced the quality of lint desired by mills. The program was developed by research, extension, and marketing agencies of the Department of Agriculture in cooperation with the Extension Service in the States.

The one-variety community usually obtained enough foundation seed annually from an experiment station or a commercial breeder to plant about 1 percent of the amount required for the entire community. The increase of this seed was used to plant about 10 percent of the community the second year.

During the third year, the rest of the community was planted with the second-year seed increase. Seeds produced the third year were sent to oil mills for crushing. Each member of the community organization received new seeds each year.

The plan started in the Southeast in the early 1930's and grew rapidly. The marked improvement in the yield and in the quality of the crop of the Southeast was due largely to the results of the one-variety program.

Other advantages were the assurance of a dependable supply of good seeds of an adapted variety, improved ginning facilities, and effective marketing systems. By 1948, in the 17 cotton States, 352,839 members in 2,275 communities were growing 11,549,000 acres of cotton in standardized one-variety communities. This amounted to about 50 percent of the total planted acreage.

It was realized at that time that the one-variety community program had served its purpose. It was replaced in most areas by the Smith-Doxey improvement groups, which were made up of groups of cottongrowers who signed up with their custom ginner or local warehouseman for receiving free classing and marketing news services. The growers in a given group were expected to grow the same variety, to obtain seed from a dependable source, and to produce lint of good quality. Some of the improvement groups were obligated by agreement or required by State legislation to plant 100 percent of their acreage to one variety.

The program in the San Joaquin Valley of California is unique. About 750 thousand acres of cotton are grown there, and the production of any variety except Acala is prohibited by law. The present Acala 4–42 variety was developed by the Department's Cotton Field Station at Shafter, Calif. The station supplies the California Planting Cotton Seed Distributors with about 45 pounds of self-pollinated seeds each year. The distributors multiply the seeds throughout four generations, by which time the quantity is adequate to supply all cotton producers with certified seed. Fresh seeds reach the final grower each year because the cycle is a continuous procedure.

Acala is resistant to the diseases prevailing in the locality and has high yield and good fiber. The cotton gins there do a highly specialized processing job and deliver a uniform product to the spinners.

BECAUSE the distribution of seeds of alfalfa involves all segments of the seed industry throughout the United States, marketing procedures followed for alfalfa are given to illustrate the way the trade operates. A similar pattern is followed in marketing the seeds of other forage legumes and grasses.

Two kinds of growers produce alfalfa seed.

The casual grower may be a small farmer, who may make either a crop of seeds or a crop of hay. His decision depends on the weather and the income he expects from each. He treats the production of seeds not as his major

business but as an alternative crop. The versatility of the all-purpose harvest combine accounts in part for the sizable role this type of producer has in national production.

Such growers are spread throughout the western half of the Nation. Their production is almost entirely limited to uncertified seed, the agronomic merits of which are more often determined by the area of production than by genetic background. Such growers accounted for about one-half of the 130 million pounds produced in 1959.

Seeds produced by these growers ordinarily follow a rather involved route to market. Usually the farmer sells the seeds to a small country accumulator in the production area. The accumulator may rough clean or finish clean, depending on the quality in any given crop year and upon the ultimate area of use.

The country accumulator usually bulks seeds from several growers together to make a large unit of one quality for easier sale. He may sell through a broker to a large wholesaler in the producing area, or he may sell to the wholesaler direct. He similarly may sell to a wholesaler in the consuming area. He makes limited sales to retailers and sometimes to consumers.

The grower of alfalfa seeds we have described rarely is under contract. He usually sells his production on competitive bids at harvesttime.

There is a serious, more purposeful grower who makes the production of alfalfa seeds his business. He farms primarily in the specialized production areas of California and to a lesser extent in the other Western States. Often he grows a variety eligible for certification and produces his seeds under the regulations and surveillance of the State seed-certifying agency. The grower may produce under some form of contract for a wholesaler. He may be a member of a cooperative, or, completely independent, he may sell to the highest bidder.

This type of grower is replacing the casual producer. As a source of supply, he is more permanent. His seeds usually are mechanically and genetically superior. He may be a small, medium, or large operator. Some have their own cleaning facilities and distribution outlets, but most have their seeds custom cleaned and limit their marketing activities to sales to large wholesalers in their area of production. The production-area wholesaler, in turn, usually sells his seed directly or through a broker to a wholesaler in an area of use. While usually wholly independent, the western wholesaler may be tied by contract, pricing policy, custom, or ownership directly to midwestern or eastern distributors.

A noteworthy development in the production of alfalfa seeds and in marketing practices themselves has been the emergence of California as the Nation's leading producing State. California in 1948 harvested 21 thousand acres that yielded 215 pounds an acre—a production of 4.5 million pounds of seeds. California in 1958 harvested 167 thousand acres of alfalfa seeds, yielding 390 pounds per acre, for a crop of 65 million pounds.

The revolution in growing alfalfa seeds of varieties adapted to the Northern and Central States in the southern latitudes upset traditional trading practices and upset existing marketing channels. It was caused by the discovery that there need be no loss of the desirable genetic characteristics in superior varieties grown one generation outside their area of adaptation.

Such production had to be controlled closely. The crop improvement associations in Arizona and California were the first to undertake the initial supervisory responsibility. They handled it skillfully. A rapid transition from old to new areas of production occurred. The longstanding problem of inadequate supplies of identifiable, superior varieties was solved. New growers, new cleaning plants, and new seed companies undertook the task of growing, processing, and marketing. A 14-fold increase in California's alfalfa production resulted.

Out of the developments in marketing, the West in general and California in particular emerged as the determining force in pricing and marketing seeds and in quality.

SOME ALFALFA wholesalers have introduced their own varieties in recent years. Contractual arrangements with the growers have changed somewhat as a result.

As with hybrid corn, the wholesaler agrees to take the contract grower's entire production. An identical price is paid to each grower of the variety. The grower agrees to sell only to the company that originated the variety. The originating firm, in turn, controls the seed stock. Usually no specific price is agreed upon at the time the seed is planted, but some premium normally is paid to the grower after the market for competitive varieties has been established.

The proprietary nature of such a variety alters certain marketing procedures. The broker is rarely used. The wholesaler in the production area and the country accumulator have lesser functions. Except for differentials in freight costs and services rendered, such a variety sells for the same price to the same class of trade throughout the season and does not reflect the day-to-day market fluctuations of the varieties that are more subject to the law of supply and demand.

The trend in the production and distribution of alfalfa seed seems to be toward this type of operation.

EXCEPT for the dramatic switch in production areas that occurred for alfalfa, much the same marketing story can be repeated for other small-seeded legumes—red clover, alsike clover, crimson clover, lespedeza, white Dutch clover, Ladino whiteclover, and sweetclover. The growers usually are different, but the country accumulator, the wholesaler, and the retailer may be the same operators who handle alfalfa.

Unlike alfalfa, much of the production is in areas of heavy consumption of seeds. The wholesaler's function therefore is as a production-area and a consumption-area wholesaler.

Some growers who specialize in producing seeds produce red clover in Idaho, Oregon, and Washington, and Ladino whiteclover in California. Most of the domestic supply of red clover seeds, however, is produced by the casual grower. No one State continuously has maintained leadership in production. Some Midwestern States may be large exporters one season and deficit areas the next. Moisture, prices of hay, and general weather conditions make the determination.

While the Pacific Northwest produces a substantial amount of red clover seed, the harvest in the Central States usually dictates the worth of the crop, even though their volume is unpredictable. Ohio, for example, had a crop of 4.3 million pounds between two crops of 10 million pounds. This variability in production calls for extreme maneuverability for all who engage in marketing and processing.

Normal procedure one year becomes abnormal the next. Marketing channels and practices are resolved only after individual seedsmen appraise their local situation as it affects and is affected by the whole. Generally speaking, marketing practices on these items are somewhat disorganized, because long planning is impossible.

Of the clovers, neither publicly nor privately developed certified varieties have cut materially into the use of the so-called common seed. No privately developed varieties are available in quantity. Ladino whiteclover has been an exception. It was mostly certified, not because there were superior varieties but because of the need to distinguish it from the medium-small types of whiteclover.

The four main companion grasses for legumes—smooth bromegrass, timothy, tall fescue, and orchardgrass—are grown by qualified growers in areas adapted for their seed production. There has been only limited effort to grow the improved varieties specifically for seed in large volume outside their areas of adaptation for forage. The trend, however, is toward this type of production. Marketing channels for these four grasses normally follow the established pattern from grower to wholesaler to retailer.

Most of the seed of miscellaneous forage and cover crops—such as cowpeas, vetches, field peas, lupines and millets—is produced by the "in-and-out" grower and does not follow definite marketing patterns. The grower seldom produces seed on a contract, and the wholesale seedsman is often bypassed in the marketing of them.

As with some of the clovers, areas of production and consumption of seeds often are the same. Much seed is distributed on a farmer-to-farmer basis. Some producers sell their crops to wholesale or retail seedsmen, who have processing and storage facilities and are willing to assume the market risks. This seed moves through normal channels to retailers and farmers.

Notable exceptions in this group are seeds of sudangrass and millets. Several public institutions have started breeding and improvement programs. A number of improved varieties, such as Piper sudan, Starr and Gahi pearl millets, have been released. Most of the seeds of the Piper sudan is produced in California and the pearl millets in the Southwest, outside of the major consuming areas. They usually are certified. Often they are grown under contract to wholesalers in the producing area, who move the seeds in normal market channels, as described for the alfalfa produced in the West.

SEEDS OF flue-cured tobacco often are sold over the counter in 1-ounce containers. Small amounts are needed to establish the individual plots or acreages. This, combined with the low total cost of seed per acre in comparison to the gross value of the resulting crop of tobacco leaf, influences marketing procedures.

The tobacco farmer who seeks out

the best seeds is rewarded for his efforts by high yields, disease-resistant stands, and leaf of good quality. He usually is willing therefore to pay a premium for good varieties. By doing so, he makes possible the continuance of breeding and research programs. This has stimulated private interest, so that a major part of the flue-cured tobacco acreage is planted to privately developed varieties.

Certification is important in the distribution of tobacco seeds. The foundation to registered to certified pattern is preserved, but, unlike most other crops, a high percentage of registered seed is sold to farmers.

Marketing channels usually omit the traditional wholesaler function. The private breeder-producer sells directly to the retailer. In addition, breeders of improved varieties usually produce their own seeds and so bypass the contract grower. The maintenance, production, and harvesting of varieties of tobacco are highly technical operations that are not adapted to contract growing.

Some farmer-growers of tobacco seeds buy privately developed or publicly developed varieties. From these they grow, process, and package certified seed, which is usually sold direct to the retailer.

New tobaccos developed by public agencies generally follow the regular channels established for the release and distribution of varieties of field crops. Breeder seed is released to the recognized foundation seed organization, which makes the first multiplication. This seed, designated as foundation seed, is sold to growers for producing registered or certified seed.

Uncertified seed creates problems. In some areas, Georgia in particular, the farmer may be able to obtain bulk seed at no charge from the warehouse where his leaf tobacco is auctioned. The planting of poor seeds from deteriorated stocks may be the result.

The exportation of tobacco seeds from the United States is prohibited by Federal law.

Import-export trading of other items is becoming an increasingly important consideration for American seedsmen. Much of the imports are handled through import brokers. Such seeds usually go to an established domestic wholesaler, who introduces them into his normal trade channels. Importations of some crops contribute materially to our total supplies. Orchardgrass from Denmark and bromegrass from Canada are examples.

Seeds of farm crops once were sold in significant volume at retail by mail-order houses. Wider distribution of supplies, a standardization of qualities and varieties, and the elimination of terminal markets have cut heavily into mail-order distribution. Today a small percentage, probably less than 5 percent, is sold in this way.

Our discussion of marketing practices is applicable equally to both independent and cooperative enterprises. At each level, cooperatives account for an important percentage of the total seed business. Just as with independents, their activity by crop varies considerably. Of some items they handle only a little. For others, usually at the grower-producer level, their position may be an important one.

Most cooperatives engaged in handling seeds perform either an accumulation service for the grower-producer or a distribution service at the consumer level. Some do both.

With a few minor exceptions, basic marketing procedures are altered but little by certification. The grower to wholesaler to retailer norm is maintained. Certification as a mechanism to protect the identity of privately developed varieties may have a larger role in the future.

D. K. CHRISTENSEN *is vice president of Northrup, King & Co., Minneapolis.*

EARL SIEVEKING *is manager of the Hybrid Seed Corn Division, Funk Brothers Seed Co., Bloomington, Ill.*

J. W. NEELY *is vice president and director of plant breeding, Coker's Pedigreed Seed Co., Hartsville, S.C.*

Grass Seeds for Lawns and Turf

ROBERT W. SCHERY

THE PRODUCTION and use of seeds for lawns and turf have grown in a few decades to match almost any agricultural enterprise.

The volume of the marketed seeds is not quite so great as that of alfalfa and corn, but the land upon which it is sown probably outvalues the acreage in corn and alfalfa.

It is an outgrowth of America's move to the suburbs; a desire for attractive lawns; an expanded highway program that calls for parklike rights-of-way; the establishment of new airports, golf courses, and industrial parks; and the continuing search for attractive turf for cemeteries, athletic fields, public buildings, schools, and parks.

We spend an estimated 2 to 3 billion dollars yearly to create and maintain about 12 million acres of nonagricultural turfgrass. The land value of this acreage is perhaps 25 billion dollars. Its seeding utilizes more than 100 million pounds of grass seeds annually. Of this "lawn seed" (to distinguish it from agricultural usage), about one-third is of first quality—mostly perennial species of attractive texture. One-third is permissible but not of top quality—mixtures with lesser amounts of quality species and some coarse or impermanent species. One-third is of a trashy sort—impermanent "hay-grass" mixtures.

The grasses that make up lawn mixtures originally were pasture species.

Many of us can remember how people scattered the sweepings from haymows around the farmstead to make lawns. This casual use of agricultural seeds gradually gave way to the sowing of better, cleaned seeds, packaged for lawn use even if it were of agricultural origin and to growing and harvesting seed specifically for fine turfs.

As the industry has progressed, standards have risen so that good mixtures now contain essentially weed-free seeds of fine-textured species, guaranteed to germinate satisfactorily. Some bulking with agricultural seed still continues in trash mixtures for mass-outlet sale, at a price, to unsuspecting homeowners.

The greatest market is in northern States. Species adaptable to cooler climates start readily from seeds, of which an abundant supply can be produced economically. Moreover, because of apomixis—reduced sexual crossing—the bluegrasses and lawn fescues maintain their identity well in varietal selection.

Seed sales in the South have centered mostly around common bermudagrass and, to a lesser extent, bahia, carpet, and centipede, with a little unselected zoysia. The improved varieties of bermuda and zoysia must be vegetatively planted, as they do not come true from seeds. St. Augustine, an inadequate seeder, also is planted vegetatively, as is much centipede turf.

The plains west of eastern Kansas have had no great development of the lawn types tailormade for that climate. There has been some commerce in and selection of buffalograss, a species able to exist with limited rainfall.

Several of the gramas, lovegrasses, wheatgrasses, and such have been seeded now and then for turf, but none is so attractive as the conventional eastern turfgrasses.

Because cities generally have enough water to permit irrigation of lawns and the use of the familiar humid-zone species, little commerce has arisen in specialties for arid lands.

The production of grass seeds is detailed in earlier chapters. Here I review three of the major species as examples of how production bears on quality, supply, and costs.

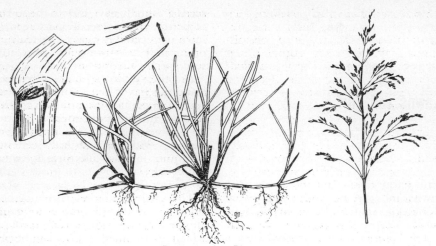

Poa pratensis—Bluegrass

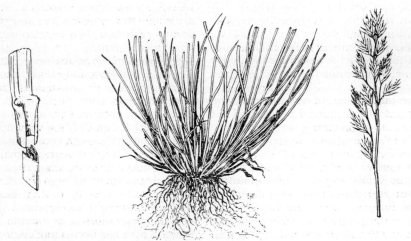

Festuca rubra—Red Fescue

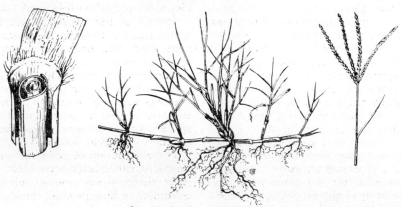

Cynodon dactylon—Bermudagrass

Vegetatively planted southern species (like creeping bentgrasses for northern golf greens) must be dismissed with the mere notation that they are mostly nursery grown in their appropriate climatic areas. Improved varieties can be bought at turfgrass establishments in the South and the Southwest.

The three leaders are the bluegrasses; varieties of fine fescue, mostly from Oregon; and bermudagrass.

Domestic and perennial ryegrasses account for most of the seed going into temporary cover (as winter grass in the South) or the cheaper mixtures. Production of ryegrass is as much for agricultural purposes as for lawns, and I pass over this segment of the industry.

KENTUCKY BLUEGRASS was the settler's partner in early colonization. Production gradually shifted from the East to west of the Mississippi as lands became more valuable and intensively cropped in the Corn Belt. The only center of production remaining in the East is the section near Lexington, Ky., where tradition and especially favorable soils continue to make bluegrass and livestock important.

In the western district—northward and westward from Missouri—production of seed of natural Kentucky bluegrass likewise works in partnership with livestock. Seed is harvested from the same turf grazed or mowed for hay at other seasons. Experience has demonstrated the appropriate management of this ecological complex, so that grazing, fertilization, control of weeds, and suchlike have become perfected. Seed harvesting moved northward and westward, as the bluegrass volunteered on the newly plowed up prairie. Minnesota, North Dakota, and South Dakota are important sources of natural bluegrass seed in some years, as are Iowa, Missouri, and Kentucky.

Economic, biologic, and marketing advantages reside in the system that has evolved for the production of natural bluegrass seed. Use by livestock of the acreage during nonseeding seasons constitutes a sort of subsidization of seed production on what has become expensive, heavily capitalized land. Furthermore, most sods have lain unpampered for years, some since colonization. The diverse strains that result should be especially hardy because they have been subject to whatever natural selection there might be for generations. Midcontinent seed also is closer to the main urban markets, and so there are transportation advantages.

On the other hand, because bluegrass volunteers everywhere in the East and Midwest, it becomes difficult to keep selected lines pure if pure lines should be wanted for certain attributes. Also, with the multiple uses to which such acreage is put, it sometimes is difficult to manage especially for seed. Consistently high yields, which may reduce unit harvesting costs, are not certain. The cultivation of named selections consequently has moved mostly to the newer, often irrigated, lands of the Pacific Northwest.

In a few sections, Kentucky especially, some farmers may own their own stripping machines, care for the pastures carefully, and harvest and deliver seed to local cleaning plants. Green seed—fresh, uncured seed, which is subject to fermentation and loss of viability unless it is spread out to cure within a few hours—may be sold at a few cents a pound to the cleaner and be cured—dried—in the curing yards of that company.

Larger farmers may operate their own curing yards. Sometimes they buy green seed from neighbors to supplement their supply. The cured seed may be sold to the cleaning plant or it may be custom cleaned on a fee basis.

In the western district, where extensive areas must be covered, most stripping is done by fleet strippers belonging to companies large enough to capitalize them and their maintenance. Farmers may arrange for use of stripping machines by any of numerous agreements. Sometimes the farmer supplies tractors and labor, and the company furnishes the machines. The crop is shared. The farmer may then sell his share to the operator for cash. Or, a company may buy stripping rights to farm acreage. Or, strippers may be issued to a farmer with an understanding that the green seed be delivered only to the operator's curing yard. Independently stripped lots of seed are subject to visual judgment by an experienced bluegrass hand at the curing yard to determine its worth. A percentage for dockage is agreed upon by buyer and seller, upon estimate of the quality of the green seed—fullness and maturity of seed, the amount of trash and weeds, the moisture content, and so on.

Such varieties of bluegrass as Arboretum, Delta, Merion, Newport, and Park generally are row cropped by the usual agricultural procedures. Many of the large growers in the Northwest operate their own cleaning plants and undertake all operations from production through to wholesale sales.

Growers have banded together to form associations to promote their particular varieties, some of which are produced under certification. The usual plan is to levy a voluntary assessment of a few cents a hundredweight, to pay for promotion in the eastern market area.

Weather greatly influences supplies of bluegrass seed, especially seed of natural Kentucky bluegrass. Bluegrass that is well cured and cleaned retains its viability for years if it is properly stored. Years of heavy production yield enough carryover supplies to offset a lean year. Prices therefore tend to have some stability, although the market generally reflects supply and demand: Heavy production, lower prices; a lean crop, higher prices.

Early harvest, starting in Kentucky and Missouri, is watched closely as an indicator of price trends. The intensity of harvest farther North will depend partly on the abundance and quality of the earlier southern crop. Should crops in Kentucky, Missouri, and Iowa be lean, with prices rising,

activity will be intense in the Dakotas. If, on the other hand, southern supplies are good, only the best acreage in the North will be harvested. An abundant year reduces the price, because of the pressure on supplies and because seed is then more selectively and economically harvested, and marginal acreage is bypassed.

Thus bluegrass seeds exhibit a production duality: Hardy, natural Kentucky bluegrass from east of the Rockies, favored economically by nearness to markets and "subsidization" by livestock; and premium varieties grown agronomically solely for seed in the Pacific Northwest.

Production averages more than 20 million pounds annually from both sources.

THE SECOND major component of good mixtures of lawn seeds for northern regions is the red fescue complex.

There are no especially favored production areas in the Eastern States, such as for bluegrass, where red fescue has become a pasture dominant. Thus, without "livestock subsidization," red fescues cannot compete well for agricultural acreage in the East. Fescue forage has been utilized to some extent in western Canada, however.

Most of the United States production consequently has become concentrated in the Pacific Northwest, especially in Oregon. There the improved varieties are grown under exacting agricultural procedures. High purities and germinations are achieved through close attention to factors of quality.

Without eastern competition, western production dominates the fine fescue market, except for imports, primarily from western Canada.

The domestic production of all varieties, usually more than 10 million pounds a year, often is about matched by imports.

Many of the growers of fescue are also growers of bentgrass, which is produced almost exclusively in the benign climate of western Oregon-Washington.

PRODUCTION of bermudagrass is less than that of bluegrass and lawn fescue. It was more than 7 million pounds in 1960. Bermuda invasion in the South was as ubiquitous as bluegrass in the North; today it volunteers widely throughout the warmer regions.

Agriculturally, the production of bermuda seed never has been able to compete successfully with other land uses in the Southeast. Thus, just as the growing of lawn fescue moved to the Pacific Northwest, production of bermuda seed ended up in the Southwest, primarily near Yuma, Ariz.

Formerly much bermudagrass seed was harvested in old alfalfa seed fields, in which the grass had volunteered. Alfalfa was especially prone to give way to bermuda on saline places. Where it was in relatively pure stands, this bermuda sod provided excellent yields of seed.

Planting and cultivation recently has been expressly for seed. No pasturing is done. Yields are reliable under irrigation. Harvest is in June and again in November. Because bermuda exhibits sexual crossing, selections do not come true from seed. Thus the only significant marketing distinction depends on whether the hulls are removed or left. Seeds with the hulls removed germinate more promptly. A pound contains about 40 percent more seeds and commands a premium price.

SEED customarily is cleaned to the accepted standards for the species at cleaning plants in the general producing area.

Most cleaned lawn seed is shipped in 100-pound sacks (sometimes 50-pound sacks) in carload lots to blenders or packagers in the sections where it is planted.

Brokerage and distribution services route some lots, but carload or part-carload shipments frequently are made directly from the seed cleaner to the packager's warehouse. There suitable blends for the trade area and the merchandising program of the packager are made. Most seed nowadays reaches the consumer prepackaged under private brand.

In the North, the chief consuming region for lawn seed, several varieties or species are customarily mixed, or blended. If the selection is skillful, the usefulness of a seed mixture thus is broadened, and adapted grasses are supplied to satisfy the many local variations in growing conditions—shade or sun, wet or dry, close or high clipping, heavy or light fertilization, and so on.

The increasing importance of lawn seeds has spurred research on the ecological question of how grasses best get along together. As a result, the top mixtures have improved.

Many blends limit or exclude bentgrass, once almost always a component of a quality mixture. Bentgrass, inherently an excellent turf species because of its low, fine growth and spreading stolons, has differing requirements from the bluegrass-red fescue component of quality mixtures; under humid conditions it tends to form disruptive colonies in the sward, within which other species may not flourish.

Other studies have pointed out how serious a setback even moderate quantities of quick "nursegrasses" may cause the desired permanent species and how insufficient seeding densities make coarse "weeds" of some plantings.

GOOD, PACKAGED mixtures of lawn seeds can be purchased at any hardware or garden store.

For Tennessee and northward, the mixture should be based primarily upon bluegrasses and the red fescues. A small percentage of quick nursegrass, such as ryegrass or redtop, may be tolerated, but they should not exceed 15 to 5 percent, respectively, of the mixture.

Tall fescue (Alta or Kentucky 31) is best avoided, except for rough areas and playfields, where coarseness is not important. The tall fescues are deep rooted and persistent. Once established, they may stool to clumps that cannot be removed except by hand digging.

The choice of lawn seeds cannot be separated from the kind of attention the lawn will receive. Presuming appropriate species have been included, how the planting is maintained will be more important than subtle differences in variety or percentage proportions in the mixture.

Full success with a new planting depends on cultivation of the soil and fertilization. Phosphorus should be prominent in fertilizer mixed into the seedbed, since it moves down through the soil only slowly.

A seeding must have constant moisture to sprout quickly. The moisture can be best insured by mulching. Straw, the usual mulch material, may be spread two or three straws deep. It helps prevent drying and reduces soil wash.

Once a seeding is established, the kind of grass determines care. Bentgrass needs close mowing, which is best done with a reel mower, and frequent fertilization, watering, control of diseases and weeds, and so on. Bluegrasses and fescues require less care. They profit most from fertilization in autumn and high clipping (for which a rotary mower is appropriate).

Any turf looks best if it is kept free from weeds. That is easily possible by the use of 2,4-D and any of the various crabgrass killers. Weeds are always less a problem under high mowing than if the lawn is scalped.

In the South, seeded grasses are fewer and have little varietal differentiation. Blending is practiced less than in the North. Bermuda, like bentgrass, is aggressive, and should have its own special management. It is usually sown by itself, planted in spring or summer, because it grows only in the warm season.

After bermuda goes dormant in autumn, some of the northern grasses may be intersown for color in winter. Annual ryegrass is used oftenest. As it dies the following spring, the bermuda can recover. Some lawnsmen are com-

ing to the conclusion that other less competitive northern species, such as bluegrass, *Poa trivialis*, *Poa annua*, and fescue, offer less aggressive competition to the comeback of bermuda in the spring.

BLENDING of seeds, once done by hand, now often is mechanized. In automated operations of the larger companies, storage bins feed seeds directly into a weighing chamber and storage repository. In elaborate plants, appropriate controls can be set to introduce so much of several varieties. Each is checked for weight as it is introduced. The mixture is tumbled in rotating drums for complete mixing.

When the blend is ready for packaging, a worm screw in the center of the storage bin recirculates the seeds so that no differential sorting of types occurs as a result of their differing sizes, weights, or surface characteristics. Thus early and late packages from a blend lot will be identical.

In blending, the packager-seedsman has opportunity to exercise skills that may give him a better product and competitive advantage.

He has opportunity to produce or obtain from reliable sources the cleanest, fullest seeds.

Even though most seeds meet conventional marketing standards, as determined by purity and germination tests, subtle differences may occur, such as size of individual seeds, origin, kind of weeds, and proportion of chaff. Many packagers insist on standards above conventional specifications and pay a premium for such seeds. Beyond this, they may subject seed to a supplemental cleaning to remove the last traces of chaff and weeds. Such exceptionally clean, heavy seeds should give better performance in the lawn.

Skillful blending considers the use to which the turf will be put and the climate where the seeds are to be sold. A company has ample latitude to develop mixtures or blends it feels offer special advantages.

Most lawn seeds are packaged in

units ranging from a few ounces to many pounds. Cardboard boxes constitute the usual package, but much is marketed in plastic sacks. As long as the seeds are not subjected to unduly high humidity or exceptionally warm temperatures, almost any packaging will keep seed satisfactorily. Most seeds endure well if the moisture content is low and temperatures are no higher than room level. Cold will not harm seeds; indeed, frozen seeds remain viable exceptionally well.

Every step of the way, lawn seeds must meet requirements of State and Federal laws. The laws were passed originally to regulate agricultural seeds at a time when lawn seeds were relatively unheard of. Consequently, some are questionable—for example, many noxious weeds troublesome in agriculture do not persist in a mowed lawn. Standards for germination and purity, however, govern nongenetic qualities in lawn seeds the same as in agricultural applications. All seeds entering commerce are subject to the laws of the State in which they are sold and to the Federal Seed Act when shipped interstate.

Seeds in commerce are continuously sampled by control officials. They must be properly labeled or tagged to indicate weeds, germination, and purity. They must conform to State requirements as to weeds considered noxious in that State. Should the test samples not conform to label statements or requirements, a stop-sale order is issued, and the seeds are impounded. The purveyor may then be subject to civil proceedings. States have laboratories for checking samples, and many private laboratories analyze seeds on a fee basis.

BULK SALES from 100-pound sacks on the floor are becoming a thing of the past. Only packaged seed is available in many garden centers. This leads to vigorous merchandising and efforts toward brand identification—on the whole, a good development in that it fixes responsibility more certainly. A

list of ingredients, with germination percentages and weed content, must appear on the retail package.

If the customer will familiarize himself as to the preferable species for his climate, he can decide readily the quality of a purchase. He will be less apt to buy lawn seed by price and buy according to what is in the package.

Research departments of major seedhouses and industry groups provide reliable instructions for use of their products. Their staffs keep abreast of the research nationally and interpret findings for public benefit. The hope is that the public will be induced to choose its grasses ever more wisely.

THIS EVER-GROWING responsibility of the seed industry to gather and disseminate sound information is recognized by many.

There also is a trend toward horizontal integration. So many products that affect the performance of a seeding are introduced each year that a seed company cannot risk ignorance of herbicides, insecticides, fertilizers, soil amendments, sprinklers, mowers, applicators, and a host of other items.

The realization is growing that one who plants seeds is less interested in seeds as such than in the hoped-for outcome of planting the seeds—a good lawn. A good lawn will result only from good seeds that are treated correctly. That means that one must have information about correct fertilization, watering, mowing, and so on if users of seeds are to be satisfied.

Many seedsmen therefore have become well-rounded experts, who have learned a great deal about the chemicals and equipment that can help good seed become good turf.

ROBERT W. SCHERY *is director of the Lawn Institute, Marysville, Ohio. He is a native of Missouri and was educated at Washington University, from which he holds a doctorate. He is the coeditor and co-author of* The Flora of Panama *and the author of two books,* Plants for Man *and* The Lawn Book.

The Responsibilities of
the Seedsmen

JOHN F. SCHIFFMAN AND ROBERT W. SCHERY

THE SEED industry has a responsibility to see to it that Americans have plenty of clean, plump seeds of guaranteed purity and germination, suitable heredity, and good potentiality.

The responsibility is one for men, not boys.

The seed trade, a hybrid of agriculture and commerce, has been affected by a ferment in both. Mechanization and applied research have revolutionized production. The trend is toward greater specialization and unprecedented outlays for research and equipment. Merchandising has assumed great importance—a development somewhat strange to agriculture.

An industry that long accepted low margins of profit and modest promotion now faces a need to tell consumers about an increasingly complex system.

Few industries have asked so little profit from their own progress. Years are spent to create a new variety, but the variety, after its brief moment of glory, becomes the property of everyone, without royalty.

Hybrid corn—the sole "invention" of the seed industry to spawn explosive growth—is the glowing example of a seed that yields enough income to assure rapid progress. New developments have not been equally rewarding financially in other sectors.

Much of the industry therefore has relied on public institutions for much basic development. The industry has always acknowledged its debt to the research programs of agricultural colleges and the Department of Agriculture and has supported them.

Because newer varieties are especially selected for expected qualities, the "origin" of seeds fades from importance as an indicator of adaptiveness. The seed trade always has assumed its responsibility for purity and germination, but realizes the need for independent checking to assure varietal reliability on creations newly developed at experiment stations.

The basic crop creations have originated mostly at State and Federal agricultural experiment stations, where time and facilities are available to tackle long breeding programs. After release, the industry tackles large-scale isolation to protect lines from outside pollination, and the even more costly hand pollination or growing under glass necessary with some crops. The seedsmen may further refine strains to meet the needs of growers and markets. Thus, scores of regional strains of Great Lakes lettuce were developed to meet growers' needs. The puny, wild-type marigold on short stems has been continuously selected and improved to yield giant hybrids in an array of colors. And so on.

Much of the seed industry is experiencing a strengthening of research within individual companies. A skilled scientific staff has become an integral component of important seed houses. It is not uncommon today for a major firm to have hundreds of varieties under trial, with thousands of trial rows for observation and evaluation. Such companies maintain several well-equipped breeding stations and experienced production men, who use modern methods and equipment and excellent facilities to provide superior seeds.

Hybrid corn has been a stimulating example to other segments of the industry—should not hybrid vigor and the sale of F_1 seed be applicable to many species? The accumulation of combining and inbred lines, which yield distinctive F_1 seed, offers opportunity to build the only unique asset likely to befall a seed corporation. Such assets should enable the concerns to support further research that leads to accelerated progress.

The industry has barely begun widespread utilization of company-developed combining stocks. F_1 petunias and marigolds, tetraploid snapdragons, seedless triploid watermelons, male-sterile lines of onions, and other innovations indicate that the threshold has been crossed elsewhere, too.

The industry is also accepting responsibility toward basic research. Progressive firms have sponsored, through the American Seed Trade Association, the Seed Research Foundation, dedicated to furtherance of basic research by whatever individuals and laboratories, private or public, are most capable of carrying it out. The first projects, sponsored through grants to three colleges, deal chiefly with studies on seed germination and keeping. There is realization that without greater basic understanding of seeds, applied research will progress less efficiently.

Meanwhile, individual companies continue their research efforts, which have already yielded such spectacular improvements as disease-resistant species of the cabbage group, cotton varieties with high-quality lint, hybrids of sweet corn, better canning beets, disease-free beans, high-yielding and uniform carrots, earlier large-ear sweet corn, mosaic-resistant cucumbers, green beans and squash for the freezer, sutureless cantaloups, compact celeries, a series of hybrid snapdragons, and many of the "All-America" garden selections.

Every technique in plant breeding is used, including mass selection, single-plant selections, hybridization, the chemically induced variations, and irradiation. Breeding programs are guided by the requirements of seed users, determined from reports of salesmen and company research men, who visit the growing areas.

IT IS LESS easy to generalize about responsibilities for maintaining supplies. That the supply of seeds has been sufficient to meet the major needs attests to good planning and maintenance of production. This service to the Nation and the economy has been unfaltering, bolstered by a system of branch warehousing in areas of sizable consumption. Within small, specialized markets—with differing traditions and needs—there may be temporary deficiencies, but even then seeds of complementary type usually are obtainable. For lawns, for example, a little more Oregon-grown red fescue can be used should Kentucky bluegrass be in short supply because of drought—or vice versa, when the supply of fine fescue is lean.

The industry cooperates with Government to provide reports as to seed stocks and indicates at intervals the supply status of major trade items. Production programs are based on many guiding factors from numerous sources, and estimates require periodic adjustment. Past records, sales reports, customers' demands, breeding and trial notes, and performance records from experiment stations provide data for forecasting future needs for each item.

Growers typically overplant somewhat to assure ample supply, regardless of weather. This is not entirely unselfish, since markets once sacrificed are regained with difficulty. Larger concerns generally hedge against the weather by growing their seeds in several locations; it is unlikely that disaster will strike everywhere in any given year. Many concerns produce in the West under irrigation, where a crop failure is hard to imagine. Cropping under irrigation in the arid region is the next surest thing to a controlled greenhouse environment.

A seedsman may risk thousands of dollars and years of precious time on the shape of a carrot or the shade of a petunia—only to see public taste change or a market disappear by the time the variety is ready. The breeding work of years may vanish in minutes, as when almost the whole supply of new bush sweetpeas burned in the field. A few successes must then bear the overhead of many failures.

Seldom is an entire genetic stock risked on any one planting or in any one year. This valuable germ plasm, the real wealth of the industry, is more likely stored in fireproof vaults, and only the necessary seed stock is withdrawn periodically. Thus, should there be disaster in the field, the genetic line is not lost—only the production of that year. Adequate supplies of quality seeds thus are maintained year after year.

ANOTHER responsibility has to do with marketing.

Some concerns may grow the seed they sell. Some independent growers take their chances on the open market. Growers often combine as a cooperative, sharing the expected market and accepting the average price that cooperative marketing may bring. The greater technical service that a cooperative can muster may be of benefit to all participants.

Items in limited markets, such as seeds of garden vegetables and flowers, commonly are grown under contract. The risks are apparent, when, for example, contracts for seed of a biennial such as carrot must be made 2 years before delivery, with no idea of the markets ahead or possible change in public taste.

No matter what the production scheme, production is still at the caprice of the weather, and yields are never sure. The smaller specialty markets are especially risky, because they are generally not very extensible; too great production can be as disastrous for profits as too little.

The seed industry has always been responsive to the consumers' needs. When lettuce growers wanted changes in size of head to satisfy the buyer's wishes or needed disease-resistant selections for less risky production, breeders in the industry responded with the improved types. Even such details as the curve of a bean or the color of its pod, comparative abundance of carrot tops and roots, and preferences as to color and shape in many crops have received quick attention. Earliness for the market and shipping or storage qualities are vital to the marketing of perishable products. Seedsmen have been alert to meet demand and have generally been able to satisfy any reasonable requirement.

Through the years, production of seed has shifted westward. Cleaning of seed also moved. There is no profit in shipping debris from fields in the West to plants in the Midwest for cleaning out and discarding there. No doubt commerce in seeds will continue in the direction of products refined at the source and marketed as standard units of quality merchandise rather than bulk poundage that must be repeatedly rehandled.

Standards have risen accordingly, so that any reliable firm would decline to market seeds containing appreciable amounts of harmful weeds or nonviable seeds. State and Federal seed laws and testing of samples back up the producers. Thus, the responsibility of industry is everywhere assured for mechanical purity and proper labeling to indicate germination and content of weeds.

A TREND toward bigness is noticeable among seedhouses, although nowhere are there the giant corporations of heavy industry.

Improvement of resources through continued expansion and growth affords greater opportunities in research and merchandising. The intimately supervised family operation of the past is becoming a producing, distributing, and marketing enterprise that has an efficient sales force, widespread warehousing of adequate supplies, and professional staffs experienced in shipping and selling.

The industry, however, can never separate itself from its agricultural heritage or from the seasonal aspects of its operations.

The seed industry thus generally parallels agriculture, in which bigger, professionally managed farm operations account for more and more of the production and reap the advantages of capacity use of equipment and the discounts of quantity buying. The passing of personal service from local seedstores may be regretted, but the trend that brought the supermarket is touching sales of seeds.

The industry learns more each year about handling, storage, and testing of seeds. Thus it discharges its responsibility for carrying quality products all the way to the consumer. Touchy items, such as asters, onions, and parsnips, are packaged in special foils, plastics, or controlled-humidity cans. That quality will be stressed increasingly in the sale of seeds seems assured, as homeowners and agricultural managers become more aware of values.

Many seedhouses have developed their own full line of products and provide the necessary popular information to see that these are used correctly. No longer are chemical names and fertilizer formulas obscure to the seedsman, as he strives to sell not just seeds but a crop.

The industry constantly seeks adapted varieties for climatic conditions. Research departments retain bloodlines of regional significance that grandfather never dreamed existed. They maintain liaison with local experts, so that the best possible advice for the area in which the seeds are marketed can accompany the seed. Improved instructions on sowing and crop needs may result in as much progress as has the creation of the improved varieties themselves.

JOHN F. SCHIFFMAN *is vice president of the Hygrade Seed Co., Fredonia, N.Y. He has been active in the American Seed Trade Association, having served as chairman of the wholesale packet division and as such was a member of its board of directors.*

ROBERT W. SCHERY *is director of the Lawn Institute. He has been a member of the teaching and research staff of Washington University, senior technician for the Rubber Development Corp., lecturer at the University of Wisconsin, and botanist for chemical and seed companies.*

The Four Types of
Seed Trade Associations

WILLIAM HECKENDORN AND
ROY A. EDWARDS, JR.

THEIR TRADE associations keep the producers, conditioners, and distributors of seeds informed of developments that bear on their business.

Each of the four types of associations (State, regional, national, and specific interest) serves its own purpose and deals with its own problems.

The State associations keep abreast of State laws that affect seedsmen in the State. There were 34 active State seed associations in 1961—in Alabama, Arizona, Arkansas, California, Colorado, Connecticut, Florida, Georgia, Idaho-eastern Oregon, Illinois, Indiana, Iowa, Kansas, Kentucky, Louisiana, Michigan, Minnesota, Mississippi, Missouri, Montana, Nebraska, New York, North Carolina, North Dakota, Ohio, Oklahoma, Oregon, Pennsylvania, South Carolina, Tennessee, Texas, Virginia, Washington, and Wisconsin.

Some of them employ executive secretaries to aid in their work of issuing bulletins, distributing reports of the experiment stations, and conducting meetings.

Most State groups hold annual meetings, at which regulatory and management problems are discussed, current advances in research and breeding are reported by scientists, and many educational and national problems are considered.

Many State associations sponsor educational and informational short courses and clinics.

The Illinois Seed Dealers' Association has cooperated with the University of Illinois in sponsoring an annual series of meetings throughout the State to acquaint dealers and farmers with new developments in the use of fertilizers, insecticides, and improved agricultural practices.

In other States, such as Mississippi, the associations and the State colleges have developed short courses in seed technology and in operating procedures for seed plants. Short courses have been conducted in Oregon, Iowa, Indiana, and other States in teaching seed analytical work to employees in the seed industry.

Scholarship and grant programs are other activities whereby the seedsmen tell their story and in turn stimulate interest in agriculture. A single organization represents grain and seed interests in some States.

State associations are particularly important in giving voice to the smaller businesses that do not generally sell seeds in interstate commerce.

The seed and soil clinics and short courses the associations sponsor give distributors of seeds a chance to become more familiar with the work of agricultural experiment stations so they can give better service to farmers.

As a result of the clinics, distributors of agricultural chemicals and fertilizers have become more familiar with the research work in the colleges, and they, in turn, demonstrate the benefits of improved practices in their communities. The seed and soil clinics have become a roundtable to explore problems and to help all concerned groups to work more closely together.

A number of States have organized State councils, whose members represent the groups interested in breeding, producing, and distributing seeds and include officials from the offices of seed law enforcement, agricultural experiment stations, farm organizations, crop improvement associations, seed analysts, and others. The purpose of a State council is to discuss regulatory and legislative questions before the introduction of legislation or the promulgation of new regulations.

REGIONAL associations deal with agricultural characteristics and trade of geographical areas. There are five: Pacific Seedsmen's Association, Southern Seedsmen's Association, Western Seedsmen's Association, Atlantic Seedsmen's Association, and Northern Seedsmen's Association.

The Pacific Seedsmen's Association draws its membership primarily from seedsmen located in States west of the Rocky Mountains. It is active in educational and promotional programs, conducts business surveys, and develops statistical information for its members. A continuous program of developing uniform State laws pertaining to the seed industry is another one of its main objectives.

The Southern Seedsmen's Association, composed of seedsmen in the 13 Southern States, has been instrumental in constructive national legislation concerned with the agricultural conservation program. The association furnishes informational aid and support to dealers through promotional programs, group insurance, advertising aid, and recommended business operations. It also supports an annual seedsmen's short course at the Mississippi State College and holds a trade exhibit in conjunction with the annual meeting.

The members of the Western Seedsmen's Association live and work in the Mississippi River Basin. It is a forum of midwestern buyers and sellers of seeds. At meetings each November in Kansas City, Mo., members hear crop reports and determine conditions of supply and demand, which help them prepare to meet requirements for the following planting season.

The Atlantic Seedsmen's Association was organized because of the development of situations that affect more than one State. One such has to do with seeds of turfgrasses, of which the States in the region use a great deal. The launching of an interstate highway program made it important that the seed industries become better informed on maintenance of roadsides in all States of their area. Members of the association met to discuss the matter.

The Northern Seedsmen's Association actively encourages the use of seeds of northern-grown, winter-hardy legumes. The climate of the area served by the association was one of the regional conditions that brought the association into being. The Northern Central States are a source of a large volume of seeds harvested annually from plantings that have withstood this cold climate for many years.

THE AMERICAN Seed Trade Association, a national organization, represents the seed industry of the United States.

It was organized in 1883 by 35 garden-seed firms that got together to cope with unjust damage claims, excessive tariff on seeds, and high postage rates. A farm-seed group was added to the association in 1930. Hybrid seed corn interests were included in the organization in 1942.

The ASTA has a board of directors, four commodity divisions, six service divisions, and numerous committees. The interests of the association are shown in the names of the commodity divisions—Farm Seed Division, Garden Seed Division, Hybrid Corn Division, and the Lawn and Turfgrass Division. The service divisions are Mail Order, Wholesale Packet Seed, Retail Store, Brokers, Associates, and Asta, the younger seedsmen's division.

Each division has its own staff of officers and committees. Unlike the association's standing committees, which are appointed by the president of ASTA, the division committees are appointed by the chairman of the division. Each division has an executive committee and various other committees, depending on the scope of their activities.

In the Farm Seed Division are the Farm Seed Research Conference Committee, Seed Improvement Committee, and Verified Origin Committee. The Farm Seed Research Conference Committee organizes an annual conference, in which men of the Department of Agriculture and State colleges participate. The conference brings to the attention of the seed trade the latest advances in research having to do with farm seeds. The Seed Improvement Committee works closely with the International Crop Improvement Association and State crop improvement associations to keep the industries informed about current developments. Keeping abreast of the rules necessary to represent the parties to a contract covering the sale or purchase of seeds is the responsibility of the Trade Rules Committee. The Verified Origin Committee cooperates with the Department of Agriculture in an auditing program, whereby the origin of certain farm seeds is checked by records that must be maintained by the receivers of such seeds.

The Garden Seed Division comprises the Garden Seed Sales Promotion Committee, Garden Seed Research Committee, Recommended Varieties Committee, and Flower Seed Germination Committee.

The policies are developed by the division committees and implemented through the division meetings and the executive officers of the ASTA. At regular meetings of the division, various committees report and the members can express their opinions about type of program they want to follow. The Garden Seed Division is more active in trade promotion than some other divisions. To promote the sales of garden seeds, the division expends approximately 40 thousand dollars annually. Another activity is a consistent program of weeding out obsolete varieties and acquainting the public with the importance and advantages of improved varieties.

The Hybrid Corn Division conducts an annual Hybrid Corn Industry Research Conference. A record of the proceedings is published and distributed widely to colleges and universities and students of agronomy without charge.

The Lawn and Turfgrass Division cooperates with highway officials in an exchange of information on the most adaptable grass to be used along roadsides under varying conditions.

The Service Divisions are concerned primarily with the movement of seeds through channels of commerce to the consumer.

NATIONAL legislation and administration of Federal laws affecting the seed industry are matters of concern to members of the American Seed Trade Association. The association is geared to represent the seed industry's interests in seeking fair, impartial, beneficial legislation and administration of laws. The association also assists in the formulation and revision of State legislation when warranted.

Cooperation with public agencies and affiliated professional societies is a cornerstone of its policies. Cordial working relationships are assured by means of liaison committees of the association with the Department of Agriculture, International Crop Improvement Association, State agricultural experiment stations, agronomists, seed analysts, control officials, and others.

Information on behalf of the association's members is presented to keep members and the public aware of developments that affect the seed industry. A membership bulletin is published twice monthly. Following the annual convention in June, a volume of proceedings is published for the members. Proceedings of the annual Hybrid Corn Industry Research Conference and conferences on farm seeds also are published. These publications are used extensively throughout the industry and by public agencies and students.

Special pamphlets pertaining to trade rules, practices, and traffic are published periodically.

The association, through its Farm Seed Division, sponsors an annual collegiate crop-judging contest in Chicago. This contest is held in conjunction with the National Livestock Show and is attended by judging teams from many parts of the United States. In the contests, students test their ability in judging against that of students from other parts of the United States.

As A RECOGNITION of the part that communications provide in keeping the public informed of the latest developments in the industry, an annual Asta award is presented to the journalists who, in the opinion of several judges, do the best job in keeping the public informed.

The first Asta awards were presented in June 1955. Since that time 17 additional awards have been presented to outstanding farm and garden writers.

The association has distributed two motion pictures about farm seeds, "The Farm Seed Story" and "Seeds and Science."

The association in 1955 established the American Seed Research Foundation, an organization that seeks to encourage basic research on seeds. Its aim is to study seeds to find out more about how they perform.

Three projects approved by the foundation have to do with the development of rapid tests of viability of seeds, the deterioration of seeds in storage, and the evaluation and classification of selected types of degeneration revealed within germinative seed by the use of the tetrazolium test. Named as project leaders were Don F. Grabe of Iowa; William P. Caldwell and James C. Delouche, Mississippi; and R. P. Moore, North Carolina.

The association cooperates with the American Society for Horticultural Science in developing lists of names in use on new varieties of vegetables. Lists of names of obsolete varieties are published periodically.

The association has made grants-in-aid for research on seeds to universities and agricultural experiment stations. Among a few of the projects in which the association has cooperated with agricultural experiment stations are the development of a manual for the selection of competent seed analysts, studies on clover and alfalfa, and improved laboratory techniques.

The association has also worked with the Association of Official Seed Analysts and the Society of Commercial Seed Technologists in their various publications.

Arbitration, group medical insurance, insurance for specialized errors and omissions, and annual trade shows are among the other services provided members of the American Seed Trade Association.

The specific commodity promotional groups and associations also serve segments of the seed industry.

The All-America Selections, sponsored by members of the American Seed Trade Association's Garden Seed Division, promotes the introduction of new vegetable and flower varieties through an award system consisting of nationwide trial grounds for new varieties. Eminent judges select the outstanding trial-ground entries. At their discretion and subject to final vote of the Board of Directors of the All-America Selections Council, exceptional new vegetable and flower varieties are awarded All-America distinction. To finance the program, winners of the awards return fixed percentages of the sales price of winning varieties.

The National Garden Bureau sponsors an information and public relations program developed by the association's Garden Seed Division to encourage gardening. The Better Lawn & Turf Institute is an association to foster more effective grass seeding practices. The Certified Alfalfa Seed Council and the Merion Bluegrass Association are similarly constituted promotional programs. The Field Seed Institute is an association that studies economic trends in the seed business.

WILLIAM HECKENDORN *is executive secretary of the American Seed Trade Association. His headquarters are in Washington.*

ROY A. EDWARDS, JR., *is president of Rudy-Patrick Seed Co., Kansas City, Mo. He was president of the American Seed Trade Association in 1959–1960.*

Statistics and Trends

THOMAS J. KUZELKA AND W. H. YOUNGMAN

STATISTICS are yardsticks for measuring the present in terms of the past and for making plans for action.

Farmers have felt a need for statistics of production and prices since the middle of the 19th century, when agriculture began to emerge from the level of self-sustenance. Many believed that they were at a disadvantage in bargaining because they knew less about crop production than did the people to whom they sold.

Agricultural statistics made their greatest growth in wartime. Some data were available as early as 1839, but the gathering of statistics was first made part of the work of the Department of Agriculture in the war period of 1862 and was greatly expanded in each subsequent period of conflict.

The Federal Census of Agriculture for 1849 gathered statistics on field seeds. The data for that year and for each succeeding decennial census up to 1909 were limited mostly to group totals for clovers and grasses. The census for the latter date provided separate totals for timothy seed, in addition to the group totals. The Census of 1919 was expanded further to include figures for seed of red clover. Statistics on imports and exports likewise were submerged in group totals for most kinds before 1910.

Although other fragmentary statistical information was collected by some States and the Department of Agriculture at earlier dates, the official estimates of acreage, yield, production, farm price, and value of production did not begin until 1919. Such production totals as were available for the years before 1919 included some partly cleaned and thresher-run seeds and therefore are not comparable with the succeeding series, which is on a clean-seed basis.

Some figures on the production of seeds were collected before 1938 by the Hay, Feed and Seed Division of the former Bureau of Agricultural Economics. They were integrated into the official series after 1938, when all functions of collecting statistics on seeds were transferred to the Agricultural Estimates Division, which is now a part of the Agricultural Marketing Service of the Department.

The urgent need for statistical information during the Second World War brought a rapid expansion of the work. Estimates of production were available in 1919 for only four kinds of field seeds, including alfalfa, red and alsike clover combined, and timothy.

Sweetclover and lespedeza were added in 1924, as production of each kind became increasingly important. Other kinds were added later. The estimating program included 47 kinds of field seeds, and 46 kinds and more than 250 types and varieties of vegetable seeds by 1950. The number of seed crops and the States where seeds are grown changed periodically as production increased or declined and as the urgency of need for statistics developed or waned.

The number of crops of field seeds for which estimates were made was reduced from 47 to 28 in 1952, because by that year supplies of many kinds were far above domestic needs and price supports for hay and pasture seeds were discontinued.

The list of the 28 kinds that remained in the estimating program since 1952 includes alfalfa, red clover, alsike clover, sweetclover, white (Dutch) clover, Ladino clover, crimson clover, lespedeza, timothy, redtop, orchardgrass, Kentucky bluegrass, Merion Kentucky bluegrass, sudangrass, smooth bromegrass, crested wheatgrass, chewings fescue, red fescue, tall (Alta and Ken-

tucky 31) fescue, bentgrass, Austrian winter peas, lupine, hairy vetch, common vetch, purple vetch, common ryegrass, perennial ryegrass, and mustard.

The list of vegetable seeds includes practically all the leading kinds and types used for the fresh market and processing.

FORECASTS and estimates of seed production are made by the Crop Reporting Board of the Agricultural Estimates Division. It also compiles and publishes data on prices, value of production, carryover, disposition, supply, and disappearance of seeds.

A typical forecast employs two kinds of questionnaires. One is mailed to a representative list of growers in the areas of production. The other is mailed to a list of country shippers.

Growers are asked to report acres cut and to be cut for seed and pounds of seed harvested "this year" and "last year." Other questions relate to carryover of old crop seeds, disposition of the seeds produced in the previous year, and quantities sold each month.

Country shippers are asked to give their opinion on the percentage of change in acreage harvested and to be harvested for seeds in their buying area, approximate quantities of seeds harvested and to be harvested for the current year and the previous year, and pounds of seeds purchased from growers each month of the previous year's seed-buying season. Followup mailings are made to nonrespondents to increase the returns.

The data from the questionnaires that are returned constitute a sample, or cross section, of all growers. The acreage in the sample may represent 5 percent of the growers who produce a particular kind of seed in a State or as high as 30 percent in another State. The average size of the sample for all the States is nearer the lower percentage.

A sample of this size usually is large enough to provide reasonable accuracy of the estimates. The sample from the country shippers represents one-third to three-fourths of all shippers handling the seeds in the producing area.

The growers' and shippers' indications of percentage of change in acreage for the current year, as compared with the preceding year, are interpreted separately for each State by use of regression charts. This method allows adjustments for any bias that may be due to selectivity in mailing lists, underreporting of large crops, overreporting of small crops, and other factors. The degree of bias is established over a period of years by known benchmark observation points such as the 5-year Federal Census of Agriculture, annual State farm census, and annual crop-check information. Yield data are interpreted by means of chart relationships in a similar manner as is done for acreage.

Because forecasts of seed production are made close to the beginning dates of harvest, the forecast frequently differs from the final estimate. Such influences as inclement weather at harvesttime, depressed prices, and lack of demand are the chief reasons for such differences. Thus, in order to obtain a more accurate appraisal of change in acreage and yield from the previous year, it is necessary to resurvey the growers that reported in the forecast and to include other growers who harvested seed. This is done by means of an acreage card, which is sent to a much larger random list of growers throughout the State. This card asks about the acreage harvested and to be harvested for all crops, including seeds.

Two indications are obtained from this source. First is the ratio to land in farms—the total reported acres of a particular seed crop expressed as a percentage of the acres of all land in farms in the entire sample. Second is the "identical" percentage of change in acreage, obtained by matching the current reports of individual growers with their previous year's reports.

As in the case of the forecast, these indications are interpreted on charts.

Additional information is also obtained on yields per acre through the use of an acreage and production inquiry, which is sent after harvest to a smaller list of respondents. The information as to yield from it and from the special forecast inquiries is supplemented by judgments as to indications of yield, obtained from the October, November, or December farm reports. The latter are mailed to a list of established crop reporters.

The composite data from all these sources as to acreage and yield form the basis for the preliminary estimate, which is published in December.

Some information also is obtained by statisticians in field offices through interviews with seedgrowers, buyers of seeds, and county agents. The statisticians often make field counts and observe the set of seed before harvest.

THE PRELIMINARY estimates published in December may be revised the following year if additional information indicates a need for revision. The new data may be a cleaner crop-check of all known cleaners in a State, State farm census enumerations of acreage and production, certified seed records, verified origin records, and additional indications on yield per acre. Data from the Federal Census of Agriculture become available every 5 years and set benchmarks that help to true up the level of the estimates.

STATISTICS for vegetable seeds are compiled from reports of growers and companies who produce seeds. Much supervision by trained workers and a large outlay of land and equipment are required for growing and storing vegetable seeds. Fewer than 100 companies comprise the seed-growing industry in the United States. Practically all report to the Crop Reporting Board. The sum of their data provides the basis for the totals, as little adjustment is usually necessary for nonrespondents. Statistics are compiled for 264 kinds, varieties, or types of seeds.

The reporting questionnaire for veg-

Production and Disposition of Red Clover Seed

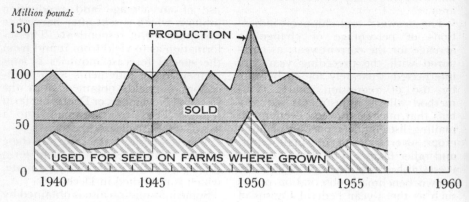

Million pounds

Production and Disposition of Alfalfa Seed

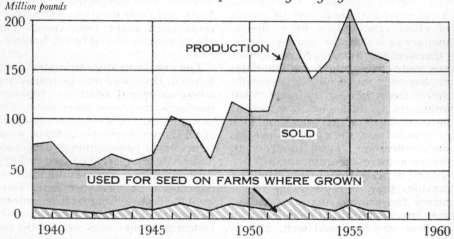

Million pounds

etable seeds is one of the longest used by the Crop Reporting Board. It was prepared in cooperation with a representative group of seedsmen. The list of varieties is revised at about 5-year intervals to include new varieties. Older and obsolescent varieties are included in group totals and published as "other varieties."

Three surveys of vegetable seeds are made annually by the Crop Reporting Board.

One, as of December 1, asks for acres harvested and preliminary production of clean seed for the current crop.

The second, as of March 15 the fol-

lowing year, asks for the final acres harvested and production for the previous year and the prospective acres and production for the new crop that is to be planted.

The third survey is made as of June 30 and obtains the quantities of vegetable seeds carried over from previous crops. This survey involves a large list of dealers, many of whom are not necessarily growers of vegetable seeds. It includes wholesale and large retail companies that are known to carry over large amounts of vegetable seeds. It does not include small retail establishments.

The information from the three surveys and data on imports under the Federal Seed Act, published by the Grain Division of the Agricultural Marketing Service, provide indications of the total supply of vegetable seeds.

Statistics for vegetable seeds were first compiled for official use in 1916 and were continued through 1923. Production increased rapidly after 1916, and by 1923 it had reached surplus proportions. Because of waning interest on the part of the seed industry, the estimates for vegetable seeds were discontinued after 1923 but were reinstated in 1940.

Changes in classifications and groupings between the two periods make comparisons of production difficult.

Such comparisons as can be made show that 1941–1945 average production was more than double the 1916–1920 average for garden beets, cabbage, carrot, kale, muskmelon, parsley, garden peas, pepper, spinach, summer squash, and turnips; and one half larger to almost double for pole beans, parsnip, radish, sweet corn and tomatoes. The 1941–1945 average production was lower than 20 years earlier for pumpkin and salsify.

Comparison of 1916–1920 data with average production in 1951–1955— which represents the adjustment period after the war—reveals that production in the latter period was lower for cabbage, carrot, onion, parsley, parsnip, pumpkin, salsify, spinach, winter squash, and celery and higher for beans, garden beets, cucumber, kale, lettuce, muskmelon, garden peas, pepper, radish, summer squash, sweet corn, tomatoes, and turnips.

Seed production in the United States paralleled the domestic demand throughout most of the country's history. Up to 1940 or so, however, the national output of some field seeds was inadequate for planting needs. As more land was brought under cultivation, more seeds were produced. Relatively large imports of alfalfa, clovers, millets, orchardgrass, winter rape, ryegrass, and vetch were needed up to 1940 to balance the supplies with the increasing demand.

From the beginning of American agriculture through the first three quarters of the 19th century, many farmers were self-reliant with respect to seeds. But after that period they began gradually to depend for their seed sources on specialized producers nearby and on seed dealers, some of whom could offer a wider choice of either local or imported seeds.

Seed corn is an example. The early settlers obtained seed corn from the Indians. Later the farmers saved some of their crops for seed, but as they learned that certain varieties were better than others, they obtained a large part of their requirements from dealers. Although dealers handled relatively large quantities of seed corn by 1890, the bulk of the seed planted by farmers was homegrown. Dealers began to handle an increasingly larger percentage after the introduction of successful hybrid varieties. Only one-tenth of 1 percent of the total American acreage in corn was planted with hybrid seed in 1933, but about 96 percent of the total was planted with hybrid seed in 1960.

While corn is an extreme example because the production of hybrid seed corn is controlled largely by commercial companies, somewhat the same trends have operated with seeds for which production is highly specialized. In 1953–1957, farmers sold more than 90 percent of their annual production for such crops as alfalfa, alsike clover, Ladino clover, whiteclover, ryegrass, chewings fescue, red fescue, bentgrass, bluegrass and redtop. But for other seeds as red clover, timothy and lespedeza, farmers continue to use much of their homegrown seeds.

ALFALFA and red clover were the principal hay legumes in the United States during the first quarter of the 20th century. Timothy was the principal grass. Alsike clover was used to a lesser extent in limited areas, mostly in mixtures with red clover and tim-

Trend in Harvested Acreage of Leading Kinds of Hay

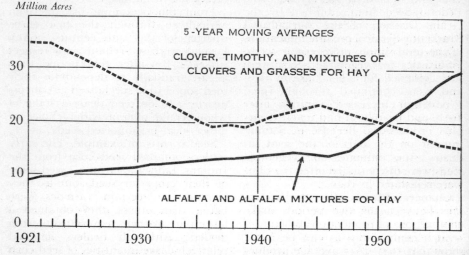

Trend in Seed Production of Important Kinds Used for Hay

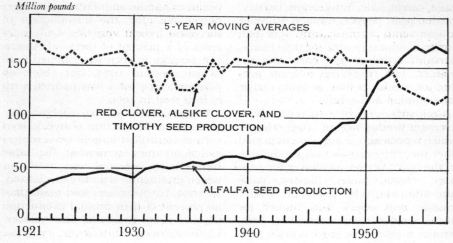

othy. Sweetclover, another versatile legume suitable for soil building, hay, and pasture, rose to prominence after 1920, when farmers in the Corn Belt used it extensively in rotations. Lespedeza gained popularity slowly for nearly two decades after its introduction, but by 1940 it was the leading hay crop in the Southeast.

Alfalfa and clover-timothy hay comprised 76 percent of the country's tame

hay acreage in 1919–1923. The remaining 24 percent of the acreage was grain hay, cowpeas, and several miscellaneous kinds. Alfalfa and clover-timothy constituted 73 percent of the total of tame hay in 1954–1958. Although there was little change in the total acreage of these two leading hays—43.8 million acres and 44.7 million acres, respectively, for the two periods—the alfalfa hay acreage increased more than threefold while clover-timothy hay acreage declined to less than one-half.

The trends in hay are influenced gradually by changes in the various classes of livestock and by experimental results that demonstrate advantages of one kind of hay over another for specific uses.

An example: Timothy hay is good feed for horses and mules. It follows that the demand for timothy was far greater when the number of horses and mules in the United States was at peak numbers of 26.7 million in 1918, compared with 3.1 million head in 1960. Horses and mules have almost vanished from farms and cities, and the demand for timothy hay and timothy seed is likewise on the downtrend.

The hay acreages relinquished by timothy, red clover, and other kinds have been replaced largely by alfalfa, bromegrass, fescues, wheatgrass, vetches, and other legumes and grasses.

The trends for the leading hays were reflected also in seed production. The production of alfalfa seed increased from 23 million pounds in 1919–1923 to 171 million pounds by 1954–1958. The total production of seeds of red clover, alsike clover, and timothy declined from 177 million pounds to 116 million pounds.

THE PRODUCTION of grass seeds likewise kept pace with changes brought about by improved practices in farm management and by expansion in city and urban developments. The construction of new highways with wide rights-of-way created a demand for large quantities of the turfgrass seeds. Rates per acre of seeding grass waterways and shoulders and slopes on highways are several times higher than rates used for other domestic uses.

Although the longtime trend in seed production was upward in response to normal demand, production received a great impetus following the First World War, and especially during and following the Second World War, when shortages of seeds occurred. The war-

time economy required additional quantities of seeds for use abroad. Specialization was accelerated by technological advances in the development of new varieties, insecticides, herbicides, and the increased use of fertilizers for production of seeds. Expediency dictated a shift in production of seeds from the Corn Belt and the Midwestern States, where seeds were more or less a byproduct of acreage grown largely for hay and pasture, to the irrigated States of the Far West.

The two wars stimulated the production in the United States of the field and garden seeds that had formerly been imported. The Nation's supplies for almost all kinds reached surplus positions by 1950. The shift of production to the irrigated areas aided the self-sufficiency movement, as it enabled growers to produce yields several times larger than yields from nonirrigated acreage. Price supports and loan programs offered growers by the Government for many kinds of seeds during the decade beginning with 1943 to encourage production demonstrated that the Nation's production potential of both field seeds and vegetable seeds is far in excess of domestic needs.

THE TOTAL amount of 27 kinds of field seeds used for domestic purposes reached peak levels in 1949 and 1950. Since that time, use declined somewhat in line with the shrinking land area devoted to production of food and fiber crops. Disappearance totaled 875.6 million pounds in 1953–1957, 4 percent less than the average of 913.5 million pounds for the preceding 5 years but 41 percent more than the 1939–1943 average of 623.1 million pounds. Most of the reduction during the 1950's occurred in the kinds of seeds used mainly for hay, crop rotation, and winter cover.

The use of clovers for hay and crop rotations has been declining almost steadily since 1950. Red clover and sweetclover are used extensively for those purposes in the North Central

Domestic Disappearance of Field Seeds

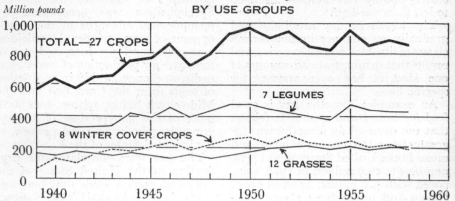

Million pounds   BY USE GROUPS

Legumes—Alfalfa, red clover, alsike clover, sweetclover, whiteclover, Ladino clover, and lespedeza; Winter Cover Crops—Austrian winter peas, crimson clover, lupine, hairy vetch, common vetch, purple vetch, common ryegrass, and perennial ryegrass; Grasses—Timothy, redtop, orchardgrass, Kentucky bluegrass, Merion Kentucky bluegrass, sudangrass, smooth bromegrass, crested wheatgrass, chewings fescue, red fescue, tall fescue, and bentgrass.

and North Atlantic States. The use of clovers is largely dependent on changes in acreages of the leading grain and hay crops. Increased acreages of such crops as corn, oats, and soybeans generally are accompanied by decreases in acreages of clovers and alfalfa.

Conversely, acreage reductions in the main cereal and grain crops usually are absorbed by increased seedings of legume hays. This pattern has operated up to 1956. Thereafter, much cropland was included in the Acreage Reserve and Conservation Reserve programs. Regulations in these programs prescribe guidance in the use of various kinds of seeds for specific purposes, such as soil erosion and soil cover.

The declining use of the leading clovers is offset in a large part by an uptrend in alfalfa. The increase in production and use of alfalfa since 1944 has been phenomenal. Farmers used nearly one-third more alfalfa seed in 1952–1957 than during the 5-year period 15 years earlier. Much of the credit for the expansion is given to general improvements in varieties for specific purposes, but some credit must be given also to the Agricultural

Conservation cost-sharing programs of the Department of Agriculture, which provided financial assistance for purchase of lime, fertilizer, and seeds, and thus helped to establish stands in some areas where alfalfa had not been grown successfully.

THE USE of winter cover crops in the South has been displaced to a large extent by oats, rye, and other lower priced seed crops, which provide winter grazing for the South's expanding livestock population.

The need for legumes as a source of nitrogen is being met by more extensive use of commercial fertilizer. Lack of Government price supports for seed production is another factor that helped accelerate the trend away from the use of the usual legume winter cover crops as soil builders.

The use of several grasses was on the increase during the 1950's—orchardgrass, chewings and red fescue, bentgrass, Merion Kentucky bluegrass, sudangrass, and ryegrass. The increase in this group was offset partly by the declining use of several older grasses, chiefly timothy, redtop, smooth bromegrass, and crested wheatgrass. Little or no change was indicated for tall fescue and Kentucky bluegrass.

By 1950 the United States attained export status in seeds, but we import many kinds from almost every corner of the earth. It is likely that this relationship will continue, because certain kinds can be obtained in the desired amounts at less cost from other countries.

For instance, we have depended on Denmark for our supply of seeds of Danish bluegrass (*Poa trivialis*) and orchardgrass; on Australia for much of our seed of dallisgrass; on Canada for several kinds, including red fescue, sweetclover, bromegrass, alsike clover, Canadian wildrye and Canada bluegrass; and on France and Italy for some of our seeds of crimson clover and birdsfoot trefoil, when they have exportable surpluses. Japan is a regular supplier of flower and vegetable seeds, as are Denmark, the Netherlands, and France.

Japan is our best market in the Far East for seeds of grasses and legumes. Thailand buys a large part of her vegetable seeds from the United States. Our merchants supply a goodly proportion of the vegetable and flower seeds needed in South American countries, as well as seeds of some kinds of grasses and clovers.

Our expansion in the production of alfalfa seed in the Pacific Coast States has given us a major share of the world's market. The United States produces alfalfa seed for several countries, including France, Germany, Greece, Sweden, and Canada—that is, we are growing seed of their domestic varieties on a contract basis.

Formerly the United States was the major source of Kentucky bluegrass seed, but now we compete with Denmark and the Netherlands. Because of our oversupply of seeds of common ryegrass in the 1950's, we exported varying amounts to European markets. Perennial ryegrass seed also moved abroad in some volume, as did bentgrass.

Seeds of Ladino clover, which we formerly imported from Italy, are produced in California and Oregon in substantial volume. There was a period when it was in oversupply in the United States and was cheaper than whiteclover seeds, and several countries imported Ladino seeds from the United States. We are now exporting fairly large quantities of seeds of Ladino clover to Europe and Japan. Chewings fescue, similarly, was imported from New Zealand, but now we are the major exporter.

We exported seeds of orchardgrass up to about 1949. Then it became apparent that orchardgrass, well managed, is a good grass for pasture and hay and fits well in grass-legume mixtures. Our domestic seed production has expanded, but we also import millions of pounds of seeds each year to supplement the domestic crop. Meadow fescue is another crop whose seeds we formerly exported, but now import to meet our limited needs. We can buy it so cheaply that our farmers do not consider it a worthwhile crop to produce.

What has been said about foreign trade in seeds of grasses and legumes applies to a considerable extent to seeds of such field crops as vetch, Austrian winter peas, and rape.

High costs of land, labor, and equipment have affected the production of some of our vegetable and flower seeds. We could produce our supply of spinach seeds in the Pacific Northwest, but it is cheaper to buy them from Denmark and the Netherlands. Consequently, much is imported. Some of the hybrid seeds are imported from countries where labor costs are lower than in the United States. This trend may continue, and imports could be increased from countries where production is dependable.

The interest in American-grown seeds is not accidental. During the Second World War, our Allies obtained large amounts of seeds to meet their needs. This was continued for some years after the war under the United Nations National Recovery Act program, and many thousands of tons of seeds were shipped to oversea countries to help them restore production.

THE VARIOUS U.S. AGENCIES charged with working in other countries to help improve economic conditions tested many American-bred varieties of crops in the foreign experiment stations. In addition, other Government agencies have sent seeds abroad, as have private firms. It is not strange therefore that many American varieties have demonstrated their superiority and are in demand.

This is true of our varieties of hybrid corn. Corn is widely grown, and many American varieties have been found to be greatly superior to the native kinds. Shipments of hybrid seed corn attained considerable volume, but by the mid-1950's, when some countries began to produce their own hybrids, there was a noticeable decline in exports. Except in countries where the acreage of corn is small, this decline in exports can be expected to continue, although the question of relative costs enters at this point. This is especially true since much of our hybrid seed corn exports represents the less desirable sizes that would otherwise be sent to the feed-grain markets. Much of the seed therefore is marketed at a substantial discount below seed corn prices in the United States, but still sufficiently above the cash-grain market to be attractive to some of the growers of hybrid seed. Because there is no question as to the genetic qualities and the size is of little concern where hand planting is practiced, these low-cost seeds should continue to be attractive to the importers.

THOMAS J. KUZELKA *is Head of the Seed Section, Field Crops Statistics Branch, Agricultural Marketing Service. He is a graduate of Doane College and the University of Nebraska.*

W. H. YOUNGMAN *was a market specialist in seeds in the Foreign Agricultural Service when he retired in 1959. He joined the Department in 1926.*

The Economics of Seed Production

CHESTER O. MCCORKLE, JR., AND
A. DOYLE REED

THE PRODUCTION of seeds in the United States has evolved from the simple procedure of saving part of a crop to plant the next year into a highly specialized enterprise.

Today's producer of seeds must have special equipment, follow rigid production methods, and observe scientific cleaning and testing procedures.

The early farmer was little concerned with prices or markets. Today's producer is faced with a highly sensitive price mechanism and, for some kinds of seeds, a complex marketing structure.

Seed production was formerly an art, which consisted of knowing which seeds to select from a field. Seed production today is dependent on scientific knowledge of the transmission of hereditary characteristics, an understanding of supply and demand, and a high level of managerial ability.

Much seed is still produced for use locally by the grower or for sale to other farmers in the area. There is increasing demand, however, for seeds of improved varieties and disease-resistant strains and for plants with characteristics adapted to specific uses or localities.

Seeds of a large number of crops cannot be produced satisfactorily in the areas of major production because of weather, diseases, and difficulties in isolating fields to prevent cross-pollination.

Sometimes a seed crop cannot compete economically with other crops in the area or with the production of seeds in other areas.

The part of the plant used commercially sometimes is different from the seeds or includes more than just the seeds. Production of seeds from these crops may require more specialized production methods and equipment that a farmer who produces the crops for their primary use does not have.

Four main types of seeds are grown in areas where production is concentrated. The production of seeds of vegetables and flowers tends to concentrate in rather limited geographical areas. Seeds of grasses and field crops are produced more widely. Climatic factors, such as atmospheric humidity and seasonal distribution of rainfall, are critical in determining location.

The area suitable for production of seeds is far greater than that required to meet the needs, but concentration within adapted districts takes place as the growers gain experience and processing and marketing facilities are established.

Specialty production of crop seeds was centered originally in the Eastern States, but it has moved west. Further westward movement is not possible. Therefore, barring unforeseen disease or pest problems, the location of production of many seed crops may be stabilizing. This is not to say that specialty seed production is adapted only to the West or that profitable production can be undertaken only in the West.

A meaningful economic analysis of specialized production in the United States must consider the kinds of farms on which seed crops are grown; the interrelationships between seed crops and other enterprises with which they are combined; the nature of production practices; and the inputs, costs, and returns from seed production.

There is no "typical" organization of seed farms. The company-owned seed farm and farms that produce only seeds and the general-crop farm on which an occasional small acreage of a seed crop is planted are the extremes in organization.

In between are such growers as those who grow Ladino clover primarily for seed but have a minimum of crops for rotation purposes. Very often a sheep enterprise is combined with Ladino clover to take advantage of the supplementary and complementary relationships that exist. Growers of seed of melons are primarily field-crop farmers who work a small acreage of melon seed into their organization.

Still another use of seed crops within the total farm organization is illustrated by the producer of "common" alfalfa, who may let a crop go to seed if he expects the price to rise high enough to make the seed more valuable than the hay crop. Nearly all seed crops (except flowers) are grown by farmers as one enterprise in a total farm organization.

When he considers a seed crop for his farm, the farmer must determine how well that crop fits into his total farm organization. Physical considerations include its machinery, labor, water, and management requirements relative to the needs of the other enterprises and the total quantities of these resources available at various times during the year.

Economic questions he must think of are the capital requirements of the crop, the expected price, and probable net returns compared with alternative enterprises. Of utmost importance in the farmer's mind are the possible yield, price, and income variations he may experience from year to year.

In terms of farm organization, seed crops are considered as cash crops. This is particularly true with specialty seed crops, which have no use except for sale as seeds. In that, specialty seed crops are unlike corn and wheat, which can be fed if the seed price is unsatisfactory. Relative profitability of other crops, limited total demand for seed crops, and possible extreme fluctuations in one or more of the components of net income with seed crops have led farmers interested in growing seeds to limit the proportion of the total resources of the farm going to the production of seed crops.

An elaborate system of contracts between specialty-crop seed producers and seed companies has emerged.

Given the abundance of resources capable of producing seed, the contract system, together with other institutional constraints, have been necessary to avoid chaos in the seed market. Much of the potential fluctuation in production and prices of seeds from year to year has thus been eliminated.

FLOWER SEEDS are produced almost entirely by the seed companies on land they own or lease. The entire supply of domestically produced seeds is grown each year on a few thousand acres. In terms of value, it is estimated that more than 85 percent of the seed is produced in two counties in the central-south coastal areas of California.

Since total requirements can be met from such a small acreage of seed, it is only logical that individual companies have gone into seed production to achieve close coordination between production and marketing.

Exacting technical requirements of the production of flower seeds also encourage company production. The need for continuous and exclusive development of new varieties through breeding and selection in order to compete with other companies for the home gardener's interest further supports the growth of seed production by the seed companies.

Producer markets comparable to those existing for other types of agricultural production therefore do not exist. Were they to develop, individual growers, aware of occasional high prices, would be tempted to plant limited acreage to seed. The obvious result would be widely fluctuating prices from year to year, and many growers would find it impossible to realize even harvest costs in some seasons. Annual quantities required of some seeds are sufficiently small that no acreage is planted in some years if the seeds remain viable.

A small amount of flower seeds is produced by individual growers. Before planting, the grower signs a contract with a company to assure a market outlet. Contracts commonly specify isolation distances, kind and varieties to be planted, and division of responsibilities in the production and harvesting.

Contracting to produce flower seeds has not been prevalent among growers, however, because of the heavy labor inputs, the constant attention required for seed crops of flowers, and the small acreages. A few varieties of seeds have been grown under contract mainly in California. Among them are zinnias, pansies, sweetpeas, petunias, and larkspurs, but even for them the amount contracted by any one grower seldom exceeds 10 acres.

Major expense items are cultivation and thinning, control of diseases and pests, roguing, fertilization, and harvesting. Expenses of irrigation may also be sizable in some places.

Land preparation includes preparation of seedbed, usually a preirrigation, and sometimes prefertilization. Costs of preparing the seedbed, including working up beds, approximate 6 dollars an acre. Preirrigation costs of labor and water may be 5 dollars to 7 dollars an acre, depending on water conditions and amount applied. When fertilizer is applied before planting, the cost including application varies between 25 dollars and 50 dollars an acre, depending on the material and quantity.

Even when grown under contract, the seed company supplies the seeds and often does the planting. These costs are relatively minor for the common flower seeds; the total seed cost seldom exceeds 5 to 7 dollars an acre.

Additional fertilizer usually is applied as sidedressing or in the irrigation water during the period of early growth. Fertilizer materials usually contain relatively higher amounts of phosphorus and sometimes potash than those used in general crop production. Excessive growth of foliage that would result from heavy nitrogen application is to be avoided in seed production.

When used, the applied cost of fertilizer approximates 5 to 15 dollars an acre.

Weeds must be controlled in the production of flower seeds, particularly during the early period of flower growth, when mechanical cultivation can be practiced. Hand cultivation often is necessary later and is extremely costly. If thinning is required, hand cultivation is accomplished at the same time. Costs of weeding vary according to the practices employed. Mechanical cultivations may number between 4 and 12, depending on the weed growth, type of flowers, and other factors. Each cultivation at today's prices costs approximately 2 dollars an acre. Total cultivation costs per acre can vary between 8 and 24 dollars. Hand hoeing and thinning may vary from 40 dollars to more than 250 dollars an acre, depending on weed conditions and the particular crop.

Irrigation is necessary throughout the western growing areas, but the total requirements depend on the season of growth, soil conditions, and the particular crop. Timing of irrigation is critical to the production of high yields of quality seed. Irrigation must be stopped as the seeds begin to mature. Individual crop requirements are best determined through experimentation on each site. Water costs may be 15 to 20 dollars an acre; irrigation labor may add 15 to 30 dollars. Total irrigation costs, excluding preirrigation, typically are 30 to 50 dollars.

Control of pests and diseases is essential in the production of high yields of good flower seeds; otherwise, growers have no chance to recover the large cash outlays required to grow them. A continuous program of dusting and spraying is required. Early treatments are often hand applied. Machines, including airplanes on company seed farms, are used at later stages of maturity. DDT and the organic phosphates are used commonly against insects. Several applications of sulfur and other materials may be needed to control various plant diseases.

The pest and disease control program on flower seeds typically costs between 10 and 60 dollars. Local conditions occasionally make necessary more frequent applications and higher costs. Fieldmen of the agricultural chemical companies often observe continuously and closely the insect populations and evidence of disease. Their recommendations on control measures usually are followed. Producers of flower seeds have become aware of the possibility of drift of toxic materials, which may leave residues.

If hand pollination is required to produce seeds, the companies grow the seeds in order to assume the exacting care and the high labor costs. Frequently this type of operation will necessitate production in greenhouses.

Harvesting seeds of most flowers involves hand cutting of the mature flower stalks and placing them on canvases to finish drying. Care must be taken to avoid shattering and loss of seeds. When production is by contract, the company often does the harvesting and threshing, the costs of which vary widely according to yield and crop.

The costs of harvesting and threshing pansy seeds, for example, can vary from 100 to 500 dollars an acre, depending on the yield. Harvesting and threshing zinnia seeds often require repeated passing of the flower heads through the thresher to remove all of the seeds, but usually does not exceed 100 dollars an acre.

Several charges must be considered by the producer before he can estimate his total cost and net return—land charges, rent or taxes and interest on investment, compensation insurance on labor, depreciation on equipment, and interest on the money invested in equipment, prorated according to its use. Rents on land suitable for producing flower seeds approximated 75 dollars an acre in 1961. If the land is owned, taxes plus interest on investment in the land were about 65 dollars an acre. Other overhead costs should not exceed 10 to 15 dollars an acre.

Total costs thus may vary from approximately 250 dollars to more than 1 thousand dollars an acre. Costs are even higher for some crops on small acreages that require additional hand labor for pollination. Compared to per-acre costs for other seed crops and other types of crops, the costs seem high, but, relative to expected returns, they usually are not excessive. Considering the attention they need, the production risks, variability in yield, and the small acreages on which they are grown, gross incomes well above production costs are justified.

The farmers who grow a small acreage of flower seeds under contract include it as one enterprise in their total farm operation. Usually the other enterprises are irrigated row crops, irrigated forage crops, such as alfalfa, and possibly some small grains. When the flower seeds are included as a part of the total farm organization, greater opportunity exists to control pests and diseases, reduce weed infestations, and add stability to the net income of the farms that could not be attained with seed crops alone.

NEARLY ALL vegetable seeds are grown under contract between a grower and a seed company. The company retains ownership of the seeds. Seed companies like to deal with the well-established, experienced growers and may offer inducements to sign them.

The contracts usually specify: The seeds of a specified amount and variety to be furnished by the company, the acres to be planted and the location of the field, the isolation from similar species that must be maintained, the provisions for cleaning, germination and purity standards, the price to be paid, and the place and dates of delivery.

The contracts also may specify the cultural practices to be followed; these are usually closely supervised by the company.

The company normally does all of the roguing and furnishes the harvest or other special equipment, either as a

contribution under the contract or for a nominal charge.

The seed companies usually do not finance the grower directly, but may make arrangements for the various suppliers to extend credit and cosign with the grower.

Most of the vegetable seeds are produced by general-crop farmers, who include a relatively small acreage of seed in their rotation. Few growers specialize in seed production as their major enterprise.

Much of the production of vegetable seeds in California is concentrated in the Central Valley on the relatively large farms, where the operators have the necessary flexibility to work such crops into their rotations and can bear the financial risk.

Most of the production in the Intermountain areas is on 80- to 120-acre farms, where the small acreage planted to a seed crop has a rather rigid place in the crop rotation.

Several examples illustrate some of the general types of cropping systems used. Many of the rotations listed change from year to year to adjust for weather, expected prices, diseases, insect pests, and other conditions.

Seeds of carrots, onions, and table beets produced in central California usually are grown in a rotation of tomatoes, sugarbeets, alfalfa (3–4 years), and seed. Some of the other crops that may be included in the rotation are barley, milo, corn, and minor crops.

Seed of melon and cucumbers—watermelon, cantaloup, Persian, honeydew, and similar types—produced in the Sacramento Valley area of California are grown in rotations that include tomatoes, sugarbeets, alfalfa, alfalfa seed, barley, milo, dry beans, safflower, sudangrass, and corn. The contracts for melon seeds typically call for planting the crop late in the season so it will not be profitable to sell any of the crop on the fresh market.

Seeds of garden beans in south-central Idaho are grown on farms of usually about 120 acres. A rotation may include alfalfa (3 years), beans

(2–3 years), sugarbeets or potatoes, and grain. Sometimes the sugarbeets or potatoes are omitted from the rotation, and a grain crop, such as wheat, may be inserted between the alfalfa and the beans.

Most of our seed of sweet corn is produced in Idaho on family farms of 80 to 100 acres. A common rotation is alfalfa, corn seed (1–2 years), sugarbeets, and grain. The contracts contain more specifications with respect to production practices than do those for most vegetable crops.

The wide range of seed crops and conditions of climate, soil, water, contracts, and size of farm preclude a comprehensive presentation of costs. For example, carrot seeds are produced by growing the carrots and harvesting and replanting them to produce seed. Some farmers perform all these operations and have costs over 2 years to produce one crop of seeds.

In some instances, the company furnishes the stecklings—small roots used for subsequent planting for seed production—at no direct cost to the farmer but pays a lower price for the seed. Costs are seldom available when a small amount of seed is needed and can be grown by one or a few growers.

Most of the carrot seed is produced in California and Idaho. Acreages produced by any one grower are relatively small and often are not a part of an established rotation but occupy fields free of weeds, insects, diseases, isolated from other carrot fields, and conveniently located. Six or more irrigations a year are required. Pesticides must be applied several times during the year. Yields vary from 700 to 1,700 pounds of clean seed an acre.

The stecklings are usually furnished by the seed company in California. The production of stecklings by the seedgrower is commoner in Idaho; thus seed production is a 2-year deal— one year to produce the stecklings and another year to grow the seed. During the winter storage period, losses of stecklings as great as 50 percent may occur.

The variable costs of producing stecklings in 1959 were about as follows (in dollars per acre): Land preparation, 8; fertilizing, 15; seeding, 10; chemical weed control, 40; disease control, 30; cultivating, 3; irrigation labor, 6; water, 18; harvesting, 130; hauling, 50; crates and storage, 110. The total was 420 dollars.

The fixed overhead costs were: Taxes, 6; office, 6; depreciation on equipment and irrigation system, 12; interest on equipment and irrigation system, 6; and land interest on 600 dollars at 6 percent, 36. The total of overhead costs was 66 dollars, and the total cost per acre was 486 dollars.

One acre of stecklings will plant 6 to 10 acres for seed production at a rate of about a ton of stecklings to the acre. Stecklings cost 50 to 80 dollars an acre of seed produced. Winter losses may increase this to 100 to 160 dollars.

Production of onion seed is similar to production of carrot seed in that the bulbs are produced one year and transplanted for seed production the following year. If onion seed is produced in the same area as carrot seed, many of the costs will be the same. Planting the onion bulbs is more expensive than planting carrot stecklings because the bulbs must be placed upright by hand. Onions also require a little more irrigation. Harvesting is more complicated, since the seed heads must be cut by hand and dried on canvas before threshing.

The onion bulbs are planted in the fall. After they root, they are covered with soil and left dormant in the field through the winter.

Bulbs usually are furnished by the seed company in California, but in other production areas may be produced by the seedgrower. The production of bulbs is similar to the production of carrot stecklings, except that the bulbs are harvested and then replanted rather than stored.

The cost of producing the bulbs in 1960 was: Land preparation, 8; fertilizing, 15; seeding, 10; cultivating, 6; irrigation labor, 6; water, 18; weeding,

ESTIMATED COSTS OF PRODUCING SELECTED FIELD CROP SEED IN CALIFORNIA, 1959

	Alfalfa	Ladino clover	Sudangrass
VARIABLE CULTURAL COST:			
Land preparation			$5.00
Plant			2.50
Clip and rake		$3.00	
Fertilize		6.00	12.00
Irrigate	$25.00	20.00	9.00
Weed control	20.00	4.50	
Pest control	17.00	5.00	
Bees	16.50	4.00	
HARVEST:			
Mow and rake		3.00	5.00
Defoliate	7.00		
Combine	15.00	15.00	12.00
Rethresh		20.00	
Haul	.75	.50	2.00
Cleaning, etc	9.25	15.25	10.00
FIXED OVERHEAD:			
Taxes	12.50	4.00	8.00
Miscellaneous	10.00	6.75	8.50
Depreciation and interest on equipment	3.00	7.00	10.00
Depreciation and interest on stand	6.00	6.00	
Interest on land	42.00	15.00	36.00
Total cost	184.00	135.00	120.00
Credit for hay	6.00	15.00	
Net cost	178.00	120.00	
Yield (pounds)	500	300	2,000
Cost per pound	0.36	0.40	0.06

ESTIMATED COSTS OF PRODUCING SELECTED GRASS SEED, 1959

	Common rye	Perennial rye	Chewings fescue	Alta fescue	Highland bent
Labor	$7.50	$4.00	$7.00	$6.50	$5.00
Tractor	3.00	1.00	2.00	2.00	2.00
Truck	.25	.25	.25	.25	.25
Other equipment	4.00	3.00	4.00	4.00	4.00
Fertilizer	3.00	5.00	8.00	6.00	4.00
Seed	2.00				
Sacks	3.00	2.00	2.00	2.00	2.00
Spray	.25	.25	.25	.25	
Seed cleaning and testing	3.00	2.00	15.00	10.00	10.00
Taxes [1]	5.00	5.00	5.00	5.00	5.00
Stand depreciation		4.50	1.00	4.00	1.00
Interest on land [2]	20.00	20.00	20.00	20.00	20.00
Total cost	51.00	47.00	64.50	60.00	53.25
Credits [3]	3.00	2.00	8.50	20.00	3.25
Net cost	48.00	45.00	56.00	40.00	50.00
Yield (pounds)	600	400	300	300	200
Cost per pound	0.08	0.11	0.19	0.13	0.25

[1] Taxes vary with tax rate and assessed valuation. The figure included represents a midpoint for land on which grass seed is grown.

[2] Interest on land varies widely with type of land on which seed is grown. Interest charges vary from an estimated 4 to 35 dollars per acre.

[3] Straw, pasturage, or hay.

75; pest control, 30; harvesting, 32. The total variable production cost was 200 dollars.

The fixed overhead costs were: Taxes, 6; office, etc., 6; depreciation on equipment and irrigation system, 12; interest on equipment and irrigation system, 6; land interest on 500 dollars at 6 percent, 30. The total overhead was 60 dollars. The total cost per acre was 260 dollars.

An acre of bulbs will plant 2 to 3 acres for the second year seed crop: Sufficient bulbs to produce an acre of seed will cost 80 to 130 dollars.

For vine crops—cucumbers, watermelons, cantaloup, squash, pumpkins—production methods and equipment are similar. Major areas of production are California, Oregon, and Colorado.

Land preparation for a crop of melon seed is similar to that for other seed crops, except that a preirrigation is usually necessary because of the late planting date. No special cultural practices are necessary other than the ordinary weed and pest control, fertilization, and irrigation. Harvesting is done with a special thresher, which may be furnished by the seed company or owned by the grower. The melons or cucumbers are picked by hand and tossed into the thresher as it moves across the field. After threshing, the seed must be washed and dried; the cost therefore is higher than that of most of the vegetable seed crops.

The production of sweet corn seed works well in a rotation of alfalfa, sweet corn, sugarbeets, and grain on the Idaho farms where most of it is grown. Corn seed ranks next to sugarbeets in profitability as a cash crop on these farms. It is a good crop in the rotation. A picker is the only special equipment required.

The contracts offered by the seed companies for corn are more specific than are the contracts for most seed crops. The seed company retains ownership of the seed. Acreages, prices, and general cultural practices are specified. The seed to make the specific hybrid is also stipulated. The company supervises detasseling. Contracts set harvest dates and manner of harvest, require a germination of 90 percent, and specify no frost or other damage. Roguing is done by the company.

Much of our pea seed is produced in the Palouse region of eastern Washington and northern Idaho, where farms typically have 500 acres or more and are primarily wheat farms. Peas are the second most profitable crop. A common rotation is grain, peas, grain, and fallow. Legumes for hay or green manure may occasionally replace the fallow. Farming is done with large-scale equipment. Little labor is hired except at harvesttime. Recent expansion of production of pea seed in the Columbia Basin of central Washington has taken place.

Yields range from 700 to 2,000 pounds an acre.

More than 95 percent of the production of pea seed is under contract. The seed company furnishes the seed, supervises the growing of the crop, and does the necessary roguing.

SEED OF field crops of one or more types is produced in nearly every agricultural area in the United States.

Little difference exists in the cultural practices used for the commercial crop and the seed crop of small grains, soybeans, and dry beans. Recleaning and seed treatment are additional costs for wheat, oats, and barley seed. Soybeans require similar additional inputs for seed, but losses in recleaning tend to be somewhat higher because of mechanical damage to the seed. In producing cotton for seed, cultural practices are similar to commercial production, but additional cultivation—by machines and hand hoeing—is necessary to control weeds. Additional expenses for cleaning the ginning equipment before ginning seed lots must be borne by the grower. With dry beans, the only expenses added for seed production are when roguing is required. A higher loss in recleaning may reduce yield slightly.

In producing seeds of hybrid corn

and grain sorghum, there are both additional cost considerations and income adjustments. First, since hybridization requires cross-pollination, alternate blocks of males and females must be planted. Planting costs are thus increased. Grain sorghum fields are rogued from 6 to 9 times to remove off-type plants. Detasseling of corn by hand to insure the desired cross is an additional labor expense, but the achievement of male sterility may eliminate this operation. Because only the seed from the female plants are of the desired hybrid type, only part of the total yield of hybrid corn and hybrid sorghums produced in the seed field can be sold at seed prices.

Growers specializing in alfalfa for seed supply most of the seed. Those who let their plantings for hay go to seed if the price is high enough also account for a sizable amount. Nearly all of the alfalfa grown for seed in California and the Columbia Basin of Washington is planted in rows. The hay produced on these stands is chopped and spread or given to anyone who will harvest and remove it from the field.

In California, rotations consist of 2–3 years of alfalfa seed and 2 years of such crops as cotton, melons, and grain. The seedgrower may farm these rotation crops himself or rent the land to someone else. Or he may be a "migratory" tenant farmer producing seed on several farms as fields become available that have appropriate crop histories for meeting the requirements for certified seed.

In some other major producing States—primarily in the Great Plains and the Intermountain area—alfalfa seed is usually taken from stands planted for hay. The first cutting is almost always for hay. The second and third may be for hay or seed. Per acre costs for seed production vary from 11.50 to 15 dollars per acre, depending on the method of harvesting. The farms are multienterprise farms, many of which include livestock enterprises.

Most of the seeds of Ladino clover are produced in the Sacramento Valley of California on soils that are not adapted to the production of deep-rooted crops. Much of this production is on land which was originally used for dryfarmed barley and sheep pasture. Many of the growers have retained their sheep enterprise and utilize the early spring growth of Ladino for pasture. Ladino is usually grown in rotation lasting about 8 years—4 years of Ladino and then 4 years of a combination of sudangrass, corn, barley, and other shallow-rooted crops. The land must not have grown whiteclover unless it was certified Ladino for 4 years to be eligible to produce certified seed. Most of the producers of Ladino seeds

ORGANIZATION, INCOME, AND EXPENSES OF A TYPICAL FARM IN THE SACRAMENTO VALLEY AREA OF CALIFORNIA PRODUCING SUDAN SEED

	Acres	Yield (tons)	Price	Gross income Per acre	Gross income Total	Cost[1] per acre	Net income Per acre	Net income Total
Tomatoes	125	20	$22	$440	$55,000	$340	$100	$12,500
Sugarbeets	125	20	12	240	30,000	190	50	6,250
Alfalfa	300	7	22	154	46,200	110	44	13,200
Milo	100	2½	42	105	10,500	90	15	1,500
Barley	250	1½	37	55.50	13,875	30	25.50	6,375
Sudan seed	100	1	100	100	10,000	85	15	1,500
Total	1,000	....	....	....	165,575	....	......	41,325
Interest on land	.....	....	....	....	....	....	......	36,000
Net profit	.....	....	....	....	....	....	......	5,325

[1] Interest on investment in land is not included.

own their equipment except for possibly suction machines for harvesting the seed on the ground from shattering. Much of the suction harvesting is done by custom operators for a percentage of the crop.

The production of sudangrass seeds is concentrated in California, Texas, and Colorado. Sudangrass will grow successfully under many different soil conditions and in combination with many crops. In California, for example, sudangrass may be grown in combination with tomatoes, sugarbeets, alfalfa, Ladino clover, corn, barley, and milo. It may be grown in combination with rice on a different type of soil.

No special cultural practices are required except that the crop may have to be mowed or swathed and dried in the windrow before threshing to avoid losses from shattering.

PRODUCTION of grass seeds exhibits extremes similar to those found with other seed crops, both in terms of total acreage and in the relative importance of the crop in individual farming operations. Some have small seed fields and care for them as time can be spared from other activities. Commercial producers give the seed crop care comparable to any other crop of equal possibilities of net return.

Grass seeds in the Great Plains, the Intermountain region, and the Pacific Northwest are produced under both dryfarmed and irrigated conditions. Some are planted in solid stands, but row plantings can be cultivated and irrigated more effectively. Seeds are also taken from native stands of some grasses when the set of seed and market are favorable.

Forage, as well as seeds, is usually produced on grass stands in this region. Typically, the farms producing small grains and livestock find a grass seed enterprise to be well adapted and profitable. An additional cash income from seed and additional forage for livestock are provided. As a multiple-purpose planting, relative prices of seed, forage, and livestock determine to a large extent whether seeds are harvested from a given grass planting in any year.

In the predominantly irrigated regions of the West, grass plantings on farms are primarily for the production of seed. Per-acre inputs and costs are greater, but yields are generally higher as a result of more intensive cultural practices. Plantings tend to be small, however, and are invariably conducted as one of several enterprises on a farm. Farmers experienced in the production of other types of seeds under irrigated conditions often add a grass-seed enterprise. They usually have the necessary experience and equipment. When added to other seed enterprises on a farm, the production costs can be reduced by taking advantage of supplementary relationships which exist. Established contacts with the seed markets may further contribute to a profitable grass seed enterprise on these farms.

BY ANY measure, the production of seeds in the United States is an important agricultural enterprise. Yet an analysis of the agriculture in the major seed-producing areas indicates that seed production is relatively less important than other enterprises, both within the area and on individual farms. There are usually other crops that on the average will bring higher net returns than seed crops.

The organization and financial structure of a typical farm producing sudangrass seed in the Sacramento Valley area of California illustrates this point. Sudangrass seed is considered an important crop in the area, but it typically occupies only about 10 percent of the crop acres of the farm, produces only 6 percent of the gross income, and contributes about 3.5 percent of the net income.

Sudangrass is a good rotation crop because it uses much of the same machinery as milo and barley, thus making more complete use of these capital items. It also loosens the soil, and many crops can be planted in the stubble with a minimum of soil preparation. The rather wide variation in prices and yields makes this a good speculative crop when the income of the farm is fairly stable as a result of including such crops as tomatoes and sugarbeets grown under contract and barley and alfalfa.

On a farm that produces alfalfa seed in the San Joaquin Valley area of California, the seed crop occupies 60 percent of the land area and furnishes 50 percent of the gross income. Even so, the seed crop provides less than 30 percent of the net income.

Thus, for two of the dominant forage seed crops in California, the seed enterprise represents a relatively insignificant part of the total income at average yields and prices.

One reason why a farmer elects to grow a seed crop is that he sees a chance to make high net returns on a small acreage. Some flower crops occasionally offer such possibilities. High yields sold at a favorable price can provide substantial net returns. If the acreage required is small, the total cash outlay may still be within the reach of the operator of a relatively small farm.

Another reason is that some seed crops provide an opportunity to use resources that for one reason or another cannot be used as effectively by other enterprises.

In some areas, producer contracts that stipulate a purchase price are attractive to many farmers. Such a contract may appear to add a measure of certainty to the farm income, although this added certainty may be more imaginary than real because of the many other variables that affect income. Contracts of this type may also help the farmer to obtain production credit.

Farmers often are willing to sacrifice the opportunity for very high incomes to avoid excessive variation in income, particularly if available capital is limited. This argument is often advanced to explain the farmers' reluctance to increase the proportion of land allocated to seed production. For some seed crops, particularly the few flower seed crops grown by individual farmers, this explanation may be valid. Wide year-to-year fluctuations in yield and price where not stipulated in a contract may occur.

Available evidence fails to support this argument when applied to many of the field crop seeds. Often, the variation in yield, price, and income are equal to or lower than those for other crops grown on the same farms. This is particularly true of seed crops grown under contract on irrigated farms in the West.

A part of the income of a farm operator is due to his skill in making managerial decisions and accepting responsibility for the decisions. The level of income in agricultural production thus is related to the managerial skills required and the financial responsibilities to be assumed. Since good management is essential to successful production of seeds, the management income to individual producers should be relatively high over time. Yet evidence we have suggests that this is not necessarily the case.

The answer lies in the fact that responsibility for many of the management decisions in seed production is retained by the contracting seed company and, in some cases, it assumes substantial financial responsibility ordinarily borne entirely by the producer in other production lines. Thus what appears to be a wrong allocation of returns between producer and contracting company often may be quite in keeping with the relative contributions of the two parties to the production of seeds of many specialty crops.

CHESTER O. MCCORKLE, JR., *is an associate professor of agricultural economics and an associate agricultural economist in the agricultural experiment station and on the Giannini Foundation at the University of California in Davis.*

A. DOYLE REED *is an extension economist in farm management at the University of California.*

APPENDIX

꙲ ꙲

A Selected List

of Publications

Andersen, Alice M.: *Handbook on Seed-borne Diseases*, 58 pages. Published by the Association of Official Seed Analysts. 1958.

Barton, Lela V.: *Storage and Packeting of Seeds of Douglas-Fir and Western Hemlock.* Contribution Boyce Thompson Institute, volume 18, pages 25–37. 1954.

Barton, Lela V.: *Storage of Some Flower Seeds.* Contribution Boyce Thompson Institute, volume 10, pages 399–428. 1939.

Bass, Louis N.: *Packaging and Storage of Kentucky Bluegrass and Creeping Red Fescue Seed.* Proceedings of the Association of Official Seed Analysts, volume 49. Pages 63–67. 1959.

Beal, J. A., Haliburton, W., and Knight, F. B.: *Forest Insects of the Southeast: with Special Reference to Species Occurring in the Piedmont Plateau of North Carolina.* Duke University School of Forestry, Bulletin 14, 168 pages, illus. 1952.

Berbee, J. G., Berbee, Flora, and Brener, W. H.: *The Prevention of Damping-off of Coniferous Seedlings by Pelleting Seed.* (Abstract) Phytopathology, volume 43, page 466. 1953.

Birdseye, Clarence, and Birdseye, Eleanor G.: *Growing Woodland Plants.* 223 pages, New York: Oxford University Press. 1951.

Boyce, J. S.: *Forest Pathology*, 550 pages, illus., New York: McGraw-Hill Book Co. 1948.

Brown, E., Holmes, F. S., et al.: *History of the Association of Official Seed Analysts*, 51 pages, 1941. Published by the Association of Official Seed Analysts.

Ching, T. M., Parker, M. C., and Hill, D. D.: *Interaction of Moisture and Temperature on Viability of Forage Seeds Stored in Hermetically Sealed Cans.* Agronomy Journal, volume 51, pages 680–684. 1959.

Christensen, C. M.: *Deterioration of Stored Grain by Fungi.* Botanical Review, volume 23, pages 108–134. 1957.

Clark, E. R.: *Drill Box Surveys*, Proceedings of the Association of American Seed Control Officials Conference. 1957.

Clark, E. R.: *Drill Box Surveys*, 39th Annual Report of International Crop Improvement Association. 1957.

Cottrell, H. J.: *Tetrazolium Salt as a Seed Germination Indicator*, Nature, volume 159, page 748. 1947.

Crocker, Wm.: *Life Span of Seeds, Growth of Plants*, chapter 2, pages 28–66, New York: Reinhold Publishing Corp. 1948.

Dickson, James G.: *Diseases of Field Crops*, 2nd Ed., 517 pages, New York: McGraw-Hill Book Co. 1956.

Doyer, L. C.: *Manual for the Determination of Seed-borne Diseases*, 59 pages, Wageningen, The Netherlands; H. Veenman and Zonen. 1938.

Du Pont Seed Treating Manual, 30 pages; E. I. du Pont de Nemours & Co., Wilmington, Del. 1960.

Fifty Years of Seed Testing. 101 pages. Published by the Association of Official Seed Analysts. 1958.

Frear, D. E. H.: *Pesticide Handbook*, 11th ed., 249 pages, State College, Pa.: College Science Publishers. 1959.

Frear, D. E. H.: *Pesticide Handbook*, 12th ed., 265 pages, State College, Pa.: College Science Publishers. 1960.

Hall, Carl W.: *Drying Farm Crops*, 336 pages, Ann Arbor, Mich.: Edwards Bros., Inc. 1957.

Harmond, J. E.: *Some New Ideas for Cleaning Those Hard-To-Handle Seeds.* Crops and Soils, volume 12, number 3. December 1959.

Henderson, James: *Fanning Mill Operation and Screen Nomenclature.* Seed Processors Short Course Proceedings, pages 21–26. Oregon State College. February 1957.

541

Hughes, H. D., Heath, M. E., and Metcalf, D. S.: *Forages; the Science of Grassland Agriculture*, 724 pages, Ames, Iowa: Iowa State College Press. 1951. Revised 1960.

Hume, H. Harold: *Azaleas, Kinds and Culture*, 200 pages, illus., New York: Macmillan Co. 1948.

International Code of Nomenclature for Cultivated Plants. Regnum Vegetabile, volume 10. Formulated and Adopted by The International Commission for the Nomenclature of Cultivated Plants of the International Union of Biological Sciences. 1958. Distributor for the United States: American Horticultural Council, Dr. Donald Wyman, Arnold Arboretum, Jamaica Plain 30, Mass.

International Rules for Seed Testing, Proceedings of the International Seed Testing Association, volume 21 (1). 1956. Published by the International Seed Testing Association.

International Rules for Seed Testing. Proceedings of the International Seed Testing Association, volume 24 (3). 1959. Published by the International Seed Testing Association.

International Rules for Seed Testing. Proceedings of the International Seed Testing Association, volume 25 (1). 1960. Published by the International Seed Testing Association.

Isely, Duane: *Determination of Variety or Type in the Laboratory and Greenhouse—Literature Review*, Proceedings of the Association of Official Seed Analysts, volume 46, pages 75–97. 1956.

Isely, Duane: *Employment of Tetrazolium Chloride for Determining Viability of Small Grain Seed*. Proceedings of the Association of Official Seed Analysts, volume 42, pages 143–153. 1952.

Isely, Duane: *Seed Analysis*, 163 pages; Ames: Iowa State College Book Store. 1951.

Lakon, G.: *The Topographical Method for Determining the Germinating Capacity of Seeds*. Plant Physiology, volume 24, pages 389–394. 1949.

Leopold, C. A.: *Auxins and Plant Growth*, 354 pages, Berkeley, Calif.: University of California Press. 1955.

McAtee, W. L.: *Distribution of Seeds by Birds*. American Midland Naturalist, volume 31, pages 214–223. A bibliography of 94 articles with a table of seed preferences of 44 species of birds. 1947.

Martin, A. C., Zim, H. S., and Nelson, A. L.: *American Wildlife and Plants*, 500 pages, illus., New York: McGraw-Hill Book Co. 1951.

Midyette, J. W., Smith, H. L., and Copeland, T. G.: *Checking Variety Claims on Oats, Barley, and Soybeans by Laboratory and Field Tests*. Proceedings of the Association of Official Seed Analysts, volume 47, pages 96–104. 1957.

Miles, S. R., Carter, A. S., and Shenberger, L. C.: *Tolerances and Sampling for Purity Analyses of Seed*. Proceedings of the Association of Official Seed Analysts, volume 48, pages 152–166. 1958.

Mitchell, John W. and Marth, P. C.:

Growth Regulators for Garden, Field, and Orchard, 129 pages, Chicago: The University of Chicago Press. 1947.

Muenscher, W. C.: *Growing Virginia Bluebell from Seed*. Wild Flower, volume 14, pages 57–58, figure 1–2. 1937.

Noble, Mary, Tempe, J. de, and Neergaard, Paul: *An Annotated List of Seed-borne Diseases*, 159 pages, Kew, England: Commonwealth Mycological Institute. 1958.

Owen, E. B.: *The Storage of Seed for Maintenance of Viability*. Commonwealth Bureau of Pastures and Field Crops, Bulletin No. 43, 81 pages (Literature Review). England. 1956.

Papavizas, G. C., and Christensen, C. M.: *Grain Storage Studies. XXV. Effect of Invasion by Storage Fungi upon Germination of Wheat Seed and upon Development of Sick Wheat*. Cereal Chemistry, volume 34, pages 350–359. 1957.

Porter, R. H.: *Detection and Classification of Seed-borne Organisms, Their Effect on Germination and Their Control by Seed Disinfection in Laboratory and Field*. Proceedings of the Association of Official Seed Analysts, volume 28, pages 195–213. 1938.

The Preservation of Viability and Vigor in Vegetable Seed, Asgrow Monograph No. 2, 31 pages, New Haven, Conn.: Asgrow Seed Co. 1954.

Proceedings, 1958 Short Course for Seedsmen, State College, Miss. 176 pages.

Proceedings, 1959 Short Course for Seedsmen, State College, Miss. 167 pages.

Qasem, Subhi A., and Christensen, C. M.: *Influence of Moisture Content, Temperature, and Time on the Deterioration of Stored Corn by Fungi*. Phytopathology, volume 48, pages 544–549. 1958.

Steffek, Edwin F.: *Wild Flowers and How To Grow Them*, 192 pages, New York: Crown Publishing Co. 1954.

Strong, R. G., and Lindgren, D. L.: *Effect of Methyl Bromide and Hydrocyanic Acid Fumigation on the Germination of Barley*. Journal of Economic Entomology, volume 52, pages 319–322. 1959.

Taylor, Norman. *Wild Flower Gardening*, 128 pages, Princeton, N.J.: Van Nostrand Co., Inc. 1955.

Tuite, John F., and Christensen, C. M.: *Grain Storage Studies. XXIV. Moisture Content of Wheat Seed in Relation to Invasion of the Seed by Species of the Aspergillus glaucus Group, and Effect of Invasion upon Germination of the Seed*. Phytopathology, volume 47, pages 323–327. 1957.

Tukey, H. B.: *Plant Regulators in Agriculture*, 269 pages, New York: John Wiley & Sons. 1954.

Tyler, L. J., Murphy, R. P., and MacDonald, H. A.: *Effects of Seed Treatment on Seedling Stands and on Hay Yields of Forage Legumes and Grasses*. Phytopathology, volume 46, pages 37–44. 1956.

Walker, J. C.: *Diseases of Vegetable Crops*, 529 pages, New York: McGraw-Hill Book Co. 1952.

Walker, John C.: *Plant Pathology,* 707 pages, New York: McGraw-Hill Book Co. 1957.

Wheeler, W. A., and Hill, D. D.: *Grassland Seeds,* 734 pages, Princeton, N.J.: Van Nostrand Co., Inc. 1957.

Wherry, Edgar T.: *Wild Flower Guide,* 202 pages, Garden City: Doubleday & Co., Inc. 1948.

Government Publications

Cooper, H. W., Smith, James E., Jr., and Atkins, M. D.: *Producing and Harvesting Grass Seed in the Great Plains,* U.S.D.A. Farmers' Bulletin 2112. 1957.

Crosier, W. F., Nittler, L. W., and Waters, E. C.: *The Quality of Seed Oats Collected from New York Farms in 1958,* Bulletin No. 785, Geneva, N.Y.: New York State Agricultural Experiment Station. April 1959.

Grass, The Yearbook of Agriculture, 892 pages, Washington, D.C.: Government Printing Office. 1948. $2.

Gray, R. B.: *Harvesting with Combines,* U.S.D.A. Farmers' Bulletin 1761. 1955.

Growing Peanuts, U.S.D.A. Farmers' Bulletin 2063. May 1954.

Growing Safflower, An Oilseed Crop, U.S.D.A. Farmers' Bulletin 2133. February 1959.

Growing Seed Flax in the North Central States, U.S.D.A. Farmers' Bulletin 2122. November 1958.

Growing Soybeans, U.S.D.A. Farmers' Bulletin 2129. February 1959.

Hamilton, Louis P., and Wooton, W. M.: *Grass Seed Production,* Arizona Agricultural Experiment Station Bulletin 228. 1950.

Harlan, Jack, Ahring, Robert M., and Kneebone, William R.: *Grass Seed Production Under Irrigation in Oklahoma,* Oklahoma Agricultural Experiment Station Bulletin B–481. 1956.

Jones, G. D., Smith, F. J., and McVickar, M. H.: *Nitrogen on Orchardgrass Pays.* Virginia Agricultural Experiment Station Bulletin 404. March 1947.

Klein, Leonard M., and Harmond, Jesse E.: *Suction Reclaimer for Shattered Seed,* Agricultural Research Service 42–24. March 1959.

Manual for Testing Agricultural and Vegetable Seeds, U.S.D.A. Handbook No. 30, 440 pages. 1952.

Mitchell, J. W., Livingston, G. A., and Marth, P. C.: *Test Methods with Plant-Regulating Chemicals,* U.S.D.A. Handbook No. 126, 68 pages. 1958.

Natti, J. J., and Schroeder, W. T.: *Protectant Seed Treatments for Vegetable Processing Crops,* New York Agricultural Experiment Station Bulletin 771, 46 pages. 1955.

Patterson, J. K., Schwendiman, J. L., Law, A. G., and Wolfe, H. H.: *Producing Grass Seed in Washington.* State College of Washington Extension Miscellaneous Publication 41. August 1956.

Plant Diseases, The Yearbook of Agriculture, 940 pages, Washington, D.C.: Government Printing Office. 1953. $2.50.

Protecting Stored Seed from Insect Attack, U.S.D.A. Agricultural Marketing Service Bulletin 64, 16 pages. 1955.

Rampton, H. H.: *Alta Fescue Production in Oregon,* Oregon Agricultural Experiment Station Bulletin 427, July 1945, reprinted March 1949.

Sesame Production, U.S.D.A. Farmers' Bulletin 2119. November 1958.

Spencer, J. T.: *Seed Production of Ky 31 Fescue and Orchard Grass as Influenced by Rate of Planting, Nitrogen Fertilization and Management,* Kentucky Agricultural Experiment Station Bulletin 554. June 1950.

State Noxious-Weed Seed Requirements Recognized in the Administration of the Federal Seed Act. U.S.D.A. (Revised annually.)

Stodola, F. H.: *Source Book on Gibberellin 1828–1957,* ARS 71–11, Northern Utilization Research and Development Division, ARS, U.S.D.A., Peoria, Ill. 1958.

Stoeckeler, J. H., and Jones, G. W.: *Forest Nursery Practice in the Lake States,* U.S.D.A. Handbook 110, pages 1–17, illus. 1957.

Stored-grain Pests, U.S.D.A. Farmers' Bulletin 1260, 46 pages. 1958.

Sumner, D. C., Goss, John R., and Houston, Byron R.: *Merion Bluegrass Seed Production,* California Agricultural Experiment Station Circular 470. October 1958.

Wakeley, Philip C.: *Planting the Southern Pines,* U.S.D.A. Agricultural Monogram 18, pages 26–56, 65–67, 215–216, illus. 1954.

Wolff, Simon E.: *Harvesting and Cleaning Grass and Legume Seed in the Western Gulf Region.* 1951.

Woody-plant Seed Manual, U.S.D.A. Miscellaneous Publication 654, 416 pages. 1948.

SOME CHARACTERISTICS OF SEEDS OF A SELECTED LIST OF CULTIVATED PLANTS

The following table lists in the first column the common and Latin names of some common cultivated plants.

The second column shows the nature of the parent plant—whether it is an annual, a biennial, or a perennial species. (A=annual, B=biennial, and P=perennial.) Plants shown as A–B or B–P may exhibit either of the two kinds of behavior, depending on cultural conditions and management.

Most seeds germinate over a wide range of temperatures—slowly at the lower part of each respective range and more quickly at the medium to medium-high parts of the range. Relatively high temperature may impede or prevent germination.

The temperatures shown in this table are very favorable for germination of the respective seeds, but are not necessarily the best naturally occurring soil temperatures at which to plant seeds in the spring for the growing of a crop in field or garden. In general, the vegetable seeds shown as tolerant to cool soil must be planted in the spring when soil temperatures are lower than shown, lest the growing crop encounter unfavorably hot weather. Freshly harvested seeds of most of these will germinate better after they are chilled a few days while moist at about 50° F.

The showing of two temperatures for vegetable seeds, as 68°–86°, represents a daily alternation of 16 hours at the first and 8 hours at the second. This alternation roughly simulates the change of night and day temperatures of the soil near the surface. Most species germinate faster and better under such alternating temperatures than under constant temperature. For the seeds of ornamentals the two temperatures indicate a favorable range but not a daily alternation. Exact optimum alternating temperatures have not been determined for these seeds as they have for "farm" and vegetable seeds.

Two figures are shown for the time for germination of vegetable seeds at the specified temperatures. The first figure is the time at which most good seeds in a sample that will germinate will have done so. Seeds that would not germinate at these temperatures by the second time interval are unlikely to have value for planting at the time of such a test. For the seeds of ornamentals, the two figures indicate the normal time within which most seedlings will appear above ground at the temperature shown, following proper planting.

VEGETABLE PLANTS

Common and Latin names	Plant habit	Approximate seeds per ounce	Germination Time	At temperature	Notable characteristic or requirement
		Number	Days	Degrees F.	
Artichoke—*Cynara scolymus*	P	700	7–21	68–86	Tolerates cool soil.
Asparagus—*Asparagus officinalis*	P	700	7–21	68–86	Do.
Asparagusbean—*Vigna sesquipedalis*	A	225	5–8	68–86	Requires warm soil.
Beans:					
Garden—*Phaseolus vulgaris*	A	100–125	5–8	68–86	Do.
Dry edible—*Phaseolus vulgaris*	A	100–125	5–8	68–86	Do.
Lima—*Phaseolus lunatus*	A	25–75	5–9	68–86	Do.
Runner—*Phaseolus coccineus*	A	25–30	5–9	68–86	Do.
Beet—*Beta vulgaris*	B	1,600	3–14	68–86	Tolerates cool soil.
Broadbean—*Vicia faba*	A	20–50	4–14	68–86	Do.
Broccoli—*Brassica oleracea* var. *botrytis*	A–B	9,000	3–10	68–86	Do.
Brussels sprouts—*Brassica oleracea* var. *gemmifera*	B	9,000	3–10	68–86	Do.
Cabbage—*Brassica oleracea* var. *capitata*	B	9,000	3–10	68–86	Do.
Cabbage, Chinese—*Brassica pekinensis*	A–B	18,000	3–7	68–86	Do.
Cardoon—*Cynara cardunculus*	P	700	7–21	68–86	Do.
Carrot—*Daucus carota*	B	23,000	6–21	68–86	Do.
Cauliflower—*Brassica oleracea* var. *botrytis*	A–B	9,000	3–10	68–86	Do.
Celeriac—*Apium graveolens* var. *rapaceum*	B	72,000	10–21	50–68	Requires cool soil.

Celery—*Apium graveolens* var. *dulce*..	B	72,000	10–21	50–68	Requires cool soil.
Chard, Swiss—*Beta vulgaris* var. *cicla*.	B	1,600	3–14	68–86	Tolerates cool soil.
Chicory—*Cichorium intybus*........	P	27,000	5–14	68–86	Do.
Citron—*Citrullus vulgaris*.........	A	300	7–14	68–86	Requires warm soil.
Collards—*Brassica oleracea* var. *acephala*.	B	9,000	3–10	68–86	Tolerates cool soil.
Corn, sweet—*Zea mays*...........	A	120–180	4–7	68–86	Requires warm soil.
Cornsalad (fetticus)—*Valerianella locusta* var. *olitoria*.	A–B	....	7–28	68	Tolerates cool soil.
Cowpea (southern pea)—*Vigna sinensis*.	A	225	5–8	68–86	Requires warm soil.
Cress:					
Garden—*Lepidium sativum*.....	A	12,000	4–10	68	Light sensitive.
Water—*Rorippa nasturtium-aquaticum*.	P	150,000	4–14	68–86	Tolerates cool soil.
Cucumber—*Cucumis sativus*........	A	1,100	3–7	68–86	Requires warm soil.
Dandelion—*Taraxacum officinale*....	B–P	35,000	7–21	68–86	Tolerates cool soil.
Eggplant—*Solanum melongena* var. *esculentum*.	A	6,500	7–14	68–86	Requires warm soil.
Endive—*Cichorium endivia*.........	A–B	27,000	5–14	68–86	Tolerates cool soil.
Kale—*Brassica oleracea* var. *acephala*.	B	9,000	3–10	68–86	Do.
Kale, Chinese—*Brassica oleracea* var. *alboglabra*.	B	9,000	3–10	68–86	Do.
Kohlrabi—*Brassica oleracea* var. *gongylodes*.	B	9,000	3–10	68–86	Do.
Leek—*Allium porrum*.............	B	11,000	6–14	68	Requires cool soil.
Lettuce—*Lactuca sativa*...........	A	25,000	7	68	Requires cool soil. Some varieties light sensitive.
Muskmelon (including cantaloup)—*Cucumis melo*.	A	1,300	4–10	68–86	Requires warm soil.
Mustard—*Brassica juncea*..........	A	18,000	3–7	68–86	Tolerates cool soil.
Mustard, spinach—*Brassica perviridis*.	A	15,000	3–7	68 86	Do.
Okra—*Hibiscus esculentus*..........	A	500	4–14	68–86	Requires warm soil.
Onion—*Allium cepa*..............	B	9,500	6–10	68	Requires cool soil.
Onion, Welsh—*Allium fistulosum*...	B	....	6–12	68	Do.
Pak-choi—*Brassica chinensis*........	A–B	18,000	3–7	68–86	Tolerates cool soil.
Parsley—*Petroselinum hortense* (*P. crispum*).	B	18,500	11–28	68–86	Do.
Parsnip—*Pastinaca sativa*..........	B	12,000	6–28	68–86	Do.
Pea—*Pisum sativum*..............	A	90–175	5–8	68	Requires cool soil.
Pepper—*Capsicum* spp.............	A	4,500	6–14	68–86	Requires warm soil.
Potato—*Solanum tuberosum*.........	P	....	.....	68	Tolerates cool soil.
Pumpkin—*Cucurbita pepo*..........	A	100–300	4–7	68–86	Requires warm soil.
Radish—*Raphanus sativus*.........	A	2–4,000	4–6	68	Requires cool soil.
Rhubarb—*Rheum rhaponticum*......	P	1,700	7–21	68–86	Tolerates cool soil.
Rutabaga—*Brassica napus* var. *napobrassica*.	B	12,000	3–14	68–86	Do.
Salsify—*Tragopogon porrifolius*......	B	1,900	5–10	68	Requires cool soil.
Sorrel—*Rumex acetosa*............	P	30,000	3–14	68–86	Tolerates cool soil.
Soybean—*Glycine max*............	A	175–350	5–8	68–86	Requires warm soil.

VEGETABLE PLANTS—Continued

Common and Latin names	Plant habit	Approximate seeds per ounce	Germination Time	Germination At temperature	Notable characteristic or requirement
		Number	Days	Degrees F.	
Spinach—*Spinacea oleracea*........	A	2,800	7–21	59	Requires cool soil.
Spinach, New Zealand—*Tetragonia expansa.*	A	350	5–28	50–86	Germinates irregularly.
Sweetpotato—*Ipomoea batatas*......	P	....	.....	77	Break or remove seedcoat.
Squash—*Cucurbita moschata* and *C. maxima.*	A	200–400	4–7	68–86	Requires warm soil.
Tomato—*Lycopersicon esculentum*....	A	11,500	5–14	68–86	Do.
Tomato, husk—*Physalis pubescens*...	A	35,000	7–28	68–86	Do.
Turnip—*Brassica rapa*............	B	15,000	3–7	68–86	Tolerates cool soil.
Watermelon—*Citrullus vulgaris*.....	A	200–300	4–14	68–86	Requires warm soil.

ORNAMENTAL PLANTS

Common and Latin names	Plant habit	Approximate seeds per ounce	Emergence Time	Emergence At temperature	Notable characteristic or requirement
		Number	Days	Degrees F.	
Achillea—*Achillea filipendula*.......	P	225,000	7–14	65–75	
African-violet—*Saintpaulia ionantha*.	A	750,000	21–28	65–75	
Ageratum—*Ageratum mexicanum*....	A	200,000	21	65–75	
Alyssum—*Lobularia maritima*.......	A	90,000	14	65–75	
Amaranthus—*Amaranthus tricolor*...	A	28,000	14–21	65–75	
Asclepias—*Asclepias tuberosa*.......	P	4,500	21–28	65–70	Requires cold treatment.
Aster—*Callistephus chinensis*........	A	12,000	14–21	65–75	
Aster Stokes'—*Stokesia cyanea*......	P	3,300	28–42	65–75	
Aubrietia—*Aubrietia deltoidea graeca*.	P	150,000	14–21	65–75	
Babysbreath—*Gypsophila paniculata*.	P	34,000	7–14	65–75	
Balloon Flower—*Platycodon grandiflorum.*	P	28,000	14–21	65–75	
Balsam—*Impatiens balsamina*.......	A	3,300	14–21	65–75	
Beard tongue—*Pentstemon gloxinioides*.	A	55,000	14–21	65–75	
Begonia—*Begonia semperflorens*......	A	1,000,000	14–21	65–75	
Bells of Ireland—*Molucella laevis*...	A	42,000	21–35	50	
Bird of Paradise—*Strelitzia reginae*..	A	140	21–28	65–75	
Black-eyed-susan—*Thunbergia alata*.	A	1,100	14–21	65–75	
Bleedingheart—*Dicentra spectabilis*..	P	6,000	.....	.....	Seed must be frozen.
Browallia—*Browallia viscosa*.......	A	240,000	14–21	65–75	
Butterfly Flower—*Schizanthus* species.	A	60,000	7–14	65–75	
Calceolaria—*Calceolaria herbeahybrida*.	A	600,000	14–21	65–75	Plant on surface.
Calendula—*Calendula officinalis*.....	A	3,000	14–21	65–75	
Calliopsis—*Coreopsis tinctoria*.......	A	90,000	14–28	65–75	
Cape-marigold—*Dimorphotheca aurantiaca.*	A	9,500	14–21	65–75	
Candytuft—*Iberis coronaria*........	A	9,500	7–21	65–75	
Candytuft, Hardy—*Iberis sempervirens*	P	11,500	14–21	65–75	
Canna—*Canna generalis*..........	P	100	56	65–75	Soak seeds. Sow on surface of soil with bottom heat.
Canterbury-bells—*Campanula medium.*	A	50,000	14–21	65–75	

Carnation—*Dianthus caryophyllus*...	A	14,000	14–21	65–75	
Castorbean—*Ricinus communis*.....	A	25	14–21	65–75	
Celosia—*Celosia argentea cristata*....	A	28,000	7–14	65–75	
Cerastium—*Cerastium tomentosum*...	P	19,000	14–28	65–75	
Christmas-cherry—*Solanum prendo-capsicum.*	A	12,000	21–28	65–75	
Chrysanthemum—*Chrysanthemum ca-rinatum.*	A	9,000	14–35	65–75	
Cineraria—*Senecio cruentus*.........	A	150,000	14–21	65–75	
Clarkia—*Clarkia elegans*...........	A	90,000	7–14	65–75	
Clove Pink—*Dianthus plumarius*....	P	25,000	14–21	65–75	
Coleus—*Coleus blumei*............	A	100,000	14–21	70–80	
Columbine—*Aquilegia* species.....	P	15,500	21–28	65–75	
Coneflower—*Rudbeckia hirta*.......	A	85,000	14–21	65–75	
Coralbells—*Heuchera sanguinea*.....	P	750,000	14–21	65–75	
Cornflower—*Centaurea cyanus*......	A	7,000	14–28	65–75	
Cosmos—*Cosmos bipinnatus*........	A	5,000	14–28	65–75	
Coreopsis—*Coreopsis grandiflora*.....	P	11,000	14–21	65–75	
Crossandra—*Crossandra infundibuli-formis.*	A	4,000	49–84	75–80	
Cup-and-saucer—*Campanula calycan-thema.*	P	120,000	14–21	65–75	
Cup-and-saucer vine—*Cobaea scan-dens.*	A	375	14–21	65–75	
Cup-flower—*Nierembergia frutescens*.	A	175,000	14–21	65–75	
Cuphea—*Cuphea llavea miniata*.....	A	7,000	14–21	65–75	
Cyclamen—*Cyclamen indicum*......	A	2,500	21–28	65–75	
Cynoglossum—*Cynoglossum amabilis*.	A	5,000	14–21	65–75	
Dahlia—*Dahlia pinnata*...........	A	2,800	14–21	65–75	
Daisies:					
English—*Bellis perennis*........	P	135,000	7–14	65–75	
Painted—*Pyrethrum roseum*.....	P	18,000	7–14	65–75	
Shasta—*Chrysanthemum maximum*	P	21,000	14	65	
Transvaal—*Gerbera jamesoni*...	A	8,000	14–21	65–75	
Datura—*Datura suaveolens*........	A	870	14–21	65–75	
Delphinium—*Delphinium elatum*....	P	10,000	21–28	55–65	
Delphinium Chinensis—*Delphinium chinensis.*	A	20,000	14–21	60–70	
Didiscus—*Trachymene caerulea*......	P	10,000	14–21	65–75	
Everlasting—*Helichrysum bracteatum monstrosum.*	A	36,000	14–21	65–75	
Exacum—*Exacum affine*...........	A	1,000,000	14–21	65–75	
False-indigo—*Baptisia australis*.....	P	1,700	21–28	65–75	
Feverfew—*Matricaria capensis*......	P	145,000	14–21	65–75	
Forget - me - not—*Anchusa myosotidi-flora.*	P	10,500	21–28	65–75	Freeze seed 72 hrs. before sowing.
Foxglove—*Digitalis purpurea*.......	P	180,000	14–21	65–75	
Gaillardia—*Gaillardia picta*........	A	14,000	14–21	65–75	
Gayfeather—*Liatris scariosa*......	P	9,500	21–28	65–75	
Geranium—*Pelargonium zonale*.....	A	6,000	28–42	55–65	
Globe-amaranth—*Gomphrena globosa*	A	5,500	14–21	65–75	
Globethistle—*Echinops ritro*........	P	650	14–21	65–75	
Gloxinia—*Sinningia speciosa*........	A	800,000	14–21	65–75	
Golden Cup—*Hunnemannia fumariae-folia.*	A	8,000	14–21	65–75	
Golddust—*Alyssum saxatile*........	P	30,000	21–28	65–75	
Gypsophila—*Gypsophila elegans*.....	A	24,000	14–21	65–75	
Heliotrope—*Valeriana officinalis*....	A	50,000	21–28	65–75	
Hollyhock—*Althaea rosea*..........	P	3,000	14–21	65–75	
Honesty—*Lunaria biennis*.........	P	1,500	14–21	65–75	
Impatiens—*Impatiens holsti*........	A	66,000	21–28	70–75	Need warmth and moisture.
Incarvillea—*Incarvillea grandiflora*...	P	6,000	14	65–75	
Kalanchoe—*Kalanchoe blossfeldiana*.	A	2,500,000	7–14	65–75	
Lantana—*Lantana camara*.........	A	1,300	42–49	65–75	Sow with bottom heat.

ORNAMENTAL PLANTS—Continued

Common and Latin names	Plant habit	Approximate seeds per ounce	Emergence Time	Emergence At temperature	Notable characteristic or requirement
		Number	Days	Degrees F.	
Larkspur—*Delphinium ajacis*	A	8,000	21–28	55–65	
Lavender—*Lavandula vera*	P	32,000	14–21	65–75	
Leopards-bane—*Doronicum caucasicum.*	P	18,000	14–21	65–75	
Lily-of-Peru—*Alstroemeria chilensis*	P	1,600	42–56	55	Germination erratic.
Linaria—*Linaria maroccana*	A	600,000	14–21	65–75	
Lobelia—*Lobelia erinus*	A	700,000	14–21	65–75	
Lupine—*Lupinus polyphyllus*	P	1,000	21–28	65–75	
Marguerite, Hardy—*Anthemis kelwayi.*	P	85,000	21–28	65–75	
Marigold—*Tagetes* species	A	10,000	7–14	65–75	
Marvel-of-Peru—*Mirabilis jalapa*	A	325	14–21	65–75	
Mignonette—*Reseda odorata*	A	27,000	14–21	65–75	
Monkshood—*Aconitum napellus*	P	10,000	....	.....	Requires cold treatment.
Morning-glory—*Convolvulus* species.	A	650	21–28	65–75	Hard seedcoat.
Moss rose—*Portulaca grandiflora*	A	280,000	14–21	65–75	
Nasturtium—*Tropaeolum majus*	A	175	14–21	65–75	
Pansy—*Viola tricolor*	A	20,000	14–21	65–75	
Periwinkle—*Vinca rosea*	A	21,000	14–21	65–75	
Petunia—*Petunia hybrida*	A	285,000	7–14	65–75	
Phlox—*Phlox drummondi*	A	14,000	14–21	65–75	
Physalis—*Physalis alkekengi*	P	18,000	21–28	65–75	
Pincushion-flower—*Scabiosa atropurpurea.*	A	4,500	14–21	65–75	
Plumbago—*Plumbago capensis*	A	2,000	21–28	65–75	
Poppy, Iceland—*Papaver nudicaule*	A	275,000	7–14	65–75	
Poppy, Oriental—*Papaver orientale*	P	140,000	7–14	65–75	
Primrose, Cape—*Streptocarpus hybridus.*	A	750,000	14–21	65–75	
Primula—*Primula obconica*	A	130,000	21–28	65–75	
Queen-Annes-lace—*Daucus carota*	A,P	36,500	14–21	65–75	
Red-hot-poker—*Kniphofia uvaria*	P	20,000	21–28	65–75	
Rockcress—*Arabis alpina*	P	120,000	21–28	65–75	
Salpiglossis—*Salpiglossis sinuata superbissima.*	A	125,000	14	65–75	
Sanvitalia—*Sanvitalia procumbens*	A	50,000	7–14	65–75	
Saponaria—*Saponaria ocymoides*	P	5,500	14–21	65–75	
Scarlet Sage—*Salvia splendens*	A	7,500	14–21	65–75	
Siberian Wallflower — *Cheiranthus cheiri.*	P	19,000	14–21	65–75	
Snapdragon—*Antirrhinum majus*	A	125,000	7–14	65–75	
Snow-on-the-mountain—*Euphorbia heterophylla.*	A	5,000	7–14	65–75	
Spider-plant—*Cleome spinosa*	A	12,500	7–14	65–75	
Statice—*Limonium sinuata*	A	350	14–21	65–75	
Stock—*Mathiola incana*	A	16,000	14	65–75	
Summer-cypress—*Kochia childsii*	A	45,000	7–14	65–75	
Sunflower—*Helianthus annus*	A	650	14–21	65–75	
Sweetpea—*Lathyrus odoratus*	A	350	14	65–75	
Sweet-william—*Dianthus barbatus*	B	25,000	14–21	65–75	
Sweet-Wivelsfield—*Dianthus chinensis*	A	25,000	14–21	65–75	
Thrift—*Armeria alpina*	P	32,000	21–28	65–70	
Tithonia—*Tithonia rotundifolia*	A	3,500	14–21	65–75	
Tobacco, flowering—*Nicotiana affinis.*	A	400,000	7–14	65–75	
Verbena—*Verbena hortensis*	A	10,000	21–28	65–75	
Viola—*Viola cornuta*	P	24,000	14–21	65–75	
Zinnia—*Zinnia elegans*	A	2,500	7–14	65–75	

ESTIMATED COSTS OF PRODUCING COMMON VEGETABLE SEEDS, 1959

Types of costs	Table beet	Broc-coli	Cabbage	Carrot	Cauli-flower	Celery	Lettuce	Melon	Onion	Garden peas	Radish	Sweet corn
VARIABLE CULTURAL:												
Land preparation	$8	$10	$10	$8	$10	$10	$10	$15	$18	$5	$11	$8
Fertilization	30	17	18	27	18	74	22	16	27	1	10	20
Planting	3	2	2	[1] 25	2	3	3	5	[1] 45	8	3	7
Irrigation	21	22	24	24	24	31	20	15	29	……	19	15
Cultivations	5	4	5	3	5	8	7	6	6	2	4	5
Chemical weed control	……	……	……	15	……	……	……	……	……	……	……	……
Thinning	……	20	25	……	25	……	22	……	……	……	20	……
Hoeing and weeding	15	10	10	5	10	10	10	13	8	……	7	15
Dusting and spraying	20	8	11	20	11	20	12	5	26	1	6	20
Other cultural labor	……	5	15	3	15	……	……	……	3	……	……	35
HARVESTING:												
Cutting	……	……	……	……	……	……	……	……	65	2	……	……
Hand labor	35	25	25	……	23	50	34	……	22	……	15	……
Threshing	30	20	20	[2] 50	20	60	30	50	6	5	……	20
Washing and drying	……	……	……	……	……	……	……	25	……	……	……	……
OVERHEAD:												
Taxes	10	10	10	10	10	10	10	10	10	2	10	6
Miscellaneous	12	11	14	12	11	13	14	14	14	1	14	6
Depreciation on equipment	7	7	7	7	7	7	7	7	7	5	7	5
Interest on equipment	3	3	3	3	3	3	3	3	3	2	3	2
Interest on land	36	36	36	36	36	36	36	36	36	16	36	36
Total per acre	235	210	235	248	230	335	240	220	325	50	165	200
Yield (pounds)	1,500	1,000	1,200	1,000	350	1,100	400	400	600	1,200	1,200	2,500
Cost per pound	0.16	0.21	0.20	0.25	0.66	0.30	0.60	0.55	0.54	0.04	0.14	0.08

[1] Stecklings or bulbs furnished by seed company.

[2] Where the plants must be pulled by hand because of excess grass in the field, the harvesting costs will be doubled.

SOME CHARACTERISTICS OF SEEDS OF SPECIES USED AS ROOTSTOCKS FOR TREE FRUITS AND NUTS

The following table lists the common name in the first column and the Latin name in the second column.

All tree fruit and nut crops are perennials, producing crops annually. No specific length of life can be indicated since this varies with growing factors in the various geographic localities.

Most deciduous tree fruit and nut seeds require afterripening, which is effected by storage in a damp substrate, such as peat and sand, at temperatures in the neighborhood of 40° F. The length of such afterripening period seems to be related to the length of the natural cold season in which the fruit was originally native. Some seeds, such as those of citrus, appear to require very short or no chilling. Germination after the chilling requirement has been satisfied is dependent on environment and is variable in optimum temperature. Some species respond more slowly than others.

Longevity of viability of seeds is dependent on storage temperature and moisture. A decrease or increase of the times shown can be effected with conditions. Cherry seeds lose viability rapidly if they become too dry. Citrus seeds are surface dried but cannot stand air drying. Peach and apricot seeds have longer life if kept air dry at moderate temperatures.

Common name	Latin name	Approximate seeds per ounce	Afterripening needed for germination (days)	Speed of germination at optimum temperature (days)	Length of viability (years)
Almond	Prunus amygdalus	12–15	50	15	5
Apple	Malus domestica	600–1,000	75–100	30	2–3
Apple (crab)	Malus pumila	1,000	75	30	2–3
Apricot	Prunus armeniaca	18–20	60	15	5
Cherry (Mahaleb)	Prunus mahaleb	300–350	100	15	1–3 cool-dry.
Cherry (sweet) (Mazzard)	Prunus avium	150–160	100–120	15	1–2 cool-dry.
Cherry (sour)	Prunus cerasus	200–250	100–120	15	1–2 cool-dry.
Citranges	Poncirus trifoliata	200–300	None	10–15 at 55° F.	Up to 1 year in polyethylene bag at 45°.
	Citrus sinensis				
Citrus macrophylla	Citrus macrophylla	200–300	None	do.	Do.
Fig	Ficus carica		Propagated by cuttings.		
Filbert	Corylus maxima		Propagated by cuttings.		
Grapefruit	Citrus paradisi	150–200	None	10–15 at 55° F.	Do.
Lemon (rough)	Citrus limon	200–300	None	do.	Do.
Lime (sweet)	Citrus aurantifolia	300–400	None	do.	Do.
Orange (sweet)	Citrus sinensis	200–300	None	do.	Do.
Orange (sour)	Citrus aurantium	200–300	None	do.	Do.
Orange (trifoliate)	Poncirus trifoliata	200–300	None	do.	Do.
Peach	Prunus persica	8–10	100	15	5
Peach (David)	Prunus davidiana	10–14	100	15	5
Pear	Pyrus communis	750	60–90	45	2–3 dry.
Pear (Oriental)	Pyrus calleryana	1,000	60–90	45	3
Pear (Oriental)	Pyrus serotina	1,000	60–90	45	3
Pear (Oriental)	Pyrus ussuriensis	1,000	60–90	45	3
Pecan	Carya pecan	8–10	30–90	20	1–3

Plum (American)	Prunus americana	50-55	150	30	4-6
Plum (Bessey)	Prunus besseyi	60-170	80-100	15	4-6
Plum (Damson)	Prunus insititia	100-120	100-120	30	4-6
Plum (Japanese)	Prunus salicina	20-40	60-100	15	4-6
Plum (domestic)	Prunus domestica	26-30	120	30	4-6
Plum (Myrobalan) (cherry plums)	Prunus cerasifera	60-70	80-100	30	4-6
Plum (Marianna)	Prunus cerasifera	50-70	100	30	4-6
Plum (Wild Goose)	Prunus munsoniana	120-140	80-100	15	4-6
Quince	Cydonia oblonga			Propagated by cuttings.	
Tangelo	Citrus reticulata ×	200-300	None	10-15 at 55° F.	Up to 1 year in polyethylene bag at 45°.
Tangerine (Mandarin)	Citrus reticulata	300-400	None	do.	Do.
Tung	Aleurites fordii	10-15	30-60	10	1-3
Walnut (Eastern black)	Juglans nigra	3	60-120	30	3-5
Walnut (Northern Calif. black)	Juglans hindsii	2-4	60-120	30	3-5
Walnut (Persian)	Juglans regia	2	30-60	20	1-3
Walnut (Paradox hybrid)	Juglans hindsii × J. regia	3-4	60-80	25	3-5
Walnut (Royal hybrid)	Juglans hindsii × J. nigra	3-5	60-100	25	3-5

U.S. SEED EXPORTS BY TYPE, QUANTITY AND VALUE, 1946–47 TO 1958–59

Year	Grasses and legumes		Other field seeds		Seed corn		Vegetable seeds		Sugarbeet		Flowers		Total	
	1,000 pounds	1,000 dollars	1,000 pounds	1,000 dollars	1,000 pounds	1,000 dollars	1,000 pounds	1,000 dollars	1,000 pounds	1,000 dollars	1,000 pounds	1,000 dollars	1,000 pounds	1,000 dollars
1946–47	29,092	9,826	12,482	1,207	N.A.	N.A.	16,305	6,784	8,992	2,235	416	598	67,287	20,650
1947–48	22,823	3,506	13,643	1,710	N.A.	N.A.	7,125	4,886	10,219	3,445	213	415	54,023	13,962
1948–49	23,177	6,660	7,600	655	29,120	2,271	4,871	3,961	3,248	690	136	268	68,152	14,505
1949–50	12,790	4,051	3,210	372	25,144	1,905	2,912	2,310	766	130	156	235	68,284	9,003
1950–51	17,611	4,967	7,326	661	13,552	951	3,599	1,701	413	78	175	279	42,676	8,637
1951–52	13,945	3,637	4,330	459	13,384	1,123	3,465	1,935	852	142	195	359	36,171	7,655
1952–53	7,404	2,705	1,079	83	11,088	926	3,254	3,049	849	143	174	324	23,848	7,230
1953–54	26,663	6,491	65,976	1,625	13,722	855	4,057	2,688	647	123	158	395	110,773	12,177
1954–55	49,953	14,985	5,468	420	15,568	1,187	4,030	2,956	810	173	227	614	76,056	20,335
1955–56	31,199	6,831	6,837	704	43,680	3,672	4,122	3,249	100	19	153	410	86,091	14,885
1956–57	42,974	13,476	11,238	913	21,484	1,755	4,568	3,494	723	186	250	560	81,237	20,384
1957–58	45,927	11,372	15,846	782	18,592	1,624	4,396	3,040	271	56	214	605	85,846	17,479
1958–59	38,603	9,998	10,112	749	13,014	1,697	3,943	3,230	473	97	319	650	66,464	16,421

N.A.—Not available.

Source: Foreign Agricultural Service. Compiled from records of Department of Commerce.

SOME SEED CHARACTERISTICS OF COMMERCIALLY

Most American forest trees reproduce primarily from seeds. To restore and maintain good and sow seeds either directly on the land or in nurseries to produce seedlings which can be provide food for many birds and small mammals. Many of the berry, fleshy fruit, and nut

Species	Time of— Flowering	Seed dispersal	Commercial seed-bearing age [1]
1. Alaska-cedar (*Chamaecyparis nootkatensis*)....................	Early spring.	Fall–spring....	*Years* ....
2. Alder, red (*Alnus rubra*)...........	....do......	Nov.–Dec......	20–100........
3. Ash, green (*Fraxinus pennsylvanica*)..	May........	Oct.–May.....	20–?........
4. Ash, white (*F. americana*)..........	Apr.–May...	Sept.–Dec....	20–175.......
5. Aspen, quaking (*Populus tremuloides*).	....do......	May–June.....	20–70+......
6. Baldcypress (*Taxodium distichum*)...	Mar.–Apr...	Oct.–Dec......	?.............
7. Basswood (*Tilia americana*)........	June–July...	Fall–spring....	15–100+.....
8. Beech, American (*Fagus grandifolia*).	Apr.–May...	After first heavy frost.	40–?........
9. Birch, sweet (*Betula lenta*).........	....do......	Sept.–Nov.....	40–?........
10. Birch, gray (*B. populifolia*).........	....do......	Oct.–Jan......	8–50........
11. Birch, yellow (*B. alleghaniensis*).....	....do......	Nov.–Feb......	....
12. Birch, paper (*B. papyrifera*)........	Apr.–June...	Sept.–Apr.....	15–70+.....
13. Boxelder (*Acer negundo*)............	Mar.–May...	Sept.–Mar.....	....
14. Butternut (*Juglans cinerea*).........	Apr.–May...	Sept.–Oct.....	20–80........
15. Catalpa, northern (*Catalpa speciosa*).	May–June...	Oct.–Mar.....	20–?........
16. Cherry, black (*Prunus serotina*).....	Mar.–June...	June–Oct......	10–125.....
17. Chestnut, American (*Castanea dentata*).	June–July...	Oct.–Nov......	....
18. Coffeetree, Kentucky (*Gymnocladus dioicus*).	June........	Sept.–Mar.....	?.............
19. Cottonwood, eastern (*Populus deltoides*).	Feb.–May...	Apr.–June.....	10–death.....
20. Cypress, Arizona (*Cupressus arizonica*).	Spring......	Sept.–following years.	....
21. Douglas-fir (*Pseudotsuga menziesii*)...	Spring–summer.	Aug.–Sept.....	9–600........
22. Elm, American (*Ulmus americana*)..	Feb.–Apr....	Mar.–June.....	15–300.......
23. Elm, rock (*U. thomasii*)...........	Mar.–May...	May–July.....	20–250......
24. Elm, slippery (*U. rubra*)...........	Feb.–Apr....	Apr.–June.....	15–200......
25. Fir, balsam (*Abies balsamea*).......	May........	Sept.–Nov.....	20–60+......
26. Fir, California red (*A. magnifica*)...	June........	Sept.–Oct.....	Middle-age...
27. Fir, Fraser (*A. fraseri*)............	May–June...	Oct.–Nov......	....
28. Fir, grand (*A. grandis*)............	Spring......	Sept.–Oct.....	20–100+.....
29. Fir, noble (*A. procera*)............	?...........	Oct...........	50–100+.....
30. Fir, Pacific silver (*A. amabilis*).....	Spring......	Oct...........	....
31. Fir, white (*A. concolor*)............	May–June...	Sept.–Oct.....	40–100+.....
32. Hackberry (*Celtis occidentalis*)......	Apr.–May...	Oct.–winter....	....
33. Hemlock, eastern (*Tsuga canadensis*).	May–June...	Sept.–winter...	30–400+.....
34. Hemlock, western (*T. heterophylla*)..	Spring......	Sept........	25–200+.....
35. Hickory, bitternut (*Carya cordiformis*).	Apr.–May...	Sept.–Dec.....	30–175.......

IMPORTANT NORTH AMERICAN FOREST TREES

forest stands, it is necessary to provide favorable conditions for natural seeding or to gather planted. This requires an understanding of seed habits and characteristics. Most tree seeds species also are a source of food for larger mammals, including man.

Frequency of good seed crops [2]	Weight per 1,000 cleaned seeds [3]		Seed dormancy [4]		Average laboratory germination
	Average	Range	Kind	Occurrence	
Years	Grams	Grams			Percent
Occasional...	4. 20	2. 52–6. 87	Embryo?......	General?....	1
4..........	. 68	. 42–1. 25	....do........	General.....	27
1+.........	26. 22	18. 44–41. 24	Embryo.......	....do......	42
3–5........	45. 36	24. 92–82. 47	....do........	....do......	38
4–5........	. 13	....	None.........	Quite gen....	59
3–5........	94. 50	49. 85–348. 92	Embryo + resinous seedcoat?	General.....	12
1+.........	90. 72	56. 70–151. 20	Embryo, impermeable seedcoat, tough pericarp.	....do......	34
2–3........	263. 50	197. 22–348. 92	Embryo.......	....do......	85
1–2........	. 70	. 49–. 92	Embryo?......	....do......	43
1+.........	. 11	. 09–. 13	....do........	....do......	64
1–2........	1. 01	. 50–1. 63	....do........	....do......	27
1+.........	. 33	. 11–. 74	....do........	....do......	34
1+.........	38. 44	30. 24–55. 32	Embryo.......	....do......	33
2–3........	15, 120. 00	11, 340. 00–30, 240. 00	Embryo + hard seedcoat?	....do......	65
2+.........	21. 60	15. 12–28. 35	None?.........	General?....	75
1 1........	94. 50	56. 00–146. 32	Embryo + hard seedcoat?	General.....	63
1+.........	3, 489. 23	2, 835. 00–4, 536. 00	Embryo.......	....do......	72
1–2........	1, 649. 45	1, 242. 74–2, 160. 00	Impermeable seedcoat.	....do......	75
1+.........	1. 30	. 77–2. 27	None.........	Quite gen...	88
1+.........	11. 34	7. 69–16. 80	Embryo?......	General.....	26
3–7........	10. 80	6. 67–22. 68	Embryo + hard seedcoat?	Variable.....	65
1+.........	6. 67	4. 77–9. 45	Embryo.......	Some, but not all lots.	63
3–4........	64. 80	50. 40–90. 72	None.........	General.....	85
2–4........	11. 06	8. 40–12. 96	Embryo.......	In northern sources.	17
2–4........	7. 56	4. 80–15. 12	....do........	Some, but not all lots.	22
2–3........	68. 73	41. 24–113. 40	....do........	....do......	25
....	8. 10	6. 57–10. 31	....do........	....do......	42
2–3........	19. 55	10. 24–36. 00	Embryo?......	Some, but not all lots?	28
Infrequent...	31. 07	23. 50–40. 50	Embryo.......	Some, but not all lots.	24
2–3........	40. 14	30. 44–55. 32	....do........	....do......	22
2–4........	30. 04	16. 68–55. 32	....do........	....do......	34
1+.........	105. 49	84. 00–129. 60	Embryo, seedcoat?	General.....	41
2–3........	2. 43	1. 26–3. 44	Embryo.......	Variable.....	38
2–5........	1. 53	. 89–2. 06	....do........	....do......	56
3–5........	2, 907. 69	2, 451. 89–3, 628. 80	....do........	General.....	55

SOME SEED CHARACTERISTICS OF COMMERCIALLY

	Time of—		Commercial seed-bearing age [1]
Species	Flowering	Seed dispersal	
			Years
36. Hickory, mockernut (*C. tomentosa*)..	Apr.–May . . .	Sept.–Dec.	25–200. . . . . .
37. Hickory, pignut (*C. glabra*).	. . . .do.	. . . .do.	30–300. . . . . .
38. Hickory, shagbark (*C. ovata*).	Apr.–June. . .	. . . .do.	40–300. . . . . .
39. Hickory, shellbark (*C. laciniosa*). . . .	. . . .do.	. . . .do.	40–350. . . . . .
40. Honeylocust (*Gleditsia triacanthos*). . .	May–June. . .	Sept.–Feb.	10–100. . . . . .
41. Incense-cedar (*Libocedrus decurrens*).	January.	Oct.–Nov.	20–200+ . . . . .
42. Juniper, Rocky Mountain (*Juniperus scopulorum*).	Spring.	Long persistent .	10–300. . . . . .
43. Larch, western (*Larix occidentalis*). . .	. . . .do.	Aug.–Sept.	40–60+ . . . . . .
44. Locust, black (*Robinia pseudoacacia*). .	May–June. . .	Sept.–Apr.	6–60. . . . .
45. Maple, red (*Acer rubrum*).	Feb.–May. . .	Apr.–July.	. . . .
46. Maple, silver (*A. saccharinum*).	Feb.–Apr. . . .	Apr.–June. . . .	35–? . . . .
47. Maple, sugar (*A. saccharum*).	Mar.–May. . .	Oct.–Dec.	?–200+ . . . . . .
48. Oak, black (*Quercus velutina*).	Apr.–May. . .	Sept.–Nov.	20–100. . . . . .
49. Oak, bur (*Q. macrocarpa*).	. . . .do.	Aug.–Sept.	35–400. . . . . .
50. Oak, chestnut (*Q. prinus*).	. . . .do.	Sept.–Nov.	20–150. . . . . .
51. Oak, northern red (*Q. rubra*).	. . . .do.	Sept.–Oct.	25–200. . . . . .
52. Oak, scarlet (*Q. coccinea*).	. . . .do.	. . . .do.	20–150. . . . . .
53. Oak, southern red (*Q. falcata*).	. . . .do.	. . . .do.	25–125. . . . . .
54. Oak, swamp chestnut (*Q. michauxii*).	. . . .do.	. . . .do.	. . . .
55. Oak, white (*Q. alba*).	. . . .do.	. . . .do.	20–300. . . . . .
56. Pecan (*Carya illinoensis*).	Mar.–May. . .	Sept.–Dec.	20–300. . . . . .
57. Pine, eastern white (*Pinus strobus*). .	Apr.–June. . .	Sept.–Oct.	15–250. . . . . . .
58. Pine, jack (*P. banksiana*).	May.	Fall–several years.	5–80+ . . . . . .
59. Pine, Jeffrey (*P. jeffreyi*).	June.	Fall–spring. . . .	8–150+ . . . . . .
60. Pine, loblolly (*P. taeda*).	Mar.–Apr. . .	. . . .do.	12–60+ . . . . . .
61. Pine, lodgepole (*P. contorta*).	June.	Fall–several years.	5–200+ . . . . . .
62. Pine, longleaf (*P. palustris*).	Feb.–Apr. . . .	Sept.–Dec.	20–350+ . . . . .
63. Pine, ponderosa (*P. ponderosa*).	Apr.–June. . .	Fall–spring. . . .	20–150+ . . . . .
64. Pine, red (*P. resinosa*).	. . . .do.	Fall–summer. . .	25–200+ . . . . .
65. Pine, shortleaf (*P. echinata*).	Mar.–Apr. . .	Nov.–Dec.	16–280+ . . . . .
66. Pine, slash (*P. elliottii*).	Jan.–Mar. . . .	Sept.–Oct.	12–150+ . . . . .
67. Pine, sugar (*P. lambertiana*).	May–June. . .	Aug.–Oct.	40–175+ . . . . .
68. Pine, western white (*P. monticola*). . .	Spring.	Fall–spring	10–300+ . . . . .

IMPORTANT NORTH AMERICAN FOREST TREES—Continued

Frequency of good seed crops [2]	Weight per 1,000 cleaned seeds [3]		Seed dormancy [4]		Average laboratory germination
	Average	Range	Kind	Occurrence	
Years	Grams	Grams			Percent
2–3	5,040.00	4,014.16–13,341.18	Embryo	General	66
1–2	2,268.00	2,016.00–2,592.00	....do	....do	85
1–3	4,536.00	3,024.00–5,670.00	....do	....do	80
1–2	15,120.00	12,960.00–18,144.00	....do	....do	..
1–2	162.00	112.00–259.20	Impermeable seedcoat.	....do	50
3	30.24	15.64–70.88	Probably embryo.	Variable	50
2–5	15.86	10.77–25.34	Embryo + seedcoat.	General	22
5–6	3.17	2.30–4.63	Probably embryo.	Variable	27
1–2	18.90	12.96–28.35	Impermeable seedcoat.	General	68
1+	19.89	11.87–35.72	Embryo	Some, but not all lots.	46
1+	324.00	238.74–504.00	None		76
3–7	74.36	49.85–141.75	Embryo		39
2–3	1,814.40	1,134.00–3,628.80	....do	General	47
2–3	6,048.00	3,360.00–11,340.00	....do	Variable [5]	45
1–2	6,048.00	4,536.00–8,247.27	None	General	82
2–3	3,240.00	1,778.82–5,670.00	Embryo	....do	58
Irregular	1,620.00	1,120.00–2,926.45	....do	....do	62
1–2	762.35	577.83–1,163.08	....do	....do	91 —
....	4,536.00	2,326.15–8,247.27	None	....do	87
4–10	3,024.00	2,160.00–6,480.00	....do	Quite gen	78
1–2	4,536.00	2,835.00–8,247.27	Embryo	General	50
3–5	16.80	8.56–22.68	....do	Quite gen	64
3–4	3.45	1.81–6.39	Probably embryo.	Occasional	68
2–4	113.40	84.00–146.32	....do	....do	68
3–10	24.65	18.14–28.35	....do	Quite gen	60
1–3	4.45	2.84–11.94	....do	Occasional	64
3–7	108.00	75.60–119.37	....do	Rare	54
2–5	37.80	19.72–65.74	....do	Occasional	59
3–7	8.72	6.39–15.12	None	General	75
5–10	9.45	7.26–12.43	Probably embryo.	Quite gen	68
1–10	31.28	28.35–34.89	....do	Occasional	61
3–5	216.00	141.75–302.40	....do	Variable	56
4–6	16.80	14.18–32.40	Seedcoat, probably embryo.	....do	48

SOME SEED CHARACTERISTICS OF COMMERCIALLY

Species	Time of— Flowering	Seed dispersal	Commercial seed-bearing age [1]
			Years
69. Port-Orford-cedar (*Chamaecyparis lawsoniana*).	Spring......	October.......	8–100+......
70. Redcedar, eastern (*Juniperus virginiana*).	Mar.–May...	Feb.–Mar.....	10–175.......
71. Redcedar, western (*Thuja plicata*)..	Apr.........	Aug.–Oct......	16–200+.....
72. Redwood (*Sequoia sempervirens*).....	Nov.–Mar...	Fall...........	20–300+.....
73. Sequoia, giant (*S. gigantea*)........	Feb.–Mar...	....do........	125–300+....
74. Spruce, black (*Picea mariana*)......	May–June...	Oct.[6].........	30–250.......
75. Spruce, Engelmann (*P. engelmannii*).	June–July...	Sept.–Oct.....	16–200+.....
76. Spruce, red (*P. rubens*)............	Apr.–May...	Sept..........	30–?........
77. Spruce, Sitka (*P. sitchensis*)........	....do......	Early fall......	35–?........
78. Spruce, white (*P. glauca*)..........	May........	Aug.–Nov.....	30–?........
79. Sweetgum (*Liquidambar styraciflua*)..	Mar.–May...	Sept.–Nov.....	20–150.......
80. Sycamore, American (*Platanus occidentalis*).	May........	Sept.–May.....	25–250.......
81. Tamarack (*Larix laricina*).........	....do......	Sept..........	40–75+......
82. Tupelo, black (*Nyssa sylvatica*).....	Apr.–June...	Sept.–Oct.....	....
83. Walnut, black (*Juglans nigra*)......	May–June...	Fall...........	12–?........
84. White-cedar, Atlantic (*Chamaecyparis thyoides*).	Mar.–Apr...	Oct.–Nov......	4–100+......
85. White-cedar, northern (*Thuja occidentalis*).	Apr.–May...	Aug.–Oct......	30–100+.....
86. Yellow-poplar(*Liriodendron tulipifera*).	Apr.–June...	Oct.–Jan......	15–200+.....

[1] Most tree species begin to bear seeds several years earlier than indicated and continue almost to death, but the most abundant production normally is between the ages indicated. Open-grown trees usually bear earlier and more abundantly than those in stands.

[2] Most trees bear some seed in the years between good crops, although total failures may occur.

[3] Seeds cleaned for commercial use. Wings, fleshy parts removed in many species.

[4] Seeds of many woody plants contain dormant embryos. Such dormancy usually can be broken by holding the seeds for 1 to 3 months in a moist medium at 0° to 5° C. Some species, chiefly legumes, have hard or impermeable seedcoats which can be overcome by mechanical

IMPORTANT NORTH AMERICAN FOREST TREES—Continued

Frequency of good seed crops [2]	Weight per 1,000 cleaned seeds [3] Average	Weight per 1,000 cleaned seeds [3] Range	Seed dormancy [4] Kind	Seed dormancy [4] Occurrence	Average laboratory germination
Years	Grams	Grams			Percent
4–5.........	2.16	.76–5.67	Embryo?......	General?....	52
2–3.........	10.50	7.69–25.77	Embryo + seed-coat?	General.....	42
2–3.........	1.10	.90–2.23	Embryo.......	Slight, variable.	51
1+.........	3.72	1.51–7.69	Probably embryo.	....do......	10
1+.........	4.98	3.44–8.40	....do........	....do......	25
4–5.........	1.12	.89–1.40	Embryo.......	General.....	64
2–3.........	3.36	2.27–6.57	....do........	Occasional...	69
3–8.........	3.24	1.57–4.54	....do........	General.....	60
3–4.........	2.16	1.13–2.93	....do........	Variable.....	60
2–6.........	1.89	1.14–3.19	....do........	General.....	50
1–3.........	5.53	5.04–6.98	Probably embryo.	....do......	70
1–2.........	2.22	1.99–3.00	....do........	Quite gen ...	35
5–6.........	1.42	1.08–2.16	Embryo.......	General.....	47
....	137.45	113.40–245.19	....do........	....do......	30
Irregular.....	11,340.00	4,536.00–22,680.00	Embryo + hard seedcoat?	....do......	75
1+.........	.99	.91–1.08	Embryo?......	General?....	84
5...........	1.31	.80–2.47	Embryo.......	Slight, variable.	46
Irregular.....	32.40	18.90–45.36	Embryo + seed-coat?	General.....	5

scarification or soaking in H_2SO_4. Several trees have seeds with both types of dormancy. In some species seed dormancy is general; others may have both dormant and nondormant seed in the same lot; and still others may vary between lots, some lots being completely dormant and others completely nondormant. Types of dormancy suspected but not proved experimentally are indicated by question mark.

[5] No embryo dormancy in species proper, but general embryo dormancy in var. olivae-formis.

[6] Black spruce cones are retained for 2 or 3 years in a state of active seed dispersal.

DATA ON SOME FOREST TREES

Common name [1]	Scientific name	Number seed/oz. Average	Number seed/oz. Range	Treatment recommended for germination [2]
Alder, red	Alnus rubra	41,500	22,600– 67,500	(a)
Ash, black	Fraxinus nigra	510	380– 590	(a)
Ash, green	F. pennsylvanica	790	580– 1,180	(a)
Ash, white	F. americana	625	340– 1,140	(a)
Aspen, bigtooth	Populus grandidentata	190,000	....	None
Aspen, quaking	P. tremuloides	225,000	....	None
Basswood, American	Tilia americana	310	190– 500	(b)
Beech, American	Fagus grandifolia	100	80– 140	(a)
Sugarberry	Celtis laevigata	270	230– 360	(a)
Birch, paper	Betula papyrifera	86,000	38,000–260,000	(a)
Birch, sweet	B. lenta	40,400	39,800– 58,300	(a)
Birch, yellow	B. alleghaniensis	27,900	17,400– 56,600	(a)
Boxelder	Acer negundo	740	510– 940	(a)
Buckeye, Ohio	Aesculus glabra	....	3– 4	(c)
Buckeye, yellow	A. octandra	....	2– 3	(c)
Butternut	Juglans cinerea	2	1– 4	(c)
Cedar (Alaska-cedar)	Chamaecyparis nootkatensis	7,400	4,100– 11,200	None
Cedar (Atlantic white-cedar)	C. thyoides	28,700	26,200– 31,200	None
Cedar (eastern redcedar)	Juniperus virginiana	2,700	1,100– 3,700	(c)
Cedar (incense-cedar)	Libocedrus decurrens	900	400– 1,800	(a)
Cedar (northern white-cedar)	Thuja occidentalis	21,600	11,500– 35,500	None
Cedar (Port-Orford-cedar)	Chamaecyparis lawsoniana	13,000	5,000– 37,500	None
Cedar (western redcedar)	Thuja plicata	25,800	12,700– 31,500	None
Cherry, black	Prunus serotina	190	300– 500	(c)
Cottonwood, eastern	Populus deltoides	21,800	12,500– 36,800	None
Cypress (baldcypress)	Taxodium distichum	300	80– 500	(c)
Dogwood, flowering	Cornus florida	280	200– 390	(a)
Elm, American	Ulmus americana	4,200	3,000– 5,900	(a)
Elm, rock	U. thomasii	440	310– 560	(a)
Elm, slippery	U. rubra	2,560	2,180– 3,370	(a)
Fir, balsam	Abies balsamea	3,720	1,870– 5,900	(a)
Fir, California red	A. magnifica	410	250– 680	(a)
Fir (Douglas-fir)	Pseudotsuga menziesii	2,610	1,250– 4,250	(a)
Fir, grand	Abies grandis	1,450	740– 2,780	(a)
Fir, noble	A. procera	910	700– 1,200	(a)
Fir, Pacific silver	A. amabilis	700	500– 930	(a)
Fir, subalpine	A. lasiocarpa	2,340	1,490– 3,200	(a)

Fir, white	A. concolor	940	520– 1,710	(a)
Gum (sweetgum)	Liquidambar styraciflua	5,100	4,050– 5,650	(a)
Hackberry	Celtis occidentalis	270	220– 340	(a)
Hemlock, eastern	Tsuga canadensis	11,700	8,300– 22,400	(a)
Hemlock, mountain	T. mertensiana	7,150	3,750– 12,900	(a)
Hemlock, western	T. heterophylla	13,700	18,500– 31,800	(a)
Hickory, bitternut	Carya cordiformis	10	8– 12	(c)
Hickory, mockernut	C. tomentosa	6	2– 7	(c)
Hickory, pignut	C. glabra	12	11– 14	(c)
Hickory, shagbark	C. ovata	6	5– 9	(c)
Hickory, shellbark	C. laciniosa	2	......	(c)
Juniper, Rocky Mountain	Juniperus scopulorum	1,790	1,120– 2,610	(a)
Juniper, western	J. occidentalis	650	500– 810	(d)
Larch, western	Larix occidentalis	8,900	6,100– 12,300	None
Locust, black	Robinia pseudoacacia	1,500	1,000– 2,200	(e)
Locust (honeylocust)	Gleditsia triacanthos	175	110– 250	(e)
Madrone, Pacific	Arbutus menziesii	125	......	(a)
Magnolia, southern	Magnolia grandiflora	360	......	(c)
Maple, bigleaf	Acer macrophyllum	190	175– 210	(a)
Maple, red	A. rubrum	1,420	800– 2,490	(a)
Maple, silver	A. saccharinum	90	60– 120	(a)
Maple, sugar	A. saccharum	380	200– 570	(a)
Oak, black	Quercus velutina	16	8– 25	(a)
Oak, bur	Q. macrocarpa	3	2– 5	(a)
Oak, California black	Q. kelloggii	7	......	(a)
Oak, cherrybark	Q. falcata var. pagodaefolia	47	......	None
Oak, chestnut	Q. prinus	6	3– 12	None
Oak, live	Q. virginiana	24	21– 32	(a)
Oak, northern red	Q. rubra	9	5– 16	None
Oak, Oregon white	Q. garryana	6	......	None
Oak, pin	Q. palustris	25	20– 34	(a)
Oak, post	Q. stellata	25	15– 40	(a)
Oak, scarlet	Q. coccinea	17	10– 25	(a)
Oak, southern red	Q. falcata	37	24– 49	(a)
Oak, white	Q. alba	9	4– 13	None
Oak, willow	Q. phellos	40	37– 43	(a)
Pecan	Carya illinoensis	6	3– 10	(a)
Persimmon, common	Diospyros virginiana	74	41– 110	(a)
Pine, eastern white	Pinus strobus	1,680	1,250– 3,400	(a)
Pine, jack	P. banksiana	8,200	4,430– 15,600	(f)
Pine, loblolly	P. taeda	1,150	1,000– 1,560	(a)
Pine, lodgepole	P. contorta	8,450	6,900– 10,300	(a)

DATA ON SOME FOREST TREES—Continued

Common name [1]	Scientific name	Number seed/oz. Average	Number seed/oz. Range	Treatment recommended for germination [2]
Pine, longleaf	P. palustris	260	240– 370	(f)
Pine, Monterey	P. radiata	1,000	810– 1,440	None
Pine, pinyon	P. edulis	120	95– 155	None
Pine, pitch	P. rigida	3,900	2,250– 5,200	(f)
Pine, ponderosa	P. ponderosa	750	430– 1,440	(a)
Pine, red	P. resinosa	3,250	1,870– 4,440	None
Pine, shortleaf	P. echinata	3,000	2,280– 3,900	(f)
Pine, slash	P. elliottii	910	810– 1,000	(f)
Pine, sugar	P. lambertiana	130	95– 200	(a)
Pine, Virginia	P. virginiana	3,300	2,500– 4,700	None
Pine, western white	P. monticola	1,690	880– 2,000	(a)
Poplar (yellow-poplar)	Liriodendron tulipifera	875	625– 1,500	(a)
Redwood	Sequoia sempervirens	7,600	3,680– 18,600	(a)
Sequoia, giant	Sequoia gigantea	5,650	3,360– 8,200	(a)
Spruce, black	Picea mariana	25,000	21,000– 31,900	(a)
Spruce, Engelmann	P. engelmannii	8,500	4,300– 12,500	(a)
Spruce, red	P. rubens	8,700	6,200– 18,000	None
Spruce, Sitka	P. sitchensis	13,100	9,700– 25,000	(a)
Spruce, white	P. glauca	15,000	8,900– 24,800	(a)
Sycamore, American	Platanus occidentalis	12,700	9,400– 14,400	(f)
Tamarack	Larix laricina	19,800	13,100– 26,200	None
Tupelo, black	Nyssa sylvatica	200	115– 250	(a)
Walnut, black	Juglans nigra	2	1– 6	(c)
Willow, black	Salix nigra	3 150,000	....	None

[1] Common names shown in parentheses are the preferred common names but are listed alphabetically according to usual usage. Thus "Alaska cedar" is listed under "cedar," although this tree is not a cedar, which name is reserved for trees of the genus *Cedrus*.

[2] Most tree seeds, except those requiring severe treatment, germinate in the spring if sown the fall before. For seed sown in the spring, stratification may be necessary or will hasten or improve germination. The stratification process, mixing seed with moist sand or sand and peat moss and storing at cool temperatures, is a substitute for the conditions of overwintering. The following treatments are recommended to improve germination:

   (a) Stratify for 2–3 months at 33°–41° F.
   (b) Soak in concentrated nitric acid for ½–2 hours, then stratify for 3–5 months at 33°–41° F.
   (c) Stratify for 4 months at 33°–41° F.
   (d) Stratify for 2–4 months at 68°–80° F., then stratify for 2–4 months at 33°–41° F.
   (e) Scarify the seedcoat or soak the seed in concentrated sulfuric acid for 20–120 minutes.
   (f) Stratify for 1–2 months at 33°–41° F.

3 Approximate.

GLOSSARY

ABERRATION (ab-burr-*ay*-shun) A nontypical form or function. A straying from the normal. Some abnormality of an individual organism or part or of a biological happening.

ABNORMAL Unusual; away from the natural pattern.

ABORT (uh-*bort*) To fail in the early stages of formation. The development of the young seed may be stopped early in its growth; its cells collapse and largely disappear.

ABSCISSION (ab-*sizh*-un) Separation of plant parts from the main body of the plant, such as the dropping of leaves, flowers, fruits, or buds. Generally associated with the formation of a special layer of thin-walled cells called the abscission layer or zone.

ACCESSORY ORGANS Attached structures that may or may not contribute to the main function of the organ.

ACHENE (ay-*keen*) A small, dry, oneseeded fruit with a thin distinct wall that does not split open.

ACORN The nonsplitting, one-seeded fruit of the oak.

ACREABLE In terms of an acre, or per acre.

ADAPTATION (add-ap-*tay*-shun) The reaction of plants to environmental conditions. One kind may respond to some conditions of soil, site, or climate favorably while another kind does not.

ADVENTITIOUS (add-ven-*tish*-us) A descriptive term for a structure that arises in an unusual place, such as a bud that develops from areas of a plant other than the base of a leaf or a leaf scar.

ADVENTITIOUS EMBRYONY (add-ven-*tish*-us em-bree-*uh*-nec) The embryo origin from a somatic diploid cell of the nucellus or integuments by a series of somatic cell divisions.

AERATION (ay-er-*ay*-shun) Bringing air into a substance or tissue. Making air, and therefore oxygen, available to a material.

AGAR A gelatinous substance extracted from a seaweed such as certain red algae. It is an ingredient used in making culture media to study the growth characteristics of micro-organisms.

AGGREGATE FRUIT (*ag*-gre-gate) Fruit developed from several pistils in one flower, as in strawberry or blackberry.

ALBINO (al-*by*-no) An organism that lacks normal color; plants that are white because of a lack of chlorophyll and other colored substances.

ALKALOID (*al*-kah-loid) An organic, nitrogenous, basic substance derived from vegetable or animal sources. Some are now synthesized. Morphine, codeine, strychnine, and quinine are alkaloidal compounds important in medicine to relieve pain or to stimulate the central nervous system.

ALLOTETRAPLOID (al-lo-*teh*-trah-ployd) A plant of hybrid origin with two sets of chromosomes from one parent and two sets from the other parent. Although four sets of chromosomes are present, associations of three or four chromosomes are rarely found at meiosis since the chromosomes contributed by the two parents are dissimilar.

AMINO ACIDS (a-*me*-no) Organic acids containing one or more amino groups ($-NH_2$) and at least one carboxyl group ($-COOH$). In addition, some amino acids (cystine and methionine) contain sulfur. Many amino acids linked together in some definite pattern form a molecule of protein.

AMYLOSE (*am*-il-los) The straight chain fraction of normal starch. The starch of normal corn is made up of two molecular types; amylose (straight chain) and amylopectin (branched chain). In both starch types the basic units consist of the sugar glucose.

ANAEROBIC (an-air-*oh*-bick) Living or functioning in the absence of air or free oxygen. The opposite of aerobic.

ANDROGENESIS (an-dro-*jen*-eh-sis) Development in which the embryo contains only paternal chromosomes.

ANGIOSPERM (*an*-gee-oh-*sperm*) A kind of plant the seeds of which are formed within a fruit.

ANNUAL The kind of plant that normally starts from seed, produces its crop of flowers and fruits, or seeds, and then dies within one growing season.

ANTERIOR A position that is forward, before, or toward the front of an object.

ANTHER (*an*-ther) The saclike structure in which the pollen is formed in the flower. Anthers commonly have two lobes or cavities, which open by longitudinal slits or by terminal pores and release the pollen.

ANTHOCYANIN (an-tho-*sigh*-ah-nin) A water-soluble plant pigment that produces many of the red and blue colors of plants; for example, the red color of apples and the red and blue colors of many flowers.

ANTIPODAL NUCLEI (an-*tip*-o-dal *new*-klee-eye) Three of the eight nuclei that result from meiosis or sexual cell division in the female organ of seed-bearing plants. They are usually in the base of the embryo sac, contain one member of each pair of chromosomes, and in most plants have no known function.

APEX Extreme point or distal end.

ARCHESPORIAL (ahr-keh-*spo*-ree-ul) Refers to the differentiated cell situated in the nucellar tissue of the ovule which is destined to undergo meiosis and give rise to the haploid generation.

ARIL A loose, fleshy bag that encloses the seed, as in the white waterlily and yew.

ASEXUAL (a-*sex*-shu-al) Nonsexual; denotes reproduction by purely vegetative means, or without the function of the two sexes.

AUTOTETRAPLOID (aw-to-*teh*-trah-ployd) A plant with double the usual number of chromosomes. Each specific chromosome is present four times and multiple associations are found at meiosis.

AUXINS (*awk*-sins) Any of several substances found in plants that may stimulate cell growth, root development, and so on.

AWN A slender bristle, such as the "beards" of wheat or rye.

AXILLARY (ax-*sill*-a-ree) Pertaining to the angle between the leaf and the stem.

BACKCROSS A plant obtained by crossing two plants that have different characters is a hybrid. Pollen of the hybrid used on either parent, or pollen from either parent used on the hybrid, produces a backcross generation.

BACTERIOPHAGE A viral agent that produces a dissolution of specific bacterial cells. Bacteriophage agents will only multiply in actively multiplying cells. Cells parasitized by phage seem to swell, burst, and disintegrate, liberating large numbers of phage particles.

BERRY A simple, fleshy, or pulpy and usually many-seeded fruit, that has two or more compartments and does not burst open to release its seeds when ripe.

BIENNIAL The kind of plant that produces vegetative growth during the first year or growing season. After a period of storage or overwintering out of doors, flowers, fruits, and seeds are produced during the second year, and the plant dies.

BIOCHEMISTRY The chemistry of life; the branch of chemistry that is concerned with biological organisms and processes.

BOLT Formation of an elongated stem or seedstalk. In the case of biennial plants, this generally occurs the second season of growth.

BROADLEAF Used in weed terminology to designate a broad group of nongrasslike plants.

BUD A plant structure that contains an undeveloped shoot or flower.

BUDDING The process of transferring a live bud from one plant to another, usually by insertion under the bark. Also, the plant process of forming buds.

BULB An enlarged, fleshy, thick, underground part of a stem surrounded by a mass of leafy scales. Scales of a bulb are actually thickened and shortened leaves. Roots develop from the base of a bulb. The lily is an example.

BULBIL   A small bulb produced above ground usually in the axil of a leaf. Sometimes spelled "bulbel."

BULBLET   Usually refers to a small underground bulb formed on a parent stem.

CALLUS   A hard or thickened layer at the base of certain grass seeds (florets).

CALLUS TISSUE   A shapeless, noncorky mass of cell growth that develops from a wounded or cut surface of a stem or root.

CALYX   (*kay*-licks)   All of the sepals of the flower; forms part of the covering of some seed.

CAMBIAL TISSUE   (*cam*-bee-ul)   The layer of cells found between the bark and the wood that gives rise to new growth. It consists of a very thin layer of cells, which normally may give rise later to either bark or wood.

CAMBIUM   (*cam*-bee-um)   A layer of cells in a stem between the bark and the wood in which cell division (resulting in lateral growth) occurs.

CARBON DIOXIDE   A gaseous compound that is formed when carbon combines with oxygen. It leaves the body chiefly when air is exhaled from the lung.

CARBON-14   One of several isotopes of the chemical element carbon. (*See* Isotope.) It is somewhat radioactive; this activity decreases very slowly with time. Carbon-14 occurs in very small, and varying, amounts in all organisms and in all organic material containing carbon. In a complicated chemical and electronic apparatus, the carbon-14 content can be used to date approximately ancient organic materials. The common isotope of carbon, carbon-12, which accounts for about 99 percent of the carbon in nature, emits no radiation.

CAROTENE   A yellow compound of carbon and hydrogen that occurs in plants, a precursor of vitamin A. Alpha, beta, and gamma carotenes may be converted into vitamin A in the body.

CARPEL   (*car*-pell)   The ovule-containing receptacle of a pistil.

CARUNCLE   (*care*-unk-l)   An outgrowth or thick appendage of the testa or outer seed-coat, as in the seed of the castor-oil plant.

CARYOPSIS   (care-e-*op*-sis)   A one-seeded fruit with the pericarp and seedcoat fused into one covering, as in corn and other grains.

CATABOLISM   (ka-*tab*-o-lism)   The breaking down in the body of chemical compounds into simpler ones, usually accompanied by the production of heat.

CATALYZE   (*kat*-ah-lies)   To induce or accelerate a chemical reaction by a substance that remains unchanged in the process.

CELL   The basic structural unit of living organisms. It is comprised of protoplasm enclosed, in plants, in a cell wall. The protoplasm consists of a nucleus and a semifluid matrix, the cytoplasm, which contains plastids and many other smaller bodies. Mature plant cells usually contain a large cavity or vacuole filled with a water solution of sugars, salts, acids, and other substances.

CENTRIFUGE   (*sen*-tri-fewj)   An apparatus that is used to spin liquids in a circular motion at high rates of speed. Particles that are suspended in a liquid medium can be separated according to their density, the heavier particles collecting at the outer rim of the circle and the less dense ones collecting in layers toward the center.

CENTROMERE   (*sen*-tro-mere)   A short segment or region of the chromosome to which the spindle fiber appears to be attached when the chromosomes are separating during cell division. In stained preparations, this region is unstained. It is the last portion of the chromosome to divide during the process of chromatids formation; however, it precedes the remainder of the new chromosome during its migration to the spindle pole.

CEREALS   Members of the grass family in which the seed is the most important part used for food and feed.

CHARACTER   An identifiable hereditary property, such as a specific component of color, a structural detail, a color pattern, or resistance to disease.

CHLOROPHYLL   (*klor*-oh-fill)   The light-absorbing pigment in plants that gives them a green color. The absorption of light by chlorophyll is the first step in the manufacture of carbohydrates from carbon dioxide and water.

CHROMATID   (*kro*-ma-tid)   A half chromosome during early stages of cell division when it is still joined to its sister chromatid. After the half chromosomes separate, the chromatids are known as daughter chromosomes. Subdivisions of chromatids are called chromonemata. They are the forerunners of chromatids in the succeeding cell division.

CHROMATIN   (*kro*-ma-tin)   The chemical carrier of inheritance. It is the complex protein material within a cell which functions in cell multiplication to reproduce identical "daughter" cells. The material readily absorbs some dyes. In prepared microscope slides of multiplying cells, chromatin is commonly the most deeply stained portion of the protoplasm within the nucleus.

CHROMATOGRAPHY (kro-ma-*tog*-ra-fe) A method for the separation of compounds from one another. Separation is accomplished as a result of the movement of compounds at different rates in a solvent allowed to flow very slowly through a porous medium, such as paper.

CHROMOMERES (*kro*-mo-mere) Granules of protoplasm occurring along the chromosome thread. They are visible during early stages of cell division and are frequently thought of as the beads on a string that comprises the chromosome. The granules may be accumulations of nucleic acids and, in this event, actually comprise the gene. On the other hand, they may be expressions of different patterns of coiling along the chromosome thread.

CHROMOSOME (*kro*-mo-soam) A rodlike body contained in the nucleus of the plant cell; the bearer of the hereditary material. (Adjective: chromosomal.)

CLIMAX The final stage and condition of equilibrium of vegetation after a series of progressional stages which have developed, without serious interruption, under the influence of a given complex of environmental factors.

CLONE A group of individuals of common ancestry which have been propagated vegetatively, usually by cuttings or natural multiplication of bulbs or tubers.

COLCHICINE (*kol*-chi-seen) An alkaloid produced by the autumn crocus. It is commonly used to induce doubling of the number of chromosomes in the nuclei of plant cells.

COLEOPTILE (*koh*-lee-*op*-tile) A sheathlike leaf of grasses and other monocotyledons that protects the delicate growing point as it emerges from the soil.

COLUMELLA (col-yew-*mell*-a) An elongated floral axis that supports the carpels in certain plants.

COMA (*koh*-mah) A tuft of hairs attached to a seed.

COMPANION CROP A crop grown with another to secure an earlier or larger return than from one crop alone.

COMPOSITE MIXTURE Breeder seed obtained by mechanically combining seed from two or more strains. The mixture is increased through successive steps in a certified seed program and distributed as a synthetic variety.

CONIFER (*konn*-i-fur) A species of plant that bears its seeds in cones, such as a pine tree.

CORM Similar to a bulb, but the stem part is much thicker and broader and the scales form only a thin layer and represent a small part of the bulk. Gladiolus is an example.

CORN In American terminology, *Zea mays*, or Indian corn; includes sweet corn, popcorn, and field types. The word is so used in this book. In Old World terminology, "corn" may mean almost any of the Old World cereal grains.

COTYLEDON (*kot*-e-*lee*-done) Seed leaves of the embryo. Usually they are thickened for storage of reserve food. They may serve as true foliage leaves.

CROSS-FERTILIZE To fertilize the ovule or ovules of one flower with the pollen from another flower; commonly refers to the fertilizing of ovules of flowers of one plant by pollen from another plant.

CROSSOVER UNIT A measurement of the degree of linkage between two genes. It is expressed in percentages. Crossing over is the interchange of corresponding segments between two homologous chromosomes before the formation of sex cells. When the terminal portion of a segmental interchange occurs between linked genes, the association between them is broken. The frequency of such occurrence is a function of nearness of the genes. The crossover units separating two genes is equivalent to the percentage of sex cells in which the association has been broken through segmental interchange.

CROSS-POLLINATE To apply pollen of one flower to the stigma of another; commonly refers to the pollinating of the flowers of one plant by pollen from another plant.

CRUCIFEROUS (croos-*if*-er-us) Pertaining to plants in the family Cruciferae. These are tap-rooted plants with four sepals and four petals arranged in crosses. They include such crop plants as radish, turnip, mustard, rape, and the many cabbagelike crops.

CRYPTOXANTHIN (crip-toe-*zan*-thin) $C_{40}H_{56}O$, a yellow carotenoid pigment in plant parts similar to xanthophyll. It functions as a provitamin A to some extent.

CUTINIZE (*kew*-tin-ize) To impregnate a cell or a cell wall with cutin—a complex fatty or waxy substance—which makes the cell more or less impervious to air and moisture.

CYTOPLASM (*sie*-toe-plasm) The contents of a cell outside the nucleus or chromosome-bearing portion. In reproduction, the male parent normally contributes only chromosomes, whereas both nuclear and cytoplasmic constituents from the female parent become a part of the offspring.

CYTOPLASMIC MALE STERILITY A type of male sterility conditioned by the cytoplasm rather than by nuclear genes and transmitted only through the female parent.

DAMPING-OFF A disease of seeds or young seedlings caused by fungi. The disease is most evident in young seedlings that topple over and die just after they emerge from the soil (postemergence damping-off). Two other types of damping-off are often mistaken for poor seed rather than disease: Germination failure, in which a seed is invaded in the early stages of germination and fails to sprout; and preemergence damping-off, in which the young seedling is attacked before it pushes its way through the surface of the soil.

DAYLENGTH The number of hours of light in each 24-hour cycle.

DECORTICATION Removal of the pith and bark from fibrous other tissues. Generally, this is a mechanical process.

DEFOLIANT (dee-*foe*-lee-ant) A chemical or method of treatment that causes only the leaves of a plant to fall off or abscise. The fruits remain attached.

DEGENERATION The progressive decrease in vigor of successive generations of plants, usually caused by unfavorable growing conditions or diseases. Virus diseases cause great loss of vigor.

DEHISCENCE (dee-*hiss*-cents) The bursting open at maturity of a pod or capsule along a definite line or lines.

DESICCATE (DESICCATOR) (*des*-ik-kate, *des*-ik-kat-er) To dry thoroughly; to remove moisture from an object definitely below the normal level. A desiccator is a laboratory apparatus for thoroughly drying substances. It commonly consists of a glass container with an airtight lid. The drying agent, a desiccant, is placed in the container with the material to be desiccated. The desiccant absorbs water and water vapor very strongly and literally takes most of the water away from the material being dried.

DETASSEL To remove the tassel or pollen-producing organ at the top of a corn plant before pollen is released.

DIAPAUSE (*die*-a-pause) In insects, a state during which growth and development is temporarily arrested. Exposure to low temperature is frequently but not always required to permit the resumption of these processes.

DICOT (dye-kot) A short synonym of dicotyledonous plant, the term refers to plants which have two seed leaves in the seed. Dicot stems always have definite wood and bark layers, and the leaf veins are branched.

DIFFERENTIATION OF CELLS (dif-er-*en*-shi-*ay*-shun) The development of specialized kinds of cells from nonspecialized cells in a growing tissue.

DIFFUSIBLE (dih-*fuze*-ih-bul) Able to spread through a system.

DIMER ACID (*die*-mer) A chemical compound in which two fatty acid molecules are combined to form a single molecule.

DIOECIOUS (die-*eesh*-us) Having stamens and pistils on different plants. The plants are unisexual; therefore both sexes must be grown near each other to produce fruit, as in American holly.

DIPLOID (dip-loid) A plant with two sets of chromosomes.

DIPLOSPORY (*dip*-plo-*spo*-ree) The formation of a diploid egg cell as a result of failure of the egg mother cell to undergo normal reduction division.

DISPERSAL (diss-*per*-sal) Spreading or scattering.

DISTAL END The part of a fruit, leaf, tuber, or root farthest from its connection with the plant bearing it.

DOMESTICATE To convert a wild plant species into a cultivated crop by selection and adaption.

DOMINANT FACTOR A hereditary factor or gene possessed by one parent of a hybrid which causes a character to be manifested in the hybrid to the apparent or near exclusion of the contrasted (recessive) character in the other parent.

DORMANCY An internal condition of the chemistry or stage of development of a viable seed that prevents its germination although good growing temperature and moisture are provided; also applied to buds.

DORMANT In a state of dormancy, a resting state that must be "broken" by time or special conditions before a seed will germinate at temperatures and moisture levels suitable for growth; applies also to buds.

DOUBLE CROSS The type of hybrid corn most commonly grown. It is the result of mating two pairs of inbred lines to produce two single crosses which are then mated to produce a double cross.

DRUPE   One-seeded stone fruit, as cherry, plum, and peach.

DRY MATTER   The substance in a plant or plant material remaining after oven drying to a constant weight at a temperature slightly above the boiling point of water.

ECOLOGY   (e-*kol*-o-gee)   The study of living organisms in relation to environment and their effects upon one another. The major classes of environmental factors relate to climate, physiography, soil, and associated organisms. Autecology is the study of the ecology of a single species. Synecology is the study of communities and associations of organisms.

ECOTYPE   (*ek*-oh-type)   A variety or strain within a given species adapted to a particular environment.

ELECTRON MICROSCOPE   An instrument that permits magnification of particles up to 200,000 diameters. Instead of having the specimen exposed to a light source, as with the standard light microscope, a stream of electrons is directed on the object. The higher resolving power of the electron microscope is largely the result of the shorter wavelength associated with electrons. The electrons are accelerated in a high vacuum through electromagnetic lenses and focused on the specimen. They are then projected on a fluorescent screen where the image of the particle may be viewed or onto a photographic plate.

EMBRYO   (*em*-bry-oh)   The rudimentary plant within the seed.

EMBRYONIC   (*em*-bry-*ahn*-ik)   Relating to, or like, an embryo; also used to denote an early or incomplete stage of development of anything.

EMERGENCE   (ih-*mer*-gents)   Issuing from a place or state.

ENDOCARP   (*en*-do-carp)   Inner layer of the fruit wall.

ENDOSPERM   (*en*-do-sperm)   The tissue of seeds, developing from fertilization of the polar nuclei of the ovule by the second male nucleus, that nourishes the embryo.

ENERGY   The capacity to do work. The energy stored in living cells as food material is released by respiration for use in growth.

ENVIRONMENT   (enn-*vie*-ron-ment)   Surroundings. A plant's environment includes the air, soil, amount of moisture, light, and temperature.

ENZYME   (*en*-zim)   A catalyst produced in living matter. It is a specialized protein capable of aiding in bringing about chemical changes. It promotes a reaction without itself being changed or destroyed.

EPICOTYL   (*epp*-e-cott-l)   The growing point of the embryo, which gives rise to the shoot, or aboveground part of the plant.

EPIDERMAL   (*epp*-e-*derm*-l)   Relating to the epidermis, or outer layer of cells. Epidermal cells usually have thickened outer walls to protect plants against drying and mechanical injury.

EVOLUTIONARY   Orderly, developmental change, usually in a definite direction.

EXOCARP   (*ex*-o-karp)   Outermost layer of the fruit wall.

EXOGENOUS   (ex-*odge*-jen-us)   Refers to a characteristic circular arrangement of plant stem parts including cambium, bark, and wood. All dicots have this arrangement of tissues.

F_1 Denotes the first generation offspring coming from the mating of two parents.

F_1 HYBRID   The first generation resulting from a cross mating of distinctly different parental types.

FAR-RED LIGHT   The radiant energy near the long wavelength side of the visible spectrum between 7,000 A and 7,500 A or 700 and 750 mμ. This is the place in the spectrum where the average eye begins to fail to detect radiation.

FASCIATED   (*fash*-ee-a-ted)   The condition whereby two or more stem growing points develop to form one broad flat stem rather than two or more single rounded stems.

FASCICLE   (*fas*-ih-kul)   A bundle of needles on a tree, as on pine or larch.

FAT   A glyceryl ester of fatty acids. Fats generally are substances of plant and animal origin. Fat may be in solid form, as butter, margarine, lard, or other shortening, or in liquid form, as the vegetable oils.

FATTY ACID   Organic compound of carbon, hydrogen, and oxygen, which combines with glycerol to make a fat.

FERMENTATION   (fer-men-*ta*-shun)   Chemical transformation induced by the activity of the enzyme systems of micro-organisms. Yeast enzymes produce carbon dioxide and alcohol from sugar. In breadmaking, the carbon dioxide causes dough to rise. Organic substances are fermented by bacteria, molds, and yeasts to a wide variety of products such as antibiotics, vitamins, food, and feeds.

FIBRIL (*fie*-bril) A small thread or very fine fiber. Normally a fiber is constituted of a bundle of fibrils.

FILAMENT The stalk that supports the anther in the flower. The filament and anther together make up the stamen.

FIRST-GENERATION HYBRID Same as F_1 hybrid.

FLORET (*flor*-et) A little flower. In grasses the floret consists of the small, inconspicuous flower with its small greenish bracts, the lemma and palea.

FLORIGEN (*flo*-ri-jen) The hormone or hormones produced by plants that causes them to change from the vegetative to the flowering or reproductive state.

FLUORESCENT (*flew*-oh-*rehs*-sent) A substance is fluorescent when upon receiving radiation it emits radiation of its own of a wavelength either the same as or different from the incident light.

FORAGE Feed from plants for livestock, such as hay, pasturage, straw, silage, and browse.

FOUNDATION PLANTING The first seed increase from the initial seed stock (breeder seed) provided by the originating agency in a recognized seed-certification program.

FOUNDATION SEED A primary source of seed of a genetically identified variety from which all increases are made.

FREESTONE A descriptive term used in relation to drupaceous fruits such as peaches, cherries, and plums to indicate that the fruit flesh does not adhere to the stone or pit containing the seed at maturity.

FRUIT (FRUITS) A fruit is a ripened (matured) ovary of a plant, together with any intimately attached parts that developed with it from the flower.

FUNGICIDE A chemical that kills or inhibits fungi. Bordeaux mixtures, ferbam, and zineb are fungicides.

FUNICULUS (few-*nick*-you-luss) The stalk by which a seed or ovule is attached to the ovary.

GAMETOPHYTE (ga-*meet*-o-fite) The part of the plant that produces gametes, or sex cells.

GEL (jel) A solid form of colloidal suspension. The process of changing certain liquid colloidal systems to a jellylike state can be achieved by cooking, like the white of an egg, or by cooling, like gelatin desserts.

GELATINOUS Thick, jellylike, somewhat sticky.

GENERA (*jenn*-er-ah) Plural of *genus*.

GENE (jeen) The unit of inheritance. The physical basis of heredity. It governs, controls, affects or conditions the transmission and development of one or more hereditary characters or traits. Its effect on a character is frequently conditioned by its interaction with other genes, the cytoplasm, and environmental factors. Genes are arranged in linear order in the chromosome. Chemically, the gene is thought to be composed of deoxyribonucleic acid, a highly complex, giant, organic, double helix molecule. Structurally this molecule is thought to consist of two spirally rising chains of linked atomic groups (five-carbon sugar molecules, called deoxyribose, alternating with phosphate groups) and a series of horizontal members or links (pairs of basic molecules) connecting the two spirals. Many viruses, which may be closely related to genes, also seem to be comprised of bundles of such molecules.

GENETICS The science that deals with the mechanisms of heredity.

GENIC BALANCE The numerical ratio of the different kinds of chromosomes and hence of genes. If each specific chromosome is present in the same number as the rest of the chromosome set, the plant is called a euploid, while plants with numerical differences are called aneuploids.

GENIC STERILITY A type of male sterility conditioned by nuclear genes. In contrast to cytoplasmic sterility it may be transmitted by either the male or female parent.

GENOMIC (jee-*no*-mick) Pertains to genome that refers to chromosome set.

GENOTYPE (*jen*-oh-tipe) The hereditary makeup of an individual plant or animal, which, with the environment, controls the individual's characteristics, such as type of flower or bony structure or shape of leaf or color of hair.

GERM PLASM The living stuff of the cell nucleus that determines the hereditary properties of organisms and that transmits these properties from parent to progeny. The expression is also used in a broad sense in referring to the total hereditary makeup of organisms. For example, geneticists and plant breeders often refer to the seeds and plants used in their research and breeding as their "collections of germ plasm."

GERMINATION The resumption of growth by the embryo and development of a young plant from the seed.

GERMINATIVE (*ger*-min-a-tive) Having the ability to grow and develop.

GIBBERELLINS (GIBBERELLIC ACID) (*jib*-er-*ell*-ens) Plant growth-stimulating chemicals produced by a fungus, *Gibberella fujikuroi*, that attacks rice, causing the stems to elongate so rapidly that they become spindly and the plants fall down. Japanese scientists found that the fungus would produce gibberellins when grown in nutrient culture. Their chemists isolated three compounds and designated them as gibberellin A_1, A_2 and A_3. British scientists later produced plant responses. Commercial preparations are available and may consist of a mixture of gibberellin A_1 and A_3 or pure gibberellic acid (A_3). The gibberellins induce many different plant effects, such as rapid stem growth, overcoming of dormancy, production of seedless (parthenocarpic) fruits, and other responses.

GIRDLING (GIRDLE) Removing a band of or cutting through the outside bark and the thin layer of cambium just underneath the bark.

GLAND Organs or swellings that usually secrete a watery or characteristic substance. Many oily and aromatic products are glandular in origin.

GLOMERATE (*glahm*-er-ate) A compact cluster forming a round mass.

GRAFT The act of transferring a piece of stem, with buds attached, to another plant, placing cambium layers adjacent so that union will occur.

GYMNOSPERM (*jim*-no-sperm) A kind of plant that produces seeds but no fruits. Since the seeds are not borne within an ovary, they are said to be naked—hence the name.

HARD SEEDS Seeds that have a seedcoat impervious to water or oxygen required for germination. Sometimes overcome by scratching or scarifying the coat or removal by brief immersion in concentrated sulfuric acid and thorough washing.

HEAT UNIT A calculated amount of heat. It consists of one degree of temperature above an arbitrary level for a duration of an hour or other time interval. The day-degree above a daily mean of 50° F. is commonly used as a heat unit in studying response of certain plants to temperature. The base level above which units are computed differs for different kinds of plants.

HEMICELLULOSE (hem-eh-*sell*-you-lohse) Cell wall compounds similar in appearance to cellulose, but more easily broken down to simple sugars. Common forms contain galactose and arabinose or glucose and xylose as well as other substances.

HERBACEOUS (her-*bay*-shus) Nonwoody, as applied to kinds of plant growth.

HERBICIDE (*herb*-i-side) A chemical or mixture of chemicals for killing plants by application to the plants or to the soil.

HEREDITARY (heh-*red*-ih-tare-y) Transmissible from parent to offspring or progeny.

HERITABLE Capable of being passed by inheritance.

HETEROFERTILIZATION (*hett*-ur-oh-*fur*-til-i-*zay*-shun) The fertilization of the egg and polar nuclei by sperm cells from different pollen tubes.

HETEROPLASTIC (*hett*-ur-oh-*plass*-tick) Refers to grafting or transplanting of tissue between two unrelated plants, especially plants of a different genus or species.

HETEROZYGOUS (*hett*-ur-oh-*zie*-gus) Not true-breeding for a specific hereditary character. A plant that does not breed true for flower color is called heterozygous for this character. Plants may be heterozygous for some characters and homozygous for others.

HIGH-AMYLOSE CORN A special type of corn that has starch with a greater than normal percentage of the straight chain starch component, amylose.

HILUM (*high*-lum) The scar left on the seed at the place of detachment from its base or seed stalk.

HOMOLOGOUS CHROMOSOMES (ho-*mol*-o-gus *kro*-mo-soms) The members of a pair of chromosomes that occur in all but the sex cells of the higher plants. Such members are structurally similar but may vary greatly as to the hereditary potential of genes carried in the chromosomes. When the embryo was formed, one member was contributed by the male and the other by the female sex cells.

HOMOZYGOUS (ho-mo-*zi*-gus) True-breeding for a specific hereditary character. A plant that breeds true for a character such as flower color is called homozygous for this character. Plants may be true breeding (homozygous) for some characters and not for others.

HORMONE (*hor*-moan) A chemical substance that is produced in one part of a plant and induces a growth response in another part, generally at extremely low concentration of the chemical.

HOST An organism, as a plant, that harbors a parasite such as a disease-producing fungus or an insect that feeds upon it.

HUMECTANT (hu-*mek*-tant) A material with a high water-attracting capacity. When added to other materials that lose water too readily, it retards loss of moisture and retains freshness. Humectants are used in tobacco, cosmetics, and some foods to stabilize moisture content.

HURL The straight, fine, smooth broomcorn structures used for the outer covering of a broom.

HYBRID VIGOR The increase in vigor over the parental types exhibited by hybrids. This increase is at a maximum in the first generation and decreases by approximately one-half in each succeeding generation of inbreeding.

HYGROSCOPIC (*high*-grow-scah-pick) Easily takes up moisture, even from water vapor in the air.

HYPHAE (*high-fee*) Threadlike strands, or filaments, that constitute the body (mycelia) of fungi. They may be divided into cells by crosswalls (septate) or be one elongated cell with several nuclei (nonseptate), coarse or fine, aerial or submerged, stiff or flexible, and exhibit different types of branching. Some hyphae are specialized for producing spores or for penetrating host tissues.

HYPOCOTYL (*high*-po-*cot*-l) The part of the axis of the embryo that gives rise to the root system of the young plant.

IMBIBE (im-*bibe*) To take up water by absorption.

IMBIBITION (*im*-bi-*bih*-shun) The taking up of liquid by absorption. In seed germination, the taking up of water by the seed from a moist medium in preparation for germination.

IMPERMEABLE (im-*per*-me-uh-bull) Impenetrable, as when a seedcoat allows no passage through of water or gases.

INBRED Successively self-fertilized; also, a plant or progeny resulting from successive self-fertilization.

INBREEDING Successively self-fertilizing a breeding line or stock through a number of generations.

INCREASE To multiply a quantity of seed by planting it, rearing the plants that grow from it, and harvesting the seeds they produce. The seeds resulting from this process also are called an increase.

INDEHISCENT (in-dee-*hiss*-cent) Not splitting open when ripe.

INDEXING Refers to the process used to test vegetatively reproduced plants for freedom from virus diseases before multiplying them.

INFLORESCENCE (in-flow-*res*-enz) The flowering axis or other specialized flowering structure of a plant, such as an umbel, raceme, spike, tassel, and panicle.

INHERITABLE Capable of being transmitted from parents to offspring.

INHIBIT (in-*hib*-it) To prevent or restrain.

INHIBITOR (in-*hib*-i-tor) A chemical substance that acts to prevent a process from occurring. Many chemicals, both natural and artificial, can act to prevent seed germination.

INHIBITORY (in-*hib*-i-tor-ee) Property of blocking or checking a process or reaction.

INOCULUM (in-*ok*-you-lum) Material, as spores, bacteria, etc., used for infecting a plant with a disease or for propagating microorganisms in controlled cultures.

INTEGUMENT (in-*teg*-you-ment) The tissue covering and surrounding the ovule. When the ovule matures, it becomes part of the seedcoat.

INTERNODE (*in*-ter-node) The portion of a plant stem between the places (nodes) from which the leaves grow.

INTERVARIETAL (in-ter-vah-*rye*-e-tal) Between two varieties.

IRRADIANCE (ear-*ray*-dee-ants) Radiation (usually meaning light) received by an object.

ISOLATE (*i*-so-late) To remove from the plant in pure form.

ISOTOPE (*eye*-soh-tope) Elemental substances having identical chemical properties, but somewhat differing atomic weights. Most of the common chemical elements have been shown to consist of a mixture of two or more isotopes. Isotopes of any one element have the same number of extra-nuclear electrons, and the same nuclear charge, but have differing nuclear masses. Today there is major interest in radioisotopes. These are basic elements that emit radioactive particles or radiations that can be detected by electronic apparatus or photographic-type film. Radioisotopes of carbon, iodine, cobalt, phosphorus, and others are now widely used in plant and animal research to study translocation of chemicals and how they react in the tissue systems.

LANOLIN (*lann*-o-lin) The fatty substance removed from sheep wool when it is scoured and cleaned. When refined, it is used extensively in cosmetics and provides a nontoxic carrier for applying plant regulators or other chemicals to the surface of plants.

LARVA The wormlike immature form of certain insects. Some are commonly called caterpillars, grubs, or maggots.

LATERAL (*lat*-er-ul) Located on or developing from the side, as a bud located on the side of a shoot.

LEAFSTALK A petiole; the footstalk or supporting stalk of a leaf.

LEGUME A plant which is a member of the Leguminosae family. These plants have the characteristic of forming nitrogen-fixing nodules. Beans and peas are examples. Also the characteristic dry, dehiscent multiseeded pod or fruit of members of this family.

LEGUMINOUS (le-*gew*-mi-nuss) Pertaining to the pea family.

LEMMA (*lem*-muh) The small greenish bract that is part of the floret in grasses.

LETHAL (*lee*-thul) So detrimental as to cause death.

LIGNIFY (LIGNIFICATION) (*lig*-ni-fie, *lig*-ni-fi-*cay*-shun) To make woody. The thickening, hardening, and strengthening of plant cells by the deposition of lignin on and in the walls of plant cells. Lignin is a complex strengthening material which chemically shows both phenolic and alcoholic characteristics.

LINEAR (*lin*-e-er) Narrow and long. Genes are said to have a linear arrangement as they are thought to occur as in a line along the chromosome.

LINKAGE Association of genes (hereditary factors) in inheritance because they are located in the same chromosome.

LOCUS (*lo*-kus) The fixed position or location of a gene on or in the chromosome.

LONGEVITY (lon-*jev*-eh-tee) Length of life. In a strict sense, the length or period of life-span, but commonly applied only to longer-than-average duration of life for the organism or material being considered.

LYSE To destroy or disorganize cells by enzymes, viruses, or certain other means.

MACERATE (*mass*-er-ayt) To finely divide and separate, as to separate seeds from fruits, either fleshy or dry, by softening and wearing away the nonseed parts.

MACROBIOTIC (*mak*-roh-bie-*aht*-ic) *Macro-:* long or large; and *biotic:* relating to life. Therefore, that which is long lived.

MAIZE (mayze) Indian corn, *Zea mays;* in America, more commonly called corn.

MALE STERILE Producing no functional pollen.

MALPIGHIAN LAYER (mal-*pig*-i-an) A protective layer or layers of cells present in the coats of many seeds. It is characteristically made up of close-packed, radially placed, heavy-walled, columnar cells without intercellular spaces. The cells often are heavily cutinized or lignified and are relatively impervious to moisture and gases.

MEDIUM (MEDIA) The supporting substance on or in which plants, fungi, and bacteria are cultured or grown. The term usually includes the nutrients as well.

MEGASPORE (*meg*-a-spor) One of the four cells that are formed in the ovule of higher plants as a result of meiosis, or sexual cell division. Megaspores contain only one member of each pair of homologous chromosomes. The enlarged cell which gives rise to the megaspores is known as the megaspore mother cell.

MEIOSIS (mye-*oh*-sis) Cell division, in which whole chromosomes pair; the members of each pair separate and pass to daughter cells, resulting in halving the chromosome number.

MEMBRANE (*mem*-brain) A thin, soft, pliable sheet or layer or the outer surface of a body of protoplasm.

MERISTEM (*mer*-i-stem) Undifferentiated tissue comprised of cells capable of undergoing cell division.

MERISTEMATIC CELLS (mer-i-ste-*mat*-ik) Plant cells that have not undergone differentiation to fit a pattern of special uses. In most cases, such cells are young cells that later develop into highly specialized tissues, such as the epidermis, transporting vessels, or sex cells.

MESOBIOTIC (*meh*-zoh-beye-*aht*-ic) *Meso-:* middle; and *biotic:* relating to life. Sometimes used in a series of longevity terms, between macrobiotic and microbiotic, to designate an average or intermediate age.

MESOCARP (*mez*-oh-karp) Middle layer of the fruit wall.

METABOLISM (me-*tab*-o-liz'm) The chemical changes within a cell that provide the energy required by a plant or animal. It embraces both constructive and destructive changes— the processes involved in the building up of protoplasm and its destruction as required for the processes that generate life.

MICROBIOTIC (*my*-crow-by-*aht*-ic) *Micro-:* small; and *biotic:* relating to life. Therefore, that which is short lived.

MICROPYLE (*my*-crow-pile) The pore or opening through which the pollen tube enters the embryo sac during the fertilization process.

MICROSOME (*my*-crow-some) A submicroscopic particle, approximately 0.05–0.2 micron (1/500,000–1/125,000 inch) in diameter, which can be isolated from living cells. Present knowledge suggests that these particles contain the enzymes that synthesize proteins.

MICROSPORE (*my*-crow-spor) The cells that develop into pollen grains. They arise through sexual cell division (meiosis) from the microspore mother cell in the anther of higher plants. Microspores contain only one member of each pair of homologous chromosomes.

MITOCHONDRIA (*my*-toe-chon-dria) Microscopic structures, which may be spherical or rod-shaped, approximately 0.5–2.0 microns (1/50,000–1/12,500 inch) in diameter, present in living cells. These particles contain organized groups of enzymes, which carry on the respiration and possibly other processes of cells.

MITOSIS (my-*toe*-sis) The division of a cell in which each chromosome splits longitudinally; the halves pass to daughter cells, each of which is identical to the original.

MITOTIC (my-*tot*-ick) Pertaining to mitosis.

MOLECULE (*mol*-e-kule) The building block of matter. The smallest portion of a compound or element that is of the same chemical identity as the mass. The molecule usually consists of two or more atoms and organic molecules, such as make up protoplasm, often contain hundreds of atoms.

MONOCOT (*mon*-o-kot) A short synonym of "monocotyledon"; it refers to plants that have single seed leaves. These plants have parallel veins in their leaves and no distinct bark and wood layers. Examples are bamboo and corn.

MONOECIOUS (moe-*neesch*-us) Having stamens and pistils in different flowers on the same plant, as in the watermelon.

MORPHOLOGY (mor-*fahl*-oh-gee) Form, structure, and development. Study of the form and structure of organisms, as opposed to the study of their chemistry and function.

MOTHER CELLS Special cells in anther and ovule that give rise to pollen and egg, the structures of sexual reproduction.

Mμ An abbreviation for millimicrons, a unit of length used to denote the wavelength of light. The visible spectrum extends from about 400 to 700 mμ.

MUCILAGINOUS (myu-sill-*laj*-i-nuss) Sticky.

MULTIPLE FRUIT Developed from a cluster of flowers on a common base, as in the fig.

MUTANT (*myoo*-tant) A plant or animal that differs from its normal or parent strain by virtue of an altered genetic characteristic.

MUTATE To change suddenly in genic constitution.

MUTATIONS New properties or characters that suddenly appear in an organism and that are not inherited from its parent; under some conditions they are transmissible to the progeny.

MYCELIUM (my-*see*-lee-um) The vegetative threadlike growth, which in fungi acts as food-taking structures for the fruiting body. (Adjective: mycelial.)

NECTAR A sweet liquid secreted by flowers attractive to insects. Bees make honey from the nectar of many flowers, and carry pollen to the pistil, thus aiding in seed formation.

NIACIN (*nye*-a-sin) One of the water-soluble vitamins of the B complex group. It is also known as nicotinic acid ($C_6H_5O_2N$) and is the precursor of the pellegra-preventing factor.

NICK The two parents for producing hybrid seed are said to nick when they produce high yields of seed of a highly productive and desirable hybrid.

NOBILIZATION A term used in the breeding of sugarcane to indicate repeated matings (backcrossing) to the "noble" canes, *Saccharum officinarum*.

NONALLELIC Two contrasting genes (hereditary factors) that occupy different corresponding positions on the two members of paired chromosomes.

NONSPECIFIC A substance or process with a number, instead of a single, of functions or actions.

NOXIOUS (*nok*-shuss) Injurious. A noxious weed is one that crowds out desirable crops, robs them of plant food and moisture, and causes extra labor in cultivation.

NUCELLUS (new-*cell*-us) Tissue in the central part of the ovule in which the embryo sac is embedded.

NUCLEIC ACID (new-*klee*-ik) Highly complex organic molecules found in the nucleus of cells. Deoxyribonucleic acid, for instance, is a giant molecule that is the chief component of chromosomes and many viruses. It is believed to be the substance that determines heredity and governs the behavior of all cells.

NUCLEUS (new-*kle*-us) The part of the plant cell bearing the chromosomes, carriers of hereditary units.

NUT A nonsplitting, one-seeded fruit, with a hard, woody shell.

NYMPH The immature stage of certain insects whose growing young resemble the parents in body form.

OCTOPLOID (*okk*-toe-ploid) A type possessing 8 repetitions of the basic haploid chromosome complement. Thus if the haploid number for a species were 10, the diploid number would be 20 and the octoploid number 80.

OFFSET A scaly bud or fleshy rosette of leaves borne on a short stem as an offshoot from the parent plant.

OFFTYPE Offtype plants in a seed field deviate in one or more characteristics from that which is usual in the strain being grown.

OPTIMAL (OPTIMUM) The most favorable.

ORGANIC ACID Contains only carbon, hydrogen, and oxygen. Among the best known organic acids are citric acid (in grapefruit, lemon, and orange juice) and acetic acid in vinegar.

ORGANISM A body or individual (a member of the animal or vegetable kingdom) exhibiting organization and organic life. The individual is composed of a number of essential and mutually dependent parts all of which partake of a common life. Bacteria and fungi are examples of micro-organisms.

OSMOTIC (ahs-*mot*-ick) Pertaining to the diffusion of substances through a membrane.

OUTCROSS The mating of a hybrid with a third parent; also an offtype plant resulting from pollen of a different sort contaminating a seed field.

OVARY The part of the pistil that contains the ovule or ovules; it ripens to form the fruit.

OVOID (*oh*-voyd) Egg-shaped.

OVULE The body within the ovary of the flower that becomes the seed after fertilization and development.

OXIDATIVE (*ox*-ih-day-tive) Refers to the processes of oxidation.

PALEA (*pay*-lee-uh) One of the greenish bracts that enclose the floret in grasses.

PALISADE LAYER (*pal*-i-sayd *lay*-er) In leaves, a somewhat compacted layer of elongated cells which underlie the upper epidermis with the long axis perpendicular to the leaf surface. In seeds, the term is used interchangeably with Malpighian layer. The term presumably derived originally from the resemblance of the palisade layer to a fence of stakes.

PAPPUS A tuft of delicate fibers or bristles at the tip of a tiny fruit, such as the feathery structure of the ripe dandelion seed that is easily blown from the head.

PARASITE One organism living on or within another (the host) and at the expense of the host. The host may or may not be destroyed in the process.

PARTHENOCARPIC (*par*-the-no-*karp*-ik) The production of fruit or a fruiting body without seeds. Examples are banana fruits, seedless grapefruit or oranges, and seedless grapes. This condition can sometimes be induced chemically by the use of plant growth regulators.

PARTS PER MILLION (Abbreviated p.p.m.) Designates the quantity of a substance contained in a million parts of a mixture or solution in a carrier, such as air or water.

PASMO (*pazz*-moe) A fungus disease of flax first observed as spots on any part of the plant above ground except the flowers. The spots may increase in size until several join together to form large irregular brownish areas. The causal organism is *Septoria linicola*.

PATHOGEN Any organism capable of causing disease in a particular host or range of hosts. It obtains its nutrients wholly or in part from another living organism.

PEDICEL (*ped*-ih-sell) Flower stalk.

PENTAPLOID (*pen*-tah-ployd) Having five chromosome sets.

PERENNIAL A plant that produces vegetative growth year after year without the necessity of replanting.

PERICARP (*per*-i-karp) The covering of a seed that is derived from the ovary wall. It may be thin and intimately attached to the seedcoat, as in a kernel of corn; fleshy, as in berries; or hard and dry, as in pods and capsules.

PETIOLE (*pett*-e-ohl) The stem of a leaf.

PHAGE-PLAQUE A clear area caused by a bacteriophage in a bacterial colony. The bacteriophage dissolves specific bacterial cells.

PHASE CONTRAST MICROSCOPE Permits the examination of living, transparent materials without resort to the usual staining procedures. Structural details, which often vary only slightly in thickness and refractive index, become visible by transformation of the phase changes of light passing through the object into corresponding variations of brightness.

PHENOMENON A fact, event, or experience that is sensed or observed.

PHLOEM (*flow*-em) Conductive tissue in higher plants through which food materials largely are transported from the leaves to the roots. The vessels through which the materials are actually conducted are called sieve tubes and are components of the phloem tissue.

PHOTOCHEMICAL Pertaining to a chemical reaction activated by light.

PHOTOPERIODISM (*foh*-toh-*peer*-ee-oh-dizm) The response of plants and animals to the relative lengths of the daily periods of light and darkness. (Adjective: photoperiodic.)

PHOTOREACTION A reaction that is initiated or hastened by light. (Adjective: photoreactive.)

PHOTORESPONSIVE Responds to or is affected by light.

PHOTOTHERMAL Pertaining to the combined effects of light and temperature.

PHYSIOLOGIC RACE Within certain groups of fungi, notably the rusts, smuts, and mildews, strains have originated which can attack or parasitize only certain specific host varieties. Individuals having the same parisitization pattern are said to belong to the same physiologic race. More than 200 physiologic races of stem rust of wheat have been described.

PHYTO- (*fi*-toe) A prefix meaning plant.

PHYTOTOXIC (*fie*-toe-*tox*-ik) Injurious to plant life or life processes.

PIGMENT (*pig*-ment) Substances that appear colored by virtue of differential absorption of radiant energy. These substances impart color to tissue of plants. Green color is a result of chlorophyll; orange and some red colors are due to many carotenoids; many red to blue colors are anthocyanins; light-yellow colors are flavones.

PISTIL (*pis*-till) The seed-bearing organ of the flower, composed of stigma, style, and ovary.

PLANT REGULATORS (growth regulators) Synthetic compounds prepared in the laboratory that induce growth responses in plants. Sometimes these responses are similar to those induced by chemicals produced by the plant itself which are true plant hormones. Plant-regulating chemicals have sometimes been mistakenly called plant hormones.

PLASTID (*plas*-tid) Small bodies or granules suspended in the cytoplasm of plant cells. Some contain pigments such as those of the chloroplasts which give the green color to plant leaves. Others contain starch or oil.

PLATED Placed on or in special media in a culture dish, usually in a petri dish, for study.

PLUMOSE (*ploo*-mohs) Feathery.

PLUMULE (*ploo*-mule) The major young bud of the embryo within a seed or seedling from which will develop the aerial portions of the plant. It usually occurs at the tip of a stemlike structure called the epicotyl, that part of the embryonic plant axis above the cotyledons.

POD A fruit that is dry and nonfleshy when ripe and splits open to release its seeds.

POLAR NUCLEI Two nuclei that fuse with a sperm cell to give rise to the endosperm, a nutritive tissue, of the seed.

POLLEN The more or less microscopic, usually yellow, bodies that are borne in the anthers of flowers and contain the male generative cells.

POLLEN PARENT The parent that furnishes the pollen which fertilizes the ovules of the other parent in the production of seed.

POLLEN TUBE A microscopic tube by which the sperm cells move to the embryo sac of the ovule.

POLLINATION (pol-lin-*a*-shun) The process by which pollen is transferred from an anther to the stigmatic surface of the pistil of a flower.

POLYAMIDE (*pol*-i-am-id) A polymer the units of which are linked together through bonds between carbon and nitrogen atoms. Nylon is a typical polyamide.

POLYMER (*pol*-i-mer) A large molecule formed by joining together small identical molecules. Polyethylene, the familiar squeeze-bottle plastic, is a polymer composed of linked units of ethylene, a gas.

POLYPLOIDY (*pol*-ly-ploid-dee) The condition in which more than two sets of homologous chromosomes are carried by the cells of a plant.

POSTERIOR (pos-*tear*-i-er) A position which is behind or to the back of an object.

PREEMERGENCE (pree-ee-*murj*-ence) Before emergence. Often refers to the treatment of the soil with weed-control chemicals after planting before the crop plants appear above ground.

PRIMITIVE Of simple derivation, or first in order of development.

PRIMORDIA (pry-*mor*-di-a) Organs in their earliest stage of development. The primordia that will develop into flowers, leaves, and stems are first visible as a dense group of cells in meristematic tissue. Later they assume the form characteristic of the organ.

PRIMORDIAL TISSUE Refers to the earliest or primary growth of a very young plant. In many plants the structure of primary growth differs from subsequent or secondary growth.

PROEMBRYO (pro-*em*-bree-o) The young embryo in the first stages of development.

PROGENY (*proj*-e-ny) Offspring. Plants grown from the seeds produced by parent plants.

PROTEIN (*pro*-te-in) An essential constituent of all living cells. Proteins occur naturally and are complex combinations of amino acids. Proteins always contain the elements carbon, hydrogen, oxygen, and nitrogen and sometimes sulfur and phosphorus.

PROTOPLASM (*pro*-to-plas-em) The essential, complex, living substance of cells, upon which all the vital functions of nutrition, secretion, growth, and reproduction depend.

PROTOTYPE (*pro*-toe-type) A pattern or original after which other objects are copies or are developed.

PROXIMAL END The end of a leaf, fruit, root, or shoot that grows closest to the stem that bears it.

PRUNE Remove vegetative parts of a plant to trim or shape it.

PSEUDOGAMOUS (soo-*dah*-gum-muss) Pertaining to pseudogamy or the type of apomixis where the diploid egg cell develops into the embryo without uniting with a sperm and fertilization of the polar nuclei is necessary for endosperm development and normal seed production.

PUBESCENCE (pyu-*bess*-cents) A hairy covering, usually of short, soft hairs.

PYCNIDIA (pik-*nid*-i-a) Globose or flasklike fungus fruiting bodies containing nonsexual spores (pycnidiospores). They are formed on the surface or more or less embedded in the tissue of the host and often open by a pore. The pycnidiospores are commonly extruded in mass or in whorls through the pore.

QUIESCENCE (kwee-*es*-ents) A state of no growth, of dormancy.

RACEME (ray-*seem*) A type of flower cluster in which single-flowered pedicels are arranged along the sides of a flower shoot terminus. There is more or less space along the shoot between the pedicels.

RADICLE (rad-i-kl) A rudimentary root, the lower end of the hypocotyl of the embryo. It forms the primary root of the young seedling.

RADIOACTIVE (*ray*-di-oh-*ak*-tiv) A substance is radioactive when a constituent chemical element is undergoing the process of changing into another element through the emission of radiant energy. Radioactivity is used as a tool in research to tag or trace the movement of compounds of interest. The presence of a compound containing a radioactive element is revealed by instruments that measure the radiant energy emitted.

RADIOISOTOPES (*ray*-dee-o-*ice*-o-topes) *See* Isotopes.

RECEPTACLE The structure to which the flower parts are attached. The receptacle may become modified in different ways, even to forming part of the fruit, as in apple and pear.

RECESSIVE GENE *See* Dominant factor.

RECESSIVENESS The condition of being recessive when a character controlled by one member of an allelic pair can be masked by the other member; the masked character is designated as recessive.

RECIPROCAL CROSSES Crosses in which two parents are used as female and male, and also as male and female, respectively.

For example, if plant A (female) × plant B (male) represents the original cross, the mating of plant B (female) × plant A (male) would be the reciprocal cross.

REGENERATION The development of new, noncorky growth from more or less mature tissue.

RELEASE Varieties or inbred lines of crop plants are subjected to repeated evaluations. Those of proved merit are made available to the public. The making available of such material is designated as release.

RENOVATION The process of restoring the productivity of plants in solid stands or rows by cultivation, fertilization, reseeding, or by other methods.

REPELLANT A material that animals try to avoid.

REPLICATE (REPLICATION) (*rehp*-li-kayt) A more or less exact duplication or repetition of a test or of an experiment to assure, or to increase, confidence in the resulting data. Five identical tests, for example, could be called five replications. Results from the five tests taken together would be more reliable than results from any one of the tests.

RESIDUAL ACTION The continued action of a material. The effect of an insecticide on insects that come in contact with it for some time after its application.

RESIN (*res*-in) Any of a large group of natural and synthetic materials similar in appearance and general characteristics to rosin, shellac, and amber.

RESISTANT A plant that is able to grow and produce a crop even though heavily inoculated or actually infected with a disease. There are various degrees of resistance; complete resistance is called immunity. A plant that is killed is classed as completely susceptible; one that grows in spite of the disease is also called tolerant.

RESPIRATION (res-pir-*ay*-shun) The metabolic processes by which a plant or animal oxidizes its food materials. Respiration provides the living system with the energy it needs for the synthesis of new material and growth.

REST A condition of a plant in which growth cannot occur, even though temperatures and other environment are favorable for growth.

RESTORER LINE An inbred line that, when crossed on a male-sterile strain, causes the resulting hybrid to be male fertile and produce pollen.

REVERSIBLE Capable of proceeding in either direction. Used to indicate a chemical reaction that can change its product back to the original substance from which it came.

RHIZOMATOUS (rye-*zohm*-uh-tus) Plants with rhizomes (creeping stems or rootstocks) below the soil surface, usually horizontally elongated. Rhizomes of grasses bear scales at the nodes and usually are slender and creeping.

RHIZOME (*rye*-zohm) A nonfleshy, more or less horizontal, underground stem.

ROGUE (roag) An offtype plant; to remove such plants.

ROOT The mineral- and water-absorbing underground part of a plant. Roots do not bear leaves, scales, flowers, or true buds.

ROOTSTOCK The bottom or supporting root used to receive a scion in grafting.

RUDIMENTARY Incompletely developed.

RUNNERS Trailing stems or branches that take root and produce new plants at the joints or ends.

SAC (EMBRYO) The sexual part of the ovule, usually in the center, which bears the egg and polar nuclei.

SAMARA (sah-*mare*-a) A nonsplitting, winged fruit, as in maple or ash. (Adjective: samaroid.)

SAPROPHYTIC (*sap*-roe-fit-ik) Subsisting on dead organic matter and commonly causing its decay.

SCARIFICATION (*scare*-i-fi-cation) The process of mechanically scarring a seedcoat to make it more permeable to water.

SCHIZOCARP (*skiz*-o-karp) Dry, two-seeded fruit of the carrot family. The fruit separates at maturity along the midline into two nonsplitting one-seeded mericarps.

SCION (*sie*-un) A portion of the shoot of a plant, such as a small branch or part of a branch, which is grafted upon a plant having a root system.

SCUTELLUM (sku-*tell*-um) A shield-shaped organ of the developing embryo within a seed. The embryo absorbs food from the scutellum, much of which is in turn obtained from the endosperm. In certain plants, like corn, it is a specially developed cotyledon.

SEED (SEEDS) A mature ovule, consisting of an embryonic plant together with a store of food, all surrounded by a protective coat. It usually develops after the fertilization of an egg cell by a male generative cell from a pollen grain. Seeds of some species develop without the intervention of the male cell; formed entirely of "mother" tissue, such seeds are called apogamic seeds.

SEED PARENT The strain from which seed is harvested in the hybrid seed field. Also commonly used to designate the female parent in any cross-fertilization.

SEEDBORNE Carried on seeds.

SEEDCOAT The outermost tissues or "skin" of a seed. Sometimes this coat is extremely hard and waterproof, preventing entrance of water to initiate germination unless it is broken, scratched, or eroded away.

SEEDLING A young plant; a plant grown from seed.

SEEDPIECE The term applied to the pieces cut from stem tissue for the purpose of vegetative multiplication. Seedpieces are not true seed and the use of the term seedpiece (occasionally abbreviated to seed) is confusing.

SEEDSTALK The erect stalk on a plant that produces flowers and seed. Applied particularly to root crops and leafy vegetable crops that produce seed after the desired product (root, head, or leaves) has fully developed.

SELECTION The practice of permitting certain individuals to reproduce and of preventing other individuals from so doing. In plant breeding, this involves the retention of apparently superior individuals and the discarding of the less desirable individuals.

SELF-FERTILIZE (SELF-FERTILE) To fertilize the ovule of a flower with the pollen of the same flower (or plant).

SELF-INCOMPATIBILITY Inability to set seed from application of pollen produced on the same plant.

SELFED Said of a pistil that is fertilized with pollen from the same plant that bears the pistil; also applied to seed resulting from such fertilization.

SEMINAL (sem-i-nal) Pertaining to the seed or germ. Seminal organs are those already developed in the embryo within the seed.

SEPALS (see-puls) The lowermost set of leaflike bracts making up the flower cup. The sepals together are called the calyx.

SET (OF SEED) Formation of seeds.

SIBBED Mated individuals having the same parentage.

SILK (CORN) The stigma and style of the female corn flower, through which the pollen tube grows to reach the embryo sac.

SIMPLE FRUIT Developed from a single pistil or ovary, which may be simple or compound.

SINGLE-CROSS PARENT The F_1 offspring of two inbred parents, which in turn is used as a parent—usually with another single-cross parent to produce a double-cross hybrid, as in corn.

SOMATIC (so-mat-ik) Pertaining to cells of the soma or body as contrasted to cells of the germinal or reproductive tissues.

SP. (SPP.) Abbreviation of "species." The expression follows the name of a genus when the single species indicated is unknown or for any other reason not specified. (Spp. is the plural.)

SPAWN A common term applied to a mixture of fungal mycelium and a nutritive organic material for the artificial propagation of mushrooms.

SPECIES (spee-sheez) A group of closely related organisms; for example, Medicago sativa is the botanical name for alfalfa. Medicago is the genus, and sativa is the species. Several species belong to the genus Medicago.

SPECIES HYBRIDIZATION The mating of two different species. Several wild species are represented in the ancestry of the cultivated rose and of many of our crop plants as well.

SPECTROMETRY (spec-trom-eh-tree) The measurement of the absorption or emission of light by a substance at specific wavelengths.

SPECTROPHOTOMETER (spek-troh-foh-tom-eh-ter) An instrument for determining the relative intensity of two colors or spectral regions.

SPERM The male generative cell that fertilizes the egg cell. Carried to the stigmatic surface of the pistil within the pollen grain, it travels down the style of the pistil within the penetrating pollen tube and near its tip. It finds its way to the egg cell within the ovule, via the micropyle, a microscopic opening.

SPERMATOPHYTE (sper-matt-o-fite) A seed-bearing plant.

SPHAGNUM MOSS (sfag-num) A bog moss belonging to the genus Sphagnum. It is frequently used as a rooting medium for plants.

SPORE In seed plants, the spore is the first cell of the gametophyte generation. The two kinds, microspore and megaspore, produce male and female gametes, respectively.

SPOROPHYTE (*spor*-o-fite) The asexual or vegetative part of the plant, as opposed to the gametophyte or sexual portion.

SPOROPHYTIC (*spo*-ro-*fi*-tick) Pertaining to the sporophyte or diploid generation which has cells with twice the gametic number of chromosomes.

STALK (*stawk*) A stemlike supporting structure, such as a peduncle or pedicel.

STAMEN (*stay*-men) The part of the flower bearing the male reproductive cells, the pollen. Each stamen is composed of a stalk (the filament) and pollen sac (the anther).

STEM The part of a plant that bears leaves, flowers, and true buds. Stems grow either in a direction opposite to the pull of gravity or in a horizontal direction—uncommonly downward.

STERILE (*stair*-ill) A plant that fails to set seed even though compatible pollen is applied to the stigma of the flower. Cross-sterile plants fail to set seed with pollen from other plants. Self-sterile plants produce no seed from their own pollen.

STIGMA (*stig*-ma) The part of the pistil that receives the pollen.

STIMULUS (*stim*-u-lus) A chemical or other treatment that excites an organ or tissue to a specific activity, such as the application of a plant regulator to a stem to induce root formation.

STOLONIFEROUS (*stow*-lahn-if-er-ous) Plants with stolons—creeping stems above or below the soil surface.

STOLONS (*stow*-lons) Laterally creeping stems at or below the soil surface, from the buds of which new plants may arise. Some stolons bear tubers at their ends (potato).

STYLE The stalk of the pistil between stigma and ovary.

SUBERIZATION (*soob*-er-ih-*za*-shun) The process by which the cut surface of a stem forms a protective, corky layer, especially in conditions of high temperature and high humidity.

SUBERIZE To heal or form a corky protective layer over a cut or wounded surface.

SUBSTRATE (*sub*-strate) A substance that is acted upon, as by an enzyme. Also, a culture medium.

SUCKER An offshoot that develops from an adventitious bud located on the roots or lower stem of a plant.

SYMBIOSIS (sim-be-*o*-sis) Living together in more or less intimate association of two dissimilar organisms, in which the association is advantageous to one or both organisms.

SYNERGID NUCLEI (si-*nur*-jid new-*klee*-eye) Two of the eight nuclei that result from meiosis or sexual cell division in seed-bearing plants. The synergid nuclei are closely associated with the egg nucleus and are usually located in the tip end of the embryo sac. Like the egg, they contain only one member of each chromosome pair. They are usually nonfunctional.

SYNTHETIC (sin-*thet*-ik) Artificially produced material as distinguished from that made by living organisms. Also applied to interbreeding population derived from the propagation of multiple hybrids.

SYNTHETIC GROWTH SUBSTANCES Chemically synthesized compounds which affect the growth of a plant. These may be the same or similar to natural growth substances which are synthesized by the plant.

SYSTEMIC (sis-*tem*-ick) Absorbed into the sap stream and passed to other parts of the plant.

TAILINGS Partly threshed material, that has passed through the coarse shakers, or "straw walkers," of a threshing machine and has passed over the fine sieve.

TASSEL (CORN) The flower cluster at the tip of a corn plant comprised of pollen-bearing flowers. The staminate inflorescence of maize.

TAXONOMY (tax-*ahn*-oh-mee) The science of classification as applied to living organisms.

TERMINAL End, as the tip of a plant shoot.

TESTA The outer covering of the seed.

TETRAPLOID (*tet*-ra-ploid) A plant with four sets of identical or similar chromosomes.

THERMAL INDUCTION The change in growth and development of plants brought about by a given temperature exposure; usually applied to the process resulting in flowering of biennial plants.

TILLER A branch arising from the base of a monocot plant, especially in the grass family.

TRAIT A synonym of character with respect to function and performance but less so with respect to form.

TRANSLUCENT (trans-*loo*-sent) The quality of a substance that permits transmission of light but diffused so that objects are not clearly visible when viewed through it.

TREFOIL A group of plants composed primarily of two species—birdsfoot trefoil (*Lotus corniculatus*) and big trefoil (*L. uliginosus* or *L. major*).

TRISOMIC (tri-*so*-mik) An otherwise diploid individual having one chromosome present in triplicate.

TUBER A much thickened underground branch or stem structure, filled with stored reserves of food and so modified as to serve as a vegetative reproductive structure. A potato is an example.

TUBEROUS (*too*-bur-us) Tuber-producing; like a tuber.

TURGID (*ter*-jid) Refers to the crisp, fresh condition found when the cells of the plant are amply supplied with water to the extent that they are fully extended. It is the opposite to wilted.

UMBELLIFEROUS (um-bell-*if*-er-us) Pertaining to plants in the family Umbelliferae. These are tap-rooted plants with minute flowers aggregated into flat or umbrella-shaped heads, and include such crop plants as carrot, parsnip, celery, dill, and parsley.

UNDERSTOCK The bottom or supporting part of a graft composed of either root or stem tissue or both.

UNSATURATED FATTY ACID A fatty acid that has a double bond between two carbon atoms at one or more places in the carbon chain. Hydrogen can be added at the site of the double bond.

UTRICLE (*you*-trick-l) A small, thin-walled, one-seeded fruit.

VACUOLE (*vak*-u-ol) A "cavity" in the protoplasm of most plant cells filled with a water solution of sugars, salts, acids, and other substances. Certain plant pigments, such as the anthocyanins, occur in the vacuole.

VARIETAL (vah-*rye*-e-tal) Pertaining to, or involving varieties.

VARIETAL HYBRID The product resulting from the mating of two varieties. The production of such hybrids was used in corn breeding to some extent in earlier years.

VEGETATIVE A descriptive term referring to stem and leaf development in contrast to flower and seed development; commonly used as a synonym of nonsexual in contrast to the sexual type of development and reproduction in plants.

VERMICULITE (ver-*mick*-you-light) is a form of mica, a mineral. Certain altered forms make ideal rooting mediums because they are light in weight, easily penetrated by air, and retain moisture.

VIABLE, VIABILITY (*veye*-uh-bul, veye-uh-*bil*-i-tee) Alive. Capable of living and developing normally. A viable seed is one which is capable of germinating under the proper circumstances. Such a viable seed may, or may not, be readily or immediately germinable. Dormant viable seeds may require lengthy specific treatments before they become immediately germinable.

VISCID (*viss*-sid) Sticky.

VIVIPAROUS (vi-*vip*-arus) As applied to plants, a relatively rare condition in which seeds germinate while still attached to the parent plant.

VOLUNTEER PLANTS Unwanted plants growing from seed that remains on the field from a previous crop.

WAVELENGTH The distance between two corresponding points on any two consecutive waves. For light it is very small and is measured in Angstrom units (A), which equal about 0.04 millionths of an inch.

WEED Any plant in a place where it is a nuisance might be considered a weed. The term is most often applied to noncultivated plants that arise unwanted in cultivated areas, lawns, pastures, or other areas used by man. Most weeds are prolific and persistent.

WINDROW (*wind*-roe) A loose, continuous row of cut or uprooted plants placed on the surface of the ground for drying to facilitate harvest.

WING A membranous or thin and dry expansion or appendage of a seed or fruit.

XANTHOPHYLL (*zann*-thoe-fill) ($C_{40}H_{56}O_2$) A yellow pigment in plant and animal products which is related to carotene and also is a precursor of vitamin A.

XENIA (*ze*-ni-a) The direct visible effects of the pollen on the endosperm and related tissues in the formation of a seed.

XYLEM (*zi*-lem) Conductive tissues in higher plants through which water and solutes move from the roots to the leaves. The conducting vessels are often called tracheae.

ZYGOTE (*zie*-goat) The fertilized egg.

INDEX

582

588

590